The Autobiography of Eleanor Roosevelt

Books by Eleanor Roosevelt

This Is My Story
This I Remember
India and the Awakening East
On My Own
You Learn by Living
The Autobiography of Eleanor Roosevelt

UN: Today and Tomorrow
(*with William DeWitt*)

The Autobiography

of ELEANOR
ROOSEVELT

Harper & Brothers Publishers New York

I DEDICATE THIS BOOK
to all those who will be spared reading the three volumes of my autobiography and who may find this easier and pleasanter to read.

As I look through it, I think it gives some insight into the life and times in which my husband and I lived, and anything which adds to future understanding I hope will have value.

E.R.

Contents

PART III   On My Own

PART IV   The Search for Understanding

Illustrations

The Roosevelts on the *Amberjack II* at Southeast Harbor, Maine
President and Mrs. Roosevelt during a western tour, 1935
F.D.R., his wife and Franklin, Jr., on election night, 1936
Mrs. Roosevelt with Queen Elizabeth in Washington, 1938
With Crown Prince Olaf of Norway, Princess Juliana of Holland, Crown
    Princess Marta of Norway and Thomas J. Watson, 1944
A group at the White House for Christmas, 1938
Mrs. Roosevelt being met, on arrival in London, October, 1942, by General
    Eisenhower, King George, Queen Elizabeth and Ambassador Winant
Visiting troops in the Southwest Pacific in 1943
President and Mrs. Roosevelt with their thirteen grandchildren in the
    White House, January, 1945
The coffin bearing the body of the President being carried into the White
    House
Mrs. Roosevelt with President and Mrs. Truman at the commissioning of
    the aircraft carrier *Franklin D. Roosevelt*, October, 1945
With General Charles de Gaulle at Hyde Park, August, 1945
Mrs. Roosevelt as a delegate at the General Assembly opening at Flushing
    Meadows, October, 1946, with Senator Connally and Senator Vanden-
    burg
In Paris, September, 1948, with John Foster Dulles, Warren Austin and
    General Marshall
In New York, October, 1952, with Senator Wiley, Senator Green, Ambas-
    sador Austin, Secretary of State Dean Acheson, Mrs. Edith F. Sampson,
    Benjamin V. Cohen, Philip C. Jessup and Ernest Gross
Mrs. Roosevelt leaving the London home of Sir Winston Churchill after
    lunching with him and Mrs. Churchill, April, 1948
Talking with President Tito at his summer estate in July, 1953

The following are grouped in a separate section after page 268
Mrs. Roosevelt with Nepal's King Tridhuvana and his two Queens in
    March, 1952
Demonstrating a western folk dance in Lahore, Pakistan, March, 1952
Watching boys at work in the Faridabad Colony near Delhi, India, Feb-
    ruary, 1952

I WANT TO SAY IN THIS BOOK a special word of thanks to Miss Elinore Denniston. I could not have done, alone, the long and tedious job of cutting that was necessary to abbreviate the three volumes into one nor have added the parts which seemed necessary for a better understanding and for bringing the volume up to date.

Miss Denniston is a most patient, capable, and helpful co-worker. Without her this volume could never have been produced. I thank her warmly and express here my deep appreciation and pleasure in working with her at all times.

E.R.

Preface

THIS IS BOTH an abbreviated and an augmented edition of my autobiography. Abbreviated because, as far as possible, material of only passing interest has been eliminated; augmented by the addition of new material that brings the book up to date. When I first embarked on the story of my life the chief problem I faced was to decide what to put in. Now, in preparing this shorter version, I have had to decide what to leave out. In both cases, the major difficulty lay in trying to see myself and my activities and what happened to me within the framework of a larger picture. It is not easy to attain this kind of perspective because, for me, as for almost everyone, I think, the things that mattered most have not been the big important things but the small personal things.

No one, it seems to me, can really see his own life clearly any more than he can see himself, as his friends or enemies can, from all sides. It is a moral as well as a physical impossibility. The most one can achieve is to try to be as honest as possible.

What my purpose has been I indicated at the end of *This Is My Story*.

It occurs to me to wonder why anyone should have the courage or, as so many people probably think, the vanity to write an autobiography.

In analyzing my own reasons I think I had two objectives: One was to give a picture, if possible, of the world in which I grew up and which today is changed in many ways. The other, to give as truthful a picture as possible of a human being. A real picture of any human being is interesting in itself, and it is especially interesting when we can follow the play of other personalities upon that human being and perhaps get a picture of a group of people and of the influence on them of the period in which they lived. The great difference between the world of the 1880's and today seems to me to be in the extraordinary speeding up of our physical surroundings.

I was for many years a sounding board for the teachings and influence of my immediate surroundings. The ability to think for myself did not develop until I was well on in life and therefore no real personality developed in my early youth. This will not be so of young people of today; they must become individuals responsible for themselves at a much earlier age because of the conditions in which they find themselves in their everyday lives. The world of my grandmother was a world of well-ordered custom and habit, more or less slow to change. The world of today accepts something new overnight and in two years it has become the old and established custom and we have almost forgotten it was ever new.

The reason that fiction is more interesting than any other form of literature to those of us who like to study people is that in fiction the author can really tell the truth without hurting anyone and without humiliating himself too much. He can reveal what he has learned through observation and experience of the inner workings of the souls of men. In an autobiography this is hard to do, try as you will. The more honest you are about yourself and others, however, the more valuable what you have written will be in the future as a picture of the people and their problems during the period covered by the autobiography.

Every individual as he goes through life has different problems and reacts differently to the same circumstances. Different individuals see and feel the same things in different ways, something in them colors the world and their lives. Their experiences and their lessons will be different in each individual case.

To me, who dreamed so much as a child, who made a dreamworld in which I was the heroine of an unending story, the lives of the people around me have continued to have a certain storybook quality. I learned something which has stood me in good stead many times—the most important thing in any relationship is not what you get but what you give.

My Hall family were typical, I think, of the early 1900's. Somewhere in the background there were people who had worked with their hands and with their heads and worked hard, but the need was no longer there and at that time the material conditions of life seemed stable.

My grandfather Hall typified the group, in his generation, that had reached a goal. He was a gentleman of leisure and enjoyed using his brains. He liked to have the stimulation of intelligent companionship but he did not feel the need to work. In his children many of the qualities of the hardfisted, hardheaded ancestors had faded away, but their world was not so stable as they thought and their money began to slip through their fingers. Today, two generations later, the world has changed so much that many of the younger members of the family have to begin again at scratch and it is interesting to see that, with necessity, many of them develop the same abilities that existed in the working forebears.

This cycle, which I have watched in my family, is one reason why, in our country, it always amuses me when any one group of people take it for granted that, because they have been privileged for a generation or two, they are set apart in any way from the man or woman who is working in order to keep the wolf from the door. It is only luck and a little temporary veneer and before long the wheels may turn and one and all must fall back on whatever basic quality they have.

This idea would never have occurred to my grandmother, for to her the world seemed more or less permanently fixed, but to us today it is a mere platitude and our children and grandchildren accept it without turning a hair.

On the other side of my family, of course, many people whom I have mentioned will be described far better and more fully by other people, except in the case of my father, whose short and happy early life was so tragically ended. With him I have a curious feeling that as long as he remains to me the vivid, living person that he is, he will, after the manner of the people in *The Blue Bird*, be alive and continue to exert his influence, which was always a gentle, kindly one.

The more the world speeds up the more it seems necessary that we should learn to pick out of the past the things that we feel were important and beautiful then. One of these things was a quality of tranquillity in people, which you rarely meet today. Perhaps one must have certain periods of life lived in more or less tranquil surroundings in order to attain that particular quality. I read not long ago in David Grayson's *The Countryman's Year* these words: "Back of tranquillity lies always conquered unhappiness." That may be so, but perhaps these grandparents of ours found it a little easier to conquer unhappiness because their lives were not lived at high tension so constantly. Certainly all of us must conquer some unhappiness in our lives.

Autobiographies are, after all, useful only as the lives you read about and analyze may suggest to you something that you may find useful in your own journey through life. I do not expect, of course, that anyone will find exactly the same experiences or the same mistakes or the same gratifications that I have found, but perhaps my very foolishness may be helpful! The mistakes I made when my children were young may give some help or some consolation to some troubled and groping mother. Because of one's timidity one sometimes is more severe with the children, or more irritated at trifles, and one feels the necessity to prove one's power over the only defenseless thing in sight.

We all of us owe, I imagine, far more than we realize to our friends as well as to the members of our family. I know that in my own case my friends are responsible for much that I have become and without them there are many things which would have remained closed books to me.

From the time of my marriage, the life I lived seems more closely allied with the life that all of us know today. It was colorful, active and interesting. The lessons learned were those of adaptability and adjustment and finally of self-reliance and developing into an individual as every human being must.

I have sketched briefly the short trip to Europe after World War I, and yet I think that trip had far-reaching consequences for me. I had known Europe and particularly France, with its neat and patterned countryside, fairly well. The picture of desolation fostered in me an undying hate of war which was not definitely formulated before that time. The conviction of the uselessness of war as a means of finding any final solution to international difficulties grew stronger and stronger as I listened to people talk. I said little about it at the time but the impression was so strong that instead of fading out of my memory it has become more deeply etched upon it year by year.

In *This Is My Story* I covered my early years, the vanishing world in which I grew up, the influences and the values that dominated that era.

In *This I Remember* I dealt with a broader and more vital period, concerned for the most part with my husband's political life during one of the most dramatic and eventful times in history, and with the gradual broadening of my own activities.

In *On My Own* I tried to give some picture of the changing world as I have seen it during recent years and of the various jobs into which I plunged in the hope that, by building international understanding and co-operation, we could hold at bay the ugly stupidity of war and learn to substitute for it, however slowly or painfully—or reluctantly—an era of brotherhood.

In the final part of this book, *The Search for Understanding*, I have added new material, covering the past few years. They have been busy years, with every half hour of every day filled and with my working day often extending from eight in the morning until well past midnight. These crowded hours have been interesting and stimulating. They have, I hope, been useful. They have, at least, been lived to the hilt.

In the long run an autobiography is valuable only if it accomplishes one of two things, or preferably both. It may help to preserve, through the eyes of an individual, a record of a way of life that has vanished, or of people who were historically important in their own era, and so add, even minutely, to our understanding of the background. Or, in a more personal way, it may help other people to solve their problems. There is nothing particularly interesting about one's life story unless people can say as they read it, "Why, this is like what I have been through. Perhaps, after all, there is a way to work it out."

Let me hasten to say that I do not suggest that my solutions should or could prove a guide to anyone. About the only value the story of my life may have is to show that one can, even without any particular gifts, overcome obstacles that seem insurmountable if one is willing to face the fact that they must be overcome; that, in spite of timidity and fear, in spite of a lack of special talents, one can find a way to live widely and fully.

Perhaps the most important thing that has come out of my life is the discovery that if you prepare yourself at every point as well as you can, with whatever means you may have, however meager they may seem, you will be able to grasp opportunity for broader experience when it appears. Without preparation you cannot do it. The fatal thing is the rejection. Life was meant to be lived, and curiosity must be kept alive. One must never, for whatever reason, turn his back on life.

E. R.

Hyde Park
December, 1960

PART I

This Is My Story

One

Memories of My Childhood

MY MOTHER WAS one of the most beautiful women I have ever seen. Her father, my grandfather Hall, never engaged in business. He lived on what his father and mother gave him.

He had a house in New York City at 11 West Thirty-seventh Street, and he built another on the Hudson River about five miles above the village of Tivoli, on land which was part of the old Chancellor Livingston estate. My grandmother's mother was a Miss Livingston, and so we were related to the Livingstons, the Clarksons, the DePeysters, who lived in the various houses up and down the River Road.

My grandfather Hall's great interest was in the study of theology, and in his library were a number of books dealing with religion. Most of them were of little interest to me as a child, but the Bible, illustrated by Doré, occupied many hours—and gave me many nightmares!

My grandmother Hall, who had been a Miss Ludlow, a beauty and a belle, was treated like a cherished but somewhat spoiled child. She was expected to bring children into the world and seven children were born, but she was not expected to bring them up. My grandfather told her nothing about business, not even how to draw a check, and died without a will, leaving her with six children under seventeen years of age, a responsibility for which she was totally unprepared.

The two eldest children, my mother and Tissie—whose real name was Elizabeth and who later became Mrs. Stanley Mortimer—bore the marks of their father's upbringing. They were deeply religious; they had been taught to use their minds in the ways that my grandfather thought suitable for girls. He disciplined them well. In the country they walked several times a day from the house to the main road with a stick across

3

their backs in the crook of their elbows to improve their carriage. He was a severe judge of what they read and wrote and how they expressed themselves, and held them to the highest standards of conduct. The result was strength of character, with definite ideas of right and wrong, and a certain rigidity in conforming to a conventional pattern, which had been put before them as the only proper existence for a lady.

Suddenly the strong hand was removed, and the two boys and the two younger girls knew no discipline, for how could a woman who had never been treated as anything but a grown-up child suddenly assume the burden of training a family?

I have been told that my mother, for the first year or so after my grandfather died, was the guiding spirit of the household, but at nineteen she was married to my father.

My mother belonged to that New York City society which thought itself all-important. Old Mr. Peter Marié, who gave choice parties and whose approval stamped young girls and young matrons a success, called my mother a queen, and bowed before her charm and beauty, and to her this was important.

In that society you were kind to the poor, you did not neglect your philanthropic duties, you assisted the hospitals and did something for the needy. You accepted invitations to dine and to dance with the right people only, you lived where you would be in their midst. You thought seriously about your children's education, you read the books that everybody read, you were familiar with good literature. In short, you conformed to the conventional pattern.

My father, Elliott Roosevelt, charming, good-looking, loved by all who came in contact with him, had a background and upbringing which were alien to my mother's pattern. He had a physical weakness which he himself probably never quite understood. As a boy of about fifteen he left St. Paul's School after one year, because of illness, and went out to Texas. He made friends with the officers at Fort McKavit, a frontier fort, and stayed with them, hunting game and scouting in search of hostile Indians. He loved the life and was a natural sportsman, a good shot and a good rider. I think the life left an indelible impression on him. The illness left its mark on him too, on those inner reserves of strength which we all have to call on at times in our lives. He returned to his family in New York apparently well and strong.

My grandfather Roosevelt died before my father was twenty-one and while his older brother, Theodore, later to be President of the United States, fought his way to health from an asthmatic childhood and went to Harvard College, Elliott, with the consent of an indulgent mother and two adoring sisters, took part of his inheritance and went around the world. He hunted in India when few people from this country had done anything of the kind.

My father returned from his trip for the wedding of his little sister, Corinne, to his friend, Douglas Robinson. Then he married Anna Hall, and tragedy and happiness came walking on each other's heels.

He adored my mother and she was devoted to him, but always in a more reserved and less spontaneous way. I doubt that the background of their respective family lives could have been more different. His family was not so much concerned with Society (spelled with a big S) as with people, and these people included the newsboys from the streets of New York and the cripples whom Dr. Schaefer, one of the most noted early orthopedic surgeons, was trying to cure.

My father's mother and his brother Theodore's young wife, Alice Lee, died within a few days of each other. The latter left only a little Alice to console the sorrowing young father. My father felt these losses deeply. Very soon, however, in October, 1884, I came into the world, and from all accounts I must have been a more wrinkled and less attractive baby than the average—but to him I was a miracle from Heaven.

I was a shy, solemn child even at the age of two, and I am sure that even when I danced I never smiled. My earliest recollections are of being dressed up and allowed to come down to dance for a group of gentlemen who applauded and laughed as I pirouetted before them. Finally, my father would pick me up and hold me high in the air. He dominated my life as long as he lived, and was the love of my life for many years after he died.

With my father I was perfectly happy. There is still a woodeny painting of a solemn child, a straight bang across her forehead, with an uplifted finger and an admonishing attitude, which he always enjoyed and referred to as "Little Nell scolding Elliott." We had a country house at Hempstead, Long Island, so that he could hunt and play polo. He loved horses and dogs, and we always had both. During this time he was in business, and, added to the work and the sports, the gay and popular young couple lived a busy social life. He was the center of my world and all around him loved him.

Whether it was some weakness from his early years which the strain of the life he was living accentuated, whether it was the pain he endured from a broken leg which had to be set, rebroken and reset, I do not know. My father began to drink, and for my mother and his brother Theodore and his sisters began the period of harrowing anxiety which was to last until his death in 1894.

My father and mother, my little brother and I went to Italy for the winter of 1890 as the first step in the fight for his health and power of self-control. I remember my father acting as gondolier, taking me out on the Venice canals, singing with the other boatmen, to my intense joy. I loved his voice and, above all, I loved the way he treated me. He called me "Little Nell," after the Little Nell in Dickens' *Old Curiosity Shop,* and I never doubted that I stood first in his heart.

He could, however, be annoyed with me, particularly when I disappointed him in such things as physical courage, and this, unfortunately, I did quite often. We went to Sorrento and I was given a donkey so I could ride over the beautiful roads. One day the others overtook me and offered to let me go with them, but at the first steep descent which they slid down I turned pale, and preferred to stay on the high road. I can remember still the tone of disapproval in my father's voice, though his words of reproof have long since faded away.

I remember my trip to Vesuvius with my father and the throwing of pennies, which were returned to us encased in lava, and then the endless trip down. I suppose there was some block in the traffic, but I can remember only my utter weariness and my effort to bear it without tears so that my father would not be displeased.

My mother took a house in Neuilly, outside of Paris, and settled down for several months, as another baby was expected the end of June. My father entered a sanitarium while his older sister, Anna, our Auntie Bye, came to stay with my mother. It was decided to send me to a convent to learn French and to have me out of the way when the baby arrived.

The convent experience was an unhappy one. I was not yet six years old, and I must have been very sensitive, with an inordinate desire for affection and praise, perhaps brought on by the fact that I was conscious of my plain looks and lack of manners. My mother was troubled by my lack of beauty, and I knew it as a child senses these things. She tried hard to bring me up well so that my manners would compensate for my looks, but her efforts only made me more keenly conscious of my shortcomings.

The little girls of my age in the convent could hardly be expected to take much interest in a child who did not speak their language and did not belong to their religion. They had a little shrine of their own and often worked hard beautifying it. I longed to be allowed to join them, but was always kept on the outside and wandered by myself in the walled-in garden.

Finally, I fell a prey to temptation. One of the girls swallowed a penny. Every attention was given her, she was the center of everybody's interest. I longed to be in her place. One day I went to one of the sisters and told her that I had swallowed a penny. It must have been evident that my story was not true, so they sent for my mother. She took me away in disgrace. Understanding as I do now my mother's character, I realize how terrible it must have seemed to her to have a child who would lie.

I remember the drive home as one of utter misery, for I could bear swift punishment far better than long scoldings. I could cheerfully lie any time to escape a scolding, whereas if I had known that I would simply be put to bed or be spanked I probably would have told the truth.

This habit of lying stayed with me for years. My mother did not understand that a child may lie from fear; I myself never understood it until I reached the age when I realized that there was nothing to fear.

My father had come home for the baby's arrival, and I am sorry to say he was causing a great deal of anxiety, but he was the only person who did not treat me as a criminal!

The baby, my brother Hall, was several weeks old when we sailed for home, leaving my father in a sanitarium in France, where his brother, Theodore, had to go and get him later on.

We lived that winter without my father. I slept in my mother's room, and remember the thrill of watching her dress to go out in the evenings. She looked so beautiful I was grateful to be allowed to touch her dress or her jewels or anything that was part of the vision which I admired inordinately.

Those summers, while my father was away trying to rehabilitate himself, we spent largely with my grandmother at her Tivoli house, which later was to become home to both my brother Hall and me.

My father sent us one of his horses, an old hunter which my mother used to drive, and I remember driving with her. Even more vividly do I remember the times when I was sent down to visit my great-aunt, Mrs. Ludlow, whose house was next to ours but nearer the river and quite out of sight, for no house along that part of the river was really close to any other.

Mrs. Ludlow was handsome, sure of herself, and an excellent house-keeper. On one memorable occasion she set to work to find out what I knew. Alas and alack, I could not even read! The next day and every day that summer she sent her companion, Madeleine, to give me lessons in reading. Then she found out that I could not sew or cook and knew nothing of the things a girl should know. I think I was six.

I surmise that my mother was roundly taken to task, for after that Madeleine became a great factor in my life and began to teach me to sew.

I still slept in my mother's room, and every morning I had to repeat to her some verses which I had learned in the Old or the New Testament. I wish I could remember today all the verses I learned by heart that summer.

Sometimes I woke up when my mother and her sisters were talking at bedtime, and many a conversation not meant for my ears was listened to with great avidity. I acquired a strange and garbled idea of the troubles around me. Something was wrong with my father and from my point of view nothing could be wrong with him.

If people only realized what a war goes on in a child's mind and heart in a situation of this kind, I think they would try to explain more than they do, but nobody told me anything.

We moved back to New York, the autumn that I was seven, to a house which my mother had bought and put in order on East 61st Street, two blocks from Auntie Bye, who lived at Madison Avenue and East 62nd Street. She had Uncle Ted's little girl, Alice, with her a great deal, and that winter our first real acquaintance began. Already she seemed much older and cleverer, and while I admired her I was always a little afraid of her, and this was so even when we were grown and she was the "Princess Alice" in the White House.

That winter we began a friendship with young Robert Munro-Ferguson, a young man sent over from England by an elder brother to make his way in the world. My father and mother had known the elder brother, Ronald (later Lord Novar), and so had Auntie Bye. The boy was taken into her house, given a start in Douglas Robinson's office, and became a dear and close friend to the entire family.

My mother always had the three children with her for a time in the late afternoon. My little brother Ellie adored her, and was so good he never had to be reproved. The baby Hall was always called Josh and was too small to do anything but sit upon her lap contentedly. I felt a curious barrier between myself and these three. My mother made a great effort; she would read to me and have me read to her, she would have me recite my poems, she would keep me after the boys had gone to bed, and still I can remember standing in the door, often with my finger in my mouth, and I can see the look in her eyes and hear the tone of her voice as she said, "Come in, Granny." If a visitor was there she might turn and say, "She is such a funny child, so old-fashioned that we always call her 'Granny.'" I wanted to sink through the floor in shame.

Suddenly everything was changed! We children were sent out of the house. I went to stay with my godmother, Mrs. Henry Parish, and the boys went to my mother's aunt, Mrs. Ludlow. My grandmother left her own house and family to nurse my mother, for she had diphtheria and there was then no antitoxin. My father was sent for, but came too late from his exile in Virginia. Diphtheria went fast in those days.

I can remember standing by a window when Cousin Susie (Mrs. Parish) told me that my mother was dead. This was on December 7, 1892. Death meant nothing to me, and one fact wiped out everything else. My father was back and I would see him soon.

Later I knew what a tragedy of utter defeat this meant for him. No hope now of ever wiping out the sorrowful years he had brought upon my mother —and she had left her mother as guardian for her children. He had no wife, no children, no hope.

Finally it was arranged that we children were to live with my grandmother Hall. I realize now what that must have meant in dislocation of her household, and I marvel at the sweetness of my two uncles and the two aunts who were still at home, for never by word or deed did any of them make us feel that we were not in our own house.

After we were installed, my father came to see me, and I remember going down into the high-ceilinged, dim library on the first floor of the house in West 37th Street. He sat in a big chair. He was dressed all in black, looking very sad. He held out his arms and gathered me to him. In a little while he began to talk, to explain to me that my mother was gone, that she had been all the world to him, and now he had only my brothers and myself, that my brothers were very young and that he and I must keep close together. Someday I would make a home for him again, we would travel together and do many things which he painted as interesting and pleasant, to be looked forward to in the future.

Somehow it was always he and I. I did not understand whether my brothers were to be our children or whether he felt that they would be going to a school and later be independent.

There started that day a feeling which never left me, that he and I were very close and someday would have a life of our own together. He told me to write to him often, to be a good girl, not to give any trouble, to study hard, to grow up into a woman he could be proud of, and he would come to see me whenever it was possible.

When he left I was all alone to keep our secret of mutual understanding and to adjust myself to my new existence.

The two little boys had a room with Madeleine and I had a little hall bedroom next to them. I was old enough to look after myself, except that my hair had to be brushed at night. Of course, someone had to be engaged to take me out, to and from classes, and to whatever I did in the afternoons. I had governesses, French maids, German maids. I walked them all off their feet. They always tried to talk to me, and I wished to be left alone to live in a dreamworld in which I was the heroine and my father the hero. Into this world I withdrew as soon as I went to bed and as soon as I woke in the morning, and all the time I was walking or when anyone bored me.

I was a healthy child, but now and then in winter I would have a sore throat and tonsillitis, so cold baths were decreed as a daily morning routine —and how I cheated on those baths! Madeleine could not always follow me up, and more hot water went into them than would have been considered beneficial had anyone supervised me.

My grandmother laid great stress on certain things in education. I must learn French. My father wished me to be musical. I worked at music until I was eighteen, but no one ever trained my ear! Through listening to my aunt Pussie play I did gain an emotional appreciation of music. She was a fascinating and lovely creature and her playing was one of the unforgettable joys of my childhood.

I would have given anything to be a singer. I felt that one could give a great deal of pleasure and, yes, receive attention and admiration! Attention and admiration were the things through all my childhood which I wanted, because I was made to feel so conscious of the fact that nothing about me would attract attention or would bring me admiration.

As I look back on that household in the 37th Street house, I realize how differently life was lived in the New York of those days, both in its houses and in its streets. There were a number of large and beautiful homes, most of them on Fifth Avenue. Madison Square was still almost entirely residential, and from 14th Street to 23rd Street was the shopping district.

In the streets there were no motorcars. Beautiful horses and smart carriages took their place. Horse-drawn stages labored up Fifth Avenue and horse-drawn streetcars ran on other avenues and crosstown streets; cabs and hansoms were the taxis of those days.

Our old-fashioned, brownstone house was much like all the other houses in the side streets, fairly large and comfortable, with high ceilings, a dark basement, and inadequate servants' quarters with working conditions which no one with any social conscience would tolerate today. The laundry had one little window opening on the back yard and, of course, we had no electric light. We were modern in that we had gas!

The servants' room lacked ventilation and comfortable furnishings. Their bathroom was in the cellar, so each one had a basin and a pitcher in a tiny bedroom.

Our household consisted of a cook, a butler, a housemaid—who was maid as well to my young aunts—and a laundress. The family consisted of my grandmother, Pussie and Maude, who had been the baby of the family until our arrival, Vallie, my older uncle, and, for brief periods, Eddie, who was some two years younger. Eddie had a roving foot and took at least one long trip to Africa which I remember.

Into this household I moved with my two little brothers and their nurse.

My grandmother seemed to me a very old lady, though I realize now that she was still quite young. She was relegated almost entirely to her own bedroom. She came downstairs when she had visitors of her own, but the drawing room, with its massive gilt furniture covered with blue damask, was the room in which she saw her guests. Her daughters took possession of the library, which was a large front room where the piano stood and where a large bow window on the street gave more light.

The dining room, in the extension at the back, was quite a bright room, having three windows on the side. Back of that was the pantry, where I spent considerable time, for the butler, Victor, was kind to me and taught me how to wash dishes and wipe them, though when I broke one he was much displeased. Sometimes when I was in disgrace and sent supperless to bed, he or Kitty, the chambermaid, would smuggle me up something to eat.

The years had changed my grandmother. With her own children she had been chiefly concerned in loving them. Discipline had been my grandfather's part. When he died she still wanted to surround them with the tenderest love, but later on she found that she could not control Vallie or

Eddie or Pussie or Maude. She was determined that the grandchildren who were now under her care should have the discipline that her own children had lacked, and we were brought up on the principle that "no" was easier to say than "yes."

Looking back I see that I was always afraid of something: of the dark, of displeasing people, of failure. Anything I accomplished had to be done across a barrier of fear. I remember an incident when I was about thirteen. Pussie was ill with a bad sore throat and she liked me to do things for her, which made me very proud. One night she called me. Everything was dark, and I groped my way to her room. She asked if I would go to the basement and get some ice from the icebox. That meant three flights of stairs; the last one would mean closing the door at the foot of the stairs and being alone in the basement, making my way in pitch-black darkness to that icebox in the back yard!

My knees were trembling, but as between the fear of going and the fear of not being allowed to minister to Pussie when she was ill, and thereby losing an opportunity to be important, I had no choice. I went and returned with the ice, demonstrating again the fact that children value above everything else the opportunity to be really useful to those around them.

Very early I became conscious of the fact that there were people around me who suffered in one way or another. I was five or six when my father took me to help serve Thanksgiving dinner in one of the newsboys' clubhouses which my grandfather, Theodore Roosevelt, had started. He was also a trustee of the Children's Aid Society for many years. My father explained that many of these ragged little boys had no homes and lived in little wooden shanties in empty lots, or slept in vestibules of houses or public buildings or any place where they could be moderately warm, yet they were independent and earned their own livings.

Every Christmas I was taken by my grandmother to help dress the Christmas tree for the babies' ward in the Post-Graduate Hospital. She was particularly interested in this charity.

Auntie Gracie took us to the Orthopedic Hospital which my grandfather Roosevelt had been instrumental in helping Dr. Newton Schaefer to start and in which the family was deeply interested. There I saw innumerable little children in casts and splints. Some of them lay patiently for months in strange and curious positions. I was particularly interested in them because I had a curvature myself and wore for some time a steel brace which was vastly uncomfortable and prevented my bending over.

Even my uncle Vallie, who at this time was in business in New York, a champion tennis player and a popular young man in society, took me to help dress a Christmas tree for a group of children in a part of New York City which was called "Hell's Kitchen." For many years this was one of New York's poorest and worst sections. I also went with Maude and Pussie to sing at the Bowery Mission, so I was not in ignorance that there were sharp contrasts, even though our lives were blessed with plenty.

Though he was so little with us, my father dominated all this period of my life. Subconsciously I must always have been waiting for his visits. They were irregular, and he rarely sent word before he arrived, but never was I in the house, even in my room two long flights of stairs above the entrance door, that I did not hear his voice the minute he entered the front door. Walking downstairs was far too slow. I slid down the banisters and usually catapulted into his arms before his hat was hung up.

My father never missed an opportunity for giving us presents, so Christmas was a great day and I still remember one memorable Christmas when I had two stockings, for my grandmother had filled one and my father, who was in New York, brought one on Christmas morning.

One more sorrow came to my father the winter that my mother died. My little brother Ellie never seemed to thrive after my mother's death. Both he and the baby, Josh, got scarlet fever, and I was returned to my cousin Susie and, of course, quarantined.

The baby got well without any complications, but Ellie developed diphtheria and died. My father came to take me out occasionally, but the anxiety over the little boys was too great for him to give me a good deal of his time.

On August 14, 1894, just before I was ten years old, word came that my father had died. My aunts told me, but I simply refused to believe it, and while I wept long and went to bed still weeping I finally went to sleep and began the next day living in my dreamworld as usual.

My grandmother decided that we children should not go to the funeral, and so I had no tangible thing to make death real to me. From that time on I knew in my mind that my father was dead, and yet I lived with him more closely, probably, than I had when he was alive.

My father and mother both liked us to see a great deal of Aunt Gracie. She was beloved by all her great-nephews and -nieces. As I remember her now, she was of medium height, slender, with clear-cut features, but always looked fragile and dainty. Ladies wore long dresses in those days, which trailed in the dust unless they were held up, and I seem to remember her generally in the rather tight-fitting bodices of the day, high in the back, square-cut in front and always with an immaculate frill of white lace or plaited linen around the neck.

Often her hands would lie folded in her lap as she told us a story and I, who loved to look at hands even as a child, remember watching them with pleasure. My Saturdays were frequently spent with this sweet and gracious great-aunt. Alice Roosevelt, Teddy Robinson, and I were the three who enjoyed those days the most.

After my father died, these Saturdays with Aunt Gracie were not allowed. My grandmother felt we should be at home as much as possible, and perhaps she feared we might slip away from her control if we were too much with our dynamic Roosevelt relatives.

The next few years were uneventful for me. New York City in winter, with classes and private lessons, and for entertainment occasionally, on a Saturday afternoon, a child or two for supper and play. My grandmother believed in keeping me young and my aunts believed in dressing me in a way which was appropriate to my age but not to my size. I was very tall, very thin and very shy. They dressed me for dancing class and for parties in dresses that were above my knees, when most of the girls my size had them halfway down their legs. All my clothes seem to me now to have been incredibly uncomfortable.

I wore flannels from the 1st of November until the 1st of April, regardless of the temperature, and the flannels went from my neck to my ankles. Of course, the attire included a flannel petticoat and long black stockings. How hot they were! And the high-button or high-laced shoes that went with them and were supposed to keep your ankles slim.

We children stayed at Tivoli in summer now with a nurse and governess, even if the others were away, and there were hot, breathless days when my fingers stuck to the keys as I practiced on the piano but I never left off any garments and, even in summer, we children wore a good many. I would roll my stockings down and then be told that ladies did not show their legs and promptly have to fasten them up again!

The house at Tivoli was big, with high ceilings and a good many rooms, most of them large. My grandfather had furnished it downstairs in a rather formal way. There were some lovely marble mantelpieces and chandeliers for candles. We had neither gas nor electricity. We had lamps, but often went to bed by candlelight. There were some vitrines with lovely little carved ivory pieces, one tiny set of tables and chairs I loved to look at, and also silver ornaments and little china and enameled pieces collected from various parts of the world.

The library was filled with standard sets of books, besides my grandfather's religious books. A good deal of fiction came into the house by way of my young aunts and uncles. It is astonishing how much Dickens, Scott and Thackeray were read and reread, particularly by Eddie.

On the second and third floors there were nine master bedrooms and four double servants' rooms and one single one. These servants' rooms were much better than those in the town house, but no one thought it odd that there was no servants' bathroom.

There were just two bathrooms in this large house, but it never occurred to us that it was an inconvenience or that it really made much work to have to use basins and pitchers in our own rooms.

We children had to take two hot baths a week, though I think my grandmother could still remember the era of the Saturday night baths. I was expected to have a cold sponge every morning.

My grandmother let me follow her about in the early mornings when she was housekeeping, and I carried to the cook the supplies of flour, sugar and coffee that she so carefully weighed out in the storeroom.

Today few servants would be content to cook in the semidarkness which reigned in that big, old-fashioned kitchen, with a large stone areaway all around it, over which was the piazza, which left only a small space for the light to filter in. The room where the servants ate had one door leading into the areaway. The laundry was a little better, because there were two doors leading out onto the terrace, and here I spent many hours.

Our wash—and what a wash it was—was done by one woman, Mrs. Overhalse, without the aid of any electric washing machine or irons. She had a washboard and three tubs and a wringer and a little stove on which were all weights of irons. The stove was ted with wood or coal.

Mrs. Overhalse was a cheerful, healthy soul, apparently able to direct her own household, come and wash all day for us, and then go back at night and finish up on her farm. She had a number of children. She taught me to wash and iron, and though I was not allowed to do the finer things, the handkerchiefs, napkins and towels often fell to my lot, and I loved the hours spent with this cheerful woman.

Pussie had an artistic temperament, and there would be days when I would go to Maude for comfort, for Pussie would not speak to anyone. Gradually I came to accept it as part of her character and to be grateful for all the lovely things she did, and wait patiently for the storms to pass.

She took me one summer with my governess to Nantucket Island for a few days—an exciting trip for a child who never went anywhere except up and down the Hudson River. After a few days I think she was bored with us; in any case, she left. The governess did not have enough money to get us home. Pussie was to return, but she forgot all about us. Finally my grandmother was appealed to and sent enough money to pay our bill and get us home.

When my young aunts and uncles were away, I was much alone. This solitude encouraged my habit of taking a book out into the fields or the woods and sitting in a tree or lying under it, completely forgetting the passage of time. No one tried to censor my reading, though occasionally when I happened on a book that I could not understand and asked difficult question before people, the book would disappear. I remember this happened to Dickens' *Bleak House*. I spent days hunting for it.

Certain things my grandmother insisted on. On Sundays I might not read the books that I read on weekdays. I had to teach Sunday school to the coachman's little daughter, giving her verses to learn, hearing her recite them, and then seeing that she learned some hymns and collects and the catechism. In turn, I must do all these things myself and recite to my grandmother.

Every Sunday the big victoria came to the door and we went to church, and my seat usually was the little one facing my grandmother. Unfortunately, the four miles were long, and I was nearly always nauseated before we reached the church, and equally so before we reached home.

I could not play games on Sunday, and we still had a cold supper in the evenings, though we did not live up to the cold meal in the middle of the day that had been my grandfather's rule.

Madeleine did succeed in teaching me to sew. I hemmed endless dish towels and darned endless stockings. Madeleine caused me many tears, for I was desperately afraid of her. I used to enjoy sliding down the moss-grown roof of our icehouse, and got my white drawers completely covered with green. I went to my grandmother before I went to Madeleine, knowing that my grandmother would scold less severely.

I was not supposed to read in bed before breakfast, but as I woke at five practically every morning in summer and was, I am afraid, a self-willed child I used to hide a book under the mattress. Woe to me when Madeleine caught me reading!

I have no recollection now of why she frightened me. As I look back it seems perfectly ludicrous, but I did not even tell my grandmother how much afraid I was until I was nearly fourteen years old, and then I confessed, between sobs, as we were walking in the woods. How silly it all seems today.

A few things I wanted desperately to do in those days. I remember that when I was about twelve Mr. Henry Sloane asked me to go west with his daughter, Jessie. I do not think I ever wanted to do anything so much in all my life, for I was fond of her and longed to travel. My grandmother was adamant and would not allow me to go. She gave me no reasons. It was sufficient that she did not think it wise. She so often said "no" that I built up a defense of saying I did not want to do things in order to forestall her refusals and keep down my disappointments.

She felt I should learn to dance, and I joined a dancing class at Mr. Dodsworth's. These classes were an institution for many years, and many little boys and girls learned the polka and the waltz standing carefully on the diamond squares of the polished hardwood floor.

My grandmother decided that because of my being tall and probably awkward I should have ballet lessons besides, so I went once a week to a regular ballet teacher on Broadway and learned toe dancing with four or five other girls who were going on the stage and looked forward to the chance of being in the chorus and talked of little else, making me very envious.

I loved it and practiced assiduously, and can still appreciate how much work lies behind some of the dances which look so easy as they are done on the stage.

Two

Adolescence

I HAD GROWN fond of the theater and Pussie took me to see Duse, the great Italian actress, when she first came to this country. Then she took me to meet her, a thrill which I have never forgotten. Her charm and beauty were all that I had imagined! I was also allowed to see some of Shakespeare's plays and occasionally to go to the opera, but my young aunts and their friends talked all the time of plays which I never went to see. As a result, one winter I committed a crime which weighed heavily on my conscience for a long time.

My grandmother told me to go to a charity bazaar with a friend. To escape my maid, I told her my friend would have her maid with her and that she would bring me home. Instead of going to the bazaar we went to see a play, *Tess of the D'Urbervilles*, which was being discussed by my elders and which I, at least, did not understand at all. We sat in the peanut gallery and were miserable for fear of seeing someone we knew. We left before the end because we knew we would be late in reaching home. I had to lie and could never confess, which I would gladly have done because of my sense of guilt, but I would have involved the other girl in my trouble.

My grandmother, after my father's death, allowed me less and less contact with his family, the Roosevelts of Oyster Bay, so I saw little of those cousins. I did, however, pay one or two short visits to Aunt Edith and Uncle Ted in summer.

Alice Roosevelt, who was nearest my age, was so much more sophisticated and grown-up that I was in great awe of her. She was better at sports, and my having so few companions of my own age put me at a great disadvantage with other young people.

18

I remember the first time we went swimming at Oyster Bay. I couldn't swim, and Uncle Ted told me to jump off the dock and try. I was a good deal of a physical coward then, but I did it and came up spluttering and was good-naturedly ducked and became very frightened. Never again would I go out of my depth.

A favorite Sunday afternoon occupation was to go to Cooper's Bluff, a high sandy bluff with a beach below. At high tide the water came almost to its base. Uncle Ted would line us up and take the lead and we would go down holding on to each other until someone fell or the speed became so great that the line broke. In some way we reached the bottom, rolling or running.

I was desperately afraid the first time we did it, but found it was not so bad as I thought, and then we clambered up again, taking a long time to get there as we slid back one foot for every two we went up.

In some ways I remember these visits as a great joy, for I loved chasing through the haystacks in the barn with Uncle Ted after us, and going up to the gunroom on the top floor of the Sagamore House where he would read aloud, chiefly poetry.

Occasionally he took us on a picnic or a camping trip and taught us many valuable lessons. The chief one was to remember that camping was a good way to find out people's characters. Those who were selfish showed it very soon, in that they wanted the best bed or the best food and did not want to do their share of the work.

My brother did more of this than I did, for he was just Quentin Roosevelt's age, and after I went abroad my grandmother let him visit Uncle Ted and Aunt Edith more frequently. My only other contact with my Roosevelt family was during an annual Christmas holiday visit, when my grandmother permitted me to spend a few days with Auntie Corinne.

This was the only time in the year when I ever saw any boys of my own age. To me these parties were more pain than pleasure. The others all knew each other and saw each other often. They were all much better at winter sports. I rarely coasted and never skated, for my ankles were so weak that when I did get out on the pond my skating was chiefly on those ankles.

I was a poor dancer, and the climax of the party was a dance. What inappropriate dresses I wore—and, worst of all, they were above my knees. I knew, of course, that I was different from all the other girls and if I had not known they were frank in telling me so! I still remember my gratitude at one of these parties to my cousin Franklin Roosevelt when he came and asked me to dance with him.

I must have been a great trial and responsibility to Auntie Corinne, who tried so hard to give every one of us a good time. But what could she do with a niece who was never allowed to see boys in the intervals between these parties and who was dressed like a little girl when she looked like a very grown-up one?

Suddenly life was going to change for me. My grandmother decided that the household had too much gaiety for a girl of fifteen. She remembered that my mother had wanted to send me to Europe for a part of my education. Thus the second period of my life began.

In the autumn of 1899, when I was fifteen, I sailed for England with my aunt, Mrs. Stanley Mortimer, and her family. She took me in her cabin and told me that she was a poor sailor and always went to bed immediately on getting on the boat. I thought this was the proper procedure and followed suit. As a result, I did not enjoy that trip at all, as most of it was spent in my berth, and I arrived in England distinctly wobbly, never having stayed indoors so long before!

I did not know my beautiful Auntie Tissie as well as I knew my two younger aunts, but I was fond of her and she was always kindness itself to me. I think, even then, she felt more at home in Europe and in England than she did in the United States. She had many friends in that little London coterie known as "The Souls." She was one of the people whom the word "exquisite" describes best.

It was decided to send me to Mlle. Souvestre's school, "Allenswood," at a little place called South Fields, not far from Wimbledon Common and a short distance from London. The school was chosen because my father's sister, Mrs. Cowles, had gone to Mlle. Souvestre's school at Les Ruches, outside of Paris, before the Franco-Prussian War. The siege of Paris had been such an ordeal that Mlle. Souvestre left France and moved to England.

The family felt that, as I was to be left alone, it would be pleasanter to know that the headmistress had a personal interest in me. Tissie took me out to see Mlle. Souvestre, and I was left there with the promise that I would spend Christmas with her in London. When she drove away I felt lost and very lonely.

There were a great many rules and the first one was that all had to talk

French, and if they used an English word they had to report themselves at the end of the day.

As my first nurse had been a Frenchwoman and I spoke French before I spoke English, it was quite easy for me, but for many of the English girls who had had little French beforehand it was a terrible effort.

On the inside of each bathroom door were pasted the bath rules and I was appalled to find that we had to fight for three baths a week and were limited to ten minutes unless we happened to have the last period, and then perhaps we could sneak another five minutes before "lights out" was sounded!

We had to make our own beds before leaving the room in the morning. When we got out of bed we had to take the bedclothes off and put them on a chair to air. Our rooms were inspected after breakfast and we were marked on neatness and the way we made our beds. Frequently our bureau drawers and closets were examined, and any girl whose bureau drawers were out of order might return to her room to find the entire contents of the drawers dumped on her bed for rearranging. I also saw beds completely stripped and left to be made over again.

The day began with an early breakfast, café au lait, chocolate or milk, rolls and butter. I think eggs were given to those who wanted them.

Mlle. Souvestre, older and white-haired and obliged to take a certain amount of care of her health, never came to breakfast, but we were well watched over by Mlle. Samaia, a dynamic little woman who adored Mlle. Souvestre and waited on her hand and foot, ran all the business end of the school, and gave Italian lessons.

To be in Mlle. Samaia's good graces you had to show practical qualities. The girls who were singled out by her to hold positions of trust were dependable, could usually do almost anything with their hands, and had the ability to manage and lead their fellow students.

It took me a long time to get into her good graces, for I was a good deal of a dreamer and an American, which to her was an unknown quantity.

Mlle. Souvestre, on the contrary, had a soft spot for Americans and liked them as pupils. A number of her pupils became outstanding women. Auntie Bye, for instance, was one of the most interesting women I have ever known.

My grandfather Roosevelt's interest in cripples had first been aroused by the fact that he had consulted many doctors in trying to do something for his eldest daughter, Auntie Bye. She was not exactly a hunchback but she had a curious figure, thick through the shoulders, evidently caused by a curvature of the spine. Her hair was lovely, soft and wavy. Her eyes were deep-set and really beautiful, making you forget the rest of the face.

Auntie Bye had a mind that worked as an able man's mind works. She was full of animation, was always the center of any group she was with, and carried the burden of conversation. When she reached middle age she was already deaf and the arthritis which was finally to cripple her completely was causing her great pain, but never for a minute did her infirmities disturb her spirit. As they increased she simply seemed to become more determined to rise above them, and her charm and vivid personality made her house, wherever she lived, the meeting place for people from the four corners of the earth.

She had great executive ability, poise and judgment, and her influence was felt not only by her sister and brothers but by all her friends. To the young people with whom she came in contact she was an inspiration and one of the wisest counselors I ever knew. She listened more than she talked, but what she said was worth listening to!

From the start Mlle. Souvestre was interested in me because of her affection for Anna, and day by day I found myself more interested in her. This grew into a warm affection which lasted until her death.

Mlle. Souvestre was short and rather stout, she had snow-white hair. Her head was beautiful, with clear-cut, strong features, a strong face and broad forehead. Her hair grew to a peak in front and waved back in natural waves to a twist at the back of her head. Her eyes looked through you, and she always knew more than she was told.

After breakfast we were all taken for a walk on the common—and you had to have a good excuse to escape that walk! From about November it was cold and fairly foggy, and the fog rose from the ground and penetrated the very marrow of your bones—but still we walked!

At home I had begun to shed some of the underclothes which my grandmother had started me out with in my early youth, but here in England in winter I took to warm flannels again, and while we had central heat, which was unusual, one had positively to sit on the radiator to feel any warmth. There were only a few of us who had grates in our bedrooms, and those of us who had open fires were envied by all the others.

I can remember crowding into the dining room in order to get as near the radiator as possible before we had to sit down. Nearly all the English girls had chilblains on their hands and feet throughout most of the winter.

Classes began immediately on our return from the walks, and each of us had a schedule that ran through the whole day—classes, hours for practice, time for preparation—no idle moments were left to anyone. Immediately after lunch we had two hours for exercises, and most of us played field hockey during the winter months.

I was as awkward as ever at games, and had never seen a game of hockey, but I had to play something, and in time made the first team. I think that day was one of the proudest moments of my life. I realize now it would have been better to have devoted the time which I gave to hockey to learning to play tennis, which would have been more useful to me later on.

When we came in at four o'clock we found on the schoolroom table big slices of bread about half an inch thick, sometimes spread with raspberry jam, more often with plain butter. Those who were delicate were given a glass of milk.

Then we studied until the bell rang, which sent us scurrying to dress for dinner. Fifteen minutes were allowed to change shoes and stockings and dress.

One day a week we did our mending in the period after four P.M.— under supervision, of course—in the school room.

In the evenings we worked again, though occasionally we were allowed to go down to the gym and dance. Most of our lessons were in French, though Miss Strachey, a member of the well-known literary family, gave us classes in Shakespeare; and of course we had German, Latin and music.

Mlle. Souvestre held her history classes in her library, a charming and comfortable room lined with books and filled with flowers, looking out on a wide expanse of lawn, where really beautiful trees gave shade in summer and formed good perches for the rooks and crows in winter.

We sat on little chairs on either side of the fireplace. Mlle. Souvestre carried a long pointer in her hand, and usually a map hung on the wall. She would walk up and down, lecturing to us. We took notes, but were expected to do a good deal of independent reading and research. We wrote papers on the subjects assigned and labored hard over them. This was the class we enjoyed beyond any other.

A few of us were occasionally invited in the evening to Mlle. Souvestre's study, and those were red-letter days. She had a great gift for reading aloud and she read to us, always in French, poems, plays and stories. If the poems were those she liked, occasionally she read them over two or three times and then demanded that we recite them to her in turn. Here my memory trained at home stood me in good stead, and I found this an exhilarating way to spend an evening.

I did not know that my grandmother and my aunts had written about me before I arrived, so I felt that I was starting a new life, free from all my former sins. This was the first time in my life that my fears left me. If I lived up to the rules and told the truth, there was nothing to fear.

I had a bad habit of biting my nails. In short order that was noticed by Mlle. Samaia, who set out to cure me. It seemed a hopeless task, but one day I was rereading some letters of my father's, which I always carried with me, and I came across one in which he spoke of making the most of one's personal appearance, and from that day forward my nails were allowed to grow.

By the first Christmas holidays I was quite at home and happy in school. Christmas Eve and Christmas Day were spent with my Mortimer family at Claridge's Hotel in London. It did not seem right to have a small tree on a table in a hotel. We had always had a big one at home, but Auntie Tissie saw to it that I had a stocking and many gifts, and the day was a happy one, on the whole.

I had been invited to spend a few days with Mrs. Woolryche-Whittemore and her family in the north of England. Her husband was rector of a church at Bridgenorth, in Shropshire, and she had five little girls, one or two about my own age. She was Douglas Robinson's sister and held closely to her American ties, so that, though I could only be considered a connection by marriage, I was made to feel like a real relative and taken into the family and treated like one of the children. I enjoyed every minute of that visit, which was my first glimpse of English family life.

For breakfast there was food on one of the sideboards in covered dishes with lamps under them to keep the food warm, and everyone helped himself to whatever he found. High tea was served in the schoolroom about four-thirty in the afternoon, and the children's father joined us sometimes and shared our bread and jam and tea and cake. Those who were very hungry could have an egg. Long walks and drives, endless games, and books on hand for any unoccupied moments made life full for the days I stayed there.

I had traveled up alone and was going back alone. There had been a good deal of discussion as to how I was to get over to Paris to see Auntie

Tissie once more before she left for Biarritz. I was to live with a French family for the rest of my holiday, in order to study French.

It was finally decided to engage one of the English inventions, a visiting maid, with good references, to travel from London to Paris with me. I had never seen her but I picked her out without any difficulty in the station and went on to Paris.

I really marvel now at my confidence and independence, for I was totally without fear in this new phase of my life. The trip across the Channel was short, and I managed to find myself a windy corner to keep from being ill, but I was glad enough, once through the customs and on French soil, to curl up in the compartment of the train, and drink café au lait poured out of those big cans that were carried up and down the platforms.

We reached Paris in the early hours of the morning. The maid went with me as far as my aunt's hotel. I spent a few hours with her and was then taken over by Mlle. Bertaux. Actually, there were two Mlles. Bertaux and their mother. They had a simple but comfortable apartment in one of the less fashionable parts of Paris, and this was to be my first glimpse of French family life.

The furniture was stuffed, as I remember it, and was of an entirely nondescript period. There was, of course, no bathroom, but hot water was brought by the *bonne à tout faire* mornings and evenings, and a little round tin tub was available if you felt you must have it.

Meals were good, but different from anything I had known. Soups were delicious, and inferior cuts of meat were so well cooked that they were as palatable as our more expensive cuts. A vegetable was a course in itself, and at each place at the table were little glass rests for your knife and fork, which were not taken out with your plate as you finished each course. The household was run with extreme frugality, and yet they lived well. The two Mlles. Bertaux were excellent guides and charming, cultivated women.

The wide avenues, beautiful public buildings and churches, everything combined to make Paris for me the most exciting city I had ever been in. I saw much of it with Mlle. Bertaux on that first visit, but chiefly we did the things that a visitor should do, not the things which, later, came to mean to me the real charm of Paris.

Mlle. Souvestre had arranged that I should go back to England under Mlle. Samaia's care, and after a delightful holiday I went back to school, hoping that I should have another chance to stay with the Bertaux family.

School life itself was uneventful, but in the world outside great excitement reigned. I had hardly been conscious of our Spanish War in 1898, though I had heard a great deal about the sinking of the *Maine* and about Uncle Ted and his Rough Riders. My grandmother and her family lived completely outside the political circles of the day and took little interest in public affairs. But I remember the joy and excitement when Uncle Ted came back and went to Albany as governor of New York.

One read in the papers of scandals and of battles but it was all on a small scale. This war of ours had hardly touched my daily life.

In England, however, the Boer War, which lasted from 1899 to 1902, was of a more serious nature, and the tremendous feeling in the country at large was soon reflected in the school. At first there was great confidence in rapid victory, then months of anxiety and dogged "carrying on" in the face of unexpected and successful resistance from the Boers.

There was a considerable group in England and in other countries that did not believe in the righteousness of the English cause, and Mlle. Souvestre was among this group. She was, however, always fair and she realized that it would be most unfair to the English girls to try to make them think as she did. With them she never discussed the rights and wrongs of the war. Victories were celebrated in the gym and holidays were allowed, but Mlle. Souvestre never took part in any of the demonstrations. She remained in her library, and there she gathered around her the Americans and the other foreign girls. To them she expounded her theories on the rights of the Boers or of small nations in general. Those long talks were interesting, and echoes of them still live in my mind.

I was beginning to make a place for myself in the school, and before long Mlle. Souvestre made me sit opposite her at table. The girl who occupied this place received her nod at the end of the meal and gave the signal, by rising, for the rest of the girls to rise and leave the dining room. This girl was under close supervision, so I acquired certain habits which I have never quite been able to shake off.

Mlle. Souvestre used to say that you need never take more than you wanted, but you had to eat what you took on your plate, and so, sitting opposite her day after day, I learned to eat everything that I took on my plate. There were certain English dishes that I disliked very much; for instance, a dessert called suet pudding. I disliked its looks as much as anything, for it had an uncooked, cold, clammy expression as it sat upon the dish. We had treacle to pour over it and my only association with treacle had been through *Nicholas Nickleby*, which did not make the pudding any more attractive. Mlle. Souvestre thought that we should get over such squeamishness and eat a little of everything, so I choked it down when she was at the table and refused it when she was not.

It was a great advantage in one way, however, to sit opposite Mlle. Souvestre, for sometimes she had special dishes and shared them with three or four of us who sat close by. When she had guests they sat on either side of her, and it was easy to overhear the conversation, which was usually interesting.

I think that I started at this period of my life a bad habit that has stayed with me ever since. Frequently I would use, in talking to Mlle. Souvestre, things which I had overheard in her conversation with her friends and which had passed through my rather quick mind, giving me some new ideas; but if anyone had asked me any questions he would soon have discovered that I had no real knowledge of the thing I was talking about. Mlle. Souvestre was usually so pleased that I was interested in the subject that she did the talking, and I never had to show up my ignorance.

More and more, as I grew older, I used the quickness of my mind to pick the minds of other people and use their knowledge as my own. A dinner companion, a casual acquaintance, provided me with information which I could use in conversation, and few people were aware how little I actually knew on a variety of subjects that I talked on with apparent ease.

This is a bad habit, and one which is such a temptation that I hope few children will acquire it. But it does have one great advantage; it gives you a facility in picking up information about a great variety of subjects and adds immeasurably to your interests as you go through life.

Of course, later on I discovered that when I really wanted to know something I had to dig in.

As the summer holidays came nearer my excitement grew for I was to travel to Saint-Moritz in Switzerland to spend my holiday with the Mortimers.

My first view of these beautiful mountains was breath-taking, for I had never seen any high mountains. I lived opposite the Catskill Mountains in summer and loved them, but how much more majestic were these great snow-capped peaks all around us as we drove into the Engadine. The little Swiss chalets, built into the sides of the hills and with places under them for all the livestock that did not actually wander into the kitchen, were picturesque, but strange to my eyes with their fretwork decoration.

However, I was totally unprepared for Saint-Moritz itself, with its streets of grand hotels tapering off into the more modest *pensions* and little houses dotted around for such patients as had to live there for long periods of time.

The hotels all bordered the lake, and the thing that I remember best about my time there was the fact that Tissie and I got up every morning early enough to walk to a little café that perched out above the lake on a promontory at one end. There we drank coffee or cocoa and ate rolls with fresh butter and honey, the sun just peeping over the mountains and touching us with its warm rays. I can still remember how utterly contented I was!

Toward the end of the summer Tissie told me that she had decided to make a trip by carriage from Saint-Moritz through the Austrian Tyrol to Oberammergau, where the Passion Play was being given. She was taking a friend with her, and I could go along if I were willing to sit either with the coachman on the box or on the little seat facing the two ladies. I would have agreed to sit on top of the bags, I was so excited at the prospect of seeing the Passion Play and all this new country.

We had only a one-horse victoria, and much of the country we drove through was mountainous, and when we climbed I got out and walked, so our progress was not rapid and we had plenty of time to enjoy the scenery.

I still think the Austrian Tyrol is one of the loveliest places in the world. We spent a night in a little inn which had housed the mad King Ludwig of Bavaria, when he went to fish in the rushing brook we saw below us. We visited his castles, and finally arrived in Oberammergau.

It was the night before the play, and because of the crowds our rooms were separated from each other in simple little village houses. We walked the whole length of the village and found the people whom we should see the next day in the holy play sitting in their little shops, selling the carved figures which they made during the winter.

The Passion Play adjourned only when people had to eat, so we sat throughout long hours of the day. I loved it, though I realize now that I must have been a tired child, for I had to go to sleep after lunch and could not get back until the end of the second period, because no one is allowed to move or make a noise during the acting.

From there we went to Munich, back to Paris, and then I returned to school.

Christmas of 1899, I was to have my wish and, with a classmate, spend the holiday entirely in Paris with the Mlles. Bertaux.

As the Mlles. Bertaux had charge of us, and as we were supposed to take French lessons every day as well as do a great deal of sightseeing, we were chaperoned and our days were carefully planned. I was getting to know Paris and to feel able to find my way about and to decide what I should like to do if I ever were free to plan my own days.

The last few days of our stay, Mlle. Souvestre was back in Paris and we went to see her. She quizzed us about what we had learned. At this time she told me frankly what she thought of my clothes, many of which were made-over dresses of my young aunts, and commanded me to go out with Mlle. Samaia and have at least one dress made.

I was always worried about my allowance, for my grandmother felt that we children should never know until we were grown what money might be ours, and that we ought to feel that money was something to be carefully spent, as she might not be able to send us any more. However, I decided that if Mlle. Souvestre thought I should buy a dress I could have it. I still remember my joy in that dark-red dress, made for me by a small dressmaker in Paris, but, as far as I was concerned, it might have been made by Worth, for it had all the glamour of being my first French dress.

I wore it on Sundays and as an everyday evening dress at school and probably got more satisfaction out of it than from any dress I have had since.

The one great event that I remember in the winter of 1901 was the death of Queen Victoria. Some of my Robinson connections had arranged for me to see the funeral procession from the windows of a house belonging to one of them. It was an exciting day, beginning with the crowds in the streets and the difficulty of arriving at our destination, and finally the long wait for the funeral procession itself. I remember little of the many carriages which must have comprised that procession, but I shall never forget the genuine feeling shown by the crowds in the streets or the hush that fell as the gun carriage bearing the smallest coffin I had ever seen came within our range of vision. Hardly anyone had dry eyes as that slow-moving procession passed by, and I have never forgotten the great emotional force that seemed to stir all about us as Queen Victoria, so small of stature and yet so great in devotion to her people, passed out of their lives forever.

By the following Easter Mlle. Souvestre had decided that she would take me traveling with her. This was one of the most momentous things

that happened in my education. The plan was to go to Marseilles, along
the Mediterranean coast, to stop at Pisa and then spend some time in
Florence, not staying in the city in a hotel, but living with an artist friend
of Mlle. Souvestre's in his villa in Fiesole, on a hill which overlooked
Florence.

Traveling with Mlle. Souvestre was a revelation. She did all the things
that in a vague way you had always felt you wanted to do. In Marseilles
we walked upon the Quai, looked at the boats that came from foreign
ports, saw some of the small fishing boats with their colored sails, and
went up to a little church where offerings were made to the Blessed Virgin
for the preservation of those at sea. There is a shrine in this church where
people have prayed for the granting of some particular wishes, the crippled
have hung their crutches there, and people have made offerings of gold
and silver and jewels.

We ended by dining in a café overlooking the Mediterranean and ate
the dish for which Marseilles is famous, bouillabaisse, a kind of soup in
which every possible kind of fish that can be found in nearby waters is
used. With it we had *vin rouge du pays*, because Mlle. Souvestre believed
in the theory that, water being uncertain, wine was safer to drink, and if
you diluted it with water, in some way the germs were killed by the wine.

The next day we started our trip along the shores of the Mediterranean.
I wanted to get out at almost every place the name of which was familiar
to me, but our destination was Pisa and it never occurred to me, the child
of regular trips from New York to Tivoli and back, that one could change
one's plans en route.

Suddenly, toward evening, the guard called out "Alassio." Mlle. Souvestre was galvanized into action; breathlessly she leaned out the window
and said, "I am going to get off." She directed me to get the bags, which
were stored on the rack over our heads, and we simply fell off onto the
platform, bag and baggage, just before the train started on its way. I was
aghast. Here we stood, our trunks going on in the luggage van and we
without rooms and, as far as I knew, in a strange place with no reason for
the sudden whim.

When we recovered our breath Mlle. Souvestre said, "My friend Mrs.
Humphry Ward lives here, and I decided that I would like to see her;
besides, the Mediterranean is a lovely blue at night and the sky with the
stars coming out is nice to watch from the beach."

Alas, we found that Mrs. Ward was away, but we spent a wonderful hour down on the beach watching the sky and sea, and though Mlle. Souvestre had a cold the next day, she did not regret her hasty decision and I had learned a valuable lesson. Never again would I be the rigid little person I had been theretofore.

As I think back over my trips with Mlle. Souvestre, I realize she taught me how to enjoy traveling. She liked to be comfortable, she enjoyed good food, but she always tried to go where you would see the people of the country you were visiting, not your own compatriots.

She always ate native dishes and drank native wines. She felt it was just as important to enjoy good Italian food as it was to enjoy Italian art, and it all served to make you a citizen of the world, at home wherever you might go, knowing what to see and what to enjoy. She used to impress on my mind the necessity for acquiring languages, primarily because of the enjoyment you missed in a country when you were both deaf and dumb.

Mlle. Souvestre taught me also on these journeys that the way to make young people responsible is to throw real responsibility on them. She was an old lady and I was sixteen. The packing and unpacking for both of us was up to me, once we were on the road. I looked up trains, got the tickets, made all the detailed arrangements necessary for comfortable traveling. Though I was to lose some of my self-confidence and ability to look after myself in the early days of my marriage, it came back to me later more easily because of these trips with Mlle. Souvestre.

In Florence, we settled down for a long visit. Spring is a lovely time in Florence and I thought it had more flavor of antiquity than any city I had ever seen. I was reading Dante laboriously and had plenty of imagination to draw upon as I walked about the city. Here again Mlle. Souvestre's belief that Americans could be trusted made my trip unique. The morningafter our arrival she took out the Baedeker, opened it at the description of the Campanile, and said, "My dear, I should be exhausted if I walked with you, but the only way to know a city really is to walk its streets. Florence is worth it. Take your Baedeker and go and see it. Later we will discuss what you have seen."

So, sixteen years old, keener than I have probably ever been since and more alive to beauty, I sallied forth to see Florence alone. Innocence is its own protection. Mlle. Souvestre's judgment was entirely vindicated. Perhaps she realized that I had not the beauty which appeals to foreign men and that I would be safe from their advances. In any case, everyone was most helpful. Even when I got lost in the narrow little streets and had to inquire my way I was always treated with the utmost respect and deference.

From Florence we went to Milan and then to Paris, where again I did my sightseeing alone. One day I met the entire Thomas Newbold family in the Luxembourg, and they wrote home that I was unchaperoned in Paris!

Back in school again for a time, and then in the early summer great excitement, for Pussie had come to Europe with the Mortimers, and she and I were to sail for home together.

I stayed with her in lodgings in London two nights before we sailed, and had my first taste of an emotional crisis on her part. I was to know many similar ones in the years to come. She always had men who were in love with her, not always wisely but always deeply!

At this particular moment she thought she was casting away her happiness forever because she was being separated from the gentleman of the moment. I stayed up anxiously most of the night listening to her sobs and protestations that she would never reach home, that she would jump overboard. Being young and romantic, I spent most of the trip home wondering when she would make the effort and watching her as closely as I could. We were on a slow Atlantic Transport Line boat and shared a cabin. Her moods were anything but placid, but by the time we reached home she was somewhat calmer.

Three

Home Again

THAT SUMMER was a stormy one. One day Pussie was annoyed with me. She told me frankly that I probably would never have the beaux that the rest of the women in the family had had because I was the ugly duckling. At the same time she told me some of the painful and distressing facts about my father's last years. The combination made me very unhappy, and Mrs. Henry Parish, Jr., with whom I was spending the summer in Northeast Harbor, had her hands full trying to console me. She tried hard to give me a good time but I knew no one and had no gift for getting on with the younger people in Northeast, where they lived a life totally different from the English school life that I was then completely absorbed in.

I wanted to get back to England to school and more traveling in Europe. After much begging and insistence I was finally told I might go if I found someone to take me over.

I went to New York, where Pussie and Maude helped me to get my first long, tailor-made suit. The skirt trailed on the ground and was oxford gray. I was enormously proud of it.

I engaged a deaconess to take the trip to London with me and return by the next boat. As I look back on it, it was one of the funniest and craziest things I ever did, for my family never set eyes on her until they came to see me off on the steamer. She looked respectable enough and I am sure she was, but I might just as well have crossed alone, for we had a rough crossing, and I never saw her till the day we landed.

In the little Cunard ships of those days (I think we were on the *Umbria*), a rough crossing meant that the steamer chairs, if they were out at all, were lashed to the railing. There were racks on the table, and when you tried to walk you felt you were walking up a mountain or down one.

33

I had learned something since my first trip, and in spite of continually feeling ill I always got on deck and sat for hours watching the horizon rise and fall, and ate most of my meals up there.

My deaconess and I proceeded to London to a large caravanserai of a hotel. The next day I went to school, carefully handed over the return ticket and enough money for her hotel bill to my companion whom I had taken care of and had rarely seen. But she had served the purpose of giving my family the satisfaction of knowing I was well chaperoned.

School was as interesting as ever. Mlle. Souvestre was glad to see me back, and I had the added interest of a young cousin at school that year. Mr. and Mrs. Douglas Robinson brought over their daughter, Corinne, and left her with Mlle. Souvestre. She was younger than I, very intelligent, and soon won her way to Mlle. Souvestre's interest and respect. In athletics she was far better than I was, and established her place with the girls more quickly than I had done.

Having Auntie Corinne and Uncle Douglas in London was a joy for me, as we were allowed an occasional weekend away and frequent Saturday afternoons if we had a relative near enough to take us out, and I know that I went up to London once or twice at least to see Auntie Corinne; later Auntie Bye was there, too.

I was only sorry that I had to go home before the coronation of King Edward VII, as they were all staying in London, where Uncle Ted would join them to act as special ambassador from our government.

During the Christmas holiday of the year 1902 Mlle. Souvestre took me to Rome. We went to a *pension* in one of the old palaces where the rooms were enormous, with high ceilings, and though we rejoiced in their beauty we nearly froze to death trying to warm ourselves over a little portable stove which had a few red coals glowing in its center.

We visited the Forum many times. Mlle. Souvestre sat on a stone in the sun and talked of history and how the men of Rome had wandered here in their togas; pointed out the place where Julius Caesar may have been assassinated and made us live in ancient history. We watched the people on their knees climbing up the "Scala Santa," and, silly little Anglo-Saxon that I was, I felt self-conscious for them!

One day we journeyed to Tivoli, with its beautiful gardens and the little loophole in the hedge through which you get a view of the city of Rome in the distance.

St. Peter's was a terrible disappointment to me, for I had remembered as a little girl kissing the toe of an enormous and heroic statue. In fact, my nurse had held me up so I might accomplish this act of reverence; but when I went back to look at the statue it was so small that I would have had to bend over considerably to kiss the toe.

When Easter came around, Mlle. Souvestre again asked me to travel with her. This time we crossed the Channel and went to stay not far from Calais with her friends, the Ribots, who lived in a house entered by a door set in a wall. You pulled a long, iron bell handle and a cheerful little tinkle ran through the house. In a few minutes you were let into a spacious and comfortable garden surrounded by a wall high above your head, making it possible to have complete privacy, which is one of the things French people strive for even in their city homes.

I do not remember the name of this small town, but I do remember sallying forth alone to look at the churches and to see what could be seen. I felt somewhat awed by our two dignified and very kindly hosts. Later I was to discover in a premier of France my host of this visit.

From there we went to Belgium and visited some other friends of Mlle. Souvestre's, taking a long trip in their coach. Then we went up the Rhine to Frankfort.

The summer was now approaching, and I knew that I must go home for good. Mlle. Souvestre had become one of the people whom I cared most for in the world, and the thought of the long separation seemed hard to bear. I would have given a good deal to have spent another year on my education, but to my grandmother the age of eighteen was the time when you "came out," and not to "come out" was unthinkable.

When I left I felt quite sure that I would return before long, but I realize now that Mlle. Souvestre, knowing her infirmities, had little hope of seeing me again. She wrote me lovely letters, which I still cherish. They show the kind of relationship that had grown up between us and give an idea of the fine person who exerted the greatest influence, after my father, on this period of my life.

I returned to Tivoli, my grandmother's country place, and spent the whole summer there. This was not a happy summer, for while I had been away my uncle Vallie, who had been so kind to me when I was a child, had been slipping rapidly into the habits of the habitual drinker. My grandmother would never believe that he was not going to give it up as he promised after each spree, but the younger members of the family realized that the situation was serious. He made life for them distinctly difficult.

Pussie was away a great deal. Maude was married to Larry Waterbury, Eddie to Josie Zabriskie and was proving himself just as weak as his brother, Vallie. This was my first real contact with anyone who had completely lost the power of self-control, and it began to develop in me an almost exaggerated idea of the necessity for keeping all one's desires under complete subjugation.

I had been a solemn little girl, my years in England had given me my first taste of being carefree and irresponsible, but my return home to the United States accentuated almost immediately the serious side of life, and that first summer was not good preparation for being a gay and joyous debutante.

My grandmother had cut herself off almost entirely from contact with her neighbors, and while Vallie, when he met anyone, would behave with braggadocio, we really lived an isolated life. No one who was not so intimate that he knew the entire situation was ever invited to come for a meal or to stay with us.

That autumn my little brother went off to boarding school. My grandmother and I took him up to Groton. She seemed quite old and the real responsibility for this young brother was slipping rapidly from her hands into mine. She never again went to see him at school and I began to go up every term for a weekend, which was what all good parents were expected to do. I kept this up through the six years he was there, just as I was to do later for my own sons.

That autumn I moved to the old house on West 37th Street. Theoretically, my grandmother lived there too, but as a matter of fact she lived at Tivoli in a vain attempt to keep Vallie there and keep him sober as much as possible.

Pussie, my only unmarried aunt, and I lived together. She was no less beautiful than she had been when I was a child. She was just as popular, with just as many beaux, and several love affairs always devastating her emotions. She went the round of social dinners and dances as hard as any debutante.

Of course, my grandmother could do nothing about my "coming out," but automatically my name was placed on everybody's list. I was asked to all kinds of parties, but the first one I attended was an Assembly Ball, and I was taken by my cousins, Mr. and Mrs. Henry Parish, Jr.

My aunt, Mrs. Mortimer, had bought my clothes in Paris, and I imagine that I was well dressed, but there was absolutely nothing about me to attract anybody's attention. I was tall, but I did not dance well. I had lost touch with the girls whom I had known before I went abroad, though afterwards I picked up some of my old relationships. I went into that ballroom not knowing one single man except Bob Ferguson, whom I had rarely seen since I went abroad, and Forbes Morgan, who was one of Pussie's most ardent admirers.

I do not think I quite realized beforehand what utter agony it was going to be or I would never have had the courage to go. Bob Ferguson introduced a number of his friends but by no stretch of the imagination could I fool myself into thinking that I was a popular debutante!

I went home early, thankful to get away, having learned that before I went to any party or to any dance I should have two partners, one for supper and one for the cotillion. Any girl who was a success would be asked by many men and accepted the one whom she preferred at the moment. These partners were prerequisites, but you must also be chosen to dance every figure in the cotillion, and your popularity was gauged by the number of favors you took home. Pussie always had far more than I had! I knew I was the first girl in my mother's family who was not a belle and, though I never acknowledged it to any of them at that time, I was deeply ashamed.

Later on, Mr. and Mrs. Mortimer gave a large theater party and supper, with dancing afterwards, for me at Sherry's, which was the most fashionable restaurant in those days. This helped to give me a sense that I had done my share of entertaining, and for one night I stood and received with my aunt and had no anxieties. Pussie and I together gave a few luncheons and dinners that winter at the 37th Street house.

Gradually I acquired a few friends, and finally going out lost some of its terrors; but that first winter, when my sole object in life was society, nearly brought me to a state of nervous collapse. I had other things, however, on my mind. I ran the house as far as it was run by anyone, for Pussie was even more temperamental than she had been as a young girl, and her love affairs were becoming more serious. There would be days when she would shut herself in her room, refusing to eat and spending hours weeping.

Occasionally Vallie would come to the house for one purpose and one alone: to go on a real spree. Pussie was no better equipped to cope with this difficulty than I was. In fact, not having any other vital interests, I had more time to handle this situation and a certain kind of strength and determination which underlay my timidity must have begun to make itself felt, for I think I was better able to handle many difficulties that arose during this strange winter than was Pussie, who was some fourteen years my senior.

A number of pleasant things happened that winter, however. Pussie's musical talent kept her in touch with a certain number of artistic people, and I enjoyed listening to her play and going to the theater, concerts and the opera with her. Bob Ferguson, who lived a pleasant bachelor existence in New York and had many friends, introduced me that year to Bay Emmett, the painter, and some of her friends, and I rejoiced that Bob and I had re-established our old friendship. He felt that he was entitled to bring me home after parties we might both attend, which was a great relief to me, as otherwise I had to have a maid wait for me—that was one of the rules my grandmother had laid down. The rule amuses me when I realize how gaily I went around European cities all by myself. However, she accepted Bob as escort, though she would not hear of anyone else having the same privilege.

He took me to several parties in Bay Emmett's studio and gave me my first taste of informally meeting people whose names I recognized as having accomplished things in the sphere of art and letters. I liked this much better than the dinners and dances I was struggling through in formal society each night, and yet I would not have wanted at that age to be left out, for I was still haunted by my upbringing and believed that what was known as New York Society was really important.

During this time I had begun to see occasionally my cousin Franklin Roosevelt, who was at college, and also his cousin, Lyman Delano, and various other members of his family and some of his college friends. His mother, Mrs. James Roosevelt, was sorry for me, I think.

Mrs. Roosevelt and her husband, who died in 1900, had been fond of my mother and, particularly, of my father, who had crossed on the steamer with them when he was starting his trip around the world. They were so fond of him that when their son, Franklin, was born they asked my father to be his godfather.

When I was two years old my father and mother took me to stay at

Hyde Park with them. My mother-in-law later told me that she remembered my standing in the door with my finger in my mouth and being addressed as "Granny" by my mother, and that Franklin rode me around the nursery on his back. My first recollection of Franklin is at one of the Orange Christmas parties, later a glimpse of him the summer I came home from school when I was going up to Tivoli in the coach of a New York Central train. He spied me and took me to speak to his mother, who was in the Pullman car. I never saw him again until he began to come to occasional dances the winter I came out and I was asked to a house party at Hyde Park where the other guests were mostly his cousins.

I did not stay so much in Tivoli the summer after I came out. I was there part of the time but paid a great many visits, for by that time I had made many friends and Mrs. Parish was kind to me as always. In the autumn when I was nineteen my grandmother decided that she could not afford to open the New York house, and the question came up of where Pussie and I were going to live. Mrs. Ludlow invited Pussie to stay with her and Mrs. Parish offered me a home.

I had grown up considerably during the past year and had come to the conclusion that I would not spend another year just doing the social rounds, particularly as I knew that my cousin's house would mean less ease in casual entertainment than I had known in the 37th Street house. She still lived with a great deal of formality and punctuality and the latter was now not one of my strong points.

Cousin Susie (Mrs. Parish) told me that I might occasionally have guests for tea down in a little reception room on the first floor, but there was no feeling that I could ask people in casually for meals. I had my maid, however, and everything was arranged so that I could go out as much as I wished, and she was more than kind in entertaining at formal lunches and dinners for me.

One thing I remember vividly. I had run over my allowance considerably and had many overdue bills, and finally Mr. Parish took me in hand and painstakingly showed me how to keep books. He would not allow me to ask my grandmother to pay these bills, but he made me pay them myself gradually over a period of time. This was probably my only lesson in handling money, and I have been eternally grateful for it.

He was tall and thin and distinguished looking, with a mustache, and while rather formal in manner he was the kindest person I have ever known.

That winter I began to work in the Junior League. It was in its early stages. Mary Harriman, afterwards Mrs. Charles Cary Rumsey, was the moving spirit. There was no clubhouse; we were just a group of girls anxious to do something helpful in the city in which we lived. When we joined we agreed to do certain pieces of work, and Jean Reid, daughter of Mrs. and Mr. Whitelaw Reid, and I undertook to take classes of youngsters in the Rivington Street Settlement House. Jean was to play the piano and I was to keep the children entertained by teaching calisthenics and fancy dancing.

As I remember it, we arrived there as school came out in the afternoon and it was dark when we left. Jean often came and went in her carriage, but I took the elevated railway or the Fourth Avenue streetcar and walked across from the Bowery. The dirty streets, crowded with foreign-looking people, filled me with terror, and I often waited on a corner for a car, watching, with a great deal of trepidation, men come out of the saloons or shabby hotels nearby, but the children interested me enormously. I still remember the glow of pride that ran through me when one of the little girls said her father wanted me to come home with her, as he wanted to give me something because she enjoyed her classes so much. That invitation bolstered me up whenever I had any difficulty in disciplining my brood!

Once I remember allowing my cousin, Franklin Roosevelt, at that time a senior at Harvard, to come down to meet me. All the little girls were tremendously interested.

I think it must have been this same winter that I became interested in the Consumers League, of which Mrs. Maud Nathan was the president. Luckily, I went with an experienced, older woman to do some investigation of garment factories and department stores. It had never occurred to me that the girls might get tired standing behind counters all day long, or that no seats were provided for them if they had time to sit down and rest. I did not know what the sanitary requirements should be in the dress factories, either for air or for lavatory facilities. This was my introduction to anything of this kind and I imagine that by spring I was ready to drop all this good work and go up to the country and spend the summer in idleness and recreation!

As I try to sum up my own development in the autumn of 1903 I think I was a curious mixture of extreme innocence and unworldliness with a great deal of knowledge of some of the less agreeable sides of life—which, however, did not seem to make me any more sophisticated or less innocent.

It would be difficult for anyone in these days to have any idea of the formality with which girls of my generation were trained. I cannot believe that I was the only one brought up in this way, though I imagine that I was more strictly kept to the formalities than were many of my friends.

It was understood that no girl was interested in a man or showed any liking for him until he had made all the advances. You knew a man very well before you wrote or received a letter from him, and those letters make me smile when I see some of the correspondence today. There were few men who would have dared to use my first name, and to have signed oneself in any other way than "very sincerely yours" would have been not only a breach of good manners but an admission of feeling which was entirely inadmissible.

You never allowed a man to give you a present except flowers or candy or possibly a book. To receive a piece of jewelry from a man to whom you were not engaged was a sign of being a fast woman, and the idea that you would permit any man to kiss you before you were engaged to him never even crossed my mind.

I had painfully high ideals and a tremendous sense of duty entirely unrelieved by any sense of humor or any appreciation of the weaknesses of human nature. Things were either right or wrong to me, and I had had too little experience to know how fallible human judgments are.

I had a great curiosity about life and a desire to participate in every experience that might be the lot of a woman. There seemed to me to be a necessity for hurry; without rhyme or reason I felt the urge to be a part of the stream of life, and so in the autumn of 1903, when Franklin Roosevelt, my fifth cousin once removed, asked me to marry him, though I was only nineteen, it seemed entirely natural and I never even thought that we were both young and inexperienced. I came back from Groton, where I had spent the weekend, and asked Cousin Susie whether she thought I cared enough, and my grandmother, when I told her, asked me if I was sure I was really in love. I solemnly answered "yes," and yet I know now that it was years later before I understood what being in love or what loving really meant.

I had high standards of what a wife and mother should be and not the faintest notion of what it meant to be either a wife or a mother, and none of my elders enlightened me. I marvel now at my husband's patience, for I realize how trying I must have been in many ways. I can see today how funny were some of the tragedies of our early married life.

My mother-in-law had sense enough to realize that both of us were young and undeveloped, and she decided to try to make her son think this matter over—which, at the time, of course, I resented. As he was well ahead in his studies, she took him with his friend and roommate, Lathrop Brown, on a cruise to the West Indies that winter, while I lived in New York with Mrs. Parish.

Franklin's feelings did not change, however.

My first experience with the complications that surround the attendance of a president at any kind of family gathering, such as a wedding or a funeral, came when my great-uncle, James King Gracie, whose wife was our beloved Auntie Gracie, died on November 22, 1903, and Uncle Ted came to New York for the funeral.

The streets were lined with police, and only such people as had identification cards could get in and out of Mrs. Douglas Robinson's house, where Uncle Ted stayed. We all drove down in a procession to the church, but Uncle Ted went in by a special door through the clergyman's house, which had a connecting passageway, and left the same way.

Only afterwards did we hear with horror that, in spite of all the precautions, an unknown man stepped up to Uncle Ted in the passageway and handed him a petition. No one could imagine how the man got in or why he had not been seen by the police. Fortunately, he had no bad intentions, but he gave everyone a shock, for had he wanted to attack Uncle Ted he could have done so easily.

In the winters of 1903 and 1904, Auntie Bye, with whom I had already stayed in Farmington, Connecticut, asked me to come to Washington to stay with her. By this time I had gained a little self-confidence and so I really enjoyed meeting the younger diplomats and the few young American men who were to be found in the social circles of Washington. I was invited to the White House to stay for a night, but I was always awed by the White House and therefore preferred to stay with Auntie Bye, where one felt more at ease. She arranged everything so well for me that I did not feel responsible for myself.

I went with Auntie Bye on her rounds of afternoon calls, and though I was aghast at this obligation, I found it entertaining. The dinners, luncheons and teas were interesting, and people of importance, with charm and wit and *savoir-faire*, filled my days with unusual and exciting experiences.

The chief excitement of the winter of 1904-05 was the marriage of

Pussie to W. Forbes Morgan, Jr. It took place on February 16, in Mrs. Ludlow's house, where Pussie was staying. Pussie looked beautiful but no one was happy. Forbes was a number of years younger than Pussie, and we knew she was temperamental and wondered how they would adjust themselves to the complicated business of married life.

Uncle Ted's campaign and re-election had meant little to me except in general interest, for again I lived in a totally unpolitical atmosphere. In Washington, however, I gradually acquired a faint conception of the political world, very different from my New York world. I also acquired little by little the social ease which I sorely needed.

Uncle Ted came occasionally to Auntie Bye's house informally, and those visits were interesting events. She went, now and then, to walk with Aunt Edith, or perhaps Uncle Ted would send for her to talk over something, showing that he considered her advice well worth having. He was devoted to both his sisters, and Auntie Corinne (Mrs. Douglas Robinson) came down to see him or he went to see her in New York or in the country. They all talked on political questions, literature or art, and his wife and his sisters, all in their own ways, made their contributions to what was always stimulating talk.

Auntie Bye had a great gift for homemaking. Some of her furniture was ugly, but wherever she lived there was an atmosphere of comfort. The talk was always lively, and there was friendliness in her unstinted hospitality. The unexpected guest was always welcome, and young or old, you really felt Auntie Bye's interest in you.

This may have been why I loved to be with her, for I was still shy and she gave me reassurance. She once gave me a piece of advice which must have come from her own philosophy. I was asking her how I could be sure that I was doing the right thing if someone criticized me. Her answer was, "No matter what you do, some people will criticize you, and if you are entirely sure that you would not be ashamed to explain your action to someone whom you loved and who loved you, and you are satisfied in your own mind that you are doing right, then you need not worry about criticism nor need you ever explain what you do."

She had lived for many years according to this principle herself. When J. R. ("Rosy") Roosevelt's wife died while he was first secretary to our embassy in London, she went over to be his hostess and take care of his children. There she met and was married to Captain William Sheffield Cowles, who was our naval attaché, and on her return to this country

William Sheffield Cowles, Jr., was born. Because of her deformity and her age, everyone was anxious about her, but courage will carry one through a great deal and the baby arrived perfect in every way and both mother and baby progressed normally to health and strength.

Uncle Will, Auntie Bye's husband, was now an admiral in the Navy, and I began to learn something about the services and to realize that these men who are our officers in the Army and Navy, while they receive little financial compensation, are enormously proud to serve their country. They and their wives have a position which is their right by virtue of their service, regardless of birth or of income. Quite a new idea to a provincial little miss from New York!

In June of 1904 I went with Franklin's mother and most of his cousins to his commencement at Harvard, the first commencement I had ever attended. That summer I paid my aunt, Mrs. Douglas Robinson, a long visit in Islesboro, Maine, where she had a cottage, and then I went up to stay with Franklin and his mother at Campobello Island, New Brunswick, Canada. Franklin came down to get me, and we made the long trip by train, changing at least twice and getting there in the evening. Of course, I had to have my maid with me, for I could not have gone with him alone!

Once there, however, we walked together, drove around the island, sailed on a small schooner with his mother and other friends, and got to know each other better than ever before. This yacht seemed to me, who was not much accustomed to any of the luxuries of life, the last word in extravagance.

In the autumn of 1904 the engagement was announced. I was asked by Franklin's aunt and uncle, Mr. and Mrs. Warren Delano, to spend Thanksgiving at Fairhaven, Massachusetts, with the entire Delano family. It was an ordeal, but I knew so many of them already and they were so kind and warm in their welcome that I began to feel I was part of the clan—and a clan it was.

My mother-in-law's grandfather, Warren Delano, had been a sea captain, sailing from New Bedford. When returning from a trip to Sweden in 1814, his boat was captured by the British and he was taken to Halifax. Finally the men were sent home, but the ship was taken from them. My mother-in-law's father, Warren Delano, remembered as a little boy the occupation of Fairhaven by the British in this same War of 1812. He and his little brothers were hurried to safety up the Acushnet River.

On retiring, Captain Delano built himself a dignified, rambling house with stone walls enclosing the lawn and garden. There was a stable in the rear. When his son, Warren Delano, my mother-in-law's father, was seventeen, Captain Delano drove him up to Boston and put him in the counting-house of his friend, Mr. Forbes. The eldest of a large family must begin early to earn his own living, and before the lad was nineteen he was sailing as supercargo on a ship which went to South America and China. This son helped to start his brothers in life and took care of his sisters and various other relatives.

He was comfortably well off when he married Catherine Lyman, whose father and mother, Judge and Mrs. Lyman, were important people in Northampton, Massachusetts. He had a house in Lafayette Place in New York, and later he built a house called Algonac at Newburgh, New York, on the Hudson River. He lived in China for many years, and was a member of the firm of Russell and Company.

After Warren Delano, the sea captain, died, the Fairhaven house belonged to all the brothers and sisters then living. Their descendants happened to be children of Warren Delano, for the other brothers and sisters had had no children.

Warren Delano, the third in line, was my mother-in-law's oldest brother, and the head of the family when I became engaged to Franklin. He managed the Fairhaven property and the trust fund that went with it. All the family went there whenever they wished.

I grew fond of some of the older members of my husband's family. Mr. and Mrs. Warren Delano were always kindness itself to me, as were Mrs. Forbes, Mrs. Hitch, Mrs. Price Collier and Mr. and Mrs. Frederic Delano.

Mrs. Hitch was the most philanthropic and civic-minded of my husband's relations. She was not only a moving spirit in Newburgh, where she lived in the old family house, but she reached out to New York City and belonged to many of the early state-wide and national movements for the bettering of human conditions. After my husband went into politics she took a tremendous interest in him and wrote him long letters about the local political situation.

Mr. Frederic Delano was still in business in those early years, but later, when he came to live in Washington, he devoted himself entirely to public affairs and became one of the leading citizens not only of his community but of the country, putting into public work the ability that had gained him a place of prominence in the business world and working as hard on his unpaid civic jobs as he had worked in the things he did which had brought him a substantial income.

All the members of my husband's family had business ability, imagination and good sense. That does not mean that they never made mistakes, but standing together as they did in a clan they usually retrieved their mistakes, and the whole family profited.

The Fairhaven house was roomy and had been added to from time to time. In it there were many interesting things. The coat of arms of Jehan de Lannoy, Knight of the Golden Fleece, and ancestor of the original Philippe de Lannoy who came to this country in November, 1621, hung over the door on a painted shield. Some shelves over the old-fashioned desks were filled with interesting little trinkets, and there were some beautiful Chinese vases.

Up in the attic were some ivory carvings done by men on the long whaling voyages. Many of these things are now in the New Bedford museum, but certain trunks held old ships' logs and family diaries, and these Franklin, in particular, reveled in.

Large family reunions had not taken place in my Hall family for many years, perhaps due to the fact that life at Tivoli, where my grandmother lived with Vallie, was not pleasant, or it may have been because we were scattered and had no mutual interests, being held together only by personal affection for each other as individuals.

Therefore, this first big family party at Fairhaven was to me something of a revelation. There was a sense of security which I had never known before. Without realizing it, it was a relief to me, who sensed in those years a certain feeling of insecurity in most of the relationships of my Hall family. Maude, for instance, was in love with her attractive husband, but financial difficulties were always lurking in the background. They seemed the gayest, most carefree of young people, and when they had come to England while I was at school, because Larry Waterbury (Maude's husband) was a member of the American international championship polo team, I watched with awe and envy the clothes that Maude wore and the constant gaiety. Theirs was a world in which pleasure dominated. Under the excitement and gaiety, however, lurked a constant sense of insecurity.

By 1902 I was already beginning to realize that debts sometimes hung over people's heads, that both Eddie and Vallie had squandered what money was left to them, that Pussie had trusted much of hers to gentlemen with good intentions but little business judgment who lost more than they made for her, so that by this time her income was considerably lessened.

My grandmother, as the children came of age, had less and less money because, as there had been no will, she had only her dower right in her husband's estate. She was barely able to meet her expenses and help her somewhat extravagant children.

Tissie's husband was well off and Tissie herself for years spent practically every penny she had on members of her family. Every one of them was conscious of financial strain, primarily because each one was "keeping up with the Joneses" in some way.

The Delanos were the first people I met who were able to do what they wanted to do without wondering where to obtain the money, and it was not long before I learned the reason for this. My mother-in-law taught me, but I am sure that any member of her family could have taught me just as well. They watched their pennies, which I had always seen squandered. They were generous and could afford to be in big things, because so little was ever wasted or spent in inconsequential ways.

If misfortune befell one of them, the others rallied at once. My Hall family would have rallied too, but they had so much less to rally with. The Delanos might disapprove of one another, and if so, they were not slow to express their disapproval, but let someone outside so much as hint at criticism, and the clan was ready to tear him limb from limb!

Before Franklin went to Harvard he had wanted to go into the Navy. His father felt that an only son should not choose a profession which would take him so much away from home. He wanted Franklin to study law as a preparation for any kind of business or profession he might enter later.

After graduating from Harvard, Franklin went to law school at Columbia University. His mother took a house at 200 Madison Avenue, and we had many gay times during the winter of 1905. Parties were given for us, wedding presents began to come, and my cousin Susie helped me to buy my trousseau and my linens. It was exciting and the wedding plans were complicated by the fact that Uncle Ted, at that time president of the United States, was coming to New York to give me away, and our date had to fit in with his plans. Finally, it was decided that we would be married on St. Patrick's day, March 17, 1905, because Uncle Ted was coming on for the parade that day.

Franklin and I were thrilled to be asked to stay with Auntie Bye for Uncle Ted's inauguration on March 4, 1905. Once at the Capitol, only the immediate family went inside. Franklin and I went to our seats on the steps just back of Uncle Ted and his family. I was interested and excited, but politics still meant little to me, for though I can remember the forceful manner in which Uncle Ted delivered his speech, I have no recollection of what he said! We went back to the White House for lunch, and then saw the parade and back to New York. I told myself I had seen a historical event—and I never expected to see another inauguration in the family!

Four

Early Days of Our Marriage

TWO WEEKS before our wedding all was frantic haste. Some of my brides-maids came to help me write notes of thanks for wedding presents, of course signing my name. One day we discovered to our horror that Isabella Selmes was writing "Franklin and I are so pleased with your gift," etc. and then signing her own name instead of mine!

The bridesmaids were dressed in cream taffeta with three feathers in their hair, and had tulle veils floating down their backs. Franklin had a number of ushers, and Lathrop Brown was his best man. My own dress was heavy stiff satin, with shirred tulle in the neck, and long sleeves. My grandmother Hall's rose-point Brussels lace covered the dress, and a veil of the same lace fell from my head over my long train.

The three feathers worn by the bridesmaids were reminiscent of the Roosevelt crest, and Franklin had designed a tiepin for his ushers, with three little feathers in diamonds. He also designed and gave me a gold watch, with my initials in diamonds and a pin to wear it on with the three feathers, which I still wear, though watches dangling from pins are not the fashion today.

My mother-in-law had given me a dog collar of pearls which I wore, feeling decked out beyond description. I carried a large bouquet of lilies of the valley.

The date chosen had an added significance for all my Hall family, as it was my mother's birthday. March 17 arrived. Uncle Ted came to New York from Washington, he reviewed the parade, and then came to Cousin Susie's house, where Franklin and I were married.

Many of our guests had difficulty in reaching the house because of the parade that blocked the streets. No one could enter from Fifth Avenue, and

49

the police guarded Uncle Ted so carefully that it was difficult for anyone to come in from Madison Avenue. A few irate guests arrived after the ceremony was over!

The ceremony was performed by the Reverend Endicott Peabody, the head of Groton School. My cousin Susie's drawing room opened into her mother's house, so it gave us two large rooms. We were actually married in Mrs. Ludlow's house, where an altar had been arranged in front of the fireplace, just as had been done for Pussie's wedding the year before.

After the ceremony we turned around to receive congratulations from the various members of our families and from our friends. In the meantime, Uncle Ted went into the library, where refreshments were served. Those closest to us did take time to wish us well, but the great majority of the guests were more interested in being able to see and listen to the President —and in a short time this young married couple were standing alone! The room in which the President was holding forth was filled with people laughing at his stories. I do not remember being particularly surprised at this, and I cannot remember that even Franklin seemed to mind. We simply followed the crowd and listened with the rest. Later we gathered together enough ushers and bridesmaids to cut the wedding cake, and I imagine we made Uncle Ted attend this ceremony. Then we went upstairs to dress. By this time the lion of the afternoon had gone.

We left amidst the usual shower of rice. One old friend of mine had not been able to be at the wedding. Bob Ferguson was laid up with a fever, which ever since the Spanish War, when he had been one of Uncle Ted's Rough Riders, came back at intervals, so before we went to our train we stopped in to see him and then took the train for Hyde Park, where we spent our first honeymoon. It is not customary to have two honeymoons, but we did, because my husband had to finish out his year at law school.

Our first home was a small apartment in a hotel in the West Forties in New York City for the remainder of the spring while Franklin continued his study of law.

It was lucky that my first housekeeping was so simple. I had a tiny room for Hall, so he could spend his Easter holiday with us, and he seemed to fill the entire apartment. Mending was all that was really required of me in the way of housewifely duties in those first few weeks and I was able to do that. But I knew less than nothing about ordering meals, and what little I had learned at Tivoli before I went abroad to school had completely slipped out of my mind.

When my mother-in-law went to Hyde Park for the summer we moved into her house, so I still did not have to display the depths of my ignorance as a housewife.

As soon as law school was over for the summer we went abroad—and with what qualms did I embark! How terrible to be seasick with a husband to take note of your suffering, particularly one who seemed to think that sailing was a joy! Luckily for me, the trip was calm, and all I remember about it is that we played a great many games of piquet and I invariably lost. I was not wise enough at that time to know that if one played cards with Franklin one must be prepared to win rarely. I claimed he had phenomenal luck. He claimed it was all due to skill!

For the first time we did things that I had always longed to do. We went first to London, and were horrified to find that in some way we had been identified with Uncle Ted and were given the royal suite at Brown's Hotel, with a sitting room so large that I could not find anything that I put down. We had to explain that our pocketbook was not equal to so much grandeur, but that made no difference. We lived in it for those first few days in London.

This is a city that my husband loved and I learned to like it better than I ever had before, because we poked into strange corners while he looked for books and prints, with clothes thrown in. But it was when we crossed the Channel that I was really excited.

In Paris we dined in strange places, ordering the specialties of any particular restaurant, whatever they might be. We wandered along the Seine and looked in all the secondhand stands. I bought clothes and some prints, but Franklin bought books, books, everywhere he went.

His French was good, so in Paris he did the bargaining, but when we reached Italy I spoke better Italian than he did. However, after a few days he gave up taking me when he was going to bargain, because he said he did better without me, that I accepted whatever the man said and believed it to be the gospel truth. He got along with his poor Italian, made up largely from the Latin which he had learned in school.

We went to Milan, and then to Venice in July. We spent the Fourth of July there. We had a delightful gondolier who looked like a benevolent bandit and kept us out on the canals a good part of the nights. He and I could understand each other moderately well. Occasionally, when we went on long trips he had a friend to help him, and then the Venetian dialect would fly back and forth, and he had to translate what his friend was saying.

We saw churches until my husband would look at no more, but he was never tired of sitting in the sun at one of the little tables around the piazza and recalling the history of Venice.

We went by gondola out to Murano and saw the glass blown, and ordered a set of glasses with the Roosevelt crest, and some Venetian glass dolphins for table decorations, both of which I still have.

From Venice we went north through the Dolomites and then we took a large, lumbering victoria drawn by two horses. It was a beautiful trip to Cortina, where we spent several days. My husband climbed the mountains with a charming lady, Miss Kitty Gandy. She was a few years his senior and he did not know her well at that time, but she could climb and I could not, and though I never said a word I was jealous beyond description and perfectly delighted when we started off again and drove out of the mountains. Perhaps I should add that Miss Gandy later became one of my good friends!

We stopped at Augsburg and Ulm, two quaint German cities, where we managed to find more interesting prints. Then we drove through the Alps to Saint-Moritz, where Auntie Tissie and her family were staying.

The fact that we drove meant that our luggage had to be light and I had one simple evening dress with me, which by this time was not in its first freshness. We arrived at the Palace Hotel to find a suite reserved for us, and the price appalled us both. We decided that as it was only for a few days our pocketbook would stand the strain. We forgot how much dressing went on in such hotels as this, and we soon found that our clothes were suitable only for one particular dining place, a balcony overlooking the lake, and the food seemed to be even more expensive here than it was elsewhere. We were much relieved when we started off again and drove out of Switzerland by way of Strasbourg and Nancy.

Franklin took pictures of this whole trip, some of them at the tops of passes where we were surrounded only by white peaks covered with snow. When we got home he never had a moment's hesitation as to exactly where they were taken. That extraordinarily photographic mind of his never forgot anything he had once seen.

Back in Paris, I collected my clothes, and we had some gay times, as some of Franklin's cousins were there also, and his Aunt Dora (Mrs. Forbes). She took us to see many places, and her apartment, which was always the center for the entire family when they went to Paris, was a most hospitable home to us.

In England we paid what was to me a terrifying visit to Mr. and Mrs.

Foljambe, who had a beautiful place called "Osberion in Workshop." It is in a part of England known as "the Dukeries," because of its many fine estates belonging to great titled families.

The most marvelous oak tree I have ever seen stood near this place, and we visited a castle which had a little railroad track running from the kitchen to the butler's pantry through endless corridors. We were shown the special rooms in which the plate was kept, more like the vault of a silversmith than a safe in a private house. The library had real charm. You entered it through a doorway from which a divided staircase led down several steps into a long room. A fireplace at the end held some blazing logs. On either side stacks came out into the room, and between them were arranged tables and chairs and maps, everything to make reading or study easy and delightful.

In this tremendous household there was only one bathroom. We had comfortable rooms with open fireplaces, and our tin tubs were placed before the fires in the morning, our cans of hot water beside them. The food was excellent but typically English. Dinner was formal and to my horror there were no introductions. We were guests in the house and that was considered sufficient.

I suffered tortures, and when after dinner I had to play bridge, which I played badly, my horror was increased by the fact that we were to play for money. My principles would not allow me to do this, so I was carried by my partner, but this scarcely eased my conscience. I felt like an animal in a trap, which could not get out and did not know how to act.

Soon after we left the United States, Isabelle Selmes's mother had cabled us that Isabelle was going to marry Bob Ferguson. They came over on their honeymoon to visit his family in Scotland. We were invited to his mother's house, in order that we might have a chance to see them. They were staying at a little watering place not far from Novar, the old family home in the north of Scotland. Up there the head of the house is known to the people as "the Novar," and for many years the present Lord Novar would take no title because he considered that "the Novar" was higher than anything the Crown could give him.

The dower house, where old Mrs. Ferguson lived, was a revelation to me, with its glorious view and the lovely gardens covering the side of the hill. I knew the Ferguson family well and they had been friends of our family for a long time.

Franklin tramped the moors with Hector, and one night, after a long day of exercise and many visits to crofters' cottages, I was awakened by wild shrieks from the neighboring bed. Mrs. Ferguson was delicate and I woke with a "Hush!" on my lips, for I did not want to have her disturbed. I had already discovered that my husband suffered from nightmares. On the steamer coming over he had started to walk out of the cabin in his sleep. He was docile, however, when asleep, and at my suggestion returned quietly to bed.

This time he pointed straight to the ceiling and remarked most irritably to me, "Don't you see that revolving beam?" I assured him that no such thing was there and had great difficulty in persuading him not to get out of bed and awaken the household.

When our early-morning tea with thin slices of bread and butter was brought in, I inquired if he remembered his dream. He said he did, and that he remembered being annoyed with me because I insisted on remaining in the path of the beam which threatened to fall off.

I was asked to open a bazaar while I was there. Any young English girl would have been able to do it easily, but I was quite certain I could never utter a word aloud in a public place. Finally, Franklin was induced to make a speech to the tenantry, and for years we teased him because he told the Scottish crofters that vegetables should be cooked in milk—an extravagance hardly within their means!

From there we went down to stay with the older brother, who was head of the house, Sir Ronald Ferguson, and his wife, Lady Helen, at their other house, Raith, on the Firth of Forth, just across from Edinburgh. This was a beautiful place, with wonderful woods and rhododendrons. My husband was tremendously interested because of the scientific forestry work which made these woods financially valuable and brought in revenue year by year.

I was fascinated by the prints which hung everywhere, even on the walls along the little back stairs which led to our rooms. My final thrill came when we went to dinner and I found the walls hung with Raeburn portraits of all the Ferguson ancestors. The first one I saw, "The Boy with the Open Shirt," I had known in reproductions since childhood but had never expected to see the original hanging in a friend's home.

This was also my first sight of a Scotsman in his dress kilts at dinner. Hector had worn them out on the moor, but I had really not had a chance to take them in, in all their glory, until this occasion.

One afternoon at tea I was alone with Lady Helen, when she suddenly asked me a devastating question: "Do tell me, my dear, how do you explain the difference between your national and state governments? It seems to us so confusing."

I had never realized that there were any differences to explain. I knew that we had state governments, because Uncle Ted had been governor of New York State. Luckily, Sir Ronald and my husband appeared at that moment for tea and I could ask Franklin to answer her question. He was adequate, and I registered a vow that once safely back in the United States I would find out something about my own government.

We had to be home for the opening of Columbia Law School, so our holiday, or second honeymoon, had come to an end. My mother-in-law had taken a house for us within three blocks of her own home, at 125 East 36th Street. She had furnished it and engaged our servants. We were to spend the first few days with her on landing until we could put the finishing touches on our house.

I was beginning to be an entirely dependent person—no tickets to buy, no plans to make, someone always to decide everything for me. A pleasant contrast to my former life, and I slipped into it with the greatest of ease.

The edge of my shyness was gradually wearing off through enforced contact with many people. I still suffered but not so acutely.

Either Maude or Pussie once told me that if I were stuck for conversation I should take the alphabet and start right through it. "A—Apple. Do you like apples, Mr. Smith? B—Bears. Are you afraid of bears, Mr. Jones? C—Cats. Do you have the usual feeling, Mrs. Jellyfish, about cats? Do they give you the creeps even when you do not see them?" And so forth all the way down the line, but some time had passed since anything as desperate as this had had to be done for conversational purposes. As young women go, I suppose I was fitting pretty well into the pattern of a conventional, quiet young society matron.

Five

A Woman

THE TRIP HOME was not pleasant, and I landed in New York feeling miserable. I soon found that there was a good reason, and it was quite a relief —for, little idiot that I was, I had been seriously troubled for fear I would never have any children and my husband would be much disappointed.

I had always been a particularly healthy person, and I think it was a good thing for me to be perfectly miserable for three months before every one of my six babies arrived, as it made me a little more understanding and sympathetic of the general illnesses human beings are subject to. Otherwise, I am afraid I would have been more insufferable than I am—for I always think we can do something to conquer our physical ailments.

Little by little I learned to make even these months bearable. In any case, I never let anything physical prevent my doing whatever had to be done. This is hard discipline, and I do not recommend it either as training for those around one or as a means of building character in oneself. What it really does is to kill a certain amount of the power of enjoyment. It makes one a stoic, but too much of a thing is as bad as too little, and I think it tends to make you draw away from other people and into yourself.

For the first year of my married life I was completely taken care of. My mother-in-law did everything for me. Like many other young women waiting for a first baby, I was sometimes nervous. A girlhood friend of mine said, "When I am a little afraid of the future I look around and see all the people there are and think they had to be born, and so nothing very extraordinary is happening to me."

Some emergencies of this period I remember vividly. We had invited some friends for dinner, and the cook departed the day before. It seemed impossible to get another one. I was simply petrified, because I knew

56

nothing about preparing a meal, and I spent the day going from employment office to employment office until finally I corralled someone to cook the dinner, and worried all the way through for fear the results would be disgraceful.

One would think that this might have suggested to me the wisdom of learning to cook, and though I remember I did take myself all the way up to Columbia University for some cooking lessons one winter I got little good out of it, for the school used gas ranges, and I learned to make special, fancy dishes only. What I needed to know was how to manage an old-fashioned coal range and how to cook a whole meal.

That winter my cousin Alice Roosevelt was married to Nicholas Longworth. Franklin had to go alone to the wedding because I was expecting my first child. On May 3, 1906, a girl whom we named Anna Eleanor after my mother and myself was born. Our trained nurse, a lovely person, Blanche Spring, played an important part in my life for many years. I had never had any interest in dolls or little children, and I knew absolutely nothing about handling or feeding a baby. I acquired a young and inexperienced baby's nurse from the Babies' Hospital, who knew about babies' diseases, but her inexperience made this knowledge almost a menace, for she was constantly looking for obscure illnesses and never expected that a well-fed and well-cared-for baby would move along in a normal manner.

During the next few years we observed much the same summer routine. We visited my mother-in-law at Hyde Park for a time and then went up to stay with her at Campobello. My mother-in-law was abroad for a part of that summer of 1906, and we had her house at Campobello. Ordinarily my husband sailed up or down the coast in the little schooner *Half Moon*, taking some friends with him, and took perhaps one or two short cruises during the summer across to Nova Scotia or to various places along the coast. He was a good sailor and pilot, and nearly always calculated his time so well that rarely do I remember his causing us any anxiety by being delayed. As a rule, he sailed into the harbor ahead of his schedule.

If they were going on a cruise from Campobello, I had to stock the boat up with food for the first few days, and after their return they always told me what delicious things they had had to eat on the boat. Apparently their idea of perfection was a combination of sausages, syrup and pancakes for every meal, varied occasionally by lobsters or scrambled eggs. My husband was the cook as well as the captain and was proud of his prowess.

One evening the next winter, we were having some people in to dinner, the nurse was out, and about six-thirty, after having her bottle and being put to bed, instead of placidly going to sleep, Anna began to howl, and she howled without stopping while I dressed for dinner. Our guests began to arrive. I called the doctor. He asked me if I thought she might have a little wind, and was I sure I had gotten up all the bubbles after her last bottle? I did not dare tell him I had completely forgotten to put her over my shoulder and had no idea whether the bubbles had come up or not. He suggested that I turn her on her tummy and rub her back, so, with my guests arriving downstairs, I told Franklin he would have to start dinner without me. I picked up my howling baby, put her over my knee on her tummy, and in a few minutes she smiled and gurgled. After I had rubbed her back for some time she got rid of her troubles and, when put back to bed, went to sleep like a lamb. I went down to dinner, but was so wrought up by this time that I felt I had to go and look at her several times during the evening, and finally succeeded in waking her up before the nurse came home. I was obliged to leave my guests again before they departed. After this experience I registered a vow that never again would I have a dinner on the nurse's day out.

I know now that what we should have done was to have no servants those first few years; so I could have acquired knowledge and self-confidence and other people could not fool me about either the housework or the children. However, my bringing up had been such that this never occurred to me, nor did it occur to any of the older people who were closest to me. Had I done this, my subsequent troubles would have been avoided and my children would have had far happier childhoods. As it was, for years I was afraid of my nurses, who from this time on were usually trained English nurses who ordered me around quite as much as they ordered the children.

As a rule, they kept the children in pretty good health and I think were really fond of them, but I had a silly theory that you should trust the people with your children and back up their discipline. As a result, my children were frequently unjustly punished, because I was unprepared to be a practical housekeeper, wife or mother.

In the winter of 1907 I had a rather severe operation and was successful in getting Miss Spring to come back to me. Dr. Albert H. Ely, who was our family doctor, performed this operation in our own house, and I was found to be considerably weaker than anyone had dreamed. As a result,

they thought I was not coming out of the ether, and I returned to consciousness to hear a doctor say, "Is she gone? Can you feel her pulse?"

The pain was considerable, but as my own impulse was never to say how
I felt I do not think I mentioned this until some time later on. I simply
refused to speak to those who approached me, and they probably thought
that I was far more ill than I really was.

During the time my husband was at law school he had long summer holidays which made it possible for us to be at Campobello. In the summer of
1907 Mr. and Mrs. Henry Parish came to stay with us. I went with my
husband to meet them on their arrival on the evening train. A thick fog
made crossing the bay blind sailing, but my husband prided himself that
with the engine he could do it and strike the exact spot he was headed for.
We reached Eastport, Maine, without any mishap, and got our cousins
aboard.

On the return trip the compass light went out. Someone brought my
husband a lantern and hung it on the main boom so he could see his course.
He rang his bell for slow speed at the proper moment, but no buoy appeared for us to pick up, no land was in sight. After proceeding cautiously
for some little time, the man on the bowsprit called out, "Hard aport," and
there, above us, loomed the Lubec docks, with just enough room to sheer
off. Much annoyed and completely mystified, my husband reset his course
for Campobello, realizing we had come through a narrow passageway and
just by luck had not found ourselves in the tide running through the Narrows. About three minutes later "Hard over" came from the bowsprit, and
we just missed a tiny island with one tree on it, which was entirely off our
course.

It dawned on my husband that the lantern swinging from the boom was
of iron and had been attracting the compass! From there on we used
matches, and found our way through the narrow pass and back to our buoy
without any further difficulties. Mr. and Mrs. Parish had an uncomfortable
time and I think were relieved that five days of solid fog made further
sailing impossible for the rest of their stay.

I was having difficulty that summer with my brother. I nagged and expected too much of him. In my most exasperating Griseldaish mood I
refused to take any further responsibility. One of my most maddening
habits, which must infuriate all those who know me, is this habit,
when my feelings are hurt or when I am annoyed, of simply shutting

up like a clam, not telling anyone what is the matter, and being much too obviously humble and meek, feeling like a martyr and acting like one. Years later a much older friend of mine pointed this out to me and said that my Griselda moods were the most maddening things in the world. I think they have improved since I have been able to live more lightly and have a certain amount of humor about myself. They were just a case of being sorry for myself and letting myself enjoy my misery.

But those first years I was serious and a certain kind of orthodox goodness was my ideal and ambition. I fully expected that my young husband would have these same ideas, ideals and ambitions. What a tragedy it was if in any way he offended against these ideals of mine—and, amusingly enough, I do not think I ever told him what I expected!

On December 23, 1907, our first boy, James, was born, and with what relief and joy I welcomed him, for again I had been worried for fear I would never have a son, knowing that both my mother-in-law and my husband wanted a boy to name after my husband's father.

This winter of 1907-08 I still think of as one of the times in my life which I would rather not live over again. We could not find any food that would agree with the new baby. Miss Spring was pressed into service, and we turned one of our living rooms into a bedroom, for we had meant to put the two babies together, but when the younger one cried every night all night that was not practicable.

I had a curious arrangement out of one of my back windows for airing the children, a kind of box with wire on the sides and top. Anna was put out there for her morning nap. On several occasions she wept loudly, and finally one of my neighbors called up and said I was treating my children inhumanly and that she would report me to the S.P.C.C. if I did not take her in at once! This was a shock to me, for I thought I was being a most modern mother. I knew fresh air was necessary, but I learned later that the sun is more important than the air, and I had her on the shady side of the house!

I also learned that healthy babies do not cry long, and that it is wise to look for the reason when a baby does any amount of prolonged crying.

My mother-in-law thought that our house was too small, and that year she bought a plot and built in East 65th Street two houses, Nos. 47 and 49. Charles A. Platt, an architect of great taste, did a remarkable piece of work. The houses were narrow, but he made the most of every inch of space and built them so that the dining rooms and drawing rooms could be thrown together and made practically one big room.

My early dislike of any kind of scolding had developed now into a dislike for any kind of discussion and so, instead of taking an interest in these houses, one of which I was to live in, I left everything to my mother-in-law and my husband. I was growing dependent on my mother-in-law, requiring her help on almost every subject, and never thought of asking for anything that I thought would not meet with her approval.

She was a very strong character, but because of her marriage to an older man she had disciplined herself into living his life and enjoying his belongings, and as a result she felt that young people should cater to older people. She gave great devotion to her own family and longed for their love and affection in return. She was somewhat jealous of anything that might mean a really deep attachment outside the family circle. She had warm friends of her own, but she did not believe that friendship could be on the same par with family relations.

Her husband had told her never to live with her children, that it was one thing to have children dependent upon you but intolerable to be dependent on them. This she repeated to me often, but I doubt if she realized that with certain natures it is advisable to force independence and responsibility upon them young.

In the autumn of 1908 I did not know what was the matter with me, but I remember that a few weeks after we moved into the new house on East 65th Street I sat in front of my dressing table and wept, and when my bewildered young husband asked me what on earth was the matter with me, I said I did not like to live in a house which was not in any way mine, one that I had done nothing about and which did not represent the way I wanted to live. Being an eminently reasonable person, he thought I was quite mad and told me so gently, and said I would feel different in a little while and left me alone until I should become calmer.

I pulled myself together and realized that I was acting like a little fool, but there was a good deal of truth in what I had said, for I was not developing any individual taste or initiative. I was simply absorbing the personalities of those about me and letting their tastes and interests dominate me.

Because my husband played golf I made a valiant effort at Campobello one year to practice every day, trying to learn how to play. After days of practice I went out with my husband, and after watching me for a few minutes he remarked that he thought I might as well give it up! My old sensitiveness about my inability to play games made me give it up then and there. I never attempted anything but walking with my husband for many years to come.

For ten years I was always just getting over having a baby or about to have one, and so my occupations were considerably restricted during this period. I did, however, take lessons rather intermittently, in an effort to keep up my French, German and Italian. I did a great deal of embroidery during these years, a great deal of knitting, and an amount of reading which seems incredible to me today when other things take up so much of my time. I doubt that there was a novel or a biography or any book that was widely discussed in the circles in which we moved which I did not read. This does not mean, of course, that I read in a wide field, for we moved still with a restricted group of friends.

On March 18, 1909, another baby was born to us, the biggest and most beautiful of all the babies—the first baby Franklin. Because of all the trouble I had had with James, I was worried about his food and kept Miss Spring with us for several months. The baby seemed to be getting on well, but I loved having her with us and insisted on keeping her until after we had been in Campobello for some time. She did not leave until sometime around the early part of August.

I had an English nurse then for the other two children. I also had a young German girl, and together they took charge of the three children.

In the autumn we moved back to Hyde Park, and I was beginning to go up and down between New York and Hyde Park. All of a sudden they notified me that all the children had the flu and that baby Franklin was very ill. No one knew how serious it might be. I dashed back, taking Miss Spring and a New York doctor with me. We spent a few harrowing days there, moved the baby to New York, but his heart seemed affected and, in spite of all we could do, he died on November 8, not quite eight months old. We took him to Hyde Park to bury him and, to this day, so many years later, I can stand by his tiny stone in the churchyard and see the little group of people gathered around his tiny coffin, and remember how cruel it seemed to leave him out there alone in the cold.

I was young and morbid and reproached myself bitterly for having done so little about the care of this baby. I felt he had been left too much to the nurse, and I knew too little about him, and that in some way I must be to blame. I even felt that I had not cared enough about him, and I made myself and all those around me most unhappy during that winter. I was even a little bitter against my poor young husband who occasionally tried to make me see how idiotically I was behaving.

My next child, Elliott Roosevelt, was born at 49 East 65th Street on September 23, 1910. I left Campobello early that summer to await his arrival in New York City. The other children returned to Hyde Park with my mother-in-law. She was in and out of New York and so was my husband, who was making his first campaign for state senator.

After my husband graduated from law school and was admitted to the bar, he worked in the firm of Carter, Ledyard and Milburn, a much-respected and old-established firm in New York City. He was doing well and Mr. Ledyard liked him, but Franklin had a desire for public service, partly encouraged by Uncle Ted's advice to all young men and partly by the glamour of Uncle Ted's example. Mr. Ledyard was genuinely disturbed but my husband decided to accept the nomination in his district, which for thirty-two years had never elected a Democrat.

My husband's branch and many of the Roosevelt family had been Democrats until the Civil War, when they became Abraham Lincoln Republicans. Later most of them returned to their Democratic allegiance, but some remained Republicans.

I listened to all his plans with great interest. It never occurred to me that I had any part to play. I felt I must acquiesce in whatever he might decide and be willing to go to Albany. My part was to make the necessary household plans and to do this as easily as possible if he should be elected. I was having a baby, and for a time at least that was my only mission in life.

Franklin was conducting a novel campaign, for no one had ever before tried to visit every small four-corners store, every village and every town. He talked to practically every farmer and when the votes were counted that election day my husband was the first Democrat to win in thirty-two years. At the same time, through that firsthand contact with the people, he had learned much of their thinking and of their needs.

I went with Franklin to one meeting before the end of the campaign. It was the first political speech I had ever heard him make. He spoke slowly, and every now and then there would be a long pause and I would be worried for fear he would never go on. What a long time ago that seems!

He looked thin, then, tall, high-strung, and at times nervous. White skin and fair hair, deep-set blue eyes and clear-cut features. No lines as yet in his face, but at times a set look of his jaw denoted that this apparently pliable youth had strength and Dutch obstinacy in his make-up.

Franklin made a good many friends in that campaign; one of them, Thomas Lynch, of Poughkeepsie, was to be a close and warm friend and follower from then on. He believed firmly that Franklin would someday be president, and showed it by buying two bottles of champagne before Prohibition, putting them away and bringing them out in Chicago in 1932 just after Franklin's nomination. Everybody at headquarters had a sip from a paper cup to toast future success.

We rented our house in New York City, and I suppose I must have gone to Albany and looked at the house which we took on State Street, though I have no recollection of doing so. I had a new English nurse with the children, Anna, James, and Baby Elliott. I was so nervous about this new baby that we took a wet nurse to be sure of having him properly fed, as it had been suggested that the first baby Franklin, who had always been a bottle-baby, might have been stronger and better able to stand his illness if he had been breast-fed.

That autumn it was also discovered that James had a murmur in his heart, and in order to take proper care of him he must not be allowed to walk up and down stairs. He was a fairly tall though thin little boy, and quite a load to carry. However, up and down steps we carried him all the rest of that winter.

Six

My Introduction to Politics

WE ARRANGED for a reception to be held in our Albany house on the afternoon of January 1 for as many of Franklin's constituents as wished to come. We arrived in the morning, and naturally we were not very well settled. I brought three servants besides the nurses, and caterers were in the house arranging for the reception, which went on interminably. People from the three counties wandered in and out for three solid hours. When it was all over and some of the debris had been removed and the caterers were out of the house, my mother-in-law and I started to move the furniture around and make the house more homelike.

I have always had a passion for being completely settled as quickly as possible, wherever I lived. I want all my photographs hung, all my ornaments out, and everything in order within the first twenty-four hours. Dirt and disorder make me positively uncomfortable.

I sallied forth that next morning to do my marketing. I received my first shock when a lady stopped me on the street with, "You must be Mrs. Roosevelt, for your children are the only ones I do not know." All my life I had lived in big cities, rarely knowing my neighbors. The realization that everybody up and down the street would know what we were doing and would pay attention to us was a great surprise.

For the first time I was going to live on my own: neither my mother-in-law nor Mrs. Paris was going to be within call. I wrote my mother-in-law almost every day, as I had for many years when away from her, but I had to stand on my own feet now and I wanted to be independent. I was beginning to realize that something within me craved to be an individual.

People were kind and I soon made friends and was very busy that year. Occasionally I went to the gallery in the Capitol and listened to whatever might be the order of business. I came to identify interesting figures. Senator Tom Grady could make a better speech than many people who are considered great orators today. Bob Wagner, "Big Tim" Sullivan, Christy Sullivan, Senator Sage, old Senator Brackett, who looked like a church deacon and was probably as wily a politician as ever paced the Senate floor, all stood out as individuals on the floor of the Senate. In the Assembly I had my first glimpse of Al Smith.

I was at home every afternoon and had tea with the children. I read to them or played with them till they went to bed. I tried having little Anna lunch with us, but after spending a solid hour over the meal on our first attempt I returned her to the nursery. Anna and James and the younger nurse had their room over the big library at the back of the house. The baby and his nurse were in the room next to ours.

Anna was fair-skinned like her father, with good features, blue eyes and straight hair which was bleached almost white by the sun. James was darker as to both hair and complexion, looking in this particular more like me. Luckily for them all, the children inherited their looks from their father's side of the family. One or two of them have eyes like my side of the Roosevelts, but eyes happen to have been rather good in that branch of the family. I had prominent front teeth, not a very good mouth and chin, but these were not handed down to any of my children.

Here in Albany began for the first time a dual existence for me, which was to last all the rest of my life. Public service, whether my husband was in or out of office, was to be a part of our daily life from now on. To him it was a career in which he was completely absorbed. He probably could not have formulated his political philosophy at that time as he could later, but the science of government was interesting—and people, the ability to understand them, the play of his own personality on theirs, was a fascinating study to him.

I still lived under the compulsion of my early training; duty was perhaps the motivating force of my life, often excluding what might have been joy or pleasure. I looked at everything from the point of view of what I ought to do, rarely from the standpoint of what I wanted to do. There were times when I almost forgot that there was such a thing as wanting anything. So I took an interest in politics. It was a wife's duty to be interested in whatever interested her husband, whether it was politics, books or a particular dish for dinner. This was the attitude with which I approached that first winter in Albany.

Here, for the first time, a man who was to become a very close friend of my husband's came upon the scene. I hardly remember meeting him. He was a newspaper correspondent, an old hand in the Albany political game, Louis McHenry Howe by name. He lived in Albany with his wife and daughter, but his home for years had been in Saratoga, so he knew the countryside and had many old friends. I saw little or nothing of the Howes that first year. I still felt myself a good deal of a stranger.

The fate of an insurgent group who stood with my husband in an early senatorial fight against Tammany influence was my first introduction into the grimmer side of machine politics. One man had a little country newspaper and depended largely on government printing of notices for his financial success. The year after, he was given none, as punishment for opposing the Democratic machine, and his paper failed. Similar stories came to us from various sources, and my blood boiled. My husband was not vulnerable but many of his friends were not in so independent a position. I realized that you might be a slave and not a public servant if your bread and butter could be taken from you; and, if you grew too fond of public life, it might exact compromises even if finances were not involved.

After the legislature adjourned I took the children to Hyde Park as usual and later to Campobello, pursuing our usual routine. My husband again had a good deal of time in summer to be with us, though he did have to spend some time in his district, and the legislature met again in August for a short session.

When I had first gone to Campobello there lived next to my mother-in-law a charming woman, a Mrs. Kuhn from Boston. When she died it was found that in her will she suggested Mrs. Roosevelt might want to buy her property, including a little point of land on the Bay of Fundy side of the island, and her house with all its furnishings, even china and glass and linen. She asked that it be offered to Mrs. Roosevelt at a nominal price in case she wanted it for her son.

My mother-in-law bought it and gave it to us, and this house became a great source of joy to me and a place with which I think my children have many happy associations.

The winter of 1912 found us back in Albany in a house on Elk Street. My first cousin, Theodore Douglas Robinson, was elected to the Assembly and came to take his seat that winter. His wife, Helen, was my husband's half niece—J. R. ("Rosy") Roosevelt's daughter—and so our relationship was extremely close and complicated.

Of course, Teddy and Franklin were on opposite sides politically, and one was in the Senate and the other in the Assembly. Both Teddy and Helen had a few close friends who were not great friends of ours, and they moved in a gayer and younger group, on the whole.

I was always more comfortable with older people, and when I found myself with groups of young people I still felt inadequate to meet them on their own gay, light terms. I think I must have spoiled a good deal of fun for Franklin because of this inability to feel at ease with a gay group, though I do not remember that I ever made much objection to his being with them so long as I was allowed to stay at home.

I remember feeling a little responsible that year for the wives of some of the new assemblymen and for the wives of some of the newspapermen, who, I had been told, were very lonely. I religiously called on them and tried to have them occasionally at my house.

I remember little of what my husband did in the legislature, except that he came out for woman suffrage. He always insisted that Inez Mulholland sitting on his desk had converted him but as a matter of fact he came out for woman suffrage two months before that memorable visit.

I was shocked, as I had never given the question serious thought, for I took it for granted that men were superior creatures and knew more about politics than women did, and while I realized that if my husband was a suffragist I probably must be, too, I cannot claim to have been a feminist in those early days.

I had lost a good deal of my crusading spirit where the poor were concerned, because I had been told I had no right to go into the slums or into the hospitals, for fear of bringing diseases home to my children, so I had fallen into the easier way of sitting on boards and giving small sums to this or that charity and thinking the whole of my duty to my neighbor was done.

I was not a snob, largely because I never really thought about why you asked people to your house or claimed them as friends. Anyone who came was grist to my mill, because I was beginning to get interested in human beings, and I found that almost everyone had something interesting to contribute to my education.

In 1909 my brother Hall had entered Harvard College. He was ready for graduation in 1912 and won his Phi Beta Kappa key, though he belonged to the class of 1913. In the spring of 1912 the authorities allowed him to go with my husband on a trip to Panama. Never having been fond

of the sea, and also being anxious whenever I went away from the children
for a long period of time, I did not accompany them on the first part of
their trip. Another member of the legisture, Mayhew Wainwright, joined
them, and they had, from all accounts, a delightful time.

In June of 1912 my brother was married to Margaret Richardson of
Boston. Hall was not quite twenty-one and she was twenty when they
started off on their honeymoon to Europe.

In the latter part of the month, my husband took me to my first political
convention. We had taken a house in Baltimore with Mr. and Mrs. Mont-
gomery Hare and Mr. and Mrs. James Byrnes.

That convention was an exciting one. In front of me in the convention
hall sat Mrs. August Belmont, who registered righteous indignation and
said she would go out and fight the party when William Jennings Bryan
practically read her husband out of it.

I understood nothing of what was going on, but I watched with keen
interest the demonstration for Champ Clark, and was appalled when his
daughter was carried around the room. The demonstrations all seemed
senseless to me, and my opinion of conventions changed little for a
number of years.

It was extremely hot. I understood little about the fight for Woodrow
Wilson's nomination, though my husband was deeply interested and was
spending a great deal of time trying to bring it about. Finally, I decided
my husband would hardly miss my company, as I rarely laid eyes on him
anyway and the children should go to Campobello, so I went home and
took them up there and waited to hear the result. I received a wild
telegram of triumph when Mr. Wilson was finally nominated. It read:

MRS. F. D. ROOSEVELT
CAMPOBELLO EASTPORT MAINE
WILSON NOMINATED THIS AFTERNOON   ALL MY PLANS VAGUE   SPLENDID
TRIUMPH   FRANKLIN.

We came down early from Campobello, because my husband had
another campaign on hand. We traveled by boat, and neither of us gave
much thought to the fact that we brushed our teeth with the water
in the stateroom pitchers. We settled the children at Hyde Park. Franklin
laid his plans for the campaign, and then we went down to an entirely

"put up" house in New York City, which we had taken back from the people who had rented it the winter before. We were to spend only one night and our old friend, Ronald Ferguson, who was over from Scotland, was to dine with us. The evening came but my husband was too ill to go out to dinner. He had a low fever and was feeling miserable. I did all I could for him, and took Ronald out to a restaurant by myself.

My husband was still miserable the next morning, so I got a strange doctor, as our regular doctor was out of town. He could not explain the fever. No one could understand what was the matter with him. I was taking complete care of him. We had a caretaker in the house who did what cooking was necessary, and I ran up and down stairs with trays, made his bed, gave him his medicine, and all went well except for the fact that at certain times of the day I felt peculiar. My husband had to take a nap after lunch every day, and I was glad enough to do the same, for the back of my head ached and I was hardly able to drag myself around. It never occurred to me that I, too, might be ill.

After this had gone on for about ten days my mother-in-law came to town one evening, having grown anxious about her son, and I told her that, as she was there, I would have my hair curled and go to bed, because I felt miserable. She kissed me and exclaimed, "You must have a fever!" She insisted that I take my temperature and we found that it was 102. The doctor came and I went to bed, and the next day tests were taken and it was discovered that I had typhoid fever. Franklin had had it when he was a little boy, so he was running only a low temperature, but they now thought he had it also. I proceeded to have a perfectly normal case, and with my usual ability to come back quickly I was up and on my feet while Franklin was still in bed and feeling miserable and looking like Robert Louis Stevenson at Vailima.

In the meantime the campaign was on, and now Louis Howe, the quiet, even then rather gnomelike little newspaper man from Albany, came to the rescue. He had grown interested in my husband at the time of the senatorial fight, and when Franklin asked him to run the campaign he accepted. Going to Dutchess County, he laid his plans and carried the district for a man who was flat on his back at the time.

Louis was an astute politician, a wise reader of newspapers and of human beings, but he was somewhat impractical, in spots. A checkbook was one of the things Louis did not understand. My husband gave him a checkbook and a certain amount of money in the bank. Each time Louis came to see my husband he still insisted that he had money in the bank. Finally, my husband was notified that the account was overdrawn. Louis still insisted he had money on hand, and when Franklin looked over the checkbook he found that Louis always added the amount of the check to the balance instead of deducting it, so of course the amount went up instead of down.

I was not favorably impressed with Louis at this time because he smoked a great many cigarettes! Remember, I was still a Puritan. I felt that his smoking spoiled the fresh air that my husband should have in his bedroom, and I was very disapproving whenever he came down to report on the campaign. I lost sight entirely of the fact that he was winning the campaign and that without him my husband would have worried himself to more of a wreck than he was and probably lost the election. I simply made a nuisance of myself over those visits and his cigarettes. I often wonder now how they bore with me in those days. I had no sense of values whatever and was still rigid in my standard of conduct.

My husband was re-elected, thanks to Louis Howe. I put the New York house in order and moved the children there, as it was too late to rent it and we had decided not to take a house in Albany for the winter, but to live in two rooms at the Ten Eyck Hotel. We commuted between New York and Albany. I went to Albany every Monday afternoon and returned to New York every Thursday morning to be with the children.

During the winter there was some talk of the possibility of my husband's being invited to join the administration in Washington but I was too much taken up with the family to give it much thought.

Seven

Washington

IN APRIL, Franklin was sent for by the President, and I stayed in New York waiting to hear what would be our fate. In a short time we got word that my husband had been appointed assistant secretary of the navy. He resigned from the state Senate and took up the work in Washington. There was an epidemic of smallpox at the time, so we were both vaccinated.

My husband had taken rooms at the Powhatan Hotel in Washington, and wanted me to come down for a time that spring. I dashed to Auntie Bye, who was in Farmington, Connecticut, to ask her what were the duties of an assistant secretary's wife. My heart sank as she gave me careful instructions on my calls. This enormous burden is no longer carried by the wives of government officials. It became impracticable during the war.

One thing Auntie Bye impressed on me was that as the wife of the assistant secretary of the navy my duty was first, last and all the time to the Navy itself. She said, "you will find that many of the young officers' wives have a hard time because they must keep up their position on very small pay. You can do a great deal to make life pleasant for them when they are in Washington, and that is what you should do."

I had come a long way since I moved up to Albany, for then I never could have paid those first calls and repeated that formula, "I am Mrs. Franklin D. Roosevelt. My husband has just come as assistant secretary of the navy." House after house I visited and explained myself in this way. My shyness was wearing off rapidly.

The autumn of 1913 we took Auntie Bye's house at 1733 N Street. It was a comfortable old-fashioned house, and the two old colored servants, Millie and Francis, who had taken care of Uncle Will when Auntie Bye

72

was away, agreed to take care of it in summer and look after Franklin when he was there alone.

There was a little garden at the back with a lovely rose arbor on the side where one could have breakfast in the late spring or summer days, and even dine on summer evenings. This little garden was kept in order by a delightful man, William Reeves, whom I got to know well. His reticence was really remarkable. We lived in that house four years, and though I talked with him often it was not until I came to the White House in 1933 that I discovered that Mr. Reeves was the head gardener there and that it had been because of his position there that he had gone to Auntie Bye during Uncle Ted's administration. He had kept it up because of his affection for her and his interest in her garden.

When we moved down to Washington my mother-in-law, as usual, helped us to get settled. We had bought a car and brought a young chauffeur with us from Hyde Park, and I had to begin in earnest to pay my calls.

My husband had asked Louis Howe to come down as his assistant in the Navy Department; Louis moved his wife and two children, one of them a fairly well-grown girl and the other a baby boy, into an apartment not far from us.

Anna was going to school with the Misses Eastman, and James began his schooling that autumn in the little Potomac School. I remember that winter primarily as one in which I spent every afternoon paying calls. We lived a kind of social life I had never known before, dining out night after night and having people dine with us about once a week.

We discovered early that unless we made some attempt to see a few people at regular intervals we would never see anyone informally, and so once every two weeks or thereabouts a few of us dined together regularly. This group consisted of Secretary of the Interior Franklin K. Lane and Mrs. Lane, a charming couple who appealed to young and old; Mr. and Mrs. Adolph Miller, old friends of the Lanes; Mr. and Mrs. William Phillips, and ourselves. William Phillips was in the State Department, and he and Caroline were old friends of ours. We put formality behind us for these evenings, and did not even seat the secretary of the interior according to rank. Franklin and I still stayed home on Sunday evenings and continued the informal Sunday evening suppers which we had always had since our marriage. I cooked eggs on the table in a chafing dish, served cold meat and salad, a cold dessert and cocoa.

I tried at first to do without a secretary, but found that it took me such endless hours to arrange my calling list, and answer and send invitations, that I finally engaged one for three mornings a week.

When I was first married I discovered that my husband was a collector. In every other respect he was both careful and economical. I never knew him in those early days to take a cab when he could take a streetcar. I have often seen him carry his bag down the street and board a car at the corner. He took great care of his clothes, never spent a great deal on himself, and there were many things that we felt we could not afford. After our first little car, we went without one for some time; and when we moved to Washington the first two cars that we had were second-hand, until I finally persuaded my husband that we spent more on repairs and had less use out of them than we would have out of a new car. The new car that we finally bought lasted until we left Washington, when he again decided that we did not need a car and sold it.

As a collector he was careful, too, and much of his collection was acquired at reasonable prices, because not many people were interested, at that time, in his field. He really knew about everything he bid for at auctions or acquired after spending hours in old bookstores or print shops.

His interest was in the American Navy and he collected books and letters and prints and models of ships. The collection was fairly sizable and interesting when he went to Washington as assistant secretary of the navy, but those years in the Navy Department gave him great opportunity to add to it. He was offered and acquired an entire trunkful of letters which included the love letters of one of our early naval officers. He also acquired a letter written by a captain to his wife describing receipt of the news of George Washington's death and his subsequent action on passing Mount Vernon. He is said to have instituted a custom which every navy ship has followed from that day to this, and which varies only according to the personnel carried by the ship. All the ships lower the flag to half mast, man the rail, toll the bell and, if a bugler is on board, blow taps.

Franklin also acquired a good model of the old *Constitution*, and his collection grew apace. At different times he collected other things. For instance, there was a period when he was fond of small chapbooks, children's books and classics published in diminutive editions, and first editions of every kind always attracted him, though he never followed any one line. Stamps were also an interest of long standing.

I have often wondered why he never handed down this love of collecting to any of our children. My only explanation is that living in the house with a collector may give everyone else the feeling that only one person in a household can indulge this taste, and even then it is a question of whether the family will have to move out in order to keep the collection intact and properly housed!

With the autumn of 1913 my life in Washington as the wife of a minor official really began. I could have learned much about politics and government, for I had plenty of opportunity to meet and talk with interesting men and women. As I look back upon it, however, I think the whole of my life remained centered in the family. The children were still small, two more were to be born during this period, and outside of the exclusively personal life there was the social aspect, which then seemed to me most important.

Nearly all the women at that time were the slaves of the Washington social system. There were two women who broke loose. One was Martha Peters, wife of Congressman Andrew J. Peters, of Massachusetts, and a sister of William Phillips. She did not care for large social functions and did not think it was her duty to her husband's career to spend every afternoon of her life paying calls on the wives of other public men.

The other woman was Alice Longworth, quite frankly too much interested in the political questions of the day to waste her time calling on women who were, after all, not important to her scheme of life. She liked the social side, but she liked her own particular kind of social life. She wanted to know the interesting people but did not want to be bored doing uninteresting things. Her house was a center of gaiety and of interesting gatherings. Everyone who came to Washington coveted an introduction to her and an invitation to her house.

I was appalled by the independence and courage displayed by these two ladies. I was perfectly certain that I had nothing to offer of an individual nature and that my only chance of doing my duty as the wife of a public official was to do exactly as the majority of women were doing.

My calls began the winter of 1914 under poor auspices, for I was feeling miserable again, as another baby was coming along the following August. Somehow or other I made my rounds every afternoon, and from ten to thirty calls were checked off my list day after day. Mondays the wives of the justices of the Supreme Court; Tuesdays the members of Congress. How many times I have wondered why my New York congressmen moved from place to place so frequently! They rarely had houses, their wives seldom came down, and to leave cards on them I had to climb up stairs in rooming houses and search every large and small hotel! Wednesdays the Cabinet, and here was a problem to be met. If Mrs. Daniels invited me to be with her on that afternoon I could not be calling on the other members of the Cabinet. Thursdays the wives of senators, and Fridays the diplomats. Miscellaneous people were wedged in on whatever days were printed on their cards or, if they had no days, on any days you happened to be near their homes. Saturdays and Sundays were free for the children.

Just as Mr. Daniels was a kind and understanding chief, Mrs. Daniels was a kind and understanding wife, and did not expect me to be with her every Wednesday. Later in the winter I tried to stay at home on Wednesdays and receive anyone who came to call on me. I had my first experience then cf entertaining ladies who spoke in three different languages and of being the only person able to interpret what was being said by one to the other!

My husband frequently came home for luncheon and brought some men with him, more often after the war began than in the first years, when he had more time for the Metropolitan Club and games of golf. This was the game he enjoyed above all others. However, when he did come home he wanted a short lunch and no time wasted. They must be able to talk freely, so I developed a habit which I have always retained. I have a little silver bell put beside my place at every meal. It belonged to my mother and is part of the recollection of my earliest days—Old Mother Hubbard with her dog under her arm. It is never far from my hand at meals. When I ring, the servants come in and take the plates away, pass the next course, and then withdraw to the pantry and stay there until I ring again. This was made the rule in Washington and has been continued wherever I am, for conversation can flow more freely. It was necessary during World War I, when conversations were frequently held which must not go beyond the people seated at the table; and I have found it always relieves a certain restraint at the table not to have someone standing behind a chair or hovering in the room.

Here, as in Albany, I tried to get in from my calls by five o'clock so as to have tea at home, and the children were always with me for an hour before their own supper and bedtime.

Somewhere around the middle of that winter—I think in early March —my husband was sent on an inspection trip to the West Coast and I accompanied him.

When we arrived in each place, a naval aide appeared and told us what we should do, for which I was thankful. I was still new at getting on and off naval ships, with all the ceremony attached thereto.

The first time Anna was with us when we bobbed up and down in a little boat, and my husband received the seventeen-gun salute fired for the assistant secretary of the navy, she buried her head in my lap because she was sensitive to noises. Afterwards she carried cotton to put in her ears. I was totally unprepared the first time the salute came, but, as I was somewhat deaf even then, the noise did not bother me.

When it came to boarding a battleship I had to wait to be told whether I went ahead of my husband or whether he went ahead of me. What did I do while he stood at salute, whom did I shake hands with, and what parts of the ship should I not visit; and when we came to leave, did I go first or last? All these questions and many more worried me during these first inspection trips. But gradually I learned. Somehow my husband seemed to know all this without coaching, and I have always wondered how he absorbed knowledge where I had to struggle and ask innumerable questions. Perhaps he grew curious earlier in life. In any case, he was able to answer most of the questions we asked him; and when we thought on occasion we had him trapped and went to an encyclopedia to prove him wrong, almost invariably he was right.

On this trip, as on most other official trips, our engagements began at nine or ten o'clock in the morning and ended somewhere around midnight. After that I wrote my letters and packed my bags.

On all these trips I started out with a great deal of apprehension, in spite of the fact that I loved seeing new places. I hated to leave my children; but once out, my fears were quiescent until we were about two days from home, and then they revived in full force, and the last night I usually imagined all the terrible things that might happen to the children before we saw them again. They might fall out of a window, or into the fire, or be run over! My mother-in-law always had an eye to the children when we were away, so there was really no cause for anxiety, but during those years they had the usual runs of colds and earaches and tonsils which are the lot of children, and, in addition, many of the less serious childish illnesses.

Any woman with children knows that she must be prepared for all kinds of vicissitudes, but it takes time to accustom yourself to these things. At first you feel that you or someone else should have prevented whatever goes wrong. Later you learn that no amount of care will ward off the accidents and all you can do is to meet them, as they come along, with a calm and steadfast spirit.

That summer of 1914 the children and I went to Campobello, as usual, but war clouds were gathering over Europe and Washington was full of anxiety. My baby was due to arrive in August and plans had been made for the doctor who had taken care of me and my four other children to fly up and be with me for the event. Miss Spring, the same nurse who was always with me on these occasions and who managed to come as often as possible when the children had any ailments, came up to keep me company. My husband came for a short holiday, my mother-in-law was in her own cottage nearby. But, instead of waiting until the right time, I woke my husband on the night of August 16, to tell him I thought he had better go to Lubec and get our old friend, Dr. Bennett. My mother-in-law heard my husband call down to the men on the *Half Moon* to bring in the little boat so he could sail over, so she came running over from her cottage to find out what was wrong.

I made everyone wait around for the whole of the next day, and the baby did not arrive until early evening on August 17. I felt guilty, for I knew Dr. Bennett had many other patients, probably much more in need of his care than I was, and I tried to make him leave, but he felt responsible and insisted on sitting around. At last it was all over and he remarked to Miss Spring, "Why, she is just like one of us. I never took care of summer people before."

Franklin Junior, the second baby to be given this name, progressed satisfactorily and I never had a pleasanter convalescence.

Franklin had arrived on July 25, but on the 29th he had a telegram to return to Washington because war seemed imminent. He wired me from there the various events as they occurred before he returned to Campobello. None of us quite realized the years of war that lay ahead. This is best illustrated by the fact that a young banker, who was married to my husband's cousin, said reassuringly to us that summer that this war could not last long; the bankers of the world could control it by refusing credits. When my husband remarked that people had always been able to find money with which to carry on war, more than one man in the financial world smiled knowingly and said it could only be a question of a few months before Europe would be at peace again.

While I was still in bed, one of the destroyers came up and spent a few days cruising around the coast. My husband gave all the young officers heart failure by insisting on taking the ship through a place that looked to them extremely dangerous, but which his intimate knowledge of the waters made safe for navigation.

I remember one occasion when he brought a destroyer through the Narrows. This is a passage running between the mainland at Lubec, Maine, and the island of Campobello. The tide runs through at great speed, except when it is slack, and at low water it would be entirely impossible to take a destroyer or any big ship through; but at high tide, if you know the passage, it can be done. My husband did it on a number of occasions, though the officers with him thought he would surely scrape the bottom.

That autumn, though he did not resign as assistant secretary of the navy, my husband ran in the September primaries against James W. Gerard for United States senator and was defeated. I remember little about the campaign. I had to stay in Campobello until September was well on, and had such a small baby that most of my attention was focused on him at the time. I do not think that my husband ever had any idea that he was going to win, and I have often heard him say that he did not think himself suited to serve in the United States Senate; and it was probably a great relief to find himself back at his desk in the Navy Department.

Eight

Growing Independence

IN THE SPRING of 1915 President Wilson appointed as commissioners to the San Francisco Fair Mr. William Phillips, who was assistant secretary of state, and my husband. Mr. Phillips went out ahead of us. I was to go with my husband and we were to accompany Vice-President and Mrs. Marshall, who were the personal representatives of the President at the fair. Much to our joy, the secretary of the interior and Mrs. Franklin K. Lane and Mr. and Mrs. Adolph Miller decided to go out at the same time.

Vice-President and Mrs. Marshall were to join us in Chicago; and, as I had never known either of them well, and the vice-president had the reputation of being extremely silent, I looked forward with some trepidation of being thrown with them on what must be rather intimate terms. I liked them both very much, and while I struggled through a number of meals with rather a silent gentleman, I discovered that he had a fund of dry humor and there was no pretentiousness about him. When he did not know a thing he said so. When he did not like a thing he said so, and usually had some amusing remark to make. We were on the back platform of the train when we crossed the Great Salt Lake. Everyone was exclaiming at the beauty around us. He removed the cigar which was rarely out of his mouth and remarked, "I never did like scenery."

I was beginning to acquire considerable independence again because my husband's duties made it impossible for him to travel with us at all times, and I was accustomed to managing quite a small army on moves from Washington to Hyde Park and to Campobello and back.

In the summer of 1915 I had not been long in Campobello when a wire came telling me that Franklin had been operated on for appendicitis in Washington. I was on my way to him when one of the men on the train came through calling my name. He handed me a telegram which said, "Franklin doing well, your mother-in-law with him. Louis Howe."

I could cheerfully have slain poor Louis because I had to claim that wire and eyes were turned on me from all over the car. So my shyness was not entirely cured. In fact, it never has been. I remember Louis Howe, years later, taking me out to dinner at a restaurant, sitting at a table he did not like, and eating food he did not like, simply because he knew I would be uncomfortable if he made me conspicuous by getting up and changing to another table or complaining about the food.

I don't suppose that kind of shyness ever really leaves one and to this day it sweeps over me occasionally when I face a crowd, and I wish the ground would open and swallow me. Habit has a great deal to do with what one actually does on these occasions, and the next years were going to give me a very intensive education along many lines.

I found Franklin's mother in Washington at his bedside and we spent some time there together. She finally felt her son was well enough for her to leave and I stayed on alone until Franklin was able to leave the naval hospital and go on board the *Dolphin* for a trip up the coast.

Ever since the beginning of World War I in Europe our country had been becoming the battleground of opposing ideas, and our family was being torn by the differences between Theodore Roosevelt's philosophy and that of President Wilson and his administration in general. I had a tremendous respect for this uncle of mine and for all his opinions. I knew that he felt we should take sides in the European war.

Woodrow Wilson, on the other hand, was determined that our nation should not be dragged into the war if it could possibly be kept out, and above everything else he did not wish our country to go in until the nation itself felt the urge to take a stand that would undoubtedly cost it much in men and money. No one had any realization of how much, and few saw far enough into the future to visualize the results that would come years later.

We had already begun to send ambulances and food to European nations. Mr. Herbert Hoover was feeding the Belgians. My husband was conscious of the pull of varying ideas and standards, and I think, being young, there were times when he wished a final decision could be reached more quickly. I often thought in later years, when he waited while younger advisors champed at the bit for action, of those early days when he played the role of a youthful and fiery adviser.

William Jennings Bryan, secretary of state, was a well-known pacifist. I was always fond of Mrs. Bryan, but in spite of my admiration for Mr. Bryan's powers of oratory there were certain things that did not appeal to me at this time.

Antiwar germs must have been in me even then, however, for I had an instinctive belief in his stand on peace. I remember Mr. Bryan had miniature plowshares made from old guns and given to many people in the government. These were greeted by some with ridicule but to me they were not in the least ridiculous. I thought them an excellent reminder that our swords should be made into plowshares and should continue in this useful occupation.

Many people were already making fortunes out of the war; those who made munitions, for instance; the growers of cotton and of wheat were finding a ready market in the nations that required more raw materials and foodstuffs than they could grow themselves, with most of their men at the front and much of their land out of cultivation.

Distinguished groups came from foreign nations to look after the interests of their own countries over here, and the social life of Washington became busier and more interesting.

In the winter of 1915-16, a large economic conference for South and Central American commerce was held in Washington, and the State Department arranged for every government official to entertain some of the delegates and their wives at different times.

The dinner that we gave I remember vividly because we never could find out how many people were going to dine with us or what their names were. A list was furnished us, but, as the people arrived, many of the names were quite different from the ones on the list. However, we finally sat down and had enough places at table.

I was getting on very well because the men on either side of me spoke English and French. I looked toward the other end of the table and saw that my husband was having a difficult time making conversation with the lady on his right. On his left he had a man who seemed able to talk to him. Later that evening I inquired how he had enjoyed his dinner companions and he answered that they were charming; the lady had been difficult to talk to as she could speak only Spanish and all he could say was: "How many children have you, madam?" to which she always responded smilingly with the number and nothing more!

The German ambassador was conscious, I think, of the general antagonism growing around him, particularly after the sinking of the *Lusitania,* but he had a few warm friends and went his way serenely enough in Washington society. The French and English ambassadors were under great pressure; many people wanted them to undertake the same kind of propaganda that the German ambassador was carrying on. The French ambassador, M. Jules Jusserand, had been so many years in this country that he had a great knowledge of the United States and its people, and the same was true of Sir Cecil Spring-Rice, the English ambassador, and neither of them would consent to much active propaganda. Perhaps they felt that there was enough interest among certain United States citizens to bring about all the propaganda that was really needed, and events later vindicated their judgment!

Sir Cecil Spring-Rice had been in this country as a young man; he had become a great friend of Theodore Roosevelt's family, and retained that friendship through the years, so that when we went to Washington one of the first houses that opened to us was the British embassy. He was a great reader and student of American history; one of the things he asked me the first time I sat beside him at dinner was which of the American histories I felt was the best. When I hesitated he remarked how strange it seemed that we citizens of the United States read so little of our own history. Sir Eustace Percy, one of the younger members of the embassy staff, was making an exhaustive study of our Civil War and had visited all the battlefields. Few young Americans do as much.

Stories of "Springy," as he was called by his intimates, and his peculiarities were current in Washington. They said that one day he came in from a long walk in the rain, went upstairs and dressed for dinner, came back to his study and sat down to read by the fire. In a short time the dressing bell rang and he arose and went back and put on all the wet clothes and came down thus dressed for dinner!

Without Lady Spring-Rice many official engagements would not have been met on time. I have been at the embassy when she has gone into his sitting room and said, "Your appointment with the French ambassador is in ten minutes and the car is at the door," and a reluctant Springy would get up from his book and his wife, put on his hat, and go to meet the French ambassador or the Secretary of State or whoever it might be.

The French ambassador and his charming wife had many friends. M. Jusserand had been one of Theodore Roosevelt's "walking Cabinet." He was a small man and had grown up in the mountains of France and was an expert climber. All his life he had taken walking trips, so he was not daunted by Theodore Roosevelt's excursions through Rock Creek Park, even when they required crossing the brook in some deep spot.

One other person stands out among the people we knew in these first years in Washington. While I cannot say I knew him well, the few opportunities we did have to be with him left a great impression upon us. The Theodore Roosevelts and Mrs. Cowles had known Mr. Henry Adams well and were constant visitors at his house on Lafayette Square. We knew some of the people who were his intimate friends and so occasionally we received one of the much-coveted invitations to lunch or dine at his house.

My first picture of this supposedly stern, rather biting Mr. Adams is of an old gentleman in a victoria outside our house on N Street. Mr. Adams never paid calls. He did, however, request that the children of the house come out and join him in the victoria; and they not only did join him, but they brought their Scottie dog, and the entire group sat and chatted and played all over the victoria.

One day after lunch with him, my husband mentioned something which at the time was causing him deep concern in the government. Mr. Adams looked at him rather fiercely and said: "Young man, I have lived in this house many years and seen the occupants of the White House across the square come and go, and nothing that you minor officials or the occupant of that house can do will affect the history of the world for long!" True, perhaps, but not a good doctrine to preach to a young man in political life!

Henry Adams loved to shock his hearers, and I think he knew that those who were worth their salt would understand him and pick out of the knowledge that flowed from his lips the things that might be useful, and discard the cynicism as an old man's defense against his own urge to be an active factor in the world of politics, a role that Henry Adams rejected in his youth.

Nine

A Changing Existence

IN MARCH, 1916, our last child was born. We named him John Aspinwell, after Franklin's uncle.

That winter of 1916 had been rather hard on my husband, because of a throat infection. He had had such a bad time with it that he had to go to Atlantic City, where his mother met him. He was supposed to take a two-week vacation, but the inactivity was more than he could bear, and in a week he was at work again. I hoped we were through with serious illness.

However, the baby was scarcely two days old when Elliott developed a bad cold and swollen glands. I thought this would amount to very little but in another day he was worse. Anything more trying than to be in bed and have a child ill in a room on the floor above I do not know, so I look back on this spring as a difficult experience. Finally we sent for an old friend of Miss Spring's, who came down from New York to take charge of Elliott and gradually nurse him back to comparative health.

From that day until he went to boarding school at the age of twelve he was a delicate small boy whom we had to watch carefully. Sometimes when I look at the strong man he has grown to be it is hard to realize the years of anxiety that went into his upbringing. From the spring of 1916 he seemed to have everything more seriously than the others, and spent days and weeks in bed. This gave him a taste for books; and I think of all the children he had the greatest pleasure in reading and developed a real appreciation of literature.

The summer of 1916 I went up, as usual, with the children to Campobello. Franklin came occasionally. That summer there was a bad infantile paralysis epidemic among children. I had never stayed in

85

Campobello late into September, but there I was entirely alone with my children, marooned on the island, and apparently I was going to be there for some time. Finally Franklin was allowed to use the *Dolphin* again, and in early October he came up, put the entire family on board and landed us on our own dock in the Hudson River.

There were beginning to be wild rumors of German submarines crossing the ocean and being seen at different places along the coast, and on the one stop we made on the way down we heard that a German submarine had been sighted and its officers had landed.

The children remained at Hyde Park until it was safe for them to travel, and I went back to Washington. From a life centered entirely in my family I became conscious, on returning to the seat of government in Washington, that there was a sense of impending disaster hanging over all of us.

The various attacks on our shipping were straining our relations with Germany and more and more the temper of the country was turning against the Germans. Stories of the atrocities in Belgium drifted in and were believed, but in spite of an increasing tenseness we had not actually broken off diplomatic relations with Germany. That winter my husband went to Haiti. The marines were in control. Franklin took with him the president of the Civil Service Commission, John McIlhenny, an old friend of Theodore Roosevelt and one of his Rough Riders. Later he was made financial adviser to Haiti and managed his difficult job extremely well, with the result that we later returned to the Haitian government the control of their own financial affairs.

This trip of my husband's was extremely interesting and took him on horseback through a good part of the island. He was far away from the coast of Santo Domingo, up in the mountains, when a cable came from the secretary of the navy announcing that political conditions required his immediate return to Washington, and that a destroyer would meet him at the nearest port. We had severed diplomatic connections with Germany and the ambassador had been given his papers and asked to leave the United States. The German naval attaché, Captain Boy-Ed, and others had finally succeeded in thoroughly arousing the antagonism of the American people by spying into American affairs. This, however, my husband did not know. When he went to the dinner given him by the Marine officers in charge of this station, he showed the decoded telegram, which he had just received, to the lady who sat next to him. She had lived so long in the parts of the world where revolutions were uppermost in people's minds that she promptly said: "Political conditions! Why, that must mean that Charles Evans Hughes has led a revolution against President Wilson."

Back in Washington, my husband plunged into intensive work, for the possibility that the United States would be drawn into the war seemed imminent. The Navy must be ready for action immediately on the declaration of war.

We found it necessary to move in the autumn of 1916 because five children were more than Auntie Bye's house on N Street was designed to hold comfortably. No. 2131 R Street was a pleasant house with a small garden at the back.

All too soon we were to find ourselves actually in the war, and during those spring months of 1917 my husband and I were less and less concerned with social life except where it could be termed useful or necessary to the work that had to be done. Again my husband frequently brought people home for luncheon because he had to talk to them, and we often entertained particular people who came from other nations because it was necessary that they should know the people with whom they were dealing.

After weeks of tension, I heard that the President was going to address Congress as a preliminary to a declaration of war. Everyone wanted to hear this historic address and it was with the greatest difficulty that Franklin got me a seat. I listened breathlessly and returned home half dazed by the sense of impending change.

War was declared on April 6, 1917, and from then on the men in the government worked from morning until late into the night. The women in Washington paid no more calls. They began to organize at once to meet the unusual demands of wartime. Mrs. J. Borden Harriman called a meeting to form a motor corps for Red Cross work. I attended the meeting but at that time I could not drive a car, so I decided that that was not my field of work.

No work was fully organized until the next autumn, but I joined the Red Cross canteen, helped Mrs. Daniels to organize the Navy Red Cross, and began to distribute free wool for knitting, provided by the Navy League.

I found myself very busy that spring, entertaining members of foreign missions who continued to come to this country to talk over the type of co-operation that we were to give the Allies. Mr. Balfour came over with a mission from England, arriving three days before the French mission. This was a quiet, unspectacular mission, but he had with him men who had served at the front and been wounded. They found their way at times to our home.

In the first French mission were Marshal Joffre and former Premier Viviani, who arrived in this country on April 25, 1917.

Franklin's cousin, Warren Robbins, was at that time attached to the State Department and was given the responsibility of accompanying the French mission and making their trip in the country as comfortable and pleasant as possible. A great crowd greeted them in Washington, and Joffre, who had been the hero of the stand at the Marne, was received everywhere with the greatest enthusiasm. People knew that his soldiers had called him "Papa Joffre" and his appearance suited this name so well that the crowd over here would often hail him in this way.

Viviani was not an agreeable personality, but he was a brilliant speaker. There were, of course, a number of people in the party, and the man who appealed to me most was Lieutenant Colonel Fabry, known as the Blue Devil of France. Before and after the war he was a newspaper editor, a gentle, quiet person to whom this nickname seemed hardly appropriate. Badly wounded many times, he was in constant pain while he was in Washington.

Before our entry into the war, many foolish people like myself said that only our financial resources would be needed and that the only branch of the service which would be called upon to fight would be the Navy. However, on our entry into the war both services were called into action, and the first plea made by the French mission was that some American soldiers be sent to France in July instead of in October, as our government had planned. The argument was that the Allies were tired and that the sight of a new uniform and of fresh men at the front would restore their morale, which was being subjected to such a long strain.

I remember most vividly the trips from Washington down to Mount Vernon on the *Sylph*, especially the first one with Mr. Balfour, Marshal Joffre and Premier Viviani. Secretary and Mrs. Daniels and my husband and I, with other members of the Cabinet, accompanied them, and their first duty was to lay a wreath on the tomb of George Washington. It was a ceremonious occasion, and as we gathered around the open iron grille at the tomb each man made a speech. How odd it must seem to Mr. Balfour to be paying honor to the memory of the man who had severed from the mother country some rather profitable colonies, but he was graceful and adequate in this rather peculiar situation.

Only when someone on the lawn at Mount Vernon told him the story of George Washington's throwing a silver dollar across the Potomac to the other shore, did his eyes twinkle as he responded, "My dear sir, he accomplished an even greater feat than that. He threw a sovereign across the ocean!"

Immediately after the declaration of war, Uncle Ted came to Washington to offer his services to the President. He had a large group of men who wished to go to the front with him. He felt he could easily raise a division and in it would be many of the best officers in the Army who wished to serve under him, such as General Wood, and many of the old Rough Riders and probably the pick of American youth. Uncle Ted could not bear the thought that his boys should go and he be left behind. He was strong and able enough, he contended, to fight in this war as he had in the Spanish War, and as he had urged the people to enter on the side of the Allies he wanted to be among the first to enlist.

On this visit he stayed with his daughter, Alice Longworth, and I went with Franklin to see him. Though he was kind to us, as he always was, he was completely preoccupied with the war; and after he had been to see President Wilson and the President had not immediately accepted his offer, Uncle Ted returned in a very unhappy mood. I think he knew from the noncommittal manner in which he had been received that his proposal was not going to be accepted.

I hated to have him disappointed and yet I was loyal to President Wilson, and was much relieved later on, when I learned that Uncle Ted's offer had been submitted to General Pershing and the War Department and that the consensus had been that it would be a grave mistake to allow one division to attract so many of the men who would be needed as officers in many divisions. Uncle Ted certainly did his best to go overseas, but it was felt that the prominence of his position and his age made it unwise for him to be in Europe. I think the decision was a bitter blow from which he never quite recovered.

I did little war work that summer beyond the inevitable knitting which every woman undertook and which became a constant habit. No one moved without her knitting.

The Navy Department was co-operating so closely with England and France that my husband hardly left Washington, but I went back and forth. He came for short periods of time to the coast of Maine. It was decided that we had no right to keep the boat which we had always used at

Campobello, and so the *Half Moon* was sold, much to the regret of both my husband and my mother-in-law. The latter had a sentimental attachment for it on account of the pleasure her husband had had in sailing her.

My brother, Hall, who was at this time working for the General Electric Company in Schenectady, was forbidden to enlist, under the rules which barred a man from everything but aviation if he was responsible for the production of war materials in the General Electric Company plant. He had been so close to Uncle Ted and his family that when all those boys enlisted he felt he must join also. He slipped away from work on the plea that he wanted to visit his uncle, and he and Quentin Roosevelt went together on July 14 and enlisted in the only branch of the service which was permissible for Hall under the circumstances—aviation.

I think both Hall and Quentin must have memorized the card for the eye test, because neither of them could have passed otherwise. Hall was called to the first school of aviation in Ithaca in late July or August. My grandmother felt strongly that he should not leave his wife and little children, and I remember my feeling of utter horror when I went to see her one day and she demanded to know why he did not buy a substitute! I had never heard of buying a substitute and said that no one did such a thing. Her old eyes looked at me curiously and she said: "In the Civil War many gentlemen bought substitutes. It was the thing to do." I hotly responded that a gentleman was no different from any other kind of citizen in the United States and that it would be a disgrace to pay anyone to risk his life for you, particularly when Hall could leave his wife and children with the assurance that at least they would have money enough to live on.

This was my first really outspoken declaration against the accepted standards of the surroundings in which I had spent my childhood, and marked the fact that either my husband or an increasing ability to think for myself was changing my point of view.

That autumn, back in Washington, real work began, and all my executive ability, which had been more or less dormant up to this time, was called into play. The house must run more smoothly than ever, we must entertain, and I must be able to give less attention to it. The children must lead normal lives; Anne must go to the Eastman School every day, and James and Elliott must go to the Cathedral School, which was in the opposite direction. All this required organization.

My mother-in-law used to laugh at me and say I could provide my chauffeur with more orders to be carried out during the day than anyone else she had ever listened to, but this was just a symptom of developing executive ability. My time was now completely filled with a variety of war activities, and I was learning to have a certain confidence in myself and in my ability to meet emergencies and deal with them.

Two or three shifts a week I spent in the Red Cross canteen in the railroad yards. During the winter I took chiefly day shifts in the canteen, for I was obliged to be at home, if possible, to see my children before they went to bed, and I frequently had guests for dinner. I can remember one or two occasions when I got home in my uniform as my guests arrived, and I think it was during this period that I learned to dress with rapidity, a habit which has stayed with me ever since.

Everyone in the canteen was expected to do any work that was necessary, even mopping the floor, and no one remained long a member of this Red Cross unit who could not do anything that was asked of her. I remember one lady who came down escorted by her husband to put in one afternoon. I doubt if she had ever done any manual labor in her life, and she was no longer young. The mere suggestion that she might have to scrub the floor filled her with horror and we never again saw her on a shift.

Once a week I visited the naval hospital and took flowers, cigarettes and any little thing that might cheer the men who had come back from overseas.

The naval hospital filled up rapidly and we finally took over one building in St. Elizabeth's Hospital for the so-called shell-shocked patients. The doctors explained that these were men who had been submitted to great strain and cracked under it. Some of them regained sanity, others remained permanently in our veterans' hospitals for mental care.

St. Elizabeth's was the one federal hospital for the insane in the country. A fine man was at the head of it, but he always had been obliged to run his institution on an inadequate appropriation, and as yet the benefits of occupational therapy were little understood in the treatment of the insane, though I knew that in some hospitals this work was being done with a measure of success.

I visited our naval unit there and had my first experience of going into a ward of people who, while they were not violent, were more or less incalculable because they were not themselves. Those who were not under control were kept in padded cells or in some kind of confinement.

When the doctor and I went into the long general ward where the majority of men were allowed to move about during the daytime, he unlocked the door and locked it again after us. We started down that long room, speaking to different men on the way. Quite at the other end stood a young boy with fair hair. The sun in the window placed high up, well above the patients' heads, touched his hair and seemed almost like a halo. He was talking to himself incessantly and I inquired what he was saying. "He is giving the orders," said the doctor, "which were given every night at Dunkirk, where he was stationed." I remembered my husband's telling me that he had been in Dunkirk and that every evening the enemy planes came over the town and bombed it and the entire population was ordered down into the cellars. This boy had stood the strain of the nightly bombing until he could stand it no longer; then he went insane and repeated the orders without stopping, not being able to get out of his mind the thing which had become an obsession.

I asked what chances he had for recovery and was told that it was fifty-fifty, but that in all probability he would never again be able to stand as much strain as before he became ill.

The doctor told me that many of our men in the naval hospital unit were well enough to go out every day, play games and get air and exercise, and that we had enough attendants to make this possible in the rest of the hospital; however, they had been so short of attendants since the war started that the other patients practically never got out. The doctor also told me that in spite of the fact that wages had gone skyrocketing during this period, the hospital had never been able to pay its attendants more than $30 a month and their board, which was low in comparison with what men were getting in other occupations.

I drove through the grounds and was horrified to see poor demented creatures with apparently little attention being paid them, gazing from behind bars or walking up and down on enclosed porches.

This hospital was under the Department of the Interior, so I could hardly wait to reach Secretary Lane, to tell him that I thought an investigation was in order and that he had better go over and see for himself. He appointed a committee which later appeared before Congress and asked for and obtained an increased appropriation. I believe this action of the secretary's enabled Dr. White to make the hospital what every federal institution in Washington should be, a model of its kind which can be visited with profit by interested people from various parts of our country.

In the meantime I was so anxious that our men should have a meeting place that I went to the Red Cross and begged them to build one of their recreation rooms, which they did. Then, through Mrs. Barker, I obtained $500 from the Colonial Dames, which started the occupational therapy work, and in a short time the men were able to sell what they produced and to buy new materials for themselves.

I was seeing many tragedies enacted in that hospital. There was a woman who sat for days by the bed of her son who had been gassed and had tuberculosis. There was a chance that he might be saved if he could get out west. She could not afford to go with him but we finally obtained permission to send a nurse.

Another boy from Texas, with one leg gone, wanted so much to get home; finally, with the help of the Daughters of the Confederacy, some of whom were our most faithful workers, he achieved his desire and I think became self-supporting.

These are just examples of the many things touching the lives of individuals which came to all of us in those days; and so far as I was concerned, they were a liberal education. Some of the stories were sordid, all of them filled with a mixture of the heroism in human nature and its accompanying frailties.

Out of these contacts with human beings during the war I became a more tolerant person, far less sure of my own beliefs and methods of action but more determined to try for certain ultimate objectives. I had gained some assurance about my ability to run things and the knowledge that there is joy in accomplishing a good job. I knew more about the human heart.

One by one, all of Uncle Ted's boys sailed. Auntie Corinne's two boys enlisted, and Monroe Robinson went overseas, as did another cousin, James Alfred Roosevelt. Harry Hooker, one of my husband's former law partners in New York City, sailed with his division.

Over and over again my brother tried to be assigned to work overseas. Over and over again he was refused, with the admonition that his value was greater where he was. He pulled every wire possible, besought my husband to use his influence, got Uncle Ted to use his, and ate his heart out because he could not get to the other side. In spite of the fact that we pointed out to him that he took his life in his hands more frequently in instructing novices than he would at the front, he was never satisfied. He always felt that if some of us had just tried a little harder we could have put him on a transport and given him his heart's desire.

All the time I knitted incessantly and worked in various ways. I wished that I might offer my services to go overseas. I was very envious of another Eleanor Roosevelt, Colonel Theodore Roosevelt's wife, who had gone over before her husband and, in spite of the regulations against wives of officers going to France, was serving there in a canteen.

My husband was engaged in naval operations and of necessity had to keep in close touch with the members of the English and French embassies. Gradually the foreign offices of England and France began to feel that their representatives were not being active enough, and Sir Cecil Spring-Rice was recalled by his government, much to the regret of his many friends in this country, who realized that he and his wife were rendering a great service to the Allied cause.

They were succeeded, in January, 1918, by Lord and Lady Reading. Everyone in Washington recognized this diplomat's great ability and liked them both.

M. Jusserand remained French ambassador until after the war was over, but a special envoy, M. Andre Tardieu, was sent over in 1918 to take up certain financial questions. My recollection is that this was not an entirely happy arrangement. M. Tardieu was an able man, but he had not, perhaps, the temperament that appealed to the French ambassador. However, the mission was successful in carrying through its business and M. Tardieu returned to France.

The winter of 1917-18 wore away and remains to me a kaleidoscope of work and entertaining and home duties, so crowded that sometimes I wondered if I could live that way another day. Strength came, however, with the thought of Europe and a little sleep, and you could sleep, and you could always begin a new day. When summer came I decided that I would spend most of it in Washington to help out at the canteen, for so many people had to be away.

Hot though the Hudson River was, I felt the children were old enough to stand it, particularly as my mother-in-law had built a large addition to the old house and the rooms that the children occupied were less hot than they had been because of the new insulation. I took the children with their nurse to Hyde Park for the summer and stayed with them awhile to get them settled.

I was making preparations to return to Washington, for I had promised to be on duty during the month of July. In June my husband got word that he was to go to Europe. Franklin had spoken and written to various people ever since we had entered the war, seeking to get into uniform. He stated that, "Even though this means doing far less important work for the Navy than if I continue the organization and operations' supervision, not only in the department itself, but also in the patron bases, in the transport service and in many shipyards, I will be in active service."

Then came orders to go overseas and report on the operations and needs of the many American naval and aviation bases and ships in European waters. He obtained a promise that when this was done he would be permitted to return to Europe as a lieutenant commander.

He sailed on the destroyer *Dyer* on July 9, 1918. The *Dyer* was convoying a number of transports taking troops to France. Franklin was naturally much excited at the prospect of this trip, and it gave him great satisfaction to feel that he was going to the front.

Neither his mother nor I could see him off, because they sailed under secret orders; and I realized at the time that it was for her a fearful ordeal, for he was the center of her existence. Luckily, she had the grandchildren to keep her busy, and there were numerous activities in which she took her full share in Hyde Park and Poughkeepsie.

I went back to Washington and spent all day and most of the night at the canteen. I had nothing else to do. Many of the members were away, and in the heat, to which I was quite unaccustomed, I was anxious to keep busy. No place could have been hotter than the little corrugated-tin shack with the tin roof and the fire burning in the old army kitchen. We certainly were kept busy, for we were sending troops over just as fast as we could train them, and we knew now that it was manpower that the Allies wanted as much as our financial resources or the assistance of the Navy.

It was not an unusual thing for me to work from nine in the morning until one or two the next morning, and be back again by ten. The nights were hot and it was possible to sleep only if you were exhausted. When my month was up and others came to take my place, I went to Hyde Park to be with the children and my mother-in-law.

In early September we began to expect to hear of my husband's start for home; but before that news came I received word, on September 12, 1918, that my uncle, Douglas Robinson, had died.

We finally heard that my husband had sailed from Brest to return to this country. A day or so before the ship was due, my mother-in-law and I received word through the Navy Department that Franklin had pneumonia and that we were to meet him on arrival with a doctor and an ambulance. We left the children at Hyde Park and went to my mother-in-law's house in New York, for our own house was rented. The flu had been raging in Brest and Franklin and his party had attended a funeral in the rain. The ship on which they returned was a floating hospital. Men and officers died on the way home and were buried at sea.

When the boat docked and we went on board I remember visiting several of the men who were still in bed. My husband did not seem to me so seriously ill as the doctors implied, but we soon had him settled in his mother's house.

All but one member of my husband's party were seriously ill. Fortunately, they all recovered. With them on the boat, coming to this country for a visit, were Prince Axel of Denmark and his aides. When they felt the flu coming on they consulted no doctor but took to their berths with a quart of whisky each. In the course of a day or two, whether because of the efficacy of the whisky or because of their own resistance, they were practically recovered.

The question of the children's schooling was beginning to weigh heavily upon my mind, so soon after Franklin was better I moved the children who had to be in school back to Washington and commenced commuting back and forth until the whole family was together again.

Franklin improved steadily but he required good nursing and care for some time, for the pneumonia left him very weak. He went to Hyde Park for two weeks, and about the middle of October was well enough to return to Washington and turn in his official reports, firsthand observations of naval activities in the North Sea, the Irish and English channels, and some of the Belgian, British and French ports. He was preparing to resign and join the naval battery in France when word came late in October that Germany had suggested to President Wilson that peace would be discussed.

As soon as we returned to Washington the flu epidemic, which had been raging in various parts of the country, struck us with full force. The city was fearfully overcrowded, the departments had had to expand and take on great numbers of clerical workers. New bureaus had been set up, girls were living two and three in a room all over the city, and when the flu hit there were naturally not enough hospitals to accommodate those who were stricken. The Red Cross organized temporary hospitals in every available building, and those of us who could were asked to bring food to these various units, which often had no kitchen space at all.

Before I knew it, all my five children and my husband were down with the flu, and three of the servants. We succeeded in getting one trained nurse from New York, as Miss Spring was not available. This nurse was put in charge of Elliott, who had double pneumonia. My husband was moved into a little room next to mine, and John, the baby, had his crib in my bedroom, for he had bronchial pneumonia. There was little difference between day and night for me, and Dr. Hardin, who worked as hard as he possibly could every minute of the time, came in once or twice a day and looked over all my patients. He remarked that we were lucky that some of us were still on our feet, for he had families with nobody able to stand up.

In the intervals of cooking for this galaxy of invalids, my cook prepared food to go out, as we had pledged ourselves to send it every afternoon. If all the children were asleep, I went in the car and visited the Red Cross unit I had been assigned to supply and tried to say a word of cheer to the poor girls lying in the long rows of beds. Like all other things, the flu epidemic finally came to an end.

These emergencies of domestic and family life were extremely good training. Gradually I was learning that what one has to do usually can be done, and my long association with Miss Spring had made me a fairly practical nurse. Fear of being left alone to care for my children had vanished. In fact, I had had sense enough in the past few years to send my nurse away in the summer for short vacations and take charge of my last two babies myself. At least I was no longer the inexperienced, timid mother, and the older children say that in consequence the younger ones were never so well disciplined as they were! Of course, the truth of the matter was that I had gained a sense of values and no longer fussed about nonessentials nor allowed myself to be stampeded by the likes and dislikes of a nurse or governess.

The feeling was growing everywhere that the end of the war was in sight. President Wilson's messages to the people of other nations made a deep impression. Ever since the Allied armies had been under the supreme command of Marshal Foch a turn had come for the better in the military affairs of the Allies. Suddenly, on November 7, we got word that an armistice had been signed and pandemonium broke loose, but a few hours later it was declared a mistake and everybody's spirits sank.

Four days later, on November 11, 1918, the real Armistice was signed and the city of Washington, like every other city in the United States, went completely mad. The feeling of relief and thankfulness was beyond description.

Ten

Readjustment

SOON AFTER the Armistice my husband heard that he would have to go abroad after the New Year to wind up naval affairs in Europe, dispose of what could be sold and ship home what could be used here again.

It was so soon after his recovery from pneumonia that it was dangerous for him to be subjected to the winter climate of either France or England, so it seemed wise for me to sail with him, which I could do, now that the war was over.

As we were not to sail until early January, we were at home for Christmas with the family. My mother-in-law usually came to spend Christmas with us if we did not go to her. Our only other guests as a rule were Louis Howe and his family.

Uncle Ted was ill in the hospital when we sailed, but none of us dreamed that it was anything very serious. On the way over we were saddened to receive by radio on January 6 the news of his death. I knew what his loss would mean to his close family, but I realized even more keenly that a great personality had gone from active participation in the life of his people. The loss of his influence and example was what I seemed to feel most keenly.

Admiral Wilson, in command at Brest, came aboard with Admiral Moreau when we arrived. Admiral Wilson boasted that he had the best apartment to be obtained in Brest, with the only bathtub in the town, but the water ran only during certain hours of the day. Most of the people of the town carried all their water from taps placed at intervals along the streets.

Admiral Wilson took me to see something of the country while Franklin worked. General Smedley Butler had finally succeeded in lifting the camp

98

a little out of the mud by building duckboard paths everywhere, but constant rain still made it no paradise.

My husband's business completed, we went to Paris where he spent some busy days. My first duty was to call on all our superiors. Luckily, they all lived in the same hotel except, of course, President and Mrs. Wilson. Franklin and I went together to call on the President of France and sign his book. Later we went again to be received formally and pay our respects.

We were staying at the Ritz Hotel and I was thrilled one day to see at luncheon Lady Diana Manners, for she had always been to me a character in a storybook. She was very beautiful, but some of the glamour of my storybook princess was gone after I had actually seen her.

A great effort was being made to revive the beautiful gay city Paris had once been. The city itself was unchanged but practically every Frenchwoman was dressed in black, and, though the tradition of long black mourning veils was forbidden, the older women could not be prevented from wearing them.

I went with my husband's aunt, Mrs. Forbes, to the oldest military hospital in Paris, the Val de Grâce, where remarkable plastic surgery was being done. I dreaded this but it was not quite so bad as I feared, though I saw all I cared to see of people whose faces were being made over by one operation after another.

We also visited what is known as the Phare, the hospital for the blind where the patients were being taught to manage for themselves and acquire a skill that would enable them to earn a living or at least keep their hands busy.

We dined one night with Belle and Kermit Roosevelt, and Teddy Roosevelt, who was a colonel in the Army, left their apartment that night to go to the American hospital to have an operation on his leg. This hospital I visited later with Mrs. Woodrow Wilson. She left a few flowers at each boy's bed, and I was lost in admiration because she found something to say to each one.

Few people came to France at this period without picking up some kind of germ and the day before we left for London I realized that I was running a temperature, with considerable pain in my side. We were to be on our way the next day, driving over the front where our soldiers had fought with the British and nothing, if I could help it, was going to prevent me from taking that trip.

I got up the next morning at six-thirty, dressed and left, sitting on the back seat of a car, feeling, whenever the road was rough, that a knife was stabbing my side, but the rest of the time, on the whole, I was fairly comfortable.

We made a number of stops, one at the Saint-Quentin Canal. They wished to show us what our troops had done and so we walked to the bottom where the canal runs between steep banks. The cut is about sixty feet deep and the sides were lined with dugouts. I wondered if the state of my feelings would give me an approximate idea of the way the soldiers felt on the cold, gray, foggy morning when they, with full packs on their backs and rifles in their hands, plunged down one side of the canal and climbed up the other. The enemy was afraid to fire until they were well under their guns for fear the approaching army might be their own men. In that way, while armored tanks plowed the plain, the canal itself with its high banks, was taken.

We drove along the straight military roads with churned mud on either side of us, and deep shell holes here and there. Along the road there were occasional piles of stones with a stick stuck into them bearing the name of a vanished village. On the hillsides stumps showed that once there had been a forest.

When we reached Amiens that night I had to confide in my husband that I had a pain and thought I might have caught cold. After dinner I obtained a hot-water bottle and managed to sleep fairly well and was up and able to be interested in the cathedral when we started out at eight o'clock the next morning. The bags of sand which had been placed around the cathedral to protect it made it difficult for us to appreciate its beauty.

Commander Royes met us at Folkestone and when we reached London we were met by Admiral Sims and naval constructor Smith, who took us to the Ritz Hotel. The next day an English doctor came and looked me over. I had pleurisy and was told to stay in bed. I attempted to obey his orders for one day, but as the men all had to be about their business and the telephone and doorbell rang incessantly, I was in and out of bed so often that I decided, even if I could not go out, it was better to be up and dressed.

In the course of a few days I began to feel better. The doctor shook his head gloomily and was convinced I was going into a rapid decline. In fact, he told me to be examined for tuberculosis as soon as I reached home. I was quite sure, however, that I was recovering, and Major Kilgore and Commander Hancock did everything possible to make me comfortable.

Finally, his work was done and Franklin with his aide left for Belgium and then to go down to see the Marines stationed at Coblenz on the Rhine. I moved from the hotel to Muriel Martineau's house and spent four days there.

We were to sail for home with President and Mrs. Wilson, and on February 4 we left by train for Brest. I remember our great excitement when Mr. Grasty, the *New York Times* correspondent, brought us a copy of the charter of League of Nations. What hopes we had that this League would really prove the instrument for the prevention of future wars, and how eagerly we read it through!

President Wilson had been acclaimed by the French people as a savior; his position in his own country seemed impregnable. No organized opposition had as yet developed. His trip had been a triumphant one, and now the people of France stood everywhere to watch for his train in the hope of getting a glimpse of him.

Our first glimpse of the President and Mrs. Wilson and their party was when they came on board the *George Washington*. We were already on the ship and stood behind the captain to welcome them. One funny incident occurred which threw the naval officers into quite a bustle of excitement. Instead of following the prescribed procedure, the President refused to go ahead of his wife and Miss Benham, her secretary, and they boarded the battleship first, a situation unheard of in naval regulations. Nothing happened, however, and when the President came over the side, ruffles rolled out from the drums and "The Star-Spangled Banner" was played and nothing really essential was left out of his welcome.

We lunched one day with the President and Mrs. Wilson. At the table was Ambassador Francis, returning from his post in Russia, a kindly humorous man, giving one a feeling of latent strength. The other guests were Captain McCauley, Dr. Grayson and Miss Benham. In my diary I noted that the talk was, as usual on such occasions, an exchange of stories, but the President spoke of the League of Nations, saying: "The United States must go in or it will break the heart of the world, for she is the only nation that all feel is disinterested and all trust." Later he said he had read no papers since the beginning of the war, that Mr. Tumulty clipped them all for him, giving him only important news and editorials. My diary comment was: "This is too much to leave to any man."

It was, I learned later when my husband became president, a problem of allotting time. Franklin reserved certain periods for his study of the press, particularly the opposition press, and, at least while Louis Howe was with him, he was always closely informed on all shades of opinion in the country. This firsthand awareness of what people are doing and thinking and saying is essential to a president. When this information is filtered through other people, or selected with a view to what a few individuals think the President should know, the inevitable result is that this source of information is dangerously curtailed or misleadingly slanted. This is fatal in the formulation of far-reaching decisions.

We landed in Boston and went through the streets in a long procession. We could see the President and Mrs. Wilson ahead of us, the President standing up and waving his hat at intervals to the crowds that lined the streets. Everyone was wildly enthusiastic and he never sat down until we reached the Copley Plaza Hotel.

At the hotel word was brought that Governor and Mrs. Calvin Coolidge would be glad to have us lunch with them and Mayor and Mrs. Andrew Peters. The President was to make a speech after luncheon and he and Mrs. Wilson did not feel that they could attend a social gathering beforehand.

Thus it fell to my lot to meet a future president of the United States and to know perhaps before the rest of the country how silent the gentleman could be! I regarded his silence on that occasion as a sign of the disappointment he felt at not having Mrs. Wilson to talk to, but I have since decided that even Mrs. Wilson could not have brought forth a flow of conversation!

Immediately after lunch we went to Mechanics Hall and the mayor in greeting the President came out for the League. We were all very much stirred by the President's speech, which was one of the best I ever heard him make. Strange as it may seem, the governor of Massachusetts, Mr. Calvin Coolidge, committed himself to "feeling sure the people would back the President."

We went on to Washington. At every station cheering crowds greeted the President until long after dusk. This was my first experience of the kind and very moving, because the people seemed to have grasped his ideals and to want to back them.

We had been gone not quite two months but it was a great relief to be back with the children.

My household soon functioned as smoothly as ever and my life was not so filled with war work, though much of the hospital work continued unabated and the pathetic funerals in Arlington were frequent in the spring. The government brought back the bodies of many of our men from the battlefields or hospitals in Europe. Sometimes men died on the transports. The funerals were held in Arlington Cemetery if the family desired, and some members of the family usually attended. The Red Cross would detail some of its members to attend and take flowers, and I can never go to a military funeral today without the vision of those scenes and the pictures of certain faces rising before me.

That spring of 1919, on the side of my official duties, I had my first personal contact with the cause of woman suffrage. Back in the Albany days my husband had been for it. Through the years courageous women carried on a constant fight for ratification of woman suffrage by the different states. It looked as though their fight was nearing a successful end and therefore the opposition rallied its forces.

Coming down on the train one day to Washington from New York, I happened to meet Alice Wadsworth, wife of Senator James Wadsworth, who, with her husband, had always been much opposed to woman suffrage. We lunched together and she spent the time trying to persuade me to come out against the ratification. I was noncommittal, for I considered any stand at that time was outside my field of work. I think she had hopes that she might make a convert of me. Before she could succeed, the amendment was ratified, and soon after I undertook work which proved to me the value of a vote. I became a much more ardent citizen and feminist than anyone about me in the intermediate years would have dreamed possible. I had learned that if you wanted to institute any kind of reform you could get far more attention if you had a vote than if you lacked one.

The Navy Department was, of course, busy liquidating the war setup as rapidly as possible. Secretary and Mrs. Daniels went abroad in March, which left my husband in charge during their short trip. Any absence on the part of the secretary made the assistant secretary acting head and gave him opportunity for closer contact with the President.

The President, after presenting his plan to Congress, was having a very hard fight. Senator Lodge felt that Congress should have been consulted sooner; in fact, should have had representatives on the European delegation. He became the leader of the criticism of the President's plan. The fight went on all through the spring.

President Wilson went back to Europe on March 6, 1919, to sign the Treaty of Versailles, feeling sure that the people were with him. The tension between the President and Congress during this period was great, and thoughtful people both here and abroad were wondering about a situation in which the Executive, charged with the duty of dealing with foreign nations, might come to an agreement and the agreement be turned down by the Senate, as had been done before.

Perhaps the answer is that these agreements should be worked out in conjunction with the leaders of Congress instead of by the Executive alone, but one cannot always be sure that even the leaders of Congress can carry all their followers with them. It is interesting, however, to find out how often Congress has not agreed with the Executive and has refused to ratify treaties negotiated by the President and the secretary of state; it leads one to wonder if some more satisfactory means should not be found.

President Wilson returned July 8, 1919, and on September 3 started out on a campaign to take the cause of the League of Nations to the American people. The President was taken ill on this trip, but recovered enough to walk off the train and into his car and into the White House when he returned on September 28.

This same year many of us realized that my grandmother Hall was failing, and on August 14 word came that she had died at her home in Tivoli, where she would have wished to be. I was in Washington, and Franklin and I went on to Tivoli to help my aunts with the last few things that could be done.

I wondered then and I wonder now whether, if her life had been less centered in her family group, that family group might not have been a great deal better off. If she had had some kind of life of her own, what would have been the result? When she was young she painted rather well. Could she have developed that talent? I know that when she was young she might have had friends of her own, might even have married again. Would she have been happier, and would her children have been better off? She was not the kind of person who would have made a career independently; she was the kind of woman who needed a man's protection. Her willingness to be subservient to her children isolated her, and it might have been far better, for her boys at least, had she insisted on bringing more discipline into their lives simply by having a life of her own.

My grandmother's life had a considerable effect on me, for even when

I was young I determined that I would never be dependent on my children by allowing all my interests to center in them. This conviction has grown through the years, and in watching the lives of those around her I have felt that it might have been well in their youth if they had not been able to count on her devotion and her presence whenever they needed her.

Up to a certain point it is good for us to know that there are people in the world who will give us love and unquestioned loyalty to the limit of their ability. I doubt, however, if it is good for us to feel assured of this without the accompanying obligation of having to justify this devotion by our behavior.

It is hard sometimes to realize what factors in our experience have influenced our development, but I am sure that my grandmother's life has been a great factor in determining some of my reactions to life.

On October 28 I went to the House of Representatives when the King and Queen of the Belgians and the crown prince were received there. It was an interesting occasion, and I was impressed by the soldierly bearing of the King and by the Queen's graciousness.

My husband arrived back from a hunting trip in time to take the usual trip down the Potomac with the royal party. Franklin had visited them at the front and again on his trip in 1919 and felt great admiration for them. He had been much drawn to their daughter, the Princess Marie José, who reminded him of his own daughter, Anna.

I could not help feeling a little sorry for Crown Prince Leopold. He was so carefully watched and his constant companion was an army officer many years older than himself. If he was out of his parents' sight for a few minutes, they were sure to inquire where he was. There were no "off the record" trips or entertainments for this young prince, and we had glimpses of what it meant to be trained to be a king.

In October, also, I had my first contact with women's organizations interested in working conditions for women. The International Congress for Women Workers, with representatives from nineteen nations, met in Washington. Because of the number of foreign delegates to be present, they tried to find wives of government officials who could speak foreign languages to attend various social functions, and so Lily Polk and I went to tea one afternoon. I liked all the women very much indeed, but I had no idea how much more I was going to see of them in the future.

On November 10, 1919, the prince of Wales, later King Edward VIII, arrived in this country and there was again the usual wreath-laying at Mount Vernon, and we met the young prince at several formal dinners. I marveled at the ease with which he conversed with older people. His usual neighbors at dinner were the vice-president's wife, Mrs. Marshall, and Mrs. Lansing, wife of the secretary of state. He did, however, manage to break away and go to some dances with younger people when formal official affairs were over.

Sir Edward Grey had come over that autumn to take up the work at the British embassy for a short time. He was almost blind and was being treated by Dr. Wilmer, our great eye doctor. Sir Edward had insisted that he could not take over the responsibility of this office unless his old friend and colleague, Sir William Tyrrell, came with him, and so this delightful pair spent a few months in this country. Because of Sir Edward Grey's affection for Uncle Ted, the name of Roosevelt was a key to his affections and we saw a great deal of him.

We invited Sir Edward and Sir William to have their Christmas dinner with us and attend our Christmas tree, our only other guests being my husband's mother and, as usual, Louis Howe and his family. They accepted, much to our joy.

Alice Longworth, Mrs. Leavitt, my grandmother Roosevelt's old friend, and Miss Spring, who was now with her most of the time, came over to join our Christmas party.

Eleven

The 1920 Campaign
and Back to New York

IN JUNE, 1920, my husband went out to the San Francisco National Convention of the Democratic party and I took the children to Campobello, where I received a telegram from Secretary Daniels, saying that my husband had been nominated as candidate for vice-president to run with Mr. James M. Cox, who was the Democratic nominee for president. The message read:

IT WOULD HAVE DONE YOUR HEART GOOD TO HAVE SEEN THE SPONTANEOUS AND ENTHUSIASTIC TRIBUTE PAID WHEN FRANKLIN WAS NOMINATED UNANIMOUSLY FOR VICE-PRESIDENT TODAY STOP ACCEPT MY CONGRATULATIONS AND GREETINGS STOP WILL YOU BE GOOD ENOUGH TO SEND MY CONGRATULATIONS AND GREETINGS ALSO TO HIS MOTHER AS I DO NOT KNOW HER ADDRESS.

JOSEPHUS DANIELS

I was glad for my husband, but it never occurred to me to be much excited. I had come to accept the fact that public service was my husband's great interest and I always tried to make the necessary family adjustments easy. I carried on the children's lives and my own as calmly as could be, and while I was always a part of the public aspect of our lives, still I felt detached and objective, as though I were looking at someone else's life.

My husband stopped to see Mr. Cox on the way home. Both of them later visited President Woodrow Wilson, preparatory to laying plans for the issues that would be fought out in the campaign. It was decided that the League of Nations should be the main issue.

My husband sent me word that his notification would take place at

107

Hyde Park and to bring Anna and James back from Campobello for the occasion, and to arrange to go back to Washington for a few days and then start west to attend Mr. Cox's notification at Dayton, Ohio. I was to take Anna on this trip and send James back to Campobello with his grandmother.

This notification meeting was the first really mammoth meeting to be held at Hyde Park. The gathering was the predecessor of many others, but I sympathized with my mother-in-law when I saw her lawn being trampled by hordes of people. My admiration for her grew through the years as I realized how many political guests she had to entertain in her house, where for so many years only family and friends had been received. The friends were chosen with great discrimination and invitations were never lightly given by my husband's father and mother. Mrs. Roosevelt was quite remarkable about this plunge into the national political picture and made the necessary adjustments in her life in a remarkable way.

Mr. Henry Morgenthau, Jr., and the committee of Hyde Park and Poughkeepsie friends arranged the details of Franklin's homecoming and his notification. Anna and I went with Franklin to Washington for a few days of terrible heat. While there I made the arrangements for giving up the house and Franklin resigned as assistant secretary of the navy, and that period of our life in Washington was over.

Franklin returned with us to Campobello for a brief rest and then started a strenuous campaign. I stayed with the children, got James ready for school and took him to Groton in late September. He seemed to me very young and lonely when I left him, but it was a tradition in the family that boys must go to boarding school when they reached the age of twelve, and James would be thirteen the following December, so of course we had to send him. I never thought to rebel then, but now it seems ludicrous to have been bound by so many conventions. I unpacked his trunk, saw his cubicle was in order, met some of the masters, said good-by to Mr. and Mrs. Endicott Peabody, the heads of the school, and went back to Hyde Park.

I did not stay there, however, but started immediately on the last campaign trip with my husband, a four-week trip which took us as far as Colorado. I was the only woman on the car. Franklin had a private car attached to different trains and on it were his secretary, Mr. Camellier; a young man who did general secretarial work, James Sullivan; Louis Howe; Marvin McIntyre, who was in charge of the train, the working out of

Anna Hall Roosevelt, the author's mother, in 1886. *Franklin D. Roosevelt Library*

Eleanor Roosevelt with her brother Elliott in 1891, and (below) about a year later with her father, Elliott Roosevelt, and her brothers, Elliott and Hall. *Franklin D. Roosevelt Library*

Eleanor Roosevelt with her horse (far left) at her grandmother Hall's country home at Tivoli, New York. *UPI*

Franklin Roosevelt at Fairhaven, Massachusetts, en route to Groton, autumn, 1897. *Franklin D. Roosevelt Library*

The author in her wedding gown, March 17, 1905. *Franklin D. Roosevelt Library*

On their honeymoon Eleanor and Franklin Roosevelt visited friends in Strathpeffer, Scotland. *Franklin D. Roosevelt Library*

In a gondola in Venice, photographed by her husband. *Franklin D. Roosevelt Library*

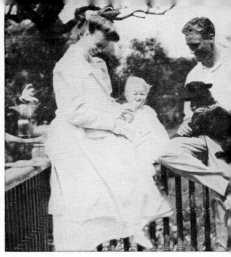

The young Roosevelts (left) at Hyde Park in 1913, with Mr. and Mrs. Henry Parrish, *Culver Service;* (right), with Anna in 1907; and (below), the Roosevelt family at Campobello, N.B., in 1920. *Franklin D. Roosevelt Library*

As wife of the Assistant Secretary of the Navy, Eleanor Roosevelt accompanies her husband on an inspection tour, *UPI;* (below), the Democratic candidate for Governor with his family at Hyde Park in 1928: (l. to r., standing) Curtis Dall, James Roosevelt; (seated) Elliott, Mrs. Roosevelt, Anna, F.D.R., his mother; (in front) John and Franklin, Jr. *Wide World*

In the Monroe Room at the White Hou (right). Portrait above the mantel is Theodore Roosevelt I, father of Preside Theodore Roosevelt. *Bradford Bachra*

Reading the congratulatory telegram from Herbert Hoover, conceding his defeat in the 1932 presidential election. *N.Y. Daily News Photo*

Greeting the Easter egg rollers, with Buzzie, Sistie and Anna Roosevelt Dall, April, 1933. *UPI*

The First Lady at the inaugural ball, March, 1933, with (l. to r.) Mrs. Cary Grayson, Ray Stannard Baker, James Roosevelt, Rear Admiral Cary T. Gr son, retired, and Brigadier General William T. Horton, retired. *Wide Wor*

A descent into a coal mine in Ohio, 1935. *UPI*

An inspection trip to Puerto Rico in 1934. *N.Y. Daily News Photo*

On a bridle path in Rock Creek Park, Washington, in 1933. *UPI*

Mrs. Roosevelt with her grandchildren, Sistie and Buzzie Dall, on the White House lawn where she had slides, sandboxes and swings built for them. *UPI*

On the *Amberjack II* at Southeast Harbor, Maine; (l. to r.) the author, F.D.R., James; (directly behind) Franklin, Jr., and John; (extreme left) Nancy Cook. *UPI*

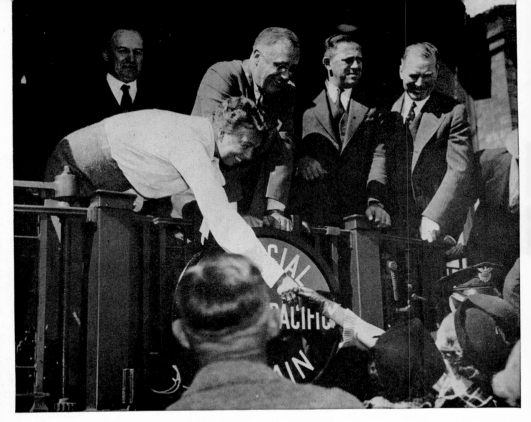

The President and Mrs. Roosevelt stop at Fremont, Nebraska, September, 1935, during a western tour, *Franklin D. Roosevelt Library;* and (below), F.D.R., his wife, and Franklin, Jr., on the porch of their Hyde Park home on election night, 1936. *UPI*

With Queen Elizabeth in Washington, D.C., during the state visit of the royal couple in June, 1938. *UPI*

At a dinner given by the Netherland-American Foundation in January, 1944, with (l. to r.) Crown Prince Olaf of Norway, Princess Juliana of Holland, Crown Princess Marta of Norway and Thomas J. Watson. *Wide World*

Gathered at the White House for Christmas, 1938: (l. to r.) Mrs. James R. Roosevelt, the President's sister-in-law, Eleanor Roosevelt, Mrs. James Roosevelt, the President's mother, the President, James Roosevelt and his wife, Franklin, Jr., and Harry L. Hopkins, then Secretary of Commerce; in front, Sara Roosevelt, James's daughter, and Diana Hopkins. *Wide World*

Arriving in London during October, 1942, Mrs. Roosevelt is met by General Dwight D. Eisenhower, King George, Queen Elizabeth and Ambassador John Winant, *Wide World;* and (below), the First Lady visits the troops in the Southwest Pacific in the fall of 1943. *Franklin D. Roosevelt Library*

President and Mrs. Roosevelt with their thirteen grandchildren in the White House on the occasion of his fourth inauguration, January, 1945. (Front, l. to r.) Christopher Roosevelt, son of Franklin, Jr.; Anne Sturges Roosevelt, John's daughter; back of her, Haven Clark Roosevelt, John's son; John Roosevelt Boettiger, Anna's son; Elliott Roosevelt, Jr.; Kate and Sara Roosevelt, James's daughters. (Back, l. to r.) Buzz Boettiger, Anna's son; Sistie Boettiger, Anna's daughter; William Donner Roosevelt, Elliott's son; Chandler Roosevelt, Elliott's daughter; David Boynton Roosevelt, Elliott's son, and Franklin D. Roosevelt, III. *Franklin D. Roosevelt Library.*

The coffin bearing the body of the President is carried into the White House. Mrs. Roosevelt is escorted by Vice Admiral Wilson Brown, the President's naval aide, on her right and White House usher Charles Claunch at her left. *Wide World*

With General Charles de Gaulle (right) in the rose garden at Hyde Park after he placed a wreath on the late President's grave in August, 1945. *Wide World*

Mrs. Roosevelt with President and Mrs. Truman at the commissioning of the aircraft carrier *Franklin D. Roosevelt,* October, 1945. *UPI*

As a delegate to the United Nations: (upper left) at the General Assembly opening at Flushing Meadows, October, 1946, with Senator Tom Connally and Senator Arthur H. Vandenburg; (upper right) in Paris, September, 1948, with John Foster Dulles, Warren Austin, U.S. Ambassador to the UN, and General George C. Marshall, Secretary of State; (below) in New York, October, 1952, with (front, l. to r.) Sen. Alexander Wiley, Sen. Theodore Green, Ambassador Warren Austin, Secretary of State Dean Acheson, (rear, l. to r.) Mrs. Edith F. Sampson, Benjamin V. Cohen, Philip C. Jessup and Ernest Gross. *Wide World*

Mrs. Roosevelt leaving the London home of Sir Winston Churchill after lunching with him and Mrs. Churchill in April, 1948. *Wide World*

Talking with President Tito of Yugoslavia at his summer estate on the Island of Brioni in July, 1953. *Wide World*

itineraries, and so on; Tom Lynch, our old friend from Poughkeepsie, who acted as disbursing officer, paying all bills, and so on; and Stanley Prenosil, who was the only newspaperman assigned continuously to covering the vice-presidential candidate.

I had never had any contact with newspaper people before. My grandmother had taught me that a woman's place was not in the public eye, and that idea had clung to me all through the Washington years. It never occurred to me to do more than answer through my secretary any questions that the reporters asked about social events. I gave as little information as possible, feeling that that was the only right attitude toward any newspaper people where a woman and her home were concerned.

But the years had taught me a certain adaptability to circumstances and I did receive an intensive education on this trip, and Louis Howe played a great part in this education from that time on. Ever since the Albany days he had been an intimate friend and coworker of my husband's. At times I resented this intimacy, and at this time I was very sure of my own judgment about people. I frequently tried to influence those about me, and there were occasions when I thought that Louis Howe's influence and mine, where my husband was concerned, had clashed; and I was, of course, sure that I was right.

Louis was entirely indifferent to his appearance; he not only neglected his clothes but gave the impression at times that cleanliness was not of particular interest to him. The fact that he had rather extraordinary eyes and a fine mind I was fool enough not to have discovered as yet, and it was by externals alone that I had judged him in our association prior to this trip.

In later years I learned that he had always liked me and thought I was worth educating, and for that reason he made an effort on this trip to get to know me. He did it cleverly. He knew that I was bewildered by some of the things expected of me as a candidate's wife. I never before had spent my days going on and off platforms, listening apparently with rapt attention to much the same speech, looking pleased at seeing people no matter how tired I was or greeting complete strangers with effusion.

Being a sensitive person, Louis knew that I was interested in the new sights and the new scenery, but that being the only woman was embarrassing. The newspaper fraternity was not so familiar to me at that time as it was to become in later years, and I was a little afraid of it. Largely because of Louis Howe's early interpretation of the standards and ethics of the newspaper business, I came to look with interest and confidence on the writing fraternity and gained a liking for it which I have never lost.

My husband was busy most of the day, when not actually out on the platform of the car, or at meetings in the various cities where we stopped. He had speeches to write, letters to answer, and policies to discuss. In the evenings, after they got back to the train, all the men sat together in the end of the car and discussed the experiences of the day from their various points of view and the campaign in general from the point of view of what news might be coming in from newspapers and dispatches.

Frequently for relaxation they started to play a card game, which went on until late. I was still a Puritan, thought they were an extremely bad example, and was at times much annoyed with my husband for not conserving his strength by going to bed. I did not realize how much he received through these contacts and how impossible it would have been, after the kind of days he was putting in, to go placidly to sleep.

Louis Howe began to break down my antagonism by knocking at my stateroom door and asking if he might discuss a speech with me. I was flattered and before long I found myself discussing a wide range of subjects.

Stephen Early had been borrowed from the Associated Press and acted in a personal capacity as advance man for this trip and went ahead of us for publicity purposes. He only now and then joined us on the train but was always in close touch. All these men were to become good friends of mine in the future.

That trip had many amusing incidents, and as the newspapermen and I became more friendly, they helped me to see the humorous side. They would stand at the back of the hall when Franklin was making the same speech for the umpty-umpth time and make faces at me, trying to break up the apparent interest with which I was listening. When I followed my husband down the aisle and the ladies crowded around him and exclaimed over his looks and charm, they would get behind me and ask if I wasn't jealous.

On this trip I saw a great deal of our country that I had never seen before; though I had not begun to look at the countryside or the people with the same keenness which the knowledge of many social problems brought me in the future, still I was thrilled by new scenery, and the size of my own country, with its potential power, was gradually dawning upon me.

We ended this trip very weary, for four weeks is a long time to be on the road, but when we reached Buffalo, New York, I who had never seen Niagara Falls insisted on seeing them. Though my husband went to Jamestown, New York, for political meetings, I took the day off and Louis Howe went with me to Niagara Falls.

One of the standing jokes of that campaign was a reference to the day in Jamestown and certain photographs which were taken of lovely ladies who served luncheon for my husband and who worshiped at his shrine. He had to stand much teasing from the rest of the party about this particular day.

It was impossible, of course, to make any arrangements for the children. Our house in New York was rented for another year to Mr. and Mrs. Thomas W. Lamont, and so we decided it would be better for Anna and Elliott to spend the winter at Hyde Park. I went to Vassar College to find a tutor to take over their schooling. A charming girl, Jean Sherwood, was recommended and we all liked her so much that she came to us that autumn and spent the entire winter with the two children at Hyde Park.

It still remained a question what would happen to the rest of us in case of either election or defeat, but most of us were fairly sure that defeat was in store. Even then I was beginning to wonder what was the point of these long campaign trips, where the majority of people who came to hear you were adherents of your own party. Only now and then would a heckler appear in the audience, and he was usually the type who could never be changed from the opposition point of view.

I still think campaign trips by anyone except the presidential candidates themselves are of little value. In 1920, however, the kind of campaign my husband made was considered reasonable.

Come what might, we had to live somewhere and my husband would probably go to work somewhere. He had already made arrangements to resume the practice of law. The old firm of Marvin, Booker and Roosevelt had ended with the war and he decided to form a partnership with Grenville Emmet and Langdon Marvin, under the firm name of Emmet, Marvin and Roosevelt.

The election was an overwhelming defeat, accepted philosophically by my husband, who had been prepared for the result. In this campaign I had taken no active part in the work at headquarters, but I had been in once or twice and had met my husband's office manager, Charles McCarthy. He had a young secretary during the campaign, Miss Marguerite

LeHand. It was through this association that she first came to my husband as a secretary and she remained with him as his private secretary until her last illness.

I did not look forward to a winter of four days a week in New York with nothing but teas and luncheons and dinners to take up my time. The war had made that seem an impossible mode of living, so I mapped out a schedule for myself. I decided that I would learn to cook and I found an ex-cook, now married, who had an apartment of her own, and I went twice a week and cooked an entire meal which I left with her for her family to criticize. I also attended a business school, and took a course in type-writing and shorthand every day while I was in New York.

Before I had been in New York many days I was visited by Mrs. Frank Vanderlip, who was at that time chairman of the League of Women Voters for New York State. She asked if I would join the board and be responsible for reports on national legislation. I explained that I had had little or no contact with national legislation in Washington, that I had listened a great deal to the talk that went on around me, and that I would be interested but doubted my ability to do this work. Mrs. Vanderlip said she was sure I had absorbed more than most of the New York members of the board knew and that I would have the assistance of an able woman lawyer, Miss Elizabeth Read. She would take the Congressional Record, go through it and mark the bills that she thought were of interest to the league, send for them and even assist me to understand them if I required any assistance.

With this assurance, I finally agreed that I would attempt to do the work. I decided that I would go to Miss Read's office one morning a week and devote that time to the study of legislation and bring home the bills that needed further study before I wrote my monthly reports.

I felt humble and inadequate when I first presented myself to Elizabeth Read, but I liked her at once and she gave me a sense of confidence. It was the beginning of a friendship with her and with her friend, Miss Esther Lape, which was to be lasting and warm. Esther had a brilliant mind and a driving force, a kind of nervous power. Elizabeth seemed calmer, more practical and domestic, but I came to see that hers was a keen and analytical mind and in its way as brilliant as Esther's.

My husband was working hard; he went occasionally to men's dinners, and I remember many pleasant evenings spent with Elizabeth and Esther in their little apartment. Their standards of work and their interests played a great part in what might be called the "intensive education of Eleanor Roosevelt" during the next few years.

My mother-in-law was distressed because I was not always available, as I had been when I lived in New York before. I had long since ceased to be dependent on my mother-in-law, and the fact that my cousin Mrs. Parish suffered from a long illness, lasting several years, had made me less dependent on her. I wrote fewer letters and asked fewer questions and gave fewer confidences, for I had begun to realize that in my development I was drifting far afield from the old influences.

I do not mean that I was the better for this, but I was thinking things out for myself and becoming an individual. Had I never done this, perhaps I might have been saved some difficult experiences, but I have never regretted even my mistakes. They all added to my understanding of other human beings, and I came out in the end a more tolerant, understanding and charitable person. It has made life and the study of people more interesting than it could have been if I had remained in the conventional pattern.

I was back on one or two boards for charities, such as the Bryson Day Nursery, but I had developed an aversion to serving on boards and having no personal contact with actual work. I tried to seize whatever opportunities for actual contact with people the nursery presented, but it was not very satisfactory.

Twelve

Trial by Fire

THE SUMMER of 1921 found us all going to Campobello again and various visitors coming up for short or long periods. There was a certain amount of infantile paralysis in some places again that summer, but it was not an epidemic, particularly among children, as it had been a few years before.

My husband did not go up with us, but came early in August, after we were settled, bringing quite a party with him. He did a great deal of navigating on Mr. Van Lear Black's boat, which he had joined on his way up the coast.

While Mr. Black and his party were with us, we were busy and spent days on the water, fishing and doing all we could to give them a pleasant time. My husband loved these waters and always wanted everybody who came up to appreciate the fact that they were ideal for sailing and fishing. The fishing is deep-sea fishing and rather uninteresting unless you go outside and into the Bay of Fundy or have the luck to do some casting into schools of fish as they came in.

Mr. Black had left and we were out sailing one afternoon in the little *Vireo* which my husband had bought after giving up the *Half Moon*, in order that the boys might learn to sail. On our return trip we spied a forest fire, and of course we had to make for shore at once and go fight the fire. We reached home around four o'clock and my husband, who had been complaining of feeling logy and tired for several days, decided it would do him good to go in for a dip in the land-locked lake called Lake Glen Severn, inside the beach on the other side of the island. The children were delighted and they started away. After their swim Franklin took a dip in the Bay of Fundy and ran home.

When they came in, a good deal of mail had arrived and my husband

114

sat around in his bathing suit, which was completely dry, and looked at his mail. In a little while he began to complain that he felt a chill and decided he would not eat supper with us but would go to bed and get thoroughly warm. He wanted to avoid catching cold.

In retrospect I realize he had had no real rest since the war. A hunting trip after the campaign had been strenuous, and plunging back into business had not given him any opportunity to relax and he had been going on his nerves.

We had Mrs. Louis Howe and her small boy, Hartley, staying in the house with us. Mr. Howe arrived a little later. He had stayed in the Navy Department after my husband left, to look after his papers and be of any assistance he could to the incoming assistant secretary, who happened to be Colonel Theodore Roosevelt. When Louis finally left the Navy Department he was considering an offer to go into business on a rather lucrative salary, and decided to take his holiday at Campobello before he made up his mind.

The next day my husband felt less well. He had quite a temperature and I sent for our faithful friend, Dr. Bennett, in Lubec. Dr. Bennett thought my husband had just an ordinary cold and I decided that the best thing to do was to get everybody else off on a camping trip, though I was sufficiently worried not to consider going myself.

The trip lasted three days, and by the time the campers were back it was evident that my husband's legs were getting badly paralyzed. Dr. Bennett wanted a consultation and we found that Dr. Keen was in Bar Harbor, Maine. By now Mr. Howe had arrived and he went with Captain Calder to meet Dr. Keen. Dr. Keen decided that it was some form of paralysis but could not explain it. By this time my husband's lower legs were paralyzed.

For a little while he showed no improvement. The days dragged on and the doctors kept saying he must have a nurse, but it was hard to get one, so I kept on taking care of him and slept on a couch in his room at night. His temperature at times was very high. It required a certain amount of skilled nursing and I was thankful for every bit of training Miss Spring had given me.

Finally my husband's uncle, Frederic Delano, begged us to have the well-known infantile paralysis doctor, Dr. Lovett, come up from Newport. He examined my husband carefully and after consultation told me it was infantile paralysis.

I was in a panic because, besides my own children, we had Mr. Howe's little boy with us. I asked Dr. Lovett what the chances were that some of the children would come down with it. He said that probably none of them would do so since they had not already become ill.

After Dr. Lovett's visit, we finally got a nurse from New York, called Miss Rockey, but Dr. Lovett had been so flattering as to certain aspects of my husband's care, not knowing that I had been the only nurse on the case, that it was decided I should continue to do a certain amount of the nursing. This I did until we were finally able to move him back to New York.

My mother-in-law returned from abroad and came up to see my husband and then returned to New York to get things ready for us. When it was considered safe, we obtained a private car in which to move my husband. Dr. Bennett agreed to go down with us, and it was arranged that the car was to be switched around in Boston so we would be able to go straight into New York without any change. This move required a great deal of planning.

Mr. Howe had made up his mind to give up all idea of taking the position that was open to him and to come back to his old boss, because he saw quite plainly that his help was going to be needed. From that time on he put his whole heart into working for my husband's future. The handling of his mail and the newspapers all fell entirely into Louis's hands.

At first we tried to keep all news out of the papers, not wanting to say anything until we knew something definite about the future. Of course we were anxious to make the trip home as inconspicuous and unsensational as possible. We put Franklin on an improvised stretcher and took him down from the house over the rough ground and stony beach and put him into the small motorboat, chugged two miles across the bay, carried him up the steep gangway, and placed him on one of the drays used for luggage in that northern part of the country. Every jolt was painful, as we walked to the station and the stretcher went into his compartment through the window.

The strain of this trip must have been great for my husband. First of all, a sense of helplessness when you have always been able to look after yourself makes you conscious every minute of the ease with which someone may slip and you may be dropped overboard, in transferring from the dock to the boat. In addition, he had not wanted crowds to witness his departure, and of course there was not only kindly interest in Eastport but there was a certain amount of interest inspired by newspapers in other parts of the country that were trying to find out just what was the matter.

We finally reached New York, and here again my husband was taken out of the car through the window and then by ambulance to the Presbyterian Hospital.

There followed days and weeks at the hospital. Dr. Lovett came occasionally, but his young associate, Dr. George Draper, was in charge most of the time.

The children were all back at school and stopped in to see him every day, with the exception of James, who was in Groton. The time seemed endless but he actually came home before Christmas.

Franklin's mother was really remarkable about this entire illness. It must have been a terrific strain for her, and I am sure that, out of sight, she wept many hours, but with all of us she was very cheerful. She had, however, made up her mind that Franklin was going to be an invalid for the rest of his life and that he would retire to Hyde Park and live there. Her anxiety over his general health was so great that she dreaded his making any effort whatever.

Though Franklin was in bed most of the time, Miss Rockey took charge of him except in the afternoons. Then I had to be at home. He was tall and heavy to lift, but somehow both of us managed to learn to do whatever was necessary. For several weeks that winter his legs were placed in plaster casts in order to stretch the muscles, and every day a little of the cast was chipped out at the back, which stretched the muscles a little bit more. This was torture and he bore it without the slightest complaint, just as he bore his illness from the very beginning. I never but once heard him say anything bordering on discouragement or bitterness. That was some years later, when he was debating whether to do something which would cost considerable money, and he remarked that he supposed it was better to spend the money on the chance that he might not be such a helpless individual.

In many ways this was the most trying winter of my entire life. It was the small personal irritations, as I look back upon them now, that made life so difficult. My mother-in-law thought we were tiring my husband and that he should be kept completely quiet, which made the discussions about his care somewhat acrimonious on occasion. She always thought that she understood what was best, particularly where her child was concerned, regardless of what any doctor might say. I felt that if you placed a patient in a doctor's care you must at least follow out his suggestions and treatment. The house was not overlarge and we were very crowded.

My husband's bedroom was at the back of the house on the third floor, because it was quieter there. I had given my daughter, who was fifteen that winter, the choice of a large room at the front of the third floor, which she would be obliged to share with the nurse during the afternoon and early evening, or a small room on the fourth floor rear, next to Elliott's room. This she would have entirely to herself. She chose the latter.

Mr. Howe took the big room on the third floor, as he had come to live with us during the week, because his wife could find no apartment in New York which was suitable both to their needs and their purse. During the weekends he journeyed to Poughkeepsie, where his wife and little boy were installed in a house and his daughter was at Vassar College. He was downtown most of the day at my husband's office, so the nurse could use his room undisturbed.

We had a connecting door into a room in my mother-in-law's house on the fourth floor, so the two little boys and their nurse had those rooms. This accounted for all the bedrooms and left me with no room. I slept on a bed in one of the little boys' rooms. I dressed in my husband's bathroom. In the daytime I was too busy to need a room.

The boys soon became entirely oblivious of the fact that their father had ever been ill. By spring he would sit on the floor with the little boys in the library, and they would play with him without the slightest idea that he was not able to do anything he wished to do in the way of rough-housing with them.

Anna, however, felt the strain of the overcrowded house and the atmosphere of anxiety. I had put her in Miss Chapin's School. I canvassed several schools and decided that Miss Chapin had the kind of personality which would appeal to me. I hoped the same relationship would grow up between Anna and Miss Chapin as I had had with Mlle. Souvestre. I did not realize how set and rigid New York schools were and that a girl coming in from outside would be looked upon by all the children as an outsider and would hardly be noticed by the teachers. Anna was very unhappy, though I did not realize it. She felt lost, and the different methods of teaching bewildered her. She tried to hide her feelings by being rather devil-may-care about her marks and her association with the other girls.

Someone had suggested to her that it was unfair that she should have a little fourth-floor room and Mr. Howe should have the large room on the third-floor front. Because of constant outside influences, the situation grew in her mind to a point where she felt that I did not care for her and was not giving her any consideration. It never occurred to her that I had far less than she had. There were times at the dinner table when she would annoy her father so much that he would be severe with her and a scene would ensue, then she would burst into tears and go sobbing to her room.

I knew nothing, of course, of what had been said to her and went on rather blindly thinking that girls of fifteen were far more difficult to bring up than boys.

I realize now that my attitude toward her had been wrong. She was an adolescent girl and I still treated her like a child and thought of her as a child. It never occurred to me to take her into my confidence and consult with her about our difficulties or tell her just what her father was going through in getting his nerves back into condition.

I have always had a bad tendency to shut up like a clam, particularly when things are going badly; and that attitude was accentuated, I think, as regards my children. I had done so much for them and planned everything and managed everything, as far as the household was concerned, for so many years that it never occurred to me that the time comes, particularly with a girl, when it is important to make her your confidante. If I had realized this I might have saved Anna and myself several years of real unhappiness. I would have understood her a great deal better because she would have been able to talk to me freely, and she would have understood me and probably understood her father and all he was fighting against.

As it was, I am responsible for having given her a most unhappy time, and we can both be extremely grateful for the fact that finally the entire situation got on my nerves and one afternoon in the spring, when I was trying to read to the two youngest boys, I suddenly found myself sobbing as I read. I could not think why I was sobbing, nor could I stop. Elliott came in from school, dashed in to look at me and fled. Mr. Howe came in and tried to find out what the matter was, but he gave it up as a bad job. The two little boys went off to bed and I sat on the sofa in the sitting room and sobbed and sobbed. I could not go to dinner in this condition. Finally I found an empty room in my mother-in-law's house, as she had moved to the country. I locked the door and poured cold water on a towel and mopped my face. Eventually I pulled myself together, for it requires an audience, as a rule, to keep on these emotional jags. This is the one and only time I remember in my entire life having gone to pieces in this particular manner. From that time on I seemed to have got rid of nerves and uncontrollable tears, for never again has either of them bothered me.

The effect, however, was rather good on Anna, because she began to straighten out, and at last she poured out some of her troubles and told me she had been wrong and she knew that I loved her and from that day to this our mutual understanding has constantly improved.

Today no one could ask for a better friend than I have in Anna or she has in me. Perhaps because it grew slowly, the bond between us is all the stronger. No one can tell either of us anything about the other; and though we may not always think alike or act alike, we always respect each other's motives, and there is a type of sympathetic understanding between us which would make a real misunderstanding quite impossible.

Dr. Draper felt strongly that it was better for Franklin to make the effort to take an active part in life again and lead, as far as possible, a normal life, with the interests that had always been his. Even if it tired him, it was better for his general condition.

The previous January Franklin had accepted an offer made by Mr. Van Lear Black to become vice-president of the Fidelity and Deposit Company of Baltimore, in charge of the New York office, and he had worked there until his illness. Mr. Black was a warm friend and kept his place for him until he was well enough to resume his work.

Mr. Howe felt that the one way to get my husband's interest aroused was to keep him as much as possible in contact with politics. This seemed to me an almost hopeless task. However, in order to accomplish his ends Mr. Howe began to urge me to do some political work again. I could think of nothing I could do but during the spring I was thrown on two or three occasions with a young woman who interested me considerably. Her name was Marion Dickerman. She was interested in working conditions for women and she taught in a school. I, too, was interested in working conditions for women, harking back to the interests of my girlhood. Mrs. James Lees Laidlaw asked me to attend a luncheon of the Women's Trade Union League and become an associate member. I joined the organization and have been a member ever since. This luncheon was my second contact with some of the women whom I had first met in Washington at the International Conference for Working Women and this resulted in a long association. I have never lost touch with this group. Many of them were interested in politics, and I soon found that Marion Dickerman also was interested.

Through my acquaintance with Miss Dickerman I met her friend Nancy Cook. Miss Cook invited me to preside at a luncheon to raise funds for the women's division of the Democratic State Committee. I had been carrying on to a limited extent my work for the League of Women Voters, but I had never done anything for a political organization before nor had I ever made a speech in any sizable gathering. Here I found myself presiding at a luncheon, without the faintest idea of what I was going to say or what work the organization was really doing. That was the beginning of a warm and lasting friendship with both Miss Dickerman and Miss Cook, and through them I met Miss Harriet May Mills and Mrs. Caroline O'Day and went to work with the Democratic women of New York State.

We moved to Hyde Park, bag and baggage, and spent the whole summer there except for a short time when I took the younger children to Fairhaven for a change of air and some sea bathing. I did not even stay with them all the time, but there I became conscious of the fact that I had two young boys who had to learn to do the things that boys must do— swim and ride and camp. I had never done any of these things. I had ridden when I was a child, and up to the age of twenty, but that was far behind me. I had no confidence in my ability to do physical things at this time. I could go into the water with the boys but I could not swim. It began to dawn upon me that if these two youngest boys were going to have a normal existence without a father to do these things with them, I would have to become a good deal more companionable and more of an all-round person than I had ever been before.

All that summer at Hyde Park my husband struggled to do a great number of things which would make it possible for him to be more active. He learned to use crutches and walked every day to gain confidence. Each new thing he did took not only determination but great physical effort.

That autumn of 1922 I took Elliott to Groton School. I drove him up myself, unpacked for him and left a much more miserable little boy than even James had been. I felt that he would settle down as James had done. He was far better prepared in his work, for he had had one year at the Buckley School, where he had done very well. He passed his examinations without any conditions. My hopes were vain, however; he never really loved the school as James did.

When we went back to New York, and when my husband was there, he followed an ordinary businessman's routine. He now had a chauffeur to take him back and forth between his office and our house every day.

Through my interest in the League of Women Voters, the Women's Trade Union League and the Democratic State Committee, where now I had become finance chairman, I was beginning to find the political contacts that Louis wanted. I drove a car on election day and brought people to the polls. I began to learn a good deal about party politics in a small place. It was rather sordid in spots. I worked with our county committee and our associate county chairwoman. I saw how people took money or its equivalent on election day for their votes and how much of the party machinery was geared to crooked business. On the other hand, I saw hard work and unselfish public service and fine people in unexpected places. I learned again that human beings are seldom all good or all bad and that few human beings are incapable of rising to the heights now and then.

We were rid of a trained nurse and we never treated my husband as an invalid. Anna had graduated to the large room and we were much less crowded with James and Elliott at school. In the holidays we usually went to Hyde Park. The whole family relationship was simpler. Anna continued to tell me about things which upset her, and her trials and tribulations away from home, and I was able more intelligently to manage the various elements of our existence.

The boys at school had on the average one accident each autumn during the football season which would necessitate my bringing them home or taking them to a hospital for a short time. We had, of course, a certain amount of illness among the children at home, but my husband's general health was good and I had not been ill since John was born. There was really no time for me to think of being ill.

In winter my husband had to go south, so for two winters we had a houseboat and cruised around the Florida waters. I went down and spent short periods with him; this was my first glimpse of the South in winter. I had never considered holidays in winter or escape from cold weather an essential part of living, and I looked upon it now as a necessity and not a pleasure. I tried fishing but had no skill and no luck. When we anchored at night and the wind blew, it all seemed eerie and menacing to me. The beauty of the moon and the stars only added to the strangeness of the dark waters and the tropic vegetation, and on occasion it could be colder and more uncomfortable than tales of the sunny South led me to believe was possible. Key West was the one place I remember as having real charm.

In New York I had begun to do a fairly regular job for the women's division of the Democratic State Committee and was finding work very satisfactory and acquiring pride in doing a semiprofessional job. We started a small mimeographed paper with which Mr. Howe gave me considerable help. We finally had it printed, and in an effort to make it pay for itself I learned a great deal about advertising, circulation, and make-up. From Mr. Howe I learned how to make a dummy for the printer, and though he never considered I was really capable of writing the headlines, I became quite proficient in planning, pasting, and so on.

Miss Cook and Miss Dickerman and I had become friends in just the way that Miss Lape and Miss Read and I had been first drawn together through the work we were doing. This is one of the most satisfactory ways of making and keeping friends.

Many of my old friends I saw very little, because they led more or less social lives. I had dropped out of what is known as society entirely, as we never went out. Now and then I would go to the theater with a friend, but my free hours were few. Ever since the war my interest had been in doing real work, not in being a dilettante. I gradually found myself more and more interested in workers, less and less interested in my old associates, who were busy doing a variety of things but were doing no job in a professional way.

Slowly a friendship grew with a young couple who lived in Dutchess County, New York, not far from us—Mr. and Mrs. Henry Morgenthau, Jr. They were younger and perhaps for that reason we did not at first see so much of one another. We had many interests in common in the county, and Mr. Morgenthau and my husband were thrown more and more together. Mrs. Morgenthau came eventually to work in the women's division of the Democratic State Committee, and she and I grew gradually to have a warm affection for each other. Good things are all the better for ripening slowly, but today this friendship with Elinor and Henry Morgenthau is one of the things I prize most highly.

During these years I also came to know Mrs. Carrie Chapman Catt, Mrs. Raymond Brown, Mrs. Louis Slade, Mrs. Henry Goddard Leach, Lillian Wald, Mary Simkovitch and many other women who had a great influence on me. To all of them I shall be deeply grateful always for opening up so many new avenues of thought and work.

I was beginning to make occasional speeches and on various occasions Louis Howe went with me and sat at the back of the audience and gave me pointers on what I should say and how I should say it. I had a bad habit, because I was nervous, of laughing when there was nothing to laugh at. He broke me of that by showing me how inane it sounded. His advice was: "Have something you want to say, say it, and sit down."

Under Mrs. O'Day, who was vice-chairman of the Democratic State Committee, I did a certain amount of organization work each summer among the Democratic women of the state. I usually went with either Miss Dickerman or Miss Cook. I paid my own traveling expenses and so did Mrs. O'Day; because money-raising was hard for women we felt every expense must be kept down. Miss Cook did wonders of economical management. All the work among the women had been started by Miss Harriet May Mills, who for many years was the outstanding Democratic woman leader of New York State. Even after her retirement as vice-chairman of the state committee, she responded to every call for assistance. I was always glad of this experience because I came to know my state, the people who lived in it, and rural and urban conditions extremely well.

Since his illness my husband had undertaken the presidency of the Boy Scout Foundation, the presidency of the American Construction Council, the chairmanship of the American Legion campaign, and a number of other nonpolitical activities. His only political effort during those years was in the summer of 1922 when he helped to persuade Al Smith to run again for the governorship.

He was entirely well and lived a normal life, restricted only by his inability to walk. On the whole, his general physical condition improved year by year, until he was stronger in some ways than before his illness. He always went away in the winter for a time and in summer for a long vacation, trying in each case either to take treatment or at least to keep up exercises which would improve his ability to get about. In the spring of 1924, before the National Democratic Convention met in New York, Al Smith, who was a candidate for the presidential nomination, asked him to manage his preconvention campaign. This was the first time that my husband was to be in the public eye since his illness. A thousand and one little arrangements had to be made and Louis carefully planned each step of the way.

I had been asked to take charge of the committee to present to the resolutions committee of the convention some of the planks of interest to women. This was to be a new step in my education. I knew a little now about local politics, a good deal through the League of Women Voters and, through my Democratic organization work, about my state legislature and state politics, and I was to see for the first time where women stood when it came to a national convention. They stood outside the door of all important meetings and waited. I did get my resolutions in, but how much consideration they got was veiled in mystery.

I heard rumors of all kinds of maneuvers and all the different things that the men were talking about drifted my way, but most of the time at the convention I sat and knitted, suffered with the heat, and wished it would end.

At this convention I caught my first glimpse of Will Rogers when he wandered by the box one day and asked, "Knitting in the names of the future victims of the guillotine?" I felt like saying that I was almost ready to call any punishment down on the heads of those who could not bring the convention to a close.

Finally, in spite of all that could be done, in spite of a really fine nominating speech by my husband and the persuasion and influence of many other people in the convention, Al Smith lost the nomination. My husband stepped gracefully out of the political picture, though he did make one or two speeches for John W. Davis.

And so ended the early phases of the education of Eleanor Roosevelt, both in life and in politics.

PART II

This I Remember

Thirteen

The Private Lives
of Public Servants

AS I BEGIN this book it seems to me an infinitely more difficult task than the previous volume. In the first place, it can no longer be only my autobiography. Most people will be interested primarily in what I may have to tell about my husband.

Perhaps I shall be able to give some impressions which may help in the understanding of the stream of history during those complicated years. What I have to say, if it is to contribute anything to the understanding of his life and character and objectives, must be about him as an individual.

I do not claim that I can be entirely objective about him, but there are some things I know that I feel sure nobody else can know. Although no human being ever completely knows another, one cannot live for many years with a person without learning something about him. Other people may know certain sides of Franklin's character or particular facets of his personality better than I; but if I can contribute what I learned and what I believe to be true I may help to fill in the true picture for future historians.

The books that have already been written about Franklin show quite plainly that everyone writes from his own point of view, and that a man like my husband, who was particularly susceptible to people, took color from whomever he was with, giving to each one something different of himself. Because he disliked being disagreeable, he made an effort to give each person who came in contact with him the feeling that he understood what his particular interest was.

Often people have told me that they were misled by Franklin. Even when they have not said it in so many words, I have sometimes felt that

129

he left them, after an interview, with the idea that he was in entire agreement with them. I would know that he was not, but they would be surprised when, later, his actions were in complete contradiction to what they thought they would be.

This misunderstanding arose not only from his dislike of being disagreeable but from the interest that he always had in somebody else's point of view and his willingness to listen to it. If he thought it was well expressed and clear, he nodded his head and frequently said, "I see," or something of the sort. This did not mean that he was convinced of the truth of the argument, or even that he entirely understood it, but only that he appreciated the way in which it was presented.

There is another fact which few people realize: the President of the United States gets more all-round information than most of the people who come to see him, though any one of them may know his own subject better than the President does. The President, however, must have a general outlook which takes in over-all considerations; whereas other people think primarily about their own ideas, plans and responsibilities for the specific thing they hope to accomplish. This circumstance puts on a President the responsibility of gathering all possible points of view, of often hearing conflicting ideas on a given subject, and then of making a final decision. It is one of the most difficult things a President has to do.

In addition, the fact that he can never have a personal loyalty greater than that to the nation sometimes makes it seem as though he were disloyal to his friends; but a man holding the office of President of the United States must think first of what he considers the greatest good of the people and the country.

I know Franklin always gave thought to what people said, but I have never known anyone less influenced by others. Though he asked for advice from a great many people, he simply wanted points of view which might help him to form his final decision, and which he sifted through his own knowledge and feelings. But once he reached a decision, people flattered themselves if they thought they ever changed it.

Franklin often used me to get the reflection of other people's thinking because he knew I made it a point to see and talk with a variety of people. I did not need to go on lecture trips or to inspect projects in different parts of the country, but my husband knew that I would not be satisfied to be merely an official hostess. He often suggested that I interest myself in certain things, such as the homestead projects. For my sake he was glad when he found that for a few weeks in spring and fall I could and did go on paid lecture trips. I would not plan such trips unless I had definite commitments and had signed formal contracts; but when they were an obligation, I arranged my time so they were possible. The trips took me to many places throughout the country to which otherwise I might never have gone.

Naturally, these lecture trips gave me more money for things I wanted to do than my husband could afford to give me. At the same time I felt that Franklin used whatever I brought back to him in the way of observations and information as a check against the many official reports he received.

Often, when some matter was being fought out with his advisers, he would bring up the question at dinner and bait me into giving an opinion by stating as his own a point of view with which he knew I would disagree. He would give me all the arguments that had been advanced to him and I would try vociferously and with heat to refute him.

I remember one occasion when I became extremely vehement and irritated. My husband smiled indulgently and repeated all the things that everyone else had said to him. The next day he asked my secretary, Miss Thompson, if I could have tea in the West Hall in the White House for him and Robert Bingham, who was then our ambassador to London and about to return to his post. I dutifully served them with tea, fully expecting to sit and listen in silence to a discussion of questions with which I would not be in agreement. Instead, to my complete surprise, I heard Franklin telling Ambassador Bingham to act not according to the arguments that he had given me but according to the arguments that I had given him! Without giving me a glance or the satisfaction of batting an eyelash in my direction, he calmly stated as his own the policies and beliefs he had argued against the night before! To this day I have no idea whether he had simply used me as a sounding board, as he so often did, with the idea of getting the reaction of the person on the outside or whether my arguments had been needed to fortify his decision and to clarify his own mind.

After Franklin became president, many people told me they disagreed with him and that they were going in prepared to tell him so in no uncertain terms. They went in for their interview, but if I saw them as they came out, they usually behaved as though they had never disagreed at all. Only now and then was someone honest enough to say he had not been able to put forward his own point of view—a difficulty due partly to the effect of Franklin's personality and partly to the person's awe of the office itself.

Franklin had the gift of being able to draw out the people whom he wished to draw out and to silence those with whom he was bored, and in both cases the people were greatly charmed. When he did not want to hear what somebody had to say he had a way of telling stories and talking about something quite different. Everyone who worked with him had to learn how to handle this technique of his if they were not to find that the questions they wanted to ask or the opinions they wanted to state never got into words because Franklin talked so steadily and so interestingly that they forgot what they had come to say.

Of all his intimates only a few, I think, ever really understood how it was that people sometimes thought he was in agreement with them when he was not or had given his consent when really he had never contemplated giving it. Louis Howe always understood this trait in Franklin, and Frank Walker, Edward J. Flynn, Henry Morgenthau, Jr., and Bernard Baruch came to know it well. With none of these men was his own interest ever paramount. The interest of each was in my husband and in the work to be done and they could be objective even when their own work was involved.

I was often supposed to be a great influence on my husband politically. Over and over again people wrote, crediting me with being responsible for his action and even for some of his appointments. Frances Perkins' appointment to the Cabinet is a case in point. As a matter of fact, I never even suggested her. She had worked with Franklin in New York State and was his own choice, though I was delighted when he named her and glad that he felt a woman should be recognized.

There were times when a list of names suggested for appointment, to serve as individuals or groups, would come out and there would be no woman's name on the list. Then I might go to my husband to say that I was weary of reminding him to remind the members of his Cabinet and his advisers that women were in existence, that they were a factor in the life of the nation and increasingly important politically. He always smiled and said: "Of course. I thought a woman's name had been put on the list. Have someone call up and say I feel a woman should be recognized." As a result, I was sometimes asked for suggestions and would mention two or three names. Sometimes they were considered and sometimes they were not.

The political influence that was attributed to me was nil, where my husband was concerned. If I felt strongly about anything I told him, since he had the power to do things and I did not, but he did not always feel as I did.

I have since discovered that a great many government people to whom I referred letters regarded them as a mandate requiring prompt attention. Evidently they thought that if what I suggested was not done I would complain to my husband. Actually, all I ever expected was that they would be interested in accomplishing the things that should be accomplished, since government is supposed to serve the good of the people. I thought that every government official investigated complaints and gladly tried to correct injustices. I realize now that this was a rather naïve idea, for it is apparent from what people told me that it was often only fear of White House displeasure that set the wheels in motion. This was not true of many departments, but I suppose it is only natural that some of the older departments, where a number of civil service people feel entrenched, should not want to bother with new activities. Both Mr. Woodin and Mr. Morgenthau must have made great changes in the old Treasury Department management. The standards set, particularly after Mr. Morgenthau became secretary of the treasury, must have seemed alarming to some of the old type of civil service officials.

I felt critical of civil service officials at times. When they have been in a department for a long while they can make any change very difficult. Nevertheless, there are an astonishing number of people who want to serve their country and are willing to accept the modest security and low pay of a civil service employee simply because they feel that they are performing a patriotic service.

Consciously, I never tried to exert any political influence on my husband or on anyone else in the government. However, one cannot live in a political atmosphere and study the actions of a good politician, which my husband was, without absorbing some rudimentary facts about politics. From him I learned that a good politician is marked to a great extent by his sense of timing. He says the right thing at the right moment. Though the immediate reaction may be unfavorable, in the long run it turns out that what he said needed to be said at the time he said it.

I do not mean that Franklin never made mistakes; most of the time, however, his judgment was good. He could watch with enormous patience as a situation developed and wait for exactly the right moment to act or speak. The quarantine speech, for instance, was delivered at a time when it was necessary that people be made to think. The meeting with Winston Churchill at Argentia and the announcement of the Atlantic Charter came at a crucial point in the country's life; in the same way, the D-day prayer lifted the morale of the people at a moment when that kind of inspiration was needed.

Franklin was a practical politician. He could always be told why certain actions or appointments were politically advisable. Sometimes he acted on this advice; on the other hand, he did many things and made many appointments against the advice of the party politicians, simply because he believed they would have a good effect on the nation as a whole. And he was almost always right. However, as a practical politician, he knew and accepted the fact that he had to work with the people who were a part of the Democratic party organization. I often heard him discuss the necessity and role of local political organizations, but he recognized that certain of them were a detriment to the party as a whole. He never got over his feeling against Tammany Hall or any boss-ridden organization, though he acknowledged that some were well administered and valuable.

Though Franklin always said I was far too impatient ever to be a good politician, and though my sense of timing is nowhere near so trustworthy as his was, I have grown more patient with age and have learned from my husband that no leader can be too far ahead of his followers. Also I think my observations of conditions and of the feelings of the average people within our country are fairly trustworthy.

During the years of my husband's governorship and presidency, but particularly after we were in the White House, I had many occasions to think seriously about the problem that faces the family of a man in American public life, especially a man who becomes the subject of great controversy— hated wholeheartedly by some and loved equally wholeheartedly by others. Of necessity, the attitude toward him must carry through to the members of his family and have some effect on them all.

For the young the situation is extremely difficult. Special privileges are offered them on every side. If they do not accept, they are considered ungracious and unappreciative. If they do accept, they are accused of being selfish, arrogant and greedy and of thinking themselves important and above other people—in fact, of having all the disagreeable traits that we most dislike in the young.

I remember, for instance, when Franklin Junior, then a young college student, was arrested for speeding between Albany and Boston. His father and I hoped that he would be treated as severely as possible, so that he would learn once and for all the inevitable results of breaking the law, even when the offense is not very serious. Above all, we wanted him to learn that punishment for breaking the law falls inexorably on all alike in a democracy. I can remember our utter dismay on discovering that he had got off without even a fine.

Our trouble, of course, came not only from the way the boys were treated outside the home—given too many privileges, on the one hand, and too much criticism, on the other—but from the fact that my husband's mother adored her grandchildren and thought of them as her own. She often got angry with me because I seldom told them what was right or wrong. The reason I didn't was that I never was sure. However, everything was always black or white to her; she had no doubts and never hesitated to tell the children what she thought. As a result, they often fooled her. The two youngest members of the family particularly always treated her with an affectionate camaraderie which won from her almost anything they desired.

Franklin Junior wrecked the small car we gave him when he graduated from school, and we decided it would be a good thing for him to go without one for a while. Almost before we knew it his grandmother, at his request, had replaced the car with a much more expensive one. When we objected, she looked at us blandly and said she had not realized we disapproved. She never heard anything she did not want to hear.

My husband had some very firm ideas about what children should do once they were educated. Up to that time they shared in the family life and possessions, but he thought that the day the boys graduated they should go to work and live on their earnings.

My mother-in-law differed in only one respect from my husband in these ideas. Although she believed the children should work, she wanted them all at home under her supervision and guidance, for she had a strong feeling about holding the family together in almost matriarchal style. Consequently, she disliked having any of the young members of the family financially independent of their elders; keeping them financially dependent, she thought, was one way of keeping them at home and controlling them.

She always regretted that my husband had money of his own from his father and that I had a small income of my own; and when I began to earn money it was a real grief to her. When Franklin was ill, however, she offered him any money he needed without question and longed to have him return to Hyde Park and never work again.

In spite of my mother-in-law's dejection about my earning money, I think she eventually became reconciled to it, realizing that it enabled me to do many things for which my own income was insufficient and which would have been too great a financial drain on my husband. The money I had inherited from my parents' estate shrank during the depression years, and I ended with a very small yearly income. However, long before leaving New York City in 1933, I had begun to earn money through teaching, writing and radio work. I can remember my pleasure when I first was able to give some substantial help to the Women's Trade Union League in paying off the mortgage on their clubhouse, and to carry through some of our plans on the Val-Kill experiment.

With the first money I earned through commercial radio work, during the bad days of the depression, I established two places where girls who were unemployed and searching for work could have lunch and a place to rest. One was in the Women's Trade Union League clubhouse and the other was in the Girls' Service League headquarters on Madison Avenue. We gave the girls a hot lunch and snacks during the day, and provided facilities for sewing, mending, and the like.

The large sums I was able to earn through radio and writing during those bad times made it possible for me not only to make contributions to organized charities but also to give work or help to individuals who could not be helped through the usual channels. I do not question that I often gave to people who were not worthy; but in those years it seemed better to take that risk than to fail those who were worthy. After a few disillusionments, however, I finally made an arrangement with the American Friends Service Committee whereby they did much of the investigating and I gave them almost all the money I earned through radio. At first I had this money paid directly to them, not receiving any of it myself. Then Hamilton Fish made an attack on me in Congress, claiming that I was evading income taxes by regarding a series of radio talks as benefits. I had, of course, obtained a ruling from the Treasury Department in 1933 that it was legal to turn over the money to a recognized charity, but as long as there was any basis for questioning my right to do this I decided to have the money paid directly to me, deducted part of it toward my income tax, and sent the balance to the American Friends.

The money I earned from all my radio work and some of my writing during the years I was in the White House I felt should be used not simply for charity donations but primarily to help people help themselves. Because that is also the philosophy of the Friends, I chose them to handle the money for me. I never gave a present to any of my children out of that earned money. On some occasions I had to use part of my small principal because I had given away so much I could not meet my income tax otherwise. I did not save a single penny during those years because I thought it was not right to do so, and I left the White House with less cash in my own principal account than I had when I went to Washington.

My husband's income was never large and he had to spend some of his principal every year he was in Albany and in the White House. As he died before his mother's estate was settled, that never was of any help to him.

At the time I married my income varied from $5,000 to $8,000 a year. Franklin knew that I had little knowledge of how to handle money, and he also knew that I had no right to disturb the existing trust arrangements, under which my money was managed largely by older members of my family and I simply received the income at certain intervals.

When I look back on how little we spent in our early married days I appreciate the changes in the cost of living in the past forty years. My husband and I agreed that we would put an equal amount into the house account, and we lived easily and comfortably if not luxuriously on $600 a month.

As our household expenses grew over the years, Franklin assumed more responsibility for running the home, and gave all the children modest allowances up to the time they left school. Before they were old enough to be put on an allowance, I bought their clothes and I always bought my own; however, Franklin thought that once they had an allowance they should buy their own clothes in order to learn how to manage money. Now and then I had to rescue them by giving them useful gifts of underwear, shirts and socks. The habit has persisted and they tease me about it now.

After our daughter Anna was married, both Franklin and his mother gave her a small allowance. However, because of my husband's theory that once a male child of the family was educated he should be on his own, our two older boys, James and Elliott, were not given an allowance after they finished their schooling. They, therefore, had to begin at once to earn a living. That complicated their lives considerably, because instead of being allowed to start at the bottom and work up, they were offered jobs that gave them too high returns. And they were too young and too inexperienced to realize that they were offered these jobs only because of their name and their father's position.

Franklin had a strong feeling that our sons should be allowed to make their own decisions and their own mistakes. Occasionally some of his friends suggested that he could give the boys a little guidance, but he always said they must find things out for themselves. I think his attitude came largely from the fact that his mother had wanted to direct his every thought and deed and that he had had to fight for independence.

She always complained that she never saw Franklin alone, but if they were left together by themselves for long they often disagreed. Those two were too much alike in certain ways to be left long alone. Franklin was as determined as she was, and as the years passed he went ahead and did anything he wanted to do in spite of the fact that he had a great respect and love for his mother. But, though out of her devotion to him she did a great many things that were difficult for her, she never accepted the fact of his independence and continued to the last to try to guide his life.

Nevertheless, I often think of how much she had to put up with. For instance, though she entertained them for his sake, she strongly disapproved of Governor Smith and some of Franklin's other political acquaintances and was unable to believe that they could have any ability. Curiously enough, I think Al Smith respected her in spite of the fact that he must have known how she felt, which only made him more self-assertive in her presence. However, she was always pleasant and one had to know her to appreciate her little barbs.

I remember one time when Huey Long was lunching with me at Hyde Park and Franklin, in order to talk to him about some bill on which he wanted his support, had seated him next to himself. My mother-in-law, who could whisper louder than anyone else I ever knew when she wanted to be heard, was at the opposite end of the table. And suddenly I heard her say to the man on her right, in her piercing whisper, "Who is that dreadful person sitting next to my son?"

As a result of Franklin's long experience with his own parent, he had an almost exaggerated determination that he would not subject his sons to similar interference, and the feeling became a plan of action. As he became busier in his public life he found it impossible to take time for the boys' interests, which kept them from asking for advice they might have sought quite naturally had he been freer to give it. One after the other, James and

Elliott learned through bitter experience and it was a bitter disillusionment as well. Their early marriages came about largely because they were not really rooted in any particular home and were seeking to establish homes of their own.

For the two younger boys things were easier because, as a great concession, my husband continued their allowances until his death. Franklin Junior went to law school after he graduated from Harvard and married, so he couldn't earn money; and John started at the bottom in the merchandising business and needed something to keep him going after his marriage. When they went into the Navy they wanted to keep on paying some share of their home expenses. Having an allowance, these two had less immediate need to earn money, so they were not put through the same experiences that the two older brothers had undergone.

Perhaps it is well at this point to clear up a story that has come back to me at various times: that our youngest son, John, was a conscientious objector and a pacifist and did not want to go into the services. Like every other young man I know, he was not, in the years before we were attacked, eager to go to war. But once we were at war there never was any question for him, any more than there was for any of our other sons. Whatever had to be done for the war had to be done, and none of them dreamed of being a conscientious objector or a pacifist.

As life grew busier at the White House, my husband had less time for family affairs, and I can remember how resentful the boys were when they found they actually had to make an appointment to see their father if they wanted to talk to him privately. On one occasion one of our sons had something he felt it was important to talk over with his father, so he made an appointment. My husband was always kind and gentle, and while our son talked he seemed to be listening, though he was reading a document he held in his hand. The boy asked if he had heard him. His father answered, "Yes," but when there was a pause in the talk, he looked up and handed the boy the paper. "This is a most important document. I should like to have your opinion on it." I imagine that seemed like a slap in the face to the boy, who thought that what he was talking about was more important than anything else in the world. He looked at the paper, commented on it and left the room.

Soon a very indignant young man came to me saying, "Never again will I talk to Father about anything personal." It took me a long while before I could bring him to understand that he had happened to strike the wrong moment and that his father had paid him a compliment in asking his opinion.

It may seem that I have gone into a great deal of frank detail about our family affairs and the personal life of the family. I have done so with a purpose, because I sometimes wonder whether the American public, which encourages the press to delve into the private lives of public servants and their families, realizes how much the family of a public man has to pay in lack of privacy for the fact that he is willing to serve his country in an elective or an appointive office.

Fourteen

Private Interlude: 1921-1927

AFTER LEAVING the law office of Carter, Ledyard and Milburn in 1910 and up to the time of his illness in 1921, Franklin had been more or less continuously in public life.

His job in the Navy Department was, I believe, one of the milestones in his life. It would have been easy for him to have become just a nice young society man who, after his work in the department was over for the day, sat around in the Metropolitan Club for a while and talked with his friends. But Louis Howe decided that this was a period when Franklin had better learn something new. He insisted that Franklin find out something about labor conditions in the navy yards, which were his special province in the department, and come in contact with the men. This was Franklin's first close contact with labor, and it was one of the turning points in his development. Certainly it proved of value to him later, both as governor and as president. In both of those periods he increased enormously in his understanding of people and their needs, and with Louis's help gradually developed a political flair that gave him great confidence.

My friend Esther Lape had become member-in-charge of the Bok Foundation. At Mr. Bok's request I helped her to organize the committee and this work. From our past experience in the League of Women Voters we knew that working together would be easy. We had Esther's friend and partner, Elizabeth Read, who was practicing law in New York City, to count on too, so the thinking and planning proceeded smoothly.

In January of the year following Alfred E. Smith's 1924 state victory, Franklin became a partner in D. Basil O'Connor's law firm. The firm became Roosevelt and O'Connor, an association which continued until March 3, 1933. However, from 1924 to 1928 Franklin devoted a good part

141

of his time to finding out how far he could recover from infantile paralysis. The use of his hands and arms came back completely and he developed, because he used them so constantly, broad shoulders and strong arms; but his legs remained useless.

Little by little, through exercise and wearing braces, he learned to walk, first with crutches and then with a cane, leaning on someone's arm. The first braces were heavy; later, lighter ones were made. However, for the rest of his life he was unable to walk or stand without the braces and some help, though he could still swim and play water polo.

The perfect naturalness with which the children accepted his limitations, though they had always known him as an active person, helped him tremendously in his own acceptance of them. He had so many outside interests that he was always busy, and boredom was something he never experienced in his whole life.

Two things he could still enjoy—swimming and driving his own car, which had special hand controls. He was as good a driver as anyone I have ever known with this specially equipped car.

Franklin's illness proved a blessing in disguise, for it gave him strength and courage he had not had before. He had to think out the fundamentals of living and learn the greatest of all lessons—infinite patience and never-ending persistence.

People have often asked me how I felt about his illness. To tell the truth, I do not think I ever stopped to analyze my feelings. There was so much to do to manage the household and the children and to try to keep things running smoothly that I never had time to think of my own reactions. I simply lived from day to day and got through the best I could.

We had tried so hard to ignore any handicap he labored under that I'm sure the two youngest boys had never even thought about what their father could not do, and much of his gallant joking was merely a way of forcing himself to accept cheerfully what he could not help. I remember, for instance, one night in New York City, during a campaign, when he had to be carried on and off the speaker's platform. It was a difficult ordeal, but he passed it off with a smile and a joke.

Franklin went to Warm Springs for the first time in the autumn of 1924. It was then a run-down southern summer resort which had seen better days. The outdoor swimming pool was the one really fine thing about the place. These springs had been known since the days of the

Indians, who, even when they were at war with one another, maintained peace in that area, believing the waters had medicinal value. There is no claim made now that they have any healing powers, but the buoyancy and warm temperature of the water make it possible for one to swim for long periods without becoming tired or chilled. My husband loved the place.

For a number of years my husband went to Warm Springs every autumn, and I remember with a mixture of joy and sadness the Thanksgiving Day celebrations. There seemed so much happiness in the children's faces, but the complete gallantry of all the patients always brought a choke to my throat. Some of them were on stretchers, some in wheelchairs, some on crutches. Some hoped to get well, many faced permanent handicaps, but all were cheerful that one evening at least.

During those years before Franklin went back actively into politics a number of things I did were undertaken at Louis Howe's suggestion in order to interest Franklin. The organization of state campaigns was primarily my job and, again with Louis Howe's help, I thought up some of the best stunts that were undertaken. For instance, in the campaign of 1924 Alfred E. Smith was running against my cousin, Theodore Roosevelt, Jr., who had previously been Assistant Secretary of the Navy in the Harding administration. The recent Teapot Dome scandal—with which Theodore Roosevelt, Jr., had nothing to do—had created much excitement; so, capitalizing on this, we had a framework resembling a teapot, which spouted steam, built on top of an automobile and it led the procession of cars which toured the state, following the Republican candidate for governor wherever he went!

In the thick of political fights one always feels that all methods of campaigning that are honest are fair, but I do think this was a rough stunt and I never blamed my cousin when he retaliated in later campaigns against my husband.

It was during these years, too, that I became engaged in two enterprises with Nancy Cook and Marion Dickerman. Franklin was particularly interested in one of our undertakings. He helped to design and build a stone cottage beside a brook where we often went to picnic during the first years after he was paralyzed. The brook was called Val-Kill, so we called the cottage Val-Kill Cottage. Franklin was the contractor and the builder and, though Mr. Henry Toombs was the architect, he liked to talk over every detail. We built not only the cottage but a swimming pool in which the children and occasionally Franklin enjoyed much sport. Later we built a more elaborate pool, but by that time Franklin was the President and we had to conform to the regulations set up by his doctor and put in filtration machinery. I do not think we had any more fun, however, in the bigger and more elaborate pool than we had in the original small one, the building of which my husband had supervised.

The cottage was not an end in itself. It was the place in which Nancy Cook and Marion Dickerman lived and from which Miss Cook directed a furniture factory. Nancy Cook was an attractive woman who could do almost anything with her hands. She had long wanted to make reproductions of Early American furniture. We obtained help and co-operation from the Metropolitan Museum, the Hartford Museum, and from many individuals. We produced drawings and went to look at famous pieces of old furniture. Miss Cook had no desire to reproduce worm-eaten antiques; she wanted to use methods employed by our ancestors, and see whether she could find a market for furniture which, though the first processes were done by machinery, would be largely handmade and therefore expensive. Because the finishing was all done by hand, the wood looked and felt as though it had been used and polished for years.

My husband was greatly interested in finding some industry that could be developed in country areas such as ours, and that could perhaps furnish occupation for some of the younger men who would otherwise leave the farms. By giving them work in an industry which would yield them a fairly good income during the slack period on the farms, he thought one could keep the progressive, more active group of young people working steadily and so raise the standard of farm development in our area.

He had a great love for the soil and wanted to see it developed; but he realized that many of the farmers around us had a difficult time holding their young sons on the land, because the return for hard and strenuous work was meager. His interest in our enterprise was therefore in the training and the employment of young men in the vicinity.

Nancy Cook ran the enterprise and I put in most of the capital from my earnings from radio and writing and even used some of the small capital that I had inherited from my mother and father. The others, especially Nancy Cook, contributed what they could afford.

We kept the factory going all through the early depression years, when the employment of people seemed vitally important. At last Miss Cook found that carrying two jobs—she was also executive secretary of the women's division of the Democratic State Committee—was too much for her, so we closed the shop.

My husband's object was not achieved, and I think the idea has been proved impractical on a much larger scale in some of the homesteads which were started during the depression. Some succeeded but few returned much on the original investment. Nevertheless, in the crisis they took people off relief and gave them back self-respect and a sense of security—a considerable achievement.

Although this experiment was a disappointment to Franklin, he accepted the failure philosophically both in our own case and later in the case of the country-wide experiment. I think he felt regret; but, with the same acceptance of the inevitable which he showed in so many other matters, having tried the experiment and become satisfied that it did not work, he gave it up and sought other solutions. He hoped that some day it might work out. He always accepted things as they were and set such experiences aside as something to remember and perhaps use in the future.

I never made any money out of this furniture-making venture. In fact, I was probably one of the best customers the shop had, because I bought various pieces of furniture as wedding presents and as gifts for other occasions.

During the depression I took over the factory building and was able, through my earnings, to turn it into a fairly comfortable if somewhat odd house. Though I did not have any architectural advice, I did have the help of a friend, Henry Osthagen, an engineer. We used local labor entirely. Employing people seemed the best way to spend some of the money I was able to earn during those years. Part of the shop we made into an apartment for my secretary, Malvina Thompson, and I frequently went there to work quietly with her; the rest of the building became a guest cottage, which we used when the big house was overcrowded—something that often happened during the years when my husband was president. Since turning the old Hyde Park house over to the government, I have made the converted shop building my year-round home.

During the early years of my acquaintance with Nancy Cook and Marion Dickerman I became associated in the Todhunter School with Miss Dickerman, who was first the assistant principal and then the principal. It was a private school for girls from the primary grades through high school. Miss Todhunter, who was British, finally sold the school to Marion

Dickerman, Nancy Cook and myself and went back to England. I began teaching there in 1927. I taught only the older girls because I considered that it took far less training to teach them than to teach the younger children. I gave courses in American history and in English and American literature and later we tried some courses in current events which I hope were more practical than are many of the courses given to sixteen- and seventeen-year-old girls. We visited the New York City courts and I think many young people learned a great deal from sitting in one of the children's courts for an hour. Those whom their parents allowed to go I took to see the various kinds of tenements that exist in a city like New York, as well as the big markets and various other places. All this made the government of the city something real and alive, rather than just words in a textbook.

In spite of my political activities and having to run the Executive Mansion in Albany, after my husband was elected governor, I continued to teach for two and a half days a week, leaving Albany on Sunday evenings and returning on Wednesday afternoons. It was rather strenuous when we were in Albany, but, of course, fairly easy when we were at Hyde Park, as we were there for longer periods, when the legislature was not in session. For a while, after we went to Washington, I conducted a class for graduates and their friends, first on a weekly and then on a monthly basis.

Fifteen

The Governorship Years: 1928-1932

IN THE SPRING of 1928, when it looked as though Governor Smith would be the candidate for the Presidency on the Democratic ticket, Mrs. Belle Moskowitz asked me to organize the women's end of the office for the national campaign.

That June my husband went with our son, Elliott, to the Democratic National Convention, which met in Houston, Texas. Elliott was thrilled at the chance to be with his father, but I had no desire to take part in the hurly-burly of a convention—the 1924 convention had given me all I wanted of that type of experience. My husband stood the Texas heat remarkably well and came back to Hyde Park feeling that he had had a great part in bringing about the nomination of Alfred E. Smith.

Franklin and I had long supported Governor Smith politically because of his social program; we believed that he sought the welfare of the average man and woman. Franklin remembered how after the Triangle Fire in 1911 in New York City Governor Smith had worked for better factory laws in our state. This fire had been a shocking disaster, in which a great many girls and women had been burned to death because of the lack of fire exits and fire protection in the factory.

Because Governor Smith had spent the greater part of his life in one state and practically in one city, he had certain shortcomings; nevertheless, we felt that he understood the needs of the people and that he had a genius for government; and we never doubted his integrity. His memory was prodigious and his method of talking to people during the campaigns, particularly in his own state, which he knew so well, was remarkably effective.

Franklin did not feel he could do a great deal of work in the campaign, but he came into the office occasionally, and he headed the Businessmen's Division, sat in on planning meetings and made some speeches. He assigned

147

Louis Howe to represent him at the headquarters full time, working with Governor Smith, John Raskob, Edward J. Flynn and others.

It was not until I began to see the full alignment against us that I became doubtful of success. Governor Smith was a Roman Catholic, and the kind of propaganda that some of the religious groups, aided and abetted by the opposition, put forth in that campaign utterly disgusted me. If I needed anything to show me what prejudice can do to the intelligence of human beings, that campaign was the best lesson I could have had.

In 1928 I was still fairly young and could put in prodigious hours of work, but I sometimes wonder how any of us, particularly Miss Thompson and Miss Tully, lived through that campaign. It proved that work is easier to carry if your heart is involved. Miss Thompson was interested because I was interested; and Miss Tully, who had been Cardinal Hayes's secretary, probably felt a religious interest in the campaign in addition to her admiration for Governor Smith.

Grace Tully was young and very pretty, and had been extremely well trained by Cardinal Hayes. Our work was somewhat different from that to which she had been accustomed, but it was good preparation for her future work with my husband and Miss LeHand.

In the fall, after school began, I did not go into the office until noon on the days I taught, but I stayed until the work was finished at night, often well after midnight. Then I went home to do my school papers and was at school the next morning at half past eight. On the other days I was in the office at nine o'clock in the morning and stayed until late in the evening.

Speaking was still something of an ordeal for me, so it was understood that my part of the work would involve simply organizing the office, handling the mail, greeting women visitors, consulting on requests for speakers; in fact, just being generally useful. Mrs. Mary Norton, congresswoman from New Jersey, as head of the women's speakers' bureau, made the arrangements for women speakers, and all requests were referred to her.

Elinor Morgenthau and Nancy Cook, who were working with the Democratic State Committee, moved with their staff to the General Motors Building for the campaign. Then, in the latter part of the summer of 1928, the vice-chairman of the Democratic National Committee, Mrs. Nellie Tayloe Ross, moved into her office at the national headquarters, with Mrs. James O'Mahoney as her assistant. Mrs. Ross had served as governor of Wyoming after the death of her husband, who had been the previous governor.

Her arrival at headquarters meant that we started to make plans for an extensive speaking trip for her, and she was always in demand for activities at headquarters. We kept her pretty busy. I remember one day I had Miss Tully scurrying everywhere to find her while a tea party waited to greet her. She was found completely exhausted, lying on the floor of our diminutive restroom, trying to regain enough energy to face shaking hands with several hundred people.

Later, she continued in active government work and became director of the mint of the Treasury Department, remaining a popular speaker with women's groups.

In September of that year I motored to Groton with our youngest son, John, to put him in boarding school. By then I had come to feel that once a child went to boarding school there never again could be the strong ties with and the dependence on the family that had existed up to that time. I had never been a convinced advocate for boarding school for the twelve-year-old but my husband, who had not gone to boarding school until he was fourteen, always felt that the loss of those two years was a hardship, because by the time he entered the school the other boys had already formed their friendships and he remained always a little the outsider.

The day I took each boy to school, unpacked his clothes and settled him was always a terrible day for me, and when it came to the last child, it was particularly hard.

Even though I was teaching school and working in the national campaign headquarters in New York City, I attended the New York State Democratic Convention in Rochester that fall. I mention this here to tell the story, as I remember it, of how my husband was finally induced to run for the governorship.

The afternoon before the nominations were made, John J. Raskob, then chairman of the National Democratic Committee, and Governor Smith asked me to come to talk with them. I had heard that Governor Smith wanted my husband to run. However, I knew Franklin felt he should continue his treatment at Warm Springs. They told me how much they wanted him to run, and asked me if I thought it would really injure his health. I said I did not know; that I had been told the doctors felt that if he continued with his exercises and swimming at Warm Springs he might improve. My husband once laughingly said that if he lived long enough he might be able to walk again, but progress was slow and I sometimes wondered how much more could be achieved.

Both Governor Smith and Mr. Raskob insisted that they did not want to urge anything that would injure Franklin's health. If, however, it was not simply his health but other reasons which kept him from consenting, they would like to know it. I said I did not think any other reasons were paramount and that Franklin felt the possibility of making further improvement in his health was worth a try. Also, having undertaken a heavy financial responsibility in Warm Springs, he felt an obligation to try to make it a success.

Finally, after Governor Smith, Mr. Raskob and I talked over the situation, they asked me if I would be willing to get my husband on the telephone and ask him to run for governor. They had been trying all day to reach him and had not been able to do so. I answered that I would not ask him to do anything he felt he should not do, let alone run for office.

They put in a call to my husband for me early in the evening and found that he had gone to Manchester, Georgia, to make a speech and could not be reached until he returned to Warm Springs. I finally succeeded in getting Franklin on the telephone at the Foundation after his return. He told me with evident glee that he had been keeping out of reach all day and would not have answered the telephone if I had not been calling.

I had just time enough to tell him that I had called because Governor Smith and Mr. Raskob begged me to, and that I was leaving him to Governor Smith because I had to catch a train. Then I ran. I can still hear Governor Smith's voice saying, "Hello, Frank," as I hurried from the room to gather up my belongings and catch the train. I did not know until the following morning when I bought a newspaper that my husband had been persuaded to accept the nomination. I never heard him say later whether he regretted his decision or not. Having decided, he put any other possibility out of his mind.

Louis Howe was not happy about Franklin's candidacy. He always thought in terms of the future, and he had planned that Franklin should be a candidate four or eight years later. Louis feared that if Governor Smith lost nationally, it might not be possible for Franklin to carry the state for the governorship, which might spoil any chance he had for future political office.

I used to laugh at Louis and say one could not plan every move in this world, one had to accept circumstances as they developed. Louis hated to do that. He liked to feel that he dominated circumstances and, so far as it was humanly possible, he often did.

Comparatively speaking, I knew very little about the 1928 campaign for the governorship. Since I had started to work in the national office, Franklin felt I was obligated to continue there, and that took the greater part of my time. I did go to hear him speak occasionally, and he made a complete campaign throughout the state. I think he did not expect to carry the state if Governor Smith lost the Presidency, and when we left the state headquarters at a late hour on election night we were still uncertain of the outcome. The next morning, when the final figures were in, my husband was governor-elect by a very narrow margin. He had a feeling that it was a great tribute to have been elected while Governor Smith, who had such a large following in the state, had been defeated.

On that election night I visited the national as well as the state campaign headquarters, and I thought that Governor Smith accepted his defeat very gallantly. It must have been hard for him to have Franklin elected while he himself was defeated, but he never showed it in any way. He went back to work in the state and on January 1, 1929, he received us when we went to Albany.

Many people have suggested to me that when Governor Smith asked my husband to run for the governorship, while he himself was running for the Presidency, he had it in mind that he would still be able to direct the work of the governor.

One of the ways in which he undoubtedly expected to keep his hold on the state government was through Mrs. Belle Moskowitz. He suggested a number of times to my husband that she would be invaluable to him, and each time Franklin replied that while he had great respect for Mrs. Moskowitz's ability and knew what her advice and help had meant to Governor Smith, he felt it would be unwise for him to retain her in his own close administrative circle. He thought it impossible for anyone to transfer loyalty after working so long and so closely with someone else.

Governor Smith had asked Franklin to nominate him for the Presidency and to run on the state ticket as governor because Franklin would bring him needed strength. However, I think that Governor Smith did not have much confidence in the Harvard man who had a different kind of education and who cared about many things which meant little or nothing to Governor Smith.

There are two kinds of snobbishness. One is that of the man who has had a good many opportunities and looks down on those who lack them.

The other kind is rarely understood, that of the self-made man who glories in his success in overcoming difficulties and admires greatly people who have achieved the things he considers of importance. Governor Smith had a great deal of respect for material success, but he tended to look down upon a man like Franklin who was content not to make a great deal of money so long as he had enough to live comfortably.

In those days I think that in some ways I understood Governor Smith better than Franklin did, because during my intensive work with the Democratic State Committee, while Franklin was ill, I had had more opportunity to observe him from different points of view. While he and Franklin had known each other for a long time, they were never really intimate. Franklin thought only of his ability as an administrator, as a campaigner, as a statesman and as a governor, and he had the greatest admiration for his knowledge of government.

I agreed that he had an extraordinary flair for government and that his memory and his knowledge of New York State were phenomenal. Indeed, I believed in him and considered him a great man in many ways, and I worked for him. I thought that had he been elected president, he would have chosen his Cabinet well, even though his knowledge of the country as a whole was slight and his advisers in the state knew little of the nation. However, I never felt he could have handled our foreign relations or gauged what was happening in the world. Also, I thought him less of a humanitarian than most people did, crediting Mrs. Moskowitz with the social welfare plans for which he was generally acclaimed, and which he carried out, I thought, largely because he knew they were politically wise.

It was natural for him to feel that he was responsible for Franklin's success in politics, since he had urged my husband to run for governor. Franklin himself, however, felt the request to run had been made to help Governor Smith, and it was on that basis and that basis alone that the appeal had been considered.

In many ways Governor Smith did not know my husband. One of Franklin's main qualities was that he never assumed any responsibility that he did not intend to carry through. It never occurred to him that he was not going to be the governor of New York with all the responsibility and work that position carried. That ended the close relationship between my husband and Governor Smith, though there was no open break, so far as I ever knew.

Franklin had some clear ideas about state government. He studied the reorganization plans that had been initiated under Governor Smith and he approved practically everything that he had done. Franklin's attitude toward the objectives that later were developed on a national scale was apparent in his approach to questions in the state. For instance, he pushed old-age pensions.

As governor, Franklin also showed his interest in labor and his belief in labor's rights. He felt that workers should receive the same consideration that management's rights received; and when times became hard, the theory that government had a responsibility toward the people was incorporated in the state policies. Franklin had been accused of giving labor too much power, but his effort was simply to equalize the power of labor and capital. As a close student of history, he knew how great and unhampered capital's power had been during some previous administrations.

His particular personal interest was in soil conservation and forestry. However, his interest in the development of water power, in the Indian problem, transportation, education, and finally in relief and general welfare was also stimulated by his experience as the administrator of a state. All these objectives, as well as his understanding of them, were expanded during the presidential years. And because he had traveled so extensively even before he was president, he knew how different the problems were in different areas of the country. All this was excellent preparation for the years ahead.

Once back in public affairs, Franklin's political interests and ambitions reawakened. When he found he could again play an active part in politics he took a satisfaction in the purely political side of the struggle, in achieving new office. It is hard to dissociate his ambition and enjoyment of the science of politics for its own sake from his desire to achieve through political action real gains for the people, first of the state, then of the nation, and finally of the world. The objectives grew as circumstances developed the need for them and the horizons broadened as time went on and we, as a nation, were swept into a position where the world was depending on us.

In Albany he had the experience of working with legislative groups in which his political party was in a minority. Later, in Washington, I often wished that it were possible for him to carry out with the Democratic representatives there the kind of educational work he had done in Albany. There were occasional meetings when all the legislation backed by the administration was talked over and explained and the entire campaign mapped out. My husband always said the group in Congress was too large and he did not see how it was possible to hold the same type of meeting.

The years in Albany cast their shadow before them. Frances Perkins was in the New York State Labor Department, Harry Hopkins was doing a job on relief and welfare, Dr. Thomas Parran was commissioner of public health, Henry Morgenthau, Jr., was conservation commissioner. Many experiments that were later to be incorporated into a national program were being tried out in the state. It was part of Franklin's political philosophy that the great benefit to be derived from having forty-eight states was the possibility of experimenting on a small scale to see how a program worked before trying it out nationally.

My own life during those governorship years was a full one. In my teaching I really had for the first time a job that I did not wish to give up. This led to my planning to spend a few days every week in New York City, except during the school vacations.

My husband, who loved being on the water, found that the state of New York had a small boat used by state officials for canal travel on inspection trips. He decided to use it himself during the summers for the same purpose. During the day we would leave the boat and visit various state institutions. This was valuable training for me. I had paid occasional visits to state prisons, insane asylums or state hospitals for crippled children, but never with the intention of looking into the actual running of any institution or gauging its good and bad points.

The head of the institution that we were visiting usually got into the car with my husband and drove around the grounds, pointing out what new buildings were needed and where they should be built. In this way Franklin gained a personal knowledge of the exterior of the institution which helped him when he met with the legislative appropriations committee.

Walking was so difficult for him that he could not go inside an institution and get a real idea of how it was being run from the point of view of overcrowding, staff, food, and medical care. I was asked to take over this part of the inspection, and at first my reports were highly unsatisfactory to him. I would tell him what was on the menu for the day and he would ask: "Did you look to see whether the inmates were actually getting that food?" I learned to look into the cooking pots on the stove and to find out if the contents corresponded to the menu. I learned to notice whether the beds were too close together, and whether they were folded up and put in closets or behind doors during the day, which would indicate that they filled the corridors at night! I learned to watch the patients' attitude toward the staff, and before the end of our years in Albany I had become a fairly expert reporter on state institutions.

In the summer of 1929 we made an inspection trip on the canal which eventually brought us out to a point from which Franklin went down the St. Lawrence River to discuss the St. Lawrence Waterway with Canadian and United States officials.

That summer, with the two younger boys, I went to Europe. My husband had particularly wanted me to show them the fronts over which our men had fought in World War I, Quentin Roosevelt's grave, and some of the cemeteries. I had already pointed out to them in the little villages of England the monuments to the men who had been killed in that war. The cemeteries, with their rows and rows of crosses, made an impression on the boys, but they were, of course, unable to gather the significance of the new buildings in the old French villages and towns. To young Americans, new buildings were not strange, and while I was impressed by the way nature had covered her scars in the woods and fields, I pointed out to the boys the whitened stumps and the fact that the trees were young, showing that whole forests had been mowed down just a few years ago. In the fields I pointed out the ditches, which had been dug by soldiers for protection, and the curious holes made by bursting shells, now covered with grass.

My older son said to me one day: "This is a funny country. There are only boys our age and old men coming out of the fields. There don't seem to be any men of father's age." That was simply another proof that the war had taken from France a heavy toll of her young men from 1914 to 1918.

This same sense of the loss of a generation came to me vividly at the first organizational meeting of the United Nations in London, in 1946. So many of the Europeans were older men who had made the effort with the League of Nations and were doubtful about a second international effort to keep the world at peace. The loss of a generation makes itself felt acutely twenty to thirty-five years later, when many men who would have been leaders are not there to lead.

Back in Albany, I became immediately submerged again in the busy routine of my life as mother, governor's wife and teacher, and there were few breaks until the state campaign of 1930. That was an easy campaign, and it was a satisfaction to all of Franklin's supporters that he won the largest vote cast for any Democrat up to that time in a gubernatorial election. This circumstance had the double advantage of making Franklin strong in the state and strong as a potential candidate for the Presidency. This prospect did not interest me particularly but it did interest his political supporters.

During his terms as governor of New York he attended many of the Governors' Conferences, because he felt that they were important. Whenever possible he wanted the advantage of contact with other governors for the discussion of problems. Sometimes I went with him. I remember particularly one of the last Governors' Conferences, at which President Hoover started to make an address. The wind blew away his papers and he was so completely dependent on them that he had to break off his speech.

In the course of that conference, which was at Richmond, Virginia, all the governors were invited to dine at the White House. My husband was already considered one of the strongest possible candidates for the Democratic nomination for president. I was familiar with the way in which guests had to stand in the East Room at a state dinner before they were received by the President and his wife, so I was worried about Franklin, who had to have somebody's arm and a cane. In addition, he became tired if he stood without support for any length of time.

We arrived a little ahead of time, since we knew we should have to walk rather slowly down the main hall to get into line, and then we waited and waited. The President and Mrs. Hoover did not appear. My husband was twice offered a chair, but he thought that if he showed any weakness someone might make an adverse political story out of it, so he refused each time. It seemed as though he was being deliberately put through an endurance test, but he stood the whole evening very well, though the half hour before President and Mrs. Hoover appeared was an ordeal.

This idea may seem preposterous but in political life you grow suspicious. The strategists on both sides weigh how far they can go without awakening in the people a feeling that the rules of fair play have not been observed. You hear a whisper of this or that, but the whispers are never brought to the attention of the candidates and no official recognition is given to them.

I can hardly remember a campaign in which, in our village of Hyde Park, scurrilous things were not said about my husband and his mother and myself, and even about the children. Some of my friends came to me in anxiety because they had heard a story that my husband did not have infantile paralysis but had some other disease which was progressive and would eventually attack the brain.

During the 1932 campaign Louis Howe heard that the Republicans planned to issue a statement claiming that infantile paralysis was a progressive disease which eventually affected the brain. Louis immediately asked Dr. George Draper, a leading authority on polio, who with Dr. Lovett had taken care of Franklin, for a counterstatement which he could use if necessary. Dr. Draper gave him a full statement, from the medical point of view, refuting any such ideas. He noted that Sir Walter Scott had had infantile paralysis when he was a small boy, and no one could point to any impairment in his brain.

My husband's mother was never happy about the gossip and rumors concerning her and her son and her grandsons. Disagreeable letters upset her very much, and the statement that she was paid by the government for the use of her house at Hyde Park as a summer White House distressed her above everything. She was proud of her home and extremely happy when her son and his family and friends could be with her, and nothing would have induced her to accept money from any source. In any case, there was at no time a suggestion of government pay, and after her death my husband continued to pay the expenses of the house and grounds out of his own pocket.

All people in public life are subject to this type of slander. Circumstantial evidence can almost always be produced to make the stories that are circulated about their private lives seem probable to the people who want to believe them. A man who chooses to hold public office must learn to accept the slander as part of the job and to trust that the majority of the people will judge him by his accomplishments in the public service. A man's family also has to learn to accept it. In my husband's case, even his little dog, Fala, came in for his share of false accusations.

Sixteen

I Learn to Be a President's Wife

FRANKLIN DID NOT tell me when he decided to run for the Presidency, but I knew that for a year or more everything that Louis Howe had undertaken for my husband had been with the idea of broadening his acquaintance-ships and knowledge of conditions throughout the country. This little man was really the biggest man from the point of view of imagination and de-termination I have ever known. He made few personal friends and he judged most of those by their loyalty to "the Boss," as he called my hus-band. He was one of the few people who never said "yes" when he meant "no."

It was Louis Howe who mapped out the preconvention campaign. The strategy and the choice of men were left largely to him and, though he talked his plans over with Franklin, he really "masterminded" the whole campaign. He loved the sense of power and, though he wanted a few people to know he had it, on the whole he preferred anonymity. It was he who chose Edward J. Flynn and James Farley to play their important roles, though Franklin liked and trusted them both. Ed Flynn came to understand much that my husband believed in and worked for. Jim Farley believed in the man for whom he worked, but he was not so much concerned with the ideas and ideals for which the man stood. He had a marvelous gift with people; he could do a prodigious amount of work, and he carried his share of the burden as magnificently as did Louis and Ed Flynn.

There were many other devoted and loyal men who believed in my hus-band and who, contributing generously of their time and money, worked directly in the campaign. Among them were Frank Walker, the Henry Morgenthaus, Sr. and Jr., W. Forbes Morgan, and Bernard Baruch. These men gathered about them other men who became active in planning to

158

meet future problems. The men who formed the so-called brain trust were
picked chiefly by Louis Howe and Sam Rosenman. They were a group
with whom Franklin consulted in laying plans to meet the problems ahead,
lawyers, professors, politicians, all gathered together to think out ways
and means of doing specific things. The original "brain trust" consisted of
Professor Raymond Moley, Professor Rexford G. Tugwell, and Judge Samuel I. Rosenman. Later, Adolf Berle was brought in and on certain occasions Dr. Joseph McGoldrick and General Hugh Johnson were consulted.

Through the whole of Franklin's career there never was any deviation
from his original objective—to help make life better for the average man,
woman and child. A thousand and one means were used, difficulties arose,
changes took place, but this objective always was the motive for whatever
had to be done. In the end, in spite of all his efforts to prevent it, a war
had to be fought, because the inexorable march of events showed that only
by war could fascism be wiped out. The persecution of the Jews was only
the beginning of the persecutions that would have been inflicted upon
all those who differed from the Fascist leaders. All freedom for the average
man would have gone, and with its going, the objectives that Franklin and
all other men in democratic nations believed in would have been lost.

While Franklin's desire was to make life happier for people, mixed with
it, as I mentioned earlier, was his liking for the mechanics of politics, for
politics as a science and as a game which included understanding the mass
reactions of people and gambling on one's own judgment.

Franklin always felt that a president should consider himself an instrument chosen by the people to do their bidding, but that he should also
consider that as president he had an obligation to enlighten and lead the
people.

I have never known a man who gave one a greater sense of security. I
never heard him say there was a problem that he thought it was impossible
for human beings to solve. He recognized the difficulties and often said that,
while he did not know the answer, he was completely confident that there
was an answer and that one had to try until one either found it for himself
or got it from someone else.

I never knew him to face life or any problem that came up with fear, and
I have often wondered if that courageous attitude was not communicated
to the people of the country. It may well be what helped them to pull themselves out of the depression in the first years of his administration as president. He knew quite well that he could not pull them out with the best

policies in the world unless the people themselves made those policies work. But he believed in the courage and ability of men, and they responded.

From the personal standpoint, I did not want my husband to be president. I realized, however, that it was impossible to keep a man out of public service when that was what he wanted and was undoubtedly well equipped for. It was pure selfishness on my part, and I never mentioned my feelings on the subject to him.

The nominating convention was held in Chicago, with Senator Thomas J. Walsh as permanent chairman. Franklin owed much to his skillful handling of the convention.

Alfred E. Smith also was a candidate for the nomination and had many ardent supporters. I think he felt that gratitude should have compelled Franklin to withdraw in his favor, since he had been instrumental in getting Franklin to re-enter public life previously. My husband believed that he could meet the tremendous crisis the country was facing better than anyone else in the party. A man must have this confidence in himself or he could never undertake the heavy responsibilities of leading a nation. People used to comment to me on the egoism of my uncle, President Theodore Roosevelt. I know many people felt that Franklin D. Roosevelt had the same quality. Undoubtedly he did to a certain extent; a man could not carry the burdens of the Presidency otherwise.

The regular machinery of the Democratic National Committee, which handled the tickets to the convention, was, of course, favorable to Smith, and refused to give a fair proportion of tickets to our convention committee. The day after my husband made his acceptance speech, however, a large carton of convention hall tickets was sent to our suite in the Congress Hotel!

As each state delegation to the convention was pledged to support my husband's nomination, that state was painted red on a large map of the United States which hung just outside the Franklin D. Roosevelt headquarters in the Congress Hotel. One morning it was discovered that during the night someone had pasted a large sign over the map: "It's votes not acres that count!" The Smith supporters were suspected.

The night before my husband was nominated, we sat up until morning in the Executive Mansion. Two days later, my husband, John, Elliott, and I flew to Chicago where Franklin was to accept the nomination.

The plane trip was something no candidate had ever before undertaken and it created considerable excitement. Previously, the candidate had not been notified officially of his nomination until later in the summer.

Mr. Raymond Moley has stated that he wrote that acceptance speech. I feel sure he was never aware of the things that happened in connection with it. There were two versions of the speech. Evidently they were somewhat alike, and thus the confusion must have come about. My husband wrote one speech himself, dictated to a stenographer in Chicago over the long-distance telephone from Albany, Franklin, Miss LeHand, Miss Tully and Judge Rosenman taking turns at dictating.

That speech, together with one that Mr. Moley and Mr. Tugwell wrote as an improvement on it, were brought by Louis Howe when he met us at the Chicago airport. As he started to hand both versions to my husband, Franklin said: "Oh, I've revised it and have a new draft in my pocket. I have been working on it in the plane." The one in his pocket was the one he read at the convention, though he read through the others and consented to include one or two things that Louis felt were especially important and that were not in Franklin's own revised draft.

Governor Smith and his family and supporters did not wait to congratulate Franklin but left Chicago immediately. The other candidates stayed and felt less bitter.

In September Franklin started on a long campaign trip across the country. Some of the children accompanied him but I did not join him until he reached Williams, Arizona, on the way home. Fortunately, one or more of the children were always able to be on all the campaign trips, for he loved having some of the family with him. They not only helped to entertain people on the train but also kept him amused, for we made it a family practice to look for funny incidents to make him laugh.

Exhilarated as always by contact with people, Franklin came home from the 1932 campaign trips with a conviction that the depression could be licked. He had an extraordinarily acute power of observation and could judge conditions in any section from the looks of the countryside as he traveled through. From him I learned how to observe from train windows; he would watch the crops, notice how people dressed, how many cars there were and in what condition, and even look at the washing on the clotheslines. When the CCC was set up, he knew, though he never made a note, exactly where work of various kinds was needed.

On the 1932 campaign trips Franklin was impressed by the evidences of our wastefulness, our lack of conservation, our soil erosion; and on what he saw he based his plans for action. But the thing he felt most strongly was that there was a vitality in the people that could be salvaged. I believe it was from his faith in the people that he drew the words of his first inaugural address: "The only thing we have to fear is fear itself."

The campaign speeches and later the fireside chats, as they came to be known, entailed a great deal of work on Franklin's part. In the campaigns the subjects were carefully chosen, the places and times to speak discussed with many advisers. Then the research began. Franklin expected the people assigned to this to bring him arguments on both sides of the question, and as much information on the subject as it was possible to gather. He went over all their material carefully and picked out the facts that were to go into the speech; then he gave it to those whom he entrusted with the writing of the first draft. When they brought this back to him, he worked over it with them two or three times.

I have known him, even after a draft had been submitted for literary criticism to the best person who had been asked to help from that point of view, to read the final copy over and over again, put in words or take them out, transpose sentences, and polish it until he knew it by heart and it completely represented his own thought.

I have sometimes been asked what role I played in connection with my husband's speeches. The answer is that I played no role at all. It is true that he sometimes used parts of letters or paragraphs from articles I gave him to look at; and I often read his speeches before he actually delivered them. But that was the extent of it.

His voice lent itself remarkably to the radio. It was a natural gift, for in his whole life he never had a lesson in diction or public speaking. His voice unquestionably helped him to make the people of the country feel that they were an intelligent and understanding part of every government undertaking during his administration.

The night of the election we were in New York City, and I circulated between the State Committee headquarters and those of the National Committee.

I was happy for my husband, because I knew that in many ways it would make up for the blow that fate had dealt him when he was stricken with infantile paralysis; and I had implicit confidence in his ability to help the country in a crisis. Naturally he had wanted to win, and he wanted this opportunity to serve his country in public life.

But for myself I was deeply troubled. As I saw it, this meant the end of any personal life of my own. I knew what traditionally should lie before me; I had watched Mrs. Theodore Roosevelt and had seen what it meant to be the wife of a president, and I cannot say that I was pleased at the prospect. By earning my own money, I had recently enjoyed a certain amount of financial independence and had been able to do things in which I was personally interested. The turmoil in my heart and mind was rather great that night, and the next few months were not to make any clearer what the road ahead would be.

Life began to change immediately. As soon as my husband's election was established, the Secret Service assumed responsibility for his protection. Our house in 65th Street was filled with Secret Service agents, and guests were scrutinized and had to be identified when Franklin was in the house.

Herbert H. Lehman had been elected governor. We turned the Executive Mansion over to him and Mrs. Lehman on Inauguration Day, January 1, 1933, and drove to Hyde Park. The work of the governorship was familiar to Mr. Lehman, so he took over with complete confidence.

Soon after the New Year my husband paid a visit to Washington. President Hoover asked him if in the interim before inauguration he would take joint responsibility for certain policies, but Franklin felt that until he had the control he could not share the burdens.

Later in the winter I paid the customary visit to Mrs. Hoover and decided how, on moving in, I was going to use the rooms. She showed me some of the rooms herself, but when I asked to see the kitchen, she turned me over with relief, I am sure, to the housekeeper and to Ike Hoover, the chief usher in the White House, whom I had known in President Theodore Roosevelt's day.

Inauguration of 1933 was not a lighthearted occasion for the man going out of office or for the man coming in or for the people of the country as a whole. President Hoover had been through a trying period. His great anxiety had been reflected in his inability to preserve his equanimity in his daily contacts with the people in the White House. We were told afterwards how difficult it had been for him even to say good morning or smile at the people of his household.

He was a victim of circumstances and of economic and political beliefs that could be changed only by a complete crisis and courageous new actions. He had served the country well during World War I, and there is no question but that during his term of office he wanted to do what was best for the country. He has, since those unhappy days, rendered service to his country and to the world on numerous occasions.

My husband often told me of his drive with Mr. Hoover from the White House to the Capitol and of how he, Franklin, tried to keep up a cheerful conversation in the face of a silent companion. Crowds were cheering and unconsciously my husband responded, until he realized that Mr. Hoover was sitting motionless. There was hope in my husband's heart and mind, but he realized that could not be the state of mind of the man sitting next to him. Finally, as they reached one of the government buildings which had been begun during Mr. Hoover's administration, my husband found himself remarking on the "lovely steel." It must have sounded inane, but it indicates how desperate he was in his search for small talk.

The condition of the country was so serious on that Inauguration Day, March 4, 1933, that little time was given to purely social amenities. Almost at once my husband began calling meetings, and the first thing that happened was the bank holiday. I was concerned because we had been staying at the Mayflower Hotel for two or three days and I had no extra cash. I went to my husband and asked him what would happen if we needed some money, particularly since the boys, some of them, had to leave soon. He smiled and said he thought we should be able to manage whatever was absolutely necessary. I began to realize then that there were certain things one need not worry about in the White House.

In the first days of his administration my husband was too busy finding ways and means of meeting the financial crisis in the country to be bothered with anything else, so I went to work to organize the household and the secretarial side of the office which did the work for the President's wife.

The inauguration was on a Saturday. The following day Miss Thompson and I went over the White House from basement to attic, looking into closets and generally inspecting the entire house. Unconsciously, I did many things that shocked the ushers, especially Ike Hoover. My first act was to insist on running the elevator myself without waiting for one of the doormen to run it for me. That just wasn't done by the President's wife.

Mrs. Hoover had furnished what we called the West Hall as a solarium, with birds, wicker furniture and plants. I decided to use that end of the wide hall as an extra sitting room, and in order to hurry things along I helped with the moving and placing of the furniture, much to the horror of the household staff.

Fortunately for me, Miss Thompson had been willing to go with me to Washington. She had lived in New York while my husband was governor and had made only occasional trips to Albany. Until now Miss Tully had helped me as well as Franklin, but from the time we went to Washington she worked only for him.

Long before Inauguration Day, Mrs. James M. Helm had offered to help us out at the White House on a voluntary basis for a "few days," until we learned our way about. Mrs. Helm, the daughter of an admiral and the widow of an admiral, had lived in Washington for many years and knew all those formidable people called the "cave dwellers," a term applied to the few people who really live in Washington and are not birds of passage. Franklin and I had seen her with the President and the second Mrs. Wilson in Paris, when Mrs. Helm was Mrs. Wilson's secretary. Franklin liked her very much, so we were all equally grateful for her offer of assistance.

The mail kept piling up around Miss Thompson's desk—letters, books, gifts and various other packages. She tried to cope with it singlehanded, because no one had told us we had a staff to help us, until finally Edith Helm could stand it no longer and said: "Why don't you give that mail to Mr. Magee? He is sitting downstairs with nothing to do and he is there with his staff to help you." After that we worked out a system which operated very well, and we were always complimented on the fact that all the mail was answered in a fairly short time after it was received.

Later Edith Helm's volunteer work developed into the permanent position of social secretary. Miss Thompson soon found that handling the mail and doing my personal work was all she could possibly manage, and she had as little interest in mastering the intricacies of Washington social life as I had.

From the beginning I made it a habit to breakfast in the West Hall at eight or half past. My husband breakfasted in bed and I always went to his room as soon as his breakfast tray was brought up. I stopped only to say good morning, for he liked no conversation at this hour, which he devoted to reading all the newspapers.

After breakfast each morning I went to my desk in my sitting room to see in turn the housekeeper, the usher and the social secretary. My grandmother and my mother-in-law had taught me how to run a house and I assumed, in accordance with their teachings, that all good housewives made out their own menus, put away and gave out the household linen, bought the food and gave all the orders for the day. In the White House I learned this was done under the housekeeper's supervision. As far as the house was concerned, I had no work and little responsibility.

I had brought down a housekeeper, Mrs. Henry Nesbitt, who had worked for me at Hyde Park in the League of Women Voters. Her husband came down with her to do the bookkeeping. She herself did the buying, prepared the menus and generally supervised the household. She was the first person who came to see me after breakfast every morning, with her menus prepared for the day. I tried to tell her approximately how many people were expected for meals, but we soon discovered that the number frequently changed at the last minute, so she had to be prepared for any contingency.

I was surprised to find how inadequate the arrangements were for the household help in the White House. A few of them had rooms on the third floor and stayed at night. Most of them came in by the day, as they do in most southern communities, but the arrangements for changing their clothes, as well as their dining-room facilities, were extremely inadequate. I tried to organize things more comfortably but I never was happy about it until extensive changes were made on the basement floor.

Some aspects of housekeeping in the White House might be of general interest. For one thing, I think few people realize what the expenses are of a man who holds a public office such as the Presidency or even a governorship. Both New York State and the federal government pay the wages of the household help, but whatever it cost to feed them came out of my husband's own pocket. In Albany we had eight or ten regular household employees and in the White House usually about thirty. I have always thought that the governments of both the state and the nation should pay for their food.

In the White House the yearly thousands of visitors meant that we had to employ many more people than we should otherwise have needed, simply to keep the public rooms clean. In addition, the Christmas parties that we gave every year for the guards and all the people working in the White House, on the grounds and in the garage were paid for by my husband. Formal parties and state dinners were paid for by the government, but if Franklin and I had any of our children or personal friends at a formal dinner, we had to pay their pro rata share of the cost. Then, of course, the requests for contributions were countless—and a president is always expected to give more generously than anyone else. Every president, I am sure, leaves the White House poorer than he was when he went in.

All this made the bookkeeping and the housekeeping complicated jobs. There were also complications and difficulties about purchases made for the White House. Nothing that is worn out and discarded can disappear. It must be produced when you say you have bought something to replace it. As a result, warehouses are filled with old furniture which is disposed of only when there is no longer a square foot of room left. If the housekeeper has to buy even a new tea strainer, the old one has to be kept in case she is asked to produce it.

Everything is used until it is worn out. Any items no longer usable are destroyed in the presence of witnesses. Anything of historical interest, such as the gold piano and the old elevator cage, is placed in the Smithsonian Institution.

The replenishing of curtains and rugs and the re-covering of walls and furniture in the formal rooms have to be seen to carefully and constantly, because a house that is always on exhibition should look its best at all times. Mrs. Hoover told me that some visitors wrote her that one of the curtains over the large staircase window had a darn in it, not realizing that the height and size of the windows made new curtains a great expense.

Every morning after Mrs. Nesbitt and I finished our discussion of the relevant housekeeping matters the usher would come to my sitting room. His purpose was primarily to check over the comings and goings of guests and members of the family. He also had to have a list of any people who were coming to see us, because otherwise they would not be admitted.

Then Edith Helm would arrive with her list of invitations to public functions, of receptions I should hold, or whatever else she thought I ought to do. These three interviews took comparatively little time. I think Edith Helm often felt I did not take enough interest in the social side of the White House duties, but at that time they seemed to me rather unimportant; indeed, there never came a point when I felt the world was sufficiently stable for us to take time to think very seriously about purely social matters.

Certain duties, however, which I thought at first were useless burdens I later grew to realize had real meaning and value. For instance, the teas. It seemed to me utterly futile to receive anywhere from five hundred to a thousand people of an afternoon, shake hands with them, and then have them pass into the dining room to be given a cup of tea or coffee by Mrs. Helm and Miss Thompson.

I soon discovered that, particularly to people from out of town, the White House has a deep significance. It is a place where the people's hospitality is dispensed to the representatives of other countries; in a way, it is with a sense of ownership that citizens of the United States walk through the simple but dignified and beautiful rooms. To many people the White House symbolizes the government, and though standing and shaking hands for an hour or so, two or three times a week, is not an inspiring occupation, still I think it well worth while. I did it regularly, three times a week, during the winter months.

At the first few receptions of each season my arms ached, my shoulders ached, my back ached, and my knees and feet seemed to belong to someone else.

My husband found the formal receptions tiring, since standing for a long period of time with braces on was something of an ordeal. He tried never to have more than a thousand people to greet, and after the reception was over he went upstairs at once.

All protocol was foreign to me, and until I learned that it was really required for two purposes—protection and orderly procedure—I resented it deeply, as do most Americans. One congressman's secretary, in replying to a formal invitation for him, addressed the envelope to "The Chief of the Proletariat" instead of "The Chief of Protocol," which indicates how little protocol means to the average American.

Washington lives by a rigid schedule. Some of it I think unnecessarily complicated but by and large I know it is necessary. The foreigners living in Washington would understand no other procedure. Also, the importance that most Americans attach to the posts they hold, whether elective or appointive, is probably justified; for in prestige most public servants find their only return. Certainly the financial returns are slight in comparison to what the majority of them could earn in business or in a profession.

Mrs. Helm had the help of the State Department on all questions of protocol. This relieved me of all responsibility. I never had to seat a formal dinner table.

I added a few parties to the social calendar of the White House—a so-called Gridiron Widows' party, and teas and a garden party for the women who held executive or administrative positions in the government. Every year the newspapermen invite the President to the Gridiron dinner. Women are never allowed to attend, not even the women of the press. I decided it would be fun to have an evening party for the women on the same night, not only newspaperwomen but wives of newspapermen, and the Cabinet wives.

As for the teas and the garden party for the women executives, I discovered that a great many women who held rather important positions in the government had never been in the White House or met the wives of the secretaries heading their departments. I had one large garden party in the spring and a series of teas during the winter season for these women, and I invited the wives of the Cabinet members to receive with me.

I include here a sample of my social calendar for one week. I think you will see that a president's wife is not exactly idle.

Monday
1:00 p.m.   Lunch with Mrs. Hull
4:00 p.m.   Tea for 175 guests
5:00 p.m.   Tea for 236 guests

Tuesday
1:00 p.m.   Lunch with Mrs. Garner
4:00 p.m.   Tea for members of Delaware Democratic Club
4:30 p.m.   Tea for foreign diplomats' wives
7:00 p.m.   Dinner for 22
9:00 p.m.   Judicial reception

Wednesday
4:00 p.m.   tea for 266 guests
5:00 p.m.   tea for 256 guests

Thursday
1:00 p.m.   Formal luncheon for 52 guests
4:00 p.m.   Tea, women's division of Infantile Paralysis Foundation
5:00 p.m.   Tea for Executive Board of the Federation of Women's Clubs

Friday
1:00 p.m.   Lunch for wives of cabinet members
8:00 p.m.   Diplomatic dinner—94 guests
            197 additional guests for music after dinner.

I am also giving some figures on the number of people who visited the White House in normal years as well as the number who had tea, lunch or dinner, or evening refreshments in the White House.

During the year of 1939:

4,729 people came to a meal
 323 people were house guests
9,211 people came to tea
14,056 people were received at teas, receptions, etc.; all of them had
some light refreshments
1,320,300 people visited the public rooms of which 264,060 had special
passes from their Congressmen to see the state dining room, the Red
Room, the Blue Room and the Green Room.

The average attendance at the Easter Egg Rolling was 53,108. The
record shows that 180 children were lost and found; two people were sent
to the emergency hospital; six people fainted and twenty-two had to be
treated for small abrasions.

After I finished the morning routine of seeing the three people I have
already mentioned—Mrs. Nesbitt, Mrs. Helm and the usher—Miss Thompson came into my sitting room to begin work on the mail. We had to work
out a completely new system for handling the correspondence. We found
that most of the mail in former administrations had been answered by
form letters; Ralph Magee, head of the correspondence bureau, had copies
of forms used in President Cleveland's administration!

After I had fulfilled my obligations to my guests, whether at formal or
informal parties, I signed the mail and read such letters as I had not seen
before, wrote on other letters an outline of what I wanted said in reply
and laid aside those that I had to dictate answers to. This often kept me
busy far into the night. Before I went to bed I returned these baskets to
Miss Thompson's desk so she could work on them in the morning. As
soon as she came to my desk in the morning we attended to the letters
that had to be dictated.

Personal work, such as my column, articles, books, radio scripts and the
like, was always done on overtime for which I personally compensated
Miss Thompson so that there could be no question of her using time that
belonged to the government for work that was purely personal. This work
was done in the evenings and on Saturdays and Sundays. In all the years
we were in Washington I could never drive Miss Thompson away for a
holiday, so she had much accumulated leave which she never used and

which, under civil service rules, she could not claim when we left Washington.

From March, 1933, to the end of the year I received 301,000 pieces of mail. The year before the 1940 election I received about 100,000 letters. The campaign for a third term, the draft, and various other administration measures caused it to increase. During the war it assumed large proportions but was, of course, of an entirely different character than it had been during the depression years.

The variety of the requests and the apparent confidence that I would be able to make almost anything possible always worried me. Many of the requests, of course, were not honest. I tried from the beginning to find people in various communities to whom I could refer letters that sounded desperate. Miss Thompson was always accusing me of being too softhearted, but I caught her once about to send money for a dress and shoes and underclothes to a young girl who wrote that she was going to be graduated from high school, was to be the valedictorian of her class, and had only her brother's overalls and shoes to wear. She, too thoughtfully, I felt, included a page from a mail-order catalogue with sizes, colors, prices, and so on, all carefully written in. I was suspicious and asked someone to investigate and we found the whole story was untrue. The child's parents were fairly comfortably off, and she was not the valedictorian of her class—she wasn't even graduating. She simply wanted some new clothes.

In addition to the regular duties I have already mentioned, there were my press conferences. I soon discovered that the women reporters in Washington were living precariously. People were losing their jobs on every hand, and unless the women reporters could find something new to write about, the chances were that some of them would hold their jobs a very short time.

Miss Lorena Hickok, who had been assigned by the AP to "cover" me, pointed out many of these things, because she felt a sense of responsibility for the other women writers. My press conferences were her suggestion. I consulted Louis Howe and he agreed that I should hold them regularly for women reporters.

I realized that I must not trespass on my husband's prerogatives, that national and international news must be handled by him, but it seemed to me there were many things in my own activities that might be useful. It was new and untried ground and I was feeling my way with some trepidation.

Louis Howe was responsible for my confidence in newspaper reporters. He had a high regard for his own craft and insisted that newspaper people were the most honorable group in the world. I took it for granted that the women would be as honorable as the men, and my confidence was seldom betrayed.

Every press conference was a battle of wits, and at times it was not easy for me, nor, I imagine, for them. For instance, when they were trying to find out whether Franklin would run for a third term, they asked all sorts of trick questions, such as: "Will the social season next winter be the same as usual?" Or: "Where would you hang all these prints in Hyde Park?" Usually I was able to detect the implications of the questions and avoid any direct answer, for Louis Howe had trained me well. My press conferences did not bother me or my husband as much as they seemed to worry other people. I believe the reporters and I came through with mutual respect.

Seventeen

The First Year: 1933

DURING THE EARLY White House days when I was busy with organizing my side of the household, my husband was meeting one problem after another. It had a most exhilarating effect on him. Decisions were being made, new ideas were being tried, people were going to work and businessmen who ordinarily would have scorned government assistance were begging the government to find solutions for their problems.

What was interesting to me about the administration of those days was the willingness of everyone to co-operate with everyone else. As conditions grew better, of course, people's attitudes changed, but fundamentally it was that spirit of co-operation that pulled us out of the depression. Congress, which traditionally never has a long honeymoon with a new president, even when the political majority is of his party, went along during those first few months, delegating powers to the President and passing legislation that it would never have passed except during a crisis.

Soon after the inauguration of 1933 we began to have a succession of visitors whom after dinner Franklin would take upstairs to his study. There were two reasons why these particular people were invited to the White House those first years. One was that the economic and political situation in the world made it necessary for him to establish contacts with the leaders of other countries; the other was his desire to build new contacts for better understanding on this continent and abroad.

For the heads of nations, Franklin worked out a reception which he thought made them feel that the United States recognized the importance of their governments. If the guests arrived in the afternoon we had tea for the entire party; afterwards, all but the most important guests went to a hotel or to their own embassy. Later Blair House, across Pennsyl-

173

vania Avenue, was acquired by the government and arranged for the use of important visitors. The head of a government spent one night in the White House, accompanied by his wife if she was with him. There usually was a state dinner with conversation or music afterwards. The following morning Franklin and his guest would often have another talk before the guest went over to Blair House or to his embassy.

One of our first guests in 1933 was Ramsay MacDonald, who came with his daughter, Ishbel. We enjoyed meeting him, but even then we sensed in him a certain weariness. The loss of his wife had been a great blow to him. In many ways his daughter was a more vivid and vital person than he.

I think Franklin believed even then that it was most important for the English-speaking nations of the world to understand one another, whether the crisis was economic or, as later, military. This did not mean that he always agreed with the policies of these other countries; but he recognized the importance to us and to them of good feeling and understanding and co-operation.

The prime minister of Canada also came to stay with us that first spring, so that he and my husband and the prime minister of Great Britain could more or less co-ordinate their common interests.

In the same period Edouard Herriot, the French statesman, also arrived in Washington. As I look over the lists of what seem to be an unbelievable number of guests that first year, I find that we received an Italian mission, a German mission, and a Chinese mission, and even a Japanese envoy who came to lunch. Other guests included the governor general of the Philippines, Frank Murphy, later on the Supreme Court, who brought with him Manuel Quezon; the prime minister of New Zealand, who came with his wife to lunch; and His Highness Prince Ras Desta Dember, special ambassador of the Emperor of Ethiopia.

The President of Panama also paid us a visit. He was not the only guest from our own hemisphere. There was a stag dinner for the Brazilian delegation; we received a special ambassador from the Argentine; the Mexican envoy came to lunch; and the Brazilian envoy returned, after a trip through the country, to report on his travels.

Franklin had a deep conviction that we must learn to understand and to get on with our neighbors in this hemisphere. He believed it was up to us, who had been to blame in many ways for a big brother attitude which was not acceptable to our neighbors, to make the first effort. So even at that early date he was beginning to lay down through personal contacts the policy of the Good Neighbor, which was to become of increasing importance.

From the time we moved to Washington in 1933, Louis Howe became more and more of an invalid. At first he was able to be in his office and to keep his finger on much that was going on, and the second bonus march on Washington by the veterans of World War I he handled personally.

The first march, which had taken place in Mr. Hoover's administration, was still fresh in everybody's mind. I shall never forget my feeling of horror when I learned that the Army had actually been ordered to evict the veterans from their encampment. In the chaos that followed, the veterans' camp on the Anacostia flats was burned and many people were injured, some of them seriously. This one incident shows what fear can make people do, for Mr. Hoover was a Quaker, who abhorred violence, and General MacArthur, his chief of staff, must have known how many veterans would resent the order and never forget it. They must have known, too, the effect it would have on public opinion.

When the second bonus march took place in March of 1933 I was greatly worried for fear nothing would be done to prevent a similar tragedy. However, after talking the situation over with Louis Howe, Franklin immediately decided that the veterans should be housed in an old camp and provided with food through the relief administration. Louis spent hours talking with the leaders. I think they held their meetings in a government auditorium and were heard by the proper people in Congress. As a result, everything was orderly.

Although Louis often asked me to take him for a drive in the afternoon, I was rather surprised one day when he insisted that I drive him out to the veterans' camp just off Potomac Drive. When we arrived he announced that he was going to sit in the car but that I was to walk around among the veterans and see just how things were. Hesitatingly I got out and walked over to where I saw a line-up of men waiting for food. They looked at me curiously and one of them asked my name and what I wanted. When I said I just wanted to see how they were getting on, they asked me to join them.

After their bowls were filled with food, I followed them into the big eating hall. I was invited to say a few words to them—I think I mentioned having gone over the battle fronts in 1919—and then they sang for me some of the old army songs. After lunch I was asked to look into several other buildings, and finally we came to the hospital that had been set up for them.

I did not spend as much as an hour there; then I got into the car and drove away. Everyone waved and I called, "Good luck," and they answered, "Good-by and good luck to you." There had been no excitement, and my only protection had been a weary gentleman, Louis Howe, who had slept in the car during my entire visit.

Most of us who watched Louis could tell that he was failing. He sat a good deal of the time in his room, surrounded by newspapers, but up to the last few months his advice was still valuable. He died on April 18, 1936, at the naval hospital in Washington. He had lived in the White House until a short time before his death.

I always felt that the loss of Louis's influence and knowledge and companionship was a great blow to my husband. Louis had seemed to have an acute sense of the need for keeping a balance in Franklin's appointments, making sure that my husband saw a cross section of people and heard a variety of points of view. While Louis was alive, I had fewer complaints from various groups that they had been excluded than ever again. Considering how many people want to see the President and how hard it is to keep some semblance of balance, I think Louis did a remarkable job. He tried to see that all points of view reached Franklin so that he would make no decision without full consideration.

The President's wife does not go out informally except on rare occasions to old friends. Now and then, in the spring, Elinor Morgenthau and I stole away in my car or hers, and stopped in at some little place for lunch or tea. Driving my own car was one of the issues the Secret Service people and I had a battle about at the very start. The Secret Service prefers to have an agent go with the President's wife, but I did not want either a chauffeur or a Secret Service agent always with me; I never did consent to having a Secret Service agent.

After the head of the Secret Service found I was not going to allow an agent to accompany me everywhere, he went one day to Louis Howe, plunked a revolver down on the table and said, "Well, all right, if Mrs. Roosevelt is going to drive around the country alone, at least ask her to carry this in the car." I carried it religiously and during the summer I asked a friend, a man who had been one of Franklin's bodyguards in New York

State, to give me some practice in target shooting so that if the need arose I would know how to use the gun. After considerable practice, I finally learned to hit a target. I would never have used it on a human being, but I thought I ought to know how to handle a revolver if I had to have one in my possession.

Always, when my husband and I met after a trip that either of us had taken, we tried to arrange for an uninterrupted meal so that we could hear the whole story while it was fresh and not dulled by repetition. That I became, as the years went by, a better reporter and a better observer was largely owing to the fact that Franklin's questions covered such a wide range. I found myself obliged to notice everything. For instance, when I returned from a trip around the Gaspé, he wanted to know not only what kind of fishing and hunting was possible in that area but what the life of the fisherman was, what he had to eat, how he lived, what the farms were like, how the houses were built, what type of education was available, and whether it was completely church-controlled like the rest of the life in the village.

When I spoke of Maine, he wanted to know about everything I had seen on the farms I visited, the kinds of homes and the types of people, how the Indians seemed to be getting on and where they came from.

Franklin never told me I was a good reporter nor, in the early days, were any of my trips made at his request. I realized, however, that he would not question me so closely if he were not interested, and I decided this was the only way I could help him, outside of running the house, which was soon organized and running itself under Mrs. Nesbitt.

In the autumn I was invited by the Quakers to investigate the conditions that they were making an effort to remedy in the coal-mining areas of West Virginia. My husband agreed that it would be a good thing to do, so the visit was arranged. I had not been photographed often enough then to be recognized, so I was able to spend a whole day going about the area near Morgantown, West Virginia, without anyone's discovering who I was.

The conditions I saw convinced me that with a little leadership there could develop in the mining areas, if not a people's revolution, at least a people's party patterned after some of the previous parties born of bad economic conditions. There were men in that area who had been on relief for from three to five years and who had almost forgotten what it was like to have a job at which they could work for more than one or two days a week. There were children who did not know what it was to sit down at a table and eat a proper meal.

One story which I brought home from that trip I recounted at the dinner table one night. In a company house I visited, where the people had evidently seen better days, the man showed me his weekly pay slips. A small amount had been deducted toward his bill at the company store and for his rent and for oil for his mine lamp. These deductions left him less than a dollar in cash each week. There were six children in the family, and they acted as though they were afraid of strangers. I noticed a bowl on the table filled with scraps, the kind that you or I might give to a dog, and I saw children, evidently looking for their noonday meal, take a handful out of that bowl and go out munching. That was all they had to eat.

As I went out, two of the children had gathered enough courage to stand by the door, the little boy holding a white rabbit in his arms. It was evident that it was a most cherished pet. The little girl was thin and scrawny, and had a gleam in her eyes as she looked at her brother. She said, "He thinks we are not going to eat it, but we are," and at that the small boy fled down the road clutching the rabbit closer than ever.

It happened that William C. Bullitt was at dinner that night and I have always been grateful to him for the check he sent me the next day, saying he hoped it might help to keep the rabbit alive.

This trip to the mining areas was my first contact with the work being done by the Quakers. I liked the theory of trying to put people to work to help themselves. The men were started on projects and taught to use their abilities to develop new skills. The women were encouraged to revive any household arts they might once have known but which they had neglected in the drab life of the mining village.

This was only the first of many trips into the mining districts but it was the one that started the homestead idea. The University of West Virginia, in Morgantown, had already created a committee to help the miners on the Quaker agricultural project. With that committee and its experience as a nucleus, the government obtained the loan of one of the university's people, Mr. Bushrod Grimes, and established the Resettlement Administration. Louis Howe created a small advisory committee on which I, Mr. Pickett, and others served. It was all experimental work, but it was designed to get people off relief, to put them to work building their own homes and to give them enough land to start growing food.

It was hoped that business would help by starting on each of these projects an industry in which some of the people could find regular work. A few small industries were started but they were not often successful. Only a few of the resettlement projects had any measure of success; nevertheless, I have always felt that the good they did was incalculable. Conditions were so nearly the kind that breed revolution that the men and women needed to be made to feel their government's interest and concern.

I began to hear very serious reports of conditions in Logan County, West Virginia, where for many years whole families had been living in tents because they had been evicted from company houses after a strike. All the men had been blacklisted and could not get work anywhere; they were existing on the meager allowance that the State of West Virginia provided for the unemployed. Now the tents were worn out, illness was rampant, and no one had any medical care. Finally Mrs. Leonard Elmhirst and I established a clinic to take care of the children. When I told my husband of the conditions there he said to talk to Harry Hopkins and to tell him that these families must be out of tents by Christmas. It was done, and for two years, out of my radio money and Mrs. Elmhirst's generosity, we tried to remedy among the children the effects of conditions which had existed for many years.

I came to know very well a stream near Morgantown called Scott's Run, or Bloody Run, because of the violent strikes that once occurred in the mines there. Some of the company houses, perched on hills on either side of the run, seemed scarcely fit for human habitation. The homestead project started near Morgantown was called Arthurdale and took in people from all the nearby mining villages.

One of the first people to go to Arthurdale was Bernard M. Baruch, who helped me to establish the original school and always took a great interest in the project, even visiting it without me on some occasions. I have always hoped that he got as much satisfaction as I did out of the change in the children after they had been living on the project for six months.

The homestead projects were attacked in Congress, for the most part by men who had never seen for themselves the plight of the miners or what we were trying to do for them. There is no question that much money was spent, perhaps some of it unwisely. The projects were all experimental. In Arthurdale, for instance, though the University of West Virginia recommended the site, apparently nobody knew what was afterwards discovered—that there was a substratum of porous rock which finally caused great expense in making the water supply safe. Nevertheless, I have always felt that many human beings who might have cost us thousands of dollars in tuberculosis sanitariums, insane asylums, and jails were restored to usefulness and given confidence in themselves. Later, when during World War II, I met boys from that area I could not help thinking that a great many of them were able to serve their country only because of the things that had been done to help their parents through the depression period.

Nothing we learn in this world is ever wasted and I have come to the conclusion that practically nothing we do ever stands by itself. If it is good, it will serve some good purpose in the future. If it is evil, it may haunt us and handicap our efforts in unimagined ways.

Years later, after the Social Security Act was passed, I saw how it worked in individual cases in this area. There was a mine accident in which several men were killed, and my husband asked me to go down and find out what the people were saying. One man received the Carnegie medal posthumously because he had gone back into the mine to help rescue other men. His widow had several children, so her social security benefits would make her comfortable. In talking to another widow who had three children and a fourth about to be born, I asked how she was going to manage. She seemed quite confident and told me: "My sister and her two children will come to live with us. I am going to get social security benefits of nearly sixty-five dollars a month. I pay fifteen dollars a month on my house and land, and I shall raise vegetables and have chickens and with the money from the government I will get along very well. In the past probably the mine company might have given me a small check and often the other miners took up a collection if they could afford it, but this income from the government I can count on until my children are grown."

Two other events of that first autumn in Washington stand out in my mind. On November 17, 1933, Henry Morgenthau, Jr., was sworn in as undersecretary of the treasury in the Oval Room in the White House, thus starting on his long and arduous labors in the Treasury Department. When Secretary Woodin resigned, Henry Morgenthau succeeded him and held the office until shortly after my husband's death, when he also resigned and left Washington.

On that same day my husband and Mr. Litvinov held the final conversations on the recognition of the Soviet Union. There was considerable excitement over the first telephone conversation between the two countries which took place between Mr. Litvinov in the White House and his wife and son in Russia. The ushers noted it in their daily record book because, while there had been overseas conversations with many other European countries, this was the opening of diplomatic relations with Russia.

Needless to say, among some of my husband's old friends there was considerable opposition to the recognition of Russia. His mother came to him before the announcement was made to tell him she had heard rumors that he was about to recognize Russia, but that she felt this would be a disastrous move and widely misunderstood by the great majority of their old friends.

Not only his old friends but with various other people my husband had frequent run-ins over the new theory that government had a responsibility to the people. I remember that when Senator Carter Glass insisted that Virginia needed no relief, Franklin suggested that he take a drive with him to see some of the bad spots. The senator never accepted his invitation.

The opening of diplomatic relations with Russia and our relations in this hemisphere were the administration's first points of attack in our foreign policy, but the major emphasis in those early years was and had to be on questions of domestic policy and our internal economic recovery.

As I look back over the actual measures undertaken in this first year I realize that the one in which my husband took the greatest pleasure was the establishment on April 5, 1933, of the Civilian Conservation Corps camps. The teen-age youngster, the boy finishing high school, the boy who had struggled to get through college, were all at loose ends. There was no organization except the Army that had the tents and other supplies essential for a setup of this kind, which was why part of the program was promptly put under its jurisdiction.

Franklin realized that the boys should be given some other kind of education as well, but it had to be subordinate to the day's labor required of them. The Civilian Conservation Corps had a triple value: it gave the boys a chance to see different parts of their own country, and to learn to do a good day's work in the open, which benefited them physically; also it gave them a cash income, part of which went home to their families. This helped the morale both of the boys themselves and of the people at home. The idea was his own contribution to the vast scheme of relief rehabilitation planning.

This was followed on June 16 by the National Recovery Act, with General Hugh Johnson in charge. The basic importance of the NRA was that it made it easier for the industrialist who wanted to do the right thing. The chiseler and the man who was willing to profit by beating down his labor could no longer compete unfairly with the man who wanted to earn a decent profit but to treat his employees fairly. The NRA was declared unconstitutional almost two years later. I thought this was unfortunate, for it seemed a simple way to keep bad employers doing what was right.

The Public Works Administration, which came into being on the same day, made it possible for the government to plan and undertake public works during this period of depression. It helped to take up the slack of unemployment by lending money to the states for projects that they could not finance by themselves.

Five months later, in November, 1933, the Civil Works Administration was set up and in time put four million unemployed to work.

In my travels around the country I saw many things built both by PWA and by CWA. I also saw the results of the work done by CCC. The achievements of these agencies began to dot city and rural areas alike. Soil conservation and forestry work went forward, recreation areas were built, and innumerable bridges, schools, hospitals and sanitation projects were constructed—lasting monuments to the good work done under these agencies. It is true they cost the people of the country vast sums of money, but they did a collective good and left tangible results which are evident today. They pulled the country out of the depression and made it possible for us to fight the greatest and most expensive war in our history.

Perhaps the most far-reaching project was the Tennessee Valley Authority. That was Senator George Norris' greatest dream and no one who witnessed the development of the Authority will ever forget the fight he put up for something that many people ridiculed. The development had been begun during World War I, but at the end of that war most of the work was stopped. Nothing further was done until my husband, who understood Senator Norris' vision, supplied the impetus at a time when it could accomplish the maximum results for the country. With the demands of a possible war in mind, Franklin insisted on pushing work on the TVA as rapidly as possible. He believed even then that under certain circumstances war might come soon, and he knew if that happened we would need everything the TVA could make available.

In the campaign of 1932 my husband and I had gone through some of the TVA area, and he had been deeply impressed by the crowds at the stations. They were so poor; their houses were unpainted, their cars were dilapidated, and many grownups as well as children were without shoes or adequate garments. Scarcely eight years later, after the housing and educational and agricultural experiments had had time to take effect, I went through the same area, and a more prosperous region would have been hard to find. I have always wished that those who oppose authorities to create similar benefits in the valleys of other great rivers could have seen the contrast as I saw it. I realize that such changes must come gradually, but I hate to see nothing done. I wish, as my husband always wished, that year by year we might be making a start on the Missouri River and the headwaters of the Mississippi. Such experiments, changing for the better the life of the people, would be a mighty bulwark against attacks on our democracy.

Eighteen

The Peaceful Years: 1934-1936

THE YEARS from 1934 to 1936 seem to me the least anxious of any we spent in the White House. The reforms instituted were beginning to put the country back on a more even keel; good feeling existed generally between capital and labor and between the President and Congress; and in our family life we had gradually managed to adapt our private traditions and habits to the exigencies of the White House.

In the spring of 1934 Franklin suggested that I make a trip to Puerto Rico. General Blanton Winship, governor of the island at that time, was faced with great difficulties. Labor conditions were bad, and there was not enough food for the constantly increasing population. The sugar companies owned large tracts of land and, because the work was seasonal and the wages pitifully small, the workers practically starved in off-seasons. Rexford Tugwell, who was then in the Department of Agriculture, was going down to make a study of what could be done in that field, and my husband thought if I went, too, it might show the people that he was really interested in conditions there.

Following the careful program laid out for me, I visited a number of rural schools, some of which were trying to improve the quality of education offered the children. I also saw the homework done by the women. Factory wages were low and the amount paid for homework was unbelievably small. Little girls sat all during their lunch hour in school embroidering handkerchiefs in order to add a few pennies to the family income.

The conditions in rural homes were unsanitary enough, but in the towns they were even more shocking. I remember going down a street, looking into the houses of factory workers. Most of them consisted of two rooms; the back room had no light, and practically the only light in the

184

front room came through the doorway. There were no screens and, of course, no plumbing or other modern conveniences. Many of the women cooked out of doors on little stoves.

The real slums were actually worse, in the capital city. Huts made of bits of tin and scrap iron and wood picked up after the last hurricane were built out over the water. We walked on duckboards placed precariously over the piling, and the water came up under every house.

There was one slum which clung precariously to the side of a cliff. Here goats and other animals lived under the houses. Again, there was no sanitation, and typhoid was common. If it had not been for the climate and the diet of rice and beans bought from the United States, there probably would have been a great deal of rickets. Tuberculosis took a heavy toll. Every year more and more children were born, which made the question of population a matter for serious thought.

From Puerto Rico we went to the Virgin Islands where, bad though some of the conditions were, they seemed slightly better than in Puerto Rico. Efforts were being made there as well as in Puerto Rico to put up some new houses, but the people had to be taught how to use them. They did not know how to live decently even under better physical conditions, because the circumstances under which they had been forced to live had made cleanliness almost impossible.

On my return I begged my husband to send down some labor people and industrialists to look over the situation. Some of my friends have since gone there to develop new industries and I think several small industries are going successfully. When Mr. Tugwell later became governor of Puerto Rico, he tried to carry out many of the ideas he had thought, on his first trip, might help, but the islands still remain a difficult problem and one which the United States is far from having solved satisfactorily.

In the summer of 1934 my husband decided to make a trip through the Caribbean and the Panama Canal and out to Hawaii, taking with him our two youngest sons, Franklin Junior and John. The newspapermen traveled on a separate ship, visiting Franklin every now and then. I remember his telling me with gleeful chuckles that he had had to provide the newspapermen with the historical background of most of the places where they stopped. Once they reached Hawaii, he and the boys had a wonderful time. He enjoyed meeting the native Queen and eating poi, which few members of the party really liked.

In the winter of 1936 Louis Howe finally moved from the White House to the hospital. We kept telling him and ourselves that he was going to improve and come back again, but suddenly word came that he had died. It was one of the greatest losses that my husband sustained. He was to have others and all were hard to bear, because in public life you can have no private time for sorrow. Duties must be performed and your own feelings must be suppressed. Louis's death deprived my husband of a close relationship and the satisfaction of having someone near to whom he could talk frankly, whose advice he might not always follow but whose presence was stimulating.

Louis Howe's death left a great gap in my husband's life. I have always felt that if Louis had lived the number of people drawn closely but briefly into the working and social orbits of Franklin's life would have been fewer. For one reason and another, no one quite filled the void which unconsciously he was seeking to fill, and each one in turn disappeared from the scene, occasionally with bitterness which I understood but always regretted. There are not many men whose personal ambition is to accomplish things for someone else, and it was some time before a friendship with Harry Hopkins, somewhat different but similar in certain ways, again brought Franklin some of the satisfaction he had known with Louis.

What worries we had in those two years from 1934 to 1936 were largely such personal ones as this. In fact, we approached the campaign of 1936 with a feeling that the country was getting back on its feet. I did no formal work in that campaign, though I visited the campaign headquarters and went with Franklin on some of his trips. To tell the truth, I never felt it was good taste to go out and electioneer for my husband, so in none of the campaigns did I take any particular part in the political activities unless I was specially asked to for some specific reason.

When the returns came in on election night, Maine and Vermont were found to be still in the Republican fold. My husband said with a wicked twinkle in his eye: "I knew I should have gone to Maine and Vermont, but Jim wouldn't let me."

There was no uncertainty or waiting for the returns this election. As usual we were at Hyde Park, where the dining room on election night was always turned into what seemed to me the nearest thing to a newspaper office. The machines on which news came in were set up in a little room off the dining room. Franklin himself had telephones, long dispatches were handed to him by relays of people, and everybody made out averages. I was expected to show interest in the returns, but also to be with his mother in the library to help entertain the guests and keep them out of the dining room, except for a few favored individuals. The newspaper people would come and be given refreshments, and finally, when the returns came in, the people of the village of Hyde Park would have a torchlight parade and come to greet my husband. We would go out on the porch and listen to a few words from him, usually shivering in the cold.

When we went back to Washington in 1936, Franklin was received with great acclaim, and his second term of office began auspiciously. He had carried with him a big Democrat majority in the Congress, and the party members felt so secure that they began to believe they could do anything they wanted. That is a bad attitude for any group to adopt, particularly when responsible for the smooth running of a country that has only just become stabilized after a great depression.

Throughout all those early years in Washington, one of Franklin's major interests was in changing the bad feeling that existed between us and our Latin-American neighbors. After the November elections he made a personal effort to implement this policy by attending the Inter-American Conference for the Maintenance of Peace, held in Buenos Aires, in 1936. He was deeply touched by the evident enthusiasm that his trip created and particularly happy that he seemed able to inaugurate the good feeling that he so greatly desired to see grow.

This trip and all other trips that had diplomatic significance were planned in consultation with Secretary Hull and the State Department. Sumner Welles, Franklin's able undersecretary of state, was not only particularly well informed about South American affairs but also very much in sympathy with what Franklin was trying to do in Latin America, and he supported the Good Neighbor policy wholeheartedly. Franklin found him an excellent coworker and counted on him for help with detailed background information. I think, however, that Franklin's own good will toward the governments and people of these countries was an important aid to the State Department in making our policy effective.

On the way home Franklin stopped in Uruguay. He always liked to tell the story of his greeting by the President of that country. When they met, he assured Franklin that he need not worry about anything happening to *him*, but since he, the President of Uruguay, had been threatened, Franklin must not be surprised if there were some shots. However, the President of the United States would not be the target. My husband got into the car and drove around, but in telling about it afterwards he said he could not help wondering if he might not get hit by mistake, even though he was not the target. However, no one was shot that day.

From Uruguay they went to Brazil, and Franklin again was much pleased by the enthusiasm that his visit called forth. It was there that he was given the gifts for me that later created so much comment in one of the newspaper columns and in radio broadcasts. For this reason I think it wise to tell the whole story here.

Undersecretary Welles was asked by President Vargas and his wife if they might send some gifts to me, for they knew the rule that no president of the United States or any government official could accept personal gifts from a foreign government while in office. Senhora Vargas sent me a beautiful hammered silver tea set and she and her husband together sent me, from their collection, a large aquamarine, one of the biggest and most perfect stones in the world. My husband presented me with these gifts on his return and I was deeply impressed by them, but realized that only in the White House or at some official gathering could such a large tea set be used. The stone was kept in my safe at the White House.

After Franklin's death I gave the tea set to the airplane carrier, U.S.S. *Franklin D. Roosevelt*, and I hope that the Brazilians were pleased to see it on the ship when she made a good-will visit there shortly after being put into commission.

I gave the aquamarine to Bernard Baruch in order that he might make some inquiries about its value. I had tried to have it appraised, but no jeweler seemed able to tell me its exact value. At that time Drew Pearson, the columnist, announced that I was about to sell this stone, that it had been given to my husband and not to me, and that it was valued at $25,000. I was appalled at the thought that I might be accused of having kept out of my husband's estate something that had actually belonged to him.

I had not wanted to give this stone to the Franklin D. Roosevelt Library because I felt it had little connection with any of my husband's collections. I hoped to do something with it that would in some way benefit the Brazilian people. Fortunately, I discovered that Mr. Welles knew all about the presentation of this gift to my husband for me, and he told me that it would give great pleasure to the Brazilian people if the stone were placed with Franklin's other collections in the Library at Hyde Park. It is there now.

While Franklin was in South America, Miss Thompson and I went on my first real lecture trip. In the spring I had undertaken four lectures in the Middle West and I had not felt happy about them; this was to be my first trip under the W. Colston Leigh Lecture Bureau.

These trips gave me a wonderful opportunity to visit all kinds of places and to see and get to know a good cross section of people. Always during my free time I visited as many government projects as possible, often managing to arrive without advance notice so that they could not be polished up for my inspection. I began to see for myself some of the results of my husband's actions during the first hundred days of his administration, and in meeting and talking with people all over the country I got the full impact of what the new programs had meant to them. It was evident that the home and farm loans, for example, had saved many a family from outright disaster.

Of course, I always reported to Franklin upon my return, but aside from any value my reports may have been to him, I had another, more personal, reason for wanting to make these trips. All the years I lived in Washington I was preparing for the time when we should no longer be there. I did not want to give up my interests in New York City, because I always felt that someday I would go back. I never anticipated that so many years would pass before I left Washington. I kept expecting to leave at the end of every four years.

During those years in Washington we tried to maintain our home traditions as well as those that had been established in the White House, particularly in regard to the celebration of holidays. Christmas Eve in Washington was usually a busy day for me. I started by going to a party for underprivileged children, given by the welfare council at the National Theater. Then I joined my husband to wish all the people in the executive offices a merry Christmas.

Usually at lunchtime I had to be at the Salvation Army headquarters, where we had a service just before the food baskets were given out. I am afraid that during the depression years these services had an unchristian effect upon me, because invariably, before receiving their baskets, the poor wretches were told how grateful they should be. I knew if I were in their shoes I would be anything but grateful. From there I went to the Volunteers of America for the same sort of service and giving of food baskets, returning home in time for the afternoon party in the East Room.

After the party my husband and I and any of the family that were with us went to the lighting of the Community Christmas Tree, where my husband broadcast a Christmas message. Then he would return to the White House while I went on to a Christmas tree in one of the alleys (the slums of Washington), where again we sang carols. As I looked at the poor people about me I could not help wondering what Christmas could mean to those children.

Returning home I would find my husband reading Dickens' *The Christmas Carol* to any of the family that were gathered together. Having a great sense of the dramatic, he always put a good deal of drama into his reading of the parts about the ghosts. Whenever he read anything aloud like this, he acted it out straight through, which was why he held the attention of the little children so well, even before they could understand the meaning of the words. After the stockings had been filled, Miss Thompson and I nearly always went to midnight services at St. Thomas Church.

My husband liked to be in the White House on New Year's Eve. We always gathered a few friends, and at midnight in the oval study the radio was turned on and we waited with the traditional eggnog in hand for midnight to be announced. Franklin always sat in his big chair and, as the President, would raise his glass and say: "To the United States of America." All of us stood and repeated the toast after him. Somehow the words were especially meaningful and impressive in that house and gave a touch of solemnity to the personal greetings that followed.

Nineteen

Second Term: 1936-1937

FRANKLIN DID NOT talk a great deal about the work he was doing, eithei at meals or in private family conversations. Most of us felt that when he was with his family he should have a respite from the concerns of his office.

When an administration bill was up before Congress, we often found that the number of Congressmen coming to his study in the evenings increased. I learned that I must make an evaluation of the bills on which he had to get support. He calculated votes closely on what was known as the administration policy, and considered "must" legislation.

Only bills that were "must" legislation got full administration support. In the first years these were largely economic measures; later on, they were measures for defense. While I often felt strongly on various subjects, Franklin frequently refrained from supporting causes in which he believed, because of political realities. There were times when this annoyed me very much. In the case of the Spanish Civil War, for instance, we had to remain neutral, though Franklin wanted the democratic government to be successful. But he also knew he could not get Congress to go along with him. To justify his action, or lack of action, he explained to me, when I complained, that the League of Nations had asked us to remain neutral. By trying to convince me that our course was correct he was simply trying to salve his own conscience, because he himself was uncertain. It was one of the many times when I felt akin to a hairshirt.

I also remember wanting to get all-out support for the anti-lynching bill and the removal of the poll tax, but though Franklin was in favor of both measures, they never became "must" legislation. When I would protest, he would simply say: "First things first. I can't alienate certain votes I need for measures that are more important at the moment by pushing any measure that would entail a fight." And as the situation in Europe grew worse, preparations for war had to take precedence over everything else. That was always "must" legislation, and Franklin knew it would not pass if there was a party split.

Often people came to me to enlist his support for an idea. Although I might present the situation to him, I never urged on him a specific course of action, no matter how strongly I felt, because I realized that he knew of factors in the picture as a whole of which I might be ignorant.

One of the ideas I agreed to present to Franklin was that of setting up a national youth administration. Harry Hopkins, then head of the WPA, and Aubrey Williams, his deputy administrator and later head of the National Youth Administration, knew how deeply troubled I had been from the beginning about the plight of the country's young people. One day they said: "We have come to you about this because we do not feel we should talk to the President about it as yet. There may be many people against the establishment of such an agency in the government and there may be bad political repercussions. We do not know that the country will accept it. We do not even like to ask the President, because we do not think he should be put in a position where he has to say officially 'yes' or 'no' now."

I agreed to try to find out what Franklin's feelings were and to put before him their opinions and fears. I waited until my usual time for discussing questions with him and went into his room just before he went to sleep. I described the whole idea, which he already knew something of, and then told him of the fears that Harry Hopkins and Aubrey Williams had about such an agency. He looked at me and asked: "Do they think it is right to do this?" I said they thought it might be a great help to the young people, but they did not want him to forget that it might be unwise politically. They felt that a great many people who were worried by the fact that Germany had regimented its youth might feel we were trying to do the same thing in this country. Then Franklin said: "If it is the right thing to do for the young people, then it should be done. I guess we can stand the criticism, and I doubt if our youth can be regimented in this way or in any other way."

I went back to Harry Hopkins and Aubrey Williams the next day with Franklin's message. Shortly after, the NYA came into being and undoubtedly benefited many young people. It offered projects to help high school and college youngsters to finish school, and provided training in both resident and nonresident projects, supplementing the work of the Civilian Conservation Corps in such a way as to aid all youth.

It was one of the occasions on which I was proud that the right thing was done regardless of political considerations. As a matter of fact, however, it turned out to be politically popular and strengthened the administration greatly.

I am reminded here of a story Miss Thompson told about the time I visited one of the prisons in Baltimore with Mr. Maury Maverick, who was in charge of prison industries during the war and wanted me to see the salvage work being done there. In order to fit the trip into my schedule I had to leave the White House early without saying good morning to Franklin. On his way to the office, he called to Tommy and asked where I was. "She's in prison, Mr. President," Tommy said. "I'm not surprised," said Franklin, "but what for?"

As time went by I found that people no longer considered me a mouthpiece for my husband but realized that I had a point of view of my own with which he might not at all agree. Then I felt freer to state my views. However, I always used some care, and sometimes I would send Franklin one of my columns about which I was doubtful. The only change he would ever suggest was occasionally in the use of a word, and that was simply a matter of style. Of course, this hands-off policy had its advantages for him, too; for it meant that my column could sometimes serve as a trial balloon. If some idea I expressed strongly—and with which he might agree —caused a violent reaction, he could honestly say that he had no responsibility in the matter and that the thoughts were my own.

Though Franklin himself never tried to discourage me and was undisturbed by anything I wanted to say or do, other people were frequently less happy about my actions. I knew, for instance, that many of my racial beliefs and activities in the field of social work caused Steve Early and Marvin McIntyre grave concern. They were afraid that I would hurt my husband politically and socially.

One afternoon I gave a garden party at the White House for the girls from the reform school in Washington, most of whom were colored. Steve thought that was unwise, politically, and I did get some bad publicity in the southern papers. Steve felt the same way about my work with the members of the American Youth Congress. Franklin, however, never said anything to me about it. I always felt that if Franklin's re-election depended on such little things that I or any member of the family did, he could not be doing the job the people in the country wanted him to do.

I know Franklin felt the same way. Many of his political advisers, as well as some of the family, were deeply troubled over Elliott and Anna's divorces, feeling that they would react unfavorably on my husband's political career. In each case Franklin had done what he could to prevent the divorce, but when he was convinced that the children had made up their minds after careful reflection, it never occurred to him to suggest that they should subordinate their lives to his interests. He said that he thought a man in politics stood or fell by the results of his policies; that what the children did or did not do affected their lives, and that he did not consider that their lives should be tied to his political interests.

Sometimes Franklin carried his disregard of criticism too far. I was appalled when, in 1937, he asked James to come to Washington as one of his secretaries. James was delighted, for he had always been interested in politics and thought the opportunity to help his father a great chance to learn much and be really useful. I, however, could foresee the attacks that would be made on his father for appointing him, and on James himself, and I could imagine all kinds of ways in which, through his necessarily political activities, he might get himself and his father into trouble. I protested vehemently to Franklin and told him he was selfish to bring James down. I talked to James and tried to persuade him not to come, but he could see no objections. Finally I was silenced by my husband saying to me: "Why should I be deprived of my eldest son's help and the pleasure of having him with me just because I am the President?" It did seem hard and what he said had a point. Nevertheless, I was unhappy, and I think my fears were justified by what actually happened.

Jimmy did a good job and it meant a great deal to Franklin to have him, but he was more vulnerable to jealousies and rivalries than were the other secretaries, and he did get into trouble when he began to work with people in Congress. As a result of the work and anxiety, he developed ulcers of the stomach and eventually had to go out to the Mayo Brothers hospital for an operation. They told James the nervous strain was bad for him, and he accepted their advice not to return to his duties at the White House.

In 1937, about the time he brought Jimmy to Washington, Franklin became much troubled over the decisions that the Supreme Court was rendering. His advisers were divided, some of them feeling that it was unwise to have any change made in the Court. Franklin felt that if it was going to be possible to pass progressive legislation only to have it declared unconstitutional by the Supreme Court, no progress could be made. He also felt that people became too conservative as they grew older and that they should not be allowed to continue indefinitely to wield great power.

The defeat of the Supreme Court bill seemed to me to be a real blow to Franklin, but he spent no time in regrets and simply said, "Well, we'll see what will happen."

Later he was able, little by little, to change the complexion of the court. He remarked one day that he thought the fight had been worth while in spite of the defeat, because it had focused the attention of the public on the Supreme Court and its decisions, and he felt that aroused public interest was always helpful. He had a firm belief in the collective wisdom of the people when their interest was awakened and they really understood the issues at stake.

Though I had been in complete sympathy with what he was trying to do, I used to think that he might have saved himself a good deal of trouble just by waiting awhile, since it was death and resignations that really gave him the opportunity to appoint new people to the Supreme Court. However, if he had not made the fight, perhaps fewer people would have resigned.

As we neared the Congressional election in 1938, I could see that Franklin was again troubled. The way he had felt about the Supreme Court was in line with the way he felt about reactionary legislators. He believed it was essential to have liberal congresssmen if his liberal program was to continue. The fact that the Democratic party had a large majority had not unified it as a fighting group, but rather had divided it into factions; at times it seemed that within the Democratic party there was, to all intents and purposes, a group of people who might work better with the more conservative Republican party. This situation led to a division among the presidential advisers and within the Cabinet, and resulted finally in what was known as "the purge."

If there were political mistakes in this campaign, some of them, I think, might have been avoided if Louis Howe had been alive. After Louis's death, Franklin never had a political adviser who would argue with him, and still give him unquestioned loyalty. Louis gave Franklin the benefit of his sane, reasoned, careful political analysis and even if Franklin disagreed and was annoyed, he listened and respected Louis's political acumen.

Whether he ignored his advice or not, at least all the reasons against the disputed action had been clearly stated and argued.

In Harry Hopkins my husband found some of the companionship and loyalty Louis had given him, but not the political wisdom and careful analysis of each situation. Louis would argue, but Harry would not do this. He gave his opinion honestly, but because he knew Franklin did not like opposition too well—as who does?—he frequently agreed with him regardless of his own opinion, or tried to persuade him in indirect ways.

Louis Howe had been older than Franklin and, because he had helped him so greatly in so many ways during his early political life, could be more independent than Harry Hopkins. Franklin, in turn, shaped Harry; he widened his horizons and taught him many things about domestic politics and foreign affairs. Consequently, Harry's opinion did not carry the weight with Franklin that Louis's had.

Jim Farley would argue with Franklin, but never very effectively, because his reasons for advocating a course were always those of political expediency. Ed Flynn told him the truth as he saw it and argued fearlessly, but he was not always on hand. Consequently, after Louis died, Franklin frequently made his decisions without canvassing all sides of a question.

Much, of course, can be done by the vice-president, the speaker of the House, the party leaders both in the Senate and in the House, and the Cabinet members, if they develop strength in Congress. In the last analysis, however, the President is the one responsible for the action of his followers; when they do not follow, he feels that his leadership has been weakened. Of course, it is impossible to have 100 per cent agreement within a party, particularly when that party has a comfortable majority in Congress, but the larger proportion of it must be united to be effective.

Of course, Franklin did not expect Congress to go down the line on every occasion. From his lifelong study of American history, and from his own experience, he keenly appreciated the value of the checks and balances established in our government by the Founding Fathers. He realized that the willingness of Congress to vote whatever powers were necessary to meet an emergency was not a situation it was desirable to perpetuate in a democracy.

Franklin never resented constructive criticism from the members of Congress. What he did resent was the refusal of certain congressmen to understand the over-all needs of the country, the narrow point of view which let them pit their local interests against the national or international interest. Franklin always said that no leader could get too far ahead of his followers, and it was because he felt that Congress was close to the people that he had a healthy respect for its reaction to any of his proposals.

Franklin's activities in the campaign of 1938 were thought by many people to have been a political mistake. I am not a good enough politician to know, but I have tried here to set forth the reasons that I think actuated him.

Harry Hopkins threw his whole heart and all his abilities into organizing relief on a national scale. He was a man whom I not only admired but came to have a deep trust and confidence in. Later, after the death of his second wife, I began to see a side of him that I had not known before. It is a natural development, I imagine, to seek entertainment and diversion when your life is lonely. What surprised some of us was the fact that Harry seemed to get so much genuine pleasure out of contact with gay but more or less artificial society. People who could give him luxuries and the kind of party in which he probably never before had the slightest interest became important to him. I did not like this side of Harry as much as the side I first knew, but deep down he was a fine person who had the courage to bear pain and who loved his country enough to risk the curtailment of his life in order to be of service, after all chance of fulfilling any personal ambition was over.

My own work had to go on regardless of anything else. When I first went to Washington I had been writing a weekly column and a page in the *Woman's Home Companion*, as well as many articles for other magazines.

The weekly column seemed a dull affair, and finally an enterprising gentleman, Monte Bourjaily of the United Feature Syndicate, had an idea that he thought would vastly increase its interest. He said he felt sure that if I would write a daily column in the form of a diary it would be of great interest to the people of the United States, who were curious about the way anyone who lived in the White House passed his time, day after day. At first I thought it would be the most dreadful chore; but I was so dissatisfied with what I was doing in the way of writing that in January, 1936, I decided to sign a five-year contract with the United Feature Syndicate for a daily column, which would be shorter and perhaps for that reason easier to do. From that time on I wrote a column six days a week, and only once failed to get it in on time. I wrote Sundays through Fridays, which meant that I had Saturdays off. When I went on trips I sometimes had to write a number of columns ahead. Otherwise, I wrote the column during the morning or at noon every day, though occasionally, if the following day looked like a very busy one, I wrote it in the middle of the night before. It had to be in by six P.M. Writing this column became so much of a habit that when people remarked that it must be difficult to do I was always a little surprised.

When I went to the South Pacific in 1943 on a five weeks' trip, I did not take anyone with me to act as secretary. Every night, after a long day of hard work, I painfully typed my own column unless I had been able to do it on a flight during the day. I learned to type many years ago but, not having had much practice, I am slow, and it took me a long time to write about what I had done during the day.

The *Ladies' Home Journal* page, which I wrote from 1941 until the spring of 1949, when I moved over to *McCall's*, was an experience suggested to me by Mr. and Mrs. Bruce Gould and Mr. George Bye, who was then my literary agent. The page turned out to be a successful feature and is something that I really enjoyed, though I was much amused by some of the questions. Occasionally they were rude and personal, but on the whole, they came from people sincerely seeking information or asking for help. At first, unable to believe that people would really ask me some of the questions which were sent me, I accused the editorial staff of making them up. As a result, they always sent me the letters on which the questions were based. Frequently they took a number of letters containing questions on similar subjects and made one composite question.

At least, I have never known what it was to be bored or to have time hang heavily on my hands.

Twenty

The Royal Visitors

THE ARRIVAL of the Swedish crown prince and princess in the United States in the summer of 1938 marked the beginning of a series of visits from members of Europe's royal families. The people of Europe were deeply troubled by the general feeling of unrest and uncertainty on the Continent and were looking for friends in other parts of the world—hence their sudden interest in the United States.

The crown prince and princess were making a trip through the country to visit the various Swedish settlements, and on July 1 came to stay at Hyde Park, where we had a dinner for them. In May, the following year, the day after a dinner and musical for the President of Nicaragua and Señora de Somoza, we entertained the crown prince and princess of Denmark at tea. In June we had another South American guest when the chief of the Brazilian Army paid my husband a visit, and later that same month the crown prince and princess of Norway arrived and came to tea. They, like the other royal guests, visited the settlements of their countrymen here, later coming to Hyde Park for a short time.

In each case we had a few people to meet them at dinner and a picnic at Franklin's newly built stone cottage on top of the hill. There are a number of Norwegians living near us at Hyde Park who asked to put on a show for the crown prince and princess of Norway. I shall always remember that as one of our pleasantest parties.

We were to come to know Princess Marta and Prince Olaf and their children very well, for during the long years of the war, though the prince was here only occasionally, the princess with the children lived in this country.

At the time of his visit our impression was that the Danish prince was more interested in his holiday than in the serious questions of the moment and had perhaps less realization of the menace of Hitler than we had expected of one in his position.

My husband welcomed these visits and encouraged everyone to come here whom he had any chance of persuading. Convinced that bad things were going to happen in Europe, he wanted to make contacts with those who he hoped would preserve and adhere to democracy and prove to be allies against fascism when the conflict came.

That same spring the King and Queen of England decided to visit the Dominion of Canada. They, too, were preparing for the blow that might fall and knew well that they would need the devotion of every subject in their dominions. My husband invited them to come to Washington because, believing that we all might soon be engaged in a life-and-death struggle, in which Great Britain would be our first line of defense, he hoped that their visit would create a bond of friendship between the peoples of the two countries. He knew that, though there is always a certain amount of criticism and superficial ill feeling toward the British in this country, in time of danger we stand firmly together, with confidence in our common heritage and ideas. The visit of the King and Queen, he hoped, would be a reminder of this deep bond. In many ways it proved even more successful than he had expected.

Their visit was carefully prepared for, but Franklin always behaved as though we were simply going to have two nice young people to stay with us. I think he gave some of the protocol people, both in the State Department and in the entourage of the King and Queen, some difficult moments.

There was one person, however, who looked on the visit as a very serious affair—William Bullitt, then our ambassador to France. He sent me a secret memorandum, based on experience gained from the King and Queen's visit to Paris the year before, in which all the smallest details were noted. I still keep that memorandum as one of my most amusing documents. Among other things he listed the furniture which should be in the rooms used by the King and Queen, told me what I should have in the bathrooms and even the way the comfortables on the beds should be folded. He admonished me to have a hot-water bottle in every bed, which I did, though the heat of Washington must have made them unbearable. One thing that was listed and that I was never able to find was a linen blanket for the queen's couch. Nobody I asked on this side of the ocean knew what it might be.

The Scotland Yard people had to stay in the house, of course, and outside the King and Queen's rooms were chairs where messengers always sat. It seemed foolish to me, since the rooms were just across the hall from each other. Not until 1942, when I spent two nights in Buckingham Palace and saw how large it was, did I understand the reason for the messengers. There they wait in the corridors to show guests where to go, and to carry any messages one wishes to send.

One day before the visit I invited Lady Lindsay, wife of the British ambassador, to tea and asked her if she was being given any instructions which might be helpful to me. Lady Lindsay was an American whom I had known a long while, and we looked at things from more or less the same point of view. She looked at me rather wickedly when she said: "Yes, Sir Alan Lascelles has told us that the King must be served at meals thirty seconds ahead of the Queen. The King does not like capers or suet pudding. I told him we did not often have suet pudding in the United States and that I really had not expected the King to like capers."

In the White House there are in the dining room two special, high-backed armchairs, one for the President and one for his wife, and no one else ever sits in them at meals. They presented a great problem for the household on this occasion. Should only the King and the President have the armchairs? That did not seem respectful to the Queen, but we could not take his chair away from the President. Finally Franklin solved the difficulty. "Why don't we buy two more armchairs identical with those we now have?" This was done and all was well.

I told Franklin that British protocol required that the head butler, Fields, stand with a stop watch in his hand and, thirty seconds after he and the King had been served, dispatch a butler to serve the Queen and myself, and I inquired what was to happen about the White House rule that the president was always served first. "We will not require Fields to have a stop watch," he said. "The King and I will be served simultaneously and you and the Queen will be served next."

Then came another serious question: Should the President sit with the King on his right and the Queen on his left and me on the right of the King? Or should we follow our usual custom? Franklin finally decided we would follow the usual custom of the United States. The King would sit on my right and the Queen on Franklin's right. The reason for this decision was that since the King and Queen were going to see a good deal of us, it did not seem quite fair to box the King in between us when he had so little time in which to meet and talk with other people. Franklin later explained this to the King, who accepted every arrangement in the most charming and delightful manner.

The secretary of state and Mrs. Hull with their party had met the members of the royal party at Niagara Falls, and accompanied them on the train to Washington. There was much pageantry about their arrival and the procession to the White House. That was something my husband always enjoyed, for he liked to put on a show. I dreaded it. At the appointed time we went down to the station and, with the government officials who were members of the reception committee, stood waiting in the President's reception room for the train's arrival.

After the presentations were over, my husband and I escorted the King and Queen through the Guard of Honor, which was drawn up in front of the station. The British National Anthem and "The Star-Spangled Banner" were played, and there was a twenty-one gun salute. Then the inevitable photographs were taken and finally my husband and the King and the Queen and I got into our respective cars and started with military escort on the slow drive to the White House. There were crowds all along the way and I was fascinated watching the Queen. She had the most gracious manner and bowed right and left with interest, actually looking at people in the crowd so that I am sure many of them felt that her bow was really for them personally.

In spite of the heat, a light cover had been placed by her footman over her knees when she got into the car. She sat upon a cushion which I afterwards discovered had springs to make it easier for her to keep up the continual bowing. The same arrangements were made for the King.

Immediately on our arrival at the White House, what is known as a Diplomatic Circle was held in the East Room for the heads of all the diplomatic missions and their wives. At that time the British ambassador, Sir Ronald Lindsay, was dean of the diplomatic corps, so he presented the chiefs of missions and their wives to the King while Lady Lindsay presented them to the Queen.

After lunch, the King and my husband in one car and the Queen and I in another drove about Washington. Our route was given out beforehand, so that people could have an opportunity to see Their Majesties. It meant, of course, that we had little chance to talk except when we were driving where people could not line up on the sidewalks. At one point the Queen endeared herself to me by saying suddenly: "I saw in the paper that you were being attacked for having gone to a meeting of the WPA workers. It surprises me that there should be any criticism, for it is so much better to allow people with grievances to air them; and it is particularly valuable if they can do so to someone in whom they feel a sense of sympathy and who may be able to reach the head of the government with their grievances."

While we were out, some amusing things had happened at home. The housekeeper, Mrs. Nesbitt, was harassed and when she was harassed she usually went to Miss Thompson. The fact that the many servants quartered in our servants' rooms were requiring as much attention as she had expected to give to everyone combined was an unexpected burden. The first intimation of any difficulty between our staff and the royal servants came when the housekeeper reported that the King's valet was making unreasonable demands and did not like our food and drink. Even the ushers were not having an easy time, for they were not accustomed to having protocol hold good among the servants. As the Queen's maid was walking down the middle of the second floor hall on her way from the Queen's room to the elevator, one of the ushers asked her if she would tell the lady in waiting that the Queen wanted her to come to her room. The maid drew herself up and said, "I am the Queen's maid," and swept down the hall. The usher, who by this time was exhausted by the heat and the extra work, reported, "Oh, so you're a big shot?"

When finally everyone got to bed that night, they must all, including the King and Queen, have breathed sighs of relief.

The next morning, before Their Majesties left the White House, they walked down a line of newspaperwomen and greeted them, then went to the British embassy, where they received members of the British colony, and from there to the Capitol. At the Capitol they were received by the vice-president and by Speaker Bankhead, and escorted to the rotunda where they received members of the Senate and the House. After that they met us on the U.S.S. *Potomac* and we had lunch on the way down the river. At Mount Vernon the usual ceremony was observed and the King laid a wreath on Washington's tomb. Time was growing short, and some people who had driven out there were presented to the King and Queen as they hurriedly got a glimpse of the old Mount Vernon house and grounds.

On the way home we stopped at Fort Hunt to visit a Civilian Conservation Corps camp. My husband, of course, could not walk with the

King and Queen, but I have a vivid recollection of that visit; it taught me many things.

The King walked with the commandant of the camp toward the boys, who were drawn up in two lines in the broiling sun. A large bulletin board had been put up with pictures of the various camps throughout the country, showing the different kinds of work done by the boys, but he did not stop to look at them.

As we went down the long line, the King stopped at every other boy and asked questions while the Queen spoke to the intervening boys. I, of course, walked with the Queen. At the end of the first line, the commandant was prepared not to go down the second one, but the King turned automatically and started down. He asked really interested questions, such as whether they were satisfied with their food, what they were learning and whether they thought it would help them to obtain work and, lastly, how much they were earning.

He had explained to us beforehand that for a long time he had had a summer camp for boys from the mining areas of Great Britain. He had been deeply troubled to find that many boys had no conception of doing a full day's work, because they had never seen their fathers do a day's work, many of Great Britain's miners having been on the dole for years. This spoke volumes for the conditions of the mining industry in Great Britain, but the King seemed interested chiefly in the effect it had on these young men; he wanted to set up something as useful as the CCC camps in Great Britain.

When we reached the end of the second row of boys, the commandant said: "Your Majesty, the day is so hot that, while the boys have prepared their barracks and mess hall for your inspection, we shall all understand if you do not feel it wise to cross the field in this sun." The King responded: "If they expect me to go, of course I will go." This was a kind of *noblesse oblige* that I had not often seen in our own officials with whom I had inspected CCC camps and NYA activities and other projects.

The Queen and I followed slowly across the field in the hot sun, and I saw one of the most thorough inspections I have ever witnessed. They looked at the shelves where supplies were kept, and when they heard the boys made their own equipment, they had tables turned upside down to see how they were made; they looked into pots and pans on the stove, and at the menu; and when they left there was little they did not know.

In the sleeping barracks the King felt the mattresses and carefully examined shoes and clothes.

My husband had carefully coached me for the tea party that followed this trip, for he said the King had particularly asked to meet the heads of all the agencies which were contributing to the recovery and doing new things in the government. As I introduced each agency head I was supposed, as briefly as possible, to outline the work that person was doing, and then give the man or woman, as the case might be, about three minutes alone with the King, then take him over to the Queen and present the next person to the King. I had rather dreaded trying to engineer this and wondered how I was going to condense the introduction into a brief enough explanation, but I soon found that my explanation could be very short, for the King seemed to know at once, as I spoke the name, what the person was doing, and he started right in with questions. I had expected to have a hard time keeping the line moving; I had watched my husband's secretaries struggling with him and it was impossible, if he got interested, to pry anyone away, but the King proved much more amenable.

The party seemed to go off successfully for all concerned. I was so impressed with the King's knowledge that at the next meal at which I sat beside him I asked him to tell me how he knew what work every person in our government did. He told me that before he came he had made a study of the name and occupation of everyone in the government; that the material had been procured for him, and was only part of his preparation for this trip to Washington.

After they left we took a train to Hyde Park, where we had the day to prepare for the twenty-four hours which the King and Queen were to spend with us there. My husband always loved taking people he liked home with him. He felt he knew them better once they had been to Hyde Park.

The day in New York City was interesting but completely exhausting, for Mayor LaGuardia had filled every minute to overflowing. As the day advanced the King and Queen realized they were going to be late reaching us; but they were not told how late they were until they actually started, whereupon the King insisted on stopping and telephoning at intervals along the way.

We sat in the library in the Hyde Park house waiting for them. Franklin had a tray of cocktails ready in front of him, and his mother sat on the other side of the fireplace looking disapprovingly at the cocktails and telling her son that the King would prefer tea. My husband, who could be as obstinate as his mother, kept his tray in readiness, however. Finally the King and Queen arrived and I met them at the door and took them to their rooms. In a short time they were dressed and down in the library. As the King approached my husband and the cocktail table, my husband said, "My mother does not approve of cocktails and thinks you should have a cup of tea." The King answered, "Neither does my mother," and took a cocktail.

Two startling things happened at dinner. They seem funny now, but they caused my mother-in-law much embarrassment. We had brought up the colored butler from the White House. My mother-in-law had an English butler who, when he heard that the White House butlers were coming up to help him, was so shocked that the King and Queen were to be waited on by colored people that he decided to take his holiday before Their Majesties came, in order not to see them treated in that manner!

Just exactly what happened to our well-trained White House butlers that night I shall never know. My mother-in-law had the extra china that was needed put on a serving table that was not ordinarily used, and suddenly in the middle of dinner the serving table collapsed and the dishes clattered to the floor. Mama tried in the best-bred tradition to ignore it, but her stepdaughter-in-law, Mrs. James Roosevelt Roosevelt, from whom she had borrowed some plates for the occasion, was heard to say, "I hope none of my dishes were among those broken." As a matter of fact, the broken dishes were part of a set my husband had been given; none of the old family china suffered.

One would think that one mishap of this kind would be enough for an evening, but just after we had gone down to the big library after dinner there was a most terrible crash; the butler, carrying a tray of decanters, glasses, bowls of ice, and so on, fell down the two steps leading from the hall and slid right into the library, scattering the contents of the tray over the floor and leaving a large lake of water and ice cubes at the bottom of the steps. I am sure Mama wished that her English butler had stayed. I wrote about this in my column at the time because I thought it was really funny, but my mother-in-law was indignant with me for not keeping it a deep, dark family secret.

Dinner had been so late that the evening was soon over and we all retired, leaving Prime Minister Mackenzie King and the King to talk with Franklin. It seemed so late when they came upstairs that I felt sorry for them, but the next day Mackenzie King told my husband that the King had knocked on his door and asked him to come to his room for a talk; he added that the King had said: "Why don't my ministers talk to me as the President did tonight? I felt exactly as though a father were giving me his most careful and wise advice."

The next day, after we had all been to church, people from far and near came to Franklin's cottage for a picnic. I had corralled two friends to cook hot dogs on an outdoor fireplace, and we had smoked turkey, which Their Majesties had not tasted before, several kinds of ham cured in different ways from different parts of the United States, salads, baked beans, and a strawberry shortcake with strawberries from Henry Morgenthau's farm in Dutchess County.

When the picnic and the handshaking were over, my husband invited the King to swim with him in the pool. I hoped the Queen would feel she could relax in the same way, but I discovered that if you were a Queen you could not run the risk of looking disheveled, so she and her lady in waiting sat by the side of the pool with me while the men were swimming.

After a quiet dinner we took the King and Queen to join their train at the Hyde Park station. Their luggage and all the rest of their party were on board. Their Majesties had said good-by to everybody and were about to get on the train when the Queen suddenly came back to me and said: "Where is the man who has been driving the King? I want to thank him." I found my husband's chauffeur and the Queen thanked him for the care with which he had driven.

The royal couple stood on the rear platform of the train as it pulled out and the people who were gathered on the banks of the Hudson suddenly began to sing, "Auld Lang Syne." There was something incredibly moving about the scene—the river in the evening light, the voices of many people singing this old song, and the train slowly pulling out with the young couple waving good-by. One thought of the clouds that hung over them and the worries they were going to face, and turned away and left the scene with a heavy heart.

Twenty-one

Second Term: 1939-1940

MANY PEOPLE may have forgotten how worried we were about the young people in our country during the early days of the depression. How deeply troubled these young men and women were was shown by the fact that many of them felt it necessary to leave their homes, because they could not find jobs and could not bear to eat even a small amount of what little food their families had.

I felt that in any efforts they made to help themselves or one another the young people should have all the consideration and assistance their elders could possibly give them. My deep concern led to my association with various youth groups and to my meeting with many young people who either were brought by their elders to Washington or came through an organization of their own.

I believed, of course, that these young people had the right to be heard. They had the right to fight for the things they believed in as citizens of a democracy. It was essential to restore their faith in the power of democracy to meet their needs, or they would take the natural path of looking elsewhere.

One of the most prominent young people's organizations of this unsettled time was the American Youth Congress. It spread all over the country and worked closely with other youth groups, such as the Southern Youth Council and the Negro Youth Congress.

During one of their meetings in Washington the leaders of the AYC came to see me and told me what they were trying to do. In time I came to know some of them quite well. I like all young people and those in the American Youth Congress were an idealistic, hard-working group. Whether they were Communist-inspired from the beginning I have never

208

known. After I had been working for them for a while accusations began to be made, and I had a number of the leaders come to my sitting room in the White House. I told them that since I was actively helping them I must know exactly where they stood politically. I asked each one in turn to tell me honestly what he believed. In every case they said they had no connection with the Communists, had never belonged to any Communist organizations, and had no interest in Communist ideas. I decided to accept their word, realizing that sooner or later the truth would come out.

The first direct contact that Franklin had with the American Youth Congress came after I was fairly sure that they were becoming Communist-dominated. Ordinarily, Franklin had little time to devote to individuals or even to particular groups. On February 10, 1940, the American Youth Congress organized a parade and a meeting in Washington, and I thought it advisable to ask Franklin to speak to them. It rained that day, and a wet group stood out in the south grounds, expecting to be patted on the back. Instead, Franklin told them some truths which, though they might be unpalatable, he thought it wise for them to hear. They were in no mood for warnings, however kindly meant, and they booed the President.

When the leaders of several youth organizations were summoned to appear before the Dies Committee, I sat through most of the hearings, because I had heard that when the members had before them people of little influence or backing, their questions were so hostile as to give the impression that the witness had been haled before a court and prejudged a criminal. If there is one thing I dislike it is intimidating people instead of trying to get at facts. At one point, when the questioning seemed to me to be particularly harsh, I asked to go over and sit at the press table. I took a pencil and a piece of paper, and the tone of the questions changed immediately. Just what the questioner thought I was going to do I do not know, but my action had the effect I desired.

Because I dislike Gestapo methods in this country, I have never liked that kind of Congressional committee. I doubt that they ever harm the really powerful, but they do harm many innocent people who are unable to defend themselves.

On one occasion my husband and I were given a confidential list of organizations which were considered Communist or subversive or un-American, a list compiled by the FBI for the use of the Dies Committee. People who belonged to any group on that list or who had even contributed to any of them were *ipso facto* under suspicion. We found that among those listed as contributors to two or three of these organizations were Secretary Stimson, Secretary Knox and my husband's mother. Franklin and I got particular amusement out of the inclusion of her name; we could picture her horror if she were told that the five or ten dollars she had given to a seemingly innocent relief organization put her among those whom the Dies Committee could easily call before it as belonging to subversive organizations.

I once asked the Dies Committee and the FBI point-blank what evidence they had on any of the young people they were talking so loosely about. They told me they had none. A book written later by a woman in Washington states that Mr. Dies offered me information which I refused to read. The fact of the matter is that I invited Mr. Dies to lunch and asked specifically for information; he never sent it to me.

After my decision to part from them, the young people of the Youth Congress accused me of having been "sold down the river to the capitalists," and some of them picketed the White House with a peace group.

When news was received that Germany had invaded Russia, however, the Youth Congress held another mass meeting and clamored for cooperation with Russia and for greater preparation for war. They even sent me a telegram saying: "Now we can work together again." The war was suddenly no longer an imperialistic war, and the pickets were called off at the White House.

Of course, I never worked with the Youth Congress again. I could not trust them to be honest with me.

I wish to make it clear that I felt a great sympathy for these young people, even though they often annoyed me. It was impossible ever to forget the extraordinary difficulties under which they were growing up. I have never felt the slightest bitterness toward any of them. I learned from them what Communist tactics are. I discovered for myself how infiltration of an organization is accomplished. I was taught how Communists get themselves into positions of importance. I learned their methods of objection and delay, the effort to tire out the rest of the group and carry the vote when all their opponents have gone home. These tactics are now all familiar to me. In fact, I think my work with the American Youth Congress was of infinite value to me in understanding some of the tactics I had to meet later in the United Nations!

During the summer of 1939 we spent a great deal of time at Hyde Park. When the news finally came that Hitler's troops had gone into Poland, Franklin called me at Hyde Park at five o'clock in the morning. All that September day I could not help remembering the good-by to the King and Queen and the lump that had come into my throat as they stood on the back platform of their departing train. Now their people faced the final hour of decision.

As I look back over the whole year of 1939, it seems to me that my husband's major efforts were bent on trying to avert total war in Europe and to awaken us here to the need for preparation. Perhaps he might have saved himself the trouble of these various efforts, yet one would not like to feel that the President of this country had not done all he could to try to change the threatening course of history.

His actions during this year and the next were only a continuation of the line of action he had begun to follow as far back as 1936. Immediately after the failure of the London Naval Conference, he had secured from Congress money to construct additional battleships and airplane carriers. The following year, in his quarantine speech in Chicago, he warned the country of the worsening political situation abroad and of the dangers it held for the United States; and he tried to persuade the people that this country should make a definite and positive effort to preserve the peace. The opposition this speech aroused was so great that Franklin realized the people were not yet ready to go along with any drastic steps toward international co-operation.

All through the Czech crisis in 1938 he continued his attempts to save the peace, through appeals to Hitler and the heads of other countries. After Munich, he blamed Neville Chamberlain for weakness, but said that England had let her defenses go down so much that there was perhaps nothing else the prime minister could do. To ensure that our country would never be found similarly unprepared was now Franklin's greatest concern.

In January he asked Congress for funds to expand our air force and construct new naval air bases. In April he warned the country of the approach of war in Europe and sent a personal message to both Hitler and Mussolini, appealing for a ten-year pledge not to attack or invade other countries. In late August Russia and Germany signed their non-aggression pact. Franklin sent a peace appeal to Hitler, King Victor

Emmanuel of Italy, and President Moscicki of Poland, urging settlement
of the Danzig-Polish Corridor issue. On the following day he sent another
message to Hitler.

Then Hitler invaded Poland. Convinced that further peace efforts would
be unsuccessful, Franklin on September 21 urged Congress to repeal the
embargo on the shipment of arms under the Neutrality Act, which he
had signed reluctantly in 1937, at the time of the Spanish Civil War. In
December Franklin appointed Myron Taylor as his special representative at the Vatican.

The letters between my husband and the Pope seem to indicate that
this appointment was one of the wise preliminary steps in the preparation for war, although it created a certain amount of difficulty among
some of our Protestant groups. Mr. Taylor was well known and respected,
and most people felt that the Pope could be a potent force for peace at
this time and that we should have some direct tie with him. I do not
think Franklin regarded this appointment as creating a permanent diplomatic post, but he thought it a necessity during a period of emergency.

During this year Franklin had persuaded his mother to deed, with him,
to the United States government a piece of their property on the Post
Road. Frank Walker headed a committee, made up of a number of other
friends, to collect the money to build a library at Hyde Park. The war
had its influence in this, too. For a long time Franklin had felt that it
would be a great advantage if the important papers and collections of the
country were not all crowded together in one building. In case of war,
the European countries would have to scatter their collections, since one
bomb could completely destroy the historical records of the whole nation.
In particular, he realized that Congress was never likely to give the Congressional Library sufficient appropriation for the continuing flow of public
papers to be brought rapidly up to date and made available to those who
wanted to study them. He also thought it would be easier to deal with a
particular period if all the records relating to it were in one place. Intending to give his own papers and many other interesting things to the
library, he believed he could persuade other people who had been active
in the life of the period to do the same thing.

I shall never forget his pleasure and pride in laying the cornerstone of
the library on November 19 of that year. It was a simple but moving
occasion. His strong feeling for history added greatly to his pleasure in

knowing that here, on his own land, there would be gathered in one building the record of the period of his country's history in which he had had a part.

The next year, 1940, had the disadvantage of all election years; everything that happens seems of necessity to have a political slant. Though the war in Europe was moving inexorably on and Hitler seemed to be sweeping all before him, some people were concerned only with the effect that any move of Franklin's would have on the chances of the Democratic party for success in the next election.

Nevertheless, throughout the year he took additional steps which, though each one in itself seemed unimportant, together tended to prepare the country for the ordeal before it. In February he urged the immediate purchase of strategic war materials; in April the combat areas were defined; and in May he asked for additional appropriations of over one billion dollars for defense. These moves were justified, since Hitler was moving fast.

Dunkirk was a sad and anxious time for us in the White House as well as for the people of Great Britain. When the full story was told, the heroism of the people on that embattled island and the way the Royal Air Force defended the country called forth admiration from everyone in the United States. We understood the kind of courage and tenacity that Winston Churchill was beginning to put into words, words that expressed the spirit of the British people in the months following Dunkirk.

It was this admiration of good sportsmanship that made my husband so bitter against Mussolini when he came into the war against France. The familiar phrase "stab in the back," which some of his advisers begged him to leave out of his Charlottesville, Virginia, speech was largely a tribute to the spirit which he recognized in the people of Great Britain and which he felt the leadership of Mussolini never fostered in the Italian people.

The occasion for that speech was the commencement at the University of Virginia Law School, where Franklin Junior was graduating. It was a curious trip; we were all there; a trip to one's son's commencement is normal; but that was not a normal and happy occasion. The times were fraught with promise of evil. Franklin's address was not just a commencement address; it was a speech to the nation on an event that had brought us one step nearer to total war.

Immediately after the speech I went to Hyde Park, leaving my husband and Franklin Junior in Washington. I knew by that time that those who thought the war inevitable had persuaded Franklin that he could not refuse to run for a third term if he were nominated.

So much has been said about the third term issue that I can contribute only my own impressions. I never questioned Franklin about his political intentions. The fact that I myself had never wanted him to be in Washington made me doubly careful not to intimate that I had the slightest preference.

Although I never asked my husband what he wanted to do, it became clearly evident, from little things he said at different times, that he would really like to be in Hyde Park and that the role of elder statesman appealed to him. He thought he would enjoy being in a position to sit back and offer suggestions and criticism. There were innumerable things that all his life he had meant to do—write on naval subjects, go through his papers, letters, and so on. He had the library at Hyde Park and had even agreed on a job which he would take on leaving the White House. As I remember, he was to write a longish editorial or article at stated intervals for one of the large New York magazines. He had built a small stone cottage to which he could retreat when too many people came to the big house; and while he was furious when people called it his "dream house," nevertheless it was part of his dream.

I had every evidence to believe that he did not want to run again. However, as time went on, more and more people came to me saying that he must run, that the threat of war was just over the horizon and no one else had the prestige and the knowledge to carry on through a crisis.

I had been deeply troubled by the fact that I saw no one being prepared to take Franklin's place, and on several occasions I asked him if he did not think he should make a definite effort to prepare someone. Franklin said he thought people had to prepare themselves, that all he could do was to give them opportunities and see how they worked out. I felt that he, without intending to do so, dominated the people around him and that so long as he was in the picture it was hard for anyone to rise to a position of prominence. Finally, I came to realize that no man could hand another more than opportunity.

I heard many other people discussed as possible candidates, but as the time for the convention drew nearer I could see that it was going to be extremely difficult to have anyone else nominated. First, the Democratic party had not found anyone else it thought could keep it in office and, second, serious-minded people were worried about the war.

Before the convention actually opened it was evident that Franklin was going to be nominated and would run; I think he had been persuaded that if he were nominated he could not refuse. I believe he did not honestly want the nomination. If he had not been nominated, he would have been completely satisfied, and would have lived his life very happily; and yet when you are in the center of world affairs, there is something so fascinating about it that you can hardly see how you are going to live any other way. In his mind, I think, there was a great seesaw; on one end, the weariness that had already begun, and the desire to be at home and his own master; on the other end, the overwhelming interest that was the culmination of a lifetime of preparation and work, and the desire to see and to have a hand in the affairs of the world in that critical period.

Finally I said to Franklin: "You have made up your mind you will not go to the convention even if you are nominated but that you will speak over the radio, and that means, I hope, I do not have to go." He said firmly that it was his definite intention that neither he nor I should go. I told him in that case I would go to Hyde Park and stay at my cottage and get the big house ready, so that when the convention was over he could come up for a rest.

Miss Thompson and I went to Hyde Park. Life was going placidly when one day the telephone rang. Frances Perkins was on the wire. She said: "Things look black here; the temper of the convention is ugly. The President should come to Chicago if he wants Mr. Wallace nominated; but if he won't come, I think you should come." I told her I thought it utter nonsense for me to go, but she ought to tell my husband her feeling and that he ought to go if anyone went. Miss Perkins rang off, saying she would talk to Franklin. When she called him, he told her he was not going to the convention, but that if he were nominated he wanted Henry Wallace as his running mate.

The next day Frances Perkins called me again and said that my husband had told her he would be willing to have me go if she felt it was essential. I said: "Franklin may be willing, but how do I know how Jim Farley feels about it? I certainly am not going out there unless he invites me. I know there is bad feeling because Harry Hopkins has been more or less running things and perhaps has not been very tactful, and I am not going to add to the hard feelings." She then wanted to know whether I would go if Jim asked me to, and I said I should have to ask my huband first. After she had finished talking, I called Franklin and told him what

Frances Perkins had said and asked him what he wanted me to do. He said: "It might be nice for you to go, but I do not think it is in the least necessary." I said: "If Jim Farley asks me to go, do you think it would be wise?" He replied: "Yes, I think it would be."

Then I waited, and later in the morning the telephone rang and Jim Farley asked me to come out. Since he was in rather a hurry, he asked me to talk to Lorena Hickok, who was then working with Charles Michelson on publicity for the Democratic National Committee. She told me she felt it was important for me to come and that Jim Farley really wanted me.

The next day we landed in the late afternoon in Chicago. Jim Farley met me at the airfield. The newspaperwomen were in the airport, and he asked me to see them at once. I told him I had nothing to say, but he thought I had better see them, so I got through the interview as best I could, saying as little as possible.

Then Jim Farley and I drove alone into Chicago. On the way he told me that Franklin had not talked to him since the convention opened and had never told him who was his choice for vice-president. I was horrified to realize that things had come to this pass between the two men, because I always had a feeling of real friendship for Jim Farley. He told me why he thought that Jesse Jones or William B. Bankhead or Paul McNutt or some other candidate should get the nomination. He also told me that Elliott, who was a resident of Texas at that time and a member of the delegation from that state, was planning to second Jesse Jones' nomination.

I said that before anything happened he should talk to my husband. I went directly to the hotel where Jim Farley had his office and called Franklin. I told him what Jim had said. I also told him I had just learned he had not talked to Jim and I suggested that he talk to him and tell him how he felt. I expressed no preference for any candidate; and I think the account of the convention which Jim Farley gave in his book, as far as my part is concerned, was his impression of what I said rather than what I actually said. He quoted me as saying to my husband: "I've been talking to Jim Farley and I agree with him, Henry Wallace won't do. I know, Franklin, but Jesse Jones would bolster up the ticket, win it business support and get the party contributions." Jim Farley had said these things to me and I repeated carefully what he had said, but I never expressed a preference or an opinion on matters of this kind, and I am sure I did not change my habits on this occasion.

When Jim Farley got on the telephone, my husband evidently told him that Mr. Wallace was the person he wanted. Jim argued with him rather halfheartedly and Franklin finally said it must be Wallace. He felt that Wallace could be trusted to carry out our policies on foreign affairs if by chance he, Wallace, found himself hurled into the Presidency. Franklin's feeling then was so strong that he was willing to insist on his running mate and thereby give him a chance to prove his ability. It was then that Jim Farley said: "You're the boss. If you say so, I will do all I can to nominate Wallace, but I will have to work fast." He turned to me and said he would have to get hold of Elliott, because he was about to second the nomination of Jesse Jones, that Paul McNutt was strong too, and we would have to get to the Convention Hall as quickly as possible. We drove there immediately and I could see that Jim was much disturbed.

As soon as we got to the Convention Hall he turned me over to Frances Perkins and Lorena Hickok, and disappeared. I went to my seat immediately, got hold of Franklin Junior and told him to find Elliott, because I was most anxious that he should not nominate anyone and so appear to be in opposition to his father's desires. Elliott came over and we talked for a minute, and I found that Jim Farley had already reached him with the information, so he did no nominating.

I saw Ed Flynn and a number of other people walking about, and many of them spoke to me briefly. Suddenly in the midst of the turmoil and confusion, Frank Walker came over to me and said: "We think now is the time for you to speak."

I made up my mind that what I said would be brief. I had prepared nothing, but I decided to base my short speech on the conversation I had heard in the hotel. If Franklin felt that the strain of a third term might be too much for any man and that Mr. Wallace was the man who could carry on best in times such as we were facing, he was entitled to have his help; no one should think of himself but only of the job that might have to be done.

The only way to accomplish my aim was to persuade the delegations in the convention to sink all personal interests in the interests of the country and to make them realize the potential danger in the situation we were facing. While I spoke there was complete silence. It was striking after the pandemonium that had existed.

Then the balloting began. Franklin Junior and I kept tallies on the roll calls, and for a while Mr. Wallace did not do well. The convention was decidedly out of order; the galleries were packed with special groups favoring different candidates, and confusion was rampant. Word began to get around, however, that Mr. Wallace was to be the candidate. Mrs. Wallace sat beside me. I doubt if she had ever tried to follow a roll call before. She looked very unhappy and asked: "Why do you suppose they are so opposed to Henry?" I did not have time to explain that probably most of the people had been sent in purposely to demonstrate for someone else.

As soon as Henry Wallace's nomination as Franklin's running mate was announced, I left Convention Hall, asking Mrs. Wallace to congratulate her husband for me. I drove directly back to the airfield and got on the plane. As we started to taxi down the field someone waved frantically. We stopped and I was told to come back, that my husband was on the telephone. He told me that he had listened to my speech and that I had done a very good job. Harry Hopkins was on another wire, waiting to speak to me, and he said practically the same thing. Then I dashed back to the plane and we took off.

The next morning my car was waiting for me at LaGuardia Field and I drove straight to Hyde Park, where I found myself in time for a nine-o'clock breakfast. I felt as though it had all been a dream with a somewhat nightmarish tinge. I had to come down to earth quickly, however, and write my daily column just as though the past eighteen hours had not seemed the longest I had ever lived through.

When Franklin and I next met we talked the whole thing over. I told him that he should not leave Jim so uninformed, that I realized that the rift had become deep and that he had simply hated to call him. Franklin always insisted, however, that Harry Hopkins had had no headquarters and no official authority. Harry had simply gone ahead and acted on his own. I believe it was one of those occasions when Franklin kept hands off because to act was so disagreeable to him; only when he was forced to act did he do so. My going out, talking to Jim, and calling Franklin forced him to say definitely what he wanted, but he never told me this in so many words, though on several occasions he said to others, "Her speech was just right."

All this was in July. The campaign really began in September. On

September 2 Franklin spoke at the Chickamauga Dam celebration, near Chattanooga, Tennessee.

The next day he announced the agreement to send Great Britain fifty of our over-age destroyers in exchange for naval and air bases in Newfoundland and the West Indies; and about two weeks later, on September 16, he signed the Selective Service Act.

Then I began to feel that war was close. Elliott had already enlisted. He had had some aviation training and hoped to get into the Air Force. His eyes were bad but a new kind of lens, which he had acquired, enabled him to take off and land an airplane, and he had his civilian pilot's license.

A little while later he was commissioned captain and sent to Wright Field. Inevitably, he was attacked in the 1940 campaign because he had been made a captain. It was one of the many issues used by the opposition in the hope of defeating Franklin. It always seemed unfair to me that Elliott should have to suffer because his father decided to run for a third term, but fairness does not enter into political strategy. Franklin and I had long since learned to accept such personal attacks; but Elliott was bitter, because he saw other people appointed to the same rank in exactly the same way, frequently with less background and fewer qualification than he had.

I resented criticisms of this kind deeply for him and for our other children, but it is useless to resent anything; one must learn to look on whatever happens as part of one's education and make it serve a good purpose. At the same time I could be amused at the attacks on me personally, especially the large campaign buttons announcing "We don't want Eleanor either," which many women wore.

Neither Franklin nor I ever minded the disagreeable things my cousin Alice Longworth used to say during the various campaigns. When the social season started after the third campaign, in which she had been particularly outspoken, she was invited as usual to the diplomatic reception. General Watson, Franklin's aide, wondered if she would have the face to come; in fact, he was sure she would not. Franklin was equally sure that she would be there, so he and Pa Watson made a bet on it. On the night of the reception, when Alice was announced, Franklin looked at Pa with a grin, and said in a loud voice: "Pa, you lose!"

It was during this campaign that the "guru letters" were brought to light and there was great excitement about the chance of their being used against Mr. Wallace. I did not know Henry Wallace well, but my feeling was that he had simply been carried away by his intellectual curiosity. He was not realistic enough to appreciate how these letters would look to people who did not have the same kind of curiosity.

When it came to Mr. Wallace's renomination in 1944, the men who went out through the country to get the feeling of the people reported back that there was a strong belief that Wallace was too impractical to help the ticket. Franklin's faith in Wallace was shaken by that time, anyway; he said that Wallace had had his chance to make his mark, and since he had not been able to convince the party leaders that he was the right person for the job, it was not possible to dictate again who was to be the candidate. Franklin had a fatalistic feeling that if there was work for him to do he would be here to do it. If not, he believed the leaders should have a man of their own choice with whom to carry on.

Franklin had intended to make no speeches in this campaign except over the radio, but he finally was persuaded to make a few. He liked Wendell Willkie very much; he never felt the bitterness toward him that he felt toward some of his other opponents, and I do not remember his ever saying anything derogatory of him in private conversation. I myself thought Mr. Willkie courageous and sincere, and I liked the way he stood for certain principles.

Franklin was always fairly confident of success, though he said one could never be sure until the votes were counted. However, this was the election he was least certain of winning, not only because Mr. Willkie was a strong candidate but because he thought the third term issue would be a greater hurdle than it proved to be. As usual, I wanted him to win, since that was what he wanted, and I would have been sorry for his sake if he had been defeated. I knew, though, that if he lost he would go on living a good and full life, for he was a philosophical person who accepted and made the best of whatever happened.

Twenty-two

The Coming of War: 1941

IN FEBRUARY, 1941, the Grand Duchess of Luxembourg came to stay and we had the customary parties. In that month, too, Harry Hopkins was sent to England to maintain personal contact between Franklin and the British government, for Ambassador Kennedy was about to resign and the new ambassador had not been appointed. I recalled Harry's disgust with some of our career diplomats during a previous trip to observe living conditions in various European countries. He had said to me on his return: "They are so busy socially that they haven't time to find out anything about working or agricultural conditions."

Mr. Willkie came to see my husband one day and the household was so anxious to get a glimpse of him while he sat waiting in Franklin's study on the second floor of the White House that suddenly many people had errands that took them down the hall. I would have gone myself, but I didn't hear of his visit until Franklin told me of it later.

June was a difficult month, because Missy LeHand was taken ill, the beginning of her long, last illness. However, life in the White House had to go on just the same. On the 17th, Crown Princess Juliana of the Netherlands and her husband, Prince Bernhard, came to stay, and through the summer we had a number of other visitors, including, in August, the Duke of Kent and, in October, Lord and Lady Mountbatten. Later, the Duke and Duchess of Windsor came to lunch with my husband, though I had to be away to keep a long-standing engagement.

Early in August my husband, after many mysterious consultations, told me that he was going to take a little trip up through the Cape Cod Canal and that he wished to do some fishing. Then he smiled and I knew he was not telling me all that he was going to do.

221

I had already learned never to ask questions when information was not volunteered, and it became almost an obsession with me as the war went on. Because I saw a great many people I might let something slip that should not be told, so I used to beg my husband to tell me no secrets. Many times it was impossible not to know something was afoot, but if I made no effort to find out what, my knowledge was pretty vague.

Franklin invited some friends to go with him for the first few days of this Cape Cod cruise, and the trip was well covered in the news. He was seen by crowds of people from the shores of the canal and then—blank! Later he loved to tell the story of how he changed from the presidential yacht to the U.S.S. *Augusta*, which steamed up the coast and into the harbor of Argentia, where he met Prime Minister Churchill.

The story of that meeting has been told often and Franklin Junior and Elliott, who were there, could describe their part in it far better than I. To both boys the meeting with their father came as a pleasant surprise. Elliott had been doing exciting work. After he enlisted he had been sent to Wright Field for training and then assigned to a group going to Gander Lake Field. Because he was in that area, he was ordered to Argentia in August when his father and Prime Minister Churchill met to discuss the Atlantic Charter. Elliott had no idea why he was being hauled off the job he was on and sent to Argentia, and when he saw all the ships lying in the harbor he was a most surprised young man.

The same surprise awaited Franklin Junior. Being in the Naval Reserve, he had been called into the Navy before we were in the war and was executive officer on a destroyer, convoying merchant ships to England, and a most unpleasant job it was. It can be very cold in the North Atlantic in late winter and the early spring, so he had been beseeching all the family to send him warm clothes, and told tales of coming into Portland, Maine, practically encased in ice. Because of this duty, however, his ship had the good luck to be assigned to guard the President and the prime minister. Arriving in Argentia, he received word that he was to report to the commander in chief on board such-and-such a ship. He was considerably uneasy and thought to himself: "Now, what have I done?" It never occurred to him that the commander in chief was not Admiral King, so when he walked on board and saw his father it was a pleasant surprise and a great relief.

On his return, Franklin seemed happy that the Atlantic Charter had been agreed upon and announced and that he and Mr. Churchill had had the chance to begin to know and to like each other. He had met Mr. Churchill before, but had not really known him. He felt that this meeting had broken the ice and said he knew now that Churchill, who he thought was typical of John Bull, was a man with whom he could really work.

The fact that he had pulled off the trip without being discovered gave him a keen sense of satisfaction. He used to chuckle as he told of the presidential yacht sailing quietly through the Cape Cod Canal for a whole day with a gentleman more or less like Franklin in size, wearing a cap pulled well down over his eyes, sitting on the deck waving.

As the years went on, I was more and more careful to know as few secrets as possible, and Miss Thompson, whose office was off the main hall near the elevator on the second floor, became practically a recluse, making it a point to tell everybody that she knew nothing about my husband's business.

Even in my press conferences I established the fairly well-understood pattern that affairs of state were not in my bailiwick but were dealt with by my husband in his news conferences. Occasionally, when I was asked for my personal opinion on some matter I would give it, and later I would be told that a good correspondent could not afford to miss my press conferences because I often foreshadowed my husband's point of view. As a matter of fact, Franklin and I would rarely have discussed the subject, and only when it was one on which I felt justified in expressing my own point of view did I answer questions on affairs of state. I suppose long association makes people think along the same lines on certain subjects, so these coincidences were not so very extraordinary.

After he came back from Argentia, Franklin was increasingly busy; but fortunately he decided to go to Hyde Park for the weekend of September 4, because his mother, who had seemed to pick up after her return from Campobello and to be well again except for a slight cold, took a turn for the worse. On September 7 she died. It was a great sorrow to my husband. There was a close bond between them in spite of the fact that he had grown away from her in some ways and that in later years they had often not been in sympathy about policies on public affairs.

Franklin's mother had always wanted to die in her own room at Hyde

Park, and to be buried simply in the churchyard, with the men who had worked for her on the place for many years carrying the casket. Her wishes were carefully observed.

The same night that my mother-in-law was dying, my brother Hall, who had a little house not far from my cottage at Hyde Park, was taken ill. We took him to Vassar Hospital in Poughkeepsie, and the day of my mother-in-law's funeral I had him moved to Walter Reed Hospital in Washington at his insistence. Having been there for treatments made necessary by his service in World War I, he wished to go back to the same doctors.

As soon as we could, after my mother-in-law's funeral was over, we returned to the White House, and the next few weeks I spent watching my brother die. He was so strong that his heart kept him alive long after most people would have peacefully sunk into oblivion, and now and then he would recognize me when I went into his room. On September 25 he died, and the funeral was held in the White House. Franklin and I took his body to Tivoli, New York, to be buried in the Hall family vault there.

The loss of a brother is always a sad breaking of a family tie, but in the case of my brother it was like losing a child. He had come to live with us when we were first married and from then on Franklin and I had been his closest family; whatever happened to him, in spite of his great desire for independence, he always came to us. I had watched with great anxiety a fine mind gradually deteriorate. He had such a strong physique that he was sure he could always regain his self-control, even though he voluntarily relaxed it for a while. You could never convince him that it is hard to shake a habit you have once let get hold of you.

Fundamentally, I think Hall always lacked self-control. He had great energy, great physical strength, and great brilliance of mind but he never learned self-discipline. Whenever his responsibilities became irksome he tended to thrust them aside and to feel that it was unfair that he should be asked to make any concessions to circumstances that he did not wish to make. As a result of this attitude, his first marriage went on the rocks. While there were undoubtedly many contributing factors, I always felt that a major one was his lack of discipline and his unwillingness to compromise or make adjustments in the light of other people's needs. In fact, he saw only with great difficulty any point of view but his own and then only when his respect for a person's strength of character was deeper than his instinctive desire to attain his particular objective.

As I look back on the life of this man whom I dearly loved, who never reached the heights he was capable of reaching, I cannot help having a great sense of sorrow for him, knowing that he must often have felt deeply frustrated and disappointed by his own failure to use the wonderful gifts that were his.

Sorrow in itself and the loss of someone whom you love is hard to bear, but when sorrow is mixed with regret and a consciousness of waste there is added a touch of bitterness which is even more difficult to carry, day in and day out. I think it was in an attempt to numb this feeling that I worked so hard at the Office of Civilian Defense that fall.

On September 22, a few days before Hall died, I agreed to take charge for Mayor LaGuardia of the activities that were not strictly defense activities but allied and necessary for the protection of the civilian population as a whole.

Elinor Morgenthau volunteered to work as my assistant. I soon found that every activity which Mayor LaGuardia did not want in his part of the program was thrust into my division. His work as mayor of New York City prevented him from giving his full time to organizing civilian defense. The few group meetings we had left me with the impression of great hurry and a feeling that decisions were taken which had not been carefully thought out. Frequently heads of divisions, including myself, were unable to discuss with him some of the things we hoped to get settled. The mayor was more interested in the dramatic aspects of civilan defense, such as whether or not cities had good fire-fighting equipment, than in such things as building morale.

One day, while I was staying in my small apartment on 11th Street in New York, I invited Mr. LaGuardia to luncheon with me, for there was something I particularly wanted to talk with him about. I planned a simple lunch, but in the midst of the preparations my maid, who had worked with me off and on for years, went to Miss Thompson completely upset and said she could not cook for the mayor. Miss Thompson reminded her that she had cooked for the President and that the mayor was an easy person to please.

After lunch the mayor, as he was leaving, said: "My wife never asks me where I have been nor whom I have seen, but she always asks me what I have had to eat. Today, I can truthfully say I did not have too much!"

I put in many hours every day at the Office of Civilian Defense, carrying on my own work at home by toiling every night. In the White House someone makes the rounds every hour to see that all is well. One morning my husband said: "What's this I hear? You didn't go to bed at all last night?" I had been working on my mail without regard to time, and when it began to get light, I decided it was not worthwhile going to bed. The man patrolling the house had seen my light under the door, heard me moving about and had reported it to the household, and someone told my husband. I did not do that very often, however.

I soon discovered that the thing I had feared was true! I could not take a government position, even without salary or paid expenses, without giving ample opportunity for faultfinding to some members of the opposition in Congress and even to some of our own party people who disagreed with certain policies. I did not much mind what they said about me, but when I found that anyone I appointed was in trouble merely because I appointed him, I did mind.

I hope that, despite these troubles, at least the trip I made with Mayor LaGuardia the night after Pearl Harbor was helpful. If I was able to give impetus to the work on the West Coast and, by the mere fact of going out there, to quiet many of the rather hysterical fears prevalent at that time, then the country benefited and the trip justified my short term of office in the OCD.

Pearl Harbor day began quietly. We were expecting a large party for luncheon and I was disappointed but not surprised when Franklin sent word a short time before lunch that he did not see how he could join us. He had been increasingly worried and frequently at the last moment would tell me that he could not come to some large gathering that had been arranged. The fact that he carried so many secrets in his head made it necessary for him to watch everything he said, which in itself was exhausting. In addition, anxiety as well as the dampness had made his sinus bad, which necessitated daily treatments of his nose. I always worried about this constant treatment, for I felt that, while it might help temporarily, in the long run it must cause irritation. Sometimes Franklin decided to eat alone in his study, sometimes he had Harry Hopkins or a secretary eat with him, or some person with whom he wished to talk privately.

Harry Hopkins ate with Franklin in the study that day and there were thirty-one of us at lunch. By the time lunch was over the news had come of the attack on Pearl Harbor, but we did not hear it until we went up-stairs, when one of the ushers told me. The information was so stunning that there was complete quiet, and we took up our next occupation in a kind of vacuum. I saw my guests off, and waited till Franklin was alone to slip into his study, but I realized he was concentrating on what had to be done and would not talk about what had happened until this first strain was over. So I went back to work.

A few minutes after three o'clock the secretaries of war and navy, Admiral Beardall, my husband's naval aide, secretaries McIntyre and Early, and Grace Tully were all in Franklin's study on the second floor of the White House. They were soon joined by General Marshall and the secretary of state. Later, when my husband and I did have a chance to talk, I thought that in spite of his anxiety Franklin was in a way more serene than he had appeared for a long time. It was steadying to know that the die was cast. One could no longer do anything but face the fact that this country was in a war; from here on, difficult and dangerous as the future looked, it presented a clearer challenge than had the long uncertainty of the past.

The next day was a busy one for us all. I went to the Civilian Defense Office that morning at nine o'clock as usual, but came back to the White House shortly before twelve to go with my husband to the Capitol to hear him deliver his message to a joint session of Congress. I was living through again, it seemed to me, the day when President Wilson addressed the Congress to announce our entry into World War I. Now the President of the United States was my husband, and for the second time in my life I heard a president tell the Congress that this nation was engaged in a war. I was deeply unhappy. I remembered my anxieties about my husband and brother when World War I began; now I had four sons of military age.

It was a very impressive occasion, one of those occasions when a spirit of unity and strength prevailed. There was no criticism—only an acceptance of the fact that something had happened to us which, as a nation, we had to face.

We knew that the Pearl Harbor attack had set us back a long way, that before us stretched endless months of building up our forces. We might have to retreat, because we had been a peace-loving people and as a nation had not wanted to prepare for war. We had been denied the wherewithal to fortify our islands in the Pacific by people who backed their representatives in Congress in the feeling that Japan did not want war with us. Many believed that only our insistence on preparation for war would force Japan to make war on us. The mistakes of those who thought that way are obvious today, but before Pearl Harbor they were not so obvious, and many patriotic people honestly believed that Japan was not planning war on us. The war in China was far away, and they thought that was all the Japanese were interested in. They did not realize that we were an obstacle to the fulfillment of the Japanese schemes for complete domination in the Pacific.

In retrospect, it is easy to see things that were obscure at the time. My husband had long suspected that these Japanese dreams of grandeur and domination existed. I remember his concern about Guam and the other islands of the Pacific as far back as when he was assistant secretary of the navy. His suspicion of Japan was based on his own ideas of what made the Pacific safe for us, and in all the war games in the Pacific Japan was always the enemy. But anyone who dared to voice such suspicion would immediately have been called a warmonger. After Franklin's message to Congress, war was a grim reality to the whole country.

From the Capitol I went straight back to the Civilian Defense Office and stayed there most of the afternoon. I got home at a quarter before six and Miss Thompson and I were at the Washington airport at ten minutes past seven, ready to start with Mayor LaGuardia to the West Coast. As I was leaving, I had a glimpse of Elliott, who arrived to make an overnight stop at the White House. He was taking training in navigation and was on a final flight before graduation. The course had been speeded up because of the war. Immediately after that, Elliot went on patrol duty on the West Coast.

Miss Thompson and I were still working in a small forward compartment on the plane when they brought me a message that had been received by the pilots: a San Francisco paper had announced that the city of San Francisco was being bombed by the Japanese. I was asked to tell Mr. LaGuardia. Just before our next landing I awakened him, and he put his head out of the curtains, looking for all the world like a Kewpie. When I gave him the message, he asked me to get off when we landed and telephone the Washington airport for verification, saying: "If it is true, we will go direct to San Francisco." It was so characteristic of him that I glowed inwardly. One could be exasperated with him at times, but one had to admire his integrity and courage. I telephoned and found that it was a rumor without verification, so I went back to the plane and the mayor decided we should continue to Los Angeles.

As we proceeded we began to receive instructions. First the pilot had orders to land us at Palm Springs, but finally we were allowed to land at an almost completely deserted airport in Los Angeles. There everything was shrouded in mystery, since most airline travel had been stopped.

Mayor LaGuardia had a field day talking to everybody about fire-fighting equipment and defense preparation. As he could not go down to San Diego, I left him in Los Angeles and went without him; it meant that he was ahead of me the rest of the trip, so I got the full impact of his visits on all the officials. His complete courage and lack of fear had a wonderful effect on everyone, but I did not know and never have known how much all our plans, both his and mine, really helped, since so much equipment was lacking that they could not do many of the things that were considered essential. He did get the organizing of doctors and medical supplies started and he did a great deal to spur the reorganizing of fire departments. I talked about the other activities, going up as far as Seattle on this trip. I worked all day and traveled to my next stop by night train since no planes were flying after dark. It was a queer sensation to be on a train with all the lights concealed—even the headlight on the locomotive was dimmed—and no lights to be seen outside.

I was back in Washington on December 15. I had been gone seven days and had traveled and worked unceasingly. That same afternoon Elinor Morgenthau and Justice Justine Polier, Betty Lindley and Anna Rosenberg, all of whom were helping Elinor, came to give me the latest news of the OCD from the office front. We discussed plans and policies and then some gossip, but I was getting hardened to gossip. Never did I have a more unfavorable press than at that time, but I did not give it much thought. I knew someday I would be out of it and if it did Franklin no harm, I had no feelings about it for myself. Franklin stayed serene and untroubled through it all.

There was gossip, too, about Harry living in the White House. Some people felt that since he had not been elected to any office he should not live there at government expense. They never seemed to understand that all the food eaten in the White House is paid for by the President and that therefore Harry was no added expense to the taxpayers.

And Harry did indeed do all—and more—that Franklin expected of him.

Once the war was started and he grasped the seriousness of the situation, he put the running of the war ahead of everything else. As far as he was concerned, war needs were paramount. My husband felt the same. I, however, could not help feeling that it was the New Deal social objectives that had fostered the spirit that would make it possible for us to fight this war, and I believed it was vastly important to give people the feeling that in fighting the war we were still fighting for these same objectives. It was obvious that if the world were ruled by Hitler, freedom and democracy would no longer exist. I felt it was essential both to the prosecution of the war and to the period after the war that the fight for the rights of minorities should continue.

I wanted to see us go on with our medical program not only in the field of military medicine but in the whole area which concerned children and young people. I thought the groundwork should be laid for a wide health program after the war. Harry Hopkins could not be bothered. He felt that money could not be diverted to anything which did not have a direct bearing on the fighting of the war. He was probably right, but I never could entirely agree with him.

After the Pearl Harbor attack, all activity in the White House centered more than ever on preparations for war. The Supply Priorities and Allocation Board began its meetings, and Franklin had more and more appointments with the military people and with people like Mrs. Anna Rosenberg, who was one of his close links with labor. Next to military operations, labor was the most important consideration in our preparation for war.

The Russian ambassador came on two occasions to see my husband; and Crown Princess Marta of Norway, who must have been deeply troubled through all those days, came to gain reassurance and talk over the situation.

Meanwhile I continued working at the Office of Civilian Defense, organizing a youth division. I also tried unsuccessfully to get the Cabinet wives to take some responsibility for the hordes of girls pouring into Washington to work in the various departments.

The whole OCD episode was unfortunate. I had been reluctant to take the job and had done so only at the insistence of Harry Hopkins and another of my husband's advisers. Franklin himself was neutral, though he told me he thought it would help Mayor LaGuardia. When the mayor found what a controversial person I became he was appalled at having me; and I did not blame him for disclaiming any responsibility for the "dreadful" things that some members of Congress felt I had done. After the mayor resigned from the OCD I was instrumental in obtaining his successor. The mounting wave of attack in Congress finally convinced me that I was not going to be able to do a real job in the OCD, so on February 20, I, too, resigned, leaving Judge Landis a prickly problem which he handled well.

It is history that as soon as Prime Minister Winston Churchill heard of the Pearl Harbor attack he made up his mind to come to the United States. His trip was top secret and none of us knew until shortly before he arrived that he was coming.

A few days before his visit, my husband sent for Miss Thompson and asked her whom I had invited to stay in the house over Christmas. He also asked to see the list of people invited to dinner. In all the years that we had been in the White House he had never paid much attention to such details, and this was the first time he had made such a request. He gave no explanation and no hint that anything unusual was going to happen.

When we learned that Mr. Churchill was coming on December 22, everyone scurried around to get ready. The Monroe Room on the second floor had to be turned into a map room and an office for the British delegation, and we shifted beds around to make room for all our Christmas guests.

My husband, on that memorable day of December 22, saw the Russian ambassador, the Chinese ambassador, and the Dutch minister, besides filling innumerable other engagements. He left shortly before six in the evening to meet the British prime minister, and they all arrived at the White House at six-thirty. We had quite a houseful, but it represented only a small quota of those who came over with Mr. Churchill.

I had been asked by Franklin to have tea ready in the West Hall for our British guests, but I found on their arrival that they preferred more stimulating refreshments. We were seventeen at dinner that night. I had come back to Washington that morning on the night train from New York City and had spent a good part of the day at the Office of Civilian Defense. I had gone to the Salvation Army Christmas party, to a Catholic Charities Christmas party, and the Alley Christmas tree programs, so I had added a good deal to the already heavy official program of the day. I still remember that as time wore on that evening I caught myself falling asleep as I tried to talk to my guests.

On this visit of Mr. Churchill's, as on all his subsequent visits, my husband worked long hours every day. The prime minister took a long nap every afternoon, so was refreshed for hard work in the evening and far into the night. While he was sleeping, Franklin had to catch up on his regular work. Even after he finally retired, if important dispatches or messages came in, he was awakened, no matter what the hour, and nearly every meal he was called on the telephone for some urgent matter. It always took him several days to catch up on sleep after Mr. Churchill left.

A number of people have accused me at various times of having no sense of propriety, because frequently I had what they called unimportant people to meet important ones. Throughout the war years the comings and goings of official people was shrouded in mystery, and it was never as simple as it now sounds to make arrangements for them. They arrived and they left suddenly, and none of us were warned beforehand. This often accounted for my having conflicting engagements and for the presence of people whom I might not have invited had I known in advance what was going to happen.

During this first visit of the British prime minister I had invited Mr. and Mrs. Louis Adamic, Monroe Robinson, my cousin, and several others to dinner on January 13. Of course, when I invited them I had no idea that Mr. Churchill would be there. After dinner I took Mr. and Mrs. Adamic, Monroe Robinson and Miss Thompson to the Philadelphia concert, and the evening seemed to me of casual interest.

The reason for asking Mr. and Mrs. Adamic was that I had read a book of his, *Two-Way Passage*, which I thought interesting. Because I was always looking for new points of view to interest my husband, I had given him the book to read.

No one was more surprised than I when Mr. Adamic wrote a book, *Dinner at the White House*, based on this occasion. He seemed to think every smallest detail of the evening had some particular significance or meaning behind it. It was the supreme example of how much can be made of how little. In the book Mr. Adamic repeated a story which was most derogatory to the British prime minister; in fact, the whole book was anti-British and anti-Churchill. Mr. Churchill hotly resented it and sued Mr. Adamic in Great Britain, where the libel laws are somewhat different from ours. Of course, Mr. Adamic to the contrary, the whole evening had been a completely casual affair.

In these first talks which my husband and the prime minister had, they faced the fact that there was a long drawn-out war ahead during which there would be many setbacks, and that both of them, as leaders of their nations, would have to be prepared to bolster the morale of their people. To explain to one's country that there must be a long period while the military forces are being trained and armed, during which production will be one of the most important factors, and that meanwhile people must be patient and hope at best to hold the line is no easy or popular thing to do.

I always had great admiration for the way in which Mr. Churchill did this. In some ways he was more blunt with the people of Great Britain than my husband ever was with us. The British people were closer to the danger and I suppose for that reason could better understand the blunt approach.

Twenty-three

Visit to England

IN RETROSPECT, the thing that strikes me about these days is my triple-barreled effort to work with the OCD, carry out my official engagements, and still keep the home fires burning. I wonder particularly how I ever managed to get in all the trips I took. At the same time my husband was having more and more meetings with the Cabinet, military advisers, foreign diplomats and labor people. In one morning he saw Major General Joseph W. Stilwell, the Greek minister, and David Dubinsky.

The list of White House guests was interestingly varied during the first half of 1942. It seems to me that everyone we were to know well during the next few years began coming at about that time; and all the royal families whose countries had been overrun sooner or later appeared, looking for assistance. Each was given a formal dinner; whatever else they got, of course, I do not know.

One of the most interesting and peculiar visitors was Alexander Woollcott, who came to the White House in January and spent four days with us. I doubt if it would have been possible to have had Mr. Woollcott as one's guest very long in any ordinary household, because he required a good many things that the ordinary household could not easily provide. For instance, he wanted coffee at all hours, and he invited guests for meals in his bedroom or in a sitting room where he could be alone with them. My work and my engagements kept me away from the house a good part of the time, but late one afternoon I returned just as he was leaving for an engagement. As I came in the door he said: "Welcome, Mrs. Roosevelt, come right in. I am delighted to see you. Make yourself at home."

Among our other guests in 1942 were Prime Minister Mackenzie King, President and Señora Quezon. In May Foreign Minister Molotov came,

234

accompanied by his interpreter, Mr. Pavlov. I was not at home when they arrived so he was given a stag dinner, but the following morning Mr. Molotov came into my sitting room with Mr. Pavlov, to have a talk with me. He talked about social reforms in his country and in mine, and he hoped that I would some day visit the U.S.S.R. I had already been told of an incident that had caused much quiet amusement. One of the White House valets was astounded when he unpacked Mr. Molotov's bag to find inside a large chunk of black bread, a roll of sausage and a pistol. The Secret Service men did not like visitors with pistols, but on this occasion nothing was said. Mr. Molotov evidently thought he might have to defend himself, and also that he might be hungry.

I liked him and I was impressed by Mr. Pavlov's English, which, he told me, he had learned from American students in Russia. He must have been gifted with a good ear, for he had no accent. I think Mr. Molotov, too, could understand English, for he often began to answer questions without waiting for the translation.

The King of Greece was with us on June 10, and on the 14th there was an impressive Flag Day ceremony in the state dining room of the White House, at which the secretary of state and the diplomatic representatives of twenty-seven other nations were present.

I spent a good deal of time in New York City that spring, emptying our house and Mrs. James Roosevelt's. We had lived in these houses since 1908 and one can imagine the accumulation of the years. My mother-in-law never threw anything away. It was a tremendous job.

Mr. Churchill was with us again from the 21st to the 25th of June. The friendship and affection between my husband and Mr. Churchill grew with every visit. It was evident that Great Britain and the United States would have to co-operate in any case, but the war could be carried on to better advantage with the two nations closely united through the personal friendship of Mr. Churchill and my husband. The two men had many interests in common, in addition to the paramount issue of the war. They were men who loved the sea and the Navy. They knew a great deal of history and had somewhat similar tastes in literature. Both of them had read much biography. Their companionship grew, I think, with their respect for each other's ability.

I remember the day Tobruk fell. Mr. Churchill was with us when the news came, and though he was stricken, his immediate reaction was to say, "Now what do we do?" To neither of these men was there such a thing as not being able to meet a new situation. I never heard either of them say that ultimately we would not win the war. This attitude was contagious, and no one around either of them would ever have dared to say, "I am afraid."

Franklin knew and understood Mr. Churchill's background. He seemed to agree when I said on one occasion that I thought the time that would be hardest for Mr. Churchill would be after the war. The world that had existed before the war had been pleasant as far as he was concerned; his tendency would be to want to go back to it, even though he might realize that there was no way in which one could go back to a prewar world.

My husband often said he felt sure Mr. Churchill would retire from office after the war ended, but I gathered that he expected that he and Mr. Churchill and Mr. Stalin would still be in office for at least a short time afterward and have something to say about the policies laid down. He felt that the world was going to be considerably more socialistic after the war and that Mr. Churchill might find it difficult to adjust to new conditions. A remark made to him by Mr. Stalin in one of their talks gave him hope that there might be, after the war, more flexibility in Communism than we actually have seen so far.

Franklin had been wondering aloud what would happen in their respective countries if anything happened to any of the three men. Stalin said: "I have everything arranged in my country. I know exactly what will happen." My husband said: "So much depends in the future on how we learn to get along together. Do you think it will be possible for the United States and the U.S.S.R. to see things in similar ways?" Mr. Stalin responded: "You have come a long way in the United States from your original concept of government and its responsibilities, and your original way of life. I think it is quite possible that we in the U.S.S.R., as our resources develop and people can have an easier life, will find ourselves growing nearer to some of your concepts and you may be finding yourselves accepting some of ours."

This, of course, was casual conversation, and I give it as I remember hearing my husband repeat it. It encouraged him to believe that confidence could be built between the leaders and that we might find a way to live in the world together, each country developing along the lines that seemed best for it.

My husband had great confidence in his own ability to understand others and to make them understand our motives and the needs and realities of a situation. One of his reasons for being willing to meet with the heads of other nations outside the country, when they were unwilling to come here, was his feeling that he could convince them better by personal contact than by letter or telephone. I think Franklin accepted what other men in high office said, and believed that if he kept his word they would keep theirs. But he was never prone to overlook a breach of contract.

I shall never cease to be grateful to Mr. Churchill for his leadership during the war; his speeches were a tonic to us here in the United States as well as to his own people. The real affection which he had for my husband, and which was reciprocated, he apparently never lost. It was a fortunate friendship. The war would have been harder to win without it, and the two men might not have gone through it so well if they had not had personal pleasure in meeting and confidence in each other's integrity and ability.

The day before Mr. Churchill left in June, 1942, young King Peter of Yugoslavia came to the White House and afterwards Franklin said to me: "That young man should forget that he is a king and go to work. In the long run, he would be better off." I think of that now when I see him with his wife and child. Waiting around for a throne is not really a satisfactory business.

That spring we had Crown Princess Marta and her children and household at Hyde Park. During the war she usually spent a week or more with us each spring and autumn on her way to some place for the summer or back to Washington for the winter. We came, for that reason, to know them all very well and I shall never forget some of the things I learned about the bringing up of royal children. Prince Harald seemed devoid of fear, and though he was frail when he first came, I can remember his swimming when the water was extremely cold. I thought he ought to come out and get warm, but I was told that the water in Norway was colder and that he must become accustomed to the cold.

The names of the people who came to see me that year recall a great many activities. One of the guests who gave my husband and me the greatest pleasure was John Golden, who always went to any amount of trouble to put on a performance or to find something he thought Franklin would enjoy. Franklin once told him that the first play he had ever seen was *The Black Crook,* which he had stolen away to see without the permission of his parents. John Golden found one of the original copies of the play and had it beautifully bound for him, which gave Franklin much real pleasure. He also did a tremendous amount of work for the servicemen, getting them free tickets for plays and movies, giving prizes for the best plays written by enlisted men, and putting on a show, the proceeds of which went to the Army and Navy Relief.

In August we had our first visit from Queen Wilhelmina of the Netherlands. My press conference ladies wanted to meet her, and she did attend one conference the morning after her arrival. During the course of the meeting she said something about the increase in tuberculosis in Holland under the Nazis, which she immediately afterwards regretted, fearing the Nazis would retaliate against her people. So I had to chase after the women and insist that everything the Queen had said about tuberculosis must be off the record.

This was Franklin's second meeting with the Queen of the Netherlands. The first had been when he called on her while she was staying with Princess Juliana in Massachusetts, not many miles from Hyde Park. Crown Princess Marta, who was staying with us at the time, went with him and she told with amusement how Franklin announced to the Queen that he had been nervous before meeting her because he had heard she was one of the most awesome of crowned heads. His respect for her increased with each meeting and both he and I came to have a warm affection for her.

The next event of real importance to me was my husband's decision that I should accept Queen Elizabeth's invitation to go to Great Britain to see the work the women were doing in the war and to visit our servicemen stationed there. I did not know that one of the reasons my husband was eager to have me go over was that those men would shortly be leaving for North Africa for the invasion.

Franklin had received some tentative inquiries about whether I would be interested in going over and seeing the role that the British women were playing in the war. Naturally the British looked upon my visit as providing an opportunity to get that story told in the United States, for the Queen, knowing I wrote a column and made speches fairly frequently, felt that I had access to the people here.

When my husband asked me how I would feel about going, I assured him that if he thought it might be helpful I should be delighted to go. Knowing that the North African invasion was coming off soon, he said that in addition to observing the work of the British women he wanted me to visit our servicemen and take them a message from him.

The trip to Great Britain seemed to offer me a chance to do something that might be useful. I asked Tommy if she would be willing to go with me, since I did not want to obligate her to make a trip that might entail some risk. She was entirely willing. I suppose the saving fact for all human beings at such times is that they never think anything is going to happen to them until it actually happens.

Before I left the United States, Harry Hopkins had told me not to pay too much attention to our ambassador, Mr. Winant, but to be sure to consult Averell Harriman on everything. I had known Mr. Winant for a long time and I had great respect and admiration for him, as did my husband. I made no answer to Harry's suggestion except to say that I had known Averell Harriman since he was a small boy because he had been an intimate friend and schoolmate of my brother's, so I certainly hoped to see him in London. I firmly determined, however, that I would consult Gilbert Winant and take his advice. I was sure that Averell Harriman would not have agreed with Harry, because he knew what a wonderful reputation Mr. Winant enjoyed with the British officials.

After Mr. Winant met us I was relieved of many anxieties. On the train we went over the proposed itinerary. I thought it was a bit strenuous, but later it was expanded to include much that I had never dreamed of doing. The itinerary had been gone over by the Queen and by Lady Reading, who was to take charge of me during a part of the visit. Mr. Winant would come for me the next morning; when we left the palace his apartment and maid would be at our disposal. I was not conscious of the need for protection, but both the prime minister and the ambassador felt I would be safer and have more privacy in his apartment than in a hotel.

I had been worried by the thought of having to visit Buckingham Palace, but I was determined to live each moment, aware of its special interest. Though certain situations might be unfamiliar and give me a feeling of inadequacy and of not knowing the proper way to behave, still I would do my best and not worry. Nevertheless, as we neared London I grew more and more nervous and wondered why on earth I had ever let myself be inveigled into coming on this trip.

Finally, we pulled into the station. The red carpet was unrolled and the stationmaster and the head guard on the train, both of them looking grand enough to be high officials of the government, told me that the moment to get off had arrived. There stood the King and Queen and all our high military officials. The only person in the whole group whom I felt I really knew was Stella Reading.

After the formal greetings, the King and Queen took me in their car, while Tommy was taken in hand by the lady in waiting and two gentlemen from the royal household, and we drove off to Buckingham Palace.

The King and Queen treated me with the greatest kindness. The feeling I had had about them during their visit to the United States, that they were simply a young and charming couple, who would have to undergo some very difficult experiences, began to come back to me, intensified by the realization that they now had been through these experiences and were anxious to tell me about them. In all my contacts with them I gained the greatest respect for both the King and the Queen. I did not always agree with the ideas expressed to me by the King on international subjects, but the fact that both of them were doing an extraordinarily outstanding job for their people in the most trying times stood out.

When we arrived at the palace they took me to my rooms, explaining that I could have only a small fire in my sitting room and one in the outer waiting room, and saying they hoped I would not be too cold. Through the windows they pointed out the shell holes. The windowpanes in my room had all been broken and replaced by wood and isinglas and one or two small panes of glass. Later the Queen showed me where a bomb had dropped right through the King's rooms, destroying both his rooms and hers. They explained the various layers of curtains which had to be kept closed when the lights were on; informed me that there would be a messenger outside my door to take me to the drawing room at the proper hour for dinner, and then left me to my own devices.

Buckingham Palace seemed perfectly enormous to me. The suite I had was so huge that when Elliott saw it he said that after this I would have to take the long corridor at the White House for my bedroom, because the one I had would never again seem adequate. The wardrobes were wonderful, the kind one longs for at home, but the 55-pound limit on baggage made my few clothes look pathetic hanging in those wardrobes. I wondered what the maid thought when she unpacked them. One evening dress, two day dresses, one suit and a few blouses, one pair of day shoes and one pair of evening shoes comprised my wardrobe for a visit to Buckingham Palace! One of the newspaperwomen, for want of something better to write about, later reported that I had worn the soles of my one pair of shoes through. The head usher at the White House read the story and thoughtfully sent me another pair.

Everything in Great Britain was done as one would expect it to be. The restrictions on heat and water and food were observed as carefully in the royal household as in any other home in England. There was a plainly marked black line in my bathtub above which I was not supposed to run the water. We were served on gold and silver plates, but our bread was the same kind of war bread every other family had to eat, and, except for the fact that occasionally game from one of the royal preserves appeared on the table, nothing was served in the way of food that was not served in any of the war canteens.

My visit to Great Britain was the beginning of a real friendship with Gil Winant. He was a shy person, but he had great intellectual integrity, a vivid imagination, which enabled him to understand situations that he had never experienced, and a sensitiveness to other people that enabled him to accomplish things many of his friends thought beyond his powers. He grew to love Great Britain and her people, and I think the statesmen who bore the brunt of the burdens during the war trusted and depended upon him.

I myself can never be grateful enough to him for the kindness with which he mapped out my trip and for the things he told me which helped me to carry out my task among the British people better than I might otherwise have done. He was a selfless person who gave little thought to his own comfort, but much thought to helping his friends. He made the time I spent in London both pleasant and comfortable. I shall always miss him, for he came to be one of the people that I looked forward to seeing from time to time. I cannot describe what it was he gave his friends. I do not even know that he considered me any more than an acquaintance, but I prized highly what he gave me; and I had a feeling that he shed light in dark places. He worked unceasingly in the hope of a better world for future generations.

With the King and Queen I had my first real look at the devastation—blocks upon blocks of rubble. Our first stop was at St. Paul's Cathedral, partly because the King and Queen wanted to give the faithful watchers who had saved the cathedral the satisfaction of a visit from them and partly so that I could stand on the steps and see what modern warfare could do to a great city.

I spent a weekend at Chequers, the country estate given by Lord Lee to the British government for the use of British prime ministers. There I watched Prime Minister Churchill playing a game on the floor with his grandson and noticed the extraordinary resemblance between the two. Mr. Churchill once remarked that his grandson didn't look like him, he just looked like all babies.

Mrs. Churchill was attractive and charming. One felt that being in public life she had to assume a role and that the role was now part of her. She was careful not to voice any opinions publicly or to be associated with any political organizations. Over the years, my admiration and affection for her have grown. She has had no easy role to play in life, but she has played it with dignity and charm.

For security reasons I had to have a code name, and someone with a sense of humor—I suspected my husband—had decided that "Rover" was appropriate. A hypothetical organization called "Rover's Rangers" had been organized by the young men at the United States embassy in London, with my husband as the "Starter."

After lunch one day we were scheduled to visit Elliott's unit at a place called Steeple Morden, but the chauffeur, who, for my protection, was a Scotland Yard man and not a regular driver, lost his way and we could not find the camp. No one who was asked would tell us how to get there— also for security reasons—so finally someone telephoned back to the United States embassy: "Rover has lost her pup" and asked for directions!

With Mrs. Churchill I went to visit a maternity hospital, and also to see how the women in the several branches of the military service were trained. During one of these visits, the air-raid warning sounded, but the girls went right on with what they were doing and paid no attention. I saw girls learning how to service every kind of truck and motorcar and to drive every type of vehicle; I even saw girls in gun crews, helping the men to load the guns. I visited factories in which women did every kind of work, and I visited one group of girls whose job it was to fly planes from one part of the country to another. Since it was unwise to keep a concentration of planes anywhere in Great Britain, these girls took over the plane when a pilot landed and flew it either to a place where it would be well camouflaged or to a repair shop.

At one time or another during this trip I visited Red Cross clubs of all types—our own American Red Cross, the British Red Cross, and St. John's Guild. At that time Harvey Gibson, the dynamic head of the Red Cross in Europe, was expanding its facilities in a remarkable manner, and though I occasionally heard that this or that particular club was doing something that my informant considered detrimental to the morale of the men or women, on the whole I thought the Red Cross was doing, in its recreation program at least, an outstanding job.

During this visit to England I started the practice, which I continued on subsequent trips, of collecting from the boys to whom I talked the names and addresses of their families, so that I could write to them on my return to the United States. I had quite a collection before I was through.

I also made a tour of the camps where our servicemen were stationed and ended it by spending one night with Queen Mary at Badminton. This was something that Franklin had particularly wanted me to do because King George V and Queen Mary had been kind to his mother when she visited England. He thought of Queen Mary as in some ways rather like his mother, and therefore made a point of my seeing her.

Here again I had the same sense of strain that I had felt before visiting Buckingham Palace. I was told that we must arrive at six o'clock—not five minutes before or five after, but at six sharp. To my surprise, Queen Mary met me at the door and took me to her sitting room, the only small room in that house, as far as I could see, and one which had a good fire. After a talk, she took me to my room, which, though cold and barnlike, was furnished grandly with Chinese Chippendale furniture. She showed me where the bathroom and the w.c. were, and they were cold too.

Tommy's room was as cold as mine. We dressed and went down to dinner, arriving in good time. At dinner I sat on the Queen's left, the princess royal on her right, the Duke and Duchess of Beaufort, the young relatives who owned Badminton, at either end of the table. General Knox, who seemed to manage the household, Lord Hamilton, gentleman in waiting to the Queen, and a lady in waiting completed the party.

After dinner, which was not a hilarious meal and during which I made valiant efforts at conversation, we went into the drawing room and stood for fifteen minutes. Queen Mary looked regal and every inch a queen, with many ropes of pearls and many sparkling bracelets and rings. She wore a black velvet evening gown and an ermine jacket. Then she asked me to her sitting room and also asked the princess royal if she wished to accompany us. Tommy was left with the others and soon escaped. I looked in on her when I was politely dismissed to go to bed, and found her already in bed because it was the only way to keep warm. However, I really enjoyed my visit and had a great admiration and real affection for Queen Mary after that.

She gave me, to bring back to Franklin, a photograph of herself, fully dressed with hat, veil and gloves, sawing a dead limb off a tree, with one of her dispatch riders, a young Australian, at the other end of the saw. She told me to tell my husband that she cared as much about the conservation of trees as he did and was sending him this photograph to prove it. Nothing I brought him from that trip gave him more pleasure than the photograph and the message, and he always felt that Queen Mary was a grand person.

Under Stella Reading's guidance I visited universities and innumerable factories, stayed on estates where the grounds were now being used for agricultural purposes and in country houses whose owners, now living in one small part of them, had turned them into nurseries for evacuated or wounded children. I saw the way the Women's Voluntary Services had organized to perform innumerable duties, from moving into a town which had just been bombed and needed everything from food to laundry service, to looking after the billeting of workers who had been moved from one factory to another.

Our days usually began at eight o'clock and ended at midnight, but I was so interested that at the time I did not even realize how weary I was gradually becoming. We wrote the column every day at whatever time we could fit it in, and sometimes in rooms so cold that Tommy's fingers would hardly work.

This was a nation at war, going through moments of great uncertainty and stress. But what I have often marveled at has been the people's stanchness and their ability to carry on during the years after the war and to accept the drabness of their lives.

One of the workers with whom I talked told me that the hardest thing was to keep on at your job when you knew the bombs were falling in the area of your home and you did not know whether you would find your home and family still there at the end of your day's or night's work. When we lunched with some of the women who were daily feeding the dockworkers, they told me: "We used to look down on the dockworkers as the roughest element in our community. We were a little afraid of them; but now we have come to know them well and will never feel that way again."

Women from many different backgrounds, who had never worked together before, were working side by side, just as the men were fighting side by side. These British Isles, which we always regarded as class-conscious, as a place where people were so nearly frozen in their classes that they rarely moved from one to another, became welded together by the war into a closely knit community in which many of the old distinctions lost their point and from which new values emerged.

When I visited a center where bombed-out people were getting clothes and furniture and other supplies, one young woman with a child in her arms and another dragging at her skirt said to me very cheerfully: "Oh, yes, this is the third time we have been bombed out, but the government gives us a bit of help and you people in America send us clothes. We get along and none of us was hurt and that's the main thing."

Back in London I had dinner with Prime Minister and Mrs. Churchill. During the dinner I had a slight difference of opinion with Prime Minister Churchill on the subject of Loyalist Spain. The prime minister asked Henry Morgenthau whether we, the United States, were sending "enough" to Spain and whether it was reaching there safely. Henry Morgenthau told him that he hoped we were, and I said I thought it was a little too late, that we should have done something to help the Loyalists during their civil war. Mr. Churchill said he had been for the Franco government until Germany and Italy went into Spain to help Franco. I remarked that I could not see why the Loyalist government could not have been helped, and the prime minister replied that he and I would have been the first to lose our heads if the Loyalists had won—the feeling against people like us would have spread. I said that losing my head was unimportant, whereupon he said: "I don't want you to lose your head and neither do I want to lose mine." Then Mrs. Churchill leaned across the table and said: "I think perhaps Mrs. Roosevelt is right." The prime minister was quite annoyed by this time and said: "I have held certain beliefs for sixty years and I'm not going to change now." Mrs. Churchill then got up as a signal that dinner was over.

Before I left for home my aunt, Maude Gray, Tommy and I drove out one day to Windsor Castle, for I wanted to report to Queen Elizabeth on my trip. While we were talking in her sitting room, the King, who had spent the day visiting our air force troops, came in with the children. Both the King and I had rather bad colds, which necessitated a good deal of attention to our noses. As we drove away from Windsor Castle my aunt said to me in shocked tones: "Darling, I never was so humiliated in my life. Your using those nasty little tissues and wadding them in your hand while the King used such lovely sheer linen handkerchiefs! What could they have thought!"

As the time for my return trip approached, my husband and Ambassador Winant and the prime minister discussed how I should travel. Tommy and I had our return passage on an American Export Lines plane. Both Ambassador Winant and the prime minister pointed out that, while I might not be concerned personally with the possibility of the Germans' discovering I was on a plane bound for Lisbon, I would be jeopardizing the other passengers. Finally, after many conversations over the transatlantic telephone, my husband, who did not want me to travel on a military plane, gave in and said: "I don't care how you send her home, just send her."

Twenty-four

Getting on with the War: 1943

AFTER WE HAD been back from London a few days a Washington columnist wrote for his paper a story asserting that Miss Thompson had asked me for a few days off to go to see her mother, who was ill. I was alleged to have said: "Why, Tommy, I didn't know you had a mother, but I am afraid we are much too busy for you to be away now."

It was so ridiculous that neither of us was annoyed. Miss Thompson wrote to the gentleman as follows:

"Your column quoting my request for a few days' holiday and Mrs. Roosevelt's alleged reply has just been brought to my attention.

"For your information, my mother died in 1928 and in order that there be no confusion about which parent I wanted to visit, my father died in 1932. Nothing could give me more satisfaction than to be able to visit either or both of my parents and get back to my job. If you, in your omnipotence, can tell me how to accomplish this, I shall be most grateful."

Needless to say, there was no answer to this letter and no correction in the column.

The day I arrived home we had a large dinner for the President of Ecuador, who was to be an overnight guest. I should have liked at least one evening to catch up on my family, for I had been away several weeks, but this is a pleasure a public person cannot always count on.

Very soon I began to realize that there would shortly be other trips about which I had better know very little. On January 9, 1943, Franklin left for Miami, Florida, and took off on the 12th for Casablanca. It was his first long trip by air across the water and I had hoped he would be won over to flying, but instead he disliked it more than ever.

Admittedly, a flight like this in time of war entailed some personal

247

danger, but that was something Franklin never gave a thought to. Long ago, when Mayor Cermak was killed, Franklin and I had talked it over and decided that that kind of danger was something you could do nothing about. You cannot be protected from a person who does not care whether he is caught or not. The only possible course is to put the thought of danger out of your mind and go ahead with your job as you feel you must, regardless of what might be called its occupational risks. In the case of the Casablanca trip there was also the fact that Franklin was doing an unprecedented thing, and he knew there would be criticism. That again was a consideration he could not let weigh with him. All the arrangements for the trip were made through the Secret Service; his departure was as secret as possible; the flag which indicates that the President is in residence was never taken down from the White House, and I went on with my daily routine exactly as though he were there.

When Franklin returned he was full of stories. He loved particularly to tell us how he had made Mr. Churchill unhappy by teasing him about his "bad boy," General de Gaulle. Mr. Churchill, of course, was responsible for General de Gaulle and the general had proved difficult about going to the meeting. Back of Franklin's teasing, however, there had been a serious purpose because he had felt that if Mr. Churchill put the screws on, General de Gaulle would have to come to Casablanca, since Great Britain was providing him with the money necessary to carry on his activities at the time. When the general did go, it was not altogether a happy meeting.

Afterwards when I questioned him about the meeting, Franklin said, "General de Gaulle is a soldier, patriotic, yes, devoted to his country; but, on the other hand, he is a politician and a fanatic and there are, I think, in him almost the makings of a dictator."

Another thing Franklin talked much about was the horrible conditions of the natives in the places he had stopped. He never minced words in telling Mr. Churchill that he did not think the British had done enough in any one of the colonial areas he had seen on this trip to improve the lot of the native peoples. He agreed with me that the United States, too, had a serious responsibility in Liberia, which we had never lived up to, and I was particularly happy when Edward Stettinius later went ahead with the plans for Liberia which he discussed with Franklin at that time. He formed a company to develop the natural resources of the country—a project that was only a dream when he talked with my husband after his return from Casablanca.

In early February I made a trip to Portland, Maine, where Cary Bok met me and took me to Camden to visit his shipyard, where he was building wooden vessels. This was something in which Franklin was greatly interested.

Later in the month I flew to Des Moines, Iowa, with Colonel Oveta Hobby, head of the WAC, to inspect their main training station. While I was there I took a side trip to speak at a college in Columbia, Missouri, and was back in the White House in plenty of time to greet Madame Chiang when she first arrived in this country. At that time she was in the Medical Center in New York City for treatment.

Madame Chiang seemed so small and delicate as she lay in her hospital bed that I had a desire to help her and take care of her as if she had been my own daughter. Occasionally I took someone to see her because I felt she would tire of seeing only me, and many people were anxious to meet her.

When it came time for her to leave the hospital we offered her our house in Hyde Park for a few days before she came to Washington. She spent several days there and then, accompanied by two nurses and her nephew and niece, Mr. and Miss Kung, who acted as her secretaries, she came to the White House and stayed until the 28th of the month. She should have been an invalid with no cares; but she felt she had work to do, that she must see important people in our government and in the armed services who could be helpful to China, and that she must fulfill certain official obligations.

I shall never forget the day I went with her when she addressed the House of Representatives, after meeting the senators. A little, slim figure in Chinese dress, she made a dramatic entrance as she walked down the aisle, surrounded by tall men. She knew it, for she had a keen sense of the dramatic. Her speech, beautifully delivered, was a remarkable expression of her own conception of democracy.

I saw another side of Madame Chiang while she was in the White House, and I was much amused by the reactions of the men with whom she talked. They found her charming, intelligent, and fascinating, but they were all a little afraid of her, because she could be a coolheaded statesman when she was fighting for something she deemed necessary to China and to her husband's regime; the little velvet hand and the low, gentle voice disguised a determination that could be as hard as steel.

A certain casualness about cruelty emerged sometimes in her conversations with the men, though never with me. I had painted for Franklin such a sweet, gentle and pathetic figure that, as he came to recognize the other side of the lady, it gave him keen pleasure to tease me about my lack of perception. I remember an incident at a dinner party during one of her visits which gave him particular entertainment. John L. Lewis was acting up at the time, and Franklin turned to Madame Chiang and asked: "What would you do in China with a labor leader like John Lewis?" She never said a word, but the beautiful, small hand came up and slid across her throat, a most expressive gesture. Franklin looked across at me to make sure I had seen, and went right on talking. He enjoyed being able to say to me afterwards: "Well, how about your gentle and sweet character?"

Her two young secretaries created a slight confusion when they first arrived in the White House, because her niece, Miss Kung, insisted on dressing like a man, and the valets, thinking I had made a mistake in assigning the rooms, unpacked Miss Kung under the impression that she was Mr. Kung. Then they went to the ushers' office and reported that I had made a mistake, only to learn much to their confusion that they had unpacked a lady. Franklin was also confused by her type of dress and when she came into the study where we all met before dinner, he greeted her as "my boy." Harry Hopkins quickly wrote a note saying: "This is Miss Kung." Franklin tried to cover up by saying blandly: "I always call all young things 'my boy' "; but everyone knew quite well that her clothes had completely fooled him. I do not believe she was offended by his mistake, for that was the impression she was trying to give. She hated being a girl—I suppose in protest against the inferior position sometimes assigned to women in China.

After Madame Chiang left us, she made a long trip by special train throughout the United States, out to the West Coast and back. It must have been a strenuous and difficult trip for her, and after her return she questioned Tommy carefully. Tommy and I had taken practically the same trip, following in her footsteps, a few days behind her, and heard about her everywhere. What mystified Madame Chiang was how it was possible for us to travel alone while she had forty people, yet never enough to do the things she needed to have done.

She asked Tommy who packed our bags, and Tommy said she packed hers and I packed mine. She then asked who answered the telephone, and Tommy said that whichever one of us was nearer it answered. She also asked who took care of the mail and telegrams and was told that we did it jointly. Her next question was, who looked after our clothes, and Tommy told her that if a dress needed pressing, we asked the hotel valet to do it. Finally she asked about my safety. Tommy explained that we did not consider "protection" necessary, since everyone was good to us, but that, of course, in various cities people would sometimes be assigned to meet us at the train and see us off and motor us about if we were going to be in large crowds; that this, however, was entirely dependent upon how the local authorities felt.

I have never asked for or wanted protection and in all the miles I have traveled and the many places I have visited I never have had an unpleasant incident. People might become a bit too enthusiastic; but it was all kindly meant and I felt it was because they loved my husband. I have had a tail pulled off my fur scarf as a souvenir, but nothing worse than that has ever happened.

During the month of April I went on a short trip with Franklin to inspect some war plants in Mexico and to meet the President and spend a few hours in Monterrey. It was an interesting trip to me, because it was the first time I had been in that country. My impression of the city is rather vague, for we drove fast and were watching the crowds rather than the city itself; however, Mexican hospitality, as expressed at the dinner we all attended and in the kindness of everyone with whom we came in contact, made a deep impression on the whole party. We traveled back with a feeling that Mexico was a close neighbor in spirit. My husband already felt close and friendly to the Mexican people, but to many of us this was a new experience.

I imagine every mother felt as I did when I said good-by to the children during the war. I had a feeling that I might be saying good-by for the last time. It was a sort of precursor of what it would be like if your children were killed. Life had to go on and you had to do what was required of you, but something inside of you quietly died.

At the time of World War I, I felt keenly that I wanted to do everything possible to prevent future war, but I never felt it in the same way that I did during World War II. During this second war period I identified myself with all the other women who were going through the same slow death, and I kept praying that I might be able to prevent a repetition of the stupidity called war.

I have tried, ever since, in everything I have done, to keep that promise I made to myself, but the progress that the world is making toward peace seems like the crawling of a little child, halting and slow.

May was a busy month in 1943. The President of Bolivia and his foreign minister stayed at the White House on two separate occasions. President Benes of Czechoslovakia and Prime Minister Mackenzie King each spent a night with us, and later the President and the President-elect of Liberia came. Their visit was a direct result of my husband's visit to Liberia on his way back from Casablanca.

Early one morning in July I was called on the telephone and guardedly told that there had been an engagement in which Franklin Junior's ship had been bombed. They thought it was getting into Palermo safely. That was all. It was long before I heard the details. After the ship had been bombed, it was taken into Palermo, where it continued to be shelled at intervals. It was tied to another ship, and men were injured on both of them. Franklin Junior had the good luck to be able to save one boy's life by carrying him down to the other ship's doctor. At the time he did not notice that he himself was hit in the shoulder, but to this day little pieces of shrapnel are there to remind him of it.

Eventually Franklin Junior's ship went to Malta for repairs and was still at Malta when he got word that he was to meet his father, who was on his way to Cairo. He was delighted at the chance of seeing him, but when Franklin told him he would like him on the trip as his aide, young Franklin's joy changed to determination that nothing of the kind was going to happen. After the repairs on his ship were completed, it would have to get home, and he knew it would be an anxious trip because the ship would not really be in top-notch condition. He felt he could not let the ship go back without him, after all he and his shipmates had been through together.

Franklin Junior and his father had quite an argument about where his first duty lay. The ship won in the end and his father gave him a letter of orders to return to it. Young Franklin realized that he could never show those orders to anyone, because security demanded that no one know his father was in the area. He had a difficult time getting back to Malta with no orders that he could show to get priority for the return trip.

Twenty-five

Visit to the Pacific

I DO NOT REMEMBER when my husband first suggested that it would be a good idea for me to take a good-will trip to the Pacific, though I do remember the suggestion came because he felt that Australia and New Zealand, being so far away, had been rather neglected in the matter of visitors. Both countries were exposed to attack and the people were under constant strain and anxiety. We had had to send a great number of our servicemen out there, an influx which had added considerably to the strain and which had been, for people whose own men were fighting in Africa and Italy, a disrupting even though reassuring occurrence.

Another reason for the trip was that I had received a number of letters from the women of New Zealand and Australia suggesting that, since I had seen the work of the women of Great Britain, I might be interested in coming out to see what was being done in their far-off countries.

At once I put up a strong plea to be allowed to see our men on Guadalcanal and other islands. I had done considerable visiting in the West Coast hospitals to which the early wounded from Guadalcanal and some from the 1st Marine Raider group (with which Jimmy served) were being returned; and I told my husband that it would be hard to go on doing it if, when I was to be in the Pacific area anyway, I were not permitted to visit the places where these men had left their health or received their injuries. He finally broke down and gave me letters to the commanding generals and to Admiral Halsey, saying that he was willing to have me go to Guadalcanal "if it did not interfere with the conduct of the war."

Franklin was going to the conference at Quebec on the 17th, the same day I was to leave for San Francisco, but we had a little time together at Hyde Park first. It was decided that my visit should be kept secret, so I

253

went on about my daily business as usual. Prime Minister Churchill, who was staying with us, still speaks occasionally of how surprised he was when I casually mentioned at dinner one night that I was leaving the next day for the Southwest Pacific.

He looked aghast. "What have you done about your trip?" I said all the plans had been made and the itinerary worked out. He asked who was going with me, and I said no one, because, having been subjected to much criticism on my return from Great Britain, I thought I would avoid some of it on this trip by taking up as little room as possible. I later found to my regret that some columnists were none too kind anyway, and that I might just as well have taken several people. Nothing more disagreeable could have been said. Mr. Churchill insisted on cabling to all his people in the Pacific, and they were most kind wherever I met them. I have always been grateful to him for his thoughtfulness.

I had gone to see Norman Davis, chairman of the American Red Cross, as soon as the trip had been decided on, and had asked if it would be of any assistance to him if I went to look over the various Red Cross installations and trouble spots. I hoped in this way to show that I was doing a serious job and not just running around the war area causing trouble. He said that I could be most useful, because he had been planning to send someone out there to inspect the Red Cross work. He asked me if I would be willing to wear a Red Cross uniform and make a report to him on my return.

I talked this suggestion over with my husband, since it seemed to offer a number of advantages. In the first place, uniforms meant less luggage, an advantage when traveling by air; in the second place, in a familiar uniform I would feel easier visiting hospitals and meeting servicemen. Franklin decided it would be a good idea, so I bought at my own expense the thinnest uniforms I could find, also a heavy one with a warm top coat, because I knew I would encounter extremes of weather. I conscientiously inspected every Red Cross activity in every area I visited and I hope that my reports were some compensation to Mr. Davis for the criticism heaped upon him for permitting me to go in uniform as a Red Cross representative.

Because Franklin felt that, since I was traveling on a military plane, I should not keep any of the money that accrued from my column while I was on this trip, I arranged for half of my earnings to go to the Red Cross and half to the American Friends Service Committee, also dividing between them what I earned for articles written after my return. Later I discovered that certain of the Republican members of Mr. Davis' board were afraid that if it were known I had given this money to the Red Cross some of the large donors who were strongly opposed to my husband politically would withdraw their contributions. Consequently, we never explained how I happened to go in uniform or what the financial arrangements were; however, I think it is now quite safe to give the facts.

On Christmas Island I had my first encounter with tropical bugs. When I walked into the room after supper and, putting on the light, found my floor completely covered with little red bugs, I nearly disgraced myself by screaming. Remembering that I was the only woman on the island, and that a scream would undoubtedly raise an alarm, I stamped my foot and all the little bugs scurried down through the cracks in the floor.

I saw everything the men were doing on that island, as I did on all the others I visited. Right from the beginning I followed my sons' advice, which was none too self-flattering, considering that they were officers. They had said: "Mummy, don't take every meal with the brass. See that you have a meal with the noncommissioned officers and get a noncommissioned officer to drive you around, and get one meal with the enlisted men themselves." The only way to accomplish the last was to get up and eat breakfast with the men before six o'clock.

I used to wonder how the pilots ever found the little dots of coral islands in that vast expanse of ocean. Having to come down so close to the water to land was a curious sensation at first, but I became accustomed to it.

Having no one with me as a secretary, I had to write my column either at night or during flights in the daytime. I am such a slow typist that this meant an extra two hours' work for me almost every day. However, when I had a long flight I could often write enough for two or three columns, which helped when I had an overcrowded schedule at some stop. I lost thirty pounds and when I got home I realized I was more tired than I had ever been in all my life. But I was not ill and the work got done—nothing else mattered.

When I reached Noumea and met Admiral Halsey, I presented my letters from my husband. The admiral has told his own story of how much he dreaded my coming. He did not dread it any more than I did, but I determined to do as well as I could, and if it was possible to get up to Guadalcanal. The admiral refused to give me the slightest inkling of what he had decided about that and told me in no uncertain terms that I would have to go to New Zealand and Australia first and that he would make his decision on my return. I thought I noticed a slight change in his attitude before I left; perhaps some good reports were coming to him from the hospitals and the various places I had already visited.

Wherever I went I met people I had seen before. That the many trips I had made in the United States during the depression years had an unforeseen by-product was evident as I walked through the hospital wards. Occasionally when I spoke to a boy, he would say he had seen me last when I spoke at his commencement or on some other occasion; then if I recalled something about his home town his whole face would light up, and I would feel that the endless miles I walked every day were worthwhile.

I stayed with the governor general and his wife while I was in the capital of New Zealand, and again with the governor general and his wife on Fiji, invitations I owed to Mr. Churchill's thoughtfulness. Both visits were pleasant though, of course, I had to follow my usual routine. In New Zealand especially, I tried to see something of the people of the country and what they were doing, as well as of our own men.

By that time we had only rest camps and hospitals in New Zealand, but I could see the effects of the tremendous influx of our men who had gone from there, first to Guadalcanal and later to other parts of the Pacific. By the time I got there some of the New Zealand men were coming back and I got one amusing letter asking me if I would not see that our men left their girls alone. When I spoke of the letter to some New Zealand people I was told a story to illustrate the difference between the approach of the average American GI and the New Zealand soldier. A GI was on a bus one day and found himself sitting behind a lovely-looking girl with fair hair. He leaned forward and said: "Angel, what heaven did you drop from?" As an opening gambit, that speech probably would never have occurred to a New Zealand man.

In the Red Cross clubs there one of the girls told me: "There is a boy here who says he does not want to speak to you or even be in the same room with you, because he understands you advocate that all the marines who came to the Pacific be quarantined for six months after they return, before they are allowed to go home." Here was a story that I had heard before leaving home. In my talk with the boys that day I mentioned the story, adding that the families of some of the boys who had written back home about it had sent the letters on to me. I told them how surprised I had been, since I had never thought of saying anything of the kind. I had a son in the marines and he certainly would never allow me to have any such ideas. Much later, after I had tested it out and found that the story was known to the noncommissioned officers and the men, some of the older officers suggested that it might have been broadcast by Tokyo Rose. Heaven knows how it started, but it plagued me for a long time, and a similar story was told in all parts of the world. The paratroopers in Italy complained that I had said the same thing about them, and I heard it again when I went to the Caribbean. Quite evidently it was propaganda designed to detract from the value of any contacts I might make, whether at home in the hospitals or on various trips.

While I was in New Zealand I visited Rotorua, the home of the Maoris, who had shown our servicemen much hospitality. The head guide, Rangi, who showed me about, was a wonderful woman, brilliant, witty and dignified.

When I reached Australia I stayed for a while at Canberra with the governor general and his wife, Lord and Lady Gowrie, who were kindness itself; I shall never feel grateful enough to them for all they did to make my visit useful and pleasant. I spoke to vast audiences and visited many hospitals, rest homes for our nurses, and recreation centers for our men. Boy after boy told me how kindly he had been treated in Australian homes, and that was equally true in New Zealand; however, Australia had a greater number of our men in proportion to her population. Nevertheless, they stood up under the strain in a remarkable manner.

In a rest home for nurses I asked one young nurse what she objected to most. She said, "The rat that sits in the middle of my floor and will not move no matter how much noise I make." Rats, insects and snakes were things one had to contend with daily in the hospitals on the islands, and one girl told me of waking up to find a snake neatly coiled on the outside of her netting. She could not get up until someone came and did away with it.

Many of these girls were working in hospitals where water was sometimes almost impossible to get; one cupful to a patient a day had to do for drinking and washing. The mud was so deep at times that even with the GI boots and trousers tucked into the tops it was difficult to get around. But I never heard any of them really complain.

It was in Australia, in a Red Cross club, that I had an interesting talk with some young men. They were mostly air force boys, some of them from West Virginia, and the discussion turned to John Lewis and the coal strike. I told them of a boy in a hospital who had said: "I come from West

Virginia. I'm a miner. It isn't the miners who are wrong; they've got a real grievance and they don't understand about us. You know that."

I was glad I knew mining areas well enough to realize that it was not even entirely John Lewis' fault. It was the fault of all of us, who should have paid attention long ago to the conditions under which the miners worked and not have left it to John Lewis to get for them the only benefits they had received up to that time. But the boys who had been miners themselves, or whose fathers were miners, had a difficult time trying to explain to their companions that there was any justification for a coal strike in wartime.

Back at Noumea, I still did not know whether I was to be allowed to go to Guadalcanal or was starting homeward. The last evening, after I had spent the day doing all the things that had been arranged for me by Admiral Halsey, he announced that I was to be ready to leave the next morning at eight o'clock for Efate. I was not to mention the name of the island because the Japs had never bombed it and we had some of our biggest hospitals there. He hoped that they did not know we were established there. From Efate I would go to Espiritu Santo and then on to Guadalcanal.

My diary may be worthy quoting:

> By six a.m. we were on Guadalcanal where we had breakfast with the commanding officer on the airfield; he is a great friend of Admiral Halsey's. At one point he was lost and everyone turned out to find him, including the admiral himself.
>
> Then the army officers came to get me, and as we drove off the trucks with the men who were working on the field were just coming in. Coletta Ryan and I leaned out to wave. At first there was complete surprise on the faces of the men, and then one boy in stentorian tones said: "Gosh, there's Eleanor." I am never quite sure whether to take this as a compliment or to be a little ashamed of it, but they were so evidently pleased to see women, we had to laugh and go on waving. The commanding officer was plainly horrified to have me treated with such levity, so I tried to make believe I considered it a great compliment.
>
> I visited all the improvements which have been made since this part of the island came into our possession. There are thought to be some Japs still on the other side of the island and there are still air raids.

One of the things which I shall never forget on Guadalcanal is my visit to the cemetery. The little church there was built by the natives and given to the soldiers, they even made an altar and the altar vessels, carving them beautifully and decorating the church with symbols which have special meanings for them—fishes of various kind which mean long life, eternity, etc. It was very moving to walk among the graves and to realize how united these boys had been in spite of differences in religion and background. The boy's messkit or sometimes his helmet hung on the cross which some friend would have carved with the appropriate symbol of the Jewish or Catholic or Protestant faith. Words that came from the heart were carved on the base, such as "He was a grand guy"—"Best buddy ever."

At 5:30 I went to the dinner that had been arranged and then back to the hospital to finish the wards. There was an air-raid alert just as we were driving in, which meant that we had to take to the shelter in the hospital grounds, with all the patients who could walk. For a short time there was a rather tense atmosphere, but somebody started to sing and we all joined in. When the all-clear sounded I went through the wards I had not covered before. I was much interested to see what the effects of the alert would be on those who could not leave their beds and go to the shelter. I saw only two men who were badly affected. . . .

The return trip to Hawaii was again made by way of Christmas Island because an attack was being made on the route we originally planned to take and it was thought not safe for me to go that way. My time on Christmas Island was short and I visited only one boy, about whom the doctor was very much worried. At the hospital I made him promise that he would try to get well if I would try to see his mother on my return. I did see her, and fortunately he recovered and came to see me when he got back to the United States.

This time I stayed some days in Hawaii, where I saw the training given under actual fire—and was greatly impressed by it—visited a great number of hospitals, and a New York State regiment. Judith Anderson met me at luncheon at one of the hospitals. She and Maurice Evans were giving Shakespearean plays on the islands in this group—*Macbeth* at the time—and it was a wild success. She told me with satisfaction that some of the boys would wait outside and ask her "who this guy Shakespeare" was and tell her it was the first time they had seen a real play with living people in it, and ask to be allowed to come again the next night because they did not think they got everything there was in the play. They were audiences such as few actors and actresses ever meet and I think repaid fully everything which Miss Anderson and Mr. Evans put into their trip.

Finally I took off for home. I have a lasting recollection of landing in California and having to sit in the plane while all the outer air was shut off and we were squirted thoroughly with disinfectant.

I had been to Hawaii, Christmas Island, Penryhn Island, Bora Bora, Aitutaki, Tutuila, Samoa, Fiji, New Caledonia; Auckland, Wellington, and Rotorua in New Zealand; Sydney, Canberra, Melbourne, Rockhampton, Cairns, Brisbane in Australia; Efate, Espiritu Santo, Guadalcanal and Wallis.

War trip number two was over.

Twenty-six

Teheran and the Caribbean

HAVING TOLD the story of my two trips to parts of the world where actual war was going on and where, of necessity, one saw the results of the war in the hospitals, I think I should say something of the impressions these trips left with me.

At first I could hardly bear the hospitals. There was, of course, a certain amount of pure physical fatigue from walking miles of hospital wards day after day; but that was nothing in comparison with the horrible consciousness of waste and feeling of resentment that burned within me as I wondered why men could not sit down around a table and settle their differences before an infinite number of the youth of many nations had to suffer.

The most horrifying hospitals were those in which the men who had been mentally affected by the experiences they had been through were treated. I could tell myself, of course, that these men would probably have broken under other circumstances, that there must be something wrong with our civilization when our young people were so vulnerable to mental illness and that we must work to discover the reasons and try to change them; nevertheless, my horror at seeing people who had broken mentally and emotionally made me lie awake nights.

There were times in the other hospitals when it was hard to accept the gallantry of the men themselves without showing how deeply sorry I was for them. I knew that that was the last thing they wanted and that their brave front of casual cheerfulness was put on to prevent people from showing that they were sorry.

Many of the boys I saw in hospitals are now leading happy and useful lives, but they carry with them, day after day, the results of the war. If we do not achieve the ends for which they sacrificed—a peaceful world in which there exists freedom from fear of both aggression and want—we have failed. We shall not have paid our debt until these ends are achieved.

One development gives me great hope for the future. Women have always come to the fore in wartime, but I think in World War II they took responsibility in more fields than ever before—in factories, on the farms, in business, and in the military services. They were an indispensable part of the life of the country. This was true in Great Britain, in Australia, in New Zealand, in France, in all occupied countries in Europe, in Russia, and in the United States. Women have become conscious also of the need to take part in the political life of their country. In the European countries more women are today playing an active role in public life than would have been possible before the war; and I am sure we are going to see great developments in the Asiatic area too. This, to me, is a hopeful sign, for women will work for peace as hard as they worked for the war.

On November 9, 1943, forty-four nations signed the agreements for the United Nations Relief and Rehabilitation Administration. The first administrator was former Governor Herbert H. Lehman of New York. Mr. Lehman proved by the way he set up his organization and conducted the work that he was a good organizer and had the patience of Job.

On November 11 Franklin left for his second war trip. He was to meet the Generalissimo and Madame Chiang in Cairo. This would be his first meeting with the Generalissimo, and Madame Chiang was to act as interpreter. Mr. Churchill met Franklin in Cairo and the talks went well.

Because at that time the U.S.S.R. was not at war with Japan, Marshal Stalin was reluctant to meet with the head of the Chinese government; consequently, when the talks in Cairo were over, Mr. Churchill and Franklin went on to Teheran to meet Marshal Stalin. This was the first meeting between Marshal Stalin and my husband. Franklin went to it with the determination that, if possible, there was going to be good will and understanding between them. I knew he was going to exert himself to the utmost to win the confidence of Stalin and to establish a better relationship between our two governments.

After Franklin had been in Teheran for only a day, Stalin insisted that, because of the rumors of unrest among the native people of Iran, the president must move into the same area of the city that he was in. Mr. Churchill was next door and the Russian soldiers could more easily protect them all.

Afterwards my husband told me that he felt there was a great distrust on the part of Marshal Stalin when they first met, and he had no idea, on leaving, whether he had been able to dissipate any of it or not. He added that he intended to see that we kept our promises to the letter. He hoped that Great Britain would be able to also, and said he would do all he could to help them do it. He felt that by keeping our word we could build the confidence of this leader whose people, though fighting on our side, still did not trust us completely. The U.S.S.R. needed all the help that we, with our great power of production, could give, while we were more than grateful for the fact that fighting in the U.S.S.R. kept so many German divisions busy.

In 1933 my husband had recognized the U.S.S.R., which had been isolated since 1918, and I am sure that at Teheran he made Marshal Stalin feel that his good will was genuine. After this meeting the co-operation among the three men grew steadily closer.

Franklin returned to Washington on December 17, exhilarated by the trip, full of new interests and seemingly in better health. Because of his keen interest in everything he saw and everyone he met, each trip seemed to have this effect on him.

Back in Washington, in January, 1944, we welcomed John's wife, Anne, and Haven and the baby, Nina, for an indefinite visit. Johnny had gone off with his ship on her trial trip and wanted Anne to settle the children in the White House so she would feel free to join him wherever he might put into port, if only for a day.

This visit was the occasion of one of the stories that we always enjoyed in the family. Franklin liked it so much that he continued to embellish it every time he told it. Johnny called me one evening just before Anne and the children were to come. I was out, so he talked to his father. First he told him when Anne would arrive and then proceeded to tell him about the various things that must be ordered and prepared for their arrival. Finally he said, "Be sure to order the diaper service." Franklin, who had never heard of it, said, "What did you say?" Johnny replied, "The diaper service." This bewildered his father who asked, "Is there anything wrong with the baby? We always boiled ours."

In February Anna arrived for an indefinite stay with little Johnny because her husband expected to be stationed in Washington for a while. Her two older children were in boarding school. Anna's presence was the greatest possible help to my husband. She saw and talked to people whom

Franklin was too busy to see and then gave him a digest of the conversations. She also took over the supervision of his food. In fact, she helped him in innumerable ways. Everything she did was done capably and she brought to all her contacts a gaiety and buoyancy that made everybody feel happier because she was around.

On the 4th of March Tommy and I left for our 13,000-mile plane trip in the Caribbean area. My husband had insisted that I take this trip. Because the war had receded in that area, the men stationed there felt they were in a backwater and chafed to be where they could do what they considered a more important job. Nevertheless, we had to have men there to guard and watch for submarines, because there was so much traffic to Europe, Asia and Africa. Franklin wanted the men to realize that he knew and understood the whole picture and believed they were doing a vital job—that they were not forgotten, even though they were not on the front line.

I was getting a little weary of the criticism heaped on me for taking these trips, but because my husband insisted that my visit to the South Pacific had been a success in that it had accomplished what he had hoped for, I decided to make this tour. He mapped it out, and I took Miss Thompson with me. The entire trip, from March 4 to March 28, was by air, and in that period we visited Guantánamo, Cuba; Jamaica; Puerto Rico; Virgin Islands; Antigua; St. Lucia; Trinidad; Paramaribo; Belém, Natal and Recife in Brazil; La Guaira; Caracas; Curaçao; Aruba; Barranquilla; Canal Zone; Salinas; Galápagos Islands; Guatemala; Havana, Cuba. From Havana we flew straight home.

Puerto Rico was seething with activity and did not seem to me at all like the quiet, restful spot I had visited ten years previously. Rex Tugwell was the governor of the island at the time of my second visit, and he was trying out some of the ideas he had become interested in during his first survey; and Adrian Dornbush was doing research to develop new uses for Puerto Rican materials—bamboo, sugar cane, palms, and the like.

I was joined in Belém by the wives of some of the Brazilian government officials, who had been sent to meet me, and by our ambassador, Mr. Caffrey, and his wife. I enjoyed having them with me on my visit to Natal and Recife, where, as in Belém, I saw all the army and navy activities and inspected the recreation facilities.

The airfield at Recife had a special fascination for me because it was from there the men were checked out to start their long trek across the ocean. I had a chat with a boy who was getting his last orders before leaving for India, where he would be flying the Hump—one of the most dangerous trips. He had just been home on leave, and he told me that when flying low over some of the midwestern country on his way back to a base near his home, he had looked down and said to himself: "I wish I could say to you people below me, 'Do you know how lucky you are? What wonderful lives you have? How rich is your security in comparison to the millions of people I have seen in India and China?' " He was one of the many boys who, in India, saw famine at firsthand; I doubt if any of them will ever forget it.

One place my husband allowed me to go that was not, strictly speaking, a service base was Venezuela. I was driven from the airport up a steep road to Caracas. Franklin had said it was one of the most beautiful roads he had ever seen, and I agreed with him after driving over it. We were told that the road was built entirely by hand by men and women who had worked on it for several years; it was a sort of WPA project. My visit was merely one of good will but while I was there I learned something of the awakening interest among women of the country in the better care and feeding of children.

After a brief stop in Colombia we flew to the Canal Zone, where I was able to get a good view of the Panama Canal from the air. General Brett and Admiral Train had mapped out quite an active tour there, and I was glad to be able to visit boys in lonely camps, to ride in a PT boat to inspect the base, and in general to see as much of our men as possible.

I had an unexpected pleasure in Panama. The U.S.S. *Wasp*, the ship on which my son John was assistant supply officer, was going through the day I arrived and since he had four hours shore leave, he came to see me. It was the last time I saw him until the end of the war.

On leaving the Canal Zone I paid a brief visit to Ecuador, where a few men were stationed, and then flew to the Galapagos Islands. Quite a number of people thought this was an unnecessary trip, and various USO entertainers had been persuaded not to go there, to the great disappointment of the men. However, it was one place where my husband insisted I go, because he knew the men there were probably having a duller and more trying time than men stationed anywhere else in the world. After visiting it, I realized that he was right. We were much amused at the sign over the door: "Women Invited." We were the only women who had ever been on this island!

The climate at the coast station in Guatemala was terrible; the men found the heat and the insects and reptiles hard to bear. Over the door of their recreation room they had a sign: "Home of the Forgotten Men." Guatemala City, however, had a delightful climate and had I been on a pleasure trip I should have liked to spend some time visiting the old capital and some of the Indian villages.

The President of Guatemala gave a formal reception for me in his palace; all were seated according to protocol and brought up to be presented to me in groups according to rank or position. The palace is luxurious. As I was entering the building to attend this reception, escorted by our military officers, a flashlight bulb exploded, and before I could take a breath Guatemalan soldiers seemed to spring up out of the floor, and our officers seized my arms and rushed me away. It had sounded like a shot and no one was taking any chances.

Since this trip was not within easy reach of the enemy, it was publicized before I left, and countless mothers, wives, sweethearts and sisters wrote to beg me to try to see their menfolk. When I left home, I took with me a file of cards with the names and identification numbers of the men I'd been asked to look up, and as I reached each place, I gave the cards of the men stationed there to one of the officers and asked, if possible, to see them. The young men would be told, without explanation, to be at a certain place—usually an officer's room—at a given time. They would arrive, nervous and apprehensive, and when I appeared would invariably look surprised and greatly relieved. On my return I had letters to write to hundreds of people, because during the trip many other boys I met asked me to write to their families back home.

On this trip, too, I managed to have meals with the enlisted men, the noncommissioned officers, and the officers. It meant breakfast at 5:55 A.M. and not 6:00, dinner at noon, and supper at 5:00 or 5:30 P.M. In one place some Puerto Rican soldiers brought Miss Thompson and me our coffee at breakfast time all prepared the way they like it—mostly sugar and canned milk.

Everywhere I went I was treated with the greatest courtesy and consideration, though some of the top-ranking officers were frank in telling me they had not anticipated my visit with pleasure. Nevertheless, Ambassador Caffrey and some of the generals and admirals were kind enough to write to Washington that my trip had been helpful, and I have always hoped that I was able to give the men some pleasure and encouragement, which had been my husband's thought in suggesting this tour.

We stopped at Havana on the way back, where, as in any foreign country I visited, I met the government officials or their deputies. This always gave me a welcome opportunity to learn something about the country itself and to express the good will of our people toward our neighbors to the south.

We landed back in Washington, after having covered 13,000 miles by air, and many, many miles on foot going through hospital wards, camps and so forth.

In two days both Tommy and I felt that the trip already lay far behind. The accumulated work demanded such concentration to catch up that we were back in the daily routine almost before we had an opportunity to report on what we had seen and done.

Twenty-seven

The Last Term: 1944-1945

ALL THROUGH the winter of 1943-44 my husband had run a low fever at intervals and we thought he had picked up a bug on the trip or perhaps had acquired undulant fever from our cows at Hyde Park. Franklin seemed to feel miserable, which was not astonishing, considering that he had been through so many years of strain. Finally, on April 9 he made up his mind that he would go down and stay with Bernard Baruch at his plantation, Hobcaw, in Georgetown, South Carolina. Mr. Baruch had offered to take in his whole entourage.

There were times when Mr. Baruch differed with my husband on policies. There were also times, as often happens to any president, when the people around him became jealous of outside advisers such as Mr. Baruch and made it difficult for cordial relations to exist. However, my husband was inclined to be impervious to stories or rumors about anyone who he felt could be helpful; and, since Mr. Baruch is one of the people who can ignore the past, he was always ready to be useful when called upon. The personal relationship remained unbroken through all the years Franklin and I knew him.

Hobcaw was just the right place for Franklin, who loved the country and the life there, and he stayed almost a month. One day Anna and I flew down for lunch, along with the prime minister of Australia and his wife, Mr. and Mrs. Curtis, and I came home feeling that it was the best move Franklin could have made. I have always been grateful to Mr. Baruch for providing him with that holiday.

June 6, 1944, was a red-letter day. We had known for a long time that invasion preparations were being made, but everything had been kept very secret. When the time came, Franklin went on the air to give his D-day

Mrs. Roosevelt joins Nepal's King Tridhuvana and his two Queens during a short visit to the mountain kingdom's capital city of Katmandu in March, 1952. *Wide World*

Demonstrating a western folk dance at a reception in Lahore, Pakistan, March, 1952. *UPI*

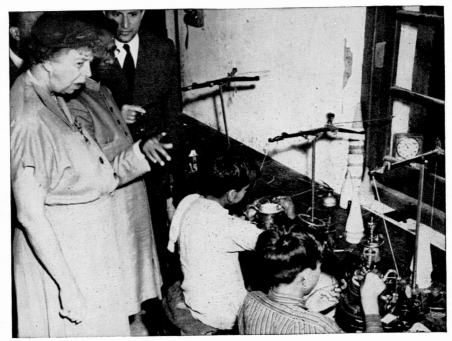

Watching boys at work in the hosiery section of the Faridabad Colony for displaced persons near Delhi, India, February, 1952. *Wide World*

Rehearsing for a reading of *Peter and the Wolf* with a Japanese symphony orchestra in Tokyo, Japan, May, 1953. *Franklin D. Roosevelt Library*

Mrs. Roosevelt leaving Idlewild Airport, New York, March, 1955, to observe the evacuation of Jews from North Africa to Israel in her capacity as honorary chairman of the nonsectarian community committee for the UJA. *Wide World*

Talking with former President Harry S. Truman in June, 1957, when he received an honorary Doctor of Laws degree at Brandeis University, of which Mrs. Roosevelt is a member of the Board of Trustees. *Wide World*

With Alfred Landon (left) and Norman Thomas (right) at a Disarmament rally in Madison Square Garden, called by the National Committee for a Sane Nuclear Policy, June, 1960. *Wide World*

In September, 1957, the author interviewed Nikita Khrushchev at Yalta, *Wide World;* and (below) visited a collective farm in Tashkent, Uzbek Republic. *UPI*

Mrs. Roosevelt being interviewed on her arrival in Moscow, September, 1959, as part of a delegation of the American Association for the United Nations. During her stay she studied Soviet education and facilities for the handicapped. *UPI*

At the opening of *Sunrise at Campobello,* New York, January 30, 1958, with former Secretary of the Interior, Oscar Chapman and Mrs. Chapman, and Ralph Bellamy, who portrayed F.D.R. in the play. *Wide World*

With Mrs. Winston Churchill (above) at Foyles Literary Luncheon, London, August, 1959, in honor of the publication of Eleanor Roosevelt's *On My Own. UPI*

In Beersheba, Israel, in March, 1959, her granddaughter, Nina (far right), purchased a camel. *Wide World*

John, James, Elliott, and Franklin, Jr., with their mother, 1958. *UPI*

Bernard Baruch escorting Eleanor Roosevelt to dinner at the Astor Hotel, New York, where he received honors from City College, November, 1960. *Wide World*

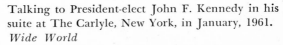

Mrs. Roosevelt with Leroy Collins at the Democratic National Convention, June, 1960, after she seconded the nomination of Adlai Stevenson.
Wide World

With Senator Lyndon Johnson (right) and Anthony Akers (center) during the 1960 campaign.
Wide World

Talking to President-elect John F. Kennedy in his suite at The Carlyle, New York, in January, 1961.
Wide World

Talking with Alex Quaison-Sackey, Ghana Ambassador to the UN, and Wisconsin Governor Gaylord Nelson at the UN in May, 1961. *UPI*

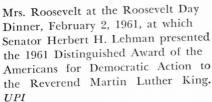

Mrs. Roosevelt at the Roosevelt Day Dinner, February 2, 1961, at which Senator Herbert H. Lehman presented the 1961 Distinguished Award of the Americans for Democratic Action to the Reverend Martin Luther King. *UPI*

Ambassador Adlai Stevenson and Mrs. Roosevelt, a member of the U.S. delegation, listen to Ghana President Kwame Nkrumah address the General Assembly in New York, March, 1961. *UPI*

prayer, and for hours our hearts were with the men on the beaches. The news came in little by little. In spite of the sorrow our losses brought to many families, it was a great relief to know that permanent landings had been made and that the liberation of Europe had really begun.

Another election lay ahead in the fall of 1944. I knew without asking that as long as the war was on it was a foregone conclusion that Franklin, if he was well enough, would run again. A number of doctors were called in and he was given a thorough physical examination. Since to hand over to anyone else at that particular point would have been extremely difficult, it was decided that if he would agree to follow certain rules laid down by the doctors, he could stand going on with his work.

There appeared in a magazine an article written by a doctor who does not give his sources of information. This doctor states that my husband had three strokes while he was in the White House, one, at least, prior to this examination. I asked Dr. Ross T. McIntire whether my husband had had a stroke and he assured me that he had never had one. It would have been impossible for him to have had a stroke without some one of us, who were so constantly with him, noting that something was wrong. My husband would have been the last person to permit doctors to slur over anything which might have made him less able mentally to continue his work.

On July 7, while I was in Hyde Park, General de Gaulle lunched with Franklin in the White House. We wondered whether this visit would change his feeling about the general, but their meeting was evidently entirely formal though pleasant, and I saw no difference in Franklin's attitude.

From the 15th of July to the 17th of August Franklin was away on a trip to the Pacific. He had been in the European area a good deal; and he wanted to establish personal contact with the officers in the Pacific area and go over their plans for the war. Consequently, a meeting was arranged in Hawaii. From there he went to Alaska and the Aleutians. It was this trip that gave rise to the extraordinary tale that Fala had been left behind on one of the islands and a destroyer sent back for him. I have no idea where this story started, though I assumed it was with some bright young man in Republican headquarters.

In July I made a trip to Lake Junaluska in North Carolina to speak before a group of Methodist women. I had been hesitant about going anywhere in the South, because my conviction that the colored people should have full civil rights had, over the years, aroused a good deal of feeling there. This hostility found an outlet, particularly in election years, in a number of disagreeable letters and editorials and I felt my presence would not be helpful. However, this group was insistent and I was glad afterwards that I went.

I had great admiration for the courage of Mrs. M. E. Tilly of Atlanta, Georgia, who was the executive secretary of the Methodist women's organization. I was told that whenever a lynching occurred she went alone, or with a friend, as soon as she heard of it, in order to investigate the circumstances. Only a southern woman could have done this, but even for a southern woman it seemed to me to require great moral as well as physical courage. She was a Christian who believed in all Christ's teachings, including the concept that all men are brothers, and though she was a white southern woman she deeply resented the fact that white southern women are so often used as a pretext for lynching. Mrs. Tilly served with distinction on President Truman's Civil Rights Committee, and gained for herself the admiration of both Northerners and Southerners.

We were all saddened by the death of Marguerite LeHand on August 2. I was glad that I had been able to see her not long before when I went to Boston to visit the Chelsea Naval Hospital. She had worked for so many years with my husband and she had been so loyal and devoted, living with us practically as a member of the family, that I knew he would feel sad not to be able to pay a last tribute of respect by attending her funeral.

On September 10 we all left for Quebec for another war conference. Mrs. Churchill was to be there with her husband and Franklin had asked me to go. At first, Mr. and Mrs. Hull had planned to go, but Secretary Hull decided that he was not well enough. Later Franklin asked Henry Morgenthau, Jr., to come up to confer on a postwar plan for Germany.

Franklin was anxious that it should be made impossible for Germany again to start a war. I heard him discuss many plans, even the possibility of dividing Germany into its original principalities. He realized that the industrial power of Germany lay in the Ruhr, and he considered the possibility of international control of that region.

He undoubtedly discussed with Henry Morgenthau all of his ideas, including the possibility of reducing Germany to a country more dependent on agriculture than in the past, allowing her only such industry as was essential to a self-supporting state, and making sure that the economy of the rest of Europe would not again be so dependent on Germany for its prosperity.

Apparently there was a lack of co-ordination among even the highest levels of government thinking, both in our own country and in Great Britain. The net result of it all seems to have been that the President's intentions were not carried out—intentions which were shared by the Supreme Commander of the European Theater, General Eisenhower.

Franklin emphasized three points which he felt were important psychologically in Germany. I think they might well be remembered today:

"The first, that Germany should be allowed no aircraft of any kind, not even a glider.

"The second, that nobody should be allowed to wear a uniform.

"The third, that there should be no marching of any kind."

The prohibition of uniforms and parades, he thought, would do more than anything else to teach the Germans that they had been defeated.

At least a month before the Quebec conference my husband had received memoranda from Secretary Hull, Secretary Stimson and Secretary Morgenthau, members of the Cabinet committee he had set up to recommend a plan for the postwar treatment of Germany. All were carefully considered, so it is fair to surmise that Henry Morgenthau's plan more closely met the needs of the situation as Franklin saw it.

Henry Morgenthau himself told the story of his last interview with my husband the night before he died. He left him with the firm conviction that Franklin was still determined "not to allow any sentimental considerations to modify the conditions necessary to prevent Germany and the German people from becoming aggressive again." Henry Morgenthau felt that these views were embodied in the Potsdam Agreement. The trouble that arose later was not because of that agreement but because of the lack of further agreement. A careful analysis of much that happened would probably show that Mr. Churchill always favored a less harsh attitude toward Germany and, as fear of Russia increased, his feeling naturally intensified.

While we were at the Quebec conference, both Mrs. Churchill and I were asked to speak in French over the radio, and there were a number of entertainments which we attended. On the 18th Franklin returned to Hyde Park with Mr. and Mrs. Churchill. Their rest there was necessarily brief because the 1944 campaign was about to begin.

Franklin opened the campaign by speaking at the Teamsters' Union dinner in Washington, Daniel Tobin being an old and warm Democratic adherent. It was at this dinner that Franklin really laid the foundation for Mr. Dewey's defeat by the way in which he told the story of Fala's indignation over the Republican accusation that he had been left behind on an island, and retrieved only at the cost of untold sums of the taxpayers' money. By ridicule, Franklin turned this silly charge to his advantage.

After that dinner the campaign was on, but I was busy with a number of things which had nothing to do with it. A conference on rural education, organized largely through Mrs. Charles Ormond Williams' interest, was held in the White House on October 4 and 5.

Shortly after my birthday I went at the regular interval to donate blood to the Red Cross. The young lady at the desk was terribly embarrassed because I had passed the sixty mark in years and no one over sixty could be allowed to give blood. I was unable to see how in a few weeks my blood could have changed, but I felt I really entered old age on October 11, 1944.

At the end of the campaign Franklin and I drove through miles of New York City streets in one of the worst rainstorms I ever remember. We did everything that had been planned, but between times we stopped in a city garage so Franklin could change into dry clothes. Riding in an open car in that downpour, he was drenched to the skin. He ended up at the apartment, which I had been trying to get him to look at ever since we sold the 65th Street houses. He had told me to get an apartment in New York City in which we could stay occasionally after we left Washington, specifying that it should be in a place where he could work in peace with no steps anywhere.

He had every intention of spending the rest of his life, after leaving the White House, in Hyde Park and Warm Springs, but realized, since he planned to do some magazine work, that he must have some place in which to stay in New York City.

I was really worried about him that day, but instead of being exhausted he was exhilarated, after he had had a chance to change his clothes and get a little rest. The crowds had been warm and welcoming and the contact with them was good for him. People had seemed not to mind standing in the rain so long as they could get a glimpse of him as he waved at them. That must give anyone a very warm feeling. People love you when they believe you have done something really worthwhile for them, and there was no question but that the people of New York City had been telling him that day how much they cared. Men, women and children had stood for hours, and as far as I could tell it had made no difference that the sun was not shining.

Dr. McIntire had worried about the campaign, but I had told him early in the autumn that I thought Franklin drew strength from contact with people. On the day of our visit to New York City I felt that I had been right and that Franklin was better than he had been at the beginning of the campaign.

That night, October 21, Franklin spoke at the Foreign Policy Association dinner. I heard afterwards that some people thought he looked ill that night, but I was not surprised because, of course, he was extremely tired. We went to Hyde Park for the election. When the returns showed that his re-election was assured, he went out on the porch as usual to welcome our neighbors when they came down to greet and congratulate him.

Franklin went down to Warm Springs for Thanksgiving and had nearly three weeks there. I was always glad when he was able to go, because he got great satisfaction out of contact with the patients, especially the youngsters. I think he felt that Warm Springs represented something that he had really been able to do for people who suffered as he had suffered.

Again that year we went to Hyde Park for Christmas. Soon after, Franklin began to plan for his trip to Yalta. I remember that he was so busy it was well into January before he had time to open his Christmas presents. He would not let any of us do it for him, so little by little, as he had a few minutes before dinner, he had the pleasure of opening his gifts, every one of which he enjoyed.

Early in January, realizing this would certainly be his last inauguration, perhaps even having a premonition that he would not be with us long, Franklin insisted that every grandchild come to the White House for a few days over the 20th. I was reluctant to have thirteen grandchildren, ranging in age from three to sixteen, together, for fear of an epidemic of measles or chicken pox, but he was so insistent that I agreed.

After the inauguration it was clearer every day that Franklin was far from well. Nevertheless, he was determined to go to Yalta, and when he made up his mind that he wanted to do something he rarely gave up the idea.

Franklin had high hopes that at this conference he could make real progress in strengthening the personal relationship between himself and Marshal Stalin. He talked a good deal about the importance of this in the days of peace to come, since he realized that the problems which would arise then would be even more difficult than those of the war period. He also told me that he intended, if possible, to see some of the Arabs and try to find a peaceful solution to the Palestine situation.

On the way back, however, General Watson, who had wanted above all else to go on the trip, had a stroke, which I knew must be causing Franklin great anxiety. Before they were out of the Mediterranean he died. Harry Hopkins also was ill on the trip and got off at Marrakech for a holiday and rest. Altogether, dark clouds seemed to be settling over the ship and I was really worried.

Many things have been said about the "surrender" of the United States' interests in the agreements at Yalta. Edward Stettinius' book answers these accusations authoritatively and I hope it will be read by everyone who has for one minute thought that Franklin was not always first concerned with the good of the United States. However, that our welfare was inextricably linked with the welfare of other countries was something he believed deeply, and he also believed we needed the friendship of other countries.

Yalta was only a step towards the ultimate solution Franklin had in mind. He knew it was not the final step. He knew there had to be more negotiation, other meetings. He hoped for an era of peace and understanding, but he knew well that peace was not won in a day—that days upon days and years upon years lay before us in which we must keep the peace by constant effort.

Though Franklin had felt confident of being able to work with Stalin when he left for Yalta, not long after he got home he began to feel that the marshal was not keeping his promises. This was something he could not overlook, and I believe he wrote him a number of extremely stern messages. He still thought, however, that in the end he could make Stalin live up to his word, and that he, Stalin, and Churchill, having fought the war together, had gained enough understanding and respect for each other to be able to work things out.

In telling of his experiences on this trip Franklin always said that one of the most interesting and colorful episodes was his meeting with King Ibn Saud. The King arrived on a destroyer, sitting with all his entourage under a canopy on deck, the sheep which he had brought for food herded at the other end of the ship. Franklin said it was the strangest-looking destroyer he had ever seen. Beautiful rugs had been spread and everything done to make the King comfortable in fairly familiar surroundings. Franklin served coffee on their arrival and the King asked permission to have his own coffee-maker prepare the ceremonial coffee, which Franklin drank with him.

The purpose of this visit was to get some kind of agreement on Palestine; also, Franklin wanted to make some suggestions about the development of the Arab countries. He had always felt strongly that they should not turn over all their oil resources to the great nations of the world but should retain enough to use in pumping water to the surface to irrigate the desert for better agricultural development. He was sure that much of the desert land had underground rivers which would make irrigation possible. He also thought that much more could be done in the way of reforestation in these countries. He had mentioned this to the Sultan of Morocco when he and Mr. Churchill had dined with him during the Casablanca conference. Franklin said Mr. Churchill did not look too happy over the idea, but the Sultan seemed enthusiastic.

He tried talking on these subjects to King Ibn Saud only to be met by the statement that the King was a warrior and would continue to be as long as he lived. He said one of his sons—and he had a great many sons— was interested in agriculture and another was interested in conservation, but that he had no interest at all in anything except being a warrior and the King of his nomad people.

The King did not want his people changed and he felt that contact with Europeans would be bad for them. When it came to Palestine, Franklin got nowhere.

On the 1st of March, Franklin addressed the Congress, and I knew, when he consented to do this sitting down, that he had accepted a certain degree of invalidism. I found him less and less willing to see people for any length of time, needing a rest in the middle of the day. He was anxious to get away and I was pleased when he decided to go to Warm Springs, where he always gained in health and strength. He invited his cousins, Laura Delano and Margaret Buckley, to go down with him.

On April 12, in the afternoon, Laura Delano called me to say that Franklin had fainted while sitting for his portrait and had been carried to bed. I talked to Dr. McIntire, who was not alarmed, but we planned to go down to Warm Springs that evening. He told me, however, that he thought I had better go on with my afternoon engagements, since it would cause great comment if I canceled them at the last moment to go to Warm Springs.

I was at a benefit for the Thrift Shop at the Sulgrave Club in Washington when I was called to the telephone. Steve Early, very much upset, asked me to come home at once. I did not even ask why. I knew that something dreadful had happened. Nevertheless, the amenities had to be observed, so I went back to the party and said good-by, expressing my regrets that I could not stay longer because something had come up at home which called me away.

I got into the car and sat with clenched hands all the way to the White House. In my heart I knew what had happened, but one does not actually formulate these terrible thoughts until they are spoken. I went to my sitting room and Steve Early and Dr. McIntire came to tell me the news. Word had come to them through Dr. Bruenn in Warm Springs, first of the hemorrhage, and later of Franklin's death.

I sent at once for the vice-president, and I made arrangements for Dr. McIntire and Steve to go with me to Warm Springs by plane that evening. Somehow in emergencies one moves automatically.

When the vice-president came I could think of nothing to say except how sorry I was for him, how much we would all want to help him in any way we could, and how sorry I was for the people of the country, to have lost their leader and friend before the war was really won.

Then I cabled my sons: "Father slept away. He would expect you to carry on and finish your jobs."

Almost before we knew it we were on the plane and flew all through the night. The next day in Warm Springs was long and heartbreaking. Laura Delano and Margaret Buckley, Lizzie McDuffie, our White House maid, Daisy Bonner, the cook Franklin always had in Warm Springs, and Prettyman, the valet, were all stunned and sad but everyone was as self-controlled and calm as possible. Though this was a terrible blow, somehow one had no chance to think of it as a personal sorrow. It was the sorrow of all those to whom this man who now lay dead, and who happened to be my husband, had been a symbol of strength and fortitude.

Finally, the slow procession moved to the railroad station and we got on the train and started for Washington. The military guard surrounded the coffin in the back of the car where Franklin had sat so often. I lay in my berth with the window shade up, looking out at the countryside he had loved and watching the faces of the people at stations, and even at the crossroads, who came to pay their last tribute all through the night.

The plans for the funeral were as Franklin would have wanted them. We had talked often, when there had been a funeral at the Capitol in which a man had lain in state and the crowds had gone by the open coffin, of how much we disliked the practice; and we had made up our minds that we would never allow it. I asked that the coffin be opened once after it was placed in the East Room, so that I could go in alone to put a few flowers in it before it was closed finally. He wanted to be remembered as he was when he was alive.

It seemed to me that everyone in the world was in the East Room for the funeral services except three of my own sons. Elliott was the only one who, by luck, could get back; he had been asked to fly in the plane which brought Mr. Baruch and several others from London. Jimmy was able to come east but he did not reach New York City until after the funeral at Hyde Park, so he joined us on the train on our way back to Washington. Langdon Marvin, Jr., who was my husband's godchild, came with Jimmy. Franklin Junior and Johnny were out in the Pacific area.

Franklin wanted to be buried in the rose garden at Hyde Park and left exact directions in writing, but he had neglected to make the arrangements necessary for using private property, so we had to make those at the last minute.

After the funeral service in Washington we traveled to Hyde Park. Again no one could sleep, so we watched out of the windows of the train the crowds of people who stood in respect and sorrow all along the way. I was deeply touched by the number of our friends who had left their homes very early to drive to Hyde Park for the funeral, and especially by the kind thoughtfulness of Prime Minister Mackenzie King. My niece (Mrs. Edward P. Elliott) was living in Ottawa at the time and he had invited her to go to Hyde Park in his special train. After the burial I stayed in the house long enough to greet old personal friends and the officials who had come up from Washington, and then went back to Washington on the same train as President and Mrs. Truman.

They were both more than kind in urging me to take my time about moving out of the White House, but I felt I wanted to leave it as soon as possible. I had already started to prepare directions so that the accumulation of twelve years could be quickly packed and shipped. As always happens in life, something was coming to an end and something new was beginning. I went over many things in my mind as we traveled the familiar road back to Washington.

I am sure that Franklin accepted the thought of death as he accepted life. He had a strong religious feeling and his religion was a very personal one. I think he actually felt he could ask God for guidance and receive it. That was why he loved the 23rd Psalm, the Beatitudes, and the 13th chapter of First Corinthians. He never talked about his religion or his beliefs and never seemed to have any intellectual difficulties about what he believed. Once, in talking to him about some spiritualist conversations which had been sent in to me (people were always sending me their conversations with the dead), I expressed a somewhat cynical disbelief in them. He said simply: "I think it is unwise to say you do not believe in anything when you can't prove that it is either true or untrue. There is so much in the world which is always new in the way of discoveries that it is wiser to say that there may be spiritual things which we are simply unable to fathom. Therefore, I am interested and have respect for whatever people believe, even if I cannot understand their beliefs or share their experiences."

That seemed to me a natural attitude for him to take. He was always open-minded about anything that came to his attention, ready to look into it and study it, but his own beliefs were the beliefs of a child grown to manhood under certain simple influences. He still held to a fundamental feeling that religion was an anchor and a source of strength and guidance, so I am sure that he died looking into the future as calmly as he had looked at all the events of his life.

At a time of shock and sorrow the lesser emotions fade away. Any man in public life is bound to have had some close relationships that were later broken for one reason or another, and some relationships that were never close and which simply slipped away; but when Franklin died, many men who had felt bitterly toward him and who without question would feel so again, at that moment forgot and merged with the great mass of people in the country who felt that they had lost someone whom they needed. Harry Hopkins looked, the day of the funeral, as though he were just about to die. After his return from Marrakech, he had been practically confined to the house, and since both men were ill, it had been impossible for them to see much of each other. I do not think that they cared less for each other or that there was any break. I think the circumstances and their own health made it difficult for them to meet and consult more often.

As I look back now I realize that unwittingly Franklin's parents had prepared him well, through contact with themselves, travel abroad, and familiarity with the customs and peoples of many countries, to meet the various situations that he faced during his public life. They certainly never intended him to be in politics, but the training they gave him made him better able to accomplish his tasks.

The so-called New Deal was, of course, nothing more than an effort to preserve our economic system. Viewing the world today I wonder whether some of the other peoples might not have stood up better in World War II had something like the New Deal taken place in their countries long enough before to give them a sense of security and confidence in themselves. It was the rebuilding of those two qualities in the people of the United States as a whole that made it possible for us to produce as we did in the early days of the war and to go into the most terrible war in our history and win it. So the two crises that my husband faced were really closely tied together. If he had not successfully handled the one he could never have handled the other, because no leader can do anything unless the people are willing to follow him.

What brought this more clearly before me were the letters that came in such numbers after Franklin's death and which are now in the Franklin D. Roosevelt Library. Touchingly people told their stories and cited the plans and policies undertaken by my husband that had brought about improvement in their lives. In many cases he had saved them from complete despair.

All human beings have failings, all human beings have needs and temptations and stresses. Men and women who live together through long years get to know one another's failings; but they also come to know what is worthy of respect and admiration in those they live with and in themselves. If at the end one can say, "This man used to the limit the powers that God granted him; he was worthy of love and respect and of the sacrifices of many people, made in order that he might achieve what he deemed to be his task," then that life has been lived well and there are no regrets.

Before we went to Washington in 1933 I had frankly faced my own personal situation. In my early married years the pattern of my life had been largely my mother-in-law's pattern. Later it was the children and Franklin who made the pattern. When the last child went to boarding school, I began to want to do things on my own, to use my own mind and abilities for my own aims. When I went to Washington I felt sure that I would be able to use the opportunities which came to me to help Franklin gain the objectives he cared about—but the work would be his work and the pattern his pattern. He might have been happier with a wife who was completely uncritical. That I was never able to be, and he had to find it in other people. Nevertheless, I think I sometimes acted as a spur, even though the spurring was not always wanted or welcome. I was one of those who served his purposes.

One cannot live the life Franklin led in Washington and keep up many personal friendships. A man in high public office is neither husband nor father nor friend in the commonly accepted sense of the words; but I have come to believe that Franklin stands in the memory of people as a man who lived with a great sense of history and with a sense of his obligation to fulfill his part as he saw it.

On the whole, I think I lived those years very impersonally. It was almost as though I had erected someone outside myself who was the President's wife. I was lost somewhere deep down inside myself. That is the way I felt and worked until I left the White House.

One cannot say good-by to people with whom one has lived and who have served one well without deep emotion, but at last even that was over. I was now on my own.

PART III

On My Own

Twenty-eight

An End and a Beginning

I RODE DOWN in the old cagelike White House elevator that April morning of 1945 with a feeling of melancholy and something of uncertainty, because I was saying good-by to an unforgettable era and I had given little thought to the fact that from this day forward I would be on my own.

I realized that in the future there would be many important changes in my way of living but I had long since realized that life is made up of a series of adjustments. If you have been married for forty years and if your husband has been president of the United States for a dozen years, you have made personal readjustments many times, some superficial, some fundamental. My husband and I had come through the years with an acceptance of each other's faults and foibles, a deep understanding, warm affection, and agreement on essential values. We depended on each other. Because Franklin could not walk, I was accustomed to doing things that most wives would expect their husbands to do; the planning of the routine of living centered around his needs and he was so busy that I was obliged to meet the children's needs as well.

I had to face the future as countless other women have faced it without their husbands. No more children would be living at home. The readjustments to being alone, without someone else as a center of life and with no children about, would be difficult. Having Tommy with me made it easier at first, for Tommy, as she was called in the family, had long been my secretary and she made coming home to wherever it might be worthwhile. But there was still a big vacuum which nothing, not even the passage of years, would fill.

I had few definite plans but there were certain things I did not want

283

to do. I did not want to run an elaborate household again. I did not want to cease trying to be useful in some way. I did not want to feel old—and I seldom have. In the years since 1945 I have known the various phases of loneliness that are bound to occur when people no longer have a busy family life. But, without particularly planning it, I have made the necessary adjustments to a different way of living, and I have enjoyed almost every minute of it and almost everything about it.

It was not always easy. At first there was seemingly a greater adjustment to be made in my outer way of life than in my inner life. Ever since my husband had become president in 1933 I had lived in the White House, which meant a public existence. In earlier days he had held various public positions, but somehow our public and private lives had meshed more easily. Then came the years of his disabling illness. Later, beginning with the governorship of New York, we were back in public life on a changed basis. There was less of a family private life. Franklin was busy and there was at all times a public life that had to be planned and arranged with care.

As I look back now I think these latter-day readjustments in life have been made easier for me by the fact that I had become used to changes ever since Franklin's illness. I think I had long been preparing for the personal adjustments that came with his death. I had always been a good organizer and I could make decisions. In the long night's trip from Warm Springs, Georgia, before my husband's funeral in the White House I had made certain definite decisions. I did not want to live in the big house on the Roosevelt estate at Hyde Park. But what would the children feel? They loved the Hyde Park house. Their grandmother had made them feel it was their permanent home. How would it seem to have it swept out of their lives?

For myself, I knew I would live in the cottage that I had made out of my furniture factory on Val-Kill Creek, two miles back from the big house at Hyde Park. Tommy already had an apartment there. My cottage has a small apartment for the couple who work for me, two living rooms, a dining room, seven bedrooms, a dormitory for young people, two large porches downstairs and a sleeping porch upstairs. The cottage was an adjunct to our lives at Hyde Park but it was mine and I felt freer there than in the big house.

In his will Franklin left the place at Hyde Park to me and to our children throughout our lives if we desired to live there. At our deaths a certain acreage, including the big house, was to go to the government. But he left a private letter to me saying that he did not think we could afford to run the place and advising me to urge the children to give the house to the government at once. He wrote that his experience with the homes of other presidents had made it clear that visitors would make private life difficult. Characteristically, he remarked that he would hate to think of us taking refuge in the attic or the cellar in search of privacy.

I was happy when the children joined with me in deciding to turn the big house over to the government as soon as it could be arranged. I soon found that I had also better liquidate the farm at Hyde Park, since it was being run with doubtful efficiency. While I had my own daughter and three daughters-in-law and two sons with me, I arranged for the division of jewelry and furs, including all that had been designated for me from Franklin's mother's estate and everything else that I felt I would not need in my new way of life. Under the will I had first choice of silver, pictures, furniture, linen, china and other things, but I decided that I would take very little. I wanted a few things for sentiment—the Turner water colors my husband had given me, some of the linen and other objects that we had used for a long time. There were some things I would need that belonged to me. But, somehow, possessions seemed of little importance, and they have grown less important with the years.

My feeling that it is a mistake to hoard possessions was confirmed when I discovered under the eaves of the Hyde Park attic some bolts of Chinese silk. They probably had belonged to Mrs. Paul Forbes, my mother-in-law's sister, and had been literally "put under the plank," as she called it, many years earlier. When I found them hidden away under the eaves the beautiful silk had been hopelessly ruined by rain water.

After all the urgent matters had been taken care of as well as possible, and I had left the White House for the last time, I went to New York, where I had taken an apartment on Washington Square a year earlier. I had thought it would be just the right place for my husband and me when he left the Presidency. When I arrived there without him at ten o'clock on the evening of April 20, Lorena Hickok was arranging boxes of flowers and carefully gathering up the cards so we would know whom to thank.

Tommy was there, too, having traveled with me from Washington. The fact that she stayed on after Franklin's death made it seem at first as though he were on one of his trips and we were living the kind of life we would have lived in any case. That first summer of 1945 I did much physical work, clearing out cupboards in the big house at Hyde Park, unpacking boxes and barrels that had come from Washington.

President Truman sent to Hyde Park a chauffeur and automobile to help me through the first month. After the chauffeur left in the middle of May I discovered for the first time what the shortage of gasoline and automobiles meant to people generally. I had no car except the little Ford fitted with hand controls which my husband used to drive around Hyde Park. It was an open car and all right for summer. But when winter came we still had nothing else except a small work truck, and Tommy and I must often have been an odd sight when, wrapped in all the rugs we could find in order to keep ourselves from freezing, we drove between Hyde Park and New York City.

There were in the summer of 1945 a number of kind friends who worried about me. One day my long-time friend Major Henry Hooker, who had been close to Franklin, telephoned to ask if he and John Golden, the theatrical producer, could call at my apartment in New York. When they arived they were very serious-faced and asked me about my plans for the future.

"I've had a number of offers of various jobs that might interest me," I said.

"Now, Mrs. Roosevelt, we have come here to offer you our services," Mr. Golden said. "We have appointed ourselves as a kind of committee to help you. We would like to have you consult us in connection with the various things you have been asked or will be asked to do. Then we could pass on whether such proposals are a good idea. In other words, we would be a committee to consider how your life is to be planned."

Miss Thompson was sitting nearby and as he talked her mouth dropped open and she gave them both an unbelieving stare. "Did I hear you correctly? You want to plan her life?"

"Exactly," Mr. Golden replied. "As old friends of the family, we feel she should be careful to do only things that count. Now, our idea is that I will provide whatever showmanship is necessary and Major Hooker will pass legal judgment . . ."

I had either to interrupt them or to burst into laughter. "Look, my dears," I said, "I love both of you dearly. But you can't run my life. I would probably not like it at all."

They departed, still warmhearted, still a little worried and perhaps a little sad. "Remember," Major Hooker said, "we are still a committee and if you need us we'll always be ready to help."

As time went on, the fact that I kept myself well occupied made my loneliness less acute. I am not sure whether this was due to my own planning or simply to circumstances. But my philosophy has been that if you have work to do and do it to the best of your ability you will not have much time to think about yourself.

The first year after my husband's death was a busy one. Many persons—Princess Juliana of the Netherlands, Madame Chiang Kai-shek, Ambassador and Madame Andrei Gromyko of Russia, General and Mrs. Eisenhower—came to call at Hyde Park. And, particularly in the summer, my children and grandchildren, nieces, great-nephews and others were often there.

The real point at which outer readjustment seemed to culminate was on April 12, 1946, when we turned the big house over to the United States government at a ceremony attended by President Truman. In my speech I told how Franklin had pictured the estate, under federal auspices, as a place to which the people of our own country and even of the world might come to find rest and peace and strength, as he had. I said I had no regrets in turning it over to the government for safekeeping. It was better to pass the house on with its contents just as it had been left by my husband, so that it might not take on the personality of those who might have made the house their home after his death. "His spirit," I said, "will always live in this house, in the library and in the rose garden where he wished his grave to be."

Readjustments in one's inner life have to go on forever, I think, but my main decisions were made by the end of the first year. It was Fala, my husband's little dog, who never really adjusted. Once, in 1945, when General Eisenhower came to lay a wreath on Franklin's grave, the gates of the regular driveway were opened and his automobile approached the house accompanied by the wailing of the sirens of a police escort. When Fala heard the sirens, his legs straightened, his ears pricked up, and I knew that he expected to see his master coming down the drive as he had come so many times.

Later, when we were living in the cottage, Fala always lay near the dining-room door where he could watch both entrances just as he had when his master was there. Franklin would often decide suddenly to go somewhere and Fala had to watch both entrances in order to be ready to spring up and join the party on short notice. Fala accepted me after my husband's death, but I was just someone to put up with until the master should return. Many dogs eventually forget. Fala never really forgot. Whenever he heard the sirens he became alert and felt again he was an important being, as he had felt when he was traveling with Franklin. Fala is buried now in the rose garden at Hyde Park and I hope he is no longer troubled with the need for any readjustments.

I have led a busy life for many years and it has not seemed less busy since the death of my husband. In the years since 1945 my life has been complicated in some ways because my working hours are long. I travel a great deal and see many people. But in another way I live very simply, so simply that not a few visitors, especially those from some distant countries where servants are plentiful as well as inexpensive, are often surprised to find that I plan the meals, do part of the daily shopping, and serve dinner for a dozen guests with a "staff" consisting of a couple in the country, one maid in town.

In the years immediately after Franklin's death I discovered that financial matters could be rather nightmarish because I was not a trained businesswoman. At first I focused mainly on cutting down expenses and earning enough money to meet my regular bills. Franklin had been too busy during the last years to settle his mother's estate, which meant that now both estates had to be settled, and this took a long time. In 1933, when we first went to the White House, I had stopped sharing many of the expenses I had previously carried jointly with my husband. This had left me free to use most of my inherited income—about $8,000 a year— for clothes, which in Washington, and for almost the first time as far as I was concerned, were an important item. Then whatever I earned by writing and speaking could be used for my personal interests and charities.

But from the day of my husband's death it was clear that I would have to meet all the daily expenses of the apartment in New York and, for a short time, of the big place at Hyde Park, which had a considerable payroll. Luckily, my husband had left me two life insurance policies. I used their proceeds while awaiting settlement of the estate, which amounted to approximately a million dollars. Then I had to make another decision.

I could live on what my husband had left me and stop working. Or I could continue to work and pay most of what I earned to the government in taxes. I don't suppose that there was really much of a decision to make because, of course, I wanted to go on working. In my new position, however, because of the tax laws I could no longer give my earnings to people or organizations in which I was interested. I had to establish a charity fund into which I put all earnings from lectures, which amounts to about 20 to 30 per cent of my income. The laws permit me to give that much to tax-exempt charities, educational institutions, hospitals and churches.

I found in time that I could live on what I earned by writing, appearing on radio or television, and reading manuscripts at $100 a month for the Junior Literary Guild. Actually, these earnings total somewhat more than I spend on living expenses, and it is a good thing they do because all the income from my inheritance and more besides is required to pay my annual tax bills.

Although I have said that I live very simply, I do not mean that my life is always quiet or that things always go smoothly. It isn't and they don't. There was one day in 1957, for example, when I had a rather busy schedule, but I firmly announced that I was reserving "a few quiet minutes" before dinner for a chat with an old friend, Lady Reading, who had just arrived from England. The day was not far along, however, before another old friend, former Governor Adlai Stevenson of Illinois, called me on the telephone. He had just returned from a trip to Africa.

"I wondered if it would be all right if I dropped by and had just a few minutes' quiet talk with you before dinner," he said.

Of course, I told him I should be delighted to see him and he and Lady Reading arrived about the same time. We had hardly settled down in the living room when the doorbell rang.

There were two young men in the hallway. One of them was wearing a bathrobe—and obviously nothing else. He was staying in the apartment above mine while the owner was away and he had accidentally been locked out.

"Oh, I forgot! I left the water running in the bathtub and it will overflow and flood the floor."

Yes, I thought, and it will all come down through my apartment ceiling!

At that moment Governor Stevenson came to the door, saying that he could no longer stand the suspense and wanted to know what was wrong. When I explained, he rose to the emergency by dashing down to the basement and turning all the knobs he could find in an effort to shut off the water for the entire building. Meantime I sent around the corner to get a locksmith. By the time he arrived Governor Stevenson had acknowledged a certain lack of success as a plumber, but the locksmith was able to open the door of the boy's apartment before we were flooded out. It was all rather amusing but it did interfere with my "few quiet minutes" with my guests. In fact, by the time we sat down again it was so late that Dore Schary had arrived to be my guest at dinner and to read for all of us the new play he had written about Franklin's illness at Campobello.

I don't normally have many quiet minutes in the day. I get up around seven-thirty most mornings. At breakfast, I read the newspapers. Then I work out the menus for the day and write instructions in "the cook's book."

By nine o'clock my secretary, Maureen Corr, has arrived to start work with me on my daily newspaper column. I have three secretaries, but not all in the same place!

After my years of work with the UN I became a volunteer in charge of organization work for the American Association for the United Nations. On my lecture tours and other journeys, Miss Corr often goes along because I must find time to do my column and a monthly page for a magazine. I dictate the column, which Miss Corr takes down on the typewriter. Then I correct it and she puts it in final shape for the messenger who comes each day before two o'clock.

I usually try to arrive at my office at the A.A.U.N. by ten o'clock. In the early 1950's when I was a member of the United Nations delegation I often had to be present for a meeting as early as nine o'clock. At the A.A.U.N. office there is always some routine work in connection with organizing new chapters—we had thirty when I took the job in late 1953 but by 1960 we had about two hundred and fifty, and sometimes there is a meeting that I must attend in the afternoon.

I try to get back to my apartment for luncheon, if possible, and then in the afternoon I usually have engagements or errands to run or friends to see or perhaps a meeting of the board of some organization in which I am active. But, if not, I start work on the mail. I receive an average of about a hundred letters a day from relatives, friends and—mostly—from strangers. Virtually all of them are answered but obviously that is a task that requires sound organization. Miss Corr opens all except my personal letters and is able to draft answers to most of them because she is familiar with what I would say.

By the time my secretaries have drafted answers to these letters there are probably only a dozen or fifteen left for me to read and answer. I go through them at odd times, whenever I have the opportunity, and scribble a note indicating my reply. Then, usually in the late evenings, when all the answers have been typed, I read and sign them all. Many times, especially if I have guests or go out during the evening, I am still signing at one o'clock in the morning. I don't have to stamp the letters that are going to towns or cities in the United States because all wives of former presidents have the franking privilege, but I do have to buy stamps for the large number of letters that I send abroad.

Occasionally I do something on radio or television. One radio broadcast across the Atlantic I remember clearly. It was with Lise Meitner, who had helped to give us the secret of the atom bomb. She had worked on uranium research in Germany in the 1930's but had been expelled from that country under the Nazi regime because of her Jewish blood. In 1945 she was in Sweden and I, in New York, was asked to speak to her on a transatlantic broadcast. It was a strange experience. While I was in the National Broadcasting Company studio prior to the start of the program, the technicians hooked us up by telephone to the studio where Dr. Meitner was waiting in Sweden. When I spoke to her I found a very famous but very frightened lady on the other end of the telephone. We could hear the NBC man in Sweden coaxing her to open her mouth and speak. She almost wept. Finally I tried to reassure her, saying: "Don't be afraid. Listen carefully to what I say and then answer slowly, thinking exactly of what you want to say, and you will be good. You really speak English well." That was only one minute before we went on the air and I prayed that she would follow my advice. She did, and I believe the broadcast was successful.

Of course, I do not spend all my time in New York City. I cannot even guess at the number of miles I travel a year, but during the winter I am on the road perhaps one week and sometimes two weeks in every month, including fairly regular trips abroad. Many of these trips to deliver lectures (I give about 150 a year) or to work for the A.A.U.N. are quick ones, because whenever I have to speak at a luncheon or dinner I try to arrange it so I can go by plane, arriving just in time to keep my engagement, and return the same evening or at least early the next morning.

I do not grow weary of travel and I do not tire easily—not so easily as some younger people I know. Sometimes, it is true, my feet hurt. What I call my "White House feet" hurt largely because of a change in the bones in my instep caused by years of standing at receptions in the White House. I generally find pleasure in travel because it gives me an opportunity to catch up on my reading. In fact, I do most of my reading for pleasure on airplanes, since at home there seldom seems to be time to pick up the many books that interest me. Incidentally, if I have a complaint about the kind of life I lead, it is that I simply cannot find time to read as much as I wish.

Twenty-nine

Not Many Dull Minutes

MY MOTHER-IN-LAW once remarked that I liked to "keep a hotel" and I probably still do when I am at Hyde Park. There usually seems to be plenty of guests there and they may include almost anyone from the Emperor of Ethiopia to my newest great-grandchild. Sometimes there are so many guests that they arrive by the busload—perhaps a group of college students from various foreign countries who come for a few hours to sit under the trees and talk with me on any subject they please, or perhaps a crowd of seventy-five or so employees of the United Nations who have been invited for a picnic.

Each year I also have a picnic for about 150 youngsters from Wiltwyck School for delinquent boys. On that occasion I always try to enlist the help of my grandchildren, who wait on the guests and organize outdoor games. We feed the boys plenty and then they usually lie on the grass for a while and I read them a story such as Kipling's "Rikki-tikkitavi" or "How the Elephant Got His Trunk." We also have a package of candy for each boy before they go home.

My picnic ground is a large one and in summers it is used perhaps once or twice a week by some school or social group and, if I am there, I always try to stop by to speak to them for a few minutes. Otherwise they have to take care of themselves. For that matter, my own guests at Hyde Park usually have to fend for themselves much of the time because there are certain periods every day when I have to be busy at my work. There are a pool where they can swim, a tennis court, a stream full of water lilies and a boat, and plenty of room for walking over the countryside—accompanied by my Scottie if he feels in the mood.

I drive my own car at Hyde Park, sometimes meet guests at the rail-

293

road station five miles from my cottage and do much of my own shopping at the roadside stands. During the summer months I keep the deep freeze well stocked and always try to be prepared to feed any number up to twenty—most of them unexpected—for luncheon.

A number of my visitors are friends or acquaintances connected with my work for the American Association for the United Nations or with my earlier life in the White House, while others are official visitors to the grave of my husband. One of the most interesting was Emperor Haile Selassie of Ethiopia, who came to Hyde Park while on an official visit to the United States. He was a slight, bearded man with dignity and strength of character and, I felt, a desire to foster freedom, peace and progress in his country. It seemed to me that the Western clothes he wore on his journey were less impressive on him than the robes and sandals of his own land, but he was a person I liked and admired.

The Department of State had, of course, made all arrangements for his visit. A representative of the department advised me that there would be nineteen persons in his entourage. He would arrive at noon and I was to meet him at my husband's grave in the rose garden. He was to visit the library, where the records of my husband's administration are kept. He positively must get to the house by one o'clock because he wanted to see a television broadcast of a film that he had made. Then, the State Department representative added sternly, it was imperative that the Emperor have a half hour alone in his room before luncheon for rest and contemplation.

I thought this a rather crowded schedule but I didn't try to argue with the State Department protocol officer. I met the Emperor and accompanied him to the library. He was much interested in modernizing his own country, and when he saw the excellent system for keeping records in the library he became excited and ordered his staff to be assembled.

"Look," he exclaimed, "study this system. Here is how you do it— here is how you keep history."

I barely managed to get him to the house on the stroke of one. He found a low stool in the living room and seated himself in front of the television set and seemed to forget everything else as the film of himself came on the screen. I am not sure that he had ever seen television before. The minutes passed and no sign that he was ready to retire to his room for the scheduled half hour before luncheon. At last I approached him.

"Your Majesty, I believe you want to rest for half an hour alone."

"Oh, no, it is not necessary to be alone. I only wanted to take off my shoes for a while and you see my shoes are off."

Another distinguished visitor to Hyde Park was Prime Minister Nehru of India, who came to luncheon one day when a number of my grand-children and their friends were there. A striking figure in his long, dark coat and white trousers bound tightly at the ankles, the prime minister seemed delighted to see the young people and after luncheon sat cross-legged in the middle of the living room and talked to them for a long time. He appeared to be just as interested in asking them questions as they were in hearing his views.

As I got to know the prime minister better, when I later visited India, I felt he was a man of great physical and moral courage. But I discov-ered that his remarkable intellectual abilities did not free him entirely from prejudice. In the dispute between India and Pakistan over Kashmir, Mr. Nehru was completely emotional because of his personal ties to Kashmir. I felt that he suffered a stoppage of all reason on that partic-ular subject and contradicted the high ideals that he normally expressed in regard to the right of peoples to decide their own destiny.

It seems to me that Secretary of State John Foster Dulles' method of dealing with Prime Minister Nehru was unfortunate and unwise. In the 1950's India was newly independent and the Indians were highly sensitive in regard to their independence. Then, too, after the Com-munists came into power in Asia, India was the only large non-Com-munist nation in Asia. Mr. Nehru firmly expects India will remain non-Communist and this is of great importance to the West. Yet Secretary Dulles made several grave errors in dealing with India. While negotiat-ing the Japanese treaties he did not go to India. Mr. Nehru felt this was an obvious slight. Then, when India and Pakistan were in conflict, we sent arms to Pakistan, theoretically at least for defense on her northern (Russian) borders. It created against us in India a bitterness that might well have been avoided by limiting our aid to Pakistan to the economic field. I cannot help feeling that Mr. Dulles failed to understand the feelings of many of the peoples with whom we deal.

After Franklin's death I did not plan to travel alone or purely for pleas-ure, but in recent years various circumstances have taken me on trips that covered a large part of the world. I do not want to tell about them in chronological order, like a secondhand Cook's tour, but I do want to say something here about the invitation I received in the spring of 1948 to visit England for the unveiling of the statue of my husband in Grosvenor Square, when I was also invited to spend a weekend at Windsor Castle.

The King and Queen were kindness itself. They showed me to my room and sitting room and told me that the King's mother, Queen Mary, was staying over at the castle in order to greet me. At dinner a Highland piper, dressed in kilts, came in to march once around the table, playing his bagpipes. There was, of course, much formality but I was impressed by the easy manner of the King, dressed during the day in tweed jacket and slacks like a country squire, and by the skill of the Queen in keeping their family life on a warm friendly level even in such a historical setting as Windsor Castle. Princess Margaret, for example, had some young friends in who promptly turned on the phonograph to listen to popular records. I was amused to notice that, like most fathers, the first thing the King said when we came into the room was: "Meg, the music is too loud. Will you please turn it down?"

On our first evening at the castle we were taken on a tour of the galleries after dinner. Like my mother-in-law at her Hyde Park home, Queen Mary knew where every painting and *objet d'art* was placed—or at least where she thought each one should be placed. She promptly observed with no particular pleasure that the King had changed the hanging of several paintings.

I was particularly struck by the then Princess Elizabeth, still a young girl at the time of my visit but very serious-minded. She came to me after a dinner given by the Pilgrims and said: "I understand you have been to see some of the homes where we are trying to rehabilitate young women offenders against the law. I have not yet been to see them but could you give me your opinion?"

I told her I was favorably impressed by the experiment. The government had taken over some of the country's historic houses that the owners could no longer afford to maintain and had put them under the care of young women prisoners, who, with expert guidance and advice, had done the work of rehabilitating the houses and gardens to preserve them as national monuments. What struck me at the time was that this young princess was so interested in social problems and how they were being handled.

One evening during my visit at Windsor Castle, when Mr. Churchill was there, we played The Game—a form of charades. Queen Elizabeth acted as a kind of master of ceremonies and chose the words that the rest of us were called upon to act out. She puzzled for some time over various words and occasionally turned to Mr. Churchill for assistance, but without success. The former prime minister, with a decoration on the bosom of his stiff white shirt and a cigar in his hand, sat glumly aside and would have nothing to do with The Game.

When Mr. Churchill, now Sir Winston, had been at the White House during the tense years of the war, he and Franklin would talk for hours after dinner. It had been a terrible strain on my husband to sit up until one or two o'clock and then have to be at his desk early the next day while his guest stayed in his room until eleven. I suppose I showed my concern about this at the time and the prime minister probably remembered it when on a later occasion in London he said, "You don't really approve of me, do you, Mrs. Roosevelt?"

Looking back on it, I don't suppose I really did—though the cigars and the various favorite drinks I had to remember had something to do with it.

I think I might interrupt my story here to say that I have seen Princess Elizabeth on several occasions since she became queen. Her loveliness does not change but she seems to me still more serious, as one might expect her to be under the burden of her duties.

On one occasion when I had been invited to the palace for a chat with her, a young secretary escorted me to my automobile. "It must be terribly hard," I said, "for anyone so young to have so many official responsibilities and also carry on as a wife and mother." He looked at me with what I thought was a surprised expression and said briskly, "Oh, no. Not at all. The Queen is very well departmentalized." How does one departmentalize one's heart? I thought.

There had been a warm behind-the-scenes controversy over the statue. Sir Campbell Stuart, head of the Pilgrims Association, which raised the money for the memorial, and the sculptor, Sir William Reid Dick, strongly felt that Franklin should be depicted standing, facing into the wind. But Winston Churchill, who was an artist himself, took issue. He argued that because Franklin could not walk the statue should show him in a sitting position.

The controversy was much in my mind after King George had spoken at the ceremony and then walked with me to the statue for the unveiling.

I pulled a cord and, as the covering dropped away, I found myself looking at a statue showing Franklin as he was some years before his death. The figure was standing, with one hand gripping a cane and with the familiar cape flowing back from his shoulders. It gave the impression of a young, vigorous man and I think that is the impression my husband would have liked to leave with the British people. I have never regretted that it was done as a standing figure.

The sculptured figure has two shallow pools on either side of it and around the pools are low marble seats where, as the landscape architect explained to me, people could come and sit and eat their lunches. Carved on the back of the four seats are the Four Freedom declarations. The architect said he felt Franklin had always liked to have the people close to him. "And here I have made this possible," he added.

Judging by what I observed when I visited Grosvenor Square in later years, the people agree with him. There are always people there and I have rarely seen the statue without at least one small home-made bouquet resting on the marble base.

Thirty

Learning the Ropes in the UN

NOW I WANT to turn back to late in 1945 when there began one of the most wonderful and worthwhile experiences in my life.

In December of 1945 I received a message from President Truman. He reminded me that the first or organizing meeting of the United Nations General Assembly would be held in London, starting in January, 1946, and he asked me if I would serve as a member of the United Nations delegation.

"Oh, no! It would be impossible!" was my first reaction. "How could I be a delegate to help organize the United Nations when I have no background or experience in international meetings?"

Miss Thompson urged me not to decline without giving the idea careful thought. I knew in a general way what had been done about organizing the United Nations. After the San Francisco meeting in 1945, when the Charter was written, it had been accepted by the various nations, including our own, through their constitutional procedures. I knew, too, that we had a group of people, headed by Adlai Stevenson, working with representatives of other member nations in London to prepare for the formal organizing meeting. I believed the United Nations to be the one hope for a peaceful world. I knew that my husband had placed great importance on the establishment of this world organization.

At last I accepted in fear and trembling. But I might not have done so if I had known at that time that President Truman could only nominate me as a delegate and that the nomination would have to be approved by the United States Senate, where certain senators would disapprove of me because of my attitude toward social problems and more especially youth problems. As it turned out, some senators did protest to

299

the President against my nomination but only one, Senator Theodore G. Bilbo of Mississippi, actually voted against me. He had been critical of statements I had made previously in regard to discrimination against Negroes, but when some of the newspapermen in Washington asked him why he opposed my nomination he replied only that he had so many reasons he would have to write a book in order to cover them all. Anyway, my nomination was confirmed by the Senate, and I still marvel at it.

I might point out here that as a delegate to the United Nations and, later, as a member of the Commission on Human Rights I received a salary that would have amounted to about $14,300 a year, except that one is paid only for the days one actually works. My transportation and hotel room bills were paid by the government and I received around $12 a day for expenses when required to travel abroad. My actual expenses always exceeded these figures, but I never knew just how much I was out of pocket because I didn't keep a complete account of them. Therefore, the only sums I could deduct from my income tax were those that I recorded for official entertainment. I suppose my service as a delegate for seven years actually cost me a considerable sum.

I did not know that I was permitted to take a secretary with me to the meeting in London and when I said good-by to Tommy I was rather heavyhearted at the thought of crossing the Atlantic Ocean alone in January. Members of the delegation sailed on the *Queen Elizabeth* and the dock was swarming with reporters and news photographers who surrounded the senators and congressmen on the delegation to get last-minute statements and pictures. Everything had quieted down, however, when I drove in my own car to the dock and got aboard rather late and managed to find my way to my stateroom.

The first thing I noticed in my stateroom was a pile of blue sheets of paper on the table. These blue sheets turned out to be documents, most of them marked "secret," that apparently related to the work of delegates. I had no idea where they had come from but assumed they were meant for me so I looked through them. The language was complicated but they obviously contained background information on the work to be taken up by the General Assembly as well as statements of our government's position on various problems.

I promptly sat down and began reading—or trying to read. It was dull reading and very hard work. I had great difficulty in staying awake, but I knew my duty when I saw it and read them all. By the time I finished I supposed that the Department of State had no more secrets from me, but I would have found it hard to reveal anything because I was seldom really sure of the exact meaning of what was on the blue sheets.

At the time I feared this was because I couldn't understand plain English when it concerned State Department matters, but I changed my mind on this score because others seemed to have the same difficulty. I remember one occasion later when our secretary of state, General George C. Marshall, summoned all members of the delegation to a special meeting to discuss our position on an important point, which is not pertinent to this story. Because of some question I asked, he evidently felt I was not clear on the matter and he went over it again.

"Is that clear?" he asked.

"I'm sorry, sir," I replied, "but that is not the way I read it in the newspapers."

Somewhat irritated, the general said that I was mistaken and that he would send me a State Department paper covering the subject.

He did and I read it carefully. Then I read it twice. Still I didn't know what our position was. I sent the paper around to one of the department's best legal minds and asked him to explain it to me. He sent me a note in reply: "If this is what they send the President on the subject, God help the President!" Then I asked one of the delegation's most experienced advisers to come to my room and showed him the blue paper.

"You must be able to explain this," I said. "You must have had a part in writing this paper."

He studied it for a while and then said, "Yes, I had, but obviously it was not intended for you or anybody else to know what this paper meant."

But I am getting far ahead of my journey to London. One day, as I was walking down the passageway to my cabin, I encountered Senator Arthur H. Vandenberg, a Republican, and before the war a great champion of isolationism. He stopped me.

"Mrs. Roosevelt," he said in his deep voice, "we would like to know if you would serve on Committee Three."

I had two immediate and rather contradictory reactions to the question. First, I wondered who "we" might be. Was a Republican senator deciding who would serve where? And why, since I was a delegate, had I not been consulted about committee assignments? But my next reaction crowded these thoughts out of my mind. I realized that I had no more idea than the man in the moon what Committee Three might be. So I kept my thoughts to myself and humbly agreed to serve where I was asked to serve.

"But," I added quickly, "will you or someone kindly see that I get as much information as possible on Committee Three?"

The senator promised and I went on to my cabin. The truth was that at that time I did not know whom to ask for information and guidance. I had no idea where all those blue documents marked "secret" that kept appearing in my cabin came from; for all I knew, they might have originated in outer space instead of in the Department of State.

Later I discovered that there was at first some concern among the Democrats on the delegation whether Senator Vandenberg would "go along" on the United States plan in London or whether he might stir up a fuss. But their suspicions proved groundless.

"When the Charter meeting of the United Nations was held in San Francisco," the senator told me, "I didn't want to be a delegate. I didn't much believe in international organization along this line, but your husband urged me to go and insisted that I could vote exactly as I felt was right. On that basis I went."

Needless to say, Senator Vandenberg became one of the strongest supporters of the United Nations; it was he who worked hard to keep the budget moderate so that there would be no danger of driving out the smaller, weaker countries. His influence meant much in the early years when support was badly needed for this bold new concept of an organization that might be our only hope of avoiding future wars.

We stayed at Claridge's in London. Our offices were on Grosvenor Square about two blocks from the embassy. When I arrived there my adviser, Durward Sandifer, said that there were one or two members of the delegation's staff who would be available to discuss with me the problems of Committee Three.

As I learned more about my work I realized why I had been put on Committee Three, which dealt with humanitarian, educational and cultural questions. There were many committees dealing with the budgetary, legal, political and other questions, and I could just see the gentlemen of our delegation puzzling over the list and saying:

"Oh, no! We can't put Mrs. Roosevelt on the political committee What would she do on the budget committee? Does she know anything about legal questions? Ah, here's the safe spot for her—Committee Three. She can't do much harm there!"

Oddly enough, I felt much the same way about it. On the ship coming over, however, State Department officials had held "briefings" for the delegates. We listened to experts on various subjects explain the problems that would be brought up, give the background on them, and then explain the general position of the United States on various controversial points. I attended all these sessions and, discovering there also were briefings for newspaper people aboard the ship, I went to all their meetings too. As a result of these briefings and of my talks with Mr. Sandifer and others, I began to realize that Committee Three might be much more important than had been expected. And, in time, this proved to be true.

One early incident in London gave me cold chills. Papers kept coming to my desk—and most of them marked "secret" or something of the sort. One morning when I walked into my office I found a notice to report at once to the security officer. I did not know where to find the security officer but, after numerous inquiries, I was directed to his office in the building. He confronted me with the fact that his staff, making their rounds at night, had found on my desk a paper that was marked "top secret." I recalled then that I had left my office at a time when my secretary was out and I had presumed that she would put all papers away when she returned and then lock up the office. Apparently she had not and I was guilty of a serious offense, which I never repeated. Thereafter I made certain that the papers were locked away in the file and that the office was locked. I also always carried personally the briefcase in which I took documents home for study, keeping it within reach or putting it in a safe place. I frequently noticed in later years, however, that information in papers marked "top secret" appeared in the newspapers even before it reached us. But that is one of the curious inconsistencies that you have to accept in government work.

Secretary of State James F. Byrnes had not accompanied the delegation, but he arrived by air soon after we reached London. He disliked delegation meetings and briefings and I never knew him to call one, except on one occasion, when the meeting was a kind of cocktail party at which we talked about our work in a desultory fashion. However, Mr. Byrnes stayed only a short time. Thereafter we had regular briefing sessions in which

State Department experts—or perhaps Edward R. Stettinius, who later succeeded Mr. Byrnes as head of the delegation—discussed each morning the important items on the day's program. These meetings were often held in a large room where around nine o'clock in the morning all the U.S. delegates and their advisers would gather, perhaps forty or fifty persons in all. Normally the head of the delegation would preside and outline the high points of the work to be done while the rest of us followed his remarks by reference to the printed or mimeographed documents that had been prepared for us by the experts before the meeting. Then, when certain complicated problems were to be discussed in detail, a State Department official with special knowledge of the subject would take over. If any points were not clear, the five delegates or their alternates would ask questions.

In this way all the delegates were able to keep up with what was going on in general—if they listened carefully and had time to read the prepared papers—and in addition each delegate and each alternate got detailed information about the particular committee or the special project on which he or she was working at the moment. These briefings became a regular part of my routine throughout the six years I was connected with the American delegation to the United Nations, regardless of whether we were in London, Paris, Geneva or New York.

I drove to the first session of the General Assembly in London with Mr. Stettinius, who was then assistant secretary of state, accompanied by Mr. Sandifer and two other young advisers. Each delegate had a desk and there were several seats behind him for his advisers. The gathering of so many representatives of the large and small nations was impressive.

The first business of the Assembly was concerned with organization and the election of the first president, Paul-Henri Spaak of Belgium, a wonderful diplomat, an eloquent orator and a statesman of stature who did much to help the United Nations get off to a good start. The first Secretary General of the United Nations was Trygve Lie, a Norwegian. He was an able man who strongly believed in the ideas behind the United Nations, which he served well. He was a positive personality, which possibly was a handicap in his position, for he eventually made enemies. It is important that the Secretary General not only should be a good negotiator but should be able to make practically everyone feel he is their friend—if such a thing is possible.

At the early sessions in London I got the strong impression that many of the old-timers in the field of diplomacy were skeptical of the new world organization. They had seen so many failures, they had been through the collapse of the League of Nations, and they seemed to doubt that we would achieve much. The newcomers were the ones who showed the most enthusiasm and determination. They were, in fact, often almost too anxious to make progress. It was fortunate that such men as Mr. Spaak and Mr. Lie were on hand and skillful enough to give the veterans new inspiration and to hold the newcomers in check when necessary.

During the entire London session of the Assembly I walked on eggs. I knew that as the only woman on the delegation I was not very welcome. Moreover, if I failed to be a useful member, it would not be considered merely that I as an individual had failed but that all women had failed, and there would be little chance for others to serve in the near future.

I tried to think of small ways in which I might be more helpful. There were not many women on the other delegations, and as soon as I got to know some of them I invited them all to tea in my sitting room at the hotel. About sixteen, most of them alternate delegates or advisers, accepted my invitation. Even the Russian woman came, bringing an interpreter with her. The talk was partly just social but as we became better acquainted we also talked about the problems on which we were working in the various committees. The party was so successful that I asked them again on other occasions. I discovered that in such informal sessions we sometimes made more progress in reaching an understanding on some question before the United Nations than we had been able to achieve in the formal work of our committees.

As a result, I established a custom, which I continued throughout the years I was connected with the United Nations, of trying to get together with other nations' representatives at luncheon or dinner or for a few hours in the evening. I found that often a few people of different nationalities, meeting on a semisocial basis, could talk together about a common problem with better results than when they were meeting officially as a committee.

As time went on, there were more and more women serving on various delegations, and ours usually had a woman alternate even while I was still a delegate. Helen Gahagan Douglas, Mrs. Ruth Bryan Rohde, and Edith Sampson all were extremely valuable on the United States delegation.

As a normal thing the important—and, I might say, the hard—work of any organization such as the United Nations is not done in the big public meetings of the General Assembly but in the small and almost continuous meetings of the various committees. In the committee meetings each nation is represented by one delegate or an alternate and two or three advisers.

The discussions and the compromises and the disagreements that occur in committee meetings are of utmost importance. At first I was not familiar with committee work and not sure of myself, but Mr. Sandifer was always seated just behind me to give me guidance. As time went on I got so I could tell merely by his reactions whether the discussion was going well or badly. If I could feel him breathing down my neck I knew that there was trouble coming, usually from the Russians.

There is a question many people have asked me about the responsibilities of a delegate to the United Nations. "You are representing your government, but do you do exactly what you are told to do or say? Do you have any latitude for self-expression or for personal judgment in voting?"

The answer is a little complicated. In the first committee meetings I attended in London I was in complete agreement with the position of the State Department on the question at issue: the right of war refugees to decide for themselves whether they would return to their countries of origin. I was uncertain about procedure, however, and often lagged behind when the chairman called for a vote. Finally, Mr. Sandifer said sternly:

"The United States is an important country. It should vote quickly because certain other countries may be waiting to follow its leadership."

After that I always tried to decide how I would vote before a show of hands was asked for and, as soon as it was, my hand went up with alacrity. In deciding how to vote, it is true that a delegate, as a representative of his government, is briefed in advance on his country's position in any controversy. In London, fortunately, I agreed with the State Department position. But later I learned that a delegate does have certain rights as an individual and on several occasions I exercised my right to take a position somewhat different from the official viewpoint.

Of course, a delegate cannot express his disagreement publicly unless he resigns, since obviously it would be impossible to have representatives of the same nation saying different things in the United Nations. But he may exercise his right to disagree during the private briefings. Before the start of a session we were told what subjects would be on the agenda. If you disagreed with the government's attitude you had the right to say so and to try to get the official attitude changed or modified. You could, if necessary, appeal to the President to intervene and you could, if there was no solution, resign in protest.

On one occasion I did object vigorously to our official decision to rescind, without explanation to our people, the position we had taken on recognizing the Franco government in Spain. I was joined by other delegates and the State Department put off action until it could explain the situation fully.

It was while working on Committee Three that I really began to understand the inner workings of the United Nations. It was ironical perhaps that one of the subjects that created the greatest political heat of the London sessions came up in this "unimportant" committee to which I had been assigned.

The issue arose from the fact that there were many displaced war refugees in Germany when the Armistice was signed—Ukrainians, Byelorussians, Poles, Czechoslovaks, Latvians, Lithuanians, Estonians, and others—a great number of whom were still living in temporary camps because they did not want to return to live under the Communist rule of their own countries. There were also the pitiful Jewish survivors of the German death camps.

The Yugoslav and, of course, the Soviet Union position, put forth by Leo Mates, was that any war refugee who did not wish to return to his country of origin was either a quisling or a traitor. He argued that the refugees in Germany should be forced to return home and to accept whatever punishment might be meted out to them.

The position of the Western countries, including the United States, was that large numbers of the refugees were neither quislings nor traitors, and that they must be guaranteed the right to choose whether or not they would return to their homes. I felt strongly on the subject, as did others, and we spent countless hours trying to frame some kind of resolution on which all could agree. We never did, and our chairman, Peter Fraser of New Zealand, had to present a majority report to the General Assembly, which was immediately challenged by the U.S.S.R.

In the Assembly the minority position was handled by Andrei Vishinsky, one of Russia's great legal minds, a skilled debater, a man with ability to use the weapons of wit and ridicule. Moscow considered the refugee question of such vital importance that he spoke twice before the Assembly in a determined effort to win over the delegates to the Communist point of view. The British representative on our committee spoke in favor of the majority report. By this time an odd situation had developed. Someone would have to speak for the United States. The question threw our delegation into a dither. There was a hurried and rather uncomfortable consultation among the male members and when the huddle broke up John Foster Dulles approached me rather uncertainly.

"Mrs. Roosevelt," he began lamely, "the United States must speak in the debate. Since you are the one who has carried on the controversy in the committee, do you think you could say a few words in the Assembly? Nobody else is really familiar with the subject."

I said I would do my best. I was badly frightened. I trembled at the thought of speaking against the famous Mr. Vishinsky. Well, I did my best. The hour was late and we knew the Russians would delay a vote as long as possible on the theory that some of our allies would get tired and leave. I knew we must hold our South American colleagues until the vote was taken because their votes might be decisive. So I talked about Simón Bolívar and his stand for the freedom of the people of Latin America. The South American representatives stayed with us to the end and, when the vote was taken, we won.

This vote meant that the Western nations would have to worry about the ultimate fate of the refugees for a long, long time but the principle of the right of an individual to make his own decisions was a victory well worthwhile.

Toward the end of the sessions we worked until late at night. The final night the vote on Committee Three's report was taken so late that I did not get back to the hotel until about one o'clock. I was very tired, and as I walked wearily up the stairs at the hotel I heard two voices behind me. Turning around, I saw Senator Vandenberg and Mr. Dulles.

"Mrs. Roosevelt," one of them said, "we must tell you that we did all we could to keep you off the United Nations delegation. We begged the President not to nominate you. But now we feel we must acknowledge that we have worked with you gladly and found you good to work with. And we will be happy to do so again."

I don't think anything could have made the weariness drop from my shoulders as did those words. I shall always be grateful for the encouragement they gave me.

Thirty-one

I Learn about Soviet Tactics

THE CONTROVERSY with the Communist-dominated countries over the fate of refugees in Germany aroused in me a desire to see for myself what had happened. I discussed my idea with Ambassador John Winant, who said he would arrange for me to visit Germany, with the aid of the Army, which was then in control of everything in occupied areas.

I was stunned and appalled by what I saw when we circled the ruins of Cologne and Frankfurt and other places that I remembered as great and crowded cities. Later when we circled Munich and looked down on the rubble of Berlin I felt that nobody would have imagined such utter, horrible destruction. Nothing could better illustrate the sickening waste and destructiveness and futility of war than what I was seeing.

Later I was to see the effects of the first atomic bomb on Hiroshima. The bombing of Germany had continued over a period of months and months. The bombing of Hiroshima was over in a few seconds. But the results were the same.

We landed first at Frankfurt, where there were a number of refugee camps, including one for Jews in Zilcheim and others for refugees from Estonia, Poland, Latvia and other countries that were now under Soviet domination.

At Zilcheim I was greeted by leaders of the Jewish refugee group. They had built a small hill with steps leading to the top where they had erected a stone monument inscribed: "To the Memory of all Jews who died in Germany." In all the Jewish camps there were signs of the terrible events through which these people had passed and of the hardships they continued to suffer, but they also showed with what courage and steadfast hope they could meet disaster.

309

In the mud of Zilcheim I remember an old woman whose family had been driven from home by war madness and brutality. I had no idea who she was and we could not speak each other's language, but she knelt in the muddy road and threw her arms around my knees.

"Israel," she murmured, over and over. "Israel! Israel!"

As I looked at her weather-beaten face and heard her old voice, I knew for the first time what that small land meant to so many, many people.

I went from Frankfurt to Berlin. With the help of American officials I managed to cover considerable ground. On a trip eleven years later I observed many differences between East Berlin and West Berlin; for instance, the brilliant lights of the Western sector and the almost complete darkness of the Eastern sector; but in 1946 I was conscious only of mass destruction and human misery.

We drove past the smashed Chancellery where Hitler had ruled and the bunker where he died and the pockmarked Brandenburg Gate that had been a symbol of Germany's greatness. Now there was desolation and the sordid, degrading sight of men and women and children dealing in the black market. Here in the shadow of the Brandenburg memorial and close to the ornate temple of Nazi imperialism all the degradation of war had come home to roost.

I also visited the quarters of refugees who had made their way from areas formerly occupied by the Germans, like the Sudetenland, to the Western sector. The people were crowded into unsanitary and ramshackle underground shelters without proper heat or water or food.

The whole journey had been a good one for me. I had grown and matured and gained confidence. After we landed in New York I wrote my thanks to the President and to the secretary of state for an unforgettable experience, and thought my work with the United Nations was over.

Not long after I returned to New York I received notice that the Economic and Social Council, which had been set up by the United Nations in London, had created a committee, the Nuclear Commission on Human Rights, to make recommendations on matters pertaining to the functioning of the UN Human Rights Commission. It was to meet in New York in the spring of 1946 and the members were named as individuals rather than as representatives of their various governments. I was asked on President Truman's invitation to be a delegate to the General Assembly.

We began work in temporary quarters at Hunter College in New York and carried on at Geneva and the United Nations headquarters at Lake Success, on Long Island, for the next two years. But during the same period I was again nominated and confirmed as a member of the United Nations delegation to the General Assembly and continued as a delegate until 1953. At the same time I was also the United States representative on the Human Rights Commission.

Thus, over the years, in one capacity or another, I saw a great deal of the Russian delegates and not infrequently felt I saw and heard too much of them, because they were usually the center of opposition to our ideas.

Perhaps Maxim Litvinov, whose wife was English, was the most skillful Russian diplomat in getting along with Western government officials. V. M. Molotov, who had been so rigid as foreign minister and who helped make *niet* such a famous word at the United Nations, was always correct and polite. But, although I saw him frequently and sometimes sat next to him at dinners, I never felt it was possible to know him well. In fact, it was difficult to know any Russian well and I suppose the Kremlin planned it that way. It was really impossible to have a private and frank talk with Russian officials.

One of the Russian delegates over a period of years was a big, dramatic man with flowing white hair and a bristling black beard, Dr. Alexei P. Pavlov, a nephew of the physiologist Ivan Petrovich Pavlov, famous for his studies of conditioned reflexes. His nephew was an able delegate but he seemed to feel the need of proving that he was a faithful Communist. He was a brilliant talker and he often gave me a difficult time in committee meetings.

More than once Dr. Pavlov arose with a flourish, shook his white locks angrily, and made a bitter attack on the United States on the basis of some report or even some rumor that had to do with discrimination against Negroes, particularly in our southern states. Of course, I always replied vigorously, pointing out that the United States had done a great deal to improve the social and economic status of the Negro.

On one occasion, when I was irritated to the point where I could no longer stand it, I interrupted him to say sternly, "Sir, I believe you are hitting below the belt." This may not have been elegant language for a diplomatic exchange but it expressed my feelings.

The Soviet delegates could be very thorough in seeking out American weaknesses or in distorting the picture of our country by citing some isolated fact to support their propaganda. Once the Russian delegate made much of what he said was a law in Mississippi forbidding any man to strike a woman with an ax handle more than two feet long. This was an example of American brutality.

"In my country," a French delegate mused, "the law forbids a man to strike a woman even with a rose, long stem or short stem."

Louis Hyde, a delegation adviser, telephoned our legal adviser in Washington to check on the allegation. The uncomfortable answer he received was that an old law something like that actually was on the books in Mississippi. In any event, we had no very strong reply.

The Russian delegates simply did not dare talk with a foreigner without taking the precaution of having a witness present, lest at some future time their superiors might accuse them of making traitorous statements. Not even brash, outspoken Dr. Pavlov, who so often berated me and attacked my stand at United Nations sessions, dared ignore this practice. One evening he and his colleague Alexander Borisov came to my apartment with several other guests. I had invited a friend who is an excellent pianist.

Dr. Pavlov listened happily, his big shock of hair falling forward and his black beard touching his chest. As they were leaving, Mr. Borisov went into the other room for his hat, leaving me alone with Dr. Pavlov. Dr. Pavlov leaned toward me and in a conspiratorial whisper said, "You like the music of Tchaikovsky. So do I!" This was as close as I ever came to getting a frank expression of opinion from a Soviet official.

I certainly do not want to give the impression that the Russian officials or representatives are surly or even unfriendly, because they are often quite the opposite. It is in official negotiation or debate that they adopt such rigid attitudes and distort facts so irritatingly and display such stubborn unfriendliness toward Western ideas. Despite their difficult official attitude, I always felt that the Americans should refuse to show unfriendliness toward representatives of the Communist bloc. Some of our delegates would not even be photographed shaking hands or talking with a Communist representative when the reporters and news photographers clustered around at the opening of each session of the Assembly or on some similar occasion. Presumably our reluctant delegates were taking the position that the Russians were mortal enemies, or perhaps they felt it would do them no good politically.

The Russians, on the contrary, were eager to be photographed shaking hands with and smiling broadly at the delegates of other nations, particularly Americans, realizing that this gave the impression all over the world that they were trying to be friendly and co-operative.

It is possible that Westerners never fully understand the complexity of the Russian character, but I constantly kept trying to do so throughout my service with the United Nations and later, because I know it is extremely important for us to learn all we can about our powerful international opposition.

I am not certain that there is any moral in these observations about my dealings with representatives of the Soviet Union. On second thought, there is, of course, a moral and a warning for those who love freedom, and it is probably best expressed by a kindly but tragic man who loved freedom very much indeed. His name was Jan Masaryk, the son of Thomas G. Masaryk, the first President and founder of the Republic of Czechoslovakia.

At meetings of the United Nations General Assembly it happened that the Czechoslovak delegation sat directly behind us. Jan Masaryk, as foreign minister of Czechoslovakia and head of the delegation, listened to the debates intently in the early days of the General Assembly, but when it came time for a vote he always followed the lead of the Russian delegation. This was not difficult to understand because the Russian armed forces practically surrounded Czechoslovakia. On one occasion he leaned forward and whispered:

"What can you do? What else can you do when you've got them right in your front yard?"

He found that what he did made no difference to the Russians. In February of 1948 the Communists seized power in Czechoslovakia by a *coup d'état* and a few days later it was announced that Jan Masaryk had died by leaping from a window.

Thirty-two

The Human Rights Commission

DURING MY YEARS at the UN it was my work on the Human Rights Commission that I considered my most important task, though as I have explained I was also a delegate to the General Assembly, which, at times when the two jobs more or less fused, caused some confusion.

Now to get back to the commission that made recommendations on the definite composition of the Human Rights Commission at Hunter College in the spring of 1946. The work in this perod was an intensive education for me in many things, including constitutional law, and I would not have been able to do much but for the able advisers who worked with me. I was more than grateful for the fact that Marjorie Whiteman, who has written a legal work on American treaties, sat behind me at almost every meeting and explained what we could or could not do for constitutional reasons. My first adviser at this time, James Pomeroy Hendrick, always remains in my mind, with Mr. Sandifer, as an ideal guide, philosopher and friend. Urbane and soft-spoken, with a quiet sense of humor, he was tireless and devoted. He never spared himself and so he made me work hard.

After I had been elected chairman of the commission I tried to push our work along as rapidly as possible. I might point out here that eventually we decided that our main task was to write an International Bill of Rights. This was to consist of three parts. First, there was to be a Declaration, which would be adopted as a resolution of the General Assembly and would name and define all the human rights, not only the traditionally recognized political and civil rights but also the more recently recognized social, economic and cultural rights. Since the General Assembly is not a world parliament, its resolutions are not legally binding on member

314

states. We therefore decided that the Declaration would be followed by a Covenant (or covenants) which would take the form of a treaty and would be legally binding on the countries that accepted them. Finally, there was to be a system for the implementation or enforcement of the rights.

We also finally recommended that the Human Rights Commission be composed of eighteen members, each of whom would represent one of the United Nations governments, and that they should be chosen on a rotating basis with due regard for geographical distribution, except for the representatives of the five great powers—the United States, Soviet Russia, the United Kingdom, France and China. As was customary, it was agreed that these five powers should be elected automatically to the new commission as members, leaving thirteen seats to be rotated among other members of the United Nations. These recommendations, however, came later. At the Hunter College sessions we were just getting started.

When we called for a formal vote on presenting our proposals to the Economic and Social Council, the Soviet Union merely recorded its "objections and dissent" to certain agreements and thus did not join in the recommendations of the preparatory commission. The Council accepted our recommendations and President Truman then nominated me as the United States representative on the commission. Being the first chairman of the commission, in addition to my duties as a delegate to the Assembly, kept me on United Nations work during five or six months of the year and I had to keep my daily schedule on a crowded timetable basis, with no minutes to spare.

I remember once when the Assembly was in session at Lake Success, Richard Winslow, who was manager of the office of the United States mission, told me that he had been urgently asked to arrange a time when I could talk to Tyler Wood, who was then assistant to Will Clayton, about a problem concerning the United Nations Relief and Rehabilitation Administration.

"Well," I replied, handing him my calendar, "here's my schedule. You figure out when I shall see him—if you can!"

He worked on the calendar for a while and then said that he and Mr. Wood would meet me at a certain hour when I would be leaving a New York hotel. They did. We got into the automobile that was waiting for me and Mr. Wood began talking. He talked until we had driven pehaps twenty blocks to the CBS studios, where I got out while they remained in the car. I did a broadcast with Mr. Dulles on some United Nations matter, then returned to the car and resumed talking with Mr. Wood while we drove from Madison Avenue to Broadway and Fifty-ninth Street. There I got out again and went into the United Nations Information Center, which was just being formally opened at ceremonies that I had promised to attend. I returned to the automobile and resumed my conversation with Mr. Wood as we drove downtown to the Hotel Pennsylvania, where Mr. Wood and Mr. Winslow left me. I continued on to my apartment at Washington Square, some twenty blocks away, but I had an appointment with Senator Austin at the Hotel Pennsylvania not long afterward, so I returned there within a short time. Arriving in the offices we had at the hotel, I discovered I had five minutes before meeting the senator, so I sat down in a big easy chair and closed my eyes.

A few minutes later I was awakened by a startled exclamation and looked up to see Mr. Winslow and Mr. Wood standing in the doorway, staring.

"How did you get here! We left you on your way home. We walked across the street, had a quick hamburger and coffee and came directly here, and you're already on the scene!"

In those days my life went long at that pace for long periods at a time and I suppose I enjoyed it, because I like to keep busy. When the United Nations headquarters was at Lake Success my schedule was complicated by the fact that I always had duties to attend to in New York early in the day and then had to drive for forty minutes to reach Lake Success in time for the opening of the Assembly or some other meeting at eleven o'clock. This suited Mr. Sandifer or any adviser because he always knew that I would be starting out at twenty minutes after ten. He could climb into my automobile with the assurance that for the next forty minutes I would be his "captive audience" and that our discussion of the day's work would not be interrupted.

In the period that I presided as chairman of the Human Rights Commission we spent most of our time trying to write the Universal Declaration of Human Rights and the Covenants, and there were times when I was getting in over my head. The officers of the commission had been charged with the task of preparing the first draft of the Declaration, and I remember that on one occasion, thinking that our work might be helped by an informal atmosphere, I asked this small group to meet at my apartment for tea. One of the members was the Chinese representative, Dr.

P. C. Chang, who was a great joy to all of us because of his sense of humor, his philosophical observations, and his ability to quote some apt Chinese proverb to fit almost any occasion. Dr. John P. Humphrey, a Canadian who was the permanent head of the Division of Human Rights in the UN Secretariat, and Dr. Charles Malik of Lebanon, one of the very able diplomats at the United Nations, also were at this meeting.

As we settled down over the teacups, one of them made a remark with philosophic implications, and a heated discussion ensued. Dr. Chang was a pluralist and held forth in charming fashion on the proposition that there is more than one kind of ultimate reality. The Declaration, he said, should reflect more than Western ideas and Dr. Humphrey would have to be eclectic in his approach. His remark, though addressed to Dr. Humphrey, was really directed at Dr. Malik, from whom it drew a prompt retort as he expounded at length the philosophy of Thomas Aquinas. Dr. Humphrey joined enthusiastically in the discussion, and I remember that at one point Dr. Chang suggested that the Secretariat might well spend a few months studying the fundamentals of Confucianism! By that time I could not follow them, so lofty had the conversation become, so I simply filled the teacups again and sat back to be entertained by the talk of these learned gentlemen.

Early in the meetings of the commission we discovered that while it would be possible to reach some kind of agreement on the Declaration, we were going to be in for a great deal of controversy with the Russian representatives, particularly Dr. Pavlov, who attempted at every opportunity to write a bit of Communist philosophy into the document. For example, at the end of practically every article the Russian proposed to amend the Declaration to read: "This shall be enforced by the state."

When such an amendment was proposed I, or one of the other Western delegates, would argue against it on the ground that this was an international declaration by the United Nations and that we did not believe it should be imposed by the power of the individual governments. We would then ask for a vote and the amendment would be defeated. But as soon as the next article was completed the Soviet delegate would again propose the same amendment and we would have to go through the whole business again with the same result, the defeat of the Soviet proposal. This naturally became monotonous but the Russians never gave up trying.

The drafting of the articles continued over many months. During our early work on the Covenants and measures of implementation it became apparent that it was going to be exceedingly difficult to agree on articles that would, if accepted, be legally binding on the various nations. This was difficult enough in regard to civil and political rights that have become fairly well accepted throughout the civilized world, but when it came to economic and social rights it seemed to me at times that agreement would be all but impossible. These articles have, however, now been adopted by the majority of the committee.

The reason for this, in part at least, was the vast social and economic differences between the various countries; the social and economic conditions in the United States, for example, as contrasted to existing conditions in a country like India. The gap was so great that it was well-nigh impossible to phrase concepts acceptable to both countries. Let me give one example to explain these difficulties.

With the aid of various specialized United Nations agencies, we set out to write the best possible article aimed at the encouragement of universal education. We achieved a preliminary draft that stated that everyone had a right to primary, secondary and higher education, the first two to be compulsory but all of them eventually to be provided free by the individual governments concerned. This might read well to a citizen of the United States but it was quite a different matter in India.

"Our economy is strained," Madame Hansa Mehta, the Indian representative, explained, "and we are trying only to give all children a primary education. What would happen if we suddenly attempted to provide secondary and higher education, too? The article should be amended to read that the goal is to be accomplished gradually, with due consideration for the economy of each country."

"The trouble with that," I replied, "is that I do not believe the United States Senate would ever ratify a treaty so vaguely worded. The senators would ask: 'What does gradually mean—five years or ten years or a hundred years?' I just don't believe they would accept it."

But if the economic problems of underdeveloped countries provided one stumbling block, the political systems of other countries, particularly the United States, provided another. Our delegation had to insist on including a states' rights clause because we could act only in regard to matters that were under jurisdiction of the federal government. We had to explain that in other matters, which were under the control of the states, we had power only to "recommend" that the states take appropriate action.

Australia and Canada were the only other countries in a similar position.

Many of the other countries resented the fact that they were being asked to commit all their people to the instruments we were drafting, whereas on certain matters the United States delegation could commit only a limited number of the people and hope that the various state governments would accept our recommendations. I could understand their resentment and their opposition to our "states' rights" system, but we always fought to get our amendment in. So far, however, the draft Covenants still lack a federal states' rights clause. We made slow progress in drafting the legally binding Covenants and even slower progress in framing measures of implementation that would provide means to enforce the Covenants.

Late in 1947 it was decided that the next meeting of the Human Rights Commission would be in Geneva, so we left for that city early in December with the idea of completing our work in time to be home for Christmas. As chairman, I knew that it would require much hard work and long hours to be able to adjourn before Christmas but I was in a determined mood and I warned all the delegations of my plans.

I immediately laid out a schedule of work that, with night sessions, I believed would enable us to adjourn by eleven o'clock on the evening of December 17.

Nobody objected to my plans, at least not until later, and I must say that everybody worked hard. My own day started at eight o'clock, when I met with my advisers at breakfast and went over the work schedule and any difficult problems. Then I would go to the Palais des Nations Unies, where the sessions were held and get through my correspondence in time for the morning session of the commission. At luncheon we usually got several delegates together to continue our discussions informally and then returned to the afternoon meeting. At night we had an after-dinner session or a meeting of our delegation. Later Mr. Hendrick and I would talk for perhaps an hour about the next day's plans, and after he had gone to bed Mrs. Hendrick would come in with a pile of personal letters on which we worked until after midnight. By the time I had dictated my daily newspaper column I was ready for bed.

This was a grueling schedule for everybody and within a few days I was being denounced—mostly in fun, I hope—as a merciless slave driver. But I must say we got through a great deal of work and kept to our schedule, for which I was very grateful to all the delegations.

We did end our work at eleven o'clock on the evening I had originally designated.

Our efforts to write a Charter or International Bill of Human Rights reached a kind of climax at the Paris sessions of the General Assembly in 1948. After our Geneva meeting we made steady progress on the Declara-tion, despite many controversies with the delegates from Communist countries.

Dr. Pavlov was a member of the commission and delivered many long propaganda harangues that appeared to be more for the purpose of pub-licizing the Communist point of view than in the hope of making changes in the Declaration. He was an orator of great power; his words rolled out of his black beard like a river, and stopping him was difficult. Usually, we had to sit and listen, but on one occasion it seemed to me that the rash accusations he brought against the United States and Great Britain were proving a real detriment to our work. Dr. Pavlov knew that most of us were getting tired of listening, but toward the end of one week when we were preparing to recess he began speaking again. He seemed likely to go on forever, but I watched him closely until he had to pause for breath. Then I banged the gavel so hard that the other delegates jumped in surprise and, before he could continue, I got in a few words of my own.

"We are here," I said, "to devise ways of safeguarding human rights. We are not here to attack each other's governments, and I hope when we return on Monday the delegate of the Soviet Union will remember that!" I banged the gavel again. "Meeting adjourned!"

Eventually we completed a draft of the Universal Declaration of Human Rights that we foolishly felt would be quickly accepted by the General Assembly, which was meeting in Paris in the autumn of 1948.

"I believe," General Marshall, who had become secretary of state, said before we left for Paris, "that this session of the General Assembly will be remembered as the human rights session."

As the session opened I was full of confidence that we could quickly get the Declaration through the formal hearings before Committee Three and have it approved by the Assembly. My confidence was soon gone. We worked for two months, often until late at night, debating every single word of that draft Declaration over and over again before Committee Three would approve its transmission to the General Assembly.

During this time I made a trip to Germany, at the request of General Lucius Clay, who asked me to address a group of German women doctors at Stuttgart. This was not an easy assignment. There had been, during the conflict with Hitler, a considerable campaign of hatred in Germany directed against me personally because I had spoken out as strongly as I could against most of the things represented by Nazism, including the persecution of Jewish people. Furthermore, any occupation force, whether good or bad, just or unjust, is detested by the people it rules, and I have never had reason to believe that an exception is made of American troops. General Clay, however, was trying with considerable success to carry out a difficult assignment in Germany and he told me he believed it might be helpful if I spoke to the women in Stuttgart. So, of course, I agreed to do so.

There was a large crowd at the Stuttgart meeting, and, as I had feared, the women were cool and reserved if not bitter toward me when I arrived at the dinner. I had no intention of letting their coldness prevent me from saying certain things I had in my mind, so I began with a denunciation of the Nazi philosophy and actions. I made it as strong as I could and I expressed the opinion that the German people must bear their share of the blame. I had not expected my audience to be pleased by such remarks and they were not. The atmosphere became cooler.

Then I talked to them more approvingly. At that time the Russians were blockading Berlin, cutting off all coal and other supplies that moved over the normal land routes and forcing the United States to organize a gigantic airlift to supply West Berlin. The purpose of the Soviets was to force the Western powers to move out of Berlin. In this crisis the German people had acted magnificently and I praised them for supporting the democracies and defying the Communist power. I talked about the future, the recovery of Germany under a democratic form of government, and the hope that the United Nations would mean the end of international wars. Slowly the audience warmed up and I could feel a change of attitude as I concluded: "And now I extend to you the hand of friendship and cooperation."

On this trip I lunched with the women doctors and they told me about their problems with their own German refugees, who had to live on the German economy because they were German citizens but could not at that time of hardship find work. They were existing under miserable and dangerous conditions. I was also told of the difficulties of tracing children taken by Hitler from conquered Poland and other lands, under his plan of destroying their nationality. As the records were found, an effort was being made to restore the children to their families. Many of them did not even know they were not of German birth.

I stayed only a little more than a day in Stuttgart but the visit taught me much and I returned with zest to the work of the Third Committee of the General Assembly.

In the final vote in Committee Three, on presenting the Declaration to the Assembly, the delegates from four Moslem countries abstained, explaining that they believed the article on religious freedom was contrary to the Koran. We consulted Sir Zafrulla Khan, the foreign minister of Pakistan, the largest Moslem nation.

"It is my opinion," he declared, "that our Pakistan delegate has misinterpreted the Koran. I understand the Koran to say: 'He who can believe shall believe; he who cannot believe shall disbelieve; the only unforgiveable sin is to be a hypocrite.' I shall vote for acceptance of the Universal Declaration of Human Rights."

In the end there was no vote cast against the Declaration in the General Assembly, but there were some disappointing abstentions. The Soviet Union and its satellite countries abstained, since the Russian delegate contended that the Declaration put emphasis mainly on "eighteenth-century rights" and not enough on economic, social and cultural rights. The delegate from Saudi Arabia abstained, saying he was quite sure King Ibn Saud would not agree to the interpretation of the Koran. South Africa also abstained, I was sad to note; its delegate said that they hoped to give their people basic human rights, but that the Declaration went too far. Two small countries were absent. The Declaration was finally accepted by the General Assembly on December 10, 1948.

After the Declaration was accepted, it seemed to me that the United States had held the chairmanship of the Commission on Human Rights long enough. So at the 1951 meeting of the commission in Geneva, I nominated Charles Malik of Lebanon, with the consent of my government. He was elected and from then on I was just a member but a most interested member, for I believed the Human Rights Commission was one of the important parts of the foundation on which the United Nations might build a peaceful world.

The commission continued to work on drafting the Covenants, but this was so difficult that the United States group finally decided that it would be possible to progress only if we moved forward a step at a time. We proposed that there be two Covenants, one covering legally binding agreements on social and economic rights and another covering political and civil rights. This plan was vigorously opposed by some delegations, including the Soviets, on the ground that the economic and social rights were the most important and that they probably would not be accepted for years if they were in a separate covenant. But it seemed to our delegation that it was better to try to get what we could at that time. The civil and political rights already were a part of the law in many countries and were not so difficult to phrase in legal language that would be generally acceptable, although we knew that even this first step would be exceedingly difficult.

We finally won our point by only four votes, but taking the first step turned out to be even harder than we had expected. Progress had been made, but the Covenants were not well drafted, nor is the drafting yet complete, and I doubt whether they are likely to be accepted in their present form. Looking back over the work that has been done, I now believe it would be best to start anew by putting into the Covenant on civil and political rights only a few basic rights on which all could agree and to provide for adding other rights as it becomes possible to have them generally accepted.

The last session of the General Assembly that I attended in Paris was in the autumn of 1951, a session that continued after a brief Christmas holiday into February of 1952. Toward the end of this session Ambassador Austin became ill and for a short time I presided over the United States delegations. The heads of other delegations expressed affection for Senator Austin personally.

"We have not always agreed with the policies of the United States," most of them said in one way or another. "But if Ambassador Austin told us something was true, we knew it was true."

I served during the autumn of 1952, but at the end of each session all delegates automatically resign to permit the President to have a free hand in choosing his representatives. In the 1952 elections, a Republican administration came into power and all of us who were Democrats knew that our services with the United Nations had come to an end. But my interest in the United Nations had grown steadily during six years, and later I volunteered to work with the American Association for the United Nations so that I would not be out of touch with the work of the one organization that has the machinery to bring together all nations in an effort to maintain world peace.

Thirty-three

Foreign Travels

ALTHOUGH I HAD been bustling back and forth across the Atlantic Ocean rather like a harassed commuter for six years, my really extensive foreign travels did not begin until 1952 after the General Assembly in Paris.

The end of my duties as a delegate later that year meant that I no longer had to adjust my life to a schedule of meetings of the Assembly or the Human Rights Commission in various cities at frequent intervals. Though it was necessary for me to spend a certain amount of time traveling in connection with my work for the American Association for the United Nations, I had much greater flexibility in my schedule and was able to take longer trips abroad, always as a newspaperwoman and sometimes also as a representative of the A.A.U.N.

I had received a number of invitations to visit various countries. One was extended by Prime Minister Nehru. The invitation stuck in my mind and, as the Assembly was ending its sessions in Paris early in 1952, I decided the time might be right. "Instead of going back to New York as usual," I remarked to my secretary, "why not go home the long way— around the world. We've already got a good start."

So Mr. Nehru renewed his invitation and our ambassador to India, Chester Bowles, seemed pleased with the idea. Another thing that influenced me was that I had long wanted to visit Israel, particularly since I had seen the Jewish refugee camps in Germany and learned more of the eagerness of most of the refugees to migrate to Israel. As soon as I began making arrangements to stop in Israel on the way to India, I was approached by Charles Malik of Lebanon, whom I had come to know well on the Human Rights Commission.

"I know that you're going to stop in Israel on the way to India," he said. "I really don't think you should stop there without visiting some of the Arab countries. You should see more than one country in the Middle East."

A little later he made arrangements for me and my secretary, Miss Corr, and we flew directly from Paris to Beirut, Lebanon, where we arrived late one evening. Beirut was a beautiful and peaceful-looking city even at night, with the Mediterranean breaking softly on its beaches. Next morning when I went out to get into the car, I discovered I was to be escorted by a lorry filled with soldiers.

I had wondered a bit about the attitude of the people toward me because I had always been outspoken in my support of the state of Israel, but everyone seemed friendly and I decided to ignore the presence of the soldiers. When we halted to visit some historic site, the truck dashed up and the soldiers leaped out to set up "lines of defense" around us. This was an indication that the government was not at all certain about the kind of reception I would be given by the people. At least the officials were taking a rather alarmist view.

Actually, there were no signs of hostility and after a short time I became thoroughly irritated by what seemed to me intolerable nonsense. I insisted that they get rid of the soldiers at once. They did so but I was certain that throughout my visit there was always a guard of some kind nearby.

I found my visit to the Arab countries extremely interesting. Lebanon is perhaps the most Westernized of the Arab countries. We had planned to drive to Syria, but there was so much snow in the mountain passes that we went by air to Damascus, an amazing city with narrow streets and bazaars.

The newspapermen to whom I talked in Syria were particularly difficult. They were bitterly nationalistic and bitterly opposed to Israel and they badgered me with questions about why I should support the Israeli cause.

"The Balfour resolution for establishment of a Jewish homeland was accepted by the United States and Great Britain after the First World War," I usually replied. "This action encouraged the buying of land by the Jews on the assurance that a homeland would be created for them in Palestine. I feel that it practically committed our government to assist in the creation of a government there eventually, because there cannot be a homeland without a government."

From Damascus I drove to Amman, Jordan, but our time was short and I had a chance to meet only two or three government officials. They were greatly concerned with the problem of the Palestinian refugees who had moved out of Israeli territory during the warfare between Israel and the Arab states and had been put into camps in Jordan. I visited many of these camps during my trips and found them distressing beyond words.

I had seen various refugees camps in Europe and had been impressed by the way the inmates kept their hopes alive and tried to make their temporary quarters into "homes" even under the most difficult conditions. I had been particularly impressed by the burning desire of many Jewish refugees to get to Israel. Now, in the Arab countries, I learned something of the grave problem of refugees from Israel.

The Arab refugee camps were the least hopeful I had ever seen. One of the principal reasons for this, I believe, was that nothing had been done to preserve the skills of the people. They seemed to have little or nothing to look forward to and nothing to do. Under such conditions the adults are likely to lose their skills and the children grow up uninstructed.

"Why," I asked my official guide, "are these people not given something to do? They might be making things to go on the market or helping to produce food. If they lose their skills they will be worthless citizens in any country they may finally settle in."

The guide gave a kind of helpless shrug. "There is unemployment in most of the Arab countries, and we cannot permit these people to seek work that would put them in competition with the citizens of the country."

The standard of living in the camps we visited was low and the housing was inadequate. I visited one tent where a woman showed us her small baby, who was ill. "The baby was bitten by a snake yesterday," the woman explained, as she put it back on the floor of the tent. There was nothing to prevent snakes from entering, and babies lying on the floor were an easy prey.

The refugees were fed on a budget of three cents per day per person. That would seem to be a pitifully small sum even for countries with a low standard of living but it represented more food than was available to some of the nomads living in the desert.

Going from the Arab countries through the Mandelbaum Gate into Israel was, to me, like breathing the air of the United States again. The

Mandelbaum Gate is nothing much, a movable barrier, with soldiers on guard. But once I was through the barrier I felt that I was among people with a purpose, people dedicated to fulfilling a purpose.

I spent seven days in Israel, the same number I had spent in the Arab countries. The health program is a monumental work. Much had been done in the past by Hadassah, which built and ran hospitals made possible by general private donations of persons in many countries.

I was greatly impressed by what the Israelis had done to reclaim the desert and make it productive, to develop the country industrially and to accept as permanent citizens hundreds of thousands of refugees from war and persecution in Europe and elsewhere. But I was even more impressed when I returned to Israel three years later and saw how much had been done in that short time.

Of course, no one should imagine that everything is perfect in Israel. The country has many large and small problems of all kinds to overcome, including the necessity for establishing a sound basis for its economic existence. A great deal has been done. The desert has been made to blossom, but there remain grave obstacles, such as the efficient use of water, to a peaceful and prosperous future. I believe that with reason and patience solutions can be found and they will greatly benefit not Israel alone but the entire area.

Not all of Israel's problems are economic. One issue that must be faced by the government is that of separation of church and state. At present the influence of the church is so great that it is often difficult to distinguish between it and the state. I was suprised to be told of a young man who had been refused the right to marry the girl with whom he was in love because she was an Orthodox Catholic. This is merely one example of the injustices that can grow out of such a situation, and the incidents will greatly increase in time. Apparently leaders of the state do not feel that their country is strong enough to undertake a solution to this problem because it would arouse bitter controversy, but someday it must be faced. When it is, I am confident there will be a separation of powers as there is in the United States.

We flew to Karachi, the capital of Pakistan, where I was to be the guest of the All Pakistan Women's Association, at the invitation of the Begum Liaquat Ali Khan.

Here, as earlier in Israel and later in India, I saw a country not only struggling with the problems that beset any young government but also suffering from the results of the partition that had accompanied the achievement of their long-sought independence. The division of this sub-continent into two independent states, one predominantly Hindu, the other predominantly Moslem, was economically painful to both parts. From the point of view of defense, too, the subcontinent is paying a ter-rible price for partition. The mountain ranges guarding its northern border made undivided India a single defense system. The Khyber Pass was one of the few breaks through which invasion was possible. But the sword of partition not only divided the land, cutting off crops from mar-kets and factories from raw materials, it also split up everything from debts and revenues to rolling stock and typewriters, including, of course, the army. So today, instead of a single strong united army deployed to meet possible aggression from without, two lesser separate armies must defend the frontiers of the subcontinent. And, instead of facing out-ward, these two armies now face each other across a line in Kashmir, over which India and Pakistan are at odds.

As in the case of the Israeli-Arab dispute, bitterness and fear of one's neighbor has resulted in spending for defense huge sums badly needed for health, housing, education, and other programs that would better the living standards of the people.

For Pakistan this division of the subcontinent had an added complica-tion. Not only was Pakistan itself separated from India, but its western portion was separated from its eastern portion by some eight hundred miles of Indian territory. Neither was it a clean cut, for no matter how the partition lines were drawn millions of Hindus and Sikhs still were left in Moslem territory and millions of Moslems in the areas that went to India.

It is against the background of these facts that we Americans must view the problems of Pakistan and India today if we are to understand the conditions that exist there and the importance of intelligent and effective help.

Some of the officials with whom I talked described to me the difficulties of those early days of independence when they were trying to get the gov-ernment set up. They worked in practically bare buildings. They had no desks, no pencils, no typewriters, no paper, few telephones. They sat on packing boxes, wrote on packing boxes, and occasionally made them into beds at night. There were no files, no statistics. More serious, there was—and still is—a grave lack of the kind of trained personnel without which it is almost impossible to carry on the business of government. A number of the members of the first Cabinet had never before held office. Nor were there bookkeepers or stenographers or clerks.

At the top there were and are, of course, some exceedingly able people who managed to get the government running; and many young people are now being trained intensively in various civil service jobs. Here the Ford Foundation is giving invaluable help, in India as well as in Pakistan.

I had met the Begum Liaquat Ali Khan at a meeting of the General Assembly in Paris and had found her delightful. After the assassination of her husband, which shocked the world, the begum had devoted herself to trying to carry out his plans for his people. It is because of her leadership and the example of the Begum Husain Malik, that the women of Pakistan have begun to free themselves of the restrictions imposed by tradition. The principal instrument through which they are acomplishing their really magnificent work is the All Pakistan Women's Association, which has set up medical clinics, established educational centers, diffused information about agricultural methods, developed skills and handicrafts.

Like all the Middle Eastern and Asian countries, Pakistan has been terribly handicapped by her lack of technical experts, people qualified to draw up, appraise and carry out the necessary development programs. To meet this need the Pakistan government, the United Nations Food and Agricultural Organization, the UN Economic Commission for Asia and the Far East, and the International Bank have wisely collaborated to set up in Pakistan a center where this kind of training is available. It seems to me to represent the best kind of international thinking and co-operation.

The spirit of the people of Pakistan is something one does not soon forget. There is courage and great vitality. They are determined to make their government succeed, and their nation a cohesive force. In talking to the men at the head of this government I was convinced that their devotion and intelligent approach, with the resolute support of the people, cannot fail to make Pakistan a great country.

We landed in New Delhi on February 27, and I was overwhelmed to find Prime Minister Nehru there to greet me, with a number of other officials and his sister, Madame Pandit, head of India's delegation to the UN. I was also extremely glad to see waiting for me Ambassador Chester Bowles and his wife. In them I was greeting good friends whom I had known for many years.

We drove directly to Government House, the official home of India's president, Rajendra Prasad, where, as protocol required, we were to spend our first night. The following day we were to move to the home of the prime minister and stay with him for the rest of our visit.

During the course of that first meeting I asked Prime Minister Nehru about a article on India's recent election, which I had read before leaving the United States. It described how people had spent days traveling through tiger-infested jungles in order to vote; how some of the primitive tribes had trekked miles across deserts, blowing little flutes, and announcing when they finally reached their destination that they had come to worship the god "Vote." Out of India's 360 million people, 90 million voted.

I told Prime Minister Nehru that I had been long enough an observer of political life to know that no great outpouring of voters occurs unless someone has done some remarkable campaigning. He beckoned me into his office and pointed to a map on the wall, which traced all his campaign trips before the election and showed how many miles he had traveled by air, train, boat and automobile—altogether 25,732. Not included, however, were the miles he traveled by bullock cart, on horseback and on foot. At the bottom of the map is a line reading: "The Prime Minister, it is estimated, talked personally to thirty million people in his audience."

The first two years of India's independence were complicated, as they were in Pakistan, by the staggering refugee resettlement problem. The country's needs were studied but there was much to be done, and everything needing to be done at once.

Nevertheless, though India has far to go, she has made an inspiring beginning. This new democracy seems to evoke the kind of passionate devotion among its leaders that our forefathers had for the democratic government they were establishing in America. Perhaps this is one of the greatest contributions the young democracies can make to the older ones. We have grown stale; we are inclined to take everything for granted. Perhaps we may draw from people who ford rivers and walk miles of jungle trails in order to vote a new sense of our responsibility and a revival of our forefathers' readiness to pledge "our lives, our sacred honor, and all our worldly goods" for the idea they believed would make this country a place worth living in.

What the leaders of India want and are determined to have is a democracy that is indigenous to their country, based on their own past and the character of their own people. It is in helping India to build in its own way and on its own strength that Ambassador Bowles has done such a remark-

able job. In the less than half year he had been in India at that time he had
made great strides in seeing that foreign aid was intelligently co-ordinated
and applied. Perhaps even more important, he had given Indians an entirely
new idea of American officialdom and a new confidence in our motives and
our good will.

We must face the fact that in the years after the war our popularity took
a terrible tumble in India, as it did throughout the Arab countries. Having
shaken off the domination of one foreign power, they are understandably
determined not to fall under the influence of any other. Even Nehru, it is
said, was at first wary of Ambassador Bowles's suggestions for Point Four
aid, lest they conceal some attempt at economic domination.

In addition, we have against us their feeling that because our skins are
white we necessarily look down upon all peoples whose skins are yellow
or black or brown. This thought is never out of their minds. They always
asked me pointedly about our treatment of minorities in our country.

As I traveled about India during the next few weeks, the immensity of
the task this new government faces became overwhelmingly apparent. India
has two problems that seem to me particularly urgent: one is how to grow
more food; the other is how to control the rising tide of her population.

With the food problem looming so large, India has had to put increased
agricultural production ahead of everything else. Right now she spends
$600 million a year and more importing food and cotton she could grow
herself, simply to maintain the present inadequate level of diet and keep
her textile mills running. She needs not so much to bring more land under
cultivation as to get more from the farm land she already has. For instance,
an Indian farmer gets only half as much wheat from an acre as an American
farmer and only about one fifth as much cotton. To introduce modern
methods to the farmers in the villages, India needs thousands of trained
men: technical specialists of all kinds, agricultural chemists, experts in soil
science, ecology and sanitation, mechanics who can repair implements,
engineers to lay out irrigation and drainage works.

Water is another problem. India's great rivers contain more than enough
for her needs but at present only a small part of the flow is being used.
Only one fifth of her farm land is regularly watered.

International co-operation in many forms is giving magnificent impetus
to improved food rations, technical assistance, health care. What can be
done in these ways was vividly dramatized to me at Etawah, a district composed of some 700,000 people, scattered among many small mud villages.

The idea for this agricultural experiment was suggested by Albert Meyer, a New York architect, who is responsible for many of India's new buildings and is designing the new capital of the Punjab. Etawah is an Indian project. We furnish technical assistance and advice, and supplies that must be bought abroad, on the self-help principle that is the basis of all Point Four aid, but the plan is an Indian plan and what has been done has been done by the Indian people themselves.

For the first two years the project was headed by Horace Holmes, a Cornell-trained American agricultural expert from Tennessee. He had lived and worked with the farmers before he began to introduce any new ways. Then he induced a few of them to try something different as an experiment, perhaps imported seeds, different fertilizer, or a better tool. When they saw the difference these things could make they tried them on their own on a larger scale, and other farmers began to follow suit.

Already they had more than doubled their crop production; wheat which had grown about a foot high was now between five and six feet high. The cattle had improved and the cows gave more milk.

After our first two days in New Delhi we started by air on a trip that was to take us over a good part of India before we returned to the capital. That trip took us to Bombay and Trivandrum, the southwest tip of India, which has the highest literacy rate in India, 50 per cent as compared to an average of 10 per cent for the rest of the country. Now, as part of her Five Year Plan, India has drawn up a program to make education free and compulsory for all children between six and fourteen years of age. This means she will need about two million teachers and thousands of new schools.

From Trivandrum we flew to Mysore and from there on a sightseeing tour to Bangalore. The peak moment of all the sightseeing for me was the Taj. I will carry in my mind the beauty of it as long as I live. At last I know why my father felt it was the one unforgettable thing he had seen in India. He always said it was the one thing he wanted us to see together.

From Agra we flew to Jaipur and at length back to New Delhi, where we stayed at Government House with President Prasad, a gentle and quiet man with great strength of character.

It was at Allahabad, where I received an honorary degree, that I encountered the effect of Communist influence on the students. It is almost always difficult for us to realize why the Communist philosophy is easier for young Indians to accept than our own. We overlook the two major factors: they rarely know what we are talking about when we speak of freedom in the abstract; their most pressing problem, from birth to death, now as it has always been, is hunger. Freedom to eat is one of the most important freedoms; and it is what the Communists are promising the people of India.

From Benares to Nepal to Calcutta—so many crowded miles, so much want, so much ferment, so much blending of the timeless with the new. So much human need—and so little human communication, at least between Americans and Indians. One of these lacks of communication comes in our sense of values. Paul Hoffman, who asked me to lunch with him and his colleagues of the Ford Foundation in Los Angeles on my way home, crystallized this point. The American dream of the Horatio Alger success story is completely meaningless to the Indian. To him it is simply an indication of a struggle for material values. What we have failed to take to him is our spiritual values. An understanding of our own spiritual foundations may be one of the bridges we need to better understanding of the East and its people. We must show by our behavior that we believe in equality and in justice and that our religion teaches faith and love and charity to our fellow men. Here is where each of us has a job to do that must be done at home, because we can lose the battle on the soil of the United States just as surely as we can lose it in any one of the other countries in the world.

In the spring of 1953 I returned from a short trip to find bad news waiting for me. Miss Thompson was in the hospital. For several days I spent most of the time there. On April 12, on the anniversary of my husband's death, I went to Hyde Park. On my return I walked into the hospital just as dear Tommy died. There had been no sudden change. She just died.

Tommy had been with me for thirty years. In many ways she not only made my life easier but she gave me a reason for living. In almost anything I did, she was a help but she was also a stern critic. No one can ever take the place of such a person nor does one cease missing her, but I am sure she would not have wanted to live to suffer the torture of being an invalid.

Though my work for the American Association for the United Nations began in the spring of 1953, it did not become intensive until autumn. Consequently, I accepted an invitation that spring to be one of a group of exchange people going from the United States to Japan. The trip was under the auspices of Columbia University, which acted as host in this country for the Japanese who came here. Our hosts in Japan were Shigeharu Matsumoto and Dr. Yasaki Takagi, who represented the International House of Japan and the Committee for Cultural Exchange.

The reason the Japanese invited me was that their women were just coming into the responsibilities of functioning in a democracy after centuries in which feudalistic concepts had dominated their lives and customs. The attempt to change over to more or less democractic concepts in a short time naturally created many problems both of a political nature and in regard to family life. Some of the Japanese leaders hoped that an American woman, talking to groups of the Japanese women and men, would be able to explain to them the meaning of democracy and the manner in which a democratic government functions.

The fact was that after World War II the United States had rather arbitrarily insisted on giving the Japanese a democratic constitution, telling them that now they were going to be a democratic country. But this did not automatically change the old customs or turn feudalism into democracy. There were various articles in the new Japanese constitution that had been taken almost verbatim from Western documents, and some of these meant nothing to the Japanese or merely confused them because of the great differences between their social and economic background and the social and economic concepts of, say, the United States or France. So a period of education obviously was necessary, and I was happy to have a chance to do whatever I could to help spread the idea of democracy.

One of the first persons I encountered in the lobby of the Imperial Hotel in Tokyo was Marian Anderson, who had been singing with great success all over Japan. Later I held a press conference. I had always heard that the Japanese were avid photographers, but I never expected to see so many news photographers as greeted us in Tokyo. I was told that Adlai Stevenson gazed in wonder at them during his trip to Japan and exclaimed: "This is a photographic dictatorship!"

I will not attempt to describe our experiences in Japan in any chronological order because we covered so much ground in the five weeks we were there, but there were some highlights that stand out in my mind. A few days after our arrival we visited Princess Chichibu, the widow of the Emperor's brother. The princess had gone to the Friests School in Washington when her father was ambassador there. After her marriage she had kept in much closer touch with the people of Japan than other members of the royal family. Her former friends came to see her regularly to talk over problems of farming and she kept busy working with the Girl Guides, similar to our Girl Scout organizations, and with Four-H clubs, which have been active in Japan since the war in an effort to help young farmers learn modern methods of production.

The next day I had an interesting meeting at the Ministry of Labor with the people who run bureaus for women in industry, for improvement of rural life, child welfare and the like. These government bureaus bear the stamp of American organization but that does not mean they operate the way they do in the United States. The organization was imposed on Japan by the occupation authorities and American methods were not entirely suited to the facts of life in Japan: the place of women in the industrial system, the necessity for children to contribute to the family income, the ability of the economy to support such public service. In order to make these organizations practical, they had to be adjusted to fit conditions in Japan, and that has been a complicated task.

There is also the important question whether such services are welcomed by the public. As I was leaving the ministry a group of Communist party women, led by an American who is married to a Japanese, were waiting outside. The American woman stared at me and seemed to be highly strung to the point of fanaticism. As I stepped out the door the group began shouting anti-American slogans.

"Go home to America! We women who went through the war do not want any more war!"

The obvious answer was, of course, that neither did I want war. It is groups such as this one that keep the fear of war constantly alive in the peoples of the free world. I made numerous inquiries about Communist activities and strength in Japan. On one occasion I met with a number of college presidents in Nara and made a point of asking them about the attitude of students and professors.

"I doubt that more than a few are really convinced Communists," one said. "However, a few can make a good deal of noise because they know what they really believe in, while the others are divided and groping to find their way."

I was inclined to believe there was more real acceptance of Marxism among the students in Japan than these college presidents were willing to acknowledge to me. They did say that democracy was not making headway among the students and that it was not being well taught.

I talked to countless groups of women in many cities of Japan and there were certain broad themes that ran through all our discussions. One was the attitude of young people toward their elders and the attitude of the elders toward the young. Since the Japanese had been urged to accept the democratic idea of free discussion, there had developed a great deal of criticism between the two groups and this antagonism was increased by the fact that the young people blamed their elders for telling them that Japan could not lose the war. Much of the authority of the elders was undermined when the Japanese armies were defeated and the Emperor was declared to be a man rather than a god. The young people became cynical and disillusioned.

There were also many questions, particularly from the students, that I answered as best I could. Sometimes I was asked why the United States used the atom bomb and how I felt about it. I tried to explain the urgent reasons that prompted our leaders to make the decision in an effort to end the war quickly, but at the same time I expressed my feeling of horror about any kind of warfare. Another question was, "Do the people of the United States understand that the young people of Japan dislike rearmament and that, in order to rearm as urged by Washington, we have to change our constitution which was adopted at the request of the United States in the first place?"

Of course, world conditions had changed since they adopted the constitution that renounced war forever, but it was not so easy to see the threat of Soviet expansion through Japanese eyes as it was through American eyes. I don't suppose my explanations of the danger to the democracies were satisfactory to people who had never experienced democratic life.

These sessions were often exhausting, particularly if there were a large number of students in the audience, but what was most tiring to me was that everything had to be translated.

I remember one charming and rather sophisticated Japanese newspaperwoman who was beautiful in her native costume yet seemed to be familiar with Western customs. She told me that her greatest difficulty at home was with the "system of the pouch."

"What is that?" I asked.

"My mother-in-law," she said, "is old-fashioned. She has a large leather pouch and each week she puts into it all the family earnings. Then all of us become dependent on her ideas of how much we should spend or whether we should spend anything. In fact, she can practically tell us how to run our lives."

I found that this custom was practiced in many places. A woman who worked in a factory told me she went home on weekends to the farm where her family lived and that she always placed her earnings on the household shrine the night she arrived. The next morning they were in the mother-in-law's pouch. I found that most of the Japanese mothers in the working class look forward to the day when they will be mothers-in-law and can tyrannize over their daughters-in-law. Slowly these outdated customs are changing under the present government but it will be a long time before they are entirely gone.

I have had many experiences in my life, but I could not help feeling a twinge of anxiety as I prepared for my interview with Emperor Hirohito, the 124th of his line, and Empress Nagako. Knowing that old habits and customs were changing, especially for the women of Japan, I felt it would be interesting to know whether the Empress was able or desired to give some leadership in these changes.

The more I talked with groups of women in Japan the more I was convinced that, while the women were a force in their homes behind the scenes, they had not gained direct equality with men as provided in their new constitution, despite the fact that there were thirty women members of the Diet, or parliament.

There were certainly some intellectuals among the prominent women in the field of labor, in farm organizations and in social work, but they could not be called the most influential in Japan from the standpoint of social prestige. They were not, if I except Princess Chichibu, finding out how the girls in the factories lived or how the farm women worked in their fields or their homes.

There was a good deal of protocol attached to this meeting with the Emperor and Empress, in which I was guided by our ambassador, John M. Allison. After we were seated in the palace the Emperor and his wife arrived. The Empress wore a kimono. As I looked at her sitting calmly with her hands in her lap, with her face unlined and impassive, I could not help wondering what lay behind that placid surface. She must be a woman of extensive education. Her husband is a student of the sciences and has written several books. The Empress had always taken an interest in child education.

We talked about conditions generally and at one point the Emperor said he had always regretted that we had gone to war in spite of his vigorous efforts to prevent it. Now he hoped we were embarked on an era of friendship and peace.

Under the new constitution his position is changed but the Emperor can be an important figure. I think he was sincere in saying that he had tried to prevent the war and I decided that, if we behaved with tact and caution, we could count on him to help us build friendly relations with the Asian world. Even at that time he was hoping that Japan would become a member of the United Nations, as it later did, and that we could all work together for harmonious international relations.

I am afraid that during this interview I did not observe the rule that one should speak only when spoken to. I asked a few questions, or rather I made some remarks intended to draw out the ideas of the Empress.

"When I visited Pakistan and India," I said, "many changes were taking place, particularly in the status and activities of women. It seemed to me that women of all classes were drawing closer together and gaining in strength because of their greater knowledge of each other."

I looked at the calm face of the Empress, waiting for her to comment. She said nothing for a few moments and then replied: "We need more education." The Emperor broke in with some comment, and I thought perhaps that would be all the response I would get from the Empress, but she seemed to be thinking over my remarks, for in a few minutes she said: "There are great changes coming about in the life of our women. We have always been trained in the past to a life of service, and I am afraid that as these new changes come about there may be a loss of real values. What is your impression, Mrs. Roosevelt?"

"In all eras of change," I said, "there is a real danger that the old values will be lost. But it seems to me much less dangerous when the intelligent and broad-minded women who have had an opportunity to become educated take the lead to bring about the necessary changes."

"Our customs are different, Mrs. Roosevelt," the Emperor broke in. "We have government bureaus to lead in our reforms. We serve as an example to our people in the way we live and it is our lives that have influence over them."

That seemed to be the final word on how far the imperial family might go in assuming leadership in the new era in Japan. But I cannot help believing that, since the older women have been such an important influence in the home in the past, the future may see greater leadership exerted by the women of high social status, including members of the entourage of the imperial family.

As I look back on my visit to Japan, many incidents stood out as illustrative of the problems of establishing a democratic form of government in the Far East, and especially of educating women to take an active part in public affairs. One day in Tokyo I attended a round-table conference at the national Young Women's Christian Association with perhaps the most representative women leaders in the country. They were gravely concerned about progress in the new era of freedom. They made me see more clearly the difficulties created by an army of occupation or even by the presence of many American boys stationed at military bases in Japan. Unfortunately, we do not train our youngsters carefully enough before sending them throughout the world. They do not always remember that they are not merely soldiers but ambassadors, representing all that their own country stands for and all that democracy means to the rest of the world. The women were particularly concerned about the spread of prostitution and believed it could be controlled only by the closest co-operation between Japan and the United States.

The education of Japanese in democratic ways also was made more difficult at times by news from the United States telling of racial discrimination, of instances in Los Angeles and Texas where the work of UNESCO was attacked as communistic, and of the methods employed by the late Senator Joseph McCarthy in his Congressional investigations. Again and again Japanese told me they were confused and bewildered by these news dispatches, which were displayed prominently in the newspapers. "Will you please explain these attitudes?" one leading Japanese businessman asked me. "Japan hopes one day to be a member of the United Nations and to work loyally with that organization. But we are unable to understand why these things happen in a great democratic nation like the United States."

On another occasion a young man showed me a news dispatch from the United States saying that the Japanese government's victory in a recent election was because the majority of Japanese were accepting the policy of gradual rearmament which had been urged on the Tokyo government by our State Department.

"Do people in the United States really believe that?" he demanded. "Everybody knows that the government in Japan has been careful to say practically nothing on the subject of rearmament. Don't you realize that there is deep resentment here because many Japanese feel the United States used economic pressure at the time of the election in order to put into office people who favor the U.S. State Department's policies? For that reason, many feel that the United States is trying to make Japan economically a slave."

These are some of the suspicions and some of the grave problems that must be overcome—and, I feel sure, will be overcome—if our relations with the Far East are to be secure. Progress has been made toward this goal, but there are constantly arising new causes of misunderstanding, so that the road is a long and rough one. Perhaps our best hope is that the Japanese as well as ourselves want peace above all. This was impressed upon me strongly at the tragic city of Hiroshima.

To arrive in Hiroshima is an emotional experience. Here is where the first atom bomb ever to be dropped on human beings was actually used. The people of the United States believe that our leaders thought long and carefully before they used this dread weapon. We know that they thought first of the welfare of our own people, that they believed the bomb might end the war quickly with less loss of life everywhere than if it had not been dropped.

In spite of this conviction, one cannot see a city and be shown the area that was destroyed by blast and fire and be told of the people who died or were injured without deep sadness. To see the home where orphans were being cared for was to wish with one's whole heart that men could learn from this that we know too well how to destroy and must learn instead how to prevent such destruction. It is useless to say that Germany started the war and even started the research that led to the atomic bomb. It is useless to remember, as I did, the feelings of my husband and of the people of the United States when he heard the shocking news of the Japanese attack on Pearl Harbor. Pearl Harbor was only the climax of years of mounting misunderstandings and antipathies throughout the world. And out of all this came Hiroshima.

But it was not just here in this sad Japanese city that men and women and children suffered. All the world suffered. So it seems to me that the only helpful thing we can do, as we contemplate man's adventure into the realm of outer space, is to pledge ourselves to work to eliminate the causes of war through action that is possible only by using the machinery of the United Nations. If we do, then the peoples may understand each other a little better; they may have a better chance to be heard.

Contemplating the fate of Hiroshima, one can only say: "God grant to men greater wisdom in the future."

Thirty-four

The Long Way Home

MISS CORR and I continued on a western route around the world, stopping first at Hong Kong, which has become a fascinating crossroads of the free world in Asia. I was kindly received at Government House by Governor General Grantham and by American diplomatic officials stationed at this sensitive spot adjoining Communist China.

"Would you like to see the border of Communist China?" the governor general asked me.

"Indeed I would," I replied, "if that is possible."

As it turned out, it was no problem at all. The British general in charge of the border patrol called for me at my hotel the next morning and we drove over the hills to a little stream that separates Hong Kong from China. To my surprise, the "line" between the free world and the Communist world at this point is only a single strand of barbed wire and there is a bridge, guarded by police, over which a considerable number of Chinese go back and forth every day. These Chinese live on the Communist side but they own land on the Hong Kong side of the border stream and are permitted to cross each morning, often driving cows or pigs and carrying their farm tools, to work the land. Then in the evening they return across the bridge to the Communist side.

There did not seem to be many guards on either side of the border, but it was patrolled regularly. Nevertheless, a number of Chinese continued to flee across the frontier to Hong Kong every day or so.

"They were storekeepers, people with small means, who would have remained at their homes," the head of the border police told me, "but they said the Communist officials kept calling them up for questioning and

342

bedeviling them until they finally decided they would stand it no longer."

Talking with other officials and with refugees I got the impression that many of those who had fled to Hong Kong were neither Communist nor anti-Communist. They just wanted to be let alone and to be given a chance to earn a living. If the government did not try to tax them too heavily, they did not really care who ran it or whether it was corrupt; they just wanted to be left in peace.

The next day I met two gentlemen who had come from Taipei (Formosa). They represented the United States Committee to Help Chinese Refugees and were also busy trying to counteract the flood of Communist propaganda literature which comes into the Hong Kong area. This propaganda was largely cheap little books with pictures that misrepresent everything done by the United States or the United Nations as bringing death and destruction. Such propaganda was circulated widely among even the poorest Chinese and, so far as I could discover, little was being done by the democracies to offset these false stories.

I could not go to Taipei and not see Madame Chiang. But I knew that if I saw her I would have to tell her I did not think her dream of regaining China was possible. I felt that Chiang Kai-shek had had his chance and had not used the right methods to unify the country, and I did not believe that he any longer had any chance to do so. So I did not visit Taipei.

I might mention here that in 1955 I made a second visit to Hong Kong and found that there was more traffic across the little bridge leading to Communist China than when I had been there the first time. There were Chinese soldiers with rifles on the other side of the border and one of them had a camera with which he took a picture of our party. Dr. Gurewitsch, who was with me on the second trip, quickly adjusted his camera and took a picture of the Chinese guards, but before he could snap the shutter all the Communist soldiers lowered their rifles and more or less concealed them behind their backs. I suppose they were acting in accordance with their instructions to avoid giving an appearance of stern military rule on the Communist side of the barrier. No one spoke, however, and we were told that there was no fraternization between the soldiers on either side of the line.

At five o'clock on a beautiful day in late June Miss Corr and I skimmed over the brown fields of Turkey and caught a first glimpse of the wonderful greens and blues of the Mediterranean just before landing at Istanbul. I had not expected anyone to meet us at that hour of the morning but, to my horror, there stood our consul general, Mr. Macatee.

"You should not have come!" I exclaimed.

"Oh, yes," he replied, always the perfect diplomat. "It is so rare for me to get up at this time of morning that I am grateful to you for the opportunity to see the world when it is so beautiful."

I could well imagine that he would have much preferred to go back to bed instead of escorting us to the Blue Mosque, Hagia Sophia, the Byzantine Wall and the Bosporus. The early-morning light made the minarets and the domes beautiful.

Much too quickly it was time to return to the airport and catch the plane to Athens. We found upon our arrival that it was a holiday. We zigzagged through narrow, twisting streets, getting our first glimpse of the Acropolis. I was pleased to learn that Governor Adlai Stevenson was in Athens and would come to tea that afternoon. We arranged to visit the Acropolis and to see some of the excavations being made in Athens under our American group.

On some of our trips we saw many signs of American influence in Greece. Near Delphi there was a huge threshing machine near the road, well labeled to show that it had come from the United States as part of the Marshall Plan. We stopped to talk with the people running the machine and they told us that it quickly did work that would have taken days with slow-moving animals and men using old-fashioned implements. It was obvious in many places that America was having an influence on the Greeks as well as on other parts of the world. But whether this was bringing us friends I did not know.

While in Athens I had the good fortune to go out to luncheon in the country with King Paul and Queen Frederika. Our embassy had handled the arrangements and, as usual, they sent a dignified but slow-moving limousine to take me from my hotel to the palace. I started out about half past eleven, rolling sedately out of the city and up into the hills to the summer palace. It was cooler there and as we were rolling happily along there was a roar of a high-powered motor behind us and a racy sports car zipped around us and went bowling along the road at high speed.

I got a quick look at the occupants and realized that the King was driving and the Queen was beside him. They were dashing along the road as if they were racing drivers out for a morning's test spin, and making the most of it. They went so fast, in fact, that before we reached the palace we caught up with two automobiles which had passed us in pursuit of the

King's car, but had broken down later.

"Those are the men who guard the King," my driver said with a chuckle.

I found the Queen to be charming, warm and intelligent. The King's personality is not so warm, but he is an able man and greatly interested in the young people of his country, where there are so many orphans from war and disaster and where so many are hungry. I believe that I receive more letters asking for help from Greece than from any other country. At luncheon the Queen told me of her efforts to alleviate this poverty.

She told me that she hoped to visit the United States to study our rehabilitation hospitals where great progress has been made in helping handicapped or crippled children. Later she and the King did make the trip. I noticed that they reserved five days at the end of their official trip for unofficial visits in New York, and I wrote the Queen a note, asking whether she had been able to see the things she wanted to see.

She replied that she had not seen any of the things she really wanted to see, so I arranged a short tour for her. We guided her to several institutions in New York City that I thought she would want to visit. We went to the new hospital on the East Side where Dr. Howard Rusk has done so much to help the recovery of crippled children. The Queen was wonderful with the patients. One little boy who had had polio attempted to show her how he had learned to walk again, but in his eagerness he slipped and fell. It was the Queen who got to him before anyone else and picked him up.

"Never mind," she said. "Many of us fall when we try to show what we can do. But I'll help you and you show me again."

Later, as we were walking in a sedate little procession, we passed a city firehouse. Looking through the big open door, the Queen saw the brass fire pole and paused.

"Do you think they would mind if I went in?"

"I'm sure they would be delighted," I said. I went in and found a fireman on duty and introduced him to the Queen. She was much interested in the equipment and asked many questions.

"Perhaps it would be possible for you to demonstrate how the men answer an alarm," I remarked to the fireman.

He said that would be simple, and rang the bell. An instant later the men began sliding down the brass pole from the second floor and quickly jumped onto their trucks. Then, last of all, their big cat came sliding down the pole. The Queen laughed and clapped her hands in delight. Then she thanked the firemen, said good-by, and we rejoined our little procession.

We left Athens by airplane on July 6, 1953, for Yugoslavia. Flying over Macedonia, in Yugoslavia, I was impressed by the fact that it looked like good farming country, in contrast to the arid appearance of the land in so many parts of Greece, particularly in the mountains.

"One reason for the difference is that the Yugoslav government has made a determined effort to reduce the number of herds of goats," a Yugoslav told me. "Goats have been almost completely forbidden in some places. I can't say this program has been entirely successful, but at least they no longer eat every blade of grass down to the roots as they often do in Greece. Why, they even eat the trees and I have actually seen them climbing up into the branches of trees to feed."

We landed in Belgrade, where I was greeted by a number of old friends from the United Nations meetings.

My main purpose in visiting Yugoslavia was to interview President Tito (or Josip Broz, to give him his real name) but I was greatly interested in learning all I could about the country and its governmental system. I wanted to make my own observations of this man who had successfully fought the German army of occupation in Yugoslavia, who had established a government closely harmonized with Communist Russia after the war and had finally broken with the Comintern, declaring his independence of the dictates of Moscow.

I had been informed correctly that Yugoslavia was very different from Russia, where for generations peasants had been accustomed to living under the strict Czarist regime, to being attached to large family estates and to doing what they were told to do. It had always been difficult to tell the Yugoslavs anything. They fought foreign invaders and they fought each other for racial and religious reasons and sometimes perhaps for no reason at all. The Montenegrins, for instance, were never really conquered through the centuries of Balkan warfare. If an invader fought his way into the country, they retired to the mountains and defied anybody to come after them. The men were such traditional warriors that the women did, and continue to do, practically all the hard, everyday work.

At a luncheon with several government officials on my first full day in Yugoslavia, one of the undersecretaries of state told of changes that were being made in industrial management. "The state," he said, "will not run the industries. They will be operated by councils of workers, and this system, where it is being tried out, already has improved production. Workers quickly find out that good management is necessary, that all must do their best and the deadwood must be eliminated if an industry is to pay."

It was obvious that the Yugoslavs were experimenting in an effort to find government theories that would permit limited individual freedom within a Socialist framework.

In the next few days the people I talked with, including American officials and newspapermen, seemed to agree that there had been great changes in the government in the past year. Decentralization of governmental power had been encouraged, which I thought was quite remarkable in a dictatorship, where the leader or leaders usually want more instead of less power. Certain supervision and a measure of ultimate control by the central government would be continued, but it was evident that many more decisions were being left to the people's committees even in the smaller village groups.

One thing that I observed almost immediately in Yugoslavia was that the people were neither worried nor afraid. I did not hear a single Yugoslav say anything about the danger of war, although their old enemy Germany was rapidly gaining strength on one side of them and they had broken with the Soviet Union and its satellites, which lie on the other side. Perhaps if you have always lived with danger you can't afford to think with fear, or perhaps the people were too busy.

Later I made a trip to Sarajevo and on the way drove to Zenica, a good coal and iron ore center which was busily trying to become the Pittsburgh of Yugoslavia. The plants had been rebuilt and enlarged after the war and were already producing three times as much as they had before.

I asked many questions about how the plants were run and cleared up some of the theories that had been explained to me in Belgrade. For example, the theory is that the plants will be run by workers' councils. But, while that is technically true, the fact is that the councils sensibly employ technical experts to operate the plants and the experts report to and are responsible to the councils. I met two American engineers employed by one plant to direct operations.

I kept finding out more about the changing industrial system. At Zagreb we visited the Rade Koncar factory, named for a factory worker who was a guerrilla leader during the war and was killed by Italian troops. The plant was making electrical transformers and other machinery needed for the development of power plants. Like others I had visited, it was operated by a workers' council and technical experts.

"Our experts are new at this kind of thing and they have made some mistakes," the manager told me. "But last year we ran at a profit."

"A profit?" I said.

"Oh, yes, that is one of the incentives for high production. After taxes have been deducted, the workers' council divides the profits, half going to pay interest and amortization on borrowed money or to improve the plant. The other half of the profits is divided among all the workers."

"Do you think that arrangement has increased production?" I asked.

The manager looked at the head of the workers' council and smiled. "Of course it has," he said.

The head of the council expressed his appreciation for the aid that had been received from the United States since the Yugoslav break with the Comintern. In fact, almost everywhere I went in the country I saw signs of the benefits of American aid and was told many times that the people were grateful.

Speaking in a general way, I found Yugoslavia a delightful place to visit and an interesting country in which to study the changing industrial, social and political system. The people were well fed, but their diet is mainly meat, fish, fats and bread. It was like asking for the moon to ask for a glass of orange juice or a lemon for your tea—unless you were at the American embassy. The prices in the shops I visited seemed high. Friends later explained that both wool and cotton have to be imported and paid for in foreign currency, which was difficult for the government to arrange, so that the prices for these goods naturally were higher than one might expect. The price of foodstuffs seemed reasonable, but I could not understand why there was so little variety. Here was a country in which 70 per cent of the population was engaged in agriculture, yet there were only a few vegetables and fruits in the markets. Officials estimated that the average family had to spend from 50 to 80 per cent of its budget on food.

I talked to a number of farmers and decided that they were the least satisfied people in Yugoslavia. This was partly because the Tito regime originally followed the Soviet pattern of collective farms. After a few years this system was not a success and it was gradually changed to permit small private farms and to encourage co-operative farming. Some collective farms continued, however, in the best farming areas. The government provided all farmers with certain tools and with fertilizers and made available machinery such as they had never had before. But of all people, the farmers the world over are the most individualistic, and the Yugoslav farmers have been slow to accept new ways.

Industrially the country has certainly made progress and important social security measures have been instituted. Medical care is provided on a universal basis and the hospitals I visited were equipped with modern laboratory and research facilities, most of which came from the United Nations or the United States. Typhoid and malaria have been largely wiped out except in a few rural areas. Generally the medical services are better than one would expect in a country that calls itself as yet underdeveloped. There are unemployment benefits and old-age pensions under the social security system, as well as payments for all children. Considering the economy of the country, these payments are generous and make a great difference in the life of the people.

Changes have also been made in the school system, and in rural areas four years of school, from the age of seven to eleven, are obligatory. Then the child can go to technical school or to a factory school for several years. In the cities high school training is free and so is instruction at the universities, which are crowded.

These are important changes in the basic structure of the country and are in considerable contrast to conditions that existed before the war. The greatest difference in postwar Yugoslavia, however, probably is at the head of the government and I was eager to talk to President Tito.

Our trip from Zagreb to Brioni to call on President Tito was one of the most delightful days I spent in Yugoslavia.

We took the plane at Zagreb in midmorning and within a few minutes, it seemed to me, we had landed and were driving by automobile into Rijeka with Mayor Eda Jardas. Later we drove on down the Istrian coast and through lovely mountain country to a point opposite the island of Brioni, where the President's boat was waiting for us.

The trip across about two miles of water to Brioni was quickly completed and we were on a wonderfully wooded island which made a perfect summer residence for a busy president. There was a hotel for guests and villas to which the marshal invited special guests. We—Miss Corr, Dr. David Gurewitsch and I—were driven in an old-fashioned victoria from the landing stage to a guest villa on the water, with a fine view of the sea. There are no powered vehicles on the island except jeeps used by the military or police units guarding the President, and the absence of noisy motors and gas fumes added to the feeling of peaceful quiet all around us.

Next morning I arrived at the President's villa alone promptly at ten o'clock, riding in a victoria. There were no obvious signs of guards or police near the villa, although no doubt the marshal is protected in an unobtrusive way, as our White House is protected by the Secret Service men. I was ushered into a large room that the marshal uses as an office. At the door I could see Mr. Vilfan and another man at a desk far across the room and it made me think of the accounts of the office of Premier Benito Mussolini in Rome, where visitors had to walk across a huge, bare space of floor to reach the desk behind which stood the stern-faced Italian dictator.

As I entered, a young-looking man came across the room to greet me. For a few moments I could not believe that this was Marshal Tito because he seemed far too youthful. It was only after he had greeted me warmly and I had seated myself on a sofa beside him that I was able to observe that his hair was graying and there were deep lines of experience in his strongly molded face. He has great charm and a strong personality. His jaw juts out and he speaks in the manner of a man who gives orders and expects them to be obeyed. But he had a sense of humor, he was pleasant to me, and he conveyed the impression of speaking frankly and honestly.

Tito spoke a little English and some German, but most of the time we spoke through our translator, Mr. Vilfan, in order to be sure that there was no misunderstanding.

Later we all went down to the dock where we got into a speedboat to go to a small island that Marshal Tito uses as a retreat when he wishes to be alone. The marshal himself piloted one speedboat, taking me with him, and seemed to get a great deal of fun out of it.

Still later in the afternoon we took a short trip on the state yacht in the Adriatic. The security officers surrounding Marshal Tito were obviously nervous about the possibility of kidnaping, and the ship was accompanied by armed vessels while military airplanes were constantly overhead or nearby.

After dinner that night I talked to the minister of interior, who was one of the guests, about the number of political prisoners.

"There are not really many political prisoners," he asserted.

"Well, how many?" I persisted. "Would you say that as many as twenty-five political prisoners were arrested in a month? Or fifty? Or seventy-five?"

"Less than seventy-five," he finally replied.

"What is the reason for most of the arrests?"

"The major reason," he replied, "is for infiltrating Soviet ideas into Yugoslavia."

This answer struck me as amusing, because that seemed to be the main thing feared by anti-Communist investigators in the United States!

Like many men who have acquired power, the President evidently loves it and has a certain vanity. But he is intelligent enough to recognize that in Yugoslavia he can have power in the long run only if the people give it to him voluntarily. As a result, I believe, he is concerned with providing a government that benefits the people, or at least enough of the people to maintain him in power.

"Do you believe the people are contented under your Socialist form of government?" I asked him.

He lit a cigarette and looked at me questioningly. "If you owned property and the government nationalized it, would you be contented?"

I said that I would not be happy about it.

"Then I will say that I don't think everybody in Yugoslavia is content. But I believe the people realize that we are doing the things that will be best for our country in the long run."

I asked him about the working of Communism in Yugoslavia, where practically everything is nationalized, although citizens have the right to own private property such as a house or a small farm of not more than twenty acres.

"We have been rather disappointed," he replied, "that many of the workers' councils have not allocated their surpluses for the good of the community as a whole but have merely divided the funds among the workers."

I asked if he considered that his country was practicing Communism.

"Communism," he answered, "exists nowhere, least of all in the Soviet Union. Communism is an ideal that can be achieved only when people cease to be selfish and greedy and when everyone receives according to his needs from communal production. But that is a long way off."

He said that Yugoslavia was developing a Socialist state that was one step toward the distant aim of Communism. "I suppose," he added, "that I might call myself a Social Democrat." Marshal Tito does not want what is being developed in Yugoslavia to be called Communism, and he also objects to the use of the term "Titoism." Every country should develop according to its own needs, he continued, and he does not want Yugoslavia to be held up as an example for others, since Yugoslavia's system might not meet the needs of any other country.

"I am not a dictator," he insisted. "We have a group—all of us were Partisans during the war—that works closely together and prepares for each step to be taken." When a law has been prepared it is published in the newspapers; then various organizations, especially the trade unions, send the government letters containing criticisms and suggestions for changes. These criticisms are carefully analyzed, Tito said, and the law is redrafted and again published in the newspapers so that the people once more will have an opportunity to express themselves about it before it is sent to Parliament for consideration.

On the basis of our conversation, it seemed to me that the President conceived of the current government as a step forward in the education of the people. He was perhaps not sure what the final steps would be, but he hoped they would lead to development of a political body along socialistic lines with a social conscience that responds to the needs of the country rather than to individual needs. I concluded that he had a concept of self-government by the people quite different from ours, because there it comes from the top rather than from the bottom. But it did not seem impossible for our type of political philosophy to live and co-operate with the system that appeared to be developing in Yugoslavia.

I commented on the American aid that had come to Yugoslavia. "I have been favorably impressed by the appreciation and gratitude of the people here for that assistance," I said. "But mere gratitude, important as it is, does not convince us that the government will not swing back to the Russian system when it has reached a point where American help is no longer needed or no longer important."

"I am ready to repeat what I told your ambassador," he said. "Regardless of whether the United States gives us help or not, the attitude of Yugoslavia toward the United States will not change."

I doubt that many people will agree when Marshal Tito describes himself as a Social Democrat. He acknowledges that the use of force by the government was necessary in his country. I felt, too, that as yet there were inconsistencies in the development of his theories of government. But I left him with the opinion that this was a powerful leader and an honest one, with some kind of long-range concept of self-government by the people. And I thought that much of the future would depend on the United States and how well we could prove that our democracy is concerned about and benefits the people as a whole.

Thirty-five

Campaigning for Stevenson

MY PARTICIPATION in political campaigns was interrupted after Franklin's death in 1945, partly because I became a member of the delegation to the United Nations and took great pains not to mix political affairs with my official duties. I believed that the questions we were dealing with at the United Nations were of the greatest importance to our country's position in the world and that they should not be approached from a partisan point of view.

In 1952 it was my opinion that Governor Stevenson would probably make one of the best presidents we had ever had, but I also believed that it was practically impossible for the Democrats to win the election because of the hero worship surrounding General Eisenhower. I did make a speech on the United Nations at the Democratic National Convention that year at the request of President Truman, and I came out for Governor Stevenson, but I did not intend to be active in that campaign and I was not.

Why, then, did I re-enter politics in 1956? I was out of the United Nations delegation at that time, and I believed as strongly as before that Adlai Stevenson would make a good president. For another thing, I had not been much impressed by the progress of what President Eisenhower called Modern Republicanism.

The Eisenhower brand of Republicanism seemed to me to be an acceptance of certain social advances that some of the younger Republicans regarded as important to the party's status in our changing domestic picture. These things usually had their origin in the New Deal days but had become so much a part of the people's thinking that Republicans who had not solidified in the old mold were willing to accept them and had

353

more or less persuaded the President to think along the same lines. President Eisenhower had seen much of the international scene and was aware of the vital importance of our role in world affairs, but the net result of his administration had not been impressive, because there were enough old-line Republicans in powerful positions to keep the party, on the whole, a conservative, businessmen's party.

Of course, the Democratic party had many conservatives in powerful positions, too, but in general it was more progressive. Some of us have long hoped for a political realignment that would result in major parties that more truly represent the conservative and progressive thinking of the people. But it is difficult to say whether that will ever be possible.

Still another thing that influenced me in getting back into politics as the 1956 campaign approached was Governor Stevenson's high standing among statesmen of other countries which are our allies or which we want to have on our side in the world struggle against Communism. After his defeat in 1952 Governor Stevenson had taken a trip around the world to study conditions in other countries and, during my own world travels, I had been greatly interested in the impression he had made on foreign statesmen. Again and again they told me that Mr. Stevenson was the kind of man who listened, who wanted to learn all the facts.

After Governor Stevenson had traveled around the world and had made a special journey to study African problems, he came to call on me one day to talk about whether he should again seek the Democratic nomination for president. He is a very intelligent man but he is also a humble man, and there were questions he was trying to resolve in his own mind.

"Don't you feel," he asked, "that there are others who would do better than I as leader of the party?"

"I cannot think of anyone else," I replied, "who has the ability to do the job you could do in meeting the most vital needs of the day."

Though I urged Governor Stevenson to run, I did not expect to take an important part in the campaign and decided to go to Europe with my two grandsons at the time of the Democratic National Convention. To my surprise, this horrified some of my friends. "If you fail to attend the convention," one of them said, "everybody will think you have changed your mind about supporting Adlai."

So finally I sent my grandsons off alone on the boat and arranged to spend a couple of days at the Chicago convention before flying to

Europe. When I arrived at the Chicago airport I was received by several supporters of Governor Stevenson. While I was en route to Chicago, former President Truman, who had begged Mr. Stevenson to run in 1952, had come out in favor of the nomination of Governor Averell Harriman of New York.

I certainly was not thrilled by this news, for various reasons. President Truman had always been especially considerate toward me. I had reported to him personally after the various meetings of the United Nations and had learned that he had a remarkable understanding of the office and duties of the President. I felt that he had had to make more than his share of big decisions as president and that he had made few mistakes in times of crisis. The mistakes he made were human mistakes in smaller things.

That morning in Chicago I was thinking of President Truman's great ability as a campaigner, and I was dismayed by the idea of pitting my political judgment against his.

I was told that I was going not to my hotel but to a press conference. When we drove to the hotel where the newspaper people were waiting I had to face more reporters and more cameras than I had ever seen before. I was fearful of the ordeal of justifying my judgment in opposition to President Truman but actually it turned out to be no ordeal at all. I said as simply and frankly as possible what I believed, and it was no more difficult than an ordinary press conference.

The reporters, of course, made as much as possible of my opposition to President Truman because it is more interesting to write about disagreements than about routine agreement. But they hadn't counted on the fact that I had previously asked President and Mrs. Truman to luncheon that day. Mrs. Truman could not come but, immediately after my press conference, I met the former President in the grillroom of my hotel. The reporters scented another story. Were we going to make a deal? In no time at all, newspapermen had taken over a large table about three feet from my elbow and were more intent on my conversation with President Truman than they were on their food.

They didn't get much to write, even if they had keen ears. We talked about everything except the convention until we had finished luncheon and then our differences were mentioned only indirectly.

"I hope you will understand that whatever action I take is because I think I am doing the right thing," President Truman said.

"Of course," I replied. "I know you will act as you believe is right and I know you will realize that I must do the same."

President Truman nodded and grinned. "What I want to do is to make this convention do some real thinking about issues," he said.

Later, when I had gone to my hotel room, I felt that I was a fish out of water and that I really had nothing to do at this convention. But I did attend a reception Governor Stevenson gave in my honor and I accompanied him on visits to various state delegations to seek their support. I saw many persons in my room, attended a luncheon for women delegates, and went before the Platform Committee twice to speak on civil rights and education.

Paul Butler, the Democratic national chairman, also asked me to speak briefly in the convention. When I got there the pandemonium was so great that I don't believe any speaker could have been heard with the possible exception of Governor Frank Clement of Tennessee, whose keynote address proved that he had a strong voice. However, what I said could be heard over radio and television, and later many persons were kind enough to say that my words gained considerable attention in the contest for delegates. In any event, I was pleased when Governor Stevenson won the nomination.

During the lively contest for the vice-presidential nomination between Senator Estes Kefauver and Senator John Kennedy, a friend of Senator Kennedy came to me with a request for support. I replied that I did not feel I could support him because he had avoided taking a position during the controversy over Senator Joseph McCarthy's methods of investigation. Senator Kennedy was in the hospital when the Senate voted censure of Senator McCarthy and, of course, could not record his position, but later, when he returned to the Senate, reporters asked him how he would have voted and he failed to answer directly.

"Oh, that was a long time ago," the senator's friend told me. "He was unable to vote and it is all a thing of the past. It should not have anything to do with the present situation."

"I think McCarthyism is a question on which public officials must stand up and be counted," I replied. "I still have not heard Senator Kennedy express his convictions. And I cannot be sure of the political future of anyone who does not willingly state where he stands on that issue."

Senator Kennedy came to see me in Chicago and I told him exactly the same thing. He replied in about the words he had previously used in talking to reporters, saying that the McCarthy censure vote was "so long ago" that it did not enter the current situation. But he did not say where he stood on the issue and I did not support him.

I did not stay in Chicago for the balloting on the vice-presidential nominee but flew back to New York the day before my plane left for Europe. I felt a sense of great relief at leaving politics behind, and I expected to play only a very quiet role in the presidential campaign. It didn't work out that way. The two months after my return proved to be among the most hectic of my life, because I ended by doing far more than I had expected to do, and I had, at the same time, to keep my lecture dates.

I thought and still think that a good business executive does not make a good government administrator, nor does an administration of businessmen make for good government. A businessman needs certain qualities for success; a government official needs a wide variety of qualities and some quite different ones. He cannot be successful unless he has a knowledge of people and politics, and there is no doubt that a number of Eisenhower appointees had to learn this in a slow, difficult manner. Often businessmen go into government with the idea that they will be the men at the top and that their orders will be carried out. This is probably the correct approach in business, but in government it is necessary to persuade others that what they want to do is the best course. Unless Congress goes along with them, they can't get results. President Eisenhower evidently felt that he could establish an administration in the pattern of big business, but such an approach to the complexities of government is not necessarily either democratic or successful—as I believe he has discovered.

In the same way, I don't believe that because a man is a successful corporation lawyer he will necessarily be the best person to direct the Department of State. Outsiders like myself do not have all the facts at their command in regard to international affairs, but surely it was blundering that carried us into the mess in which we found ourselves in 1956 in the Middle East, and still find ourselves.

Secretary Dulles served in all but two of the United Nations Assemblies in which I served. I often observed that he was rarely inclined to take a stand, to say that this was right or wrong. He shied away from decisions because he didn't like to make himself responsible for a definite program.

This probably explains why he did not come to the defense of loyal public servants in his department when they were under bitter and unfair attack, which naturally led to low morale in the State Department.

I might add that I don't believe there is much question that Vice-President Richard Nixon will succeed Mr. Eisenhower as party leader, regardless of the opposition of some Republicans. I regard Mr. Nixon as a very able and dangerous opportunist, but since 1952 he has learned a great deal. He now knows the importance of gaining the confidence of the people and he has worked hard at it and made progress. This still does not make me believe that he has any strong convictions.

One of the important duties of the President—and one that the Republican administration neglects—is to be the educator of the public on national problems. Most people do not have the time or inclination to inform themselves fully on the complex and seemingly remote problems that must be settled by government. But if he knows the issues and explains them clearly, the President is in a position to make the people aware of what must be decided and to make them feel their responsibility as citizens in reaching a decision. Without such education of the people, democracy can become a dangerous kind of government because voters are called upon to make decisions or to support decisions without having sufficient knowledge of the factors involved.

To get back to the subject of that campaign, I had gone late in September to Oregon to do anything I could in behalf of Senator Wayne Morse's race for re-election to the Senate, this time as a Democrat instead of on the Republican ticket. I had to work my political appearances into a tight schedule so that I could also keep my lecture engagements, which were often in distant cities. That was a hectic period. I recall one occasion when I (speaking from Los Angeles) was to introduce Governor Stevenson over television for a speech he was making that night in Milwaukee, but I was also scheduled to speak at a luncheon, hold a news conference, attend a reception, and then go on to San Diego to appear on another television program. Because my plane was two hours late, the day was further confused. When I reached the studio where I was to introduce Governor Stevenson I had half an hour to spare. To the horror of the studio people, I insisted on having an office stenographer to whom I dictated two newspaper columns while the political managers stood by biting their fingernails.

There were a good many other days just as crowded. Later in West Virginia, in the mining area, I continued campaigning. I stopped at a mine when the shifts were changing and talked to some of the miners, something I had not done since the early days of the depression in the 1930's. The miners were better off than in those former days and I was happy to see the changes. I felt at home in this mining environment. It took me back to the depression period when I spent much time trying to see what could be done for the people, particularly the children, of this area.

On that campaign tour I traveled in all directions. I ran into Senator Alexander Wiley, the Republican incumbent, who was on his campaign tour. Senator Wiley was having his troubles because of the opposition of his Republican colleague from Wisconsin, Senator McCarthy. President Eisenhower had not come out strongly in Senator Wiley's support, although the Senator had been a staunch administration man in Congress. But I admired the way in which he had fought for a sound foreign policy and I greeted him warmly when I saw him in Marquette. I was later told that he felt this had done him no harm in his winning campaign.

As I moved rapidly from one area to another on a tight schedule I managed it only by taking every opportunity to snatch some sleep sitting in a plane or an automobile or resting a few minutes in a chair.

This kind of thing went on for weeks. I never fooled myself about the difficulties of defeating the incumbent administration at a time when there were no great and compelling reasons for the public to make a change. If the people are fairly comfortable and there is no great unrest, they prefer to let well enough alone, and it is seldom possible to stir them by pointing out that there are grave problems ahead—in this case, in the international field. You can't expect the voters generally to respond very strongly to such a situation. But in a campaign you have to feel that you may be able to overcome your handicaps, for otherwise you will not be able to give your speeches with any conviction. So I kept telling myself that we had a chance to win and that it was worthwhile to make the strongest possible fight.

I did, however, get awfully, awfully tired of motorcades. I have no idea how many times I rode through the streets of various cities in a procession of open-top automobiles carrying candidates for national and local office. Most of them were rather silly performances. There are only two people who really become well known to the people during a campaign. In this case, one was the President, whom they knew, and the other was the head of the opposition ticket, who was trying to become president. Of course, there are some local candidates for office whom they recognize, but as far as I was concerned the motorcade always seemed ridiculous because there was no reason for anyone to bother to come out on the street to look at me.

The last days of the campaign were really strenuous and I was getting mighty tired of the sound of my own voice. My final appearances were in Washington, where I was on a television program with Senator Margaret Chase Smith at five-thirty in the afternoon and in St. Louis the same evening, where I spoke in Kiel Auditorium. Early the next morning I took a plane back to New York and got to Hyde Park in time to cast my vote, which was the last if not least important thing I could do in behalf of Governor Stevenson.

The returns, of course, were unhappy from my point of view. I felt sad because I am a strong admirer of Governor Stevenson and I believed his abilities were needed to meet the problems that would arise in the next four years. But when it was over, I was glad to be out of politics.

Later my children told me I had tried to do too much. "You're going to have to slow down," they warned me. "You're going to have to stop working one of these days and you certainly should never get involved in another such job of campaigning."

Thirty-six

Bali and Morocco

MOST OF MY journeys abroad have been in connection with official or semi-official business of some kind, but I have been fortunate in being able to combine work with sightseeing and sometimes I have been able simply to take off on my own for a short time, as I did when I visited the famous island of Bali in 1955.

I had been asked to be a delegate to the World Federation of United Nations Associations, which was meeting that summer in Bangkok, the capital of Thailand, and I was happy to accept, partly because it would give me a chance for another look at the Far East en route. I did not feel that I was well acquainted with the problems and people of Indonesia, which was long in the Dutch colonial domain but is now a federation of independent republics. And I had always wanted to see Bali, which I had read so much about and which was usually pictured as the loveliest and most peaceful of the fabled South Sea Islands.

The Dutch, I knew, were not popular in the islands after the war and apparently were becoming still less popular. Yet I had known Queen Juliana for some years and felt that she had worked hard to further a better spiritual understanding among peoples. I should like to tell a little about the Queen, because before I went to Indonesia one of the royal families of Europe I enjoyed visiting was that of Holland. I had always admired the former Queen, Wilhelmina, for her staunch courage and her insistence upon being a good Dutch housewife as well as a capable ruler.

I have a very special feeling about Queen Juliana because, like Princess Marta of Norway, she came a number of times to stay with us at Hyde Park with her husband and children. Franklin was godfather to their third daughter. She and her husband have brought up their children in

361

a democratic way and part of the time they have attended the public schools. Once when two of the children and some small friends were walking home they passed an orchard where they picked up some apples that had fallen outside the fence but which, of course, did not belong to them. The owner called the police and a little later the police telephoned the palace and informed the then Princess Juliana that her children were more or less in custody.

"Very well," she replied, "you must deal with them just as with the others. Then telephone me again and we will come get them."

All the children were reprimanded by the police and at least a couple of them received additional punishment at the hands of their parents when they got back to the royal palace.

I was the guest of Juliana before she became queen at the time the University of Utrecht awarded me a degree of doctor of laws. It was a colorful ceremony and at the end of it the princess and I drove in a carriage drawn by four horses, with great pomp and ceremony, to the women's house of the university. The women were very proud because it was not often that a woman was given a degree, and on this occasion they not only participated in the ceremony but served as outriders accompanying our carriage. The princess was at the students' house with me, and I look back on that particular incident with great pleasure.

As queen, Juliana has worked vigorously to help develop understanding among Europeans. She has sought with other Continental powers to awaken the peoples of Europe to their responsibilities. Her government has been influential in the Council of Europe and she has led in the humanitarian efforts of her country to help refugees. The pages of history will record that she was a woman who loved her fellow human beings.

So, feeling as I did about the Queen, I decided in 1955 to take advantage of my journey to Bangkok and visit the islands that in past years had been so strongly under Dutch influence.

We spent a week in Japan. The standard of living was still poor when seen through Western eyes, but I felt that conditions were improving since I had been there in 1953 and that the people looked happier. One thing that had distressed me on my first trip was the number of difficult problems that would have to be overcome to establish democratic government firmly in that country. Yet when I returned there after two years I thought that the people were accepting more and more of the important aspects of democracy. They had gradually begun to want to take part and have a say in their government. Of course, the habits and customs developed during centuries of feudalism had not been eliminated overnight, but I thought a great change was taking place in the thinking of the people.

We flew from Japan to Hong Kong and then to Manila and touched down at Jakarta. It was almost dark when we arrived in Bali, and were met by Mrs. Bagoes Oka, the charming wife of an assistant to the governor of the province. The next day we drove to the village of Ubud through country that was green and seemed to have plenty of water. We stopped at a large compound with mud walls. There was an open market at the gate with all kinds of food and handwork on display.

"This is the local rajah's house," Mrs. Oka told me. "You will stay here in one of the guest houses." The rajah was a plump little man in a sacklike gown tied in the middle with a broad sash. For economic reasons, he had converted his compound into a kind of hotel. The guest houses each had one room with mud and wood walls and washing facilities were in a small separate room which one reached by going through an archway. There was little in the way of modern plumbing.

The basic food of the people is rice for every meal, usually with vegetables, but there is a feast about once a week when they eat chicken and pork and make up for the lack of variety in their daily diet. We did not have to eat rice all the time, but I must say that later when I moved to a little Dutch hotel overlooking the water the meals were good and I was so much more comfortable that it seemed like heaven.

By the time we left Bali for Jakarta and Bangkok I felt I had seen enough dancing to last me the rest of my life, but it was the kind of dancing that goes with the island and its people and we thoroughly enjoyed our visit.

The meeting of the World Federation of United Nations Associations in Bangkok was interesting but not particularly newsworthy. We were greeted upon arrival by the prime minister, Field Marshal P. Pibul Songgram, and his wife as well as people from the United States embassy. I found the city unusual and interesting despite the fact that it was the rainy season and sheets of water fell during the afternoons.

Thanks to a hospitable government, a number of us were able to make a trip to see Angkor Wat, the famous temple of the ancient Khmer Empire of Cambodia. We went by plane over a fertile valley where, in the rainy season, there was water everywhere. While still aloft we could see the temples at Angkor Thom and Angkor Wat. I thought they were the most impressive monuments I had ever seen.

There is another journey to a new and developing country which I want to describe before I come to what was to me the most important experience in recent years. But to do it I shall have to switch back to Hyde Park to a time not long after Morocco had achieved its independence from French colonial rule.

One day Archie Roosevelt, one of the State Department's experts on the Arab world, telephoned and asked if an old friend of his could come to my house for tea. I said I should be delighted, but I was amazed when a huge limousine arrived. A small girl got out, then an American woman, then a Moroccan woman, and finally two Moroccan men carrying a huge box of flowers.

I had not been expecting such a delegation but it turned out that one of the men was the chief adviser to Sultan Mohammed V of Morocco, who later became King Mohammed V. They had come to place flowers on my husband's grave and I had thought they were just coming for tea. They explained that they had expected to meet two officials from the State Department when they reached Hyde Park, but something had gone wrong and they did not show up until later.

After we had had tea, the adviser to the Sultan arose rather mysteriously and said, "Mrs. Roosevelt, I would like to speak to you alone."

After the others had left the room, he continued, "We Moroccans never forget a kindness. The Sultan asked me to say to you that he recalls your husband as one foreign head of state who gave him disinterested advice. He wants me to say that he believes there would have been no secret treaty between France and the United States in connection with the establishment of United States air bases in Morocco if your husband had lived. But we do not blame the United States for making the treaty and we will raise no difficulties now in the negotiations on the bases between your government and ours. The Sultan also extends an invitation for you to visit Morocco."

A few months later some friends of mine in New York told me that a problem had arisen in connection with a large group of Jews in Morocco who wanted to migrate to Israel. They had been granted visas by the French government and were prepared to go but, at the last minute, the Moroccan officials raised various obstacles to their departure.

"The French constabulary has been withdrawn and there is a good deal of Arab hostility toward the Jews," I was told. "They are now in temporary camps which are crowded and unsanitary and there is fear of an epidemic. We have tried to get something done to bring about their release but with no success and we have not been able to get any word from the Sultan. Do you think you might appeal to him?"

"I will write him a letter," I said. I wrote it at once, saying that the Jews apparently were in considerable danger and also that there was fear of an epidemic that might endanger everybody in that area. I said I knew that he was interested in all people and I hoped he could do something to relieve the situation. I did not receive any reply to my letter, but not long afterward I learned that the necessary permission for the Jewish group to leave Morocco had been issued and that they had gone to Israel about two weeks after I wrote to the Sultan.

In 1957 the crown prince of Morocco and his sister visited the United States and the crown princess came to call on me. She was accompanied by the wife of the Moroccan ambassador and several other ladies, and by the Moroccan minister to the United Nations. As they were leaving, the princess spoke briefly to the minister and he turned to me.

"My princess says that her father, the Sultan, extends an invitation for you to visit our country."

Later in the winter of 1957 Dr. Gurewitsch told me that he was planning to take his daughter Grania to North Africa for a vacation, and we decided to go as a party and visit Morocco. My son Elliott and his wife joined us.

The white-robed governor of Casablanca and a representative of the Sultan were at the airport to greet us. With them was Kenneth Pendar, whom Elliott and Dr. Gurewitsch greeted joyfully. Elliott had been in Morocco with the Air Force during the war and was assigned to his father when Franklin and Winston Churchill held their historic conference in Casablanca, so he knew the area well. We spent only a day at Casablanca, before driving to the capital, Rabat.

I was much interested in the country we drove through and in the people. I have never felt that the French were the best colonizers in the world, but, for that matter, no country can give another everything that it needs. The French had left in Morocco good roads and hospitals. Under Marshal Lyautey they had also kept something of the old flavor of the country; instead of permitting ancient Arab towns to be torn down for new buildings, they had seen to it that the new construction was outside the old sections. But the French residents of Morocco had almost a monopoly on power and irrigation and the Arab fields that we drove through were burned up by a severe drought. This naturally did not make the Arabs friendly toward the French colonizers. The Arab schools were poor and the country has a low literacy rate and, as usual, the masses have a very low standard of living. The Moroccans value their independence but the government had had to start almost from scratch and there was much to be done.

Generally speaking, I thought that it was remarkable that the Moroccan people, who for the most part live in great insecurity, had not been lured into Communism.

The Sultan had been in the hospital for an operation but only a couple of days afterward he invited our whole group to the palace. We drove there late in the afternoon and were immediately ushered into the large reception room. Chairs were placed around the room in a semi-circle. There were beautiful rugs on the floor. Mohammed V awaited us in a big chair on a raised platform. Despite his recent operation, he rose to greet me and I introduced the other members of our party to him. We were served refreshments as we chatted, and he politely asked the various members of the group about their interests and occupations. After a short time the others left but he asked Elliott and me to remain for a less formal talk.

The Sultan was young and handsome, with a sensitive and kindly face. There was humor in his eyes and his slender hands were expressive as he passed the usual string of beads through his fingers. He wore long white robes, white over some delicate color, and a small cap. His conversation made it clear that he was alert and deeply concerned about the welfare of the people, their need for economic security and for aid in developing social services. But he was also well aware of the international complications affecting the Arab world. From his remarks I felt that he hoped the three North African countries of Morocco, Tunisia and Algeria might become a kind of bridge between the East and the West, helping to ease the tensions created by extremist Arab nationalism in such countries as Egypt and Syria and to bring about a better understanding among nations.

I had felt since our arrival that there was on the part of the Moroccans a greater warmth toward the United States than in other Arab countries but I did not fully understand it until we had talked with the Sultan. This attitude of friendship went back to the time during World War II when Franklin and Prime Minister Winston Churchill met at Casablanca.

The French officials then ruling Morocco paid them a formal call, and when they departed Franklin said: "Now we must see the Sultan."

Mr. Churchill looked at him without much enthusiasm. "Why should we do that?" he asked. "We have seen the French."

"We must see the Sultan," my husband replied, "because this is his country."

The Sultan was thinking about that visit when he said my husband gave him disinterested advice that convinced him of the friendship of the United States. His attitude of helpfulness had become known everywhere in Morocco and many persons told me that the assurance of the friendship of the United States was a kind of milestone in the Moroccan campaign for independence.

A few days after our talk with the Sultan I witnessed another and unusual demonstration of the friendship of the people when we visited Marrakech and the area in the foothills of the Atlas Mountains. Shortly before noon one day we started out from Marrakech in three automobiles. The countryside was parched and dusty and the roads were sometimes mere tracks of dirt. We passed a great assemblage of perhaps two hundred camels as we left the city and later came upon a well where a bullock walked slowly around and around in a circle, drawing water for irrigation of the desert fields. As we bounced across the hills we came upon a wonderful view of the little village of Demnat, which lay on a hilltop beyond a dry, brown plain with the mountains rising up behind.

There were a few travelers on the road, some driving little flocks of sheep through swirling clouds of dust as we drove to the residence of the caid, some distance from Demnat. The leading officials of the town were there to greet us and the caid had prepared the usual Arab feast, great platters of rice and mutton and sweets that must be eaten with the fingers.

After the feast the officials of Demnat accompanied us across the plain to their ancient walled town, one of the oldest in Morocco, dating back to the tenth century. The road was a rough dirt track and the dust was thick and the sun was hot, but a large and enthusiastic crowd had gathered outside the main gate of the town.

"Welcome!" they shouted as our automobile drew up. "Welcome!"

Even more impressive to me was the fact that they had made a crude American flag, which was hung over the gate, and a sign saying, "We always remember President Roosevelt!"

The more I traveled throughout the world the more I realized how important it is for Americans to see with understanding eyes the other peoples of the world whom modern means of communication and transportation are constantly making closer neighbors. Yet the more I traveled the happier I was that I happened to have been born in the United States, where there exist the concept of freedom and opportunities of advancement for individuals of every status. I felt, too, the great responsibility that has come to us as a people. The world is looking to us for leadership in almost every phase of development of the life of peoples everywhere.

But leadership is a stern, demanding role and no person or state can lead without earning that right. On my visit to the Soviet Union in 1957 I was strongly impressed—I was almost frightened—by many things that showed how hard we must strive if we are to maintain our position of world leadership.

Thirty-seven

In the Land of the Soviets

I HAVE WRITTEN frequently about my enjoyment from visiting many delightful places around the world, including the police-run state of Yugoslavia. I would not want to live in Yugoslavia, nor would anyone who values personal freedom. But I think I should die if I had to live in Soviet Russia. I traveled there extensively for almost a month in 1957. When I went to Moscow, the Stalinist dictatorship had been replaced by the less fearful—in theory, at least—dictatorship of Nikita S. Khrushchev, but the people still existed under a system of surveillance that must cause anxiety and the power over them still seemed to me a hand of steel.

My trip to the Soviet Union was one of the most important, the most interesting and the most informative that I have ever made. I tried to understand what was happening in Russia by looking at the country through Russian eyes, and unless all of us in the free world approach the Soviet Union from that point of view we are going to deceive ourselves in a catastrophic manner. I remembered that only forty years ago this great mass of people was largely made up of peasants living in houses with mud floors and, perhaps, with a farm animal or two in the kitchen in wintry months. They were illiterate. They were oppressed. They were frightened of conquest by the Germans, and for many years they were bound together by a readiness to defend their homeland no matter how hard their lives might be.

We must never forget these things when we look at what Russia is today. I looked and was frightened. My fear was not of the Communist power or philosophy, not of awesome missiles or hydrogen bombs. What I feared was that we would not understand the nature of the Russian Revolution that is still going on, and what it means to the world. If we

369

fail to understand, then we shall fail to protect world democracy no matter what missiles or earth satellites or atomic warships we produce. So I want to explain carefully why I am frightened.

I must start my explanation back in the spring of 1957 when Dorothy Schiff, the publisher and owner of the New York *Post*, invited me to luncheon and posed a question. "Would you like to go to China and write a series of articles for the *Post?*"

"I certainly would," I replied.

"You make your application to the State Department for a visa and I will make the other arrangements."

I applied to the State Department and was refused a visa. I was irritated at the time. Later some of my irritation waned. The department has a responsibility to stand behind its visas and to afford protection to citizens traveling abroad on its passports, so I felt they had a right to point out that it was impossible to provide any protection for our citizens traveling in Communist China. However, it seemed to me that the department could say that if newspapermen wanted to go to China under those conditions they were free to go, provided the Chinese government would permit them entry. In any event, I did not get a visa to China and Mrs. Schiff asked me if I would go to Russia instead.

"Yes," I replied, "but I can't go until September, and I would want to take my secretary, Miss Corr, and Dr. Gurewitsch. He can speak Russian and his medical knowledge would also be of great importance in connection with my investigation of conditions."

It took three months to get our visas approved by the Russians. At the end of August the three of us flew to Frankfurt and Berlin, where I was surprised to see how much building had been done since my last visit and how rapid the German recovery had been. From Berlin we flew to Copenhagen early in the morning and there shifted to the Scandinavian airline to Moscow. The plane was so crowded, mostly with American and British tourists, but there were also some Central Europeans from the Soviet satellite countries. We stopped at Riga for passport examination and luncheon but were not allowed to leave the airport. That afternoon we flew on across Russia. I was surprised that so much of the country we passed over was wooded, for I had always thought of Russia as treeless steppes. It was getting dark as we approached Moscow but we could see that much new construction was in progress in the city; in many places the cranes and skeletons of buildings stuck up against the skyline. There were a surprising number of airplanes, most of them two-engine craft, on the ground at the Moscow airport, about the number one would see upon landing at Idlewild or LaGuardia in New York.

Two young men from the United States embassy met us at the airport, and we were also greeted by representatives of Intourist, the Soviet travel bureau, which was arranging my schedule of travel. I was not a guest of the government but was traveling as a reporter. My interpreter was Anna Lavrova, a charming and intelligent young woman who had been my husband's interpreter when he met with Premier Stalin and Prime Minister Churchill at Yalta in 1945.

My first impression of Moscow was that there was building going up everywhere. We drove past the lower side of the Kremlin on the way to the National Hotel, and it was very impressive with its many lights and high walls.

At the hotel Mrs. Lavrova accompanied me to my apartment, a sitting room, bedroom and bath. The furnishings were ornate and heavy, yellow damask, carved table legs and a generally old-fashioned atmosphere, and the plumbing, while all right, was far from modern.

The food was generally good at the hotel and we ate almost no place else, because prices were extremely high in the few restaurants that we might have patronized. There was borscht with big pieces of meat and much cabbage in it, chicken, and, of course, tea and caviar and cakes and lots of ice cream.

The Russians generally do not dress well. The government has discouraged any display in dressing because it is not important to the economic welfare of the country. Prices of clothes are high by American standards and there is little to be said for quality or variety. As a result, the people, whether on the street or in offices or working at manual labor, are dressed warmly but monotonously, usually in dark clothes and without distinction. About the only word to be used about the dress of the people was "drab."

The day after our arrival I called at our embassy and then went to the Intourist offices, where I talked with the head of the bureau. We went over my travel plans in detail.

"I want to get as far away from Moscow as possible," I said, "because I want to see all aspects of the country. I have always been fascinated by Tashkent and Samarkand. Perhaps I could go there unless it is too far off the beaten path."

The bureau director smiled. "We have a commercial jet airplane service to Tashkent every day. The flight takes four hours."

So he put Tashkent on the schedule, and Stalingrad, and a boat trip on the Volga, and the Black Sea and Leningrad and Kiev. But once I started traveling I didn't stick closely to the schedule—much to the dismay of Intourist—and in the end I had to cancel some of the trips because of lack of time. Whenever I decided that I needed more time in some place and changed the schedule, the Intourist people went into a polite tizzy. Most Russian travelers go where they are told to go when they are told to go.

I had made requests for interviews with a number of government officials as soon as I arrived in Moscow but it proved difficult to get specific dates confirmed. When the appointments were made, however, I was received with graciousness and friendliness and was given every assistance, including permission to visit many institutes and projects under the various ministries.

After a few days of seeing the ballet, visiting museums and attending a good one-ring circus, Miss Corr and I were driven to a state farm about twenty miles from Moscow. There are two kinds of farms in the Soviet Union, state farms owned by the government, which hires and pays the workers, who have no personal interest in production; and collective farms, where the land is owned, worked collectively and managed by private owners who elect one of the group as their head. Both types of farm are under state supervision.

Workers on the farms are given a house and a small plot of land which they may cultivate for themselves. Of course, the workers on a state farm do not take the risks that a collective farmer does. The collective farmer is in difficulties in a poor year when the crops fail; in a good year, however, he is able to raise his income considerably.

The state farm I visited was called Lesnie Poljana, meaning Prairie among the Forest. The state-appointed manager told me that they had two thousand acres under cultivation and that they had a breed of milk cows, called Holmogor, for which they raised food.

"There are 550 pedigreed cattle on the farm," he said, "and 226 of them are milk producers. The milk is all shipped in cans to institutions in Moscow."

Some 230 persons worked on the farm throughout the year and about 20 others were hired in the busy summer season. Women do what we think of as men's work all over Russia, street-cleaning and section-hand work on the railroads, and they did much of the work in the cow barns at this farm. There were some milking machines but most of the milking was done by hand. The beef cattle did not look particularly well fattened and throughout Russia I found that the meat is not so tender as ours, apparently because it is not hung so long. Chickens are usually not tender, so that one rarely had roast chicken. It usually was boiled or minced in croquettes or used in soup.

Not long after visiting the state farm we took the jet airliner for Tashkent, where I had a chance to visit a collective farm. Less than four hours after we left Moscow we came down at Tashkent, some two thousand miles away.

There was more desert here than I had expected and the green areas were confined to the source of water or to irrigated sections. Part of Tashkent dates back to the twelfth century, and this old section was being slowly torn down, the streets were being widened and new, modern apartment houses were being built.

The collective farm that we visited was owned by an organization of farmers. Out of the over-all income of the farm, 7 per cent goes to the government in taxes. Another 16 per cent goes for capital reserve, 1 per cent to amortization and the like. Thirteen per cent goes into the operation of services, of which there are many, and the remaining cash is divided among members of the collective. We were told that a man might get about 8,000 rubles a year in cash on this basis, plus shelter, services, food and so on, which meant that he is fairly well off. If the crops fail, of course, he is in trouble.

Cotton was the main crop, but the farmers also raised cattle for meat and milk. There were 1,160 houses and 1,700 able workers, representing a dozen different nationalities brought together in this ancient area of Central Asia. Each farmer annually received about 30 pounds of meat, a considerable quantity of grain, and 150 pounds of potatoes, in addition to which he might raise food for himself in his garden plot and keep a cow, for which the collective provided food.

We walked around part of the farm. There was no running water in any of the houses but they all had electricity and I frequently saw a one-burner electric plate on top of an old wood range. Toilet and bathing facilities were old-fashioned—usually a privy and a bathhouse.

Every inch of land seemed to be in use. Even where small fruit trees had been planted there were growing crops. The farm had a maternity hospital and a baby clinic but, in case of serious illness, the farm people went to hospitals in Tashkent. There was a nursery, a kindergarten and a school. Children were taken care of at these institutions while their parents worked in the fields, but nursing mothers could leave their work and go to the nursery at stated hours when feedings were given.

The manager of the farm said that there had been a steady increase in production in recent years, but this collective also had increased in size and it was difficult to know whether it was operating more efficiently and getting a greater yield from the land or had just acquired more acreage. Later, in Moscow, I talked about farm production with Senator Allen J. Ellender of Louisiana, who was making his third visit to Russia. He was interested in Russian agriculture and had been in the new area in Soviet Asia where a large region was being plowed up for the first time.

The senator felt that there was serious danger that the new land might turn into a dust bowl as happened in parts of our Southwest after the protective grass had been stripped from the plains. He said he had written a letter to Mr. Khrushchev warning him of this danger, but that the Communist party chief had not seemed to pay any attention. Later, talking to a deputy minister of agriculture, I asked him about this problem, but he said that a thorough investigation had been made before the land was plowed up and that the top soil was found to be more than three feet deep.

The Russians, incidentally, had imported some of the famous Santa Gertrudis beef cattle from the King Ranch in Texas for breeding purposes. They had been shipped to Russia several years earlier and I was told that they had disappeared. I was curious about them and eventually inquired at the Ministry of Agriculture about what had happened to them.

"Oh, they are the special pets of the minister," I was told. "They were shipped to the southern part of the Ukraine and they are still there and thriving. They have also had plenty of little ones!"

The College of Music and similar institutions illustrate how the Communists operate. Forty years ago there were no music schools in the area and the songs of the region were handed down from generation to generation. Then Moscow decided that it was important to preserve the culture of each of its republics and this was an example of how they were doing it. The college in Tashkent has 350 students and 150 teachers, who constantly watch for gifted young people so that they can become teachers or enter a musical career anywhere in the Soviet Union. The state provides 6 million rubles a year to operate the college, which also had sponsored some

30 theaters for students of drama in the Uzbek Republic.

On Sundays Tashkent was alive with music. There were little squares where singers gathered on platforms to entertain whoever happened to stroll by. There were dancers and musicians, too, and the crowds wandered about from one place to another, listening to the music.

We made a quick trip by air to Samarkand, and were met by two women, who were local officials, and a historian, who told us much about this capital city of Tamerlane. The government has spent heavily to restore some of the old buildings in the "blue city" and there are wonderful old tombs with colored inlays on their façades, including the tomb of the first wife of the Mongol conqueror and the tomb of Mohammed's cousin. Earthquakes had destroyed many of the buildings but there were still two domes of an extraordinary blue color. There is also a large hospital for bone tuberculosis, which we visited and where I was impressed by the docility of the children.

The most important things I learned about the Soviet Union—and the things that may be most difficult for democratic peoples everywhere to comprehend—came to a focus when I visited the city of Leningrad. I had been absorbing various ideas from the time I landed in Moscow and was gradually approaching certain conclusions on the basis of what I had seen and heard. But it was at the Leningrad medical school, which puts great emphasis on pediatrics, that I really saw what was happening in Russia and what this may mean in the world-wide struggle between Communism and democracy.

The influence of Dr. Ivan Petrovich Pavlov, a physiologist and experimental psychologist, on the Russians today is tremendous. I knew vaguely that, before his death in 1936, Dr. Pavlov had conducted many experiments and made extensive studies of conditioned reflexes and that the Soviet government had built a special laboratory for him. But I had not realized until I saw some of the results of his work at Leningrad and elsewhere that he may well prove to be far more famous in history as the father of a system that seems to be turning the masses of Russia into completely disciplined and amenable people.

I had told the Intourist people that I would like to go to the institute of medicine oriented toward pediatrics, where I could see their methods of handling children. At the institute they asked if I would like to see an experiment. Thirty-two children taken at birth from lying-in hospitals, whose parents had died or abandoned them, were being trained. The purpose of the training was to see whether they could develop in an institution and be as advanced, healthy and happy as in an ordinary home.

The nursery was well equipped. While the head teacher and several doctors watched with me, one of the nurses, a solid, friendly young woman in white uniform and cap, demonstrated the kind of training given the babies. It was here, I later realized, that the Pavlov theories were being put into practice. The same pattern is followed in all nurseries and also by mothers training their children at home.

A six-month-old baby was brought to the nurse for his daily conditioning. The routine was simple—to hold two rings out to the baby and persuade him to pull on them as the first step in the exercises. I noticed that the baby already knew what was coming and what he was supposed to do. He held out his hands to grasp the rings as soon as he saw the nurse. Then, after holding tightly to the rings throughout the exercise, he dropped them without being given any signal and shifted to the next exercise. This was using his legs and he went through the routine without any direction from the nurse. Then he lay rigid, waiting to be picked up by his heels and exercised on his head. After that the nurse picked him up and hugged and kissed him and spent some time playing with him as any mother might do with a small baby.

This attitude of affection and loving care was customary, I observed, with children of all ages at all the institutions that I visited. The next group I saw consisted of four children about a year and a half old, who went through a more complicated routine. They came in, like a drill team, took off their shoes, put them neatly in a row and pulled out a bench from the wall. One after the other, they crawled along the bench, then walked on it, then crawled under it. Then they climbed up on exercise bars. They knew exactly what to do and when to do it, like clockwork, and when they had finished the routine each one walked over and sat on the lap of a nurse. The nurse lowered them down backwards to the floor and pulled them up again in another exercise. Then the children put on their shoes, put the bench back in place and went out. This kind of training in behavior goes on year after year as the children grow up.

What, I asked myself, does this mean in ordinary life outside the nursery or schoolroom? And as I watched the children I knew that I had already seen some of the answers in the conduct of the Russian people, the generations that are growing up or have grown up since Dr. Pavlov conducted his experiments and drew his conclusions about the conditioning of reflex action.

Because of lifelong conditioning, the government can depend on the mass of the people—there will always be exceptions—to react in a certain way to certain stimuli. The Russians today are a disciplined, well-trained people; not a happy people, perhaps, but not likely to rise up against their rulers.

But more than this—much more—Americans should never forget that by controlling the entire economy the Soviet dictatorship can use this disciplined people to do things that are difficult if not impossible in our free economy. The Communist leaders are aware of this power and know how to use it. They put far more emphasis and far more money into scientific and research projects, for example, than we do. To take just one field of endeavor: in 1956 the Russian schools graduated about 26,000 doctors. In the United States, we graduated about 6,500.

In the Soviet Union free medical care appeared to be one of the things most highly valued by the people. The Health Ministry has agencies throughout the country but the rules are made in Moscow, with some adjustments for local conditions. To become a doctor one must attend school for ten years and then study at medical school for six years and then give three years of work to the state. The emphasis at first was placed on public-health doctors. After completing his work for the state a doctor may choose his specialty and have three more years of training. I was interested to discover that a doctor is not supposed to work more than a six-hour day.

The whole Soviet Union is divided into health districts. We visited one district center in Leningrad for the care of mothers and children. It deals only with healthy children. Those who are ill are sent to a hospital. The district has 19,000 children. There are three nurseries in the city and four outside where children are sent for a more healthful atmosphere. There are 18 kindergartens and 11 schools in the district. The district medical staff of 91 persons includes 51 doctors, each of whom spends two hours in the center and four hours making calls. They told us that only one child under a year old had died in the district in 1956 and only four children under sixteen had died. There was no venereal disease and no prostitution in the district. It is significant to note that there are more than 35 such centers in Leningrad alone, with 2,000 doctors devoting themselves purely to preventive medicine.

We later visited Sochi, far to the south on the Black Sea, where there are 50 sanitariums owned by government-run industries or by trade unions. If a doctor certifies the need for a worker to go to a sanitarium during his month's vacation, 70 per cent of the cost of his care is paid by the union. The worker pays for his transportation, at a specially low rate, and also pays 30 per cent of his expenses during this vacation period. In cases of serious illness, the time spent in a special hospital or sanitarium is not counted as vacation time.

At Sochi there is a remarkable arrangement that permits either men or women workers going to the sanitariums to take along their spouses, but at extra cost. I saw many husbands and wives enjoying the beautiful beach at Sochi, lying in the sun or swimming. The people spend much time and thought preparing for their holidays; in fact, I never realized how important vacations were until I heard them discussed so fervently in the Soviet Union.

I have written mostly about agriculture and medicine in Russia, but the government is just as keenly aware of the need for research and for generous financing in other scientific fields. There was in Moscow with us an American, Seth Jackson, who was a member of a United Nations delegation visiting Russia to study problems of forestry, particularly logging. He was a technical expert from our Department of Forestry, and it was his opinion that Russia was ahead in forestry research.

"The Soviet Union has surveyed all of its forests through the efforts of the Institutes for Research in Forestry," he said. "There are twelve such institutes in this country and they have steadily improved the machinery used for logging and other purposes. The United States hasn't ever mapped all of its forests."

There was another thing that interested me in regard to the Soviet encouragement of scientific progress. Able students have been given every opportunity to work freely, but I wondered what right they had been given to think. So I asked one scientist about it.

"Oh, we are encouraged to think freely just as we are given every encouragement to work," he replied, with a smile. "We are free to discuss, to challenge and to think whatever we please." But if you ask any of them a political question, they invariably reply, "We know nothing about politics."

Later in Moscow I had an interesting meeting with the Committee of Soviet Women, who were trying to arrange for an invitation to the United States. "Why is it so difficult," one of them asked, "for us to get visas to visit your country? We have been trying for two years to arrange a visit through the State Department but have failed miserably."

"Are you sure," I asked, "that your own government would give you permission to leave Russia?"

"Certainly," she said. "We have been given unequivocal assurances from our own government."

I told them that I would try to get a group from the National Council of Women of the United States to look into the problem and possibly take some action at the State Department. These women had a great desire to see America and I felt sure that it would benefit us to have a greater interchange between the Russian people and our own people. We have completely different backgrounds and our lives are completely different. But we have to see to understand. Possibly after seeing America they would prefer their own way of life but such interchanges might lead us to sufficient understanding to work out the kind of peaceful coexistence our leaders talk about but seem unable to achieve.

There was one other phase of the conditioning of the Russian people that I observed everywhere I went in the Soviet Union, and it is one of particular importance to Americans at present. The most familiar symbol in the country is the dove of peace. You see it wherever you go. I saw it painted on the sides of trucks on the streets; I looked down from the tower of Moscow University and saw a great white dove outlined in stone in the lawn. It was on posters in distant villages. The finale of a circus I attended featured the release of a flock of doves over the audience, following a patriotic speech.

The peace campaign was launched to remind the people that they must sacrifice and work because, despite Russia's desire for peace, their great enemy, the United States, is trying to bring about a war against Russia. The dove of peace symbolizes the efforts of the Soviet Union to protect the people from an aggressive war such as our government is alleged to be planning.

We Americans and the people of the free world must never forget or ignore this kind of distorted conditioning of the Russian people, this kind of indoctrination with ideas that are false but that by repetition can be drilled into the minds not only of the Russian people but of peoples in underdeveloped countries whom the Communists seek to turn against the United States.

A totalitarian regime regulates all the news—or almost all—that is available to the great mass of people. None but a Communist newspaper can be bought in the Soviet Union, so the people get only the slanted Communist point of view on what is happening in the world. They have no other interpretation of the position of the United States and little concept of world opinion other than that fed to them by the Kremlin.

For us merely to say that their beliefs are false is not enough, because they have been conditioned to believe that Washington is plotting a war and that Moscow is striving to protect them from our aggression; and they do believe it. Almost the only news about the United States that I saw in Russian newspapers was the story of school integration troubles at Little Rock, Arkansas. When I protested that the Russians were getting a completely distorted view of the United States and of the attitude of the American people, I was usually met with silence or obvious disbelief. Or, if the person I was talking with was educated and intelligent, his reply might be: "Oh, I know nothing about politics."

It may seem ironic to us that a dove of peace has become the symbol of an American plot to start a world war, but I was convinced that we are going to have to make far greater efforts than we have made in the past if we can hope to avoid the war that the Kremlin has told the people over and over and over again that we might start.

Thirty-eight

A Challenge for the West

AS SOON AS I arrived in Moscow I requested an interview with Nikita S. Khrushchev. I was told to write a letter in which I was to state the questions I would ask Mr. Khrushchev. I did so, saying that I wanted to record his answers.

As the days flew along I became discouraged about the possibility of seeing him, although that had been one of the main purposes of my visit to Russia. I was ready to admit failure. Then, three days before my scheduled departure, my interpreter said: "I forgot to tell you, but we go to Yalta early tomorrow morning."

The next morning we departed for Yalta. After our arrival we learned that Mr. Khrushchev would send his car for us the following day at nine-thirty.

Exactly at nine-thirty we drove downhill toward the Black Sea and finally came to a gate with a soldier on guard. We passed through the gate and, a few minutes later, through another similarly guarded gate, and then we approached a comfortable but not imposing house on a lovely site looking toward the city of Yalta. We had arrived exactly on the minute set for our appointment.

We were led through the yard and to a garden, where Mr. Khrushchev was talking with another gentleman. He came to greet us and bid us welcome, a short, stocky man with a bald head and a wide smile on his round, mobile face.

Dr. Gurewitsch, who had accompanied me, set up our portable tape recorder, so there would be no misinterpreting what we said, and we settled down to talk.

"I appreciate your coming here," he said, "and I want to speak of President Franklin Roosevelt. We respect him and remember his activities be-

381

cause he was the first to establish diplomatic relations between the United States and the Soviet Union. President Roosevelt understood perfectly well the necessity of such relations. He was a great man, a capable man who understood the interests of his own country and the interests of the Soviet Union. We had a common cause against Hitler and we appreciate very much that Franklin Roosevelt understood this task. I am happy to greet you in our land."

My first question concerned disarmament. I pointed out that after World War II we reduced our army from twelve million to one million men, but then, because of the Soviet Union's actions, we were forced to rearm. In such circumstances, I said, the American people wondered how the Soviet Union could expect us to agree on disarmament without inspection.

"We do not agree with your conception," he replied. "We consider that demobilization took place in the U.S. and in the U.S.S.R. In our country men and women were all mobilized. In our country perished roughly the number of persons you mention as making up the army of your country, almost the same number, Mrs. Roosevelt. I do not want to offend you, but if you compare the losses of your country with the losses of ours, your losses just equal our losses in one big campaign. You know what terrible ruins we got. We lost our cities. That is why our country was so eager to establish firm peace. No country wished it so eagerly."

But, we pointed out, the Soviet army was bigger than ours.

"I do not reject that our army was bigger. Take a map and look at the geographical situation of our country. It is a colossal territory. If you take Germany or France, small countries who keep their army to defend either their east or their west, that is easy; they may have a small army. But if we keep our army in the east it is difficult to reach the west because our territory is so vast."

I pointed out that after the war the Russians wanted a group of neutral countries between them and Germany, that Germany was no longer a military menace and that Great Britain could not be considered a military threat. Why, then, I asked, was it not possible to do without an offensive army in Russia, since it frightened the rest of the world?

"When we increase our arms," he said, "it means we are afraid of each other. Until the troops are drawn out of Europe and military bases liquidated, the disarmament will not succeed."

I told him that after World War II we had not been suspicious of Russia. I knew that my husband had hoped we would be able to come to an understanding. "But then," I went on, "we found the Russians did not strictly keep agreements made at Yalta and we became more and more suspicious."

The discussion continued. Mr. Khrushchev appeared to think that the Americans did not really want to liberate the European and Eastern countries. Instead, they had tried to destroy the will of the people. I countered with the suggestion that the acceptance of Communism did not, in our opinion, represent the will of the people. From that point on the discussion grew more heated. Did he, I asked, believe that a Communist world must be brought about?

"Communism will win in the whole world," he told me. "This is scientifically based on the writings of Karl Marx, Engels and Lenin." He went on to assure me blandly: "We are against any military attempt to introduce Communism or socialism into any country."

Much of our discussion is irrelevant now as conditions have changed in the world. Basically, there was no possibility of meeting in agreement on a single point. Except one, perhaps, equivocal as it seemed.

"Misunderstandings have grown between our countries," I said, "and there is fear on both sides. We will have to do things to create confidence. One thing is a broader exchange of people."

"I fully agree, Mrs. Roosevelt," he said in a calmer tone.

At the end of two and a half hours of conversation I felt fully convinced that Mr. Khrushchev knew the danger that any new war would bring to civilization. He was, I decided, convinced that war would be a disadvantage to the Soviet Union and to Communism because he believed that the wave of the future was socialism and that his cause would triumph without war. He believed it, I told myself, and he would try to make the future serve his purposes.

As I was leaving, Mr. Khrushchev wished me a pleasant trip and asked, "Can I tell our papers that we have had a friendly conversation?"

"You can say that we had a friendly conversation but that we differ."

He grinned broadly. "Now!" he exclaimed. "At least we didn't shoot at each other!"

For three weeks in the Soviet Union I had felt more than at any time in my life that I was cut off from all the outside world. For three weeks I do not believe I had heard anyone really laugh on the streets or in a crowd. I had been among hospitable people but they were people who worked hard, who lived under considerable strain, and who were tired. It was only after I had landed at Copenhagen and heard laughter and gay talk and saw faces that were unafraid that I realized how different were our two worlds. Suddenly I could breathe again!

But I was frightened too, and after I reached home my nagging fear continued. I was—I still am—afraid that Americans and the peoples of the rest of the free world will not understand the nature of the struggle against Communism as exemplified by the Soviet Union. It is urgently important for the sake of our country and people that we get rid of some of our great misunderstandings and that we see clearly the things that must be done.

We are in a great struggle between two vastly different ways of life. While we must have guns, atomic weapons and missiles for retaliation against aggression, they are not going to win this struggle or prevent a catastrophic world war. Nor is belief in the idea of democracy likely to have great effect in areas where democratic institutions are not established. To overemphasize the importance of military power or to propagate merely the abstract idea of democracy is to miss the point. There is much, much more to be done if Western leadership is to be accepted by the masses of the world's underdeveloped countries, if our way of life and our hard-won freedoms are to survive—or, perhaps, if anything is to survive in the atomic age—and flourish. We must provide leadership for free peoples, but we must never forget that in many countries, particularly in Asia and Africa, the freedom that is uppermost in the minds of the people is freedom to eat.

I think it is time for us Americans to take a good look at ourselves and our shortcomings. We should remember how we achieved the aims of freedom and democracy. We should look back in an effort to gauge how we can best influence the peoples of the world. Perhaps we made the greatest impression on underdeveloped countries in the 1930's when we ourselves were making a tremendous effort to fight our way out of a great economic depression. In that period we united behind bold ideas and vigorous programs, and, as they watched us, many people in far countries of the world began to realize that a government could be intensely interested in the welfare of the individual. They saw what was happening and it gave them hope that it could happen to them too. That was a generation ago, but again today it seems to me that it is essential for us to examine carefully our actions as a nation and try to develop a program for the welfare of the individual.

In this connection I was sometimes astonished during my visit to Russia to see what the Soviet government had brought about during four decades of Communist dictatorship. Illiteracy, which was once 90 per cent, has been reduced until it is now probably less than 10 per cent. The people have been educated in every field—crafts, arts, professions, sciences—and the government has used the educational system for political purposes, to shape the people to the will of the leadership.

Educators are sent where they are most important for the purposes of the government. Doctors are sent where they can be most useful. Workers are sent to distant areas of Asia because new fields must be plowed and crops planted. This is dictatorship and it is hateful; but the results achieved by the Soviet regime are obvious to anyone visiting Russia. The water is pure; the milk is clean; the food supply is increasing; industry has made mighty strides. The people are not free, but they are better off materially every year. They know little of other countries and they are willing to accept a hard life because of the insidious Communist propaganda that unites them in fear of aggression by the United States. Most of them are sustained by a belief in communistic aims.

The Russians recognize that there are vast masses of people in Asia, Africa and parts of Latin America who are closer to the economic conditions that existed forty years ago in Russia than they are to the conditions that have existed for many years in the United States. The leaders of the Soviets can say to them: "We know your conditions. Our people were once hungry, too; not only for food but for health and education, for knowledge and for hope for the future. Look at what we have done in forty years! Take heart. We can help you."

This is a challenge to democracy. This is the real challenge, and it cannot be met by mere words. We have to show the world by our actions that we live up to the ideals we profess and demonstrate that we can provide all the people in this country with the basic decencies of life, spiritually as well as materially. In the United States we are the showcase for the possibilities inherent in a free world, in democracy. If the lives of our people are not better in terms of basic satisfactions as well as in material ways than the lives of people anywhere in the world, then the uncommitted peoples we need on our side will look elsewhere for leadership.

We have spent a great deal in grants to our friends abroad but there is more than that to the struggle for the minds of men. For example, we have taken no trouble to invite delegations from other parts of the world to look at our system and see what we are doing under government auspices. If we are to be leaders we must offer needy countries technical know-how to help them achieve the freedom to eat, and practical help in developing, step by step, a democratic way of life. It is not enough to say that we do not like the Communist idea. We have to prove that our own idea is better and can accomplish more.

We *can* accomplish more. There is no reason for us to be frightened by the scientific achievements under direction of the Soviet government, which has concentrated money and manpower on sputniks and rockets for obvious propaganda reasons. We have been complacent and given as little money and as few men as possible for work that we should have pressed vigorously. We were more interested in our comforts, in making money, and in having all the luxuries possible in this comfortable world of ours. We have to change and we *will* change that approach. If we are to lead the free world we must become a mature people—or we may one day wake up to find that fear and laziness have reduced us from a strong, vital nation to a people unable to lead other nations in the only way to win the struggle against Communism, the way of the mind and the heart.

I can think of nothing more foolish than looking at the Russian scientific achievements and saying that we must rush to catch up with them by resorting to their methods. We have always said that our objectives were those that could be achieved only by a free people. Why should a free people slavishly follow a Communist lead? We must develop all our resources in our own way. We want our people to decide whether their children shall go to school, whether they shall be scientists or playwrights or mechanics. We don't want to be told what to do. What the world wants today is leadership in the true sense, and we had better decide what we want to achieve and then go ahead and do it as leaders and not as imitators.

The only thing that frightened me in Russia was that we might be apathetic and complacent in the face of this challenge. I can well understand why the Russian people welcome the good that has come to them. But I cannot understand or believe that anything that has to be preserved by fear will stand permanently against a system which offers love and trust among peoples and removes fear so that all feel free to think and express their ideas.

It seems to me that we must have the courage to face ourselves in this crisis. We must regain a vision of ourselves as leaders of the world. We must join in an effort to use all knowledge for the good of all human beings.

When we do that we shall have nothing to fear.

PART IV

The Search for Understanding

Thirty-nine

Second Visit to Russia

FOR SOME TIME my children and my friends have been warning me that I must slow down. They tell me that I am working too hard, seeing too many people, undertaking too many activities; that my interests seem to proliferate rather than to narrow. Which is certainly true.

I am willing to slow down but I just don't know how. Even when I am aware that people have used my time unjustifiably, I find myself interested in them. Even when a new project makes demands on my already crowded schedule, I find it difficult to reject it, so long as it serves a useful purpose. But I do feel that I am too old now to undertake any course of action or embark on foreign travel unless I am convinced that it will, in some way, be useful.

I had been much troubled by my first visit to Russia, where I had spent nearly a month visiting institutions of many sorts, and had concluded by having a three-hour interview with Mr. Khrushchev. The more I thought of that visit and the conclusions I had drawn from it the more troubled I was. What seemed most frightening about the conditions I found in Russia, the trends I discerned, the possibilities I envisioned, was that the people of the United States appeared not to have the slightest grasp of their meaning in terms of our own future.

Basic in all this was the impression I had gathered from watching the training—or rather the conditioning—of children in the Soviet Union into disciplined, amenable citizens, prepared to obey any orders given them and incapable of revolt. To return to the United States after that trip and hear people talk blithely of the possibility of the Russian people's rising up against their government (a situation made inconceivable by their conditioning from babyhood) or changing their attitude toward us (when

389

every source of information is filtered through government hands) was more than disturbing. It was alarming. It meant that we were facing the greatest challenge our way of life has ever had to meet without any clear understanding of the facts.

There is in most people, at most times, a proneness to give more credence to pleasant news than to unpleasant, to hope that, somehow or other, things "will come out all right." But this was not the frame of mind that created the United States and made it not only a great nation but a symbol of a way of life that became the hope of the world. One can fight a danger only when one is armed with solid facts and spurred on by an unwavering faith and determination.

So, when Dr. Gurewitsch decided, a year after the first trip to Russia, that he would like to go back and see whether he could learn the answer to some questions in regard to physical medicine, I was eager to return to the Soviet Union and, on a second visit, without the distraction of strange first impressions, find out for myself whether my first conclusions had been sound.

Dr. Gurewitsch, his wife Edna, and I started our tour, in 1958, by attending a meeting of the United Nations Associations which was being held in Brussels because of the World's Fair.

The theme of the Brussels Exposition was "Better Living for the People Today," and on the whole I did not feel that it was as effective as it should have been. A great many people criticized our building, which annoyed me very much, as I thought it was beautiful and the layout of the landscaping was unusually fine. Inside, however, the exhibitions were not well arranged, and the mechanical displays were not working.

One of the most popular, though unplanned, features of our exhibit was the appearance there of Harry Belafonte. He had a great personal success, and his presence was most valuable as an answer to much of the criticism of the Americans on their attitude toward colored people.

The Russian exhibit was monumental. It can be summed up as marching, marching, marching, piled on marching. Pictures of young Russians marching to school, marching to factories, marching with the army, all looking young, healthy and vigorous. To most people from the Western countries that much marching is supremely dull. They had, I remember, a cyclorama which lasted for an hour and a half (with more marching, of course), but which was less interesting and less informative than the one produced by the Americans, which lasted only twenty minutes.

How much ultimate value this kind of exhibit had, either for the Russians or for us, I have no way of knowing. My own over-all impression was that the Russian exhibit gave an effect of enormous power and drive; but, though they displayed the best they had to offer to the best advantage, it was not good enough to match what we have. On the other hand, I felt that here again we had not used, in the best possible way, an opportunity to show the peoples of the world what the United States is all about.

One of the most pleasant episodes during my visit to Brussels was a luncheon with Queen Elizabeth of Belgium, whom I liked very much.

Queen Elizabeth is a musician and an artist. She paints, she does sculpture, she plays several instruments. In addition, she is a woman who plants gardens. But I think the loveliest thing about her is that she is really concerned about people. Of course, being a queen, she is cut off from people in many ways so that her approach is necessarily unrealistic, but she really wants to learn. She has a beautiful soul and a longing to be of service to humanity. She gives with great generosity, not only with her head but with her heart.

From Belgium we flew to the Soviet Union. The first five days of our visit were given up to the activities of the Soviet Association of the United Nations, which had invited all of our delegation to be its guests. This meant that we would have only a little over two weeks for the work we wanted to do and therefore we decided to concentrate on Moscow and Leningrad.

As soon as we ceased to be the guests of the United Nations, I was simply a private tourist visitor, but I had no trouble in making appointments with any department or in seeing anything I asked to see.

I did not try to see Mr. Khrushchev on this visit. I felt that he had had a great many American visitors and must have all the information he needed about us. Certainly, he had had plentiful opportunity to receive reports from those who had interviewed him.

My main object was to try to find out how many emotionally disturbed children there are in the Soviet Union and what treatment is being provided for them. The Russian answer to the problem of emotionally disturbed children lies, primarily, in their type of discipline, or conditioning of all children. They begin, as I have said before, when the child is two months old, and by the time he is seven years old the child is completely regimented. The Soviet children have little or no desire for freedom. Their conditioning and training has been carefully thought out to prevent deviation of any kind, on any level, from birth to death.

This conditioning provides, too, for the development of what one might call "safe leadership," that is, leadership within certain carefully prescribed limits.

For instance, each school class elects its president, at the age of seven years. The classes for this age group average about forty pupils. The little president marches his class into the schoolroom and tells when to get up and leave. He passes them on to two children from an older grade who see them safely out of the building. Then this little boy returns to help the teacher tidy up the schoolroom.

"How," I asked the teachers, over and over, "can you detect an emotionally disturbed child?"

They were disgusted. "Any deviation in behavior is reported immediately," they told me.

This uniformity in behavior and in response is, it seems to me, the factor which Americans fail almost entirely to understand, either in its essence or in its potentialities. This large-scale conditioning of human beings is something so new in the world that we cannot grasp it.

I should think that it would destroy initiative completely, but though I have frequently asked them, no psychologist can tell me what the results of this gigantic experiment with human beings will be.

On my first visit I had watched the training of small babies. On this trip I studied the older children, their training, their discipline, their complete absorption by the Communist system.

Whatever else a child's life in Russia may be, it is not easy. Indeed, life is easy for no one there. The children work in school from 8:45 until 1:45. If they have anyone at home, they return for a hot meal. Otherwise, this is provided by the school. For the next two hours, in the Pioneer Youth Home or room, they have exercises, supervised games, and are drilled in Marxism. Every child learns his Marxism backwards and forwards. By the time he leaves school he is prepared to take not only his skills but his political ideas with him wherever he may be sent, to whatever part of the world.

For another two hours there are outdoor games, also supervised. The Russian child is never alone. And when the school day ends he is assigned far more homework than falls to the lot of the American child.

As a part of the Pioneer Youth Movement, every big city provides a "children's palace," where the children go twice a week for two hours of various types of training and entertainment. This includes such diverse things as lectures on outer space, chess playing, storytelling, dancing and singing, and the development of handicrafts.

The one I visited was in Leningrad. The equipment was excellent and the shop equipment for training in manual arts was as good as or better than that in our own trade schools. And, of course, during the lectures or the games the training in Marxism is continued.

In the light of this standardized training, which is much the same whether one lives in Moscow or in a remote village, it is easier to understand why the teachers could tell me so promptly that "any deviation in behavior is reported immediately."

Madame Muravyeva, who was in charge of social service for the Soviet Union, told me that every schoolteacher is trained to watch for signs of physical, mental or emotional disturbance. Where such disturbances seem to be a result of home conditions, the social services work to improve these conditions. Where more drastic efforts are needed, the child is sent to a sanitarium, where, the minister of health told me, preventive therapy is used.

I was told that inadequate housing in the big cities, bad relations between parents, and undesirable conditions caused by heavy drinking could create emotional disturbances in the young.

After sitting through many classes in schools and visiting many more, I came back believing that the Russians have fewer emotionally disturbed children than we do and less of a problem with juvenile delinquency, particularly in the early years. Their problem comes primarily with those young people who go into the technicons, a type of technical school, at fourteen, because they are judged not capable of higher education. Therefore, at seventeen they are ready to take a job and suddenly, after having had every moment of the time planned and occupied, except for the hours when they work, they are free, their own masters, with their own money.

It is a heady thing to be given freedom all of a sudden, even the limited kind in the Soviet Union. So this, inevitably, creates a problem. These are the youngsters who, Mr. Khrushchev says, behave like our zoot-suit youngsters and create a problem by heavy drinking.

Those who attend technicons are much the biggest group of the young in Russia. As in any country, there is a large percentage which cannot profitably be educated beyond a certain point. In Russia, however, the search for talent, for the exceptionally bright, for the artistically endowed or the scientifically minded goes on constantly, and such exceptional young-sters are provided with every opportunity to improve their talents, increase their learning, and acquire as much education as they can absorb.

There is no fear of eggheads in Russia. They know that the speedy de-velopment of the country, which has already grown in forty years from one of the most backward to one of the most modern nations, can be achieved only by using every scrap of talent, every scrap of brains and ability they have.

I do not mean that these talented youngsters are indulged. Far from it. I visited an art school in Moscow where children talented in painting and in sculpture are given the best possible tools to work with and every op-portunity to learn. But their life is Spartan. Their beds are probably com-pletely hygienic but they are far from comfortable. Their food is sufficient to sustain life but drab as diet. The cold, even in September, in the build-ing where they live and work, struck us as we thought of what the winters must be like. Yet these children range in age from only eight to seventeen.

The corridors were lined with examples of their work and I was much interested in inspecting them. I found that what the very young did was fresh and interesting. But it seemed to me that, as they grew older, they became more imitative under their training. This was particularly accentu-ated in the field of sculpture. When I went to the class for seventeen-year-old boys and girls I felt that both the concept and the execution of practically all their work was stereotyped, tied to the past of the classical tradition, but with little individual expression or feeling for modern forms of development.

Naturally, it is a great benefit to the talented young to be afforded every opportunity to develop their skills to their utmost. Russia is the only country which, next to its politicians and scientists, pays its highest salaries and gives its highest honor to its artists and its intellectuals.

But, while the salary may be higher and the recognition greater, in some basic ways the restrictions of life in Russia are the same, whether one is at the top or at the bottom of the scale. One rule seems to hold true: there is practically no privacy in Russia.

The number of rooms you are allowed to have in an apartment depends on the number of people who are to live in it. If there are four people, there are only two rooms. On the other hand, whether you are allotted six rooms or two rooms, your rent is still only 1 per cent of your income.

Before I left New York on this second trip to Russia, a letter appeared in the *New York Times*, written by a Russian woman who challenged the paper to publish it. She wrote that she wanted to hear from American women. Russia wanted peace, she said, and we did not. What were American women doing about it? She asked foreigners to come and see her, to discover for themselves how people lived in Russia.

At the request of the *New York Times* I answered her letter, and while we were in Leningrad we went to visit her. She lived in a new house on the outskirts of Leningrad, up five flights of stairs. There was an elevator but it never ran. She welcomed us, tremendously proud of her apartment, which, from her standpoint and that of most of her fellow countrymen, was palatial.

She had five children under twelve years of age, and the son went to a boarding school but came home for weekends. She was allowed three rooms, a bathroom, and a big kitchen. This meant that the smallest boy slept in the room with his mother and father, the two girls had a bedroom, and the two older boys slept in a room which served also as dining room and living room.

Her letter, I feel sure, had been supervised and approved by the government. To her delight it had brought her a number of answers, about three hundred, I think. Some of her other correspondents had come to see her, as we did.

We found her very friendly—indeed, most Russians are personally friendly to Americans—but nothing could shake her conviction that we, as a nation, threatened Russia and wanted war. Before the end of our visit, I think we had convinced her that we ourselves did not want war, but she still believed firmly that the United States did.

Why did our country have bases? she asked. We were ringing Russia round with bases. Which, of course, is true. But that Russia could conceivably constitute a warlike threat she brushed aside as nonsense, as hostile foreign propaganda.

When we left Leningrad we were touched to find that she had bothered to come to the train, in the middle of the night, to see us off.

The visit left us with a blank feeling of failure. There was no personal hostility between us. None at all. But there was an unshaken conviction that the United States not only threatens but actually desires and seeks war. Here we are, equipped with the best communications in the world, and yet we have not learned how to use them in a way that can reach people.

The friendliness of these people, always apart from the political bias in which they have been conditioned, is astonishing. I have noticed, over and over, when they come to the United States, even if they have met you only most briefly before, they greet you as though you were a long-lost friend, almost appealing for affection.

At one time the National Council of Women arranged, through the State Department, for two Russian women to visit the United States. A group of us raised the money for the trip, hoping that if they could see for themselves something of American life and the American temper it would give them something new to tell their people on their return.

These women lived here in private homes and were free of supervision by their own government, and, naturally, by ours, while they were in this country. I cannot believe that the visit was wasted. The more such visits are sponsored the better it will be for us because, if we continue to fail to tell our story convincingly abroad, at least the evidence is here at home without the telling.

All this is a digression from the problem of emotional disturbance. We visited the Pavlov Institute, and watched the training of various types of animals. The most interesting, of course, were the monkeys but we were warned not to get too close to the cage of the big ones, particularly if they did not happen to be good-tempered at the time. We also saw dogs being trained and being experimented with in many ways. It was not difficult to see how, out of this conditioning of animals, could come the theory of the conditioning of children. We also visited institutions where children who were handicapped by illness or some infirmity were spending the summer months, and where the care was excellent.

Then we went to a hospital where people are diagnosed. Anyone who thinks that he needs help can go to a clinic. If he can cope with his problem without going to a hospital, that is fine. Otherwise, he is treated in the hospital. This place cares for those threatened with mental and emotional disturbances and provides aftercare when they have returned to their normal lives.

The interesting thing is that there appeared to be no lack of man power for nursing in the Soviet Union. Here we are lucky if one nurse has only forty patients. In the Soviet Union one nurse had no more than four patients and a really disturbed person gets almost constant attention. This is possible because all the women in Russia are mobilized.

Of course, with the modern drugs the change in the mental hospitals is very great. We did see one room where patients were still given shock treatment, but this method of therapy is gradually disappearing.

There is a shortage of some of the new drugs in the Soviet Union. I do not know how serious this may be but, of course, it would make a difference in the treatment. In the particular hospital which I visited I saw very few badly disturbed people. I remember one young girl who had come in, thinking she had a monkey in her stomach. The nurse never left her for a minute.

I returned from Russia late in the fall of 1958 and attempted after my second visit to balance my impressions against those of my first one.

What stood out most sharply were the changes. The year before, there had been only trucks on the road. Now there were a large number of small cars and a considerable number of larger cars, all of them of Russian make.

The year before, my first impression as our plane circled Moscow, had been of the number of cranes where new building was going on. This time I found a number of new apartment houses had been built and the city was expanding. There were apartment buildings going up to house two million people.

The year before, the people had appeared to be uniformly drab. Clothing was not important in the economy, so the people had to do with what was provided. This time they were much better dressed. The expression on their faces when we saw them at the end of the day's work was happier, less anxious than it had been when they were closer to the Stalin regime.

On the whole, however, the second visit intensified the basic impressions of the first.

Today the Russian people are well disciplined, amenable to direction, healthy and determined to build a place in the sun for themselves and for their country. In our thinking about them we must remember how the situation looks from *their* point of view.

They have no freedom, we say. But they never had freedom, so they do not miss it. Forty years ago they not only had no freedom they had no education, they had no health care, they had no hope of bettering their condition.

For them what has happened has been, on the whole, of great value.

And farther on there is China, 600 million people who, in eight years, have come even faster along the road to modernization—and indoctrination—than the Soviets had done in the first eight years after the revolution. Yet the only way we have found to cope with this growing danger, this mushrooming threat, is to ignore their political existence, by which they lose face and feel bitterness; and to refuse to trade with them, by which we force them to build up their own ability to produce the very things they might buy from us, thus acting as a spur to their industrialization. Surely there is no framework for building world peace and understanding through these methods.

Today we are one of the oldest governments in existence; ours has been the position for leadership, for setting the pattern of behavior. And yet we are supinely putting ourselves in the position of leaving the leadership to the Russians, of following their ideas rather than our own. For instance, when the Russians set up a restriction on what visitors to the country may be allowed to see, we promptly do the same thing here, in retaliation. Whenever we behave in this manner we are copying the methods of dictatorship and making a hollow boast of our claim that this country loves freedom for all. We owe it to ourselves and to the world, to our own dignity and self-respect, to set our own standards of behavior, regardless of what other nations do.

I came back from that second trip to Russia convinced that any talk of an uprising of the people against their government was baseless nonsense. But I came back believing more profoundly than before that, by practicing what we preach, putting democracy to work up to the very hilt, showing the world that our way of life has the most to offer the men and women and children of all countries, we could regain our lost leadership. Against those mindless millions we can oppose the unleashed strength of free men, for only in freedom can a man function completely.

Forty

The American Dream

IF THAT SECOND trip to Russia aroused deep misgivings in my mind about the efficacy of the methods we have used in recent years in meeting the Soviet challenge, a journey which I made in 1958 to Morocco and another in the spring of 1959 to the Near East made me feel that we must think through once more our whole approach to world problems.

When I visited Morocco in 1958, the King kindly sent an aide with us and we were allowed to travel through the northern part of the country. This was the first opportunity I had had to see for myself the difficulties that arise in the transition stage between colonialism and independence. The troubles that Morocco was encountering were, it seemed to me, fairly typical of the basic difficulties of all young nations in transition.

As the French withdrew from the country, taking their nationals along, the villages found themselves stripped of teachers and doctors. Countless villages were without a single person trained to give medical assistance. The Moroccans were not yet prepared to replace the doctors, the teachers, and the service employees with their own men. It may be decades before they are ready to do so. Where, then, are the necessary people to come from? I'd like to go into this a little more thoroughly later on, because I feel in that answer lies the key, or one of the major keys, to the future.

As though this acute shortage of trained men were not enough, a severe drought had cut down the food supply drastically. The United States, through church organizations, had sent a considerable amount of food to alleviate the greatest need, but conditions were still bad.

Another, and unforeseen, difficulty was that the Moroccans had established markets, which are held on different days in different towns. With this new system they abolished the middleman, who was usually Jewish.

399

This meant that Morocco found itself with a number of people who had no longer any way of making a living.

The great problem seems to be that, while people may be able to fight successfully for freedom, they may not yet be prepared to set up a stable and functioning independent government. The French pulled out, but the Moroccans had no one to replace them. They were totally unprepared for self-government. They were, in fact, much worse off than they had been a year before.

Today this is happening in a more drastic form in the Congo with the withdrawal of the Belgians. The time for colonization has, perhaps, gone forever, but some intermediate transition system is essential if chaos is not to follow.

A recent Afro-Asian resolution in the UN reveals the difficulty of the position by these words: "Inadequacy of political, economic, social or cultural preparedness" shall not serve as a pretext for denying independence. Now, we cannot deny that such a pretext has often been used in denying the right of self-determination. But it cannot be denied, either, that without some basic qualifications, self-determination will lead to self-destruction.

The visit, which I made with my granddaughter Nina in the spring of 1959, was very brief: one week in Israel, two weeks in Iran, with stopovers in Paris and London.

In Soviet Russia one is in a country where a way of life, a political and economic philosophy, has crystallized. In the Near East the situation is different, the fluctuating and uncertain position of young countries which are in transition from the ways of the past to those of the future, with no certain path to tread and with the ultimate goal still obscure. That is becoming the situation of an increasing number of infant nations as they shake off the fetters of colonialism, or of ancient laws and customs, and grope for their own place in the sun. And what that goal is to be, what kind of place they are to occupy, what political philosophy they will choose in the long run, will depend in great part on how we, in this country, prepare to meet the challenge.

Is what we are doing good enough? Have the changes that have revealed themselves in recent years, particularly in Africa and the Near East and the Latin-American countries, shown overwhelming evidence that we are doing an intelligent job, an adequate job? I am afraid not. Genuinely afraid.

To me, the democratic system represents man's best and brightest hope of self-fulfillment, of a life rich in promise and free from fear; the one hope, perhaps, for the complete development of the whole man. But I know, and learn more clearly every day, that we cannot keep our system strong and free by neglect, by taking it for granted, by giving it our second-best attention. We must be prepared, like the suitor in *The Merchant of Venice* —and, I might point out, the successful suitor—to give and hazard all we have.

It was the season of Ramadan when we reached Shiraz, Iran, to visit my daughter Anna, whose husband was stationed there. Iran, of course, is not Arab, but many of its problems are similar to those of its neighbors in the Near East. The chief problem, it seemed to me, was poverty. The mass of the people have become poorer and poorer; their health has deteriorated; and so, in a disastrous way, have its natural resources. Or, more likely, the loss of natural resources has brought about the poverty. The mountains of Iran, once clothed with forests and covered with fertile soil, are bare now. The land is desert. And with this loss of the fertility of the soil, this loss of forests, has come an inevitable economic instability.

The health of the people is generally poor, with trachoma, tuberculosis and malnutrition the biggest medical problems. The country exists in a kind of flux. The tribes are unwilling to settle down into village life until they can be convinced that such a way of life offers more advantages. They want to be sure that there will be an opportunity to work gainfully, that health conditions will be better, that there will be educational advantages.

So far as the masses are concerned, this is still preponderantly an illiterate population. While there are schools in Shiraz and even in some of the villages, the compulsory education law is not enforced.

To add to the difficulty, so far as future improvement is concerned, the Iranian has no sense of community responsibility. The position of women is still inferior. All this militates against improved social conditions that might arise from the will of the people themselves, their desire and determination to better their own lot and that of their fellow countrymen.

In Shiraz we visited the Jewish community and found it grim indeed.

These people were living in one-room huts, without sanitation. There were not even doors or windows—just holes cut in the walls so that people could go in and out, and to admit a little light. As a rule, there was a little charcoal brazier in one corner for cooking and heating. Bedding was rolled up in the daytime and covered the floor at night.

From Iran we went on to Israel, where we spent Easter week. Since my return I have tried to analyze what makes the difference in atmosphere between Israel and its Arab neighbors and the great country of Iran.

I think the greatest difference lies in an atmosphere in Israel that one does not find in many other countries. Its young people may be chiefly responsible for it. They are excited by the dream of building a country and they work at it with gusto, with all their strength, with exhilaration and a kind of exaltation that cannot fail to impress the visitor. Difficult as conditions are, long and hard as the people labor, they do it in an atmosphere of faith and hope and conviction. It is the absence of these qualities in the other countries that is so disheartening. For men cannot live without hope. If it is not engendered by their own convictions and desires, it can easily be fired from without, and by the most meretricious and empty of promises.

I was much amused on my return from Israel to discover that wherever I lectured for the next few months people appeared to be less interested in world affairs than they were in the fate of a camel that Nina had bought in Israel but which we were unable to bring into the country, at the orders of the Department of Agriculture. Eventually, the camel was given to a poor Bedouin.

What I had learned on these two trips was much on my mind when I returned home. Why, I wondered, were we not more successful in helping the young nations and those in transition to become established along democratic lines? Why was it that the Russians were doing so much better? The answer can be oversimplified and an oversimplification is false and misleading. But part of the answer, and I thought a major part, was that Russia had trained its young people to go out into the world, to carry their services and skills to backward and underdeveloped countries, to replace the missing doctors and teachers, the scientists and technicians; above all, to fill the vacant civil service jobs, prepared not only by training for the job itself but by a complete briefing in the customs, habits, traditions and trend of thought of the people, to understand them and deal with them. Where they go, of course, they take with them their Marxist training, thinking and system.

And our young Americans? Were they being prepared to take their faith in democracy to the world along with their skills? Were they learning the language and the customs and the history of these new peoples? Did they understand how to deal with them, not according to their own ideas but according to the ideas of the people they must learn to know if they were to reach them at all? Had they acquired an ability to live and work among peoples of different religion and race and color, without arrogance and without prejudice?

Here, I believe, we have fallen down badly. In the past few years I have grasped at every opportunity to meet with the young, to talk with college students, to bring home as strongly as I can to even young children in the lower grades our responsibility for each other, our need to understand and respect each other. The future will be determined by the young and there is no more essential task today, it seems to me, than to bring before them once more, in all its brightness, in all its splendor and beauty, the American Dream, lest we let it fade, too concerned with ways of earning a living or impressing our neighbors or getting ahead or finding bigger and more potent ways of destroying the world and all that is in it.

No single individual, of course, and no single group has an exclusive claim to the American Dream. But we have all, I think, a single vision of what it is, not merely as a hope and an aspiration but as a way of life, which we can come ever closer to attaining in its ideal form if we keep shining and unsullied our purpose and our belief in its essential value.

That we have sometimes given our friends and our enemies abroad a shoddy impression of the Dream cannot be denied, much as we would like to deny it. *The Ugly American,* impressive as it was, struck me as being exaggerated. True, one of the first American ambassadors I ever met in an Eastern country was appallingly like the title character in the novel. There are doubtless many others, too many others; men who accept—and seek—the position of representative of their government abroad with no real interest or respect for the country they go to, and no real interest or respect for the image of their country which they present to other people.

Such men buy their position by gifts of money to their party or seek them because of the glamorous social life they may lead in exotic places.

"Oh, you must go there. You'll have a wonderful time. And the polo is top-notch."

They often do not know the language of the country; they are not familiar with its government or its officials; they are not interested in its customs or its point of view.

The Russians—and I say it with shame—do this better. They are trained in the language, history, customs and ways of life of a country before they go to it. They do not confine themselves to official entertaining but make a point of meeting and knowing and establishing friendly relations with people of all sorts, in every class of society, in every part of the country.

When we look at the picture of Russian greed in swallowing one satellite nation after another and contrast it with the picture of American generosity in giving food, clothing, supplies, technical and financial assistance, with no ulterior motive in acquiring new territory, it is stupid and tragic waste that the use of incompetent representatives should undo so much useful work, so great an expense, so much in the way of materials of every kind.

Of course, what the Russians have accomplished in training their young people for important posts in the underdeveloped countries—which, I must repeat, may affect the future course of these countries—has been done by compulsion. That's the rub. For what we must do is to achieve the same results on a voluntary basis. We do not say to our young people: "You must go here and take such a job." But we can show them that where we fail the Russians will win, by default. We can show them the importance of acquiring the kind of training that will make them useful and honorable representatives of their country wherever they may go abroad.

Perhaps the new frontier today is something more than the new revolution in textiles and methods and speed and goods. It is the frontier of men's minds. But we cannot cast an enduring light on other men's minds unless the light in our own minds burns with a hard, unquenchable flame.

One form of communication we have failed abjectly in: the teaching of languages. Most school children have several years of inadequate teaching in one language or another. I say inadequate because the study of a language, after all, is inadequate if one cannot learn to read and write it, to speak and to understand it. During World War II the government found a simplified and most effective method of teaching such difficult languages as Japanese and Chinese to American GIs. In a matter of weeks they had mastered more of the language than formerly they would have acquired in the same number of years. And yet in our schools the old, cumbersome, unproductive methods are still in use.

It seems to me so obvious that it should not need to be said that we must increase and improve the teaching of languages to our young people, who will otherwise find themselves crippled and sorely handicapped in dealing with people of foreign races and different cultures.

These are things our children should be told. These are the conditions they are going to have to meet. They ought to be made to understand exactly what competition they will encounter, why they must meet it, how they can meet it best. Yet I rarely find, in talking with them, that they have been given the slightest inkling of the meaning of the Soviet infiltration of other countries, or that the future the Soviets are helping to build is the one with which they will have to contend. I rarely find that anyone has suggested that our own young people should have any preparation whatsoever to cope with the problems that are impending.

That is why, in the course of the past several years, I have fitted into my schedule, wherever I could, occasions to talk with the young. Sometimes they come up to Hyde Park by the busload to ask questions or to discuss problems. Sometimes I talk at their schools or colleges.

Last year, in co-operation with Brandeis University, I experimented with a new idea. I agreed to do a series of nine television programs, which were then sold to education television stations throughout the country. It worked so well that this year I have agreed to do ten programs.

In addition to this, I lectured to a class given by Dr. Fuchs on international law and international organization at Brandeis. There were only thirteen in the class, all students who hoped to go into foreign service either for business or for the government, five of them students from foreign countries. I was a little staggered by this assignment, as I felt sure that many of these young people were better versed in questions of international organization than I was. But at least I could discuss with them the tangled problems of foreign politics.

This, of course, was a specialialized sort of lecture course, and I found it interesting and stimulating, as I have always found teaching. But what I would have preferred to say to these young people was something like the following:

Today our government and the governments of most of the world are primarily concerned—obsessed—by one idea: defense. But what is real defense and how is it obtained? Of course, a certain amount of military defense is necessary. But there comes a point where you must consider what can be done on an economic and cultural basis.

It seems to me that, in terms of atomic warfare, we should henceforth have a small professional army of men who have voluntarily chosen military service as an obligation to their country. But what then? What about the hundreds of thousands of young people who leave school every year, either from high school or from college? Are they, from now on, to have no participation in contributing to the welfare of their country?

Far from it. As matters stand, we draft young men into the service, train them until they are useful, and then let them go. This seems to me monstrous waste.

It has long been my personal conviction that every young person should be given some basic training that might, eventually, be useful to his country. As I thought about it, it seemed to me that this could be handled either in school or at college, and instead of calling all young men up for compulsory military service, we could offer an alternative along these lines:

Whether you finish college, or high school, you may, if you do not want to spend two years of compulsory military training, decide what country you would like to spend two years in. You will be given two years of basic training, either during school hours or in the evenings. If you want to go, say, to Africa or to other underdeveloped countries, you will, from the age of fifteen to seventeen, be taught the language, the history, the geography, the economic background of the country. You will be prepared to take with you a skill, or be trained for the most crying need in many transition nations, to fill the civil service jobs that Russia is now so rapidly filling. Or, if you are preparing for a profession, you may make use of that.

New industries are needed in these countries, there are technical needs in almost all areas. The economy has to be bolstered in countless ways. New techniques are required in agriculture. And nearly all of these countries need teachers badly.

I was greatly interested and pleased to hear that Chester Bowles's son turned down a scholarship at Oxford University to go to Nigeria, where he plans to teach in high school for two years.

What is saving Ghana today is that Sir Robert Jackson remained in the country after the withdrawal of Great Britain. He is using all his great experience and intelligence on behalf of the people as economic adviser to the Volta River Project. He is also being aided by his brilliant wife, the famous economist, Barbara Ward.

For people in young nations, which are still in a transition stage and setting up governments, such help could be more valuable than a large standing army or economic aid, particularly when in the new country there are few people capable of administering it effectively.

As I have said, this training and use of our young has been long in my mind. Wherever and whenever I could I have advocated it. Recently with the announcement of the Peace Corps, it appears that a similar plan will at least have a fair trial. Some of our young people will be given the opportunity to take up the slack in underdeveloped countries, and to bring our skills and our attitudes and our principles to them as free men. I am delighted that this has been done, and am hopeful that it may prove to be one of the most fruitful ways we have found of sharing our American Dream with others.

President Kennedy has initiated a Peace Corps through which he hopes the ideals of young, and perhaps not so young, Americans may be expressed to people throughout the world, particularly in the underdeveloped countries which need help at the present time. The methods of choosing people and arranging with the recipient governments are still being worked out. Colleges and universities that have programs for exchange will be aided where their programs seem to be worthwhile. This will be an educational job for Americans, giving them an opportunity to get a better idea of the world in which they live and at the same time will show a spirit of service which is prevalent in this generation of Americans but which has not had great opportunity so far for expression.

A suggestion has also been made for a younger U.S. group of older high-school age to work on forestry and soil conservation throughout the U.S. This would seem to me of great value but as yet this is not even in the active planning stage as far as I know, though I hope it will materialize before very long.

I have said that the Russians have accomplished by compulsion what we must accomplish voluntarily. But there is one element of this Russian training that I have neglected to mention. I don't see why I neglected it, because it is of paramount importance. They have taught their young to feel that they are needed, that they are important to the welfare of their country. I think that one of the strongest qualities in every human being is a need to feel needed, to feel essential, to feel important. Too often our own youngsters do not feel that they are really essential to their country, or to the scheme of things. We have not had enough imagination to show them how very much we need every one of them to make us the kind of country that we can be.

In Austria, a short time ago, Mr. Khrushchev said that he expected a Communist world in his lifetime. We have no time to waste.

All this, you may say, is far from the American Dream. Not at all. The American Dream can no more remain static than can the American nation. What I am trying to point out is that we cannot any longer take an old approach to world problems. They aren't the same problems. It isn't the same world. We must not adopt the methods of our ancestors; instead, we must emulate that pioneer quality in our ancestors that made them attempt new methods for a New World.

For instance, we are pioneers today in the field of automation. There is no possibility of holding back automation, but we can, at least, profit by the mistakes of the past in dealing with it. The industrial revolution, which began in Great Britain, put machinery into the mills and threw out the people to starve.

Eventually Great Britain was much better off as a result of the industrial revolution. But, because it was not prepared to cope with it at the time, a far-reaching and unexpected thing happened. Out of the industrial revolution and its abuses came Karl Marx.

With automation we have a new situation and on the way we cope with it will depend the attitude of the world. Here we are the undisputed leaders. But we cannot handle it without planning. We must learn to foresee results before we act. We cannot afford, today, to throw a lot of people out of work without making some provision for them. True, the conscience of the people is different now; we would no longer sit by and let people starve and die. But if we are going to cope successfully, if we are to make this new technique a blessing to society and not a disaster, we have to make plans. We cannot blunder along, hoping things "will come out all right." Government, industry, labor, all these must use their best brains, must be aware of and accept their full responsibility for the situation.

With decreased work hours there will come more leisure. What is to be done with it? Masses of people now working at machines, without any opportunity for self-improvement or bettering their condition, will be afforded new opportunities. But, unless we give them a background of education, they will not know how to make use of this opportunity for advancement. If they have no capacity for development, and no enterprise beyond sitting glued to a television screen, they will deteriorate as human beings, and we will have a great mass of citizens who are of no value to themselves or to their country or to the world.

It is a new industrial revolution that we are pioneering. The eyes of the world are on us. If we do it badly we will be criticized and our way of life downgraded. If we do it well we can become a beacon light for the future of the world.

And now, I see, my new concept of the American Dream is only the old one, after all. For, while those who started our government and fought for our right to be free may have thought in Old World terms to some extent, they, too, had a conception of the Dream being universal. The Thomas Jeffersons thought of education not for a handful, not even for their own country alone, but looked forward to the day when everyone, everywhere, would have the same opportunities. Today we have achieved so much more, in many ways, than our ancestors imagined that sometimes we forget that they dreamed not just for us but for mankind.

The American Dream is never entirely realized. If many of our young people have lost the excitement of the early settlers who had a country to explore and develop, it is because no one remembers to tell them that the world has never been so challenging, so exciting; the fields of adventure and new fields to conquer have never been so limitless. There is still unfinished business at home, but there is the most tremendous adventure in bringing the peoples of the world to an understanding of the American Dream. In this attempt to understand, to give a new concept of the relationships of mankind, there is open to our youngsters an infinite field of exciting adventure where the heart and the mind and the spirit can be engaged.

Perhaps the older generation is often to blame with its cautious warning: "Take a job that will give you security, not adventure." But I say to the young: "Do not stop thinking of life as an adventure. You have no security unless you can live bravely, excitingly, imaginatively; unless you can choose a challenge instead of a competence."

Forty-one

Milestones

IN OCTOBER of 1959 I reached my seventy-fifth birthday. It was a busy day, as most of mine are, with little time for introspection. Nonetheless, it was, in a way, a milestone, and I found myself looking back along the way I had come, trying to get a long-range view of the journey I had made and, if I could, to evaluate it. I wanted, if possible, to draw a kind of balance sheet, to formulate for myself the objectives I had had and to estimate how far I had achieved them.

This kind of introspection is one in which I rarely indulge. At times, of course, it is valuable in throwing light into dark places, but its danger is that one may easily tend to become self-absorbed in one's voyage of discovery and self-analysis.

People still ask me frequently how I planned my career and what over-all objective I had in mind. Actually I never planned a career, and what basic objective I had, for many years, was to grasp every opportunity to live and experience life as deeply, as fully, and as widely as I possibly could. It seemed to me stupid to have the gift of life and not use it to the utmost of one's ability.

I was not a gifted person but I was always deeply interested in every manifestation of life, good or bad. I never let slip an opportunity to increase my knowledge of people and conditions. Everything was grist to my mill: not only the things I saw but the people I met. Indeed, I could not express adequately the debt I owe to the friends who taught me so much about the world I live in. I had really only three assets: I was keenly interested, I accepted every challenge and every opportunity to learn more, and I had great energy and self-discipline.

As a result, I have never had to look for interests to fill my life. If you are

410

interested, things come to you, they seem to gravitate your way without your lifting a hand. One thing leads to another and another, and as you gain in knowledge and in experience new opportunities open up before you.

Before my seventy-fifth birthday something else had happened that forced me to turn back and look at my past life rather than to look ahead, as I prefer doing. Dore Schary wrote *Sunrise at Campobello*, a play that dealt with my husband's serious illness and his spiritual victory over being crippled. I can remember still the evening when the dramatist read his play to me. And I can remember the strange experience of seeing it performed.

I have been asked countless times how I felt about seeing myself, my children, my husband portrayed on the stage. Did I feel a sense of recognition? Did I say, "But it wasn't like that at all?" Did I feel that my privacy as a woman had been invaded?

The truth is that I watched the play with complete detachment. It is true that when I closed my eyes Ralph Bellamy evoked the very quality and cadence of Franklin's voice and I seemed to hear him speak. But, for the rest, it seemed quite impersonal; it was a play, so far as I personally was concerned, about someone else.

I think if the average person tries to look back he will be unable to remember what he was like, or how he looked, or even, except for major matters, what he did when he was young. He can remember only what he felt. Even in the case of my children I felt that I was watching the actions of quite fictitious characters. One of the best-drawn characters in that play, by the way, was Louis Howe. True, he was less untidy than the Louis I had known, but the lines were excellent and the portrayal was true of the man.

No, it was not by seeing the character of "Eleanor Roosevelt" on the stage that I could come any closer to an analysis of the woman who had now reached seventy-five years of age.

Looking back, I could see that the over-all objective of which many people spoke to me had no existence. It seems hardly human that anyone can plan his life clearly from the beginning, making no allowances for a changing or developing character or for circumstances.

I am sure that my objectives, during those early years at least, were constantly changing. In the beginning, because I felt, as only a young girl can feel it, all the pain of being an ugly duckling, I was not only timid,

I was afraid. Afraid of almost everything, I think: of mice, of the dark, of imaginary dangers, of my own inadequacy. My chief objective, as a girl, was to do my duty. This had been drilled into me as far back as I could remember. Not my duty as I saw it, but my duty as laid down for me by other people. It never occurred to me to revolt. Anyhow, my one overwhelming need in those days was to be approved, to be loved, and I did whatever was required of me, hoping it would bring me nearer to the approval and love I so much wanted.

As a young woman, my sense of duty remained as strict and rigid as it had been when I was a girl, but it had changed its focus. My husband and my children became the center of my life and their needs were my new duty. I am afraid now that I approached this new obligation much as I had my childhood duties. I was still timid, still afraid of doing something wrong, of making mistakes, of not living up to the standards required by my mother-in-law, of failing to do what was expected of me.

As a result, I was so hidebound by duty that I became too critical, too much of a disciplinarian. I was so concerned with bringing up my children properly that I was not wise enough just to love them. Now, looking back, I think I would rather spoil a child a little and have more fun out of it.

It was not until I reached middle age that I had the courage to develop interests of my own, outside of my duties to my family. In the beginning, it seems to me now, I had no goal beyond the interests themselves, in learning about people and conditions and the world outside our own United States. Almost at once I began to discover that interest leads to interest, knowledge leads to more knowledge, the capacity for understanding grows with the effort to understand.

From that time on, though I have had many problems, though I have known the grief and the loneliness that are the lot of most human beings, though I have had to make and still have to make endless adjustments, I have never been bored, never found the days long enough for the range of activities with which I wanted to fill them. And, having learned to stare down fear, I long ago reached the point where there is no living person whom I fear, and few challenges that I am not willing to face.

On that seventy-fifth birthday I knew that I had long since become aware of my over-all objective in life. It stemmed from those early impressions I had gathered when I saw war-torn Europe after World War I. I wanted, with all my heart, a peaceful world. And I knew it could never be achieved on a lasting basis without greater understanding between peoples. It is to these ends that I have, in the main, devoted the past years.

One curious thing is that I have always seen life personally; that is, my interest or sympathy or indignation is not aroused by an abstract cause but by the plight of a single person whom I have seen with my own eyes. It was the sight of a child dying of hunger that made the tragedy of hunger become of such overriding importance to me. Out of my response to an individual develops an awareness of a problem to the community, then to the country, and finally to the world. In each case my feeling of obligation to do something has stemmed from one individual and then widened and become applied to a broader area.

More and more, I think, people are coming to realize that what affects an individual affects mankind. To take an extreme example, one neglected case of smallpox can infect a whole community. This is equally true of the maladjusted child, who may wreak havoc in his neighborhood; of the impoverished, who become either economic burdens or social burdens, and, in any case, are wasted as human beings. Abuses anywhere, however isolated they may appear, can end by becoming abuses everywhere.

I learned, too, while I was groping for more and more effective ways of trying to cope with community and national and world problems, that you can accomplish a great deal more if you care deeply about what is happening to other people than if you say in apathy or discouragement, "Oh, what can I do? What use is one person? I might as well not bother."

Actually I suppose the caring comes from being able to put yourself in the position of the other person. If you cannot imagine, "This might happen to me," you are able to say to yourself with indifference, "Who cares?"

I think that one of the reasons it is so difficult for us, as a people, to understand other areas of the world is that we cannot put ourselves imaginatively in their place. We have no famine. But if we were actually to see people dying of starvation we would care quite a bit. We would be able to think, "These could be my people."

Because of our rather extraordinary advantages, it is difficult for us to understand the other peoples of the world. We started with tremendous national resources. Our very isolation, in those early years, forced us to develop them. Many of the people who settled here had escaped from poverty and want and oppression and lack of opportunity. They wanted to forget their background and they soon did, because the difficulty of travel made it hard for them to go back and refresh their memories. So we grew

out of the past and away from it. Now it would be valuable for us to remember the conditions of that Old World. It would help us to understand
what the poorer countries need and want today.

And this, I suppose, indicates what has happened to me in seventy-five
years. Though now as always it is through individuals that I see and understand human needs, I find that my over-all objectives go beyond individuals
to the fate of mankind. It is within that larger framework that one must
think today if mankind is to survive the threat that hangs, in a mushroom
cloud, over it.

So I come to the larger objective, not mine, except as I am an American,
but America's. It seems to me that America's objective today should be to
try to make herself the best possible mirror of democracy that she can.
The people of the world can see what happens here. They watch us to
see what we are going to do and how well we can do it. We are giving
them the only possible picture of democracy that we can: the picture as
it works in actual practice. This is the only way other peoples can see for
themselves how it works; and can determine for themselves whether this
thing is good in itself, whether it is better than what they have, better
than what other political and economic systems offer them.

Now, while we are a generous nation, giving with a free hand and with
an open heart wherever there is need or suffering (that we can understand,
at least), we have one weakness that, considering our political maturity as
a nation, is rather immature. We continue to expect the world to be grateful to us and to love us. We are hurt and indignant when we do not receive gratitude and love.

Gratitude and love are not to be had for the asking; they are not to
be bought. We should not want to think that they are for sale. What we
should seek, rather than gratitude or love, is the respect of the world. This
we can earn by enlightened justice. But it is rather naïve of us to think that
when we are helping people our action is entirely unselfish. It is not. It
is not unselfish when we vaccinate the public against smallpox. It is a
precautionary measure, but nonetheless good in itself.

Other nations are quite aware that when we try to bolster up their
economy and strengthen their governments and generally help them to
succeed there is a certain amount of self-interest involved. They are inevitably going to be on the lookout to see what we want in return. Consciously we do not want anything, but unconsciously almost anything we
do, as a nation or through the United Nations, is intended to benefit us

or our cause, directly or indirectly. So there is no reason for demanding either gratitude or love.

Our obligation to the world is, primarily, our obligation to our own future. Obviously we cannot develop beyond a certain point unless the other nations develop too. When our natural resources peter out, we must seek them in other countries. We cannot have trade if we are the only solvent nation. We need not only areas from which to buy but areas to which we can sell, and we cannot have this in underdeveloped areas.

We must, as a nation, begin to realize that we are the leaders of the non-Communist world, that our interests at some point all touch the interests of the world, and they must be examined in the context of the interests of the world. This is the price of leadership.

We cannot, indeed, continue to function in a narrow orbit or in a self-enclosed system. We cannot weigh or evaluate even our domestic problems in their own context alone. We no longer have merely domestic issues. Perhaps the best illustration of this is the question I am asked everywhere in the world:

"We hear you Americans pay to keep land out of production because there is too much to eat. Is there no better way to use your ability to produce food than to get rid of it?"

This is a home question; it is literally of vital moment to the millions of starving in the world who look to us. I do not see how we can retain world leadership and yet continue to handle our problems as though they concerned us alone; they concern the world. We feel that a surplus of food is only an embarrassment. We solve it as though only we were concerned. But think of the hungry people and their bitterness as the food that could save their lives is plowed under. To say they think it highly unfair is to put it mildly.

We have never put our best brains to work on the ways we can produce to the maximum, give our farmers a better income, and still employ our surpluses in a way to solve the pressing needs of the world, without upsetting our economy or that of friendly nations who might fear we were giving food to markets they are accustomed to selling to.

We have a great variety of climate, we can grow almost anything we want. Canada can grow only wheat. There need be no clash of interests here.

How have we tried to "solve" matters up to now? We cut our acreage and store the surplus or dump it; we pay our farmers too little to give them an income on a par with that of industrial workers, so we have a dwindling farm population. No one has ever sat down and said, "This is a problem you *must* work out."

It is in ways like these, using our intelligence and our good will and our vast capacity to produce, that we can meet and overcome the Communist threat and prove that democracy has more to give the world.

All this seems like a far cry from my seventy-fifth birthday and yet I find that, as I have grown older, my personal objectives have long since blended into my public objectives. I have, of course, realized that I cannot continue indefinitely the strenuous life I now lead, the constant traveling from state to state, from country to country.

What, then? Then, I thought, even if I must relinquish much of my traveling, perhaps there is a way in which I can still reach people with things that it seems important for them to hear. The most practical way of doing this is through a radio or television program. My radio and television agent shook his head.

"You are too controversial a figure," he told me. "The sponsors would be afraid of you. Some of them feel so strongly about you that they believe the public would not buy any product on whose program you might appear."

I remembered then that some years earlier the head of the Red Cross had been afraid to accept a donation for fear that my participation would drive away other subscribers!

It is startling to realize that one is so deeply, fanatically disliked by a number of people. And yet, while I weigh as honestly as I can their grounds for disapproval, when I feel that I am right in what I do, it seems to me that I cannot afford, as a self-respecting individual, to refuse to do a thing merely because it will make me disliked or bring down a storm of criticism on my head. I often feel that too many Americans today tend to reject the thing, however right they believe it to be, that they want to do because they fear they will be unpopular or will find themselves standing alone instead of in the comfortable anonymity of the herd.

As a result, when I believe, after weighing the evidence, that what I am doing is right I go ahead and try as hard as I can to dismiss from my mind the attitude of those who are hostile. I don't see how else one can live.

One day my radio agent appeared, looking very much surprised, to say that he had had an offer for me to do television commercials for an organization that sold margarine.

"I know this isn't the kind of thing you had in mind," he pointed out, "but if a conservative firm feels that you can sell their product I think you should at least try it. It may break the ice for you."

I thought it over. I had to face the fact that I would be bitterly criticized for doing commercials. On the other hand, if this was a field I wanted to open up I ought at least to see whether I could do it, no matter how disagreeable the reaction of many people might be.

So at length I agreed. The only stipulation I made was that, outside of selling the product, I should be allowed to say one thing of my own that I thought had value. So I reminded the audience that there were hungry people in the world.

There were, of course, as many disagreeable comments as I had expected, but the program went all right and the sponsors discovered that, after all, I did not prevent people from buying their product!

This year (1960-61) I am going to introduce a program of refugee stories, as my participation in the Refugee Year work of the United Nations.

The purpose of this refugee organization, now headed by Mr. Lint, is to try to reduce the population of the refugee camps in Europe; to wipe them out if that is humanly possible. Ten years is too long for these people to have lived in camps, stateless and with no solution in sight for their problem. There are children who have never known any other life.

Actually a good deal has been accomplished. The number of refugees has been greatly reduced. Where they still remain in camps, an effort has been made to provide permanent housing and to find them jobs. A number of countries have accepted what is called "hard-core cases," those who are blind or have other disabilities. Of course, I am referring now only to the refugee camps in Europe. There are between 800,000 and a million refugees in the Near East and no one knows how many in Hong Kong and in China.

The refugees of the world are a constant and painful reminder of the breakdown of civilization through the stupidity of war. They are its permanent victims. No time in history has known anything like the number of stateless people who have existed or survived the rigors of the past thirty years.

When we closed the work of the United Nations Relief Association in the United Nations we set up the present Commission for Refugees with headquarters in Geneva. No money, however, was set aside for this. Its function is to see that these people are given papers which will allow them to get work, to make life more possible for them, though they are still stateless.

Mr. Lint discovered that there were still many who needed financial help and he requested aid for a fund which he could use for this purpose. Every year he comes to the United States to get further funds to meet these needs.

In the American Association of the United Nations we were willed a considerable sum of money which was to be applied to alleviating the conditions of refugees. We had to set up a group to handle this, and, of course, we had to have the consent of the high commissioner to turn the money over to Mr. Lint for this purpose. Before long even this ugly scar of war may be healed.

Interspersed among my other activities, traveling and lecturing, work with the A.A.U.N., radio and television appearances, I continue to entertain a number of interesting people who visit Hyde Park from time to time, sometimes to leave flowers at my husband's grave or to visit the library, sometimes to come as guests to my cottage, either through arrangements made with the State Department or independently.

Perhaps the most confusing time was in September, 1959, when the visits of Princess Beatrice of Holland and Premier Khrushchev almost overlapped. The little princess came at the time of the Hudson-Champlain celebration. Like most foreign visitors she had been feted and had listened to speeches and had attended functions until she was exhausted.

When she reached my cottage she was very tired. There was an hour free before dinner, I told her, and she said wearily to her lady in waiting, "Please open my bed."

Young as she was, she had been living under the strictest protocol and had been entertained, for the most part, by much older people, dignified statesmen, and so forth.

There was, I assured her, going to be no protocol. I planned a buffet supper, with people waiting on themselves and seated at small tables, and my guests for her were some boys from Harvard and my granddaughter, who was about her own age.

Later my granddaughter told me of their conversation. The princess told them that she was going to college and how much she valued the time there. She had even regretted losing a month from college because of her trip to America. This was the last time in her life that she would be able to live naturally with other people.

She told them, too, what difficulties arose for young people in her position. There were so few people left whom they could marry.

She was a very gentle, simple person, very sweet and simply brought up.

On the morning of the day she left Mr. Khrushchev and his wife were to arrive on their first visit to the United States. The princess and her party—we had sixteen for breakfast—left at nine in the morning. We were to feed an unknown number of members of Mr. Khrushchev's party and tables were set up and ready for them, all managed by my faithful and capable couple.

Never, I think, have I seen anything like the number of state police who were called out by our anxious government to protect Mr. Khrushchev. When I reached the library, where I was to meet him, they were lined up, side by side, all the length of the driveway and parking place. When we returned to my cottage, the dirt road which leads from the highway to the house had men stationed every few feet all the way. They had even suggested the possibility of my trees hiding malefactors who could climb them to shoot at the Communist leader. But I put my foot down at having my trees destroyed.

Anyhow Mr. Khrushchev, his pleasant and simple wife, and his entourage arrived very late at the cottage, so late they had time for nothing but a glance around and a hasty bun, which Mr. Khrushchev snatched from a table to sustain him while they rushed back to New York for his speech at the United Nations.

No shots were fired, no unpleasantness of any kind occurred, and the piles of uneaten food were disposed of by the hordes of state police. It was all rather silly.

Before his arrival there had been much speculation about what Mr. Khrushchev would get out of his visit to the United States. I don't see how, in that hasty breathless fashion, any preconception could be altered. Perhaps if he had had any chance to speak to the farmers in Iowa at leisure, he could have obtained an effective, firsthand impression of the American people, of their independence, self-respect and self-reliance. But, being hurried along, he naturally could not be expected to get a very fair impression.

But even in that rushed, cursory visit, he must have realized that we are not ripe for revolution. He must have seen for himself that while we have great prosperity we are not entirely materialistic. At least, he *may* have seen these things. I don't know. I do think, however, that if foreign leaders could visit our country quietly and on their own, they would form a much sounder impression of it than through these exhausting official receptions, parades and endless speeches.

So an account of my seventy-fifth birthday ends, in spite of me, with a discussion of foreign affairs. There is such a big, muddled world, so much to be done, so much that *can* be done if we increase in depth of understanding, in learning to care, in thinking of hunger not as an abstraction but as one empty stomach, in having a hospitable mind, open like a window to currents of air and to light from all sides.

Forty-two

The Democratic Convention of 1960

AT THE END of the presidential campaign of 1956, in which I had worked to the point of exhaustion for Adlai Stevenson, I determined that never again would I take any personal part in a political campaign.

So much for my firm intentions! My involvement in the 1960 campaign came about almost inadvertently. It grew out of a controversy in the Democratic party in New York State, where boss rule was attempting to replace the voice of the voters. The fact that my own party was involved in this particular case did not absolve me from feeling that the situation was intolerable. The morality of a party must grow out of the conscience and the participation of the voters. We cannot condemn the bosses as long as we sit back supinely and fail to wrest power from their hands and restore it to the voters themselves. In order to function at all, democracy depends upon the participation of the people in their government. It cannot survive by boss rule.

I do not believe that the people of this country would submit passively to boss rule and meekly abdicate their own rights and privileges if they were clearly aware of the situation and understood the workings of the machinery which makes bosses possible. Certainly the first step is to start not at the top but at the bottom of the pyramid and curb the power of the local city and state leaders of the political machine who, unchallenged, become the party bosses and, in a very real sense, our bosses.

The core of boss rule, naturally, is patronage. Many Americans have little idea of how the machinery of politics is handled. They have too little sense of responsibility in regard to its functioning. And yet boss rule can exist only where there is widespread indifference.

"But what can we do about it?" people ask me. "I know it is disgrace

421

ful, but we're helpless to do anything."

The answer to that, of course, is that we are not in the least helpless. We can always do something if we care enough. It was in protest against the bosses of the Republican party machine—Hanna and Platt—that Theodore Roosevelt started his Bull Moose party.

One curious feature about political reform is that so many people feel it is "disloyal" to attempt to rectify the abuses in one's own party. And yet it is obvious that political morality is dependent upon the awakened conscience and private morality of the voters. Such "disloyalty" is simply an evidence of loyalty to principle.

Two years ago, at Buffalo, both the governor and the mayor of New York said they preferred a certain candidate for the U. S. Senate. Carmine De Sapio, the boss of the Democratic machinery in New York, calmly turned them down and took it upon himself to name his own candidate. The result was that he defeated the party's chance of victory by forcing ·pon the voting public an unacceptable candidate.

Because of this highanded action, in March, 1959, Senator Herbert Lehman, Thomas Finletter and I signed a statement backing reform groups in New York City. We declared that the people were weary of bossism.

The response of the people was swift. They set up a clamor to be heard as citizens with a right to a voice in their own government. Once started, the revolt began to grow and it is still growing and gaining strength. The result was that the regular party organization discovered it would go down in defeat unless the reform groups threw in their support and worked with it. But the reform groups made clear that, unless they were free of all control from the local organization, it would not have their support. The only way to get rid of one's chains is not by complaint or lamentation. It is by knocking them off.

Now, while I was determined to take no further part in presidential campaigns, I was stirred by reading a statement made by two of our leading historians, Henry Commager and Arthur Schlesinger, Jr., who declared that, while Adlai Stevenson was undoubtedly the best candidate for the Presidency, they did not think he could be nominated and consequently they were going to support John Kennedy.

It seemed absurd to accept anyone as second best until you had done all you could to get the best. For my part, I believed the best ticket would be Stevenson and Kennedy, with the strong chance that the latter would become president at a later time.

Having made this statement, I was immediately heralded by the Stevenson backers. Nonetheless, I did not intend to go to the Democratic convention. Three of my sons were strongly backing Senator Kennedy, and it seemed pointless for me to appear on the opposite side.

However, I did not agree with the people who said Mr. Stevenson could not be nominated because he had twice been defeated. His defeat, I felt, was a result of running against the hero worship of President Eisenhower, a factor which would not exist in this campaign. I felt, too, that there was no one who could serve us better in the present crisis of world affairs or who had earned higher regard and respect among other nations.

I was finally persuaded to go to the convention, where I was distressed to find that once again I was in opposition to Mr. Truman's political stand, and I made a seconding speech for Mr. Stevenson's nomination.

The result not only of the Democratic but of the Republican convention has been such that observers in both parties were left with an acute feeling of dismay. I am not concerned at this point with the merits of either candidate. What I found, and what numbers of Americans found, horrifying was the fact that the choice of a presidential candidate, the fundamental and basic right of every American citizen, was no longer a result of public thinking or an expression of the wishes of the majority of the people of the country; that, instead, it represented the decision of the party bosses.

This kind of thing, of course, should not be allowed to go on. Our political conventions, as they now function, are as obsolete as outmoded machinery. Our present need is to evolve a new method by which the voice of the people is heard and they again arrive at their own choice of the candidates who are to lead them and to carry out their wishes in government. We cannot again permit the political bosses to dictate who the nominees are to be.

The working of smooth political machines, such as we observed in the two recent conventions, is not new. It is only an intensification of a process that has been going on for years. But now that we have seen it clearly, the time has come to say, as many people are saying, "This is intolerable. We cannot permit it to go on."

How was it possible that in the 1960 conventions the choice of candidates was made without regard to the wishes of the American citizens? The answer lies in boss rule. The effect of local organizations on the choice of a presidential candidate is, unless checked, a strangle hold.

It works like this. The delegates to a convention are appointed by the state machinery. Generally a caucus is held of the delegates of each state and they are told that the leaders have decided they are to support a certain candidate. And why do the delegates supinely do as they are told? Because most of them hold some kind of public office and do not want to risk their positions. It is the rare delegate who, like Senator Lehman, can say, "I will not serve unless I am given complete freedom to vote as my conscience dictates."

Having been committed to the machine, the delegate can only carry out instructions. He remains deaf to the voice of his constituents. He may receive thousands of telegrams favoring another candidate but he disregards them. It is not the voice of the people but the voice of the machine boss that he heeds.

During the 1960 Democratic convention in Los Angeles, a large box of telegrams was handed to Mr. Prendergast. He opened one or two, saw they were in favor of Adlai Stevenson, and threw the box away.

It must be obvious to anyone who attended or watched either or both of the conventions of 1960 that if the delegates chosen cannot represent what they consider to be the majority opinion of the people of their district they might as well stay at home. The convention could, as efficiently, be attended solely by the two or three high-ranking bosses from each state.

All that would be lacking would be the demonstrations, which are, as a rule, artificial displays of enthusiasm arranged for by the machines or the candidates themselves. These demonstrations are largely controlled, in their extent, noise and length of time, by the National Committeemen, who allot to each candidate the number of tickets to which they feel he is entitled, according to his apparent strength. This choice rests upon the decision of a single man.

It was rumored at the 1960 Democratic convention that Mr. Kennedy's group, which was undoubtedly the strongest, received a far greater number of passes than those assigned to Mr. Stevenson's headquarters.

This situation, of course, was greatly simplified in the Republican convention at Chicago, for there the people were offered no choice of candidates for the Presidency; as, indeed, had been the case with Mr. Nixon's vice-presidency in 1956.

It has been many years since, in Baltimore, I attended my first political convention for the nomination of a president. At that time I felt, and I feel still, that to select the standard-bearer of a party in an atmosphere of noise, bands and balloons, to the accompaniment of the manufactured and synthetic excitement of parades, is to strip one of the most important features of our system of its dignity and meaning. The circus has almost overshadowed the serious purpose and far-reaching effect of these deliberations. One can imagine, in horror, the effect of accompanying debates in the Senate or in the House by interpolations of noise and music from the partisans of either side of the question.

The time has come to restore the choice of a presidential candidate to the people themselves. How can this be done? One possibility has occurred to me. Instead of continuing to leave the selection of the men who, in turn, select the candidate, in the hands of the city and state committees, we should elect the delegates ourselves. The simplest and most direct procedure would be, at the primary nearest the convention, to elect the delegates to attend that convention and to have the names of all the presidential aspirants listed on the ballot. Each voter could check the name of the candidate of his choice. The delegates to the convention would be required to vote for the candidate with the majority vote in that primary.

Of course, beyond the first ballot, it might not be practicable to hold the delegate to the original choice. An occasion might arise in which there would be a deadlock and it would be impossible to come to any definite conclusion.

The answer to this seems to me to lie in the caucus held by each state delegation. In the past this, too often, has resulted in the issuing of definite instructions. If the law required a secret ballot, so that the delegates could be free to vote, as all Americans are presumed free to vote, according to their consciences, it would be possible to achieve a system that would come much closer to reflecting the wishes of the people of the United States than our present one does.

This, of course, is only a suggestion. Certainly any method would require considerable elasticity because of the various state laws. The important thing is that the whole concept of the rules governing a convention system should come before the American people to be reassessed and discussed.

Another outmoded piece of machinery in the selection of the President is the presidential primary as it now functions. The chief trouble here is that the candidates spend their time running down their rivals in the same party. The net result is to furnish a large amount of ammunition to the opposition party in the campaign. An example is the Republican use, in 1960 campaign propaganda, of everything Senator Johnson had said about Senator Kennedy in the preconvention days.

I have been talking from the point of view of a Democrat, because I am more familiar with their tactics. But it would appear that the same tactics are used in both parties. In both cases, one had the feeling that the convention did not greatly matter. The votes had been sewed up beforehand.

There is time ahead to re-examine our machinery on state and city as well as national level, to find a method to ensure that each of us can make his voice heard as independent and responsible voters. We can do it if we want to.

As Adlai Stevenson said to some of his family and friends in his living room in Los Angeles, during the hush that followed the realization of his defeat at the Democratic convention, "Cheer up. All is not lost."

Looking back on that turbulent—but prearranged—convention, I am heartened by the memory of the warm spontaneous outburst of genuine feeling and tribute and love that greeted Mr. Stevenson when he entered the hall to take his seat. Even though the delegates had been committed in advance, there was no stifling this tribute to a great statesman and a magnificent citizen.

For him, modest as he is, lacking in vanity, so incapable of self-aggrandizement that he refused to lift his hand to seek the nomination, it must have been a heart-lifting moment.

One factor of the convention that I had cause to remember afterwards was that no one knows when a television camera is turned his way, as the cameras are constantly swinging around. Unless you are constantly aware that you are under scrutiny you are apt to be caught at unexpected and embarrassing moments.

Later I received many letters from people who said they sympathized with my tears after Adlai's defeat. As a matter of fact, it was not tears I was having wiped off my cheek but someone's lipstick.

Because the plain-clothes men were afraid that when I went up to second Adlai's nomination I would be caught in a mob, they circled me about. They were very nice and very solicitous and treated me as though I were made of Dresden china. In fact, they practically carried me, with the result that we moved so slowly I thought we would never cover the ground from one side of the arena to another.

The plain-clothes men held my elbows firmly at every step. Now, this happens to be one of the few things which indicate to me that I am supposed to be unable to navigate in the ordinary manner at my age and I resent it very much. Consequently, I kept trying to get away from and shake off their helpful hands. Presumably this showed up on television, because I received a number of letters from people who wrote to assure me that I had behaved in a most rude and disagreeable manner.

I was also criticized for coming in and receiving an ovation while Governor Collins was making his excellent speech, but, because of the noise, I was quite unaware of the fact that anyone was speaking. Sometimes, even now, I am still taken aback to discover how closely one's most trivial movements are followed in this day of television. It seems as though one can find privacy only within the silence of one's own mind.

Forty-three

Unfinished Business

"YOU REALLY must slow down." This is becoming the repeated refrain of my children and all of my friends. But how can I when the world is so challenging in its problems and so terribly interesting? I think I must have a good deal of my uncle Theodore Roosevelt in me because I enjoy a good fight and I could not, at any age, really be contented to take my place in a warm corner by the fireside and simply look on.

Early in July of 1960 I went to Washington for briefings at the State Department in preparation for the meeting in Warsaw, Poland, of the World Federation of United Nations Associations.

Of course, our American Association for the United Nations is not controlled by our government, but we always ask to be told of any situation that may exist in a country to which we are to send delegates. Such background information helps us to be better-equipped citizens and better able to carry on discussions with the other United Nations associations that may be present.

This trip, which I made in September, was my first to Poland and I was able to visit two cities, Warsaw, where the meeting was held, and Cracow. No cities could have been more dissimilar. Warsaw was probably one of the most completely destroyed cities in World War II. What the Germans failed to destroy by shelling they systematically burned. Almost nothing was left standing. The people were driven out into the woods and the city was demolished, stone by stone.

When the Russians finally liberated the area, there was some discussion about rebuilding. After all, there was nothing to start from. Perhaps it would be better to pick another location and begin from scratch, but at length it was decided to rebuild on the same site.

Because the mayor felt that the people should have roots, an attempt was made, as far as possible, to build a replica of the old city. An ancient square was reproduced almost exactly. They rebuilt the old church and put back the statues. Old stones were salvaged from the rubble to be used again. On the whole, it has been very well done, for while it is a modern city, the atmosphere of the old city has been re-created successfully. True, there is one horrible building, designed by a Russian architect, almost an exact copy of the hideous University of Moscow, though not quite so large.

Cracow, on the other hand, was left untouched by the war and has retained all its Old World charm, its typically Polish features, oddly but delightfully interspersed with traces of the influences brought there by Italian alliances. In contrast, near Cracow there is one of the new steel cities, on much the same pattern as the steel cities of Russia, signifying the opening up of a balanced economy, partly industrial, partly rural, and therefore a big step forward, as it brings the people of Poland the hope of greater prosperity.

Such hope is grasped eagerly, for it is evident on many sides that Poland is still a very poor country, and the cost of all this rebuilding has been a tremendous drain on the economy.

There are the inevitable shortages of goods. One Polish housewife told me that, while there are few things for which they have to queue up, still meat is always hard to find and is unprocurable on Mondays. Prices are high, on the whole, and I think it is safe to say in general that goods are of poor quality.

The biggest expense, in Poland as in Russia, is for shoes. Clothes are expensive and the material is so poor that wardrobes have constantly to be replaced. A young American woman, married to a Pole, said that her Polish friends simply could not believe her when she told them the suit she wore was six years old. Material like that was unobtainable in Poland at any price.

Nonetheless, one is conscious of the fact that the Polish people live with vitality and enthusiasm. Certainly, I could not have met with more hospitality and solicitude. One cannot help liking the Poles, whether ministers of state or casual workers whom one has an opportunity to meet and chat with.

It seemed to me, indeed, that Poland might well serve as a much-needed bridge of understanding between the Western and Eastern nations if—

and that is the stumbling block—if it succeeds in becoming a stable economic country. This, I believe, is possible if its borders are recognized by the Western European community and it is assured of nonaggression from any source. Certainly, such a bridge is going to be essential if we are to build up the beginnings of confidence between East and West. So, perhaps, Poland's own feeling of greater security—if it can be assured by the two opposing areas—may be the opening wedge to help the others to understanding.

However, it has not yet attained the kind of economic stability, let alone the prosperity, which its people hope for and long for. The people in Warsaw, which seems to epitomize Poland, assured me that the peasants were much better off than the city people because they not only had more to eat but did not have to keep up appearances and buy so many clothes and shoes as were necessary in the cities. But when I had an opportunity to drive out into the country and when I looked at the farms and the farm buildings I felt that the life of the peasant had not yet reached a very high level of comfort.

One thing that greatly interested me was that, while Poland is a Communist state on the Soviet pattern, the Polish people have not accepted as many state controls as the Russian people have. This is particularly true of the women. They are not obliged to take their children to nurseries at a certain age and leave them in the hands of the state. As a result, many of them prefer to stay at home and take care of their own children in their own way.

Another field in which compulsion is not so binding as in the Soviet Union is health care. While the pattern of universal medical care has been laid out in Poland, there is no compulsion to make use of it.

The chief thing one is conscious of in Poland is the fear of a possible change of the new boundaries, which might deprive the country of many of the minerals that make it possible to develop an industrial economy.

Remembering Poland's position on the map and her past history, it is easy to understand her uneasiness, but the people are going about their business and there is greater prosperity as the years go by. Even though they are a completely communistic dictatorship, there is a greater sense of freedom among the people than you find in the Soviet Union. In the new steel city there are one school, two kindergartens, and two nurseries per district. The architect told me the nurseries were almost empty. The women do not want to send their babies there for fear they will catch some contagious disease. The attitude that every woman must work is not being enforced in Poland.

But if the women have not supinely followed the communistic pattern, they are, from a long and tragic history, alert and uneasy about the course of events. They asked me over and over, "Do you think your government means to give Germany atomic weapons? We are afraid of Germany, of its growth once more in military strength."

On the whole, that trip to Poland was an interesting and a rewarding one, and it made me see that in these people we could build a bridge of understanding and good will.

In a way, it is, I suppose, ironical that I have visited many Communist-controlled countries without experiencing a single unpleasant incident or encountering one act of hostility or hearing one unfriendly word. Yet here in my own country, earlier in the year, the announcement of a public appearance I was to make in St. Petersburg, Florida, was followed by a telephoned threat that the meeting would be bombed. The threat was, of course, anonymous. Such people are almost invariably cowards.

I assume that the reason for this warning was the fact that I have always been outspoken on my position in regard to the race question, and the man without a name or a face had determined that I should not be heard. Nonetheless, I went. The meeting started and, in spite of the rumors, was very well attended. I was just about to speak when someone stepped to the microphone. The police of St. Petersburg had ordered everyone to leave the building and go some blocks away while a search was made for the bomb.

I assumed, after that, the people would go home, so I was pleased and surprised to find that they had all waited and came back when the building was declared safe. But what touched me most was the gallantry of a little southern woman who sat in the front row. The editor of a St. Petersburg paper told me, with pride, that she was his mother. When she was asked to leave she refused categorically to go home.

"If I am going to be blown up," she declared, "I can't think of any better company to be blown up with."

The meeting proceeded and I made a speech. We all left in peace and quiet, without incident. It confirmed my opinion that when people really mean business they don't notify you beforehand.

Some months later, during the heat of the political campaign, I was to address an audience of schoolteachers in Indianapolis. When I reached the city I was warned that there would be few people in the old tabernacle building where I was scheduled to speak because, several days earlier, a newspaper had printed an editorial urging the teachers to boycott my lecture. Apparently the paper felt that one votes more intelligently in a presidential election if one hears only one side of the story. As my talk, however, dealt with foreign affairs and America's position in world leadership, and did not touch on the campaign, its point did not seem particularly pertinent.

To my great pleasure, I addressed ten thousand teachers that morning. Not even standing room was available in the auditorium. A free citizenry, as I think these two incidents show, is not so easily coerced as a few people would like to believe.

Whether the editorial writer of the Indianapolis paper and the anonymous dealer in threats have learned this lesson I do not know. But it occurs to me that Mr. Khrushchev on his second and stormy visit to the United States must have realized that threats are often ineffective. During that visit he suffered two major defeats in the United Nations Assembly: one when the Asian and African resolution supporting Secretary-General Hammarskjöld's actions in the Congo was passed without the Soviet amendments; second, when the delegate from Ireland was elected to the presidency of the General Assembly instead of the delegate from Czechslovakia.

I wonder if the people of this country as a whole realize how extraordinary that whole situation was. Mr. Khrushchev arrived in force, bringing with him the heads of the satellite nations, as though they were bogeys to frighten children. His only convert appears to have been Premier Fidel Castro of Cuba.

Mr. Khrushchev's objective was nothing less than the complete destruction of the United Nations, which he would have achieved if his suggestions that Mr. Hammarskjöld be ousted, that the UN be moved to another part of the world, and that a three-man governing board be set up, had been accepted. If he had been successful, the only machinery the world has through which it can work for peace would have been made impotent.

How great a loss, how disastrous a defeat for world peace and understanding and stability that would have been is evidenced these days in what is happening in the United Nations. More and more it is establishing itself as a place where reasonable decisions are being reached. In spite of Mr. Khrushchev's posturing and intemperate language, there does seem to be a gradual approach to an effort to settle international differences in the Congo. This would not have been possible if there had not existed a United Nations where all the representatives could get together to air their differences and find a *modus vivendi*. It is very important that we recognize this.

There was a time, at the outset, when people disillusioned by the League of Nations could scoff at the idea of another world organization designed to work for the peaceful settlement of international disputes. But that time has passed. Today we are seeing more and more clearly that it *can* work, that it *does* work, and it will be increasingly effective if we back it with all our strength. After all, it is because it is an effective organization that Mr. Khrushchev has been so determined to destroy it.

My estimate of Mr. Khrushchev's purpose has been challenged by Professor Golunsky, of the Soviet delegation to the UN. He says I have completely misunderstood Mr. Khrushchev. He points out that five major nations were able to agree on the establishment of the UN. Why, then, could not three heads be set up to carry it further? Obviously, this is ridiculous because, while Mr. Khrushchev's course could be represented by one of the three heads, since satellites are never allowed to differ, the Western countries have many differences and it would be impossible for one head to represent all the divergent opinions. The same thing holds true for the neutralists.

Clearly, colonialism is practically dead. In a very few places there has been some resistance on the part of colonial powers, but the great majority of the nations in Africa which are now becoming free have been granted this freedom by the colonial powers themselves.

If Mr. Khrushchev really believes in the self-determination of peoples, he should allow a free election under United Nations supervision in Estonia, Latvia, Lithuania, Albania, Hungary, Bulgaria, Czechoslovakia, Poland, East Germany—all Russian satellites.

One can well understand the desire of the emerging African states to remain free of the cold war in Europe, and one hopes that this will be possible. They have troubles enough of their own in setting up governments and in finding peaceful accommodations between their own tribes. Nkruma, head of the Ghana delegation, has suggested that an African agency, working under the UN, be responsible for the solutions of the

African situations which are probably going to arise pretty continuously for a long time. This may be a good suggestion, and I think it should be carefully discussed between the African groups themselves and the Secretary-General.

One result of Mr. Khrushchev's attack on the Secretary-General was the tremendous tribute paid to Dag Hammarskjöld in the vote of the UN special session. The adopted resolution passed 70 to 0 with a number of abstentions.

In passing the resolution the General Assembly called on all states to refrain from sending military aid to the Congo, except on request of the UN through the Secretary-General. This, of course, will only be done for a temporary period until the Congolese can work out their own difficulties and set up a central government. After that, it is hoped there will be no further need for UN military forces.

But, while Mr. Khrushchev was sternly rebuffed by the UN and endured a total defeat in his attempt to destroy the organization, one question troubled me then and still troubles me. For it was not all defeat. Mr. Khrushchev banged his shoe on the table, he shouted, he interrupted, he behaved hysterically and with gross bad manners. But this was not a pointless exhibition. There was method in it. By his clowning and his interruptions during Mr. Macmillan's excellent speech, he succeeded in forcing the newspapers to carry so much about his capers that the focus of interest was on him and therefore the impact of Mr. Macmillan's presentation was lessened.

What worried me most was that I did not feel that any one of the Western delegates succeeded in giving a real sense of inspiration about the ideals of democracy. No one said, with the force and the passionate conviction with which Mr. Khrushchev discusses Communism, what we are all about. And yet that is the one thing the Russians most fear, the one thing they cannot combat, the one thing they cannot compete with by production and more production, by space ships and space men. Indeed, it seems apparent to me that the focus has been deliberately thrown on outer space by the Russians to distract attention from our essential differences, to lead us cleverly to try to compete in outer space, to distract attention from the fact that, if people knew the true situation, knew what we stand for, what we live by, there could be no real competition at all.

Some leader must appear from the West who can put into words not the advantages of any form of economy, or any degree of production, but the inspiration of belief in the dignity of man and the value of the human individual. This is the basic difference; this is what we of the West must really fight for, and speak out about in ringing tones.

I would like to say, however, that I do not feel that we, as individuals or as a nation, gain either in dignity or in prestige by refusing to know the people who lead the great opposition to our way of life, by refusing to deal with them in friendship or at least with good manners when possible, or by refusing to learn to understand them as far as we can. To refuse to know or understand the opposition seems to me madness. It reminds me of one of the strangest attitudes during World War I when German was no longer taught in our schools, apparently on the theory that we could deal better with people with whom we could not communicate.

Because on his first visit to America Mr. Khrushchev had paid a most unsatisfactory and fleeting visit to Hyde Park and had been deprived of his lunch, I tried to make up for this situation by asking him to lunch or tea on his second visit. I got a prompt reply saying that he would be glad to come to tea.

On his arrival in this country, of course, he had proceeded to behave badly, trying to destroy the UN because he had not been able to get his own way and had been put out of the Congo just as we had been put out; trying, too, to exploit as far as possible the differences between Castro and the United States government. As a result of these antics, I had written several columns about his efforts to wreck the United Nations, so when the time for the tea arrived, I was rather dreading it.

The only other person I asked was Mrs. Kermit Roosevelt, who said she would pour. Mr. Khrushchev arrived, bringing Mr. Gromyko, Ambassador Mikhail Menshikov, and an interpreter. On the whole, our meeting was outwardly very friendly. He lost no time, however, in telling me about the growing economic strength of the Soviet Union, the increasing amount of iron ore, the fact that in twenty years they would be producing an astronomical amount of steel.

I remarked gently that if you produced that amount of steel you would have to have a market for it. That would require a rise in the standard of living in Russia and China, if they were to accomplish their objective.

As usual, within a couple of days after Mr. Khrushchev came to tea I began to receive letters that were more emotional than thoughtful and that took me to task sharply and bitterly for entertaining in my house the head of a great foreign power because his system of government happened to be different from our own. How, I wonder, do these people feel that we can learn to live together—as we must—if we cannot sit down over a cup of tea and quietly discuss our differences. At least, Mr. Khrushchev remarked at the end of our first long interview at Yalta, we didn't shoot at each other!

During all these years, of course, I have continued my regular newspaper column, which has run since 1935. After the Warsaw meeting I changed from a regular five-day column to a somewhat longer column which appears three times a week. I have continued, too, with my monthly magazine page, with my work for the A.A.U.N., with radio and television work, and with the lectures that take me far and wide.

And then, in spite of all my protestations that I would never again campaign actively, I did take part in John Kennedy's campaign for the Presidency, not so strenuously as I had worked four years earlier for Adlai Stevenson but as well as I could with the commitments I already had to carry out.

Having supported Adlai Stevenson during the convention, I was uncertain what I would do after the nomination. I withheld my decision to join Herbert Lehman as honorary chairman of the Democratic Citizens Committee of New York until I might have a chance to see and talk with the Democratic candidate and judge his qualities for myself.

When he came to see me at Hyde Park I found him a brilliant man with a quick mind, anxious to learn, hospitable to new ideas, hardheaded in his approach. Here, I thought, with an upsurge of hope and confidence, is a man who wants to leave behind him a record not only of having helped his countrymen but of having helped humanity as well. He was not simply ambitious to be president; he wanted, I felt convinced, to be a truly great president. He neither desired nor expected his task to be easy. He saw clearly the position of the United States in the world today as well as the shortcomings at home and was both too honorable and too courageous to color these unpalatable facts or distort them.

He believed that Americans could, as they have done in the past, meet and conquer the obstacles before them, but only if they knew what the obstacles were, what the conditions were, what must be done, by sacrifice, if necessary, by courage and conviction, certainly, to accomplish our ends.

And yet, because what happens in the next few years may well settle the future of the world for decades if not for longer, I waited, knowing what hinged on this election, for the first of the Great Debates. After that, I had no further hesitation. On the one side, I heard that all was for the best in the best of all possible worlds, that we lived in a country without unemployment or want, that our world leadership was unchallenged, and that it was, presumably, un-American to think differently. On the other side, I heard the less popular story, the one I had met face to face, over and over, in my travels around this country and around the world.

So I took part in the campaign. Unfortunately, I started out under a slight handicap as I picked up a virus and was far from feeling well, but I traveled to California by plane one afternoon and the next day was a fair example of what followed. In the morning, press conferences, television interviews, radio spots. A hasty bite of lunch. A long drive to a totally unimportant meeting. A long drive back. A brief rest at the home of my friend Mrs. Hershey Martin. A big meeting in a church, a meeting in a theater, a quick dinner, and a plane back to New York.

One day at home—and whenever I was at home I had meetings in various parts of the city—then a day in West Virginia, where we traveled 250 miles, stopping to shake hands and speak to outdoor crowds ten or eleven times. An hour's rest, a large rally, and back to New York by a small plane.

I campaigned in four states in the Middle West, two of which, I am glad to say, turned up in Mr. Kennedy's column. In the other two I felt I had not been very effective.

Again I say I am never going to campaign again. After all, next time I will be eighty and that would be absurd.

As the campaign advanced and I followed Mr. Kennedy's speeches, I came more and more to believe that he has the power to engender the sense of identification with him which is so important. If a man has this quality he can call out the best that is in people. Today the United States needs to be reminded of its greatness, and the greatness of a nation can never be more than the greatness of its people.

If my observation is correct, I have more hope for the solution of our problems than I have had for a long time. This does not mean that I am sure we can solve them all or that we will not make mistakes. But I do now have hope.

One feature of the campaign that dismayed and shamed me was the injection of the religious issue. It is a long time since I sat in my office and read the scurrilous literature that came into the Democratic headquarters during Alfred E. Smith's candidacy. Nothing quite so vicious happened during the 1960 campaign.

But the ugly feature was that it should arise at all. The question seems to me fairly simple. The Constitution gives us all religious freedom and we are not to be questioned about our religious beliefs. Some preposterous notions were set loose during the campaign: the Pope would dictate our form of government, our way of life, our education, our reading. The Catholic Church would dominate the nation politically as well as spiritually. This idea, of course, arises from the fact that in Spain, which is a Catholic country, the church does, for the most part, control the state. But Spain is not the United States and we have a Constitution which expressly provides for separation of church and state.

It is, I am afraid, true that frequently various religious groups endeavor to exert pressures and control over different legislative and educational fields. It is the job of all of us to be alert for such infringement of our prerogatives and prevent any such attempts from being successful. Like all our freedoms, this freedom from religious-group pressure must be constantly defended.

What seemed to me most deplorable was not the fact that so many people feared the strength of the Roman Catholic Church; it was that they had no faith in the strength of their own way of life and their own Constitution. Have we forgotten so quickly that our Founding Fathers came here for religious freedom—Protestants, Catholics, Quakers—for the right to worship God as they chose? This is our foundation stone. I, for one, believe in it with all my heart, and I reject, with shame and indignation, the fear, the lack of faith, the shaken confidence of those who would topple the stone on which we stand so proudly.

When the Great Debates had ended and another election was over, one could sit back, in a new quiet and calmness of spirit, to weigh what had happened. One thing I believe no one would challenge: the debates were a landmark in democratic procedure; they brought before the people of the whole country the candidates and their views. They stimulated a new interest in the issues, they emphasized the importance of the voting public's familiarizing itself with the issues at stake; they made the citizens, as they should be, a vital and participating element, with a stake in what happens to their country. The telling point, of course, is that, as a result of the debates, more people voted than have ever voted in the history of the country. And that was a victory for the democratic system.

And after the election—back to work. There is so much to do, so many engrossing challenges, so many heartbreaking and pressing needs, so much in every day that is profoundly interesting.

But, I suppose, I must slow down.

Index

443

73 74 75 76 77 9 8 7 6 5 4 3

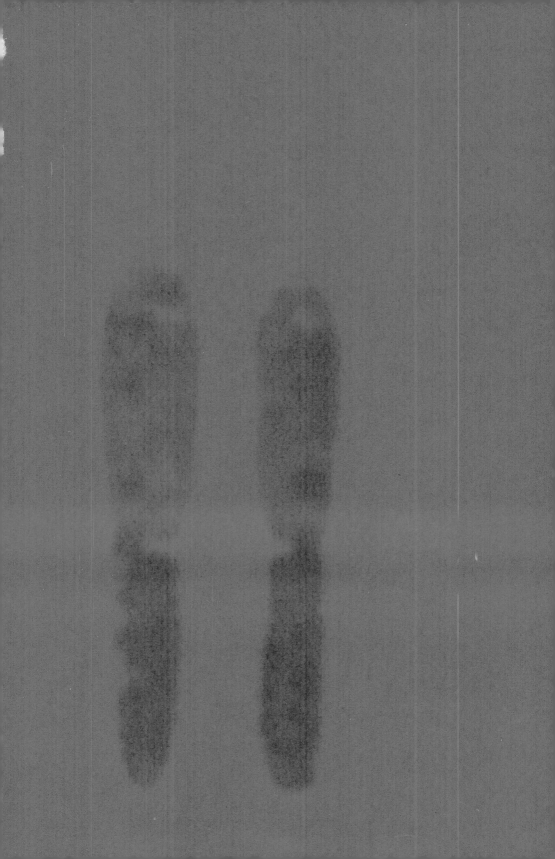

THREE GREAT NOVELS
What a Woman Wants

D1533513

Erica James, Maureen Lee, Donna Hay

Three Great Novels: What a Woman Wants

A Sense of Belonging
Dancing in the Dark
Some Kind of Hero

First published in Great Britain in 2006 by Orion,
an imprint of the Orion Publishing Group Ltd.

A Sense of Belonging Copyright © Erica James 1998
Dancing in the Dark Copyright © Maureen Lee 1999
Some Kind of Hero Copyright © Donna Hay 2003

A CIP catalogue record for this book is
available from the British Library

ISBN-13: 978 0 75287 532 3
ISBN-10: 0 75287 532 9

Typeset by Deltatype Ltd,
Birkenhead, Merseyside

Set in Minion

Printed and bound in Great Britain by
Mackays of Chatham, plc

The Orion Publishing Group Ltd
Orion House
5 Upper Saint Martin's Lane
London, WC2H 9EA

The Orion Publishing Group's policy is to use papers that
are natural, renewable and recyclable products and made
from wood grown in sustainable forests. The logging and
manufacturing processes are expected to conform to the
environmental regulations of the country of origin.

www.orionbooks.co.uk

Contents

A Sense of Belonging

To Edward and Samuel

Acknowledgements

This book couldn't have been written without the help and support of so many people and whether they want the credit (or the blame) or not, they're going to get it.

Life-saving thanks must go to Big G for those quiet, calming moments.

Glass-raising thanks to Helena who listened to numerous silly ideas being tossed around her kitchen while I poured the wine and she cooked the lunch.

Side-splitting thanks to Maureen for saying, 'Come on, that's just not on!' As ever she made me laugh at just the right time.

Courteous thanks to Morris Phillips for allowing me to pry into his business.

And the same to Susan Howard of Avocado Cards in Huddersfield.

Respectful thanks to Jane Wood at Orion, along with Selina Walker and Sarah Yorke.

Appreciative thanks to Helen Spencer for the over-the-phone consultations.

Humble thanks to all those people who shared their personal experiences of MS with me, especially Sue Argent who never minded me ringing her with yet another query. Her outlook on life, together with her extraordinary strength of character, is a truly inspiring example to us all. Thank you, Sue.

Devoted and adoring thanks to the two back-room boys, Edward and Samuel, who know exactly when to run for cover when things are going badly, and whose survival skills are improving with each book I write.

And, finally, forelock-tugging thanks to Jonathan Lloyd at Curtis Brown for being nothing like Piers Lambert!

A novel is a mirror which passes over a highway.
Sometimes it reflects to your eye the blue of the skies,
at others the churned-up mud of the road.

Henri Beyle (called Stendhal)
1783–1842

The Beginning

1

THE END

Jessica Lloyd looked at what she'd just typed, considered it for a few seconds, then allowed herself a small wry smile.

This wasn't because she had at last finished her latest novel, or indeed that these two perfectly innocuous words would irritate the hell out of her exacting agent – 'I know when it ends, Jessica, there's no need to tell me, I'm not a fool' – but because, and heaven forbid that anyone would accuse her of spouting high-sounding humbug, she happened to believe that there was no such thing as an ending. In her experience life was all about beginnings.

And today of all days she had to believe that this was true.

She switched off the laptop, stood up, stretched her arms over her head and went and leant against the white-painted wall that separated her small terrace from the rocky drop below. She rested her elbows on the sun-warmed stone and gazed out at the sweep of bay with its crystal-clear water that was holiday-brochure blue. It was a breathlessly hot June morning and the sea was calm and tranquil, benign even, but Jessica knew well enough that by early afternoon there would be a strong wind blowing in across the water, bringing with it the kind of crashing waves that wind-surfers delighted in and for which this part of Corfu was renowned.

But for now, all was still.

She went back to the shade of her vine-covered pergola, to the wooden table she had been working at, and gathered up her things and took them inside. She plugged the laptop into the printer, which squatted incongruously next to the bread bin on top of the fridge in the tiny kitchen, and set it to print her final chapter of *A Carefree Life*. While she waited for the machine to do its work she poured herself a glass of ice-cold mineral water and gulped it down. It was eleven o'clock and she had been working on the terrace since a little after seven, having got up early to finish her novel. And now that it was done she could use the rest of the day to say her goodbyes.

She had lived on Corfu for six years and for the most part she had cherished every magical timeless day that had drifted by. She had come to the island not long after her thirtieth birthday and had fallen for the charming, carefree way of life the Corfiotes so enjoyed. It had suited her own temperament perfectly.

She had also fallen in love, or what she had thought was love at the time. Now she wasn't so sure.

First there had been Christos who, if nothing else, had tried to teach her to cook, or rather his mother had. But when it finally dawned on Christos that she had absolutely no interest in cooking, and that if he wanted anything worthwhile to eat he either had to do it himself or go home to his mother, he went in search of a nice local girl who would know exactly how to produce his favourite meal of arni brizoles. There had been no bitter recriminations between them when they'd parted, just a shared sense of better luck next time.

Luck had given her Gavin.

Gavin, so sure, so confident and so amusing. He was the original free spirit, as he'd never stopped letting her know.

He had come to the island some two years before, to work as a sailing instructor, and when they'd met, like Christos, he had set about teaching her what was important to him. In his case it was sailing. She hated sailing almost as much as cooking, but had been so captivated by Gavin that she hadn't let on and had tried her best to listen to his enthusiastic instructions. She'd then tried even harder to carry them out. But it had been hopeless. Tacking into the wind was a concept she never mastered. Each lesson she would capsize the small boat at least half a dozen times – it didn't help that Gavin would shout from the shore that a child of ten could sail the wretched thing. 'Then let it!' she shouted back at him one day, abandoning the boat and swimming away from it in a monumental sulk.

If the sailing was a nightmare, the sex was a dream.

And always afterwards, whether they were lying on her bed in the moonlight or in the sun on her secluded terrace, he would sing to her or tell her jokes.

But the sex, the singing and the jokes – and thank goodness, the sailing – were all about to become things of the past.

She hadn't told Gavin what she was doing because she knew what his reaction would be if she did try and explain to him why she was leaving. There would be that little-boy-lost look, accompanied by the words, 'But you can't really mean it' – in Gavin's world, nobody ever meant what they said. He would then open a bottle of wine and insist they discuss it on the terrace beneath the stars and moon, where he knew she'd be unable to stay angry with him for more than two minutes. And because of his arrogance he would assume she was going because of him and he'd say, 'But it's just the way I am, it doesn't mean anything' and lead her to the bedroom.

Then, once they'd made love, he would whisper in her ear, 'Stay, Jessica, don't go.'

And she'd give in. Just like that.

She sighed. It wasn't good to think about Gavin too much. Not at this stage. Not when she knew how weak he could make her feel. His greatest skill, she had long since decided, was that he knew exactly how to keep her dangling. She was ashamed to admit it, but basically it was all down to sex. And it wasn't even that Gavin understood her body and knew all the right things to do with it that made him so appealing, it was more a case of the sheer force of his energy in bed that had her gasping for more. Without a doubt, if sex were ever made an Olympic sport, Gavin would be the Mark Spitz of the event.

She smiled to herself and imagined Gavin putting his latest round of infidelity down to essential training.

She poured another glass of water, quickly drank it, then decided to have a swim before taking her motor boat into Kassiopi. She went in search of her swimming costume. Just as she had changed, the phone rang.

It was her mother.

Instantly Jessica was filled with alarm. Her mother rarely called. It was always Jessica who did the phoning. The last time Anna had phoned was six months ago and it was to announce that she was being admitted into hospital for a heart bypass operation. Very calmly she had said, 'Don't go doing anything silly, Jessica, like rushing over, but I'm going into hospital for a few days. There seems to be a problem with my heart. A lot of fuss over nothing, very probably.' Within hours of the call Jessica was sitting on a plane bound for Manchester, panic-stricken that she might never see her mother again. It was a thought that had stayed with her throughout the flight and had reduced her to a tearful, sniffling wreck, much to the consternation of the man in the seat next to her.

They had never been overtly close, not like other mothers and daughters Jessica knew, who needed constantly to be together, but their love for one another was just as strong. Unfortunately, so was the need for both of them to live independently of each other.

'What is it?' Jessica asked. 'What's happened?'

'Don't fuss. I'm fine. I just wanted to see if it wasn't too late to make you change your mind.'

'No chance,' Jessica said with a light laugh. 'Everything's arranged this end and you know jolly well that I've exchanged contracts on Cholmford Hall Mews, so you can expect me as I'd originally said.'

'Remind me.'

Jessica tutted. 'Does that mean you've lost the letter I sent you?'

'I might have.'

'Honestly, Mum, you're hopeless.'

'I'm nothing of the sort. After years of having a head for paperwork I've given it up. Now get on and tell me what time you'll be arriving tonight, this call's costing me a fortune.'

'With a bit of luck I'll see you some time after eleven.'

'As early as that?'

'You really know how to make a daughter feel loved.'

'I'm working on it, Jessica, but it's not easy.'

A few moments later, when Jessica put down the phone, she found herself almost wishing the hours away until her flight. She wanted to go home. Which was strange because England hadn't been home for years.

She picked up a large towel from the back of a chair and made her way down the steep hillside path at the end of her sun terrace. At a sharp turn she paused and stood still in the fierce heat, and gazed across the expanse of sparkling water. In the distance was the Albanian coastline, its mountainous bumps blurred and hazy in the baking sunshine. All around her was the sweet smell of cypress trees and the ever present noise of cicadas hidden in the olive trees. Surely she should feel something, she thought, as she stood taking in the view and the moment. Shouldn't there be at least some feeling of regret at leaving all this, this island that had once been such a blissful paradise?

But that was the point, she supposed. It no longer was a blissful paradise.

She carried on down the path, taking care where she placed her feet on the stones that in places were loose and wobbly.

When she reached the tiny sheltered area of pebble beach that she called her own, where she kept her small boat tied to an overhanging branch of a eucalyptus tree, she placed her towel on a rock and slipped into the clear turquoise water. It was wonderfully cool and refreshing, and leaning her slim brown body forward she began swimming away from the shore, moving her arms and legs slowly and rhythmically.

Perhaps this might be something she would miss when she returned to England.

But even the thought of a chilly chlorine dip at the local swimming baths back in Cheshire could not persuade her that what she was doing was wrong.

It was in January, when her mother had gone into hospital, that Jessica had begun to feel uneasy. It was the first time that she wondered whether she hadn't been a little selfish all her adult life.

The trouble was she had been brought up by a strong, clear-minded and very independent woman, and raised with the expectation that she would be the same. Which had meant that at the earliest opportunity she had been encouraged to fly the nest and spread her wings. At no stage had she thought about marriage or ever having children, the two things just didn't come into her thinking. As a child there had been no bedtime stories of young girls being rescued by handsome princes on the look-out for a compliant, pretty wife, instead there had been tales of heroic women battling against the odds; of Joan of Arc, Amy Johnson, Florence Nightingale and even Ginger Rogers who, according to her mother, did everything Fred Astaire did but backwards and in high heels. 'Whatever you want to do,' her mother would say when kissing her good-night, 'believe you can do it and you will. And more important than anything else, make sure you enjoy what you do.'

Which might well have provoked some children into becoming high-flying achievers, but not Jessica. What it did was convince her from an early age that whatever she did it would be because she wanted to do it. She grew to be extremely single-minded and able to turn her hand to anything she chose. Her scholastic education came to an end at the age of eighteen and because she already had a passion for skiing, but couldn't afford to fund it, she decided to work as a chalet maid in a ski resort in the French Alps, where she spent what little free time she had on the slopes perfecting her technique. She'd then gone to live in Colorado, where she worked as a skiing instructor. From there she'd returned to Europe and while island hopping round Greece, with only a bulging backpack to her name, had chanced upon a holiday company desperate for an extra rep to help them out for a couple of weeks on Corfu. By the time the job came to an end Jessica knew that she had chanced upon a place that she had no desire to leave. She began working in a taverna, which was where she had met Christos, and when she wasn't serving plates of moussaka and feta salad to the tourists, along with retsina and ouzo, she was to be found on the beach with a notebook and pen. Quite unexpectedly she had discovered she had a new craving and was instantly keen to satisfy it. She had started writing a novel. It took her a year and when it was finished she posted the set of notebooks to her mother to read. Unbeknown to Jessica, Anna had then secretly typed it out and sent it off to an agent in London. Several months later, not long after Christos had given up on Jessica, she had received a letter from her mother with the news that a publisher was interested in her book. 'They're offering real money,' she wrote, 'not buttons, but hard cash. You'd better come over right away and see what you think.'

And she had. First she had met the agent to whom her mother had sent the manuscript, then the publisher. A contract was signed and when she flew back to Corfu a week later the first thing she did was to give up working at the taverna and buy herself a new set of notebooks and pens, and start writing another novel.

Now, as she climbed up the steep path to her small whitewashed house that nestled comfortably into the unspoilt hillside, she thought of the third book she had completed today, which she would take with her to England that evening on the plane, along with just a few carefully selected possessions that would remind her of Corfu. The house was rented, as was the furniture, and much as she'd come to love her locally carved olive-wood knick-knacks and brightly coloured rugs and wall hangings, it was only right that they should stay behind. They would look out of place in her new house; it would be like taking holiday souvenirs home and finding they looked silly away from their own environment, just as cheap holiday wine was best enjoyed *in situ*.

She threw her wet towel over the clothes line tied between two olive trees and experienced the uneasy feeling that her decision to leave Gavin and her idyllic life-style and return home to England was all about her finally growing up.

No more could she justify her carefree life. No more could she ignore what she felt she owed her mother. And whether her mother was prepared to admit it or not, Anna needed her daughter's help.

Just occasionally, though, Jessica had the strange and dangerous feeling that perhaps this wasn't so, that in actual fact, by some quirk of human nature, it was she who wanted her mother to need her.

Either way, it didn't matter. The truth was, at the age of thirty-six she had discovered that Corfu could not offer her what she now found she wanted more than anything else.

She went inside the house to shower and get ready to go out, more convinced than ever that what she had suspected for some time was true – she had outstayed her welcome on this lovely Ionian island. It was definitely time to move on, to go back to England where she had a new home waiting for her, not with her mother – that would be a disaster for them both – but somewhere close by, where she hoped to be able to keep a surreptitious eye on Anna.

And maybe she might even find what it was she was looking for, that setting up home at Cholmford Hall Mews would satisfy the very real sense of belonging that she was now seeking.

2

Kate Morris stared with pleasure through the large arched window in the sun-filled sitting-room of 5 Cholmford Hall Mews and experienced the sensation of having died and gone to heaven. She wondered how she would ever get anything done in the house with this beautiful view of rolling fields and woodland to gaze at all day.

Well, one thing was for sure, today was not the day to stand and dream. There was such a lot to do and she wanted most of it done before Alec came home from work that evening. She wished to surprise him, wanted very much to make their new home together perfect.

They had only moved in yesterday, so she knew that it was just possible that she was setting her sights too high, but she badly desired everything to be right.

She moved away from the window and turned her attention to one of the large packing cases in the middle of the room. She opened it, took off the protective layers of scrunched-up paper and pulled out a parcel to unwrap. It was a framed photograph of Alec and his family – the McLaren clan as she called them – taken last Christmas. There was Alec's daughter Ruth, who wasn't much younger than Kate, and her husband Adam, and their son, little Oscar, four years old and utterly adorable; dark-eyed and winsome, and Kate's favourite member of the McLaren family, other than the man she loved. And looking very much the patriarchal figure, Alec was in the middle of the picture, his tall frame dominating the photograph as he stood proudly, surrounded by his family. She ran her finger over his face, taking in the flecks of grey at his temples, the smile that had put her so thoroughly at ease when they'd first met and the new pair of gold-rimmed glasses she had helped him choose the week before Christmas. She was in the picture too. She gazed critically at herself and saw a tall girl in her late twenties looking more like a gawky schoolgirl with shoulders slightly stooped as though this would make her less visible and less out of place among a family in which she felt she didn't belong. It was a sad truth, but it was exactly how she'd always looked in her own family photographs. The final figure in the group portrait was perhaps the most important

9

member of the family ... in terms of Kate's future happiness, she suspected. It was Melissa McLaren.

Melissa and Alec had been divorced now for over two years, but Kate was astute enough to know that a formal piece of paper could never fully untie the bond that existed between a couple who had not only been married for as long as Alec and Melissa had, but who also still saw one another on a daily basis running their jointly owned company together. Kate recognised all too well that some women in her position would be unhappy with the situation in which her partner still had so much contact with his ex, but Kate was determined never to let something as petty as jealousy ruin what she and Alec had between them. Though they had only known one another for less than a year their love was as precious to Kate as anything she'd ever known.

She placed the photograph on the mantelpiece, along with some other ornaments she'd already unwrapped after seeing Alec off to work earlier that morning. It was a shame he'd needed to go in to the office today of all days, it would have been lovely to have had him here with her setting up home together.

They had met last autumn through, of all things, a dating agency – a fact that nobody in the McLaren clan was ever to know about. 'I couldn't bear for Melissa to know I'd resorted to meeting somebody this way,' Alec had told Kate. It wasn't perhaps the most flattering thing for him to say to her, but she knew and understood what he meant, and had respected his need to protect his pride. Hadn't she felt exactly the same herself?

In theory they should never have met, because of their age difference, but that particular week the computer at the agency had had a glitch and had sent out hundreds of profiles to mismatched prospective partners and, with curiosity on both their parts to blame, she and Alec had arranged to meet for a drink in a wine bar in Knutsford.

'Excuse my lack of originality,' he'd said on the phone, 'but how will I recognise you? I've never done this kind of thing before.'

'I'm tall for my age,' she'd joked, 'and I have rather a lot of hair.'

She had liked the look of him from the very first second she'd seen him enter the wine bar, without even knowing that he was her date. He'd been dressed in a loose-fitting raincoat over a linen suit and pale-green shirt that later in the evening she had realised had reflected the colour of his eyes. She had liked him even more when he'd approached her without hesitating and said, 'You have to be Kate Morris, I love your hair, it makes you look like an ethereal Burne-Jones beauty.'

According to the advice offered by the dating agency, when two people meet for the first time they should plan to spend a maximum of thirty minutes in each other's company. She and Alec had spent all evening together. They'd had a couple of drinks in the wine bar and moved on to a nearby restaurant. She had found his manner easy and comfortable. He was softly spoken, with just the merest hint of a Scottish accent, and appeared confident and perfectly composed, even though he admitted to her the following day that he had been terrified that she would think him old and boring. But there was nothing old and boring about Alec, he was spontaneous and fun, and she had fallen in love with him by the time they'd finished their meal. Later, when he had walked her to her car and had said how much he'd enjoyed the evening, he'd added, 'I don't suppose there's any hope of you humouring a middle-aged man and having dinner with me next week, is there?'

'No,' she'd answered, 'no, I don't think so.'

He'd lowered his eyes, disappointed – ever since that moment she'd never seen him look so downcast. 'I just thought it was worth asking,' he'd mumbled awkwardly, staring into the shop window behind him, 'but I quite understand, I suppose that's how this dating thing works.'

She'd reached out and rested her hand on his coat sleeve. 'You don't understand at all,' she'd said, 'I said no because I can't wait until next week. How about tomorrow evening?'

His handsome face had instantly broken into a delighted smile. 'You mean it?'

'Yes.' She'd smiled back at him. 'Why wouldn't I?'

He'd thrown his arms in the air. 'A million and one reasons why not. Like I'm twenty years older than you.'

'Actually you're twenty-one years older.'

He groaned. 'That bad, eh?'

'Old enough to be my father.'

'Doesn't it bother you?'

'So where shall we eat?'

'Here? Wherever. Wherever you want. Oh Kate, give me something that belongs to you so that I don't wake up in the morning and find you were nothing but a dream.'

Kate smiled and hoped she would never forget the memory of their first meeting. She carried on with the unpacking. When she'd cleared another two boxes she was interrupted by the sound of the doorbell. She clambered over the chaos of yet more unopened boxes in the hall and opened the front door. She was met by the sight of a woman holding a large bouquet of flowers.

'Kate Morris?'

'Yes, that's me.'

'For you.'

Kate took the flowers and watched the woman turn her florist's van round in the gravelled courtyard in front of all the mews houses and drive out through the central archway. She closed the door and walked through to the kitchen. She laid the flowers on the table and read the small accompanying card. *To my darling Kate, sorry I can't be with you on this special day. Please don't work too hard. All my love, Alec.*

Kate swallowed back tears of happiness. Nobody had ever treated her so lovingly.

3

From the kitchen window of 2 Cholmford Hall Mews Amanda Fergusson watched the florist's van drive away and felt a stab of jealousy at the sight of such a beautiful bouquet of flowers. Tony wasn't a flower person, chocolates yes, occasionally, but rarely flowers. But then that was all right, because she wasn't a sentimental person either.

She closed the dishwasher and moved on to tidying up the breakfast bar. But her thoughts were still with the pretty young girl over in number five, who she decided was probably sickeningly sentimental and was on the receiving end of similarly romantic gestures all the time from her . . . Amanda hesitated. Her what, precisely?

Husband?

No. The man who had stood on the doorstep that morning kissing her goodbye as though he couldn't bear to be parted from her was no husband. Amanda had one of those and she knew the difference: in broad daylight husbands pecked, while lovers embraced.

On the other hand, they might be newly-weds. That was it, probably. Recently married and still going through the honeymoon period. It would soon be over, just as it was with her and Tony. It hadn't slipped her notice either that there was a considerable age gap between the happy couple.

She carried on with the clearing up. In the adjoining family room she could hear the sound of Tony's six-year-old daughter Hattie, singing along to a programme on Children's BBC. Amanda listened to the little girl. She sounded relaxed and cheerful. Which wasn't always the case.

When Amanda had met Tony eighteen months before, he was still trying to get over the loss of his wife, who had died in a car accident the previous year. He was also finding it difficult to cope with the demands of his job and his young daughter. A succession of unreliable nannies hadn't helped either and had served only to disrupt Hattie's life further.

But now, at least, thanks to her, both Tony and Hattie seemed to be on a more even keel, even if at times Amanda felt she was out of her depth. Marriage to Tony wasn't all that she'd imagined it would be, but she was working on it. Tony, however, wasn't her real problem, that was Hattie.

She wished at times that Tony would trust her more with his daughter. He was too prone to step in and undermine her when she was trying her best to discipline the girl.

They had argued again last night. Hattie had been in and out of bed, one minute claiming she was thirsty, the next that she was too hot. 'I can't sleep,' she'd said. Tony had immediately suggested that Hattie come downstairs and sit with them for a while, but she had known the answer was to be firm and make Hattie realise that grown-ups needed their time together. Tony had had his way, and Hattie had sat between them on the sofa and had consequently refused to go back upstairs. Eventually she had fallen asleep, lying across Tony's chest, and he had carried her up to her room. By which time it was nearly midnight and they too had gone to bed, exhausted and bad-tempered.

'May I have a drink?'

Amanda turned round to see Hattie standing in the doorway. 'Please,' she said. '*Please* may I have a drink?'

'Please,' repeated Hattie in a bored tone.

Amanda poured out a plastic cup of apple juice. She placed it on the breakfast bar. 'Climb up on to your stool, then.'

'I want it in there,' Hattie said, pointing towards the family room and the television.

'In here or not at all. What's it to be?'

Hattie stared back at her.

Amanda sensed a battle of wills looming. 'You know the rules,' she said, 'where there are carpets, new carpets at that, you're not allowed to eat or drink.'

'Daddy lets –'

'Then Daddy's wrong.'

Hattie's eyes opened wide.

Amanda was cross with herself. Once again, not only had she cast herself as the wicked stepmother, but she had broken the cardinal rule: Daddy was never wrong. And the only way out of the problem now was either to give in – which she wouldn't – or provide a distraction. 'Why don't we go out,' she said. 'Let's go and meet the nice new lady who moved in yesterday.'

Kate had almost cleared the sitting-room of packing cases and was just considering a well-earned coffee break when she heard the doorbell for a second time that day and went to answer it.

It was the little girl she noticed first. She decided that she was a couple of years older than Oscar.

'We thought we'd come and introduce ourselves,' said the woman behind the small fair-haired child, 'we live in number two over in the

14

corner. I'm Amanda and this is Hattie.' Hattie immediately tried to hide herself behind Amanda.

'Come on now, don't be shy,' Amanda said, giving her a little shove. 'I'm afraid she can be very silly at times.'

Kate bent down and smiled at Hattie. 'Hello,' she said, 'I'm Kate. Would you like to come in and help me unpack a few boxes? I've got so much to do, it would be lovely to have another pair of hands.'

Hattie considered Kate for a moment, then pushed past Amanda and followed her inside the house.

'I was just going to make myself a cup of coffee, would you like one?'

'Please,' Amanda answered, 'but only if we're not keeping you. I can see you've still got a lot to do.'

Kate led the way through to the kitchen and swept her long hair up from her face. She held it in that position for a few seconds and looked back at the mess in the hall, which she had yet to make an impression on. 'You're so right.' She sighed, letting go of her hair and sending it cascading down her back. 'But not to worry, I'm sure I'll get it all done by this evening, especially now that I've got Hattie to help me.' She smiled down at the little girl who was busy staring at her.

'You've got lovely hair,' Hattie said unexpectedly.

'Thank you and so have you.'

'No I haven't, mine's horrible. I'd like it long like yours, but Amanda says it's easier to keep it short like this.'

'And Amanda is quite right,' Kate said diplomatically, wondering what Amanda's relationship was to this sweet girl – aunt, stepmother or child-minder? Surely not her mother. 'But maybe when you're a big girl and can look after your own hair you'll be able to have it just as you want.'

'I will,' Hattie said flatly. She gave Amanda a sideways glance.

'Now what would you like to drink?' Kate asked, aware that the rapport between her two visitors was not all that it could be.

'May I have some apple juice, please?'

'What beautiful manners you have, but I'm afraid I've only got orange juice or grape juice. Or how about some milk?'

'Milk please.'

Amanda watched the scene between her new neighbour and Hattie. If she had been jealous at the sight of the flowers arriving in the courtyard earlier this morning, she now felt an even greater sense of envy witnessing the ease with which this willowy beauty could strike up such a friendly alliance with her stepdaughter. It had taken Amanda the best part of six months to get Hattie so much as to smile at her.

'There now,' Kate said, picking up the tray of drinks, 'I think that's everything we shall need. Oh, Hattie, could you carry that tin of biscuits for me? Yes, that's the one, the large red tin. Can you manage it? Splendid.'

'Where are we going to have our drinks?' asked Hattie.

'In the sitting-room, it's the only tidy room in the house.

'Is there a carpet in there?'

'Yes,' Kate said, puzzled. 'Why?'

Hattie didn't answer but she threw another look at her stepmother.

Amanda followed behind, feeling cross and slightly left out. 'What lovely flowers,' she said, when they went into the sitting-room and she saw the enormous arrangement on a highly polished corner table. 'I saw them arrive earlier, lucky you.' She went over to take a closer look and to read the card propped up in front of the vase. When she looked back at Kate she was surprised to see that she was blushing.

'Alec is very romantic, he does things like that.'

'Is Alec your husband?' asked Hattie, taking off her shoes and making herself at home in a large comfortable wing-back armchair.

'Sort of,' Kate said, handing Amanda her cup of coffee. 'Milk?'

Amanda shook her head, hoping that Hattie would ask what 'sort of' meant.

'Sugar?'

'No, thank you.' She waited for Hattie to oblige, but the silly girl was too busy smiling at Kate, who was now passing her a glass of milk. She almost wished that Hattie would misbehave and spill the drink all over the expensive-looking fabric of the chair in which she was sitting, as she did at home sometimes, then they'd see how this beautiful serene creature would handle things.

'So when did you move in?' Kate asked, as she settled herself on a low footstool beside Hattie's chair and offered her a biscuit.

'Last week. We were the first. It's been strange being here all on our own. It's very quiet. I'm just so glad I've got a car or I'd feel completely isolated.'

Kate stared out through the large arched window that took up nearly the entire width of the far end of the room. 'But it's wonderful, isn't it? The countryside is so pretty. I don't think I shall ever want to leave. There's such a good feeling about the place. Do you feel it too?'

'Ah . . . yes,' lied Amanda. All she had felt since they'd moved in was a colossal sense of exhaustion. Running herself ragged over unpacking, then gathering swatches of fabrics and wallpaper samples was not her idea of fun, especially as she was now looking after Hattie full time because they'd taken her out of school before the end of term so that they could move house and area. For the first time since her marriage to Tony, when she'd given up her job in the building society in order to be a stay-at-home mum for Hattie, she longed for her old way of life – chasing unpaid mortgage payments was a doddle in comparison.

16

'Is there anybody else living here, or are we the only ones to have moved in?' Kate asked, offering Amanda a biscuit.

Amanda had a pretty good idea what was going on with the development as she'd made it her business to befriend Sue, the sales negotiator who worked in the show house three days a week. Though even Sue hadn't been entirely sure what the set-up between Kate and Alec was. 'Contracts have been exchanged on number one and completion has already taken place on number four,' she said.

'Any idea what the other people are like?'

'Apparently your immediate neighbour is a well-known author, a romantic novelist, but I've never heard of her, not that I read that kind of book. I prefer something with a bit more substance when I do have the time to read.'

'How interesting. Do you know her name?'

'Jessica ... Jessica Somebody or other. I can't remember her surname, which just goes to show she can't be that well-known.'

'Her name's Jessica Lloyd,' Hattie said, her mouth full of biscuit crumbs.

'Hattie,' reprimanded Amanda, 'don't speak with your mouth full.' She then turned to Kate. 'I think Hattie might be right though.'

'I know I'm right,' Hattie continued, 'because when the lady in the show house said her name yesterday I thought of Vanessa Lloyd at my old school. Is she famous?'

Kate smiled. 'I don't know about that, but I used to work in a library and Jessica Lloyd's books were never on the shelves, they were always out on loan. She's very good.'

'Oh, well then,' Amanda laughed, 'we shall have to watch ourselves and be on our guard, or we'll all end up in her next novel.'

'And what about number one, do you know who's moving in there?'

'According to Sue in the show house, he's a lonesome bachelor. She thinks he's the sort to keep himself very much to himself.'

4

'You're out of your mind!'

Josh ignored his brother and continued to drive along the narrow lane with its high hedges that in places were brushing both sides of his Shogun. He hoped they wouldn't meet an oncoming car, because if his memory served him correctly there wasn't another space to pull in for at least a quarter of a mile.

'I mean it,' Charlie persisted. 'You must be mad thinking of living out here, there'll be no night-life other than owls tu-whit, tu-whooing all hours and driving you round the bend. What's got into you?'

Still Josh didn't say anything. He had anticipated this reaction from Charlie, which was why he had deliberately only brought his brother to see the house when he'd exchanged contracts and had set a date for the removal men to move his stuff out of his flat in Bowdon. And he knew very well that his brother wasn't at all concerned about the lack of available social life that there would be out here in the country. The real line of Charlie's argument was yet to come. He didn't want to hear it, but he knew there could be no avoidance. It was inevitable. Just as so many other things in his life were inevitable.

'Is there any chance of you answering me?'

'And is there any chance of you keeping an open mind?' Josh said evenly, slowing the Shogun to negotiate a small bridge that crossed the canal. He stopped the car to admire the view, hoping it might impress his brother – that it might disarm Charlie of some of his resounding disapproval. To the right of the bridge and moored further along the tow-path was a brightly painted barge and on the bow of the boat was a Jack Russell terrier with a red spotted scarf tied round its neck; it was barking frantically at a swan passing serenely by. On the other side of the bridge and to the left was an attractive white-painted cottage with a garden that was in full flower, which led down to the tow-path where willow trees dipped their elegant branches into the water.

'Well?' said Josh.

'Okay,' Charlie muttered crossly, 'an open mind it is.'

Josh drove on. The narrow lane began to open out and the hedges shrank sufficiently to reveal fields of ripening corn swaying gently in the rippling breeze. They came to a turning to the right, which took them through an avenue of chestnut trees so large and majestic that the branches reached out across the road and formed a long leafy tunnel.

Charlie continued to sit in the front passenger seat unmoved by all the picture-postcard settings they were driving through. For the life of him he couldn't work out what Josh had been up to. Why in heaven's name had he done this crazy thing? And in secret. What had possessed him to buy a house out here in the middle of nowhere? 'Is that it?' he asked, seeing a large building ahead of them.

'Yes,' said Josh. He slowed the car and drove through the archway of Cholmford Hall Mews. He parked outside number one, which was the end property on the left-hand side of the horseshoe-shaped barn conversion. 'I'll get the keys,' he said.

He walked slowly and stiffly across the courtyard to the show house where he found the sales negotiator in the kitchen. She was perched on a bar stool reading a magazine. She closed it and slipped it under a property brochure as soon as she saw him.

'Okay if I have the key?' he asked. 'I want to show somebody round.'

'Of course, Mr Crawford. No problem.' She went to a filing cabinet tucked into a corner of the kitchen and pulled out an envelope of labelled keys. She handed him his set. 'You're moving in next week, aren't you?' she said, hoping to engage him in conversation. He really was quite good-looking, in that smooth, clean-cut kind of way you usually only saw on the telly. He had a neat dress sense too, but then she'd always liked a man in black. A shame she could never get him to talk, though. He was always polite, but not what she'd call forthcoming. He thanked her for the keys and left.

There was no sign of Charlie when Josh went back across the courtyard, but the small gate to the garden of number one was open. He found his brother standing in the middle of the recently turfed lawn. This garden mirrored exactly number five's and they were the largest plots on the development, both extending to almost half an acre, and the views across to Bosley Cloud and the Peak District were stunning.

'Admiring the view?' asked Josh.

'Not particularly, I'm getting agoraphobia. Give me the suburbs any day.'

'Philistine. Come and see inside the house.'

As they moved from one empty, echoing room to another Josh waited for his brother finally to get to the point. Charlie was rarely quiet and the uncomfortable silence growing between them was getting on his nerves. It had been the same at work recently. Without a word, Charlie was syphoning off jobs that would normally come Josh's way. Even when they had been planning their last trip to Hong Kong, Charlie had assumed that Josh would stay behind. He'd tried to make out that Josh was needed in Manchester to make sure everything was in order for their next trade fair.

'Okay,' Charlie said at last, when they'd done the full tour and were back in the sitting-room where they'd started. They stood in front of a large arched window and stared out at the garden and hills beyond. 'I'll concede that it's a great house. I'll even go so far as to say I like where it is. It has a certain countrified-meets-chic charm to it, though I couldn't see myself here, not ever. I'd feel too cut off.'

'But?'

A couple of moments passed before Charlie spoke. 'Oh, come off it, Josh, you know perfectly well what the "but" is.'

Josh shook his head. 'Please. Explain it to me.'

Charlie kept his eyes on the patchwork of uneven turf outside. He couldn't bring himself to say the words. How could he? How could he tell his brother – his best mate – that the odds were against him, that one morning in the not too distant future he could wake up unable to manage the stairs in his own home, never mind push a bloody great mower round that huge garden out there.

'You're not saying anything, Charlie. Don't tell me you're struggling to find the right words.'

Charlie turned away from the window. He faced his brother. 'Don't taunt me, it's not fair.'

Josh's face hardened. 'You're right,' he said, 'you're absolutely right. It isn't fair. It's not fair that I've got multiple sclerosis and that I should want to live in this house. I should behave myself and conform, and become the disabled person you want me to be. I should throw in the towel and move into a crappy, depressing little bungalow and have the whole place kitted out with ramps and God knows what else.'

'I didn't say that.'

'No. You didn't need to. It's been written all over your face ever since last night when I told you about this place.'

Charlie ran his hand through his hair. It was nine months now since Josh had been diagnosed as having MS and he knew he should be getting used to these sudden outbursts of anger from his younger brother, but he wasn't. If anything he was finding it more and more difficult to come up with the right response. If he were honest, he found his brother's anger frightening because he knew that it betrayed Josh's fear of his illness.

'Who said anything about a bungalow?' he said, trying to make light of Josh's accusation. 'And anyway, what was so wrong with your flat? Why the sudden need to up sticks and be so far away from everyone you know?'

Josh moved slowly across the room and went and leaned against the carved oak mantelpiece. He could feel the underside of his left foot beginning to tingle, which he knew in a matter of hours would turn into full-blown pins and needles and would spread up his leg, leaving him with barely any feeling in that part of his body. If he was lucky it would be gone by the morning. If not, it could last for days, maybe even weeks. 'If you must know, I'm tired of you all staring at me,' he said, 'you, Mum and Dad, and everyone at work, you're all giving me those same pitying looks. Poor Josh, you're thinking, only thirty-seven and destined soon to be little more than a vegetable in a wheelchair.'

Charlie flinched at his brother's words, but he couldn't stop his concern now turning to anger. He stuffed his fists into his trouser pockets. 'It's because we care about you, you ungrateful bastard!'

'And I'm sick of it,' Josh shouted back at him. 'If I haven't got much worthwhile life left then I'm bloody well going to enjoy what I have got, which means living out here in the country and being allowed to be *me*, and not some stereotyped image of a crippo that you've got in mind.'

'But it's so isolated here,' Charlie tried to reason.

But Josh was past reason. 'Good,' he shouted, 'because then you won't hear me screaming when I've had enough and done myself in!'

5

Before heading for Kassiopi, Jessica steered her boat towards a secluded bay that contained nothing but a couple of extravagantly large holiday villas surrounded by bushes of purple-flowering oleander and soaring cypress trees. Both villas had direct access on to the small sandy beach where Jessica could see and smell a lunch-time barbecue in progress. Exuberant English voices drifted across the water as children chased and splashed each other in the rock pools and parents, stretched out on sun-loungers, instinctively called out to them to be careful.

Jessica smiled at the children as they waved at her and carefully manoeuvred the boat alongside the rickety wooden jetty that had been built to serve the two holiday properties, as well as her friends' more modest house higher up the hillside. She switched off the engine, hopped out and tied the boat to the post Helen and Jack used. She then began the climb up the steep wooded slope to where they lived.

She was hot and short of breath by the time she reached their little house with its buttermilk walls partially draped in bougainvillaea and topped with a delicate coral-coloured roof. She found them both lying languidly in deck-chairs in the shade of the terrace that Jack had spent the winter months constructing. For once, Jack was wearing shorts, but as usual, apart from a sun visor, Helen didn't have a stitch on.

'Hi there,' Helen said when she saw Jessica. 'You look like you could do with something to drink.'

Jessica flopped on to a nearby chair and fanned herself with her hand. 'Please,' she said, lifting off her sun-glasses and wiping the sweat from her face, 'a keg of water should just about do it, along with the same quantity of ice that sank the *Titanic*.'

Helen laughed, which had the effect of making her large tanned breasts wobble. Jessica had always been fascinated by Helen's body: splendidly Rubensesque and the colour of terracotta, its voluptuous form contrasted with her own, which was a rather straight-up-and-down affair with just a hint of a bump here and there, had made her feel slightly less of a woman than her friend. Before Helen and Jack had made their home here on the island Helen had dressed in what she herself described as mumsy chain-store separates. Looking at her now, it was difficult to imagine that such a sensual, generous body could ever be restrained by anything so criminally dull. Helen's body was made for being on show and these days she chose to do exactly that, and proudly. She'd told Jessica how when she and Jack had arrived and they'd first stripped off their inhibited Englishness, Jack had been in a permanent state of arousal, which Helen had further boasted had done wonders for their sex life, which she said had begun to run out of steam back in Huddersfield.

'You just never learn, do you?' Helen said. 'How many years have you lived here and you still go rushing about in the heat of the day when any sensible-minded person does little more than open a bottle of wine.'

'Not sure we've got any icebergs lurking in the freezer, Jessica,' Jack said, getting to his feet, 'but I'll see what I can rustle up for you.'

Jessica watched Jack go inside and not for the first time wondered what his ex-work colleagues from the bank in Huddersfield would make of his current life-style.

Forty-eight-year-old finance managers didn't normally go in for such bohemian mores, but when Jack and Helen had come to Corfu on holiday three years ago they had returned home to Huddersfield after two weeks of bliss and decided that their lives were no longer suited to the confines of a nine-to-five existence on a smart housing estate on the edge of town. Jack had told Jessica how one morning, with his resignation neatly typed up, he had gone in to work ready to end twenty years of company loyalty and to discuss the effect this decision would have on his pension. What he hadn't been prepared for was a generous redundancy package being solicitously offered across his boss's desk. He immediately feigned disappointment and desk-thumping outrage at such treatment, then rushed to the staff toilets to dispose of his resignation.

They quickly sold their executive five-bedroomed house and moved to Corfu, and with Jack's redundancy money they bought a couple of tiny villas; one to live in and the other to rent out to tourists. And to go the whole hog, Helen rekindled an old hobby from her pre-teaching days and started painting. She now sold tasteful water-colours of the surrounding area to the very same kind of holiday-maker she had once been. Jessica affectionately called them the Tom and Barbara Good of Corfu.

'Do you think you'll ever leave here?' Jessica suddenly asked Helen.

Helen looked at her. 'What an absurd question. Are you feeling okay?'

Jack joined them on the terrace, carrying a tray of drinks. He handed Jessica a large beer mug of water with several cubes of ice, as well as another glass which contained white wine. He passed a glass of wine to his wife, who said, 'Jessica's just asked me the strangest of questions. Go on, Jessica, ask Jack and see what kind of response you get from him.'

'Fire away,' Jack said, settling himself in his deck-chair.

Jessica smiled. 'I only asked if you could ever see yourselves leaving the island.'

'It's a possibility, but only to go somewhere equally perfect.' Jack stared at Jessica. 'So what's the deal? Why the question?'

Jessica drained her beer mug of water and let a few ice cubes slip into her mouth. She crunched on them noisily.

'Well,' Helen said, 'like Jack says, what's the deal?'

'Not much, it's just that I've come to say goodbye.'

'Goodbye?' Helen and Jack looked at each other, horrified. 'What do you mean?' they said together.

'I'm going back to England.'

Helen sat up aghast. She leant forwards, her legs akimbo, completely oblivious to her nakedness.

'A-hem,' Jack said, raising his eyebrows, 'you're showing your sexy bits, Helen.'

Jessica smiled, amused that Jack hadn't lost all of his nine-to-five conventions.

Helen tutted and to please Jack slapped her legs together. 'Why, Jessica?' she asked. 'I don't understand it. It's paradise here.'

'I know,' Jessica said, 'but I think that's part of the problem. It's all too easy living as we do. It's as if we're all caught up in this wonderful balloon of a life that encapsulates the very best of everything we could ever want and . . . and I've got the feeling my own particular balloon of perfection has burst.'

Helen looked confused. 'I'm not sure I understand. What's wrong with enjoying ourselves?'

'Nothing . . . so long as it feels right.'

'And it doesn't feel right for you any more?'

Jessica turned to Jack and shook her head. 'Not any more, no. It's not enough.'

'How much paradise do you want, for heaven's sake?' cried Helen.

'I don't think it's paradise I'm searching for. Perhaps it's the opposite. I feel like I haven't earned myself a proper slot in life yet.'

'Oh, my fathers, you're not on some kind of guilt trip, are you? Don't tell me you're about to embark on some personal crusade of masochistic pleasure. You've had it too good and now it's time for a bit of punishment, is that what you're after? A hair shirt and a steady job?'

'Helen,' warned Jack, 'stop trivialising what Jessica's got to say.'

'I'm not,' she said crossly.

Jessica suddenly laughed. 'Stop it, you two. And Helen, for goodness sake stop looking so thoroughly indignant, it doesn't suit that wonderful body of yours.'

'So come on, Jessica,' Jack said, 'why the Shirley Valentine in reverse? What's brought it on?'

'I'm not sure I can explain it to you. All I know is that I no longer feel a part of life here. I don't feel I belong.'

'What does Gavin have to say?' Helen asked.

'Er ... he doesn't know I'm going.'

'What?'

'When are you leaving?' asked Jack.

'Tonight.'

'*What!*'

'Helen, will you stop saying *what* all the time.'

'Listen, Jack, I'll say what as many times as it takes to talk some sense into this girl. She can't go, she simply can't.'

Jessica said goodbye and left her friends to carry on their bickering. She took the steep path down to the beach, untied her boat, started up the engine and headed towards Kassiopi where she hoped her next round of farewells wouldn't be quite so interrogative.

When she reached the busy harbour, with its myriad fishing boats jostling for position with the many caiques waiting to take tourists for a trip along the coast, she made her way to Costas's restaurant and decided that, to be on the safe side, she would simply tell him and his family that she was returning to England to look after her mother. A Greek man like Costas would understand all about family duty and responsibility.

Costas hugged her warmly when he saw her. He kissed her many times over and slipped his arms around her waist. He took her to the back of the restaurant away from all his customers. He kissed her again and asked her in one breath how she was, how her writing was going and when was she going to get around to casting him as her next romantic hero? His English was perfect, if slightly Americanised, having been learnt while working in Chicago in a restaurant owned by one of his many cousins. He called through to the kitchen at the back of the restaurant. Instantly his mother appeared through the beaded curtain and shuffling behind her came an even older woman, Costas's grandmother. The two women beamed at Jessica. They were very fond of her, especially as she had immortalised them both in the opening chapter of her first novel which had been set in Corfu. They spoke hardly any English and even though Jessica could speak passable Greek, Costas always insisted that she spoke in English so that he could practise his interpreting skills. Jessica suspected it was because he liked to show off in front of his womenfolk.

'I can't stay long,' she said, refusing his offer of a drink and a plate or two of mezéthes, 'I've just come to say goodbye.'

'Goodbye?' he repeated, 'why?'

'I'm going back to England.'

Costas forgot all about translating for his mother and grandmother. They waited patiently for him to speak to them. But he didn't. 'For good?' was all he said to Jessica.

She nodded. 'I think so.'

He smiled.

'You don't seem surprised.'

'I'm not. I've seen it many times before. For visitors to the island its magic only lasts for so long.'

Jessica kissed him.

'What's that for?' he asked.

'For being the first to understand. Thank you.'

After leaving Costas and his family Jessica walked along the crowded harbour and crossed the square to Dimitrios, the owner of her house who, with his wife Anastasia, ran a noisy bar that unashamedly pandered to the needs of a particular type of English tourist. They served up steak and kidney pudding with mushy peas, even in August when the heat could be in the high nineties, and in the evenings they didn't bother playing bouzouki music, but showed videos of *Fawlty Towers* and *Men Behaving Badly* to amuse their customers over their beers.

Jessica chatted for a while with Dimitrios – unfortunately Anastasia was out visiting her mother – then handed him her spare set of keys to her house. She signed the necessary forms and returned to her boat.

When she finally reached Coyevinas she found Gavin waiting for her on the sun terrace.

Having said goodbye to her closest friends and dealt with the formalities of relinquishing her home, Jessica was already mentally flying back to England, ready to start her future.

But here was Gavin. Here was the present.

And just one look at him was enough to make her undo all her well-made plans.

He was leaning lazily against the wall, looking down at her as she approached the last few steps. His shoulder-length, sun-bleached hair was blowing in the afternoon sea breeze that had just started to pick up and his white T-shirt was rippling across his chest. She couldn't make out the expression on his face because he was wearing his favourite Ray-Bans, but she had the feeling that he had been waiting for her for some time and that he must have seen her little boat appear round the rocky promontory from Kassiopi and that he must also have watched her climb the steep hill path. She wondered what had brought him here at this time of day when normally he would be out teaching tourists to sail before the sea became too rough.

'Why aren't you working?' she asked, going straight inside the house.

'Pete's covering for me,' he said, following behind her and pushing his glasses up over his head.

'Why?' She frowned. *Why* was a word she'd heard too often today.

'Helen phoned me.'

'Oh.'

'What were you going to do, Jessica, write me a letter?'

She thought of the envelope in her bag. 'I'm sorry,' she said guiltily.

'No you're not.' His face took on an expression of bewilderment and reduced him to the hurt boy she had predicted.

'And are *you*?' she asked. 'Are you sorry I'm going, or are you just put out, a little inconvenienced perhaps?'

He didn't answer her. 'Helen didn't seem very clear about your reasons for leaving.'

Jessica smiled. 'She wouldn't be, she's too busy being punch drunk on Ionian nectar.'

Her metaphor was lost on him. He frowned and came towards her. 'Are you okay?'

'I think so,' she said, suddenly aware of the warmth of his body next to hers. She held her breath, knowing that if she breathed in the smell of him she would be caught in his spell and be reminded of all the pleasures soon to be denied her.

'Is it me? Is that why you're going?'

His arrogance gave her the strength she needed. How typical that he should think the world revolved around him. She took a step back from him and went outside to the terrace. He followed her and to the sound of the cicadas chirruping noisily in the nearby olive trees they both stood gazing at the sea and the shimmering outline of Albania where so much needless fighting had recently taken place.

'Your sleeping with other women did hurt me at first,' she said, determined to be honest with Gavin, but equally so that her last memory of him wouldn't be an acrimonious one. 'But then I began to realise that it wasn't our relationship that was bothering me. It was something much more significant. I woke up to the fact that there's nothing here for me any more.'

'Not even me?'

Still that arrogance! 'No, Gavin, not even you. Besides, there are plenty of other women for you, you don't need me. And I'm afraid that's something I want, I want somebody to need me.'

'Like your mother?'

She smiled. 'How perceptive of you ... and how very out of character.'

He shrugged. 'All things to all men, that's me.'

'Don't you mean all things to all women?'

He had the grace to turn away.

'By the way,' she said, sensing that their conversation was coming to an end, 'I know you don't approve of boats with engines, but you can have mine anyway. Do with it what you want.'

'Thanks.' He placed his hands on her shoulders and kissed her. 'Good luck, Jessica, I hope you find what you're looking for. Do you want a lift to the airport?'

6

Alec thought of ringing Kate to let her know that he was on his way, but he was in such a hurry to see her he didn't want to do anything that might slow him down, so he locked up the office, threw his briefcase into the rear of his Saab 900, pushed back the soft top and headed for home along the A34 going south.

It was strange not to be driving in a northerly direction on this familiar stretch of road – through Alderley Edge, then on to Wilmslow – as he'd done for as long as he could remember, but he guessed that his new route home would soon become second nature to him. He passed Capesthorne Hall on his right with its extraordinary turreted façade and toyed with the idea of getting tickets for him and Kate for the open-air summer concert that would be held there next month. Thinking of Kate again made him want to get home even faster and he pressed down on the accelerator.

He wondered if he'd ever lose this feeling of euphoria every time he thought of her. He still couldn't believe his good fortune, that a girl like Kate would even be interested in him, let alone love him.

But then so much had happened to him that he was convinced that no matter how predictable one thought one's life was, it was anything but. He for one had never imagined he would end up running such a successful greetings card company.

Neither had he ever considered ending up a divorcé.

While he would admit that his marriage with Melissa had never been perfect, he had thought that there had been enough common ground between them – namely their daughter and the jointly owned business – to keep them together no matter what. There had been the usual conflicts that life bestowed so generously on any married couple, especially a couple who lived and worked together, but he had accepted the arguments and irritations as all part and parcel of marriage. Looking back on it, perhaps he had been too passive, too inclined to remember his vows of *for better or for worse* and had simply gone along with things. But in the end Melissa had not. Melissa had seen fit to give up on what she referred to as a bad job. She had likened their marriage to a rather tedious book that one is told to read because it's a classic and never mind the boring bits, one must stick with it and see it through. Rather graphically, she'd told him that she had grown tired of wading through the same book, she wanted something new to read. 'There isn't anybody else,' she'd told him, as if this would make him feel better, 'I just don't want to be married to you any more.' Her pragmatic approach, he realised later, had at least made them both behave in a civilised manner throughout the divorce.

Initially, though, shock had rendered him unable to comprehend a life without Melissa when, one wet, miserable November evening she had moved out of their house in Wilmslow. 'I shan't be one of those grasping women,' she'd told him in the office the following morning. 'I shall just expect what is currently mine: half of the house, half of the savings and half of the business. Here's the name of my solicitor.'

That was the thing about Melissa, she was very businesslike, very organised and very together. Nothing fazed her.

No. That wasn't quite true. He had seen Melissa floored once, completely so. It was last Christmas when she'd first set eyes on Kate.

He'd heard the intake of breath, as well as the comment that followed. 'Pretty enough wrapping,' she'd whispered to their daughter Ruth, 'but is there anything worthwhile beneath those liquid eyes and the bewitching smile?'

He smiled, turned off the main road and drove through the avenue of chestnut trees towards Cholmford Hall Mews. 'Oh yes, Melissa,' he said out loud, a triumphant note to his voice, 'there's something more worthwhile than you'll ever know.'

He parked the car in front of the house and through the kitchen window that faced the courtyard he caught sight of Kate. She must have just taken a shower for he could see that she was wearing her white towelling bathrobe and had a towel wrapped around her head.

He let himself in and placing his briefcase at the foot of the stairs in the hall he called out jokingly in true Hollywood style, 'Hi, honey, I'm home.'

She came and wrapped her arms around him. 'So you are.'

He held her tightly, pressed her slight body against his own and kissed her slender neck. He breathed in the perfume of her fragrant skin. 'You smell wonderful.'

'So does supper, I hope. It's nearly ready.'

He kissed her and began loosening her bathrobe. 'Can it wait?'

'Can you?'

He pulled the towel away from her head and let her wet hair fall to her waist. 'No,' he said and took her upstairs.

Later, when they sat down to eat, Alec poured out some wine and handed

Kate a glass. 'A toast,' he said, 'to our first proper meal in our very own home.'

They chinked their glasses and smiled happily at each other in the candle-light.

'You don't mind eating in the kitchen, do you?' Kate asked. She had hoped to have had the dining-room sorted out in time, but in the end she had been too exhausted to start unpacking all of Alec's cut glass and china. Even so, she had gone to great lengths to make everything just right for them in the kitchen, setting the table perfectly for a romantic supper; napkins, scented candles, even a few flowers taken from Alec's bouquet.

'Of course I don't mind.' He laughed. 'This is wonderful. I don't know how you managed to get so much done today and cook a meal. The house looks fantastic. You're a marvel, you are, really.' He leant over and kissed her.

'So what was your day like?' she asked, basking in his praise.

'Busy. We've got trouble in the warehouse down in Oxford. I shall probably have to go and take a look some time in the next few weeks.'

'Can't Melissa go?' Kate knew it was silly, but she didn't want Alec going down to Oxford, not if it meant he might spend the night away from her.

'She could, but I'd rather do it myself. Why don't you come with me?'

'Are you sure?'

'Of course I am. We could stop the night in a nice hotel. It would give you a break from all the hard work you're putting in here.'

'I wouldn't be in the way?'

'Not at all. I'd much prefer it if you came. And besides, expensive hotel rooms have an aphrodisiac charm all of their own.'

She smiled. 'My own charm wearing thin already?'

He covered her hand with his. 'Not in a million years.'

Amanda tipped the remains of Tony's uneaten supper into the bin. Another disastrous evening was behind them. If only Tony didn't always give in to Hattie. Surely he could see that the child had him tightly wrapped around her little finger? How many bedtime stories did it take, for heaven's sake?

She went back into the sitting-room, switched on the television and began sorting out the swatches of fabric and wallpaper samples that she had collected over the past week. She really had to decide what colour scheme to have in the sitting-room. She was fed up with not having any curtains.

Upstairs in Hattie's bedroom Tony was sitting on the floor alongside his daughter. They were leaning against her bed looking at a book all about dolphins, which they'd bought on their holiday in America last year when they'd visited Sea World in Orlando.

31

'Do you remember when we were all splashed by that huge whale?' Hattie asked her father.

He smiled, remembering the holiday with fondness, not because it was supposed to have been his honeymoon with Amanda, but because it had brought his daughter such pleasure. 'Yes, we were drenched good and proper, weren't we?' He drew her closer to him.

'And then the whale came round the pool a second time and splashed us some more. Can we go again?'

Tony closed the book and placed it on Hattie's bedside table next to a framed photograph of her mother. 'Come on,' he said, 'time your pretty little head was on the pillow.'

Hattie reluctantly climbed into bed. Tony covered her with the white frilled duvet.

'So can we go again?' Hattie asked, looking up at him, her arms outstretched, waiting for a final hug.

'We'll have to see,' he said. He leant down and kissed her soft cheek. She quickly reached out to him and held on to his neck and pulled him down so that he ended up lying beside her.

'We went to see the new lady who moved in yesterday,' she said, hoping to keep her father's attention for a little longer.

'And is she nice?' he asked.

'Very nice. She's got lovely hair. It goes all the way down her back.'

'I'll look out for her. Now you really should go to sleep.' He kissed her again and made his escape.

He turned out the light and went downstairs, his head aching with tiredness. He was exhausted. He'd been up since five that morning and on the road by half past in order to see a customer in Reading for nine o'clock. The meeting had gone on until two, then he'd driven to Birmingham for another appointment. He'd finally reached home just after eight, only to find Amanda cross and out of sorts because Hattie had played her up over tea.

'Fancy a drink?' he said, when he found Amanda in the sitting-room watching the television.

'I'll make us some coffee, shall I?' she said, rising from the sofa.

He shook his head. 'I need something stronger.'

'There's some wine in the fridge. I'll get that.'

He collapsed on to the sofa, pushed aside the mess on the coffee table in front of him and put his feet up. He closed his eyes to some poor devil of a politician having his bones picked clean by a predatory Jeremy Paxman and tried hard not to think of what lay ahead after the weekend when he had an all-day meeting with one of the company bigwigs who was flying over from the States to determine the effectiveness of their UK office. 'Nothing to worry about, Tony,' Bradley Hurst had said on the phone yesterday morning, 'I want you to know that Arc is deeply invested in the UK. All I want to do is simply have ourselves a head-to-head to clarify our position.' The last time their position had been clarified by Bradley-Dewhurst-the-Butcher's-Boy, as all the sales guys in the office referred to the recently appointed vice-president of Arc Computers, their numbers had been dramatically reduced. As director of sales in the UK, Tony was only too aware that no matter how well the figures looked they would always be vulnerable to another attack from Bradley Hurst. The man was ruthless and probably went to bed at night chanting his own personal mantra – one employee less equals a dollar saved; two employees less equals two dollars saved; three employees less ... It was a short-sighted way to run a company and long term it couldn't work.

When Amanda came back into the room with a bottle of wine and two glasses she found her carefully ordered wallpaper and fabric samples scattered all over the floor and Tony fast asleep. 'Happy bloody families,' she muttered to herself.

The flight had been delayed by nearly an hour and Jessica hoped her mother wouldn't be worrying. She had tried ringing from the airport at Corfu to warn her that she'd be late, but she hadn't been able to raise an answer. She had tried again when she'd landed at Manchester, but still there was no reply from Willow Cottage. She had fought against the rapidly forming image in her mind of her mother lying prostrate on the floor, her hand inches away from the phone. Instead, she had forced herself to picture her mother doing some late-night weeding in her immaculate garden, happily ignorant of the time or of the ringing telephone inside the house.

Now, as she sat in the back of a taxi driving at a snail's pace through the dark Cheshire countryside and with only a few minutes to go before her journey would be completed, Jessica chided herself for her stupidity. Her mother had managed just fine all these years without having anyone fretting over her, especially the kind of fretting that was turning her daughter into a neurotic idiot.

Idiot had been the word that Helen had used so vociferously at the airport when she and Jack had seen her off. Gavin had offered to come as well when she'd told him that Jack was driving her to the airport, but she had said she'd rather he didn't. 'Tears and sentiment would do me no good at this stage,' she'd told him.

There had been no danger of tears or sentiment with Helen, though. She was still cross with Jessica for leaving. 'You're an idiot, Jessica. A complete idiot. But mark my words, when you've been back in England for a few months you'll wonder what you've done.'

'You're probably right,' Jessica had said, 'but I'm going anyway.'

'And another thing,' Helen had gone on, 'why didn't you tell us what you were up to?'

'Because you would have tried to stop me.'

And that was the truth. She knew she'd hurt Helen and Jack with her secrecy, but she couldn't have taken the risk of letting them know what was in her mind. If she'd told them that on her last visit to England, when her mother had gone into hospital, she'd seen a house that she was considering buying they would have gone out of their way to dissuade her.

'Been on holiday, then?' the taxi driver asked, opening his mouth to speak for the first time.

'Yes,' she said, not wanting to explain yet again why she was returning to England. The pair of chatty young lads sitting next to her on the plane, with their scalped heads, noserings and sunburnt faces and bulging carrier bags of duty free, had been at a loss to understand why she didn't want to live in Corfu for the rest of her life. 'Give me a life of sun, sex and ouzo any day,' one of them had said.

'Somewhere hot and nice?' the driver asked her.

'Very hot and very nice,' she said truthfully.

'Ah well, it'll be back to normal and the real world now, won't it? That's the thing about holidays, there's nothing lasting about them, just a few out-of-focus photographs.'

Too tired to add anything of any worth to the conversation, Jessica let the man ramble on with his personal philosophy and anxiously watched the road. Now that the driver had opened up the floodgates of dialogue he seemed to have lost interest in keeping his eyes on the dark, narrow lanes and kept turning round to emphasise a point to her.

'You'll have to slow down here,' she said, suddenly leaning forward in her seat, 'there's a small bridge and almost immediately there'll be a turning to the left. That's it.'

In the clear moonlit sky Willow Cottage looked enchanting with its white rendered walls almost hidden beneath a swathe of sweet-smelling blooms from several ancient climbing roses, as well as a clematis that had competed for space over the porch. It was exactly how Jessica always pictured the house in which she'd grown up. Her own life might have taken a few twists and turns, but Willow Cottage had not.

The taxi driver was impressed. 'If I lived here I wouldn't need to go on holiday.'

Jessica waited impatiently for the man to amble his way round to the boot for her things. Come on, come on, she muttered to herself. 'How much do I owe you?' she asked, when finally a collection of overstuffed holdalls was gathered around her feet.

'Call it twenty-four.'

I'd sooner call it highway robbery, Jessica thought as she watched the red tail-lights of the car disappear. She looked up at the house and wondered why her mother hadn't already come to the door.

No! she told herself. Keep that writer's brain firmly under control, your mother is not lying dead on the Axminster!

She tried the doorbell, but got no response. In the end she let herself in with the key that was kept hidden beneath a large stone that Anna had brought back with her in her hand luggage after one of her stays in Corfu.

She found her mother upstairs in the spare room; it was stripped of all its furniture and old flannelette sheets covered the floor. Anna was standing on the top rung of a pair of step-ladders, a paintbrush in one hand and a pot of undercoat in the other; beneath her, a ghetto blaster was blaring out *The Three Tenors* and Pavarotti was 'Nessun dorma'-ing.

Jessica went over to Pavarotti and turned him down. Her mother suddenly caught sight of her and visibly jumped out of her skin. She gave a loud scream. 'What are you trying to do, Jessica, creeping up on me like that? You frightened me to death.'

'I'm sorry,' Jessica said, immediately horrified at what she'd done – *good grief, she could have killed her mother with shock!* 'I should have thought. I'm sorry. Are you okay? Do you need to sit down?'

'I'm fine,' Anna said irritably. She came down the step-ladder and put the pot of paint on a piece of newspaper. She then looked up at her daughter and, seeing the distress in her face, thought, poor Jessica, how fragile she thinks I've become. 'It'll take more than a little bit of shock to finish me off,' she said more good-humouredly. 'Now let me put this brush in a jar of white spirit, then I'll make us a drink. How was your flight? Oh, and by the way, welcome home.'

7

It was a difficult weekend for both Jessica and Anna. Jessica spent most of it hovering anxiously over her mother, watching her every move. In turn, Anna took every possible opportunity of trying to escape her daughter's infernal gaze.

'Should you be doing that?' was Jessica's automatic response to almost anything Anna did. She said it when she found her in the spare room finishing off the undercoating to the picture rail that she had started while waiting for Jessica to arrive the night before. She said it again when she found her mother standing on a chair in the downstairs loo, changing a light bulb.

'Look, Jessica,' Anna said, 'this can't go on.'

'You're right. It can't. Now get down from that chair and let me do that.'

By Sunday afternoon the strain was really telling. Jessica found Anna struggling with a heavily loaded wheelbarrow in the garden. 'What on earth do you think you're doing?' she cried out, running across the lawn to her mother. 'You have Dermot twice a week to help you in the garden. Leave him to do the heavy work.'

'This is not heavy work. Now kindly leave me alone,' Anna said, gripping the handles of the wheelbarrow through her tattered gardening gloves and doing her best not to lose her temper. 'Go and do something useful. Go for a walk. Go and look at your new house. Anything. So long as you leave me to dig in this manure in peace.' She then pointedly turned up the volume on the Walkman that she had strapped around her waist and staggered further down the garden listening to a piece of Chopin, which Jessica could hear tinkling through the headphones.

Jessica stood and watched her mother angrily tossing fork-loads of manure on to the rose beds and, realising that her own anger needed to be assuaged, decided to go for a walk. She stamped off across the lawn towards the front of the house and to the willow trees either side of the brick steps that led down to the canal.

At first she marched furiously along the tow-path, snatching out at long blades of grass and swishing them against the undergrowth of dock leaves and buttercups, at the same time mentally shouting at her mother for her stubbornness and her stupidity, but gradually the calming effect of the canal worked its magic on her and she felt herself beginning to think more rationally.

It had been the same when she'd been a teenager. The canal had been the perfect place of refuge after she'd argued with Anna over something as trivial as the colour of her hair or the skimpiness of her clothes. They'd shout at one another, each convinced the other was wrong, then she'd race out of the house in a fit of adolescent angst and make for the tow-path. But always by the time she'd even reached the first sweeping curve in the waterway and her favourite tree, her temper would have fizzled out and she would lean against the sycamore and wonder what all the fuss had been about.

She reached the sycamore tree now and as she leant against its huge trunk, a pretty red-and-green-painted narrow boat came into view. Its occupants smiled and nodded at her. She smiled back and watched them slowly chug on with their journey.

Her anger and frustration now gone, she admitted to herself that it was obvious she would have to move into Cholmford Hall Mews sooner than she had originally planned. The idea had been for her to stay for over a week at Willow Cottage, then move into her new home, but even a weekend was turning out to be too nerve-racking an ordeal for them. She suspected that her mother was trying to prove a point with all her displays of independence and that it was merely a device for marking out the territory that belonged to Anna, which she clearly wished to retain.

With this in mind, the first thing Jessica did the next day, Monday morning, was to phone the sales negotiator in the show house at Cholmford Hall Mews. 'I know I said it would be the following week I'd move in and we'd agreed that you needed the show house for as long as possible, but is there any chance I could arrive sooner?'

'You're in luck. We've finished work on number three and we're going to use that as an impromptu show house. It's not a patch on this one, but at least it'll be somewhere for me to sit. I'm actually in the process of moving my stuff across at the moment. I should be finished by this afternoon. I don't see why you couldn't move in tomorrow if you can get your solicitor to arrange for completion to take place by then. Everything's ready for you, the carpets were cleaned on Saturday and the furniture not included in the sale has been shifted across to number three. Do you want to come and check anything?'

Jessica's first reaction was to say no, but then, thinking that it would do her and her mother good to have a break from each other, she said, 'Yes, I'll come down later, about two.'

She phoned her solicitor who said he'd arrange everything in time and after lunch she set off for Cholmford Hall Mews, which was little more than a mile away from Willow Cottage.

The day was warm and sunny, and as Jessica strolled along the lane and entered the cool tunnel of chestnut trees she found herself remembering all the times she'd played here as a child. With her mother's help she had even learnt to ride a bike properly on this flat stretch of road. Anna had never tired of telling the story of the day when Jessica had demanded that the stabilisers be removed from her bicycle. This act of 'big girlness' had meant that her poor mother had had to spend hours running alongside her, one hand on the saddle, the other nudging the handlebars whenever Jessica starting going too fast and out of control.

'Let go, let go,' she had screamed at Anna. 'I can do it, take your hand away.' And of course, the first time Anna had let go, Jessica had tumbled straight off the little bike and had ended up in a heap, with two grazed knees and a blow to her pride.

Jessica smiled to herself, thinking that her mother would probably view her as no better now than that skinny, demanding, four-and-a-half-year-old.

When she'd been that horrible child, Cholmford Hall Mews had been nothing but a sad, derelict stable block – the only surviving bricks and mortar from Cholmford Hall, which according to the local history books had originally been a grand shooting lodge. Just after the First World War the Hall was completely burnt down to its eighteenth-century foundations and for years after nobody saw fit to rebuild the house – the Cholmford family had long since run out of money. In the fifties the land was finally sold to a neighbouring farmer, who immediately cleared away the great pile of rubble and used the land for grazing. The stable block was then relegated to housing tractors and other assorted agricultural equipment and it wasn't until last year when a local building firm, on the look-out for a suitable conversion project, discovered the now thoroughly dilapidated barn and made an offer on it.

When Anna had first told Jessica about the development that was being built she had felt pangs of sorrow that her childhood haunt was to be spoiled and turned into a hideous eyesore. But then, when a few months later her mother had had her heart operation, Jessica had quickly made the decision to go and take a look at the building work. Far from spoiling the barn and the surrounding area, the builder had gone out of his way to create five good-sized homes of considerable quality that blended in perfectly with the incomparable setting. Jessica had come away impressed and within days had made up her mind to buy one of the houses. She didn't tell Anna straight away what she was doing – she needed the shock of her own actions to settle down before she could start explaining herself to her mother.

When Anna had been admitted to hospital, all Jessica had been able to think about was how much she loved her and what a happy childhood she had given her. Even her father's death when she was six years old had done nothing to dent the rosy picture she had of her formative years. She supposed it was because Anna had more than made up for the potential deficit in that area.

And now it was down to Jessica to make sure that her mother's love and kindness were returned.

Jessica moved in to Cholmford Hall Mews on Tuesday afternoon. Anna helped her. They were both the happier for it, knowing that the sooner Jessica was installed in her own home, away from Willow Cottage, the sooner they would start adapting to having each other around.

In terms of moving in there wasn't much to do. The only things that needed unpacking were the holdalls Jessica had arrived with from Corfu, along with several carrier bags of supermarket provisions and a bag of basic crockery borrowed from her mother for Jessica's empty kitchen. Between them they carried everything into the house from the boot of Anna's Fiesta parked outside in the gravelled courtyard.

'It's quite lavish, isn't it?' Anna remarked when everything was in and they'd closed the front door and she looked about the place.

'You said that the first time you saw it.'

'I know. I suppose I was hoping it might have calmed down a bit since then. It's all a bit chichi, don't you think?'

Jessica laughed. She knew exactly what her mother was getting at. The show-house-style furnishings and décor were not at all to her liking, but at the time she'd made her offer on the house it had made sense to Jessica to have everything all done – it was a bit like moving house the *Blue Peter* way; *and here's one I made earlier.*

'And those sofas will be a nightmare to keep clean,' Anna said, going over to inspect the two enormous cream sofas that were placed either side of the fireplace with a distressed-oak table between them. 'It's straight out of *Homes and Garden*. I'm not sure it's really you, Jessica.'

'What, you think I'd be better suited to something a bit more down-market? Some sawdust on the floor and a couple of barrels to sit on?'

'Don't be clever. I only meant it's hardly what you've been used to.'

'That's true enough. Come on, let's go upstairs, the bathrooms are quite something. You'll be green with envy.'

'Why do you need two bathrooms?' Anna said when she followed her daughter up the stairs.

'I don't,' Jessica said, opening a door at the top of the landing. 'It's what builders think people want nowadays. Now what do you think of that, it's the last word in des. res. luxury, isn't it?'

39

'Goodness, what a lot of edges and corners,' Anna said, peering in at the Wedgwood-blue bathroom with its white tiles and dado border decorated with Grecian urns. Opposite the bath and built around a low-level toilet and a pair of basins was a bank of cupboards and drawers. She went over and opened them all, one by one. 'What on earth will you keep in all these?' she asked.

'I've no idea. Old manuscripts, perhaps. Come and see my bathroom, it's even grander than this one. It looks over towards Mow Cop and the builders have set the cast-iron bath on a raised platform, so I'll be able to enjoy the view while having a soak.'

When they had finished inspecting the bathrooms and Anna had marvelled at the jacuzzi facility to Jessica's bath they went back downstairs. 'How about a cup of tea?' she suggested.

'Good idea, I'll put the kettle on. Oh, but I can't. I don't have one.'

'Oh, well, we'll go shopping later,' Anna said, forever practical, 'meanwhile I'll fill the teapot with water and boil it in the microwave.'

'What microwave?' Jessica asked, looking about the streamlined kitchen and seeing only a row of light-oak cupboards and a runway of spotless work surface.

Anna went over to the built-in cooker unit. 'This one,' she said. She pressed a button and a small door sprang open revealing the spotless interior of a microwave. 'You'll have to get yourself better acquainted with modern-day kitchen equipment, Jessica. I never did like that kitchen of yours in Corfu, it was so basic. The ancient Greeks were such a go-ahead lot, but I'm afraid their descendants are way behind in the white goods department these days. Ooh look, you're not the only one moving in today.'

They stood at the window and stared at a removal van as it rumbled its way into the courtyard and came to a stop outside number one. A few seconds later it was joined by a dark-blue Shogun. Anna and Jessica watched the driver get out. He was quite tall, with a slim build, and was dressed entirely in black – black T-shirt tucked into black jeans, a black denim jacket slung over his shoulder and black shoes with thick chunky soles. He started walking across the courtyard, his progress slightly hampered by a limp to his left leg.

'I do believe he's coming here,' Anna said as the figure in black drew nearer.

'I think you're right,' Jessica concurred, slipping out of view from the window. 'I wonder what he wants.'

They waited for him to ring the doorbell. But he didn't. To their amazement they heard him turn the door handle and suddenly he appeared in the kitchen.

'Keys,' was all he said. But then he looked about him and when he'd taken in the sight of Jessica's few possessions already making themselves at home on the breakfast bar his face coloured. 'Ah,' he said uncomfortably.

Jessica was a nanosecond ahead of him. 'This isn't the show house any more,' she said helpfully, 'it's number three you want.'

He looked at her as though he were going to speak and certainly Jessica could have sworn she saw his mouth open, but something must have made him change his mind, for he quickly turned and left.

'What a rude man,' Jessica said as they took up a discreet position in front of the kitchen window once more and watched him make his way over to the new show house. 'He didn't even have the manners to apologise for barging his way in here.'

'I thought he was rather dishy,' Anna said, 'in an awkward, boyish kind of way. He reminds me of that chap from *The X Files*, you know, the one with the lovely skin and the silly surname.'

'Oh, stop being so modern, Mum. Now come and show me how this blasted microwave works.'

Josh collected his keys from the woman in the show house, thankful that she'd been on the phone and had been unable to try and engage him in conversation. It was the last thing he needed right now. He hadn't been able to believe it when he'd woken this morning and found that today of all days, when he needed all his faculties to cope with the move, the power of speech was to be denied him. It was like that some mornings. He never knew what he would wake up to. Sometimes it was his hands that refused to work properly. Other days it could be his legs and this morning it had been his speech. He could form a sentence perfectly in his head, but when he actually said the words they came out all joined together like a string of sausages. It was so frustrating.

And so bloody demeaning.

He dreaded to think what those two women must have thought of him. Bad enough that he had barged his way into their house as he had, but even worse that he couldn't apologise for what he'd done.

He joined the removal men who were now all out of the van and were having a quick smoke before unloading his things. He let himself into the house. From his jacket pocket he pulled out a pen and a pad of yellow Post-its and on each page began writing: sitting-room, dining-room, study, kitchen and so on, until he had identified each room. He then went round the house sticking the appropriate piece of paper on each door. That way he hoped the men wouldn't have to keep asking him where everything had to go as each packing box had been appropriately labelled. He'd spent most of the day trying to keep himself to himself so as not to invite conversation, but there had been times when they'd been packing up at the flat when it had been impossible not to answer their questions. He'd tried his best to give them clear instructions, but he knew that they either had him down as a drunk, because his speech was so slurred, or worse, had concluded that he was a half-wit.

It was nearly seven o'clock when the removal men left Josh alone. He found the emergency box of supplies that he had packed himself – coffee, milk, tea-bags, biscuits, Mars bars, pain-killers and some Southern Comfort. He pulled out the bottle and without bothering to look for a glass he slowly climbed the stairs, taking each step with infinite care, steadying himself with his free hand against the white-painted banister. When he reached his bedroom he had to fight his way through the packing boxes to where his bed had been placed. It was exactly where he didn't want it. But no matter. He sat on the edge of it and took several large gulps of Southern Comfort. It burnt his throat and left a warm glow of apparent strength there. He knew he shouldn't drink, that the alcohol would make his co-ordination even worse, as well as slur his speech more than it already was, but he didn't care. He was exhausted and had no intention of talking to another soul that day. He planned to sleep for at least the next twelve hours. He drank some more, then tried screwing the lid on the bottle, but this simple task took all his concentration and when he'd managed it he dropped the bottle on the floor and collapsed back on to the bed.

He was asleep within seconds.

The phone rang an hour later. It wasn't easy to find as somebody – one of the removal men – had placed it under the bed. He eventually located it and fumbled with the receiver.

'Josh, it's Charlie. How's it going?'

'Iwasleep.'

'What? You're not very clear. Do you need a hand? I could come over if you want.'

'Sodoff!'

Josh banged the receiver down and lay on the bed. He tried to go back to sleep, but in spite of his exhaustion he knew he wouldn't be able to. He knew also that Charlie would ring again.

He was right. The phone rang almost at once.

'Sawry,' he managed to say.

'It's okay,' Charlie said, 'don't worry, is it a bad speech day?'

'Yess.'

'Do you need any help?'

Josh could hear that Charlie was suddenly emphasising his own clear diction, as if this would in some way help Josh's words come out right. He knew that Charlie couldn't help it, it was a knee-jerk reaction, like clearing your throat for somebody else. The last time they'd been in this situation Josh had felt angry and humiliated by Charlie talking to him as though he were a simpleton, but tonight he was too tired to feel anything.

'Josh, are you still there?'
'Yesss,' he said wearily.
'Are you very knackered?'
'Yesss.'
'Would you like some company?'
'No.'

8

Amanda wondered what on earth she was going to do.

Her mother was supposed to be baby-sitting for Hattie that evening and she had just rung to say that she couldn't make it. Tony would go mad. The relationship between the pair of them was bad enough without Rita further worsening the situation – one that had developed from the day she had taken Tony to meet her parents for the first time: the dreaded Sunday-lunch scenario – roast boyfriend and apple pie. Her mother didn't have a very high opinion of men and was never slow in publicly declaring them a species incapable of making a commitment. 'Commitment my foot,' she would often say, 'men don't know the meaning of the word. A piece of soggy loo roll has more staying power than a man.'

When she had uttered these familiar words in front of Tony he had laughed politely and asked where that left Amanda's father. 'You've been married for over thirty years, Amanda tells me, that's quite a commitment, wouldn't you say?' Since then Rita had viewed Tony with suspicion. She didn't like to be questioned.

Even on their wedding day, Rita had approached Amanda while she was slipping into her dress and suggested that it wasn't too late to change her mind.

'But I don't want to change my mind,' she had told her mother.

'Then maybe you should consider it. I'm not entirely sure you've thought this through. Is he really the right man for you? It's all been so quick.'

'A two-year engagement would be too quick for you, Mother. Now help me with my zip. And please don't worry, I know exactly what I'm doing.' Which was true, she was not the sort of woman to leave things to chance. Her mother might not realise it, but Tony was perfect for her.

She had thought that moving to Cholmford, where they would be only a few miles away from Rita, would perhaps ease the situation between the three of them. She had had visions of Rita becoming more involved with her and Tony, and especially with Hattie. She had seen her mother in the role of doting grandmother wanting to spend time with her newly acquired granddaughter. 'That's all right, Amanda,' she had imagined her mother saying, 'I'll take charge while you and Tony have some time to yourselves. A long weekend alone is just what you both need.'

She must have been crazy thinking that life could be that simple.

And what was she going to do about tonight? In an hour's time she was supposed to be having dinner with Tony and Bradley Hurst and his wife. It wasn't often that Tony discussed his work with her, but she knew that his all-day meeting with Hurst was an important one. She was aware, also, of the importance of tonight's little get-together and the part that she was expected to play. Which, if she was honest, she enjoyed. The role of corporate wife appealed to her. If she herself couldn't work, then making a career on the back of her husband's was quite possibly the next best thing. And it was another reason why she didn't want to lose this evening's opportunity of presenting herself and Tony as the perfect couple to Bradley Hurst. She quite fancied the trappings that came with Arc Computers, more important, she had her eye on the perks that came further up the organisation. Currently Tony was the UK sales director for Arc and while he seemed happy with his lot, she had other ideas. Who knows, if only Tony could show a bit more ambition, one day they might end up in America where the standard of living was so incredible.

But all this was pie in the sky. So much for being the force behind the successful husband, she couldn't even organise a baby-sitter for that evening. There just wasn't anybody to whom she could turn. Having moved here to the back of beyond where they didn't know a living soul, apart from Rita, there wasn't anyone to whom she could shout for help. Everyone they knew lived at least twenty-five miles away. It was hopeless. Well, there was nothing else for it but to ring Tony and explain. She would have to lie through her teeth and make out that her mother was, at the very least, at death's door. Which would probably bring a smile to Tony's face.

'When will Grandma Rita be here?' asked Hattie, coming into the bedroom where Amanda was staring out of the window. Hattie was all ready for bed, dressed in her Beauty and the Beast nightie and chewing on her toothbrush.

'She's not,' Amanda said flatly. 'She can't make it.'

Hattie sucked on her toothbrush. 'Does that mean you can't go out?'

Amanda moved away from the window. She went and sat in front of the dressing-table mirror and began taking out the heated rollers from her hair. 'Got it in one.'

Hattie came and stood next to her. 'Are you disappointed?'

Amanda stared back at Hattie in the mirror. 'Yes,' she said truthfully, 'yes I am, and I think your father's going to be more disappointed. In fact, I'd better ring him now while he's still at the office, before he leaves for the restaurant.'

45

'Isn't there anybody else who could baby-sit?' Hattie didn't like the idea of her father being upset.

Amanda took the last of the rollers out and shook her hair. She started brushing it. 'We don't know anybody else here, that's the problem.'

'We know Kate.'

Amanda stopped what she was doing. She thought of last Friday when the sickeningly *lovely* Kate had had Hattie eating out of her hand. She had certainly shown that she had a knack for dealing with small children, which was more than Amanda had, and she had come away after their visit consumed with jealousy that anyone could be that good with her stepdaughter. When they'd finished their cups of coffee Kate had let Hattie plunder several packing cases of books out in the hall and had even allowed her to play with her jewellery box – little more than a cheap trinket box as far as Amanda could see – which she had brought down from her bedroom. 'I'd be so grateful if you sort it out for me,' she'd said to a smiling Hattie, 'the move has made it all topsy-turvy. Do you think you could manage that?'

Amanda turned and faced Hattie. 'You're right,' she said, a glimmer of hope twinkling in the far distance, 'we do know Kate, but do you think she'd do it?'

'She might, she was very nice to me.'

The words 'to me' were not lost on Amanda. 'She's probably got plans for tonight already,' she said, brushing her hair once more. 'And anyway, what would your father say about somebody he doesn't know looking after you?'

Hattie kept quiet and carried on chewing her toothbrush.

Stupid question, thought Amanda, if there was one person who could convince Tony a bad idea was a good one it was Hattie. 'Okay,' she said, getting up from the padded stool and stepping into her black patent shoes. 'I'll go across and see Kate. It's worth a try.'

The taxi dropped Amanda off just outside the restaurant. She couldn't believe her luck that Kate had agreed only too readily to help out.

'Alec won't be home till late, so I'd be happy to look after Hattie,' she'd said. 'Let me write a note for him and I'll be over.'

Not being a child person herself, Amanda couldn't understand anyone being so keen to spend an evening cooped up with somebody else's offspring. But she was more than glad that there were people like Kate who were fool enough to do so.

She saw Tony attracting her attention from the far side of the busy restaurant and she weaved her way through the maze of tables to reach him. He kissed her cheek and introduced her to the Hursts. She had never met Bradley Hurst before and she was taken completely unawares by the sight of him. He was one of the best-looking men she had ever had the good fortune to meet. He was tall, very tall, with piercing, icy blue eyes behind a pair of rimless glasses and he had a head of thick blond hair that made him more Robert Redford – in his younger days – than the man himself; he also looked and smelt the very epitome of power and success. His wife complemented him exactly – she could have been straight out of *Murder One*, a smart-arse lawyer type, all suit, lipstick and shiny hair. They made a glamorous couple and in comparison Amanda felt like little wifey who'd forgotten to take off her pinny and slippers.

'So great to meet you,' Bradley said, up on his feet and clasping her hand in his, 'Tony's told us all about you. We even know your shoe size.' He laughed warmly and Amanda didn't doubt his words for a minute. She knew how Arc operated from the way Tony had to spend hours genning up on the people who worked for the company.

'Hi, I'm Errol,' the suit and lipstick said, now taking her turn to shake hands.

As in Flynn? Amanda wanted to ask, but she knew better than to question an American about his or her name.

They sat down and Amanda waited to see which way the conversation would go, now that she had arrived. Would there be the routine polite questions about her busy day as a stay-at-home mother? She hoped not. It was too tedious for words.

'Tony's been telling us about the new home you've just moved into,' Bradley opened up with. 'Sounds kinda interesting. A converted barn. Errol and I would just love something like that, out in New England perhaps. Connecticut would be great. Ever been to New England, Amanda?'

'No.'

'Sure thing? Tony, you'll have to fix that. Amanda would love New England, I just know it. It's the neatest place for a vacation.'

Tony made the appropriate response and retreated behind the head-nodding diplomacy he'd employed for most of that day. He'd like to fix Bradley-Dewhurst-the-Butcher's-Boy good and proper. How dare the man sit here in this bloody expensive restaurant telling him to take his wife on a lavish holiday to the States when he'd just informed him today that three of his best men would have to go. 'We're reshaping things as we head towards the millennium, Tony,' he'd started with first thing that morning, before Tony had even removed his jacket and sat down at his desk. 'We need to create a new vision, a new direction. It's all about concentrating the focus. You should see what we're doing back home, it's an exciting time for Arc. Tough, but exciting.'

Exciting for whom? Tony wanted to know. For the fortunate few who still had a job? And how the hell was he going to keep up morale in the office with everyone terrified about what would happen next? He'd be treated as a leper. He would become the enemy. Nobody would want to speak to him for fear that raising a head above the parapet would be reason enough to have it blown off.

Tony drove home listening to Amanda talking about how much she'd enjoyed the evening. 'You never told me what an interesting man that Bradley is.'

'I never told you that because he isn't.'

Amanda laughed. 'Nonsense.'

'I'm serious. The man's ruthless.'

'That's his business persona. If you're running a company like Arc you've got to be tough and stand up to people.' Secretly Amanda wished that Tony would show a bit more backbone. He'd been a right wet rag round the table during the meal, hardly opening his mouth, and when he did speak it was to come up with something as tactless as questioning Bradley's views on the state of the world's economy. Of course Bradley knew what he was talking about. As vice-president of Arc he was certainly better placed to understand these things than Tony.

'Now tell me about this woman who's looking after Hattie,' Tony said, breaking into her thoughts. 'You did leave a phone number with her, didn't you, just in case —'

'Don't worry. Of course I did. And believe me, there wouldn't have been a problem. I've never seen Hattie behave so well as she does with Kate. We should thank our lucky stars that we've got her living so close, she'll prove to be an absolute godsend, especially as your daughter seems to have fallen for her in such a big way.'

There were no lights on in the house upstairs when they reached home and when they let themselves in, all was quiet. Either Hattie was fast asleep or . . . or there was something wrong. Tony hurried through to the sitting-room, which was lit by a single lamp. When he saw Kate rise from the floor where she'd been sitting cross-legged reading a book in the soft light cast from the lamp behind her he could understand perfectly why Hattie had fallen for her. She was beautiful. Stunning.

And though the situation was completely different, he was reminded of the very first moment when he had met Hattie's mother Eve.

It had been love at first sight.

9

About an hour after leaving Tony and Amanda, Kate got into bed. She snuggled up close to Alec and laid her head in the crook of his arm. 'You didn't mind me not being here when you got home, did you?'

'Of course not,' he answered. 'What a silly question to ask.'

But Alec had minded, more than he cared to admit. He knew it was irrational, but when he'd let himself into the house and called out Kate's name and there'd been no response – only the message propped up by the microwave where his supper was waiting for him – he'd felt deflated and let down. Ever since their relationship had begun, and more particularly since Kate's job as a librarian had come to an end, he'd become used to her always being there for him when he came home from work.

Within weeks of meeting one another he had asked Kate to move in with him, to the cheerless house that he'd been renting after he and Melissa had sold what their solicitors had coldly referred to as *the matrimonial home* – he could have bought out Melissa's share in the property and stayed where he was, but he hadn't seen any point in remaining in the large family house, not when every room, every square inch of it, would remind him of the past. In what seemed no time at all after Kate had moved in with him the small, ugly house had undergone a magical transformation, it was suddenly alive and felt like a home; a proper home that was comfortable and inviting. It was as if Kate had bottled her unique, understated charm and liberally sprayed it around all the rooms. He realised very soon that the house had responded to Kate in exactly the same way that he had when she had saved him from a life that was leaden and interminably dull.

And it was that old life that he had been reminded of this evening when he had waited for Kate to come home. The empty house had dredged up memories of his being on his own after Melissa had left him. He had hated the long solitary evenings when all he'd had for company was the television and a meal for one on his lap. He had been wretched and depressed. Inevitably, it hadn't taken him long to slip into the bad habit of staying late at work, then going home for a liquid supper followed by an early night.

Melissa had been only too quick to point out that he was letting himself go. 'You're a mess, Alec,' she said one morning at work, when he'd turned up late and heavy-headed. 'And your clothes stink of whisky. Go home and change, and take a good look at yourself.'

Melissa had never believed in pulling her punches. But she had been right, as she so often was, and with more strength than he'd known he possessed he'd hauled himself out of the trough of despair and begun to think about his future. And while clearing up several months' worth of self-pitying squalor from around the house, including a bin liner of old newspapers, his eye had fallen upon the 'Encounters' page of the *Sunday Times*. Was this the answer? he'd asked himself as he'd run his finger over the numerous dating agency advertisements. In a moment of decisiveness he'd picked up the phone and rung one of the numbers. Afterwards he'd regretted what he'd done and had needed a large whisky to calm himself down. His sense of shame and embarrassment was enormous, that he, Alec McLaren, had sunk to such a pathetic point that he was prepared to meet a total stranger in the belief that somehow his life would be miraculously improved by such a meeting.

But it had been. And how!

Kate was his life. He never wanted to be apart from her, which was why he had been so miserable all on his own that evening.

Of course, he could have simply strolled across the courtyard and joined Kate at number two, but in a way he had wanted to test himself. Just how dependent on her was he?

'So tell me about your day,' Kate said, slipping over on to her side and looking into his face.

He kissed her forehead and held her close. 'Nothing special,' he said, 'though I managed to convince our friends at W. H. Smith to give us more shelf space later in the year. You wouldn't believe how tight the whole thing's becoming. Oh, and by the way, Ruth phoned.'

'What did she want?' – other than more money, Kate wanted to add, but she had promised herself that she would never criticise Alec's family, no matter how tempted she was. In her opinion, Alec's daughter was a spoilt brat; a spoilt ungrateful brat at that, who shamelessly used her father whenever she needed to.

A few months before, Ruth had told Alec that Adam's one-man-band architectural firm was going through a lean time. 'People are so miserly these days,' she had moaned to Alec over Sunday lunch, 'they just don't seem to understand that to invest in one of Adam's exclusive designs is the best investment they could ever make.'

Alec had dutifully helped out in the only way Ruth understood and had parted with a large amount of cash. 'It's only money,' he'd told Kate, when a few weeks later Ruth announced that she and Adam were leaving little

Oscar in the care of a child-minder and taking a holiday in St Lucia for a couple of weeks.

'She's after a favour,' Alec said, shifting his hand from Kate's neck and following the contour of her shoulder and then planting soft kisses on her throat.

'What kind of favour?' Kate asked nervously, raising Alec's head to her own. What on earth could Ruth want from *her*?

'I'll tell you in the morning.' He smiled and went back to kissing her.

When Tony awoke the next morning he found that Amanda's side of the bed was empty. He turned over and looked at the alarm clock. It was half past six. He closed his eyes, wishing the clock were wrong. Then he wondered where Amanda was. She was never up before him. 'You'll find I'm not a morning person,' she had told him the first night they'd slept together.

It was just one of the many little incompatibilities between them.

He pulled the duvet up over his head and wondered at the mess he had made of his life. He should never have married Amanda. Anyone could see they were wrong for each other. But then, how many other men in his position wouldn't have done the same?

Nothing could have prepared him for coping with the shock of Eve's death. One moment she had been on the telephone saying that she was just on her way to pick up Hattie from nursery and the next she was dead.

A freak accident.

A lorry with a man asleep at the wheel. It could have been anyone crushed to death on that wet, windy afternoon.

But it hadn't been anyone. It had been *his* wife. *His* Eve.

For months afterwards he'd gone around as if he too were dead. Nothing had made any sense any more. Even little Hattie had meant nothing but another problem for him to cope with. His work colleagues had helped as best they could by covering for him and continually making allowances. Friends, too, had played their part, but even the closest of them had gradually tired of the same sad story being replayed over and over.

In the end, and quite understandably, he had been left to stand on his own feet. Then he'd met Amanda at a party that his friends had insisted he went to. 'You've got to get out, Tony,' they'd repeatedly told him.

He'd given in, on the basis that after an hour he could leave if he wanted, and five minutes before his allotted time was up Amanda had walked into the kitchen where he'd been occupying himself arranging the magnetic letters on his hostess's fridge to form the words *I've had enough*.

'Enough of what?' she had asked.

If he'd been drunk he would have told her the truth, that he'd had enough of life, but because he was stone-cold sober, he'd said, 'Enough to eat.'

'Me too,' she'd said. 'Does Julie always force-feed her guests this way?'

'I wouldn't know. I've never been here before.'

'We've a lot in common then, me neither.'

Tony pushed back the duvet and thought that Amanda couldn't have been more wrong. They had nothing in common. He could see that so clearly now. He had married her because he had been a fool, a calculating fool to boot. He had seen her as a mother for Hattie, someone to organise his private life while he kept his professional one intact.

Poor Hattie, he thought as he got out of bed and went through to the bathroom for a shower. Poor, poor Hattie. He had thought he was doing the right thing in providing her with a mother, but the truth was he'd made things worse. He knew Hattie would never view Amanda as a proper mother and in a way he felt sorry for Amanda too. She was no Mary Poppins, but then neither was she Cruella De Vil. She was just Amanda, a woman who had made the mistake of getting herself involved with a man who still hadn't got over the death of his wife.

His first wife, he corrected himself. For better or for worse, Amanda was his wife now.

Downstairs in the kitchen Amanda was busy making breakfast. For a non-morning person she was feeling surprisingly cheerful. Her good mood was directly attributable to the previous evening. Late last night in bed, while Tony was asleep, she had made a few resolutions. From now on things were going to be different.

She had known all along that Tony had married her because he thought she would make his life easier. She had never deluded herself over the role she had been expected to play in his life and, more to the point, the role expected of her in Hattie's life. And that was fine, she liked nothing better than to know where she stood. But Tony had to be prepared to accept that as much as he was using her, she would use him. It was a fair bargain, in her opinion. If it was her job to take Hattie off Tony's hands, then in return it was only reasonable that his was to provide her with the life-style she wanted.

But after last night she had come to the conclusion that to get the best out of Tony – and ultimately the life-style she craved – she was going to have to work at their marriage a little harder than she'd originally imagined. She would have to appear to be giving him her unfailing support in everything that mattered to him – his daughter and his career.

It was listening to Bradley and Errol describing their 'honey pie' marriage that had made her reconsider her own. The gist of what they were saying was that if she were to shoulder the greater part of Tony's life, the more there would be for them to gain as a couple. 'I always treat Bradley's job as much mine as his,' Errol had said.

Amanda's initial response to such a comment was to scoff — only an American could have such a crass and idealistic view — but then she'd begun to wonder at what they were saying.

'Success is down to sharing the commitment of a career,' Bradley had said, 'I rely on Errol one hundred per cent. She's at home so that I can function at my best and be the success I am. Old-fashioned values keep it together, am I right, hon?'

'Absolutely,' Errol had said, 'I've had to make a few sacrifices here and there, but the rewards have certainly made up for anything I thought I'd lost.'

'And she's not just talking about the rewards of a perfectly cooked muffin.' Bradley had laughed.

Looking at the woman across the table in her smart-arsy suit, Amanda had found the image of Errol at home with a tray of blueberry muffins at the ready rather an unlikely picture.

'Brad's right,' Errol had said, 'I used to work as an attorney, but we soon found that we were pulling against each other and we just weren't getting anywhere. I suppose you could say we're centred on Brad now, we've invested my skills into his.'

'But hey, hon, you're talking to the converted. That's exactly what Tony and Amanda have done. Am I right, Amanda?'

The notion of centring herself on Tony had never before entered Amanda's head — what woman in the nineties *would ever* think of doing that?

In bed, she had asked herself the same question over and over — was it really possible that by turning herself into an Errol she could make Tony a power-hungry executive like Bradley? In the end she had decided that it was worth a try ... even if she did only pretend to be doing all that centring rubbish.

She scooped out Tony's egg from the pan of boiling water and took it to the table where she carefully placed it in the china egg-cup. Hearing footsteps on the stairs, she hurriedly poured out a cup of freshly made coffee.

Tony stood in the doorway amazed.

'Good-morning,' she said brightly, 'did you sleep well?'

He came over and continued to look amazed. He had never known Amanda to be up this early and he had certainly never heard her talk to him as though she were an air stewardess. 'It's not some kind of anniversary, is it?' he asked warily, looking at the table where he saw mats, napkins, glasses of orange juice, a pot of proper coffee and even a boiled egg. What was she up to?

She laughed and guided him to his chair. 'It's a celebration of sorts,' she said, 'it's the start of me getting my act together. Now tell me what you'd like for supper tonight.'

Supper! Good grief, it was as much as he could do to contemplate the egg in front of him. He knew he was being ungrateful, but more than anything he wished that Amanda were upstairs in bed as she usually was at this time of day, leaving him in peace with his normal hurried bowl of cereal while hovering over the sink looking out at the surrounding countryside with nothing but his own troubled thoughts for company.

Sinking into his chair and taking a fortifying sip of his coffee, he let his thoughts turn to last night. To that incredible moment when he'd first set eyes on Kate. She looked absolutely nothing like his first wife, but his whole body had responded in the same way as when he'd met Eve. His heart had jolted and his pulse had quickened, and as he'd crossed the room and held out his hand to her he had felt as though they'd met already. 'This was so good of you. I hope Hattie wasn't any trouble,' he'd said, holding on to her hand and not showing any sign of letting go of it.

'Not at all,' she'd answered, 'we chatted and then I read to her.'

'Let me guess. *The Secret Garden?*'

Kate had laughed. 'Yes, a few chapters, then we had *The Tale of Mrs Tiggy-Winkle.*'

Tony had been shocked. Not since Eve's death had Hattie let anyone read that book to her. She had loved the way her mother had read the story. Amanda had once tried it and Hattie had snatched the book out of her hands.

'We ought to thank Kate properly for last night,' he heard Amanda say.

He snapped out of his reverie. 'Yes,' he said, 'yes, you're right. How about some flowers?'

'Flowers,' Amanda repeated, her hand poised over the cafetiere to top up his coffee – flowers for a complete stranger, but rarely for her, she thought. 'We could do that, but I'm not sure it's the right thing to do,' she said slowly, thinking that Errol's marital professionalism would never allow her to stoop to anything as base or unworthy as jealousy. 'I know for a fact that her partner Alec has just bought her some.'

'Oh,' Tony said flatly. Partner. Alec. *Her partner.* He didn't want to hear words like that.

'I've got a much better idea,' Amanda carried on. 'Why don't we invite them for supper one evening, that way we can start being more neighbourly. Living out here and being so isolated it makes sense to build up a rapport with people whom we might need to rely on occasionally. What do you think?'

'Fine,' he said, pushing away his half-eaten egg. 'See what you can fix up.

I'd better get going. Bradley wanted to see me in the office early this morning before he heads off to the airport.'

'Oh, well, give him my best and tell him to stay longer next time so that we can see more of him and his lovely wife.'

Tony grimaced. The less he saw of Bradley-Dewhurst-the-Butcher's-Boy the better.

10

When Alec had left for work and Kate had finished the toast and marmalade that he had kindly brought upstairs on a tray for her, she thought about what they had discussed while Alec was getting dressed.

'You don't have to do it, if you don't want to,' he had said, 'you mustn't feel duty bound to accept because it's Ruth who's asked you.'

But Kate had known that she would accept Ruth's proposal. That it was irresistible. Looking after Oscar would be a delight. In fact, it was just what she needed until she had decided what she was going to do about getting another job.

She got dressed and went downstairs, and found that the postman had been. A scattering of assorted-sized envelopes lay on the carpet in the hall. She picked them up and carried the pile through to the kitchen where she switched on the radio and was met with a snappy John Humphrys berating some poor soul for being incompetent. She turned the dial until she found Terry Wogan being accused of the same crime by one of his loyal listeners and to the sound of the Irishman's mock outrage she began opening the mail. The envelopes were all addressed to *Mr Alec McLaren and Miss Kate Morris* and were cards wishing them well in their new home, except for one which was addressed to her only. It was from Caroline with whom she had shared a tiny terraced cottage in Knutsford before she'd moved in with Alec, and with whom she'd also worked for two years at the library.

'I've lost your new phone number, so have resorted to this – let's get together for an evening out.' Caroline had used a green felt-tip pen to scrawl her message on the inside page of the card and her writing was large and loopy – not unlike Caroline, Kate thought with a smile. The card itself was also typical Caroline and the picture showed an oil-smeared, bronzed, muscly man in the skimpiest of leopardskin swimming trunks and to one side of his bottom her friend had written, 'Now he's what I call a man!'

To say that Caroline was interested in men was a huge understatement. She was pretty much obsessed with the male species. 'I'm always hungry for a good man,' she would joke, 'the only trouble is most of them are like

56

a Big Mac, you have one and then a few hours later you're ready for another.'

No man ever stayed long in Caroline's life.

'I don't know what's wrong with men these days,' she would complain after the door of her love life had been slammed in her face yet again.

'You frighten them to death, that's what's wrong with them,' Kate had told her. 'Try not to be so pushy. Let them come up for air occasionally.'

'I'm only being me,' she would retort, 'I'll be damned if I'm going to pretend to be something I'm not.'

And if there was one quality about Caroline that Kate was in awe of it was her friend's incredible self-confidence and her implicit assumption that she was right and others were wrong. Whereas Kate had grown up believing it was she who was usually to blame for anything that went wrong and that it was her place to yield to those around her in order to make a situation work, Caroline was convinced of the opposite. The word sorry never appeared in her vocabulary, nor did the concept of being helpful, biddable or compliant ever occur to her, as her behaviour at the library showed only too plainly.

Caroline hated *the public*. She saw them as an unpleasant nuisance that got in the way of her carrying out her job as she roared about the shelves with a sense of urgency that frightened some of the more timid browsers who liked to while away their time quietly flicking through the papers and magazines. They certainly weren't up to being physically moved on when Caroline felt the need to tidy up the tables of paper-strewn reading matter. She didn't care that some of the braver users of the library called her the Gestapo behind her back.

Untidy customers Caroline could just about tolerate, but people who interrupted her and expected an answer to a daft question were the kind she had no time for. One afternoon an elderly pensioner had taken his life into his hands and had approached the desk where Caroline was hiding behind the computer reading the latest Penny Vincenzi and had asked, 'I wonder, have you got that book, you know the one all about life in a Cheshire village during the war?'

'How the hell should I know,' Caroline had snapped back. And seeing the poor man almost reduced to tears Kate had stepped in and taken him reassuringly by the arm to the selection of local history books.

Another time Caroline had caught a woman furtively eating a prawn and mayonnaise sandwich while reading a book in what she had thought was a quiet corner in among Travel and Careers. Unfortunately she had chosen a book that had made her laugh out loud and Caroline had pounced on her, not just for disturbing fellow library users, but for defacing council property by smearing page fifty-eight of *Caught in the Act* with a blob of mayonnaise.

Kate was just recalling the look of shock and bewilderment on the face of the woman when she remembered that *Caught in the Act* was one of Jessica Lloyd's novels.

Kate had noticed signs of their new neighbour moving in yesterday and she had badly wanted to pluck up the courage to go and knock on the door and introduce herself. Perhaps today she might.

But first she had to ring Ruth. She looked up at the clock – her Ikea station clock that her colleagues at the library had given her on her last day – and saw that it was nearly a quarter to nine. She went through to Alec's study and flipped through the address book to find Ruth's number. She pressed the buttons on the phone and prepared herself for a conversation with Ruth by taking several deep breaths. When the phone was picked up at the other end she was greeted with an explosion of noise. It sounded like an angry scene from a soap opera on the television, but Kate quickly realised that it was Ruth and Adam arguing. So who had answered the telephone?

'Hello,' she said cautiously.

'Hello,' said a small voice.

'Oscar, is that you?'

'Yes.'

'It's Kate.'

'Hello, I've just had my breakfast. I had a big bowl of Honey Pops.'

'Mm ... delicious, do you think I could speak to Mummy?'

'She hasn't had her breakfast and she's very cross with Daddy. He used all the milk.'

'I'm sorry to hear that, but can you tell her I'm on the phone?'

Kate listened to Oscar banging down the receiver on something hard, then strained her ear to catch him interrupting the shouting match that was still in full flow. She couldn't hear his gentle voice, but she caught Ruth's loud and clear.

'Who's on the phone? Well, why didn't you tell me, Oscar? Really, you can be so naughty at times. Kate, is that you?'

'Hello Ruth, I hope I haven't called at an awkward time.'

'It's always an awkward time in this house,' Ruth said bad-temperedly, 'it's called being married to a fool. Now has Dad put my proposal to you? He did explain that I want this done on a proper footing? I'll be paying you.'

'Yes, Alec did mention that.'

'And?'

'I'd love to help out.'

'But?'

'There is no but,' Kate said. Poor Ruth, she was so cynical and unhelpful herself she couldn't imagine anybody wanting to help her.

'You mean you'll do it?'

'Of course I will.' And feeling in control with a member of Alec's family for the first time, Kate added, 'Why don't you and Oscar come over for lunch today and we can sort out the details?'

They agreed a time and said goodbye, and after Kate had tidied up the kitchen and found that she was still feeling flushed with success at having managed a conversation without Ruth making her feel slightly less worthy than a toe-nail clipping, she decided to introduce herself to Jessica Lloyd.

Jessica took one look at the stunning girl in front of her and wanted to reach for her notebook and pen. As classic images of romantic heroines went, this one was the princess of them all. Peas under the mattress, mirrors on the wall, mislaid glass slippers, she could show them a thing or two!

'I'm Kate and ... and I don't want you to think I'm an interfering neighbour,' she said hesitantly, 'but I live next door and thought I'd just pop round to say hello. If you're busy I could come back another time.'

'I'm not busy at all. Come on in. I'm Jessica, by the way.' *Yes, come on in and let me get a better look at you!*

Jessica took Kate through to the sitting-room. 'Now before you say anything about the furniture and décor,' she laughed, 'I didn't choose any of it, so in no way does it reflect my character.'

Kate laughed too. 'It must be strange knowing that so many people have walked through your home just for the Sunday afternoon experience of poking about in a show house.'

Jessica pulled a face. 'Do you know, I hadn't thought of it quite like that. But you're right. What a horrid thought. Would you like a drink?'

'Tea would be lovely, but only if you're sure I'm not stopping you from doing anything.'

'You're not interrupting, honestly.'

Out in the kitchen Jessica filled the kettle – newly bought yesterday afternoon with her mother – plugged it in and reached for the nearest piece of paper to hand, which turned out to be an envelope from British Gas. She wrote quickly and spontaneously on the back of the envelope, trying her best to capture the stunning girl in the sitting-room. *Hair to die for*, she scribbled, *masses of copper waves right down to her waist – colour of a good sweet sherry. Tall and very slim – does she eat? Long, long legs hidden beneath faded jeans. Looks about twenty-one and makes me feel about a hundred and twenty-one! Pale complexion, probably never had a spot in her life! Greeny eyes, sort of misty in a sad kind of way. Irish background? Reminds me of those girls from* Riverdance. *Dread to think what Gavin's reaction to her would be!*

She crossed out this last comment and wrote, *Gavin Who?*

59

When she was satisfied with the thumbnail sketch, she made a pot of tea, grabbed a couple of her mother's cast-off mugs and slopped some milk into a cracked jug, also from Willow Cottage. Sooner, rather than later, she simply had to do some serious crockery shopping.

'Sorry I was so long,' she said when she joined Kate in the sitting-room. 'And I apologise for the state of this china. It's all borrowed from my mother until I get myself sorted. These poor old mugs look dreadful in here among all this chic furniture, rather out of place. A bit eccentric even. One could almost feel sorry for them.'

Kate wanted to say that everything looked fine and that anyway writers were allowed to be as eccentric as they wanted, that it was expected of them, but instead she said, 'Where have you moved from?'

'Corfu.'

Kate's eyes widened. 'Corfu? How wonderful. This is going to feel very different then, isn't it?' She suddenly lowered her gaze, conscious that Jessica was staring at her.

'I'm sorry,' Jessica said, realising that she'd been caught out. She quickly turned her attention to pouring the tea. 'I have a terrible habit of staring at people. An occupational hazard you could call it. I watch people all the time. They fascinate me.' She passed Kate her mug of tea.

'Thank you. Perhaps that's what makes you such a good writer.'

Disarming as well, thought Jessica. 'I don't know,' she said, 'am I?'

'A lot of people seem to think so, including me.'

Jessica looked awkwardly at her mother's chipped teapot. She found praise difficult to handle. Probably because she never trusted it. 'So how did you know I was a writer?' she asked.

'The woman over in number two told me ... and the sales negotiator told her. But I'd already heard of you. I'm a librarian, or rather I used to be.'

'Used to be?'

'I was made redundant. I was the last to be taken on and so naturally when all the cutbacks came into force a few months ago I was first to be asked to leave.'

'Any idea what you'll do next?'

Kate shrugged. 'I don't hold out much hope of getting another librarian job locally, but for the time being and perhaps until I really know what I want to do next I'm going to be looking after my partner's grandson.'

'Ah,' said Jessica – and thereby hangs a tale I'd like to know more about, she thought. But instead of immediately pursuing that particular line of conversation, she decided to keep it for when she and Kate knew one another a little better. She tucked her legs up underneath her on the sofa, reached for her mug of tea and settled herself in for a good gossiping session about her new bedfellows. 'When did you actually move in?' she began.

'On Thursday last week.'

'And were you the first?'

'No. There's a family over in number two –'

'With the woman who'd spoken to the sales negotiator, who'd told her all about me?'

Kate smiled. 'Yes, they were first to move in.'

'So what are they like?'

'They've a little girl called Hattie. She's really sweet.'

'And the parents, are they as sweet?'

Kate wasn't a gossiper by nature and she was reluctant to pass on what Hattie had told her last night while she had been looking after her, but having recently spent so much time alone she now found it almost impossible not to chat away with her new neighbour. And it wouldn't be gossip, really, would it, because Amanda had told her herself on Friday last week that she was Hattie's stepmother? It wasn't as if it were a secret. If it were, Amanda wouldn't have told her. 'They're very nice,' she said, 'she's his second wife ... the first was killed in a car crash. From the little I've seen of her I think Amanda finds the role of stepmother difficult. It can't be easy if you don't have a natural rapport with children.'

'And she doesn't?'

Kate shook her head, then regretted it. 'That was probably very unkind of me.'

'No worries,' Jessica said, 'I shall strike it from the record.' She was amused at Kate's discretion. A conscience as well as beauty. A beguiling combination.

They fell silent for a moment or two, until Kate said, 'We could lend you some china and anything else you're short of, if you like. Alec and I have got plenty of stuff we probably won't ever use.'

Jessica was touched. And intrigued. She wanted to know more about this Alec. She knew she was being unashamedly nosy, but meeting somebody for the first time often gave her an insatiable appetite for a dose of interrogation, especially when she was on the verge of writing a new novel and therefore on the look-out for a likely source of inspiration. 'That's really kind of you,' she said, 'but tell you what, would you like to come shopping with me this week and help me choose some things?'

Ruth finally arrived for lunch with Kate. She was over an hour late, uptight and overdressed in a Jackie Onassis-style cream suit with matching handbag, high heels and sun-glasses. She was cross, having just wasted an entire morning on an unsuccessful shopping trip to buy herself a suitable wardrobe for her new career, and while she took out her temper on her father's new home, tutting at the unimaginative design – Adam could have made so much better a job of it – Kate took Oscar outside to set the wooden table for lunch in the garden. Normally she would have had everything all neatly arranged, but she knew how Oscar liked to help her.

'Shall I put this knife here?' he asked.

'Yes please,' Kate said, 'and can you put the napkin next to it?'

They worked happily together until Ruth, tired of tutting inside alone, came out to the garden and tutted some more, saying that it was foolish to consider having lunch outside. 'The wasps will be swarming round as soon as we sit down.'

Kate held her ground and, as it turned out, the only person the wasps annoyed was Ruth. A pair hovered menacingly around her, dive-bombing her glass of orange juice or threatening an assault on her salad with its honey-and-mustard dressing. In the end they grew bored of the sport and flew away.

Kate ventured to enquire about the arrangements for Oscar. 'How many days a week will it be for?' she asked, watching Oscar who had finished his lunch and was now exploring the large empty garden.

'To begin with just two, that's until things pick up. But eventually I see myself working more or less full time. Adam needs somebody to get to grips with the administrative side of the business. The woman he's got now is hopeless. I know she's got problems at home, but these days one has to rise above that kind of thing and be the complete professional, otherwise there's simply no point.'

After hearing the sparring professionalism of Ruth and Adam arguing that morning, Kate couldn't help but wonder what the effect of their relationship might have on the business. It appalled her enough imagining the effect it must already be having on their son.

'So what time will you be wanting to drop Oscar off in the mornings?'

'Quite early, so you'll have to get your skates on. There'll be no more being spoilt by Dad bringing you breakfast in bed.'

Kate coloured and wished the wasps would come back. How did Ruth know these things? Surely Alec didn't tell her?

'Then in September, when he starts school, you'll have to take him. He's to be there at nine and he'll finish at three thirty. When you've collected him he'll need his tea. And by the way, I don't want him eating any old rubbish when he's here with you. He's to have fresh vegetables and fruit, plenty of fibre. I've got a list in my bag of meals he's to have. He's not to have any red meat, or fish fingers, or orange squash, fresh juice only. And definitely no sweets or biscuits.'

Poor Oscar, thought Kate. 'What time will you be picking him up?' She was wondering how much love she could cram into the precious hours Oscar would be with her.

'Heaven knows, to begin with. We'll both need to be flexible if this is to work.'

'Just a rough idea?' Kate persisted.

'Now don't try and pin me down, Kate. It's all very well you having worked in a cushy library where the hours are set, but outside the world of subsidy, in the real world, people have to graft all hours to get things done. I'm sure we'll soon slip into a pattern.'

'I'm sure we will,' Kate said, glancing over to Oscar who was fully absorbed in gathering buttercups and daisies by reaching one of his tiny hands through the picket fence to the weed-infested area of the neighbouring field.

'Oscar! Stop that at once,' called out Ruth, 'you'll get horrid stains all over your new Osh Kosh trousers. Now come back here where I can keep an eye on you.'

Oscar slowly withdrew his hand and wandered over to where they were sitting. He smiled up at Kate and handed her his bunch of squashed flowers.

'Thank you,' she said and gave his sun-warmed cheek a kiss. She was looking forward to having Oscar all to herself. It would be like having a child of her own.

11

More than a week after he'd moved house Josh drove through the central archway of Cholmford Hall Mews and set off to work.

It wasn't yet eight o'clock, but already the day was warm. He activated the sun roof and as it slid back he switched off the radio. He wanted to enjoy his drive in to work that morning and had no desire for his good mood to be jeopardised by the tedium of listening to bad news. He didn't want to hear another word from some unknown MEP whinging on about why Britain should or should not touch a single currency. Neither was he interested in the latest round of Northern Ireland peace talks breaking down again.

On the other hand, nor did he want any good news to eclipse his own.

It was nothing short of a miracle that he was feeling better than he had for days. This morning he'd woken up with nothing more annoying than a stiff leg to bother him. Now that was what he called bloody fantastic news! Sod the government's latest unemployment figures – the lowest on record for years – and to hell with the pre-summer bonanza of high street spending, he, Joshua Crawford, was up and running!

Okay then. He wasn't exactly running, but he was up and ready to get back to work.

He drove through the suffused green light of the avenue of chestnut trees and thought how it was that in such a relatively short space of time his expectations had been so dramatically reduced. It wasn't that long ago that if he'd have woken up with a stiff leg he would have been filled with fear, panic and anger.

When he reached the small bridge that spanned the canal he slowed the car and looked over to the pretty white cottage that he admired whenever he was passing. He envied whoever lived there. It was an idyllic spot. But then for that matter so was Cholmford Hall Mews. He drove on.

He would never admit it to his brother, or his parents, but the effort of setting up a new home on his own had been more debilitating than he'd expected. They'd all offered to help him, but he'd turned them down, wanting to prove to himself that he could manage. For the first few days after moving in he'd cursed his weakened body constantly, then he'd cursed himself for having collected so much junk. He made several trips to the council tip and jettisoned piles of stuff that should have been thrown away before the move, if not years before that. He also paid a visit to the nearest charity shop and donated countless bags of clothes that no longer fitted him because of the weight he'd lost in the past months. As well as this he handed over a bag of unused Christmas presents, including a Whistling Key Finder; some Resonating Energy Chimes, designed to relax and uplift; a Mini Carpet Bowls set and a rubber-sealed radio designed to be listened to while in the shower. They were absurd gifts and were all from his father, who took a perverse pleasure in browsing through the hundreds of mail-order catalogues that came his way. His taste for the impractical meant that for some time now both Josh and Charlie, as well as their mother, had ended up with a series of ludicrous presents.

It was while he was at the charity shop that his ego had taken an unexpected battering. He'd asked an elderly white-haired assistant whether the things in his car would be of any use. 'Always glad to have whatever's going,' she'd said and had promptly raced outside to his Shogun parked on the double-yellow lines, eager to help him unload the bags of clothes. It was a while before she realised that he wasn't able to keep pace and that he was still inside the shop, limping his way through the racks of second-hand goods. 'You should have said something, you poor old duck,' she'd said, looking pointedly at his legs, 'we'd have arranged to collect this lot from you, it would have saved you all the bother.'

His sense of frustration was enormous as he was then forced to watch a woman, who had to be at least thirty years older than him, manhandling the heavy bags from the back of his car. He'd hated himself and his situation.

Worse was to come later in the day when he started unpacking yet more boxes and came across his squash and tennis rackets, along with his skis and boots. The objects lay on the floor in the hall, reminding him, just in case he'd forgotten, that they would be of no use to him now. He banished them to the garage where they could no longer sneer at him. He hid the offending items behind an old blanket. He'd then spent the rest of the day struggling to put together a simple rack of shelves, but with each turn of the screwdriver his hands and wrists had burned until, two hours later, when all sense of feeling had gone from them he'd finally put in the last screw.

Triumphant, but knackered, he'd slept on the sofa that night, too exhausted to contemplate the stairs.

'Multiple sclerosis,' he'd been told last year by the neurologist, who had confirmed the illness to Josh, 'will take over your life and destroy it if you let it. There are certain things that you are going to have to face up to, like the chaos it will bring. Each day will be different. There's not a lot you can do to stop the unpredictable nature of MS, so the best advice I can give you is to take each day as it comes.'

The doctor had gone on to explain how the central nervous system worked and how his own was unable to send out and receive messages, which was why his body didn't work as it should. And as Josh had listened to what he was being told a feeling of relief had swept over him – he wasn't going mad after all. He hadn't imagined the weakness in his arms and legs; the occasional loss of balance and co-ordination; the heavy tiredness that without warning would suddenly come over him just as if he'd been drugged; the pins and needles; the numbness. For nearly two years he had experienced all these problems off and on, but because they came and went so quickly, as if by the flick of a switch, he had kept them to himself, but had always wondered after each occurrence whether he wasn't turning into some kind of hypochondriac. He had tried all this time to ignore what was going on, but when one morning he'd woken up and found that he couldn't see properly – everything through his right eye was blurred – he'd been terrified that he was going blind. He rushed to the nearby busy health practice, where he was quickly referred to an eye specialist, who in turn sent Josh to a neurologist. A whole series of tests followed. By this stage he had convinced himself that he was dying.

'You'll be with us for a few years yet,' the neurologist had said, when Josh had voiced his fears after he'd been given the diagnosis. 'But first things first. We need to set you up on a course of steroids to sort out the inflammation of your optic nerve.'

'Is that what's causing the blurred vision?'

'Yes. It's quite common in MS. Often it's the first conclusive evidence we have as to what we're dealing with.'

'And will it go back to normal? Will I be able to see?'

'Yes, the eye will be fine. Don't worry.'

But that was exactly what Josh started to do. Once the initial feeling of relief, that he now knew what was wrong with him, had gone, he realised that though the neurologist had given him varying degrees of help and advice, he had omitted to explain to him that there was no cure for what he had. When pressed, he admitted that there wasn't even a drug he could take to stop the illness from getting any worse.

Worry kicked in.

And anger.

How could this have happened to him? He'd always been so fit. He'd rarely been ill, not with anything significant. So why should he have multiple sclerosis? And what was there to come? He began to read up on the illness, and what he discovered only fuelled his anger and his ever-growing terror of what lay ahead.

But now, as he drove into the centre of Manchester and headed towards Deansgate, he was determined not to think about the future. It was too depressing. He joined the slow-moving queue of cars at the traffic lights and suddenly wished he weren't there, that he were back in Cholmford, in his new home.

Charlie might have joked that the place gave him agoraphobia, but Josh knew that he'd done the right thing in buying the house. He loved it already. He loved being in the sitting-room overlooking the fields of corn, bright and golden, and sharply contrasted against the adjoining fields of lush green grass, edged now and then with rows of hawthorns, oaks and beech trees, and all set against a magnificent backdrop of soft-focus hills.

What had appealed to Josh, when he'd first driven out to Cholmford after reading about the barn conversion in *Cheshire Life*, was the sense of freedom the house offered. Its isolation had immediately struck a chord with him. He had a desire to be alone, or at least to *feel* alone – given his circumstances, the coward in him reasoned that having a few people living close by wouldn't be a bad idea.

For some time he had been wanting to move as far away from Manchester as he sensibly could – the daily drive in to work had to be a realistic journey – and not just because he wanted a bit of space around him. He needed to distance himself from those closest to him.

Since his illness had been diagnosed he had felt confined – trapped even. He knew that Charlie meant well, his parents too, but their constantly looking out for him was beginning to have a suffocating effect. Trying to accommodate their response to his MS, as well as his own, was too much for him; it was like having to cope with yet another symptom of the illness. He believed, and hoped, that by moving away from their good intentions he would be able to sort himself out. God knows, he needed to.

All this he could see so clearly on a day like this when his body didn't feel as heavy as lead. When he felt comparatively well and normal it was easy to think logically and marshal his thoughts and fears. But it wasn't always so. He knew that. Too often he was irrational and as moody as hell.

He parked his car alongside his brother's TVR in the car-park behind their offices. Crawford and Sons was situated on the second floor of what had once been a Victorian warehouse, but had been converted into office space in the seventies. The first floor was occupied by a firm of solicitors and the top by a company of financial advisers. Josh had always joked that he and his brother were the only honest souls among a den of thieves.

Josh and Charlie had never considered working in anything other than the garment industry and when, thirteen years ago, their father had decided he wanted to retire early, he'd handed the business over to them. 'It's yours now,' he'd said, 'and I promise I shan't poke my nose in, it's up to you how you run it.' He'd been true to his word. Not once had he interfered with any decision they'd made.

They had worked for their father since leaving college and before that, spending all their vacations learning their craft from him, as well as developing a crucial sixth sense for a potential quickest selling line – an asset which had proved invaluable during the heady days of the Thatcherite era when there were fast bucks to be made in the garment trade and even faster bucks to be lost.

Crawford's had gone from strength to strength during the eighties and at one stage they'd had as many as forty employees. But that was then. Now things were different. With margins as tight as they were, the traditional layer of middle management had been removed from the company and they had pared themselves right down to the bone, numbering just fourteen employees to date. It was at least satisfying to know that, given the medicine they'd forced down their throats, they were still turning over the same profits as they had in the years of plenty, whereas many of their competitors who had resisted any honing down of their businesses had gone under.

Josh was convinced that their current success was due as much to their father as it was to the way in which he and Charlie had guided Crawford's through the recession and had then had the courage gradually to broaden the base of high street stores whom they supplied. The reputation and longevity of the company were just as important. Crawford's was well-known in Hong Kong where the bulk of what they sold in the UK was produced and as a consequence of their good name they were seen as a low risk. Maybe they were even liked. A few of their suppliers, the older ones in particular, still asked after their father. One always asked the same question: 'How's William?' he'd say, 'still pruning his roses?' He thought that was what all Englishmen did when they retired.

The other contributing factor to their survival was that Josh and Charlie knew their strengths. They were not innovators in the world of fashion, but followers. It was a clear distinction and so long as they remembered it Josh was sure they would continue to be a success.

He took the lift up to the second floor. When Mo, their receptionist, saw him she quickly stuffed a book under her desk. Josh was amused. For ages he and Charlie had known that Mo did most of her night-school homework during office hours, but so long as she kept doing her job as well as she did, neither of them had any complaints. He could also see that she must have raided the rail of finished samples in his office while he'd been away, for he recognised at once that she was wearing a knitted top that was part of next spring's line, as well as a pair of black PVC trousers – currently their fastest selling item. She grinned at him. 'Couldn't keep away, eh?'

'Got it in one.' He tried to sound as upbeat as he could, then attempted to stride past Mo, but the stiffness in his leg wouldn't let him. 'Charlie in his office?' he asked.

'Yes, but I've just put a call through. Shall I get you some coffee?'

'Thanks, that would be great.'

Charlie was still on the phone when Josh pushed against his door. When Charlie realised he was there he hurriedly brought his conversation to an end.

'Josh, what are you doing here? I thought you were off for another week?'

'I was getting bored,' he lied. He hadn't been bored at all. What had made him come in to work was something quite different. It was fear. He was frightened that if he stayed away too long there might not be a proper job for him to come back to. He wasn't worried that his brother would take advantage of his illness and try and squeeze him out of the business – Charlie would never do that – it was more that he was concerned that people would get used to him not being there. He was conscious, too, that for the past few months his brother had been working ridiculously long hours in order to cover for him. It couldn't go on.

He sat in the chair opposite Charlie and Mo brought in their coffee. She placed the mugs on the desk between them, which was almost buried beneath a tidal wave of faxes, contracts and specifications.

'So, how about you bring me up to date?' Josh said when Mo had left them. 'What's happened over that faulty batch of black jeans? Have they managed to get the dye fixed?'

Charlie leant back in his chair. 'Yes, after much verbal abuse they agreed there was a problem. I gave them an ultimatum by the way; one more cock-up like that and we ditch them. Is that okay with you?'

'Sure it is.' Josh felt the net of good intentions creeping over him. A year ago and Charlie wouldn't have put that question. 'And how about the problem at the warehouse?'

'I'm still dealing with that one.'

'Well, seeing as I'm back, let me sort it out.'

'Actually,' Charlie said slowly, 'I thought I'd go up there later today.'

'Meaning what?'

Charlie began sliding bits of paper across his desk. He didn't look up. 'Meaning exactly that. I'll go there later.'

Josh felt his body go taut with angry frustration. He got to his feet, placed both hands on the desk and leant forward. 'Meaning poor old Josh isn't up to it, I suppose. For pity's sake, Charlie, I'm quite capable of driving to Failsworth.' Then, summoning every ounce of energy, he marched out, slamming the door behind him. He ignored the stares of curiosity from everyone in the design area as his footsteps banged out angrily on the wooden floor. When he reached the safety of his own office he sank into his chair, sick with bitter exhaustion. He clasped his head in his hands.

A few moments later he looked up to see Charlie standing in the doorway. He came in. 'I'm sorry,' he said.

'Yeah, so am I.'

They fell silent. Then Josh spoke. 'Listen, Charlie, we need to talk. We can't go on like this . . . apart from anything else I don't have the energy. And what strength I do have I don't want to waste proving to you that I'm still capable of pulling my weight around here.'

Charlie nodded. 'Point made. Do you want to go out for lunch later and put me straight?'

'No, I've a better idea. Come back to my place tonight for supper. Meanwhile, I'll drive up to Failsworth and sort out the warehouse. Okay?'

Charlie nodded. 'Okay.'

12

Jessica had a surprise call from her agent.

It was a surprise for two reasons: one, it was so early in the morning – early enough for Jessica to be dozing in bed still – and two, to her knowledge Piers rarely called anyone until late in the afternoon – not because he was still dozing in bed, but because he'd always given her the impression that he was far too busy a man to pick up the phone before lunch-time.

He was a curious agent, with none of the smooth-tongued charm Jessica had come across in her limited dealings with the world of publishing, and his opening gambit to their conversation now was a typical example of his complete disregard for the social conventions usually employed in such circumstances.

'Jessica, is that you?' he demanded – he never announced himself; if Piers was benevolent enough to ring somebody they were supposed to have sufficient wits about them to know who he was. At the other end of the line she could make out a strange vibrating noise. Then she recognised what it was. It was Piers shaving. The cheek of the man! He was too stingy to give her his undivided attention. He was probably sitting at his desk, his phone on monitor, one of his hands guiding a Braun multi-shaver across his coal-face craggy chin and the other scrolling through an author's royalty statement on his computer screen.

'Hello, Piers, how are you?' she said defiantly. She might be in bed and still not fully *compos mentis*, but she was prepared to give the social conventions an airing, even if he wasn't.

'Flat out and with no time for small talk. I finished *A Carefree Life*.'
'And?'
'Not bad.'

Praise indeed, thought Jessica. For Piers to offer up such a charitable comment was quite something. 'Thank you,' she said.

'Much better than the previous one you churned out,' he said, the sound of the Braun still whirring away in the background.

'Kind of you to say.' *It had only reached the bestseller lists!* Why the hell did she stay with him? There were plenty of other literary agents in London she could switch to. Why did she put up with him?

Easy. She put up with him because he was dead straight with her. There was never any beating about the bush. No fawning. No bullshit. No literary snobbery. No ego massaging. And if there had ever been the merest hint of any skin-crawling sycophancy she would have dropped Piers like the proverbial hot brick. Or was it a hot potato? Well, whatever. Something mighty hot.

There was also the small matter of his undeniable talent for negotiating a cracking good contract. The advances Jessica had received since writing her first novel had been more than enough to satisfy her modest needs and had enabled her to buy her house in Cholmford Hall Mews. She had no delusions that Piers was partly responsible for her good fortune. It was just a shame he couldn't employ a touch more sweetness in his manner. A few words of encouragement wouldn't go amiss.

'I want you to come down and see me,' he said.

She sat bolt upright, terrifyingly *compos mentis* now. A summons? What had she done wrong? Did he no longer want to act for her, was that it? Or worse, had her publishers decided not to offer her another contract? Had they found themselves a new Jessica Lloyd? After all, no writer was indispensable.

'When were you thinking?' she said calmly, already worrying about her next mortgage payment.

'Day after tomorrow.'

'Day after tomorrow?' repeated Jessica, more convinced than ever that the summons was in order to impart bad news. 'But I've just moved house,' she said, grasping at any excuse to put Piers off, 'I've got so much to do. I need to –'

'I know all that, Jessica.' His tone of voice implied, don't bother me with domestic details, I'm a busy man. 'But this is important.'

'Okay, what time?'

'Be here for twelve thirty. I'll book us a table for lunch.'

She heard him switch off the razor, which was all the goodbye she received.

She went downstairs and made herself a cup of coffee, and determined not to fret over her conversation with Piers she took a kitchen chair and went outside to sit on the unimaginative rectangle of patio. She stared at her empty plot of garden and tried to visualise how it would look by the time her mother had taken it by the scruff of the neck. Anna was full of enthusiasm for creating all manner of curvy-shaped beds and filling them with seedlings and cuttings from Willow Cottage. 'I'll plant some rudbeckia against the fence for you,' she'd said only the other day, 'and then I'll throw in some campanula and verbascum. Maybe some columbine as well, though not too much, it can be very short-lived. And a hibiscus would love the sunny aspect as well as the rich soil.' Jessica was no gardener and she was more than happy to let her mother's green fingers take charge, just so long as she didn't overdo things.

She yawned and stretched out her legs in the warm early-morning sun. She glanced down at the T-shirt she was wearing and the words written across her chest – *Wind Surfers Do It Wet And Standing Up.* It was Gavin's and had been part of a small selection of his clothes that he had kept at her house. It was months since he had worn it, yet Jessica could smell him in every fibre. She had intended to leave it behind in Corfu, but at the last minute, and in a moment of weakness and indulgence, she had relented and tucked it into one of the bags. Then last night, while lying in bed unable to sleep, she had pathetically sought it out. Slipping the garment over her head, the soft, well-worn fabric had felt familiar and comfortable against her skin, and had brought back happy memories of Gavin. Within seconds she had fallen asleep.

But this morning – and before Piers's phone call – she had woken up to the smell of Gavin and had longed for him, every bit of her missing him. Well, perhaps only the physical bits – she didn't miss the mental pain he'd inflicted on her by refusing to commit himself to their relationship. But really the missing and longing had started ages ago when she had become conscious of the loss of what had attracted her to him in the beginning. When they'd first met, Gavin's sense of fun and happy-go-lucky nature had matched her own carefree persona. They had been in perfect accord with the shared view that life was best enjoyed with no more thought given for tomorrow than for yesterday.

But then things had changed.

She had started wanting to plan her tomorrows.

And it had proved fatal.

She drank the rest of her coffee, then ran a lingering hand over the front of Gavin's T-shirt. She hadn't expected to feel his absence so keenly. She had imagined that she would simply start a new way of life and that it would be without Gavin. After all, she had done it before. Each time she had moved about the world she had managed quite easily to piece together a new existence on her own. But she suspected that this time it was going to be a little more difficult because the memory of Gavin was going to be more persistent than she had anticipated.

She had thought that she would miss Corfu itself, but strangely she didn't. Every now and then she would think fondly of the quiet bay that had been home for so long and of the friends she had made. Sometimes she would recall Helen and Jack and imagine them on their terrace happily bickering like a couple of noisy cicadas. But for how long would they remain so happy? was the question that came into her mind. Might even

73

their contentment turn on them one day and poison their bickering into something altogether more damaging? She hoped not. She wanted them to be happy.

She wanted Gavin to be happy, too.

She smiled. Who was she kidding? Gavin would always be happy. He was too straightforward to be anything else. Nothing ever troubled him because he was incapable of taking anything seriously. That was why he was able to be unfaithful and not wonder at his actions. If it didn't matter to him, then why would it matter to anybody else? was his unspoken philosophy.

She hadn't thought of it before, but Gavin and Piers were quite similar. In many ways they couldn't be more different, but in other ways they were worryingly alike. It probably never crossed Piers's mind that a chance remark on his part – *Much better than the previous one you churned out* – would be deeply hurtful.

She thought now of her impending day to be spent in London and the thought appalled her. It would be stinking hot and horrendously crowded, full of worn-out tourists pointing at screwed-up maps and asking her for directions. Which would be futile because she knew London about as well as they did. On any previous trips to see Piers, or her editor, she had afterwards flown back to Corfu desperate for her little house and the peaceful tranquillity it gave her. She wasn't a city person and a day in London was just about as much as she could take.

She began to worry again what it was that Piers had to tell her. What was so important that he couldn't discuss it on the phone? Was it something to do with her recently delivered manuscript? She wondered about ringing her editor, but remembered that Cara would still be away on holiday and that *A Carefree Life* would be lying unread on her desk, awaiting her return.

Well, whatever it was that Piers had to tell her would have to wait until Friday, today she was going shopping with Kate. It was a funny thing, but the more times she saw Kate, the older and more worldly she felt. In the past all her friends had been older than her and she had been happy to play her part accordingly. But Kate was almost ten years her junior and being in her company forced Jessica to behave quite differently. So what did that say about her? The trick cyclists might mutter something about her suffering from that well-known Peter Pan syndrome and that Corfu had been her Never-Never Land. Well, the trick cyclists could say all they wanted. They could pedal themselves up their inner tubes for all she cared. She wasn't afraid of adulthood. Wasn't that the very reason she had left Corfu? Responsibility for her mother had fairly smacked her in the face and made her see where her duty lay.

And on that grown-up thought she went indoors to get dressed.

Kate was just turning the key in the lock before going to call on Jessica when she heard footsteps coming across the courtyard. It was Amanda.

'I'm so pleased to have caught you,' Amanda said, hurrying the last few paces. 'I've been meaning to have a word with you for days. Tony and I wanted to thank you for helping us out the other night and we wondered whether you and Alec would come for dinner on Saturday.'

'There's no need to go to all that trouble,' Kate said, 'it was a pleasure looking after Hattie.'

'Well, come for dinner anyway. We'd love to see you both. About eight o'clock?'

'Thank you,' Kate said. She hoped that her voice conveyed at least a hint of sincerity. 'Would you like me to bring anything?'

Amanda laughed. 'Yes, some of your magic to work on Hattie, at least then we'll get an evening without her bothering us. She can be such a nuisance at bedtime.'

'I'll see what I can do,' Kate said stiffly. She suddenly decided that what she'd suspected from her first meeting with Amanda was true. She didn't like her one little bit. She started to move away from her front door.

'Off out, then?'

The enquiry was perfectly reasonable, but Kate was reluctant to satisfy Amanda's curiosity. Just because they were neighbours it didn't mean that they had to know one another's business. And besides, she didn't want Amanda suggesting that she come along for the ride as well. She had been looking forward to her day out with Jessica and had no desire for Amanda to spoil it.

'I'm just going shopping,' she said, in an effort to be economical with the truth.

'Anywhere nice?' asked Amanda.

Before Kate could reply Jessica's front door opened and she appeared on the step. Now we're for it, thought Kate.

Amanda looked over to Jessica and gave her a little wave. She hadn't yet had an opportunity to introduce herself to this supposedly well-known author – of whose supposed fame she was yet to be convinced – and she immediately seized her chance. She moved towards Jessica. 'Hello,' she said, 'I'm Amanda and I live in number two, over in the corner.'

'Hi, Kate tells me you were first to move in. How are you getting on?'

'Slowly getting things straight, you know how it is.'

Looking at Amanda in her commodore outfit – navy blazer and perfectly pressed knee-length white shorts with creases standing to attention and two-tone blue-and-white shoes – Jessica had a sneaky feeling that Amanda's idea of getting things straight would be entirely different from her own.

75

'I just came over to invite Kate and Alec for dinner on Saturday,' Amanda went on, 'I don't suppose you'd like to join us, would you?'

Kate hoped that Jessica would say yes. She didn't relish an evening of Alec talking to Tony and her being stuck with Amanda. Her wish was granted. 'Thank you,' she heard Jessica say, 'I'd love to come. What time?'

'Eight-ish and don't feel you have to dress up, it's casual.'

'One man's casual is another man's Sunday best,' Jessica said with a light laugh.

Amanda stared blankly at her, then returned her attention to Kate, 'I hope you enjoy your shopping.'

As they drove through the archway in Kate's little Mini, she said, 'Thank you for saying yes to Amanda's invitation. I'm not sure I could have coped with a whole evening of her without some kind of moral support.'

'Well, don't you dare back out at the last minute and leave me on my own. But tell me, and bearing in mind that I've known Amanda for all of two minutes, does she have the same effect on you? Does she make you want to say or do something outrageously rude, just to see how she would react?'

Kate smiled. 'Not exactly. To be honest she makes me feel awkward and nervous. But then lots of people make me feel like that.'

'What an extraordinary thing to say.'

'But it's true.'

'I hope I don't make you feel awkward.'

When Kate didn't reply Jessica said, 'Shall I take your silence as confirmation that I thoroughly put the wind up you?'

'No. No, I was quiet because I was just thinking that you don't make me feel nervous and I was trying to work out why.' She slowed down to negotiate the bridge over the canal and noticed that Jessica was craning her neck to look at the cottage on the right. She remembered then that Jessica had told her that this was where her mother lived. 'It's a beautiful house,' she said as they drove on.

Jessica wrenched her gaze away from Willow Cottage. She knew perfectly well that Anna wasn't at home, that she was staying with friends for a few days, but she couldn't rid herself of the need to be continually checking on her mother. It was quite alarming that in such a short space of time she had become a fanatical worrier about her mother's well-being. She realised now, with a sense of very real shame, that previously she had worried less over Anna because it had been a clear case of out of sight, out of mind.

'And did you grow up there?' asked Kate.

'Born and raised, as the expression goes.'

'It's lovely,' said Kate, 'I wish I'd grown up somewhere like this.'

Jessica caught the wistfulness in Kate's words. 'Don't be fooled by a few pretty roses round the door,' she said lightly. 'Now come on, tell me where we're going.'

'I thought perhaps we could go to Macclesfield. It's fairly easy to park there and I'm sure you'll be able to get most of what you want.'

'Brilliant, the sooner I get this over and done with the better. And thanks, by the way, for driving. Mum was all set to lend me her car, but then she was invited to spend a few days with friends over in Abersoch. And that's another thing I've got to arrange.'

'What's that?'

'A car. I'll go mad if I don't get one organised soon.'

'Did you have one in Corfu?'

'No. I either walked or used my boat.'

'It sounds very romantic. Don't you miss it all? This must seem quite ordinary in comparison.'

'It's all relative. Even shopping by boat becomes ordinary in the end.'

'I suppose so.' After a while Kate added, 'I hope that's not true of love.'

'That's quite a leap of thought,' Jessica said, intrigued and hoping for some further comment.

But Kate didn't say anything else. She kept her eyes on the road and her thoughts to herself. There were times when if she thought about how much she loved Alec she became convinced that something so precious could never last. She wasn't a pessimistic person by nature, but it was as if she were waiting for their relationship to go wrong.

13

Kate and Jessica finally returned home just after six o'clock. Kate's tiny car was brimming over with carrier bags, and boxes of china and glassware and bed linen, and the larger items that they hadn't been able to squeeze into the Mini were being delivered a few days later.

Kate helped Jessica carry everything inside and after she'd said goodbye she went next door to find a message on the answerphone from Ruth telling her – not asking her – to call back immediately.

Kate took the unprecedented step of ignoring a member of Alec's family and started preparing supper. She crushed a clove of garlic, put it into a frying pan along with a large spoonful of olive oil, then chopped up an onion and while that was softening in the hot oil with the garlic she peeled and chopped some tomatoes and added them to the pan. She was just reaching for the pot of fresh basil on the window-sill when the phone rang. She had forgotten to turn off the answerphone and Ruth's voice bellowed at her from the hall.

'You can't surely *still* be out,' Ruth said bad-temperedly.

Kate was tempted to ignore Ruth again, but remembering that, to all intents and purposes, she was now an employee of Alec's daughter she decided she'd better answer the phone. She took the frying pan off the hob and went and put Ruth out of her misery.

'Sorry about that, I've just got in,' she said, stretching the truth by about twenty minutes. 'If it's Alec you want to speak to I'm afraid he's not back yet.'

'No, it's not Dad I want, it's you. I need you to look after Oscar tomorrow. I'll drop him off at about half past eight.'

'But I thought you didn't want me to have him until the week after next.'

'I know that's what we agreed, but something's come up.'

Yes, thought Kate, lunch with a friend probably. 'I'm sorry, Ruth,' she said, 'but I can't help you, not tomorrow.'

'What? What do you mean you can't do it?'

'Alec's got to go down to Oxford to the warehouse tomorrow and I'm going with him.'

'Well, surely you can go another time; Dad's always going down there.'

Kate gripped the receiver. She really mustn't let Ruth push her around in this way. 'Alec was quite keen for me to go. We were going to stop the night in a hotel and then come back the following day.'

A loud snort from the other end of the line told Kate exactly what Ruth thought about her father spending a night in a hotel with a woman twenty-one years his junior.

'Well, all I'll say on the matter is that poor Oscar is going to be devastated,' Ruth went on. 'I promised him he'd be spending the day with you and now he'll probably cry himself to sleep with disappointment. If there's one thing children need, Kate, it's stability and consistency. I didn't think I'd have to remind *you* of that.'

Kate flinched. She'd known that she would regret ever letting Ruth wheedle out of her the details of her unhappy childhood. It had been a chance remark on Boxing Day when she had met Alec's family for the first time that had led to the mortifying disclosure. She had spent all morning in the kitchen preparing lunch and trying to take her mind off the impending show-down, and while she had been willing the day not to happen Alec had been insistent that all would be well. His calmness had surprised her. She hadn't expected him to be as nervous as she was, but his jovial manner – to the point of seemingly enjoying the prospect of his ex-wife meeting her – had only added to her own anxiety. The words *trophy girlfriend* had entered her head as he'd helped her choose what to wear. By the time they arrived she was rigid with fear and she let Alec greet his family while she hid in the kitchen and listened to him taking coats and offering drinks.

'They'll love you,' he whispered into her ear when inevitably he came to find her, 'who could fail to?'

'Melissa for one,' she whispered back.

He kissed her and took her by the hand to the sitting-room.

'This is Kate,' Alec announced, his arm around her shoulder. Predictably all eyes – especially Melissa's – were on her and, wishing herself anywhere but in that room, she made a few polite noises and sought refuge in Alec's grandson Oscar, who was sitting on the floor looking at a book.

'Hello,' she said, going over to the little boy and slipping down to the floor beside him. 'Is that a Christmas present?'

He raised his head warily, stared at her with his large, thoughtful brown eyes, then said, 'Yes. Will you read it to me?'

She didn't need asking twice and leaving Alec to entertain the rest of his family she took the book from Oscar and began reading aloud to him, but in a lowered voice so as not to draw attention to herself. After a few minutes, Ruth came over and joined them. She sat in the wing-back chair in front of Kate and Oscar, and with a glass of wine in her hand she watched the pair of them closely. She also listened. Kate struggled to keep her nerves at bay and continued reading as best she could. When the story was over Oscar, who was now sitting on her lap, turned the pages back to the beginning and said, 'Read it again, *please.*' She smiled and gave him a hug, glad that she had at least made one friend in Alec's family.

'Do all children lap you up in this way?' Ruth asked.

'I . . . don't know,' she answered.

'I've always thought that it's the childlike who relate best to children. Wouldn't you agree?'

The insult was glaringly obvious and Kate said the first thing that came into her head. It proved to be entirely the wrong thing to say. 'I just like children to be happy. I know what it's like to be unhappy.'

The expression on Ruth's face changed. She snapped forward in her chair and began the process of interrogation that she must have been dying to do ever since she had learnt of her father's scandalously young girlfriend. Kate tried hard to parry the questions that were being fired at her, but her nervousness and natural distaste for deception rendered her incapable of defending herself against such a determined inquisitor. By the time Ruth had finished with her, the full details had been drawn out of her and an unspoken conclusion reached – not only had Kate's unstable upbringing set her on a course of seeking out a lover to make up for the father she had never known, but her love of children was to compensate for the love she'd never received from her own mother, who had flitted from one disastrous relationship to another. But what was wrong if that was the case? Did it really matter? Wasn't it true that everybody's actions were attributable in one way or another to their upbringing? But any amount of self-justification wouldn't quell the tide of unhappiness Ruth's questioning was causing her.

Several times during Ruth's cross-examination Kate had looked across the room for help, to where Alec was talking to Melissa, but he had been unaware of her distress.

In the end it was Oscar who came to her rescue. 'I'm hungry,' he announced. 'What's for lunch?'

'I'd better go and see,' she said, quickly lifting him off her lap and getting to her feet. He had followed her out to the kitchen and they had remained the best of friends ever since.

But now as Kate thought of her little friend her heart ached at the distress she would cause him if she didn't do what his mother wanted. She couldn't bear the thought of him crying himself to sleep that night. She tried to think of a way round the problem; a solution that would suit them all. She didn't want to let Alec down, but neither did she want to hurt

Oscar. An idea came into her head. She wasn't sure how Alec would take it, but Oscar was his grandson after all, so he couldn't object too much, could he?

But Alec did object.

'What?' he demanded, later that evening when Kate told him what she had agreed with Ruth.

'Ruth wanted me to look after Oscar and I said if it was all right with her he could come with us to Oxford . . . I thought he'd enjoy it,' she faltered. 'I thought you would, too.'

'You mean, you thought *you'd* enjoy it.'

Kate was dumbfounded. She had never heard Alec's voice so cold, or so sharp. 'I . . . I don't understand, you know I enjoy having Oscar around, I love him dearly.'

Alec turned on his heel and marched out of the kitchen. He went upstairs to the bedroom, yanked off his tie and threw it on the bed, followed by his jacket. He went and stood in front of the window and gazed out at the distant hills. After a few minutes, when his anger had subsided, a far worse emotion took hold of him. Shame. He was shattered at his sudden outburst of anger.

He didn't need to try and reason out his actions. It was all about his own insecurity. He was so terrified that he would lose Kate he was becoming irrationally possessive. He couldn't handle her wanting to spend time with anyone but himself.

Hell! He was even jealous of her spending time with Oscar.

He'd heard people talk about the demon of jealousy and what a powerful destructive force it could be, but he'd had no idea until now just how destructive.

All he wanted was to have Kate entirely to himself while they were in Oxford. He'd planned to get his visit at the warehouse over and done with as quickly as possible, then spend the rest of the time with Kate. He'd even ordered champagne to be waiting for them when they arrived at the hotel. He'd had in mind a night of seduction.

Not a night of baby-sitting!

He banged his fist down on the window-sill and Kate's small china trinket box close to his hand rattled its lid.

From downstairs he heard the sound of a door shutting and as he continued to stare out of the window he caught sight of Kate walking away from the house. He knew he ought to rush out to her, but he stayed where he was. Motionless. Bewildered. He had never known such pain. He watched her cross the courtyard and walk past the block of garages. Then she began to run, her beautiful hair fanning out behind her as she ran across the field where the nearby farmer sometimes grazed his sheep. She went into the darkness of the small copse and vanished out of sight.

'What are you staring at?'

Charlie turned away from the window and faced his brother who had just come into the room.

'You never told me you had such terrific-looking neighbours.'

'I didn't know I had.'

'Well this one was a beauty and she was running into the sunset like a frightened gazelle.'

Josh thought of the only female neighbour he'd met at Cholmford Hall Mews, bearing in mind that he'd felt like death when he'd encountered her. All he could recall of the woman from number four was that she was slim, with a terrific tan. He had the feeling, though, that she wasn't what his brother would describe as a beauty. He knew Charlie's taste in women and they were usually of the very tall, curvy variety. And as far as he knew there wasn't anybody of that description on his doorstep. But then he hadn't exactly gone out of his way to meet his neighbours, having kept himself to himself since moving in.

'So what did she look like?' he asked, going over to the leather sofa and settling himself down, glad to take the strain off his left leg, which had been hanging off him like a dead weight for most of the day. He picked up his can of beer from the glass-topped table in front of him.

Charlie came and joined him. 'I think I've just fallen in love with an angel straight from heaven.'

Josh nearly choked on his beer. 'You what?'

Charlie smiled. 'Okay then. Maybe not. But she was all willowy and gorgeous, like something out of a picture, you know, one of those Pre-Raphaelite paintings.'

'What, the ones where the women look like they've got disjointed necks?'

'Yeah, those are the ones.'

'So let me get this right. There's a woman out there in the fields with a broken neck and you fancy her?'

Charlie sighed. 'You put it so well.'

Josh got to his feet. 'I think you need another beer.'

Charlie followed him out to the kitchen and while Josh opened the fridge he lifted the lid on the pan of curry gently simmering on the hob. 'When's supper ready? I'm starving.'

Josh tossed him a can of beer. 'When we've had our conversation.' He went and sat on a stool at the island unit in the middle of the kitchen.

'Oh, it's the serious stuff now, is it?'

'Got it in one.'

Charlie sat opposite his brother. 'Look,' he said, 'I'm sorry about this morning.'

'Yeah, and so am I, I over-reacted. But if we're going to avoid any repeat performances of that little fiasco we've got to come to some kind of understanding. My body might be doing its best to convince me – and everybody else – that I'm about as useful as a chocolate teapot, but there's nothing wrong with my brain. Okay?'

Charlie nodded. 'I know that, Josh. It's just that –'

'I know what the just is, it's you thinking that you've got to cover for me. But how long do you think you can keep that up? You're shattered with all the extra work you're taking on and I don't know whether you've looked in the mirror recently, but your looks are definitely going.'

'Cheeky sod!'

'Yeah, well, do something about it. Stop treating me like a charity case and let me do my job as best I can, and get yourself home and in bed at a more realistic time each night. Otherwise we'll end up with no company to run because we'll both have blown it.'

Charlie took a long swig of beer. He looked thoughtfully at his brother. 'I hear what you're saying and in principle I agree. But . . .' he raised his hand as Josh opened his mouth to speak, 'don't leap down my throat, but how long do you think *you* can keep this up?'

'Honest answer?'

'Yes.'

'I don't know. Some days I feel fine, as if I could plod on for ever. Other days, I feel like death. But you know that already.'

'You don't think, then, that by easing off work you might . . . you know, you might prolong . . .' But he couldn't finish the question.

Josh did it for him. 'You mean, if I give up work and take it easy will I live to be sixty instead of perhaps snuffing it when I'm in my forties?'

Charlie swallowed. 'I wish you weren't so bloody blunt.'

'But that's the gist of your question, isn't it? Well?' Josh prompted when Charlie didn't answer him.

'Yes,' Charlie muttered morosely. He kept his gaze firmly on the can in his hands. He couldn't begin to imagine life without Josh. It was inconceivable. They weren't like other brothers. There was an extraordinary affinity between them that had enabled the pair of them never to tire of one another's company. They had grown up together; played together; studied together; worked together and even holidayed together. Some might say it was an unnatural relationship, that siblings could never be that close without there being something strange or sinister going on. But the truth was quite straightforward, he loved his brother and would do anything to protect him. He looked up, suddenly realising that Josh was answering his question.

'I have no idea if by taking it easy now my life will be extended, but I can only do what feels right. And what's important to me at the moment is to be able to carry on as though this whole nightmare had never started.'

'So how can I best help?'

'By supporting me, I guess.'

'That's what I've been doing.'

Josh shook his head. 'No. You've been feeling sorry for me. Pity's the last thing I need.'

Charlie crushed the empty beer can in his hand. 'Okay then. I'll try my best.' And wanting to lighten the mood – there was only so much of this he could handle – he said, 'But in return you've got to introduce me to your neighbours. I want to meet that fantastic girl who's just taken flight across the fields.'

Josh stared at the crushed can in front of him and felt a bit demolished himself. 'She's probably not real,' he said, slowly getting to his feet. 'It's just some mythical vision your body has created to taunt you with.'

It was almost dark when Alec heard footsteps on the stairs. Soft, wary footsteps.

He hadn't moved since Kate had fled. He was still standing in the bedroom, his head slumped against the cool glass of the window. He turned and faced her when she came in. She stared at him, the hurt on her face only too visible. She looked pale and fragile, her eyes wide with the pain he'd inflicted on her. He could see that she had been crying and his heart twisted with shame and guilt.

'I'm sorry,' she murmured. 'I should have asked you first about Oscar. I should have thought.'

That she could think herself in the wrong appalled Alec and in an instant he was across the room with his arms around her. He held her so tightly he heard her gasp.

'It's me who should be sorry,' he whispered, burrowing his face into her lovely hair and keeping it there. He couldn't look at her expression. Not because he couldn't risk seeing the anguish he had caused, but because he didn't want her to see the tears in his own eyes.

84

14

Thanks be to Richard Branson, thought Jessica as her train pulled into Euston Station precisely on time; the journey from hell was over.

The fat man in the seat directly opposite her – the cause of two hours and fifteen minutes of purgatory – closed his laptop and began tidying away his portable office, which, as the train had hurtled its way through the sun-dried countryside of Middle England, had steadily encroached further and further towards the small space that Jessica had tried in vain to claim as her own.

As far as Jessica was concerned journeys had a peculiar tendency to bring out the territorial, if not the killer instinct in the most passive of people. Motorways were bad enough with every driver seeing himself as king of the road, but there was nothing like a train journey really to threaten somebody's personal space. Especially if the very latest in high-tech weaponry was being employed – the mobile phone.

And the fat man opposite her must have been a top gun in the use of his.

Of course, she should have known better than to occupy a seat in the same compartment as Porky, never mind sit barely three feet away, but it had been a choice between him or a screaming baby further down the train.

Once she'd made up her mind where to sit she had offered up a smile in the hope of at least setting off on the right foot. But he had ignored her. Fine by me, she had thought, settling herself into her seat and sorting out where to put her large leather bag, which was loaded up with reading matter for the journey.

But it was clear from the word go that nobody but Porky was going to get a moment's peace all the way to London. If he wasn't shuffling through sheaves of paper or rattling the keys on his laptop, he was on the phone. And there was nothing discreet about Porky's manner of conducting business.

'Yah!' he would holler into the small phone pressed into the pudgy flesh of his face, 'Yah. Yah. Yah. Yah, just do it. Yah, thanks. Let me know how you get on. Speak to you soon.'

By the time the train reached Watford Gap, Jessica and her fellow passengers had had enough. But nobody, it seemed, was brave enough to do anything. One or two people shook their newspapers, hoping that this might be enough to shame Porky into quietening down. Someone even tutted. But it was Jessica who decided it was time for action when the horrible man heaved himself out of his seat and headed towards the buffet car. When he was completely out of sight, she leaned forward, reached for one of his yellow Post-its and wrote in large letters – *One more noise from you, Porkster, and you're DEAD!* She stuck it on the screen of his laptop. Her immediate neighbours read what she'd written and smiled their thanks and support.

'Couldn't have put it better myself,' said a tiny grey-haired lady who had been sucking Polo mints all the way from Stoke.

Porky returned with several paper carrier bags of food and drink. He squeezed his bulky frame back into his seat. But just as he'd levelled off he saw the note. He snatched it off the laptop and held it up. 'Who's responsible for this?' he demanded, glaring round at the compartment like a teacher with a class of fifth-form pranksters.

Nobody spoke. Nobody even looked at him. It was as if he didn't exist.

The remaining half-hour of the journey was wonderfully quiet.

As soon as she could, Jessica squeezed past Porky and bolted off the train. She made her way along the busy platform towards the escalator for the underground. She was in luck, a train had just pulled in and she found herself a space jammed up against a George Michael look-alike, extraordinary whiskers and all. He smelt delicious and was rather good-looking, but then after two joyful hours of Porky, Robin Cook would have scored a ten-out-of-ten rating on the hunkometer.

She got out at Charing Cross and began the short walk to Piers's office, which was situated just off Haymarket. It was now, as she made her way through the tourists sunning themselves on the steps of the National Gallery, that she began to worry – at least the awful train journey had kept her mind off her impending doom.

Jessica was convinced that her writing career was over. Last night in bed, she had tossed and turned – even Gavin's T-shirt had been of no use – as her mind had worked through the same scenario again and again: her publishers were no longer interested in her and Piers was unable to find anybody else to take her on, which was probably why he had been so uncharacteristically generous about *A Carefree Life*. Though convinced that this was the case, there was the small voice of reason suggesting that if so, Piers would be the last person to have any qualms about breaking the news to her over the phone. If an author was past her sell-by date Piers would have no problem in sending her packing. 'Jessica,' he would say, 'it's time to clear your desk. Pick up your P45 on your way out.'

By the time she reached the glass-fronted building where Piers hung out on the second floor she was sweating and her stomach was somersaulting a treat. She could barely breathe and there was a dull ache clawing at the back of her head. Nervous tension was a real killer!

She pressed the button and when the doors opened she stepped into the mirror-lined lift and hunted through her bag for a strip of pain-killers. But all she found were a couple of loose Paracetamols, chipped and coated in fluff. She gave them a rub and put them in her mouth and swallowed. One went down, but the other stuck to her tongue and at the foul taste her face twisted into the kind of distorted shape a champion gurner would have been proud of. The lift came to a sudden halt, the doors opened and in front of her stood an immaculately dressed Piers – pin-stripe trousers, light-blue shirt and Old School-style tie. Through her discomfort she was conscious that he blended in nicely with the navy-blue carpet at his feet.

'Les Dawson, I presume,' he said, when he saw her grimacing face.

It was the nearest she'd ever heard Piers get to making a joke. 'I need a glass of water,' she croaked. The tablet was firmly lodged at the back of her throat now and her taste-buds were sending out emergency distress signals. Mayday! Mayday! Poison alert! Prepare to abandon ship. Which was a smart way for her body to say that if something wasn't done soon, Piers would have a revolting mess on his office carpet.

Stella, Piers's assistant, was sent for and was given the task of sorting Jessica out, and when she finally emerged from the toilet she composed herself and allowed Stella to escort her to Piers's office. He was waiting for her.

'Sorry about that,' she said, 'it must be the air down here in London, it doesn't agree with me.'

He gave her a look as if to say, are you quite finished? Then lifted his jacket from the back of his chair and pulled it on. 'Let's go and eat.'

Jessica had rather hoped that Piers would put her out of her misery before they went to the restaurant. Perhaps he was such a sadist that he was enjoying the moment of keeping her in an agony of suspense. Oh well, if that was the case, she'd have the most expensive meal the restaurant had to offer. That would serve him right.

He took her to the Caprice.

'I was here with Nick Hornby last week,' he told her as they perused their menus.

'Who?' Jessica asked, knowing full well whom Piers meant; she'd read *Fever Pitch* as soon as the book had made it to the shelves in Kassiopi. It was the first time she'd known Piers even hint at trying to impress her. What was going on? A joke earlier and now a blatant case of social climbing. He'd be telling her next that he was a drinking chum of A. A. Gill. She shuddered at the thought.

He lowered his menu and contemplated her. 'You're going to have to get your act together, Jessica,' he said sternly. 'Now that you're back in England you'll have no excuse for being out of touch.'

Her act of out-of-touchness was her deliberate way of showing up other people's hoity-toity pretentiousness. And anyway she had never been out of touch with England. The *Sunday Times* had always been available to her in Corfu and her mother had regularly sent her videos of all the best in TV drama, though she had begun to question Anna's taste when tapes of *Star Trek: The Next Generation* had arrived in the post. 'Why should I have to get my act together?' she asked Piers. She was being bold now. Well, why not? If she was being given the old heave-ho, she might just as well go out fighting to the last.

He didn't answer her. Instead he caught the eye of a passing waitress and began ordering his lunch. When he'd finished he looked pointedly at Jessica. So did the waitress.

'I'll have the duck whatsit on a bed of asparagus, followed by the pan-fried chicken liver with rosti, and I want the liver cooked. I don't want to cut into it and find lumps of strawberry jelly.' She slapped the menu down on the table and leant back in her chair. She was really getting into the part now: recalcitrant and thoroughly obnoxious.

'In that case we'll have a bottle of red wine,' Piers said, ignoring her performance and making her feel like a naughty child. 'I think the 1994 St Chinian will be suitable.'

When they were alone he said, 'How's the new house?'

Now this was going too far. Piers making small talk. No, really. This had to stop. 'Piers,' she said, 'would you please get to the point?'

'The point?'

'Yes. Just why on earth have you dragged me all the way down here?'

He smiled. Well, it was almost a smile; a slight lifting of the corners of his mouth. For a split second he looked almost handsome. Jessica had never before considered Piers as a good-looking man, but she decided that if he could only get the hang of this smiling thing he would stand a chance of being half decent; marriage material even. To her knowledge – Stella being her main source of information – Piers had never been married and at the age of forty-seven he gave the impression of having no desire to do so. Jessica would put money on him not being gay, though why she felt so strongly on this score she had no idea. Perhaps it was his brusqueness that precluded this possibility. Not that all gay men had to go around gushing like Julian Clary.

Their wine arrived and Piers instructed the waitress to leave them to it. He poured out a large glass for Jessica and one for himself.

'I think this is what the clever-arsed folk would call a champagne moment,' he said, raising his glass, 'but you know me well enough to know that I'm not a champagne person, or clever-arsed for that matter, so this will do well enough instead. Come on, raise your glass.'

Jessica did as she was told, but viewed Piers suspiciously. He was up to something. A spot of softening up before delivering the blow perhaps?

'To your next contract,' he said. 'Congratulations.'

'My what?'

'You heard. Go on, drink up.'

She took a sip, then a gulp. Followed by an even larger mouthful. 'So why didn't you tell me this on the phone?'

He leant back in his chair. 'I wanted to tell you in person. I think the occasion merits such treatment. Nothing's definite and it's all down to you to make the final decision, but how do you feel about switching horses?'

'I think you'd better explain.'

Their first course arrived and while they flapped napkins open, sprinkled salt and pepper and poured out more wine, Piers explained. 'As you know, now that you've delivered *A Carefree Life* you've fulfilled your contract which means –'

'Which means I'm now out of contract.'

'Precisely. And I think you've outgrown where you are.'

'How do you work that out?'

'I've had an offer from another publisher who's prepared to pay a substantial amount of money for you.'

Jessica reached for her wineglass. 'How much? And which publisher?'

'One question at a time.'

She gulped her wine and tried to stop her knees from shaking under the table. It was all turning out so differently from how she'd imagined, and the combination of shock and relief was transforming her into a jittery mess. She planted both feet firmly on the ground in the hope it would keep her legs from moving. But it didn't work. They carried on banging away like pistons.

'You're being offered a two-book contract,' she heard Piers say. But suddenly he stopped and stared at her. 'Jessica,' he said, 'are you playing footsie with me?'

'Certainly not!' she squeaked. And with enormous will-power she forced her legs to be still.

He carried on, but with a curious expression on his face. 'As I was saying, it's a two-book contract and three times what you're currently being paid.'

Jessica drained her glass and goggled. The cutlery on the table began to rattle as her legs started up again.

Piers refilled her glass and said, 'Got anything to say?'

'Um ... supposing I don't like my new editor?'

Piers rolled his eyes. 'For this kind of money, Jessica, I'd make an effort to get on with Genghis Khan.'

'But I like where I am.'

'In that case you'll have to accept their lower offer.'

'Which is?'

'A two-book contract and only twice what you're currently getting.'

Jessica considered what Piers had just told her. It was difficult to take it in. One minute she was worrying about her mortgage and the next she was feeling like Barbara Taylor Bradford. 'Even if I take the lower offer, it's still a lot of money, isn't it? I mean, it's oodles more than I ever thought I'd get paid. Squillions more in fact.'

'Such a precise command of the English language you have when it comes to money, Jessica. But it's only what an author of mine deserves. How's your duck by the way?'

They left the restaurant a little after three and took a cab back to the office. Jessica had been too shocked and excited to eat a thing and had drunk far more than was good for her. She tried to sit upright in the back of the cab, but somehow she kept slipping to one side. At one point she ended up with her head on Piers's shoulder. In a more sober state she would sooner have put it inside a tandoori oven.

They sat in his office and Stella was instructed to bring them coffee. And lots of it.

'I'm not drunk,' she told Piers as she sank into a chair.

'And I'm the Archbishop of Canterbury,' he said drily.

She giggled and found she couldn't stop. She laughed and laughed until tears were rolling down her cheeks. He came over and passed her his handkerchief.

'Thank you,' she said, pressing the hanky to her face. The square of crisp linen smelt of aftershave. *Piers wore aftershave?* Why hadn't she noticed that before? She tried to picture him at home in his bachelor bathroom splashing about with bottles of Givenchy or Chanel for Men. But it was no good. All she could imagine was Piers shaving in his office, too busy to bother with anything as trivial as men's toiletries.

She looked up at him as he stood leaning against his desk, his hands placed either side of him. She suspected that he was having a crack at smiling again, that mouth of his was definitely slightly more curved than it had been a few moments ago. She suddenly wondered what he was like in bed. Underneath that stern façade was there a passionate man who was dynamite between the sheets? Never mind the bedroom, how about the office, spread-eagled across the desk? The thought that she would like to find out had the effect of instantly sobering her up. *Arrgh! She'd actually just considered the possibility of having sex with Piers!*

She reached for the cup of coffee Stella had brought in some time ago and quickly drank it, even though it was nearly cold.

'Fully recovered now?' Piers asked, regrouping to the other side of his desk.

'Er . . . yes, thank you,' she said. She tried to make her voice sound sure and businesslike, and made an even bigger effort to sit up straight. 'Sorry about that, it's the shock. You know, the excitement of it all.'

He stared at her, his head slightly tilted to one side.

He knows, she thought. He knows what I was just thinking. She squirmed in her seat.

'So,' he said slowly, 'what's your decision?'

She cleared her throat. 'Um . . . I don't know.'

He tutted. Sentiment, his expression said. Nothing but woolly-minded sentiment. 'I'm sure I don't need to remind you that you have to think of your long-term future.'

'I know all that, but it's not just the money,' she said lamely, 'it's the personal side of the working relationship that counts as well. Cara and I get on. I might not like my new editor.'

'I thought we'd already covered that.'

She frowned.

He held up his hands. 'Okay. If you don't want to make the move that's fine by me. It's entirely your decision.'

Jessica needed some time on her own to work things out. So she went to the toilet to make up her mind. It was a ridiculous thing to do, but after ten minutes of deliberation she decided that if the loo flushed perfectly first go she would stay where she was. If it took two yanks of the handle, as it normally did whenever she used a strange toilet, then she would take the money and run. She held her breath and gave the loo handle an almighty shove – Frank Bruno couldn't have put more into it.

She went back to Piers. 'I'm staying with Cara and the team,' she said firmly, but not looking him in the eye – her decision to accept a lower offer meant that Piers had just lost out financially as well.

He made no comment, but offered her another cup of coffee and insisted on personally taking her back to Euston for her train.

'It's to be the red-carpet treatment from now on, is it?' she said, as they walked along the station platform, 'now that I'm one of your big earners.'

'I've always treated you well, Jessica.'

She came to a stop. 'Piers, you've never once walked me to my train and as far as I'm concerned you've treated me abominably ever since I've known you. You take a tenth of anything I earn and make me feel like shit.'

He raised an eyebrow. 'Good to know that I'm so good at my job. And if you really want to know why I'm escorting you to your train it's because in your current state of mind I wouldn't trust you to find the end of your nose.'

15

Jessica found herself a seat in a relatively uncrowded compartment. She hoped that there wasn't a clone of Porky lurking somewhere in the carriage.

As the train pulled out of the station she closed her eyes. Her head was beginning to ache again. What was needed was a quick forty winks.

But a nap didn't work and by the time they reached Rugby she knew she was in for a migraine. The dull ache had spread to the right side of her head and was throbbing with all the intensity of a pneumatic drill. She kept her eyes shut to stop the pain caused by the blinding overhead light and when the train stopped at Crewe she went and stood in the corridor by an open window, hoping that the cool evening air would help.

But it didn't and twenty minutes later, when the train finally pulled into Cholmford Station, Jessica walked like a zombie along the deserted platform. The station was unmanned and there was no sign of a phone. She was completely alone. She cursed herself for not having arranged for a taxi to pick her up. There was nothing else for it but to walk.

She staggered along the empty lanes for almost a mile, her head feeling as though it were going to explode. She felt so desperately ill that she was tempted to lie down in the road and wait for a passing car to run her over and put her out of her misery – if only there were any cars about. She had reached the stage now where the migraine was making her feel sick and light-headed. She reckoned that her mother's house was only a mile away so she struggled on. But it was no good. She couldn't go another step. There was a gap in the hedgerow and seeing that there was a small stump of a tree hidden in the long grass of the verge, she sat down and tried to breathe slowly and deeply. All around her it was very quiet. It wasn't yet dark, but the light was fading fast. She had never felt so isolated. A perfect night for a murder, she thought. No one to hear her screams. No one to appear on the *Six O'Clock News* as a key witness. She was just cursing her mother for living in the most remote spot in the whole of Cheshire when she heard the sound of a car coming along the lane.

'Oh please, God,' she said, seeing the headlights and getting to her feet, 'let it be someone prepared to help a damsel in distress.' She stood in the middle of the road determined that the driver would have no choice but to stop for her. She didn't give a thought to her safety – the person behind the wheel could be the mad axeman of Cholmford on the look-out for his latest victim for all she cared. He could chop her up into convenient bite-sized pieces and it would be fine by her – she'd even hold herself steady so that he could get make a better job of it – because at least then her head would stop hurting. Perhaps she could insist that he start by chopping her head off first.

Josh slowed down. He switched off Michael Nyman's *The Draughtsman's Contract* and as he approached the strange figure in the road he recognised who it was. It was his neighbour from number four. He got out of the Shogun and went to her. She didn't look at all well. She was very pale and her eyes were unfocused. She was shivering, too.

'Please,' she said, 'whoever you are, can you give me a lift to Cholmford Hall Mews? And if you are a mad axeman, do you think you could treat yourself to a night off?'

He smiled. 'Okay, but just this once.' He helped her into the car.

She didn't speak for the next hundred yards, then suddenly she blurted out, 'Stop!'

He slammed on the brakes and before he could get out of the car to offer his assistance she was on the roadside bent over a clump of stinging nettles.

After a few moments she got back into the car. He handed her the box of tissues he kept in the glove compartment. 'I'm not drunk,' she murmured, 'if that's what you're thinking. I've got a migraine, it always gets me like this. I'm sorry.'

'Let me know if you need to stop again,' he said.

'Don't worry, I will.' She put her head back against the head-rest and closed her eyes. She looked really ill now. He wondered if she had recognised who he was yet.

In all, they stopped three times. When they finally reached Cholmford Hall Mews, Josh parked as close to number four as he could. He went round to her side of the car and opened the door. 'Okay?' he said. 'You're home. Have you got your keys?'

She stepped down, took a couple of paces and lurched forward, almost knocking Josh clean off his feet as she fainted against him.

Regaining his balance, he decided the best thing he could do was to push her back into the car and take her over to his place. It didn't seem fair to leave her all alone.

She came to just as he started up the engine. 'I thought I'd already got out of the car,' she said drowsily.

'You did, but you also fainted.' He drove across the courtyard.

'Oh dear, I'm making a nuisance of myself, aren't I?' she said in a small voice. 'Where are we going?'

He pulled on the handbrake. 'My house. I don't think you should be on your own. And don't worry, I promise you, hand on heart, I've taken the evening off from axe murdering.'

She looked at him for the first time. 'I've just realised who you are. You're my rude neighbour, aren't you?'

Josh frowned at this description of himself.

'Right,' he said, when they were inside the house. 'What do you normally do when you have a bad migraine like this?'

She leant back against the wall, light-headed and dizzy. 'Bed, hot-water bottle and complete darkness.'

'Okay, can you manage the stairs?' It was strange asking somebody else this question. Usually it was asked of him. They made slow progress and Josh was glad that his neighbour was unable to go any faster, at least it meant he could keep up with her.

At the top of the stairs he led her to the spare room. The bed wasn't made up, but he opened a cupboard and pulled out a duvet. He threw it on the bed, followed by a couple of pillows. He also found a hot-water bottle. 'I'll be back in a minute with this,' he said.

Downstairs in the kitchen he boiled a kettle, found a bucket – just in case – from under the sink in the utility room, filled the hot-water bottle and grabbing a box of tissues from the window-sill he slowly made his way back up the stairs. He tapped lightly on the door and went in. She was already in bed, fully dressed, judging by the lone pair of shoes on the floor. She was very nearly asleep. He handed her the hot-water bottle and put the other things on the floor beside her.

'I'll leave you to it,' he whispered, 'just give me a shout if you need anything.'

She nodded and he crept quietly away.

Jessica opened her eyes, but then immediately closed them. She didn't want to wake up. She wanted to stay where she was in Gavin's arms. They had been making love on the hot sand beneath a cloudless sky – it had been like *From Here to Eternity*, but in colour and without the messy crashing waves. But try as she might to recapture the dream, she couldn't, it was gone.

And so was her migraine.

She opened her eyes again and remembered where she was – her neighbour's spare room. She peeped under the duvet. She was fully dressed. Well, that was okay then. She looked at her watch and saw that she'd been asleep for just over an hour. She sat up slowly. Very slowly. If she moved too quickly at this stage the blinding pain would come back.

She shifted the pillows behind her shoulders and looked about her, taking in the room in the semi-darkness. For a man who had just moved house there was very little sign of him having done so. All was neat and tidy. Apart from there not being any curtains up at the window.

She could make out the sound of music coming from downstairs. It was a familiar opera, but one she couldn't remember the name of. It irritated her that she couldn't recall its title. Puccini, she decided. It was definitely Puccini. But which opera?

After ten minutes of sitting quietly she ventured out of bed. She stood up and found that the dizziness had gone, as had the nausea. She felt a bit embarrassed going downstairs. It wasn't every day that she ended up sleeping in the house of a man whom she barely knew and who had taken on more than his fair share of neighbourly kindness.

She found him in the sitting-room, bent over a mound of paperwork. From an impressive-looking hi-fi system in the corner of the room Puccini was still doing his stuff.

'Hi,' he said, when he saw that she was there. He put down his work, took off his glasses and got to his feet. 'How are you feeling?'

'Like I've been beaten over the head with a frying pan,' she said, squinting against the light.

'Is it too much for you? I'll turn it off if you like and just leave a lamp on.'

She nodded her thanks and watched him move across the room. He seemed to be limping much more than she remembered when she'd first seen him.

He caught her looking at his leg. 'It's an old skiing injury,' he said hurriedly, 'it comes and goes. Please, sit down.'

She hesitated. 'I really ought to go. You've done so much to help me, the least I can do is leave you in peace.'

'Nonsense. I'll make you a drink. What would you like?'

'Tea would be great.' She was glad that he wasn't making her feel that she should be off straight away and while he was out of the room she settled herself in a chair as far away from the lamp as possible.

Whoever her neighbour was he had good taste. The room, though sparsely furnished, was comfortable and homely. The chair she was sitting in matched the leather sofa, which was black and well worn and had a couple of terracotta-coloured cushions placed at each end. In front of it was a glass-topped coffee table that her neighbour had been working at, and on the floor was a large rectangular black-and-red rug that had Rothko stamped all over it. The other pieces of furniture were all modern in design and appeared to be made of beechwood; they contrasted stylishly with the wrought-iron lamps. There were several Italianate architectural prints in gilt frames covering the walls and either side of the fireplace were hundreds of books crammed into the built-in shelves that went right up to the ceiling. Jessica was pleased to conclude that her Good Samaritan was a man who liked to read.

Unlike Gavin.

She was sure that the last book Gavin had read was *Noddy Gets Into Trouble.*

It was a shame that she was still feeling so groggy as she would have loved to have prowled round the room and explored her neighbour's belongings.

'Have you managed to take any pain-killers, yet?' he asked, coming back with two large mugs and a packet of something under his arm.

'No,' she said, 'and that was the problem. I didn't have any with me.'

He put the mugs on the glass-topped table and handed her the packet he'd been carrying. 'Try those,' he said, sitting down on the sofa, 'they usually do the trick for me.'

'You get migraines as well?'

'Not so much these days.' Which was true. He might have a lot else going wrong with him, but hey, the migraines had eased up. Fair exchange was no robbery, as they say.

Jessica read the back of the packet, popped two tablets out of the foil packaging and swallowed them down with a gulp of tea. 'This is really kind of you,' she said. 'I don't know what I would have done if you hadn't come along.'

'It's no problem.' He smiled.

And what a smile, thought Jessica. Here's a man who could teach Piers a thing or two.

'My name's Josh, by the way,' he said, leaning back into the soft leather of the sofa and straightening his long legs, 'Josh Crawford.'

'And I'm Jessica Lloyd and I can assure you I don't normally go around throwing up in the bushes for an evening's entertainment.'

He smiled again.

Wow! When the sex appeal was being handed out this guy must have been first in the queue.

'You know, I've always meant to apologise to you,' he said.

'What on earth for?'

'For that day when I barged my way into your house for my keys. I had no idea the show house had changed.'

'Oh that. Forget it. And if it makes you feel any better my mother thought you were rather dishy. That's her phraseology, not mine.'

'And what did you think?'

'I thought you were exceptionally rude.'

He lowered his gaze, surprised at her candour. 'Then I have to hope that my rescue of you tonight has in some way made up for my appalling behaviour that day.'

Jessica smiled. 'Put like that, I have no choice but to agree fully with my mother's description of you.'

He looked up and saw from her face that she was gently making fun of him. 'Good,' he said, entering into the spirit of the conversation. 'So this mother of yours, who has such impeccable taste in men, does she live nearby?'

Jessica laughed. 'Yes, very close by. We passed her house on the way here. I would have pointed it out to you, only I was otherwise engaged. It's the one just by the canal bridge.'

He raised an eyebrow. 'There? It's a lovely house. Great situation as well.'

'Everyone says that.'

'And is that where you grew up?'

Jessica nodded and as she finished her tea the music on the hi-fi came to an end. It seemed the right time to leave. 'I really should go now,' she said, stretching forward to put her empty mug on the table.

'Must you?' he asked. It had been a while since Josh had enjoyed the company of a woman in this way and he was reluctant for the evening to come to an end.

'It's quite late,' she said, 'I'd hate to outstay my welcome.' Much as she thought she ought to be making a move, Jessica was more than happy to stay and chat. Having decided that her rude neighbour wasn't at all the uncouth monster she'd thought he was, she was keen to find out a little more about him.

'You're more than welcome to stay,' he said. 'In fact, I'd rather you did, it would stop me from working.'

Jessica glanced at the open files at the far end of the table. 'Okay,' she said, 'it's a deal.'

'Good. Would you like something to eat?'

'No thanks, but another cup of tea would be good.'

She watched him limp out of the room, then she too got up. She went over to the CD player and inspected the two tall beechwood columns of CDs. There was practically every taste in music accounted for: Northern Soul, Choral, Reggae, Frank Sinatra – *Frank Sinatra?* – Rock, Classical and Blues. She then checked the CD that they'd been listening to and found that she had been wrong. It hadn't been Puccini at all. It had been Verdi's *La Traviata*.

When Josh came back into the room, she said, 'Can we have this on again, please?'

'Sure.' He put their mugs on the table and came over and pressed the start button. They were standing very close, so close that even in the half-light Jessica could see the intense dark hue to his brown eyes as he looked at her. She could also see how dilated his pupils were. *Talk about the stuff of romantic fiction!* She cleared her throat – unnecessarily – and moved away, back to the chair in which she'd been sitting.

'So where have you been today?' he asked, also resuming his earlier position. 'You look too smartly dressed to have been out rambling.'

She cast her eyes over her sleep-crumpled suit – her one and only suit. 'I'd been down to London,' she said.

'For pleasure or for business?'

'Could London ever be for pleasure?'

'Depends on your viewpoint.'

'Well this was definitely for business and I'm afraid to say I behaved very badly at one point.'

'Oh?'

'I was given some fantastically brilliant news, having expected the reverse, and the shock of it made me drink too much over lunch, which I couldn't eat, and I very nearly made a pass at my agent, so that tells you how bad I was.' She groaned and hung her head, recalling her behaviour in the taxi and in Piers's office.

He laughed. 'There's a lot of information packed into that one sentence. Any hope of you disentangling it for me?'

She looked up and smiled. 'It'll have to be another time. I'm too tired now.'

'Well, when you've drunk your tea I'll be the perfect gentleman and see you safely across the courtyard.'

'I wouldn't want to put you to all that bother, not with your dodgy leg.' As soon as her words were out, Jessica knew she'd said the wrong thing. It was as if a cloud as black as the shirt he was wearing passed over Josh's face. 'You'll have to go easy on the skiing in future,' she said, trying to make light of the situation. 'Bones, ligaments, muscles, they're all tricky blighters, they take for ever to mend.'

'Yes,' he said flatly. 'I guess you're right.'

When Jessica had gone, Josh turned up the volume on the CD player and the final act of *La Traviata* filled the sitting-room. He threw himself on to the sofa.

He was angry.

Not with Jessica – she couldn't have had any idea that what she'd said would have meant anything to him. No, he was furious with himself. Why did he let these things get to him? Why couldn't he just brush it off? It was a chance remark. Nothing more. They were getting on fine until he'd acted like an idiot.

And there was another thing. Why had he lied? *Skiing injury! It comes and goes!* Too bloody right it does. Just what the hell had he thought he was doing?

Apart from wanting to make a good impression on Jessica.

Apart from wanting her to view him as a whole man.

Apart from convincing her that he wasn't some weak, uninspiring invalid.

Oh, to hell with it! What was the point anyway?

In spite of his anger he couldn't help but smile at the memory of the pair of them over by the hi-fi. There'd been a split second when he had thought of kissing Jessica. In the old days he wouldn't have hesitated. He would have swooped in on her and steered her towards the sofa.

He got up and went in search of something to drink. He found some Scotch in the dining-room, poured himself a large glassful and took it back to the sitting-room.

Like in the old days, he repeated to himself. The good old days before ... before everything had started going wrong. Before he'd started having trouble with his balance. Before his legs had begun to feel like lead. And before that humiliating night in Hong Kong when he'd fallen down a short flight of stairs and everyone had thought he was drunk.

He took another swig of Scotch.

His last girlfriend had run a mile when she'd found out that she was dating a guy who was likely to end up in a wheelchair.

Well, lucky old her that she could run a bloody mile. Good bloody riddance!

16

It was Saturday afternoon. The sun was high and very hot, and as it shone through the window it beckoned Tony to leave the confines of his study, where he was checking through that month's sales figures, and go outside.

It was a tempting thought and one he was inclined to take up as it would give him a welcome break from Amanda endlessly rushing about the house getting it ready for that evening's dinner party. She had dusted, cleaned and polished from the minute she had got out of bed and, for no good reason that he could understand, she seemed intent on ruthlessly cleansing the entire house from top to bottom. She was now vacuuming the hall and as she approached the study he experienced the sensation of his breath being sucked out of his body.

A walk with Hattie was definitely what he needed. He switched off his computer, stood up and turned to confront the turbo-powered monster making its way into his study.

'Why don't you take Hattie for a walk?' Amanda shouted above the din. She seemed to Tony in that moment just as much a turbo-powered monster as the machine she was wielding. 'I'm sure she'd like that.'

'Good idea,' he said, thoroughly irritated that Amanda had suggested what was already in his mind.

Hattie ran on ahead, while he strolled behind at a more leisurely pace. They took the path leading away from the development and began walking through the long grass, and as the distance between them and the house grew he thought how strange it was to be on his own with Hattie with Amanda's blessing. It was an unusual occurrence. Invariably Amanda wanted him to spend more time with her.

He knew that she had found it hard adjusting to her role as stepmother, but there had been times in the past few months – though not this week – when he had found himself impossibly torn between his wife and his daughter. Maybe it was to be expected. Perhaps a second wife had more to be insecure about than a first. With an unknown act to follow, and if the relationship was to work, it was more than likely that the new partner needed, *and deserved*, a much greater depth of love and reassurance than the previous wife. If this was true, and Tony suspected it was, then he knew with certainty that he was unable to offer Amanda what she needed most from him.

When they reached the cool shade of the copse of trees Hattie said, 'Shall we climb a tree?'

They found a suitable candidate: a small oak with a branch that was just low enough for Tony to hoist Hattie up on to it. She began moving along the thick branch to a hollow spot nearer the trunk of the tree and waited for him to join her. He jumped, caught hold of the bough and hauled himself up.

'It's great, isn't it?' Hattie said, squeezing herself close to him. 'We can see for miles. Look, there's our house, right over there.'

He stared to where she was pointing and dangled his legs beneath him. It was years since he'd climbed anything other than the corporate ladder and being here with Hattie brought back happy carefree memories from his own childhood. Days when the biggest dilemma he had had to face was whether there was time to play another game of tag in the street with his friends before his mother would call him in for tea. Now he was head to head with perhaps the biggest dilemma of his life – how to carry on with his marriage.

He had reached this depressing conclusion while driving home from work last night. He had had a lousy day, having delivered the news to three of his most experienced salesmen that they were no longer required by Arc. Throughout each session he had cursed Bradley Hurst for his short-sightedness. Letting go of good men like Dave, Alan and Richard didn't make sense. Not when they would eventually end up working for their main rivals, taking with them years of accrued knowledge and invaluable experience.

Dave had been gracious enough to say, 'No personal ill feelings, Tony. I know it's not your fault. It's the way things are done.'

But both Alan and Richard had been furious, particularly Alan, and with good reason, as his wife was expecting their third child any day. 'You're nothing but a yes man, Tony,' he'd snarled across the desk. 'And don't think we don't know how chummy you are with that bastard Hurst. Each time he comes over and gives you the latest edict you're practically kissing his arse to keep in with him.'

The insults had escalated until Tony had insisted that Alan get out of his office, which he did, leaving Tony in no doubt that Alan held him directly responsible for the loss of his job. And when driving home late last night, having the roads practically to himself, Tony had been filled with the desire to jack it all in. He'd had enough of being in a no-win situation at work. He hadn't slogged his guts out ever since leaving school to be on the receiving end of such dog's abuse.

At the entrance to the avenue of chestnut trees he had stopped his Porsche and wondered what the hell he was doing at Arc Computers. Was this really the life he had imagined for himself? And as he'd sat in the car in the gathering dark, he couldn't figure out which depressed him more, his job or his loveless marriage.

'Daddy?'

He turned and faced Hattie. He could see from her expression in the dappled sunlight that she must have been trying to attract his attention for some time.

'I'm sorry. What did you say?'

'Why do you look so sad, Daddy? Is it Mummy, do you still miss her?'

His heart twisted. 'Yes,' he said honestly. And he truly did. Every time he looked at his daughter's face he was reminded of Eve.

'Are you missing her now?'

'A little,' he confessed. The truth was that a part of him – that bit he kept from the rest of the world, including Hattie – missed Eve every day. It now occurred to him that since her death his life had lacked direction. With Eve, he had seemed set on a particular course – a shared course – and one that he'd been keen to follow. But now none of those life goals seemed important. Everything seemed shallow and trivial and uninteresting. Work. Marriage. Even the new house that he and Amanda had been so keen to buy. Though if he was honest it had been Amanda who had settled on Cholmford Hall Mews. She had hated moving into the house that he and Hattie lived in and had started going round the various estate agents in the area picking up details on all manner of properties. But then at least she'd been straight with him and said how she felt about sharing the home that he and Eve had created. Not that he would have been so insensitive as to have expected Amanda to slip neatly into Eve's shoes.

He wondered now about Amanda's sudden change of heart. Or whatever it was that had happened to her these past few days. Ever since that night out with the Hursts she had been acting differently. It was as if she had turned over a new leaf and was going out of her way to please him. It was callous of him, but he couldn't help likening her to a Stepford Wife. He'd noticed too that she was trying harder to get along with Hattie and of that he realised he should be glad. But deep down he knew that whatever Amanda was doing, without a monumental change of heart within himself it was pointless.

'It's like we've run away, isn't it?' Hattie said, looking up into his face. 'Nobody knows we're here. We could just stay here in this tree for ever and ever.'

And ever – he echoed in his head. He smiled and gave her a hug, and pulled out a packet of Opal Fruits from his back pocket. 'I sneaked them from the tin in the cupboard in the kitchen,' he confessed. He offered her the first one.

She chewed noisily on the strawberry-flavoured sweet, making great sucking noises. When she'd finished she said, 'When Kate came to baby-sit she told me that there was a pond here somewhere. Shall we see if we can find it? Maybe we could go for a paddle.'

'If you like.'

They climbed down from the tree, Tony first and then Hattie. She slipped with a light thud into his waiting arms. As they walked further into the copse, Tony had to acknowledge that his daughter's mention of Kate was stirring up yet more disquieting thoughts in him – innermost thoughts that so far he'd been unable to formulate or, more truthfully, hadn't had the courage to express with any clarity for fear of what he might discover about himself. Was it possible that whatever it was he felt for Kate was because his life was in such a mess? Were chaos and turmoil making him behave irrationally? Was his troubled mind causing him to imagine himself in love with a woman whom he didn't know? And if all this was true, what was to become of him? Was he one step away from the funny farm?

'Yucky!' said Hattie, pulling a face when they came to the edge of a large pool of murky green water, 'I don't want to paddle in that. What shall we do now?'

'How about a game of hide and seek?'

'Good idea. I'll hide first.'

'All right,' agreed Tony, 'but only on condition that you don't go anywhere near the water. Got that?'

She nodded and scampered away. 'Close your eyes and count down from fifty,' she shouted over her shoulder.

Tony did as she said and as he called out the numbers he had the sinking feeling that he was performing a countdown on his life.

When at last they had exhausted all possible hiding places Tony swung Hattie up on to his shoulders and slowly they made their way home in the hot afternoon sunshine. He was in no hurry to get back – he had no desire to be caught up in Amanda's determined attempts to impress their new neighbours – and if it weren't so hot and Hattie weren't desperate for a drink he'd have willingly stayed out longer. He had enjoyed his afternoon with Hattie and, giving her tired little legs a squeeze as they dangled over his shoulders, he made up his mind that whatever madness he was on the brink of he would spend more time with her.

As they drew level with the front door of number one he caught sight of their immediate neighbour just getting into his Shogun. He hadn't yet had the opportunity to introduce himself and seizing the moment, Tony went over to say hello.

17

At long, long last Oscar had fallen asleep.

Alec switched off the cassette player and brought a much needed end to his ordeal. Since leaving Oxford it seemed as if he'd heard the same banal song over and over – if he was forced to hear one more squeaked 'eh-oh' from the Teletubbies he'd throw the wretched tape out of the car window. He glanced sideways at Kate and saw that she was looking at him.

'Has it been very awful for you?' she asked.

'Yes,' he said, but then he smiled and reached out for her hand and squeezed it. 'Only joking. It's hard work, though, isn't it, keeping him entertained the whole time?'

Kate didn't agree, but she wasn't going to risk upsetting Alec by saying so. Their trip down to Oxford had been fun and had helped to heal the damage caused by their argument of Thursday night, but even so, Kate was anxious not to rock the boat and say the wrong thing to Alec.

He couldn't have apologised more for what he'd said to her, but she still felt the sting of his words – You thought *you'd* enjoy it. Never before had she heard Alec's usually soft voice weighted with such coldness and never would she have imagined him capable of wanting to hurt her. But he hadn't meant to hurt her, he'd told her that repeatedly in bed after she'd come back from sitting outside in the dark.

'I don't know what came over me,' he'd said, cradling her in his arms. 'I'm sorry, truly I am.' He had fallen asleep almost immediately, but she had lain awake, for the first time unsure about her future with Alec.

Only a few days ago she had thought she had discovered perfect peace at last, that the sense of belonging she had craved all her life was to be found through Alec. But lying there in the dark emptiness of the night she had begun to worry that this was not the case.

She had slipped out of bed and crept quietly downstairs and while making herself a drink she had wondered if out of need for that most basic of human requirements – to love and to be loved – she had been too hasty and unrealistic in her expectations of Alec. In her ready acceptance of a man she thought could offer her all the love and reassurance she had ever wanted, had she deliberately overlooked the one vital question she should have asked herself before she'd got so inextricably involved with him: had her upbringing led her into a situation that was doomed to fail?

But who was to say what was and what wasn't an acceptable basis for a loving relationship? What did it matter that she loved a man who was old enough to be her father? Surely all that mattered was that she loved him.

And she did love Alec.

So much so, that for him she was willing to sacrifice her desire to have children.

She had always wanted to have a child of her own, but Alec had made it very clear, right from the start of their relationship, that he didn't want any more. 'I'm too old to go through all that again,' he'd told her, 'much too old. I want to be able to enjoy myself with you, not be up in the night chasing bottles and nappies.'

And because she had felt so wonderfully secure, wrapped in his love and affection, she had been confident that she could come to terms with this ultimate sacrifice. But the longing for a child was never far away and Oscar's ever-increasing presence in her life was a poignant reminder of what she was to miss out on.

But perhaps this too was another example of her subconscious searching to resolve her own childhood.

'Penny for them?' Alec suddenly said.

'I was thinking about supper over at number two tonight,' she said. It was her first lie to Alec. Was this the start, then? Was this when they began to cover up their true feelings for fear of hurting or upsetting each other?

'Are we in for a deadly dull evening, do you think?' he asked, interrupting her thoughts once more.

She smiled, determined to put her anxiety aside. 'It would be worse if Jessica weren't going.'

'You seem to have made a good friend there; I'm glad about that.'

'Are you?' Immediately she regretted the words.

Alec took his eyes off the motorway and looked at her. 'What a strange question,' he said. 'Why wouldn't I be pleased?'

She didn't say anything, but Alec knew why she had asked it. And it served him right for playing the part of possessive lover the other night. His behaviour had told her in no uncertain terms that he wanted her all to himself, that he couldn't bear to share her with anyone. He badly wished that Thursday could be erased from their memories, but he knew it couldn't. His complete sense of unworthiness compelled him to go on seeking confirmation from Kate that he hadn't hurt her as much as he knew he had. More than anything he needed to believe that she had forgiven him. 'Are you still upset about the other night?' he asked gently.

But before Kate had a chance to reply a sleepy voice from the back of the car said, 'I need a wee.'

At four o'clock they pulled up outside Ruth and Adam's beautifully proportioned Georgian cottage. It constantly amused Kate that Adam chose to live in such an exquisite home himself, but designed for others some of the oddest houses she'd ever seen.

The sight of a bright-red MR2 on the driveway didn't amuse her, though. It was Melissa's car. And while Alec switched off the engine and unbuckled his seat-belt, she fought back the urge to brush her hair and check her face in the mirror.

Oscar ran on ahead and banged on the front door, while Kate and Alec followed behind, carrying between them an assortment of his luggage, along with his car seat. Ruth opened the door.

'I've been to Oxford,' Oscar announced excitedly. 'Kate took me on a big bus that didn't have a roof and we saw lots of –'

But Ruth wasn't listening. 'There you are at last,' she said, directing her words at Kate. 'Why didn't you phone to say you were going to be so late?'

'I didn't think we were late,' Kate answered.

'Come on, Ruth,' Alec said, oblivious to his daughter's rudeness, 'out of the way so we can off-load this little lot.'

She let them pass. 'No, not there, Dad,' she said, 'you're cluttering up the hall. Take it through to the playroom.'

Kate followed behind Alec, their footsteps echoing on the polished wooden floor. They deposited Oscar's car seat beside a row of boxes containing tidied-away building bricks and puzzles and farm animals. Kate had never seen the room littered with toys and she had the awful feeling that Oscar was rarely allowed to spoil the neatly arranged boxes.

'I don't suppose there's a drink on offer, is there?' Alec prompted.

If there was, Kate didn't want it. She wanted to be off. She didn't feel up to an encounter with Melissa. But Alec was hell-bent on a drink.

'After what I've put up with since yesterday, at the very least I deserve a triple whisky.'

Ruth took them out to the garden. It was beautifully kept, and so it should be, thought Kate, who knew that Ruth had a gardener in twice a week to see to the lawns and borders. She watched Oscar go up to his father and heard him tell him about his trip round Oxford on an open-topped bus, but like Ruth, Adam wasn't paying his son any attention, he was deep in conversation with a smartly dressed man about the same age as Alec. Kate didn't recognise the man and wondered who he was.

Disappointed, Oscar left his father's side and came back to Kate. He tucked his hand inside hers. 'They're not listening to me,' he said, his words reflecting the sadness in his face.

'Not to worry,' she whispered, 'they're just busy at the moment. Who's that man talking to your father?'

'Don't know.' Oscar shrugged miserably. 'I'm going in for a drink.'

For a few minutes Kate found herself standing alone. With a large tumbler of whisky in his hand, Alec had now joined Adam and was being introduced to the stranger.

'Hello Kate,' came a silky voice from behind her. It was Melissa. 'How was Oxford? I thought you were very brave taking Oscar away with you. I bet Alec hated every minute of it. But good for you for trying to turn him into a more participating grandparent. Though to be honest, I think you're wasting your time.'

'Alec thoroughly enjoyed himself,' lied Kate.

'I doubt that very much,' Melissa said with a laugh. 'He couldn't bear Ruth when she was that age, so there's no reason to suppose that Oscar will stand any higher in his estimation. Now if you'll excuse me I must go and have a word with Alec. Poor devil, he looks quite worn-out.'

Kate watched Melissa move away, the heels of her shoes sinking slightly into the soft lawn. Much as she didn't like Alec's ex-wife, Kate had to admit that Melissa was still a very attractive woman. She dressed in what Kate called expensive grown-up clothes and gave off an air of relaxed confidence, which in turn had the effect of making Kate feel plain and gawky, and about fifteen years old. There was an aura of poise and sophistication to Melissa which Kate knew she would never possess and she often wondered what it was that Alec saw in a girl like her, when for so long he had been married to such a beautiful woman.

As Kate watched Melissa move in on Alec, who was now on his own with Adam, she experienced the familiar wave of jealousy whenever she saw them together.

'Hello there.'

She turned to her right and realised that the unknown man, who earlier had been talking to Adam and Alec, was now at her side. At such close range, she decided that he wasn't particularly good-looking – his eyes were too pale and his jaw too square – and that he was one of those slightly overweight middle-aged men who looked as good as he did because of the expensive clothes he wore.

He held out his hand. 'Tim Wilson,' he said.

She shook hands with him. 'And I'm Kate.'

'I know,' he said. 'In fact I know lots about you.'

'You do?'

'You're Alec's girlfriend, aren't you?'

She nodded. 'So who are you?'

'I suppose you'd call me Melissa's boyfriend.'

The surprise on Kate's face must have shown.

'She's not mentioned me before, then?'

Kate shook her head.

He seemed disappointed. 'Well, it's a recent thing.'

Kate was curious and wondered why Melissa hadn't shown off the fact that she had a boyfriend. 'How did you meet?' she asked.

'Oh, the usual; dinner party, eyes across the table. How about you and Alec?'

'Much the same,' she lied.

'And how do you get on with this business of them still seeing one another every day?'

Kate followed his gaze across the garden to where Alec and Melissa were chatting.

'It doesn't bother me at all,' Kate lied again. How many lies was that today? she thought wretchedly.

He eyed her closely. 'It bothers me,' he said flatly, 'it bothers the hell out of me.'

'But Tony,' cried Amanda, 'how could you do this to me? Now the whole meal will be a disaster!'

'Nonsense, just don't give everyone such big helpings.'

Amanda tried desperately hard to keep her anger in check. But it wasn't easy. Not when she had put so much effort into that evening's meal and it had all been ruined by Tony waltzing in with Hattie after their walk saying he'd invited their other neighbour for dinner. She wasn't given to acts of the miraculous involving loaves and fishes, so just what exactly did Tony think she was going to do?

'I'm sorry,' he said, 'I should have thought. What can I do to help?'

At the sound of Tony's words she suddenly thought of her role model. Now what would Errol Hurst do if she were presented with the same situation? How would she react if Bradley were to turn up from work with an unexpected car-load of Japanese clients for supper? Calmly and proficiently capable, that was how Errol would be. There'd be no domestic histrionics. No apportionment of blame. Just a professional willingness to provide her husband with that all-important back-up so necessary in order for him to get on. Errol would be so resourceful she'd probably raid next door's fish tank just so that she could serve a meal of sushi if she thought it would help Bradley's career. Well, anything Errol could do, she could do better.

'Do you want me to go over and explain to him that we haven't got enough food?' Tony suggested. 'I'm sure he'd understand, he seemed a nice enough bloke.'

Amanda stared at Tony and slowly forced a smile to her lips. 'Oh, don't be silly. Of course I can rustle up something. Just leave it to me. And at least now the numbers around the table will be equal.' She turned away from Tony, amazed at how sincere she'd sounded. It almost made her want to laugh.

Tony was amazed too. How could Amanda be so angry one minute and apparently so understanding the next? It was bizarre. Was this a hormonal thing, he wondered, or just a case of schizophrenia?

18

At a minute past eight Jessica peeped out of her kitchen window to see if there was any sign of Kate and Alec heading for number two. But there was no sign of anybody and determined that she wasn't going to be the first to arrive she decided to ring her mother for a chat – anything to forestall the inevitable.

She had almost finished dialling the number when she remembered that Anna was still away. Damn, now what? She couldn't just sit here twiddling her thumbs. She caught sight of last Sunday's partially unread copy of the *Sunday Times*. She began idly flicking through it, until she came to the book section. She looked to see who had said what and about whom and, only too thankful that she hadn't written any of the novels that had been given the sniffy literati treatment, turned to the television guide to see what she would be missing that evening.

Mm . . . *Prime Suspect* was on at nine o'clock. Aha! The ideal delaying tactic, right in her lap, setting the new video would take for ever. She'd be drawing her pension before she made it to Amanda's dinner-table. 'Oh, sorry I'm late,' she'd be able to say, 'but videos, aren't they just the worst?' Playing the helpless bimbo would appeal to Amanda's superior air, she suspected.

At seven minutes past eight Josh looked at his watch. He then glanced out of his kitchen window, checking for some sign of movement from across the courtyard. In particular from number four.

When Tony had introduced himself that afternoon and had invited Josh for dinner, he had very nearly refused, but when Tony had said who else would be there he had instantly changed his mind. He'd enjoyed Jessica's company last night and saw no reason to be antisocial and miss out on an opportunity of seeing her again.

At ten minutes past eight Kate slipped out of Alec's arms and said, 'Come on, we'd better get a move on, we're already late.'

He pulled her back down on to the bed and kissed her. 'I wish we didn't have to go.'

'So do I, but I promised Jessica I wouldn't back out at the last minute. So hurry up and get dressed.'

He smiled. 'One more kiss and I'll think about it.'

At twenty-one minutes past eight, and much to Jessica's amazement, she found that she had managed to set the video recorder and with nothing else for it she picked up the box of chocolates for Amanda and made a move.

At twenty-two minutes past eight Josh pulled out a bottle of red wine from the wine rack in the kitchen and decided he might just as well be the first to arrive.

At twenty-three minutes past eight three front doors opened simultaneously and four dinner guests faced each other across the courtyard. Josh waited for the others to join him on his side of the development.

After the necessary introductions had been made, Jessica said to Josh, 'I didn't know you'd been invited.'

'I think I was an afterthought.'

'That makes two of us.'

They fell in step behind Kate and Alec as they led the way. Josh could quite see why his brother had been struck by the sight of Kate, she was stunning, but personally he was more taken with Jessica. She looked so much better than she had last night. Gone were the pale face and the dark-rimmed eyes, and in place was a very attractive woman. She looked great in a tight-fitting lycra top – Crawford's had sold thousands like it last year, as they had the long wrap-around skirt that she was wearing. He noted how it fell open with each step she took and he wondered how such a fantastic pair of legs had slipped his attention last night.

They were greeted by Amanda who, after being handed an assortment of flowers, bottles and chocolates, took them through to the sitting-room. Sparkling white wine with cassis was offered and as the drink was already poured out and waiting for them on a tray Josh took his fluted glass politely, wishing, though, that he'd been given the choice of a beer. He caught Jessica pulling a face at the sight of her drink and they exchanged a small knowing smile.

'Tony will be down in a minute,' Amanda said, handing Alec and Kate their glasses, 'he's just putting Hattie to bed. Why don't you all sit down?'

Jessica waited to see where Amanda would sit, then chose the sofa which was as far away as she could get from their hostess.

Josh came and joined her. 'How are you feeling?' he asked in a low voice.

'Much better, thanks. You were great last night, by the way, a true hero.'
He smiled. 'Glad to be of service.'

'What's all this, then?' asked Amanda, rudely interrupting Alec, who in answer to her question had just been explaining what business he was in. 'Who's been a hero?'

Jessica considered inventing an outrageous story about herself and Josh, but as she couldn't be sure of her audience, or that Josh would be willing to play along with her, she decided to keep the fiction to a minimum. 'Let's just say that despite the unusual circumstances we found ourselves in last night,' she said, unable to resist leading Amanda on, 'this fine young man behaved as a perfect gentleman.'

She needn't have doubted Josh.

'And it would be far from correct of me to elaborate on what Jessica has told you all,' he said, 'my lips are sealed, a gentleman never betrays a lady.'

Alec and Kate laughed, but Amanda, who was waiting for a full explanation of what was being implied, was distracted by a movement in the doorway. Jessica followed her gaze and saw a small, pretty girl dressed ready for bed. Holding her hand was a good-looking fair-haired man. Tony and Hattie, she assumed.

'Now Hattie, what did I tell you?' Amanda said. Though her words revealed little more than a hint of mild irritation, there was nothing mild about the expression on her face. Jessica could see that she was clearly cross and she remembered what Kate had said about Amanda not being ideal stepmother material.

'Hattie just wanted to come down and meet everybody,' Tony said affably. He brought his daughter further into the room.

'Well, a few seconds won't do any harm, I suppose,' conceded Amanda, 'but then it's straight to bed, young lady,' she added, 'and no nonsense. This is grown-up time.'

'Oh dear.' Jessica laughed. 'On that basis I'd better join Hattie.' The expression on Amanda's face gave Jessica every reason to suspect that she had just made herself public enemy number one.

Not long after Hattie was dispatched to bed the rest of them were ordered into the dining-room. They were told where to sit and what they were eating.

'It's a Gary Rhodes recipe,' Amanda told them in a loud voice, interrupting Tony, who was talking to Kate and Alec at his end of the table. 'I know he's a bit showy and that there's a lot of window dressing to him, but his recipes do actually work. What do you think, Kate?'

Oh Lord, thought Jessica, recognising that Amanda was going to insist that everybody participated in her dinner party, whether they wanted to or not. There would be no skulking behind napkins for any of them.

Kate took a few moments to finish what was in her mouth and politely agreed with Amanda. 'Though I quite like the Two Fat Ladies,' she added.

'Really?' asked Amanda. 'You do surprise me.'

'It's their originality that –'

'Original, I agree, but so unhygienic,' Amanda said dismissively. She then turned from Kate and fixed her attention on Josh. 'And Josh, how about you? Do you like to cook? Or are you one of those terrible *Men Behaving Badly* types in the kitchen?'

Jessica couldn't believe the crassness of the woman. Somebody shove a bread roll into that great big mouth! she wanted to shout across the table. But she was pleased to see that if Josh was at all put out by Amanda's assumption that because he was a single man he was therefore a complete dick-head when it came to feeding himself, he didn't show it.

'I manage pretty well,' he answered smoothly. 'I particularly enjoy Thai cooking.'

Jessica silently applauded Josh for his subtle slap in the chops of their hostess.

But after a long silent pause, the weight of which could have equalled any number of lead balloons, Jessica scooped up the last of her salmon mousse and thought, well, this *is* going splendidly. What fun we're all having. She wondered how Helen Mirren was getting along.

'So tell us about your writing, Jessica,' Amanda said, moving her attention around the table. 'It's not every day we have an author in our midst. I thought of writing a book once.'

Oh, here we go, thought Jessica. If she had a pound for every person who had ever said that to her she'd be up there with Jeffrey Archer.

'But I've never had the time,' Amanda went on. 'I've always been too busy.'

Yeah, yeah, yeah. She'd heard it all before.

'It must be wonderful to be able to earn a living from something as easy as writing.'

Jessica was nearly out of her seat and reaching for a gob-stopping bread roll. *Easy! She'd give her bloody easy!*

'I don't think it's quite as simple as that,' Kate said diplomatically. 'If it were, too busy or not, we'd all be doing it, wouldn't we?'

Jessica gave Kate a grateful look.

'Well, I wouldn't know about that,' Amanda carried on. 'Do you sell many books, Jessica? I saw one in the supermarket yesterday.'

'I get by,' replied Jessica. Tight bitch, she thought, noting that Amanda had said 'saw' and not 'bought'.

'I didn't know you were a writer,' Josh said, seizing a few seconds of conversational lull while Amanda chewed on a piece of cucumber.

'It's not something I go out of my way to advertise,' Jessica said – *was it any wonder when there were people like Amanda in the world?*

'Jessica's an excellent writer,' Kate said generously. 'I've read both her books.'

'So what kind of novels do you write?' Josh asked.

'Romantic comedies,' Jessica replied. 'Probably not your cup of tea; not enough explosions or car chases.'

Alec laughed. 'From what Kate tells me, your sex scenes are pretty explosive.'

'But all done in the best possible taste,' Jessica joked.

'I suppose you must have to do an inordinate amount of research,' Josh said with a playful smile.

'Oh, an inordinate amount of research,' Jessica said, matching his expression.

Josh slowly leant back in his chair. 'You must let me know if there's anything I could help you with in the future,' he said, his eyes still fixed on her.

Jessica's own gaze held firm. She took a long, deliberate sip of her wine. 'And who knows,' she said, 'I might just do that.'

Aghast at the way in which Jessica and Josh were carrying on, Amanda began gathering up the plates and cutlery. She gave Tony a get-up-and-do-something look and he immediately got to his feet and went round the table refilling glasses. He was secretly envious of the way in which Jessica and Josh were flirting with each other. It reminded him of himself and Eve. They had met on a management training course and he had been determined from the moment he'd set eyes on her to get her into bed before the end of the three-day course. By the close of day one, when they'd spent five hours solving what the tutor had called 'Mind Opening Puzzles' they had built up a flirtatious rapport. By day two they were found kissing in the hotel lift and on the final day, when they should have been attending an afternoon talk on 'There's More than One Way to Look at a Problem' they were in his hotel room making love. The memory of such a happy time in his life made him risk a glance in Kate's direction. How he longed for the evening to be over. Sitting in the same room as Kate without being able to talk to her, in the way he wanted, was unbearable.

Even more unbearable was Alec's presence.

What made it so bad was that Tony found himself liking the man. It was beyond him that he could chat so effortlessly to Alec when all the time he was imagining what it would be like to hold Kate in his arms.

'No more wine for me, thanks.'

Tony looked down to see Josh's hand covering his wineglass.

'Sorry,' he said distractedly. 'What can I get you instead?'

'Water would be fine, thanks.'

Josh watched Tony fill his water glass, then he raised his eyes to look at Jessica. She was turned slightly to her left, talking to Alec, but he had the feeling she knew full well that he was staring at her.

Last night when he'd gone to bed and thought about his evening with Jessica, he'd known that he was attracted to her and now, as he viewed her across the table, he realised that for the first time in a long while he was experiencing the urge of wanting a woman. The impulse was so strong that it was outweighing the fear and loss of confidence that had crept over him since his illness had been diagnosed. One of the aspects of MS that appalled him most was the threat of impotence. What if he couldn't perform? What if his useless body let him down? One of the specialists he'd seen at the hospital a few months ago had waved the subject aside when Josh had put it to him. 'You don't need to concern yourself about that now,' the man had said – a man who in Josh's opinion looked like he'd lost interest in sex years ago – 'worry about that when it happens,' the doctor had added. Easy for you to say, Josh had thought angrily.

And since his last girlfriend had done a runner, the subject of sex had become nothing more than a hypothetical conundrum anyway.

But now ... well now, it was very much on Josh's mind. He had the feeling that it was on Jessica's too. Or was that just wishful thinking?

Jessica was the first to say that she was tired and that she ought to be getting off home. 'It's been a wonderful evening,' she said, faking a yawn. She wasn't lying completely. Excluding Amanda, she'd enjoyed everybody's company once they'd all relaxed. She pushed her empty coffee cup away from her and stood up.

'I hadn't realised it was so late,' Josh said in turn, also getting to his feet. He didn't want Jessica rushing off without him.

Which caused Alec to say that he and Kate had had a long day and that they had better be going as well.

Thanks were made, goodbyes said, and finally the four dinner guests departed. It was past midnight and the dark sky above the courtyard was pricked with bright, twinkling stars. It was very quiet. And very still.

'Well, good-night then,' Alec said to Jessica and Josh, 'it was good to meet you both. If there's anything in the neighbourly department you need, don't hesitate to knock on our door.'

'The same goes for my door,' Jessica said, 'knock any time you need to. See you for coffee during the week, Kate.'

Kate and Alec walked away, arm in arm, their feet crunching noisily on the gravel.

'Well,' said Josh, turning to face Jessica.

'Well indeed,' she repeated.
'I don't suppose you'd fancy a nightcap, would you?'
'I thought you'd never ask.'

19

When Jessica awoke the following morning it was very late. It was getting on for lunch-time.

In Corfu she had never slept in. Early morning, before anyone else was about, had been her favourite part of the day. It was so quiet sometimes that she could hear the distant sound of goat bells high up in the hills behind her house. On days like that it was as if she had the island to herself. It was when she worked at her best. She would make a pot of coffee and a plate of toast dripping with butter – not for her the local breakfast of yoghurt and honey and the occasional fig that Helen and Jack relished – and go and sit outside on the terrace. She had never tired of the view and each morning she had lost herself in admiring the tranquil setting. She had often wished that instead of being a novelist she had Helen's skill as an artist. She would have loved to have been able to paint the myriad shades of blue, green and white that for her epitomised where she lived – sand as silvery as the moon; beaches whitened by sun-bleached pebbles; water the colour of pure turquoise; and cypress trees, lush and green, their verdant tips spearing a cloudless sky of china-blue.

Then, once she had had her fix of admiring the view, she would get down to work. The hours would slip by effortlessly as she lost herself in her latest cast of characters who were facing all manner of dramas as a result of her vivid imagination.

Thinking of work reminded Jessica that it was high time she got stuck into her next novel. When she'd had lunch with Piers on Friday he had asked her only once what she had in mind to write next – he'd probably decided not to push her, thinking that it would be unlikely that he'd get any sense out of somebody who was making such a fool of herself.

And he would have been right. He would have got more reason out of the salt and pepper pots on the table than her.

It wasn't often that she let the side down so appallingly, but on that occasion she'd certainly gone all the way. She cringed at the memory and buried her head deep into the pillow. Gavin would have loved seeing her behave so badly and wouldn't have thought twice about using it against her if she'd ever dared to show so much as the merest hint of disapproval over one of his frequent drunken binges.

She turned on to her back and stared up at the hideous lace canopy above the bed and thought of Gavin.

She wondered what he'd be doing right now. Probably he was down on the beach at Avlaki: Ray-Bans on, hair catching the breeze and no doubt putting his breath-taking charm to good use on some keen-to-please female tourist whom he'd met the previous night in a bar in Kassiopi. 'I've never tried sailing before,' the silly girl would have simpered, which was all the opening Gavin would need. 'Then I'll teach you' – his stock reply to anybody stupid enough to give him the opportunity to show off how good he was in and on the water – 'be on the beach for ten-thirty tomorrow,' he'd add, 'and I'll take you through the theory, then we'll get down to the exciting stuff. I guarantee you'll be sailing single-handedly by late afternoon and to celebrate your success we'll have a drink afterwards at the nearby taverna.' His technique was persuasive and irresistible.

She ought to know, she'd fallen for it herself.

Since leaving Corfu, Jessica hadn't once deluded herself that Gavin would be pining for her. But she did wonder whether he missed her. Just a little.

She supposed not.

If he had, he might have been in touch with her. But there had been nothing. Not one phone call. Not even a letter.

But then, what could she expect? It had been she who had chosen to end things between them.

It was a strange phenomenon, though, that one could be so involved, so wrapped up in another person, then be so entirely separate.

Mind you, with Gavin it had been a basic physical wrapped-upness rather than any meeting of minds. Jack had often asked her what she saw in Gavin and Helen had laughed at him.

'You imbecile, Jack, the man's an Adonis, what do you think she sees in him?'

Helen had been quite right. The physical attraction between them had been like a white-knuckle ride; no matter how often they made love the thrill was as great as the time before.

But gradually it had dawned on Jessica that a physical thrill was only as good as the moment it took to fulfil itself. She had then begun to want more. And poor Gavin didn't have more to offer. It had been a sad realisation, that. It had also made her feel old. Expectations in one's youth are delightfully low and straightforward, you put up with anything. But age brings with it higher and more complicated expectations from a partner, such as consideration, respect, faithfulness, understanding and, worse still, something as horrifying as a planned future.

Gavin's idea of a planned future was choosing what he was going to eat for lunch.

She sighed and got out of bed. She pushed back the curtains and leant her elbows on the window-sill. It was a glorious morning and beyond her garden, a sun-filled landscape of fields and clumps of trees presented itself to her. It was beautiful. Very different from what she had been used to for the past few years, but just as captivating. She opened the window and leant out over the white-painted sill.

She thought of Josh. He, too, was different from anybody she'd previously known.

It would have been the easiest thing in the world to have carried on their flirting to its natural conclusion last night, but when, after a couple of drinks, things had started hotting up on the sofa she had thought, Whoa! I've been here before and I'm not sure I'm in the market for a casual affair.

She had, of course, only herself to blame. She really shouldn't have encouraged him.

Mutterings of 'I'm sorry, I'm not sure I can do this' had seemed slightly ridiculous when he'd tried to kiss her – and just for the record his technique had been faultless: a subtle inching along the sofa so that their legs were almost touching, a beautifully timed silence, a lowering of his eyes to her lips, a lifting of his hand to her shoulder and then the final tilt of his head – always a heart melter that one – as he moved in for the big finish.

Except she had gone and spoilt things for him.

'My mistake,' he'd said, when he'd felt her resistance. He'd backed away from her as though she had a gun pointed at his head.

They'd then metaphorically dusted themselves down and catching sight of the awkwardness on one another's faces they had suddenly burst out laughing.

'Sorry about that,' he'd said with a grin that had enough sex appeal in it to cause her very nearly to say, oh what the heck, let's go for it, anyway!

'I'm sorry too,' she'd said, 'I've behaved outrageously all evening. It's either the fault of that awful woman Amanda, or . . .'

'Or?'

'Or it's your fault.'

He laughed. 'Fancy another drink?'

They finished a bottle of Southern Comfort and moved on to coffee, and all the time they talked. He told her about the company he and his brother ran – he had talked a lot about Charlie – and about all the travelling the pair of them had done, but he wasn't one of those men who only spoke about himself. He prompted her to speak about her own life, about growing up in Cholmford and what had led her to live such a nomadic life, and what had brought her back home. She told him about her mother and her heart condition. She even told him about Gavin. Then there was her writing. He wanted to know all about that, unlike Gavin who had never been interested in what she did, having dismissed her books as the kind of commercial nonsense anyone could do if they put their mind to it – he and Amanda would get on like a house on fire.

She had felt extremely comfortable in Josh's company, so much so that the time had flown by, and before they knew it it was nearly four in the morning. She had tiptoed her way across the gravel and let herself in, just as the first signs of dawn had begun to filter through the bruised night sky.

'Dirty stop-out,' she said with a smile, now turning away from the bedroom window and going into the bathroom, 'what *will* the neighbours think?'

In the make-do show house of plot number three Sue Fletcher, the negotiator, was tidying up her things. Her work at Cholmford Hall Mews was over. Tomorrow she would start work at a new site. She was going to miss Cholmford, it had been one of her more enjoyable assignments. It was a shame, though, that she hadn't managed to sell the last remaining plot, but she'd had a feeling all along that number three was going to stick. Everybody she had shown round the house had had the same criticisms of it – they didn't like the property being divided by the archway; they didn't like the garden; but mostly they didn't like the price. So now it would be down to an estate agent to do his best, but Sue knew as well as the next person that without a substantial drop in the asking price it would be an uphill struggle to find a buyer.

Still, it wasn't her problem. Her next challenge was an exclusive block of apartments in Altrincham.

Happy that everything was in order, she locked the door behind her for the final time and as she turned round she saw the man from number one driving out through the archway. She returned his smile and wished that all the clients she dealt with were as easy on the eye.

Josh drove like the wind to his parents' house in Prestbury. He parked his car alongside Charlie's and because it was such a hot day he walked slowly round to the back of the house, assuming that everybody would be sitting in the garden.

He was right. His brother, dressed in shorts and a T-shirt, was lolling in a hammock slung between two apple trees and his father was coughing and spluttering over the barbecue, where the coals were sending up great lung-threatening clouds of smoke.

His mother was sitting in her usual sun-lounger and was doing the usual crossword. She looked up when she realised he was there. 'Hello, Joshua,' she said, putting her newspaper down. 'We'd nearly given up on you. I was about to send Charles in to give you a call. We were getting worried.'

He went and kissed her. 'A late night,' he said by way of explanation for turning up unprecedentedly late for their monthly family get-together. He'd also woken up unprecedentedly late. Normally an early riser, he had surfaced just after twelve o'clock and it wasn't until he was munching on a bowl of muesli in the kitchen and thinking about Jessica that he'd caught sight of the calendar hanging beside the telephone on the wall. With a thud of realisation he'd remembered that he was supposed to be washed, dressed, shaved and in Prestbury within the hour. Dumping the half-eaten cereal in the sink, he had gone back upstairs to do something about his appearance. Glad that his body was at least continuing to keep up with him, as he'd stood in the shower, and conscious that he was feeling okay for yet another day, he dared to hope that his MS was entering a period of remission; that the symptoms of his illness were lessening. It had happened before. So why not again?

'Shall I get you a beer?' his father offered.

'That's all right, Dad. I'll go and help myself.'

When he went into the kitchen and pulled open the fridge door he heard footsteps following in behind him. It was Charlie. 'You want one as well?' he asked.

'Please.'

Josh handed him a can. 'I met your wondrous creature last night,' he said.

'And?'

Josh smiled. 'She's really not your type.'

'Hey, I'll be the judge of that.'

'And she's also fairly well partnered up.'

'Shit!'

'Language, Charles.'

'Sorry, Mum,' Charlie said, turning to see their mother coming into the kitchen.

'So how are things?' she asked Josh as she went over to a chopping board beside the sink and picked up a plate of vegetable kebabs.

Josh tried not to over-react. He knew his mother had to ask and that she did her best to put it in such a way as to imply that a general enquiry was being made of him, but in reality the question was much more specific. It was stupid of him, but he'd much prefer his mother to come straight out with, 'So which bit of you isn't working properly today?'

'I'm fine,' he said and, going for a deflection he added, 'and the house is pretty well organised now. You and Dad will have to come over.'

'We'd like that,' she said. 'Now go back into the garden and get some sun on you. You look far too pale and all that black doesn't help. Don't you have any clothes in any other colour these days?'

'She's right,' Charlie said as they went outside and found themselves a couple of chairs away from the smoke, 'you do look pale.'

'If you'd drunk as much as I did last night you'd be pale.'

Charlie raised an eyebrow. 'Tell me all.'

Josh told him about being invited to dinner with his new neighbours.

'So that's how you got to meet my scampering angel,' Charlie interrupted. 'What's the husband like?'

'I never said she was married. She lives with somebody, a guy called Alec.'

Charlie leant forward in his chair. 'Not actually married, eh? So all is not lost. What's he like? A right Smart Alec? Or is he some kind of brainless gladiatorial hunk who's charmed her with his pecs?'

Josh laughed. 'She's a whole lot smarter than that.'

'So come on then, what am I up against?'

'You're not going to believe it. He's got to be about fifty, grey-haired and –'

'You're winding me up!'

'Nope.'

'You mean that fantastic creature has thrown herself at a man nearly twice her age. Why?'

Josh shrugged. 'He's a nice bloke, maybe she just goes for the father-figure type. It takes all sorts.'

'Who likes the father-figure type?' asked their father, coming over and seizing the opportunity of his wife's absence from the garden to stand easy from his barbecue duties for a couple of seconds.

'A neighbour of mine whom Charlie has decided he's fallen in love with.'

Their father laughed. 'Missed the boat again, Charles, have you?'

'I wouldn't say that exactly. I reckon I'm a worthy match for a grey-haired has-been any day.'

'Nothing wrong with grey hair,' William Crawford said, running his hand through his own. 'And may I remind you that you're not short of a few threads of silver yourself.'

'Thanks, Dad.'

'William,' called a voice from inside the house, 'those chops, they're burning!'

He hurried back to his sentry post.

'So what are your other neighbours like?' Charlie asked.

'A couple with a young daughter and . . .' he hesitated.

'And?'

'And a writer.'

123

'Really. What's he like?'

'*She.*'

'Oh. Any good?'

'Not sure about her writing skills, but she's . . .' Josh's voice faltered. How exactly should he describe Jessica? The usual adjectives of striking and attractive somehow didn't seem appropriate. She was more than that. But what? Interesting? Was that how he would describe her? Or how about sententious? She was certainly to the point. She was also extremely funny. But these were hardly the normal descriptions a man would use of a woman whom he had every intention of getting into bed.

'She's what?' prompted Charlie.

Josh smiled. 'Never you mind.'

'Oh, like that, is it?'

'I should be so lucky.' Josh told his brother about Jessica's migraine and his rescue of her. He also told him about last night.

Charlie laughed. 'Well, one thing's for sure, I'll have to take back all I said about no night-life being on offer out there in the sticks. Perhaps your paleness has nothing to do with an over-indulgence of alcohol but an excess of carnal pleasure.'

'I wish.'

'You mean, she was there all that time with you last night and you didn't manage –'

'I was taking the subtle approach.'

'Get away. She didn't fancy you, did she?'

'Course she did.'

'But not enough, evidently.'

They both laughed and drank their beers. Josh listened to his parents battling it out round the hot coals – the chops were done, but the kebabs were not – and felt unaccountably relaxed. Talking to Charlie in this light-hearted way reminded him how it always used to be when they'd teased one another about their sexual prowess. It was one of the things he'd noticed when his illness had been diagnosed; overnight Charlie stopped treating him as the brother he'd always been and had started talking to him like some ancient maiden aunt. The teasing abruptly stopped. So did the mateyness. It was as if it was in bad taste to rib somebody who wasn't a hundred per cent – mocking the afflicted just wasn't on.

'What's her name?' asked Charlie, breaking into Josh's thoughts.

'Who?'

'Don't give me any of that. The woman who turned you down.'

'I told you, she didn't turn me down.'

'If you say so.'

'Her name's Jessica, Jessica Lloyd.'

'Mm . . . nice name. So what kind of writer is she?'

'She writes romantic comedies and according to your darling Kate she writes brilliant sex scenes.'

Charlie held up his hands as though giving thanks to the Lord. 'My darling Kate. How sweet the name doth sound.'

'Put a sock in it, will you? And take my advice. She won't give you a second look. She and Alec are very much a couple.'

Charlie pulled a face. 'Just because you were shunned last night, don't go sour-graping all over me.'

'I didn't say I was shunned.'

'Well what were you then?'

'I was . . . if you must know I was spoken to like I was a normal human being.'

Charlie looked at him closely. 'Meaning what?'

'I mean she didn't talk to me in that does-he-take-sugar-with-it? way so many other people do.'

'Are you getting at me?'

Josh shook his head. 'All I'm saying is that Jessica treated me like a normal bloke because she doesn't know anything to the contrary.'

'She doesn't know about your MS?'

'That's right.'

'But what if –'

'There are no what ifs. I have no intention of telling her about my illness, because at least then I won't have to put up with any crap from her.' His face broke into an expression of intense seriousness. 'She'll treat me as a man, not an invalid. And who knows, I might even get lucky.'

Charlie turned away and looked down the length of the garden, to the old rope swing hanging from the silver birch where he and Josh had played as boys – their mother joked that she still kept the rope swing as a hint that one day she hoped to have grandchildren playing on it.

He thought about what his brother had just said. He had the feeling that Josh liked this Jessica, that he viewed her as being more than just a potential one-night stand. If that was the case, and if Josh really thought there was any chance of a relationship with her, then surely it had to be founded on honesty. Not on deception.

He'd be a fool to think otherwise.

20

It was Monday lunch-time and at first glance the car-park of the Vicarage looked as if it were full. But driving round to the back of the pub, Kate spied a small space that had been ignored by everybody else and with breath-holding care she squeezed her Mini between an ugly people carrier on her left and a white-painted wooden barrel on her right, which was stocked with a large flowering hydrangea and an abundance of yellow and purple pansies that clashed horribly with the blue of the hydrangea.

She found Caroline perched on a bar stool, pretending to be reading the lunch-time menu on the blackboard to the right of her. In reality, Kate knew better. Caroline was eyeing up a group of noisy businessmen at the far end of the bar. Nothing changes, she thought. 'Hi, Caroline,' she said, tapping her friend on the shoulder.

Caroline whipped round. 'And about time, too. I've been sitting here on my own for ages. It gives a girl a bad name.'

'Sorry, the traffic was terrible, but I'm sure you've been able to amuse yourself in my absence.'

'Definitely not my type,' Caroline said, catching Kate's eyes straying over to the far end of the bar. 'They've done nothing but discuss company cars and Manchester United. What are you drinking?'

'I'll get them,' Kate said, reaching into her bag. 'What would you like?'

'Dry white wine, please.'

Kate attracted the attention of the woman behind the bar and when they'd got their drinks and ordered two prawn salads they went outside to the garden. They chose a table which had an umbrella above it. Kate sat in the shade and Caroline positioned her chair to catch the sun, and pulling off a loose-fitting silk shirt she revealed a skimpy strapless top and a pair of deeply tanned shoulders.

'It must be hell being you,' said Caroline smugly. 'You can keep your dazzling head of red hair and perfect pale skin, I'd sooner be a boring brunette any day and soak up the rays.'

'Well, at least I shan't look like a prune when I'm fifty.'

'Don't give it another thought. I shall have had the very latest in drastic surgery by then. I'll have my face stretched right round to the back of my head. I'll look sensational.'

'You'll look like Bette Davis.'

Caroline laughed. 'My word, but you're frisky today. Now tell me what you've been up to. I want to know everything. How's the big relationship going and is the sex still as good and have you found yourself another job yet?'

There was never any chicanery to Caroline's conversation. 'If I were a stronger person I'd tell you to mind your own business,' Kate said.

Caroline smiled. 'Yeah, but I know that deep down you're just dying to tell me what a wonderful time you're having so that you can rub in what a dreary depressing life I lead. Hey, do you mind moving slightly to the right? There's a drop-dead gorgeous guy sitting over there and he can't see what he's missing out on with you in the way.'

Kate obliged and finding that the sun was now in her eyes she put on her sun-glasses.

'Do you have to do that?' Caroline asked, 'those shades make you look even more glamorous; you look like Julia Roberts. Take them off at once.'

'No,' Kate said firmly, 'now stop treating me like one of the poor pensioners in the library you bully so sadistically and tell me what *you've* been up to.'

Caroline raised an eyebrow. 'My, my, Kate, who's been teaching you how to be so assertive?'

'It's you! You've taught me everything I know.'

'So that's it, I'm to be hoist by my own petard, am I?'

Their lunch arrived and when they were left alone again Caroline said, 'You're looking particularly well. Dare I ask, is that what the love of a good man does for you?'

Kate smiled and reached for her knife and fork. 'You should try it some time.'

'Ouchy-ouch! You're turning into a nasty piece of work, Kate Morris.'

'So there's still no decent man in your life, then?'

Caroline sighed. 'Chance would be a fine thing. Do you know, I'm so desperate I've thought about joining one of those dreadful introduction agencies, you know, the ones you see advertised in the paper all the time.'

Kate held her tongue. She had never confided in Caroline about how she had met Alec and she certainly wasn't about to start now – Caroline was the last person on earth that she'd trust with such a delicate and private piece of information. It still amazed her that she'd had the courage to join the agency in the first place and had done so in secret. She had thought about it for months before finally taking the plunge. It wasn't so much that there had been a lack of boyfriends in her life, it was just that they were all the wrong kind. They were either too serious or not serious enough; too quiet or too noisy; too nervous or over-confident. Having your personality traits matched to those of a like-minded man seemed a good way to cut through all the toe-curling embarrassment of a first date that was obviously going nowhere. But it hadn't been anywhere near as simple as that – there was only so much a computer could come up with – and there followed several disastrous evenings before she'd struck gold with Alec. 'So why don't you join an agency?' she asked Caroline innocently.

'But it's so desperate. I mean, the whole set-up must attract all the wrong kind of men, the flaky ones whose trousers are too short, and who wear grey slip-on shoes and want to unburden themselves on some equally sad woman.'

How tempting it was to prove Caroline wrong. 'But how do you know it would be like that?'

'Believe me, Kate. I just know.'

'Well, perhaps you should give it a try. You never know, you might meet somebody really special. I'm sure it would be worth a go. What have you got to lose?'

Caroline chewed thoughtfully on a prawn. 'Do you really think so?'

I know so, Kate wanted to say, but instead she nodded her head and sipped her fizzy water.

'Anyway, enough about my non-existent love life, tell me about yours. Any sign of the clanging of wedding bells yet?'

'Alec and I are happy enough without getting married.'

Caroline contemplated her friend. 'If you don't mind me saying, that sounded just an itsy-bitsy bit too pat; it also had the distinctive ring of an untruth behind it.'

Kate blushed.

'Doesn't he want to get married?'

'It's not something we talk about.'

Caroline scoffed. 'He's taking you for a ride, girl.'

'He's not,' Kate said indignantly, quick to leap to Alec's defence. 'And why should we change things when we're both happy with what we've got? Everything's perfect between us.'

'Mm . . .' said Caroline. She sounded far from convinced. 'Okay then,' she said, 'you give me no alternative but to test your idea of perfection. Suppose I were to put the question of, let's say, how could you possibly improve on your relationship? And don't give me any bullshit about your lives resembling a day in the life of Adam and Eve before the wily snake made his appearance.'

'That's a silly question.'

'So what if it is, give me an answer.'

Kate didn't want to. She knew what her answer was and she was frightened that hearing herself actually say the words out loud might court disaster for her relationship with Alec.

'Come on,' pressed Caroline. 'It doesn't have to be something monumental. It could be something as simple as changing the colour of his socks. Or guiding him through the tricky transition from Y-fronts to boxers.'

Kate relaxed and smiled.

'Or, of course,' Caroline went on, 'it could be something more earth-shattering like you ... like you wanting to have a baby and him not being interested because he's done that scene already.'

Don't react, Kate told herself. She's only fishing. She has no way of knowing.

'Well?'

There was no avoiding the question. She would have to come up with something credible in order to make Caroline drop the subject. 'I'd like to be rid of Alec's ex-wife,' she said with a sudden flash of inspiration. It was even true.

'Why?' latched on Caroline, 'is she a problem? He doesn't still have a thing for her, does he?'

'Heavens no!'

'How can you be so sure?'

'Really, Caroline, are you so jealous of me that you want to unravel my relationship with Alec completely?'

Caroline had the grace to look shamefaced. 'Spoil-sport,' she said. 'Come on, eat up and I'll go and fetch us another round of drinks. Same again?'

'Please.'

When Caroline returned she said, 'So if you're going to be boring and not tell me anything about you and Alec, tell me how you're managing financially and what you're doing about getting another job.'

This was much safer ground and Kate pushed her finished plate to one side and said, 'I had a bit saved for a rainy day, so I'm okay for a while, but ... but I think I'm going for a career move.'

'Oh, sounds interesting. What are you thinking of doing? With your new-found assertiveness you'd make an ideal doctor's receptionist.'

Kate smiled, but thought about what her friend had said. Had she changed? Was she really standing up for herself more these days? 'With all the cutbacks going on I really don't hold out much hope of getting another librarian's job in the immediate area, so the obvious answer is to retrain.'

'Go on.'

'What do you think about teaching?'

Caroline groaned. 'The only kind of teaching I'd consider would be in an all-boys' school with an excessive amount of sixth-form testosterone to drool over. So what age do you see yourself with?'

'Infants.'

Caroline groaned again. 'Well, you always were the only one at the library who could control the little horrors. You should have seen the state Maggie got into on Saturday when we had the first of the summer holiday story-time sessions. I thought she was going to hit this one boy who kept interrupting her. "Please Miss, please Miss," he kept whining. It was only after Maggie had finished the story and all the children stood up that she realised why the pest had been wittering on at her. He'd wanted the loo and had used the carpet in the end. Oh happy days.'

'The poor boy.'

'Poor Maggie, you mean. You know how obsessive she is about hygiene. She's becoming even more of a basket case these days. She's started wearing gloves, saying that the average library book contains more germs than a public lavatory. She reckons the books taken out by men are the worst. She's probably right.'

Kate laughed.

'So what does Alec think about you becoming a schoolmarm?'

'I haven't talked to him about it yet.'

'Why not?'

'Because I only started thinking about it over the weekend.' It was while she had been waiting for Alec to finish talking with Melissa on Saturday afternoon that the idea had begun to take root. Melissa's boyfriend, Tim, had asked her what she did for a living. When she had explained, he'd said, 'I don't recall librarians being as attractive as you.' She had felt the colour rising in her cheeks and had hoped that Melissa hadn't overheard what he'd said.

'So why aren't you still stamping books and telling people to ssh?' he'd asked.

'I was made redundant.'

'I'm sorry. Any idea what you'll do next?'

'I'm not sure, to be honest. Which I know sounds pathetically feeble.'

'Not at all, but what would you most like to do if you had the pick of any job?'

She had thought about this for a few seconds, then, seeing Oscar coming towards her, she had found her answer. 'I like children, so maybe I could do something in that line.'

'Teaching perhaps?'

'Yes,' she'd said, and responding to Oscar's hand searching for hers she'd added, 'I think I'd like that a lot.'

'Hello. Anybody at home?'

'Sorry, Caroline,' Kate said. 'I was miles away then.'

'I could tell. So what are you going to do about this career change? If you act fast now you might be able to join a teacher training course starting this autumn. Why don't you come over to the library and go through all the further education information?'

Kate drove home full of optimism, which made her realise that she must have been feeling the opposite before she'd arrived for lunch.

Since losing her job and moving in with Alec she had perhaps been too quick to put her life on hold. Being content to drift along was all very well, but it couldn't go on that way. She would spend the rest of the summer taking care of Oscar, as she'd promised Ruth, but come the autumn there would be her own life to see to.

It had been good to see Caroline again. One of her friend's greatest strengths was bullying people into sorting out their lives.

She decided to stop off at the supermarket on the way home and buy something special for supper that evening. She felt the need to celebrate the fact that a twinkling of an idea had been turned into a fully fledged decision.

She saw it as an important decision; one that she was convinced was going to make everything right again between her and Alec.

Having a new career to work for would stop her wanting something she couldn't have.

21

Jessica was fooling herself that she was working. Or rather, she was trying to fool herself that she was working.

Sitting with her head bent over a pad of foolscap and sucking pensively on the end of a pencil, she was giving an impressive performance of a writer. Only trouble was, the paper was blank and the pencil, completely unused, was as sharp as a pin.

Her attempt at putting a story-line together was not going well.

In fact, it was going depressingly badly. Not a word had been written since eight o'clock that morning. It was now ten thirty and the great Muse of romantic fiction had yet to get out of bed, apply her make-up, don her heels and make an appearance in Jessica's study.

The worry was, perhaps she never would.

Maybe the goddess who had worked so well for Jessica in the past had deserted her and had stayed behind in Corfu. 'Forget it,' the mythical Greek goddess had said to her many sisters when she'd learnt of Jessica's plans to leave the island, 'I ain't working my butt off in some freezing outpost called England!'

Jessica flung down her pencil. It bounced off the desk, hit the corner of the printer and broke its sharp point clean off.

'Serves you right,' Jessica said with childish satisfaction.

Starting a new novel in the past had never been a problem for Jessica. In fact, she had invariably enjoyed the anticipatory element of staring at a blank piece of paper and waiting for ideas to start to flow. It was at this stage, before she had progressed to working on her laptop, that she had the most fun. So long as she didn't have a single word written she could kid herself that her next novel would be her crowning glory; her *magnum opus*. It would win universal critical acclaim, the like of which had never been heard before – even Germaine Greer and A. S. Byatt would find it amusing, in a deceptively meaningful and thought-provoking way. It would race straight to the No. 1 slot of the *Sunday Times* bestseller list and it would stay there longer than Helen Fielding's *Bridget Jones's Diary*. Not only that, it would have every known television and film producer champing at the bit to serialise or Merchant Ivory it.

But that was the stuff of dreams. It was not to be taken seriously.

She stood up. It was time for another cup of coffee. Her sixth of the day so far.

Not that she was counting.

Not that she was becoming paranoid.

While she waited in the kitchen for the kettle to boil she thought of her phone call with her editor yesterday afternoon – another timely reminder that she should be getting on with the next novel. Fresh from her holiday, Cara had read *A Carefree Life* over the weekend and had phoned to say how much she'd enjoyed it. 'It's great, Jessica, definitely your best.'

'Thank you, Piers thought so, too.'

'In that case we must be sitting on the book of the decade!'

They'd both laughed, then Cara had congratulated Jessica on her new two-book contract. 'We're all thrilled here that you're staying with us.'

'You know how it is,' she had joked, 'better the devil you know.'

'We're planning a massive promotional campaign for *A Carefree Life*,' Cara had gone on to explain, 'and just as soon as the art department have done their stuff I'll let you have a copy of the jacket. Any ideas for the next book?'

'Um ... I'd rather not say just yet.'

'That's fine, don't worry, Jessica. We can always trust you to come up with something good.'

Thinking of Cara's praise now, as Jessica dunked a digestive biscuit into her coffee while staring out of the kitchen window, she felt riddled with worry – *we can always trust you to come up with something good*. Well, supposing she couldn't do it this time? Supposing she'd only ever had the three books in her and that anything she wrote now would be contrived, samey and destined for the cut-price four-books-for-a-pound stores to be found in every high street?

And there was so much money involved.

It was a frightening thought to be trusted with such an incredible weight of responsibility. This, of course, was one of the reasons why she'd turned down the more lucrative offer Piers had negotiated – the more the advance, the greater the responsibility.

What a wimp she was!

And what a dreadful and unnerving revelation it was to know that deep down she was as scared as Gavin to take on the mantle of responsibility.

She dunked another digestive into her cup and seeing it disintegrate into her coffee, she decided she needed shaking up.

The best person to do that was her mother. They'd spoken on the phone late last night, not long after Anna had arrived home from her jaunt to

North Wales, and Jessica had said that she would see her some time today. Now was as good a time as any.

As she walked along the lane to her mother's cottage Jessica tried not to think about the fruitless morning spent in her study. Think of anything, she told herself, anything so long as it has nothing to do with writing.

So she forced herself to count how many flowers in the hedgerow she recognised. She got the easy ones, the daisies and buttercups and dandelions, and even identified the patches of tufted vetch with its pretty pale-lilac flowers and the covering of groundsel greedily spreading itself along the roadside. But it was no good. No amount of nature-trailing was going to stop her worrying. Just what was she going to write about in her next novel? An idiot's guide to Cheshire's least-trodden pathways?

This whole business of not being able to write was getting her down. It was a new phenomenon to her. She had never experienced the dreaded writer's block before. But now she had. And in spades.

The inspiration for her previous books had come mostly from some of her own experiences – her first novel had featured a young backpacker; her second, *Caught in the Act*, not surprisingly had starred Gavin; and *A Carefree Life* had more than a passing similarity to her own life. Oh, but heaven help her if she was relying on her new situation to throw a shaft of illuminating light on a potential story-line, because so far, Cholmford seemed to be doing its best to keep her permanently in the dark.

Since she'd been living back in Cholmford, she had tried several times to get started, but on each occasion she had failed. And miserably. It was as if she were clean out of ideas. She had blamed it on her new surroundings to begin with, convincing herself, after each failed attempt, that the next day she would crack it. It wasn't even as though she was having trouble in getting chapter one off the ground, it was worse. Much worse. She had no characters. She had no setting. She had no story-line. In short she had a resounding zippo. No wonder she'd nearly throttled Amanda on Saturday night – *It must be wonderful to be able to earn a living from something as easy as writing*. Hah! The horrible woman should try it some time. She should try rolling up her sleeves for a day of creative black-out.

The strange thing was she could say with great authority – enormous authority in fact – what she wasn't going to write next. That was easy. She didn't want to write some thinly disguised copy of a classic. The bookshelves were full of contemporary reworkings of *Jane Eyre*, *Pride and Prejudice*, *Emma*, and more recently *Rebecca* had been given the same treatment. She was sick of bright young things always getting their man.

The other kind of novel she didn't want to write was the one about the bored, frumpy housewife, who manages overnight to shed three stone and with little more than a wave of a new mascara wand makes the sexy love interest fall at her feet.

If she was sick of bright young things getting their man, she was equally sick of middle-aged women making good.

Where was the reality?

Where was the nitty-gritty, hard-up-against-the-wall portrayal that all men were bastards and weren't worth the effort?

So, having condemned most of the popular romantic fiction currently on offer, what exactly did that leave her to get her teeth into?

A good juicy murder story?

It would be her own if Piers got wind of the mess she was in.

Oh Lord, what on earth had happened to her? Why was she so thoroughly cynical about love and romance all of a sudden?

She came to an abrupt stop in the road.

Gavin!

That was what was wrong with her. It was all his fault that she couldn't write. He had knocked the stuff of love right out of her and now she couldn't write about it.

'Damn you, Gavin!' she said out loud. A startled sparrow flew out of the undergrowth and disappeared into the safety of a hawthorn tree.

And what's more, she thought as she stomped her way along the road, having stolen her creative Muse, Gavin was very probably having his nautical way with her.

By the time she reached Willow Cottage Jessica's fury was just waiting to unleash itself.

She found her mother heaving a large rock out of the back of her Fiesta.

'Oh hell,' muttered Anna, when she saw the look of fuming anger on her daughter's face. 'I'd hoped to hide this before you arrived.'

'I bet you did!' stormed Jessica, going over to the car and pushing her mother's hands away from the enormous filched lump of North Wales coastline. 'Just what do you think you're doing?'

'I would have thought that was quite obvious.'

Jessica struggled with the rock, then pitched it into the wheelbarrow which her mother had positioned against the car. The barrow shuddered and nearly toppled under the weight of its cargo.

'In heaven's name, couldn't you have found something smaller?'

Anna smiled. 'The others are.'

'Others!' cried Jessica, now following after her mother, who was staggering behind the barrow and pushing it round to the back of the house.

'I'm building a rockery,' Anna said over her shoulder.

'I don't believe this,' Jessica said when they stood looking at a pile of stones. 'You've got enough here to rival Stonehenge.'

'Oh, don't exaggerate.'

'Well if you're not worried about your own suspension, what about the car's? You must have been dragging the boot on the ground the whole way home from George and Emily's.'

'It's my body, my car, I'll do as I please.'

Jessica frowned. Why couldn't her mother behave as she was supposed to? Why couldn't she be happy with a little light weeding and the odd coffee morning to keep her out of mischief? Why this bloody need to kill herself! 'And what was George thinking, letting you do this? I thought I could trust him.'

'Look, Jessica, I know you mean well, but do you think you could ease up a bit? And for your information, George wasn't around when Emily and I loaded the car. So don't go blaming him. Here, just help me tip the barrow to get this rock out.'

Jessica did as her mother asked. 'I'm sorry,' she said, when the stone rolled away from them and joined its compatriots, 'it's just that I can't help but worry about you.' She knew that she'd just taken out her anger and frustration on Anna.

'I know, dear. But honestly, I'm fine. Which is more than I can say for you. Now why don't you sit down for a few moments and tell me what you've been up to while I was away. Oh, and before I forget, George and Emily send their best wishes and they both loved your last book. They want to know when the next one comes out. I said you'd write and tell them yourself.'

Jessica rolled her eyes. 'Letters will be all I'll be good for at the rate I'm going.'

Anna could see that her daughter was unusually upset. 'Come on,' she said, 'sit on the swing and tell me all about it while I prune the roses.' Without waiting for a response from Jessica, she led the way.

The swing had been one of Anna's proudest achievements in the garden. It had been a present for Jessica on her tenth birthday. It was built out of a sturdy combination of wooden sleepers and metal girders, and Anna had trained clusters of baby pink roses to grow over it. Now, after all these years it resembled the prettiest of rose arbours.

Jessica sat on the wooden seat and breathed in the sweet smell of roses; the perfume was as fragrant as she remembered from her childhood. She suddenly felt sad. The time would come when one day, these beautiful roses would be nothing but a memory.

'So what's the problem?' Anna asked, pulling out a pair of secateurs from her skirt pocket and snipping away at the deadheads; she dropped them tidily into a trug on the ground.

Jessica picked up her feet and gently began swinging to and fro, setting off a steady rhythmic creaking. 'I can't write,' she said simply.

Anna carried on with what she was doing. 'You mean you've got writer's block?'

'Something like that.'

'So what are you going to do about it?'

'I wish I knew.'

'Remind me to fetch some oil out here, that swing sounds as fed up as you. Any idea what's caused this block?'

'Promise you won't tut or scoff?'

'Have I ever?'

'Frequently. Especially over Gavin. When you met him for the first time you did nothing but tut and scoff.'

Anna turned and faced her daughter. What Jessica had just said was true. She had never really taken to Gavin. 'Are you saying he's the reason for your writer's block?'

Jessica nodded.

'Dear me,' was all Anna said. She went back to her roses.

'He's made me so cynical about love and romance that I don't think I can write about it as I used to.'

Anna tutted.

'You promised!'

'No I didn't. And the answer is simple. Find somebody new to love. Have a bit of a fling to restore your faith in all things romantic.'

'I can't possibly do that!'

'Why ever not? There's nothing like a casual affair to put the spring back in your step. Now tell me how your house is coming along.'

Jessica was amazed at her mother's extraordinary suggestion. Mothers weren't supposed to go around saying things like that! Little did Anna know that Jessica had already had the offer of something to put the spring back in her step, but had turned it down. She wondered, now, why she'd done that. Why had she backed off from Josh Crawford in the way she had? Was it simply that it was too soon after Gavin? Well, chances were she was going to find out. Last night, Josh had called over to invite her to dinner this evening.

'Jessica,' Anna said with a frown, 'I'm getting more attention from that creaking swing than from you. I asked you how your house was.'

'Sorry,' Jessica said, dragging her attention back to her mother. 'It's fine, though I'm not sure how much longer I can put up with some of the décor.'

'Then do something about it.'

'I will.' Jessica smiled. How clearly her mother saw things. If there was something wrong, then Anna's immediate response was to put it right – have a fling, redecorate, whatever. She never wasted any energy complaining about a thing.

'Which room bothers you the most?' Anna asked.

'Um ... the kitchen probably, it's too slick, too much like an operating theatre.'

'Then let me decorate it for you.'

'What about Stonehenge?'

'I am capable of doing more than two things at once you know.'

'All right,' said Jessica. 'You're on.' At least if her mother was helping her it meant she could keep an eye on what she was getting up to. 'Do you think you could help me with something else?'

'Depends what it is. It's nothing to do with Gavin, is it?'

'No it isn't,' Jessica said crossly. 'I need to buy a car, and I wondered if you'd like to chauffeur me round a few garages and help me choose one?'

'When?'

'This afternoon?'

Anna looked disappointed. 'I wanted to make a start on the rockery.'

'Please.'

'Oh, all right. And don't think for one moment that by putting me off today I shall lose interest and not get around to doing it.'

'Hadn't crossed my mind.'

'Liar.'

Jessica stayed for lunch with Anna and told her about her new publishing contract.

'Does this mean you're going to be fabulously wealthy?'

'Don't be daft. It means there's a lot of hard work ahead of me ... if only I could get started.'

After lunch they went in search of a car.

'What are you thinking of buying?' Anna asked Jessica as they drove away from Cholmford. 'Something with a decent engine I hope. Will your ill-gotten gains run to something brand new and swanky? I quite fancy being driven around in style. How about a little sports car? We'd look good in that.'

'I was thinking more along the lines of a second-hand runabout.' Even though Jessica knew she was about to start earning what in anyone's book was a decent amount of money, the years of living with little more than a backpack stuffed full of frugal uncertainty had made her unable to splash out too lavishly.

'You're surely not telling me you want a boring old Metro that's been driven by a dull old dear who's never pushed it beyond third gear?'

'It'd be better than your Fiesta that's been used as a skip. Honestly, Mum, the state of this car's disgusting. When was the last time you cleared it out?' She held up a pork pie wrapper that had been stuffed into the space where cassettes were supposed to be stored.

'You're turning into a right old whinge. Where, oh where, did I go wrong with you?'

'You didn't. I'm the voice of reason.'

Anna groaned. 'Now that you've come home, I'm not going to see too much of you, am I?'

'Thanks, Mum. Love you too.'

'One can have too much of a good thing, you know.'

'I'm beginning to see that.'

'Good. Just so long as we know where we stand. Now tell me about your neighbours, what are they like? And more to the point, what's the story behind the good-looking man we saw the day you moved in? Single, married, divorced or gay?'

Jessica laughed. 'I've a good mind not to tell you.'

'You could always walk to the garage.'

'Okay, I give in.' Jessica began by telling her mother about Tony and Amanda, then moved on to Kate and Alec next door. 'I like them, they're nice. They're not married but they're very much in *lurve*. She's a lot younger than him and a real stunner, but one of those who doesn't realise it.'

'You mean, she's stupid?'

'No. There's a naïvety about her that's really quite refreshing. I'd love to use her as a character in a book one day.'

'And what about him? Is he a middle-aged lech?'

'Not at all. He's the kind of man I'd have liked as a father.' She immediately wished she hadn't said that.

'I'm sorry not to have obliged you, Jessica.'

'I didn't mean it like that.'

Anna smiled kindly at her daughter. Years ago, Jessica had always been on at her to find a husband. But what with bringing up a child on her own and running a busy employment agency, the opportunity had never shown itself. Perhaps if it had, Jessica wouldn't now be so overly attentive.

'So,' she said, 'we've covered Mrs Social-Climber and her cute husband, and Mr and Mrs Lovey-Dovey next door, how about our good-looking young man? What have you got to tell me about him? I see that you've kept him till last. Would he be any good at helping you over your writer's block?'

'Honestly, Mum, why don't you just come right out and ask if I fancy sleeping with him?'

'I thought I just had.'

Jessica feigned a look of shock and told Anna all about being rescued after her trip down to London. She went on to give an edited version of the nightcap session following Tony and Amanda's dinner party.

'And?' Anna said when she'd finished.

'And, there isn't anything else to tell.'

'You sure?'

'Kindly remember there are certain things a daughter can't share with her mother.'

'It must have slipped my memory. Didn't I ever tell you that you were adopted?'

Jessica laughed. 'Forget it. I'm not telling you any more about him. So keep your nose out of my private life and your eyes on the road, I'd forgotten what an appalling driver you are.'

She had decided not to tell her mother that she was having dinner with Josh that evening and would keep it that way until she had made up her mind where she stood with him. It was all very well her mother suggesting that she have a fling with one of her neighbours, but how would it be when it was over and she and Josh had to face each other across the courtyard?

And surely Anna was wrong? Rushing headlong into the arms of somebody, for whatever reason, so soon after Gavin didn't seem like the most sensible of ideas.

It sounded like a perfect recipe for disaster.

22

Josh read through the recipe for Thai salmon parcels one more time and got down to work.

He grated the small stump of fresh ginger, crushed the clove of garlic, squeezed the juice out of two limes, chopped up a spring onion together with some coriander, then put it all in a pyrex bowl. Next he melted a chunk of butter in the microwave, then laid out the first of the sheets of filo pastry. As he began brushing the melted butter over the thin layer of pastry he had to concentrate hard on keeping his right hand moving.

It's fine, he told himself, determined to ignore the pins and needles and stiffness that were building up in his fingers. There's nothing to worry about. It'll pass.

But the cruel voice of Past Experience said otherwise. *If you're struggling to hold a pastry brush now,* it sneered at him, *how do you think you're going to relieve Jessica of her clothing later on tonight? Just think of all those buttons and fastenings to get through.*

He told Past Experience to bugger off and carried on with what he was doing, but the brush slipped out of his hand, rolled off the edge of the island unit and landed on the floor. He picked it up and threw it into the sink, then hunted through the drawer for another. When he found one, he laid a second sheet of filo pastry on top of the first and smeared it with the melted butter.

I'll be fine, he told himself. It's only the one hand that's playing up and anyway, I could always claim I'd hurt it during the day.

How? the gloating voice sneered at him again, *a squash injury perhaps?*

He blotted out what he didn't want to face, just as he had his brother's expression on Sunday afternoon when he'd told him about Jessica. He could tell what Charlie was thinking, but he didn't care.

'I'm not looking for a big relationship that's heavy on commitment,' he'd said to Charlie, when they'd eaten lunch and were tidying the kitchen, while outside in the garden their parents dozed in the sun. 'There's no point anyway. I just want a bit of fun . . . while I still can.'

'But wouldn't you rather have something that's more meaningful?'

'Like I say, there's no point. What can I offer anyone?'

Josh knew that he was being selfish, that what he had in mind that evening was all about himself. Jessica might not have wanted to go to bed with him the other night, but he had every intention of making things turn out differently tonight. And to hell with the consequences.

He finished making the salmon parcels and went through to the dining-room to check there was nothing he'd forgotten. Everything looked in order. He'd set the table earlier when he'd got back from seeing a customer in Stoke and all that remained to be done was to light the candles when Jessica arrived.

In the sitting-room he went over to the flowers he had bought on the way home. They were large creamy white lilies and had been the most impressive-looking flowers in the shop. 'They'll last for days,' the florist had said, 'and the scent's terrific.' Now he wondered if they were a bit too much; the room seemed to be filled with their rich, powerful fragrance. He carefully picked up the vase and carried it away from the mantelpiece and positioned it on a small table beneath the open window where a cool breeze gently blew in. He stood back and stared at the lilies. He didn't know why, but they didn't look right. There was nowhere else to put them so he returned the vase to the mantelpiece. He then fiddled about with the cushions on the sofa and chairs, and straightened the magazines on the coffee table.

Bloody hell, he thought, what was he doing, turning into some neurotic housewife plumping up the cushions?

All the same, he couldn't resist going upstairs and checking the bedroom. He smoothed out the duvet which he had changed earlier, kicked his work shoes under the bed and pulled open his bedside drawer. A new packet of condoms winked back at him and before the malevolent voice that had taunted him in the kitchen had a chance to say anything, he shut the drawer and went and inspected the bathroom. All was clean and tidy. No hairs in the bath plughole and not a sign of any shavings in the basin. Even the towels were hanging straight.

He went back downstairs to the kitchen, where the tantalising smell of garlic and lime was making itself at home. He poured out a glass of wine from the bottle already uncorked in the fridge and congratulated himself. The stage was perfectly set for an evening of seduction. All that was needed was for Jessica to make her appearance.

Jessica was totally unaware of the time.

After an exhausting but successful afternoon spent car hunting with her mother, she had come home and run herself a bath. While lying back in the hot scented water and thinking about the evening ahead, the miraculous had happened – inspiration for her next novel had leapt out at her. What's more, the title had even presented itself.

And amazingly it was all down to her mother. Though heaven forbid that Anna should ever know that the credit was hers!

Not wanting to lose a single precious idea, Jessica had made a fast exit from the bathroom and with only a towel tied around her she had hurried down to the study where, on a creative high, she began throwing together a cast of characters along with a rough outline for a story.

Only when her neck and shoulders started to ache from being hunched over her desk for so long did she wonder what time it was and, remembering that she was supposed to have been getting ready to go out, she went through to the kitchen. The digital clock on the oven unit told her it was twenty to nine. She gasped in horror. She was nearly half an hour late for Josh.

She flew upstairs and threw on the first things to hand – the long wraparound skirt she had worn the other night for supper at Tony and Amanda's and a loose-fitting sleeveless top the colour of ivory, which made her look browner than ever. She slipped a pair of gold hooped ear-rings through her ears, brushed her hair and was downstairs in a matter of seconds, ready to open the front door. It was then that she realised she'd forgotten to put on any knickers. Back up the stairs, she yanked open a drawer and found that she was down to her last pair – they were years old and had seen rather more action than was decent. She wriggled into the worn-out pinky-grey cotton-and-lycra mixture and dashed downstairs again, remembering on her way out of the house to grab the bottle she'd bought for Josh.

When she knocked on his door she was flushed and out of breath.

In contrast, Josh looked like he deserved better than her cobbled-together appearance and antique knickers.

He stood there smiling at her, every inch of him heart-stoppingly, stomach-lurchingly gorgeous. And she was so busy taking him in – every little bit of his clean-cut splendid self, dressed in black jeans and crisp white T-shirt – that she almost missed the kiss being planted on her cheek. She reacted just in time and caught the benefit of his lips brushing against her skin.

'Here, this is for you,' she said. She handed him the bottle of Southern Comfort. 'Seeing as I helped you polish off the last one.'

'Thanks, we'll have a go with this later, perhaps. Come on through to the kitchen, I'm just in the middle of something.'

She followed behind him. Mm . . . nice bum, she found herself thinking. She even thought his limp was attractive and decided that it gave him an interesting air of vulnerability. As they passed what she took to be the downstairs loo, she was aware of a heady nose-clearing cocktail of Pine-O-

Fresh toilet cleaner and some kind of air freshener. Bless him. The bachelor boy had been busy.

In the kitchen, she watched him open the oven door and take out a tray of croûtons. Her taste-buds responded to the delicious smell of garlic and olive oil. 'Sorry I'm so late, by the way,' she said.

'I was beginning to wonder whether I was going to be stood up,' he said, closing the oven door with his foot and tipping the perfectly cooked croûtons into a yellow-and-blue pottery bowl. 'I would have been very disappointed.'

'Oh, I wouldn't have done that,' she said, 'standing people up isn't my style.' She had the feeling that they were flirting with one another again.

'Good, I'm glad to hear it. So what's your excuse for being late? And I shall expect something highly imaginative and original from you, no ordinary explanation will do, not from a writer.'

She laughed. 'Well, Crawford – you don't mind if I call you that, do you?'

'If it amuses you, go ahead. Though I'd like to know why.'

'How very tedious of you. But let's just say that a little formality never does any harm. It's a useful device for putting people at their ease.'

He moved across the kitchen and slid the baking tray into the sink. 'An interesting concept, with more than a hint of Oscar Wilde to it.'

'You're not accusing me of plagiarism, are you?'

He turned round and laughed. 'Oh I wouldn't dare. Now, about your excuse for being late.'

'Heavens, you're like a dog with a bone. Would you believe me if I said that burglars broke into my house in the middle of the night and stole all my clocks, thereby leaving me unable to keep track of the time?'

'No. Try again.'

'Localised earthquake?'

'Hopeless.'

'I overslept?'

He shook his head.

'Okay, I admit it, I was with another man having great but meaningless sex.'

He smiled. 'The truth at last. Glass of wine?'

'Thanks.'

He poured out a glass and handed it to her.

'Actually, I'm late because I've at last started work on my next novel.' She told him how depressed she'd been that morning. 'You can't imagine what a relief it is for me to get going again. There were a few nasty moments today when I thought I'd lost it.'

'I'm delighted to hear that you haven't. Am I allowed to know the title?'

She hesitated. Normally she didn't share too much of a new novel with anyone, not until it was firmly in her mind – a new book was like a tiny flickering candle flame, blow too hard on it and it would be completely snuffed out. But she decided to tell him. He would probably think it funny. Well, he would if he knew what her mother had suggested today. 'It's going to be called *A Casual Affair*,' she said, 'what do you think?'

It was his turn to hesitate.

'Don't you like it?' she asked, concerned.

'No. I mean, yes. Yes I do, it's great.' He lowered his gaze and busied his hands with adding the croûtons to the bowl of salad. *A Casual Affair*, he repeated to himself. Well, considering what he had in mind it was perfect.

When they sat down to eat Jessica was impressed. 'You've gone to a lot of trouble, Crawford,' she said mockingly, watching him light the candles on the table. 'Or is this the way you always eat?'

He smiled. 'Only when I want to impress somebody special.'

'Oh,' she said in a coy girlie voice, 'does that make me special?'

He passed her a dish of Jersey Royals that were coated in butter as well as a sprinkling of chopped chives. 'What do you think?'

'I think that you've a manner smooth enough to charm the devil and that I should be very wary of you. And,' she continued, helping herself to a couple of potatoes and adding them to her plate of salmon, 'a man who can cook as well as this is clearly to be viewed with the utmost suspicion. The bottom line, Crawford my boy, is that you're too good to be true. There has to be another side to you that you're keeping under wraps.'

He shook his head. 'See, there's the thing, I'm told that all the time.'

'I can well believe it. Take it from me, this new man stuff of being a whizz in the kitchen will do you no good at all. It only serves to undermine the majority of women and frighten the pants off them.'

He grinned. 'Sounds like justification enough to me. *Bon appetit!*'

The salmon was perfect, as was everything about the meal, and when they'd finished eating Josh told Jessica to go and relax in the sitting-room while he made some coffee.

Alone in the kitchen, he punched a fist in the air. *Yesss!*

Everything was going exactly to plan. They were getting along just fine. All he had to do was get some coffee down Jessica, followed by a couple of glasses of Southern Comfort, then it would be up those stairs. Yes, yes, *yesss!*

The fact that he had hardly any feeling in his right hand did nothing to dampen his confidence and he congratulated himself on his performance over dinner – he'd managed to eat with the fork in his right hand, which didn't need too much manipulative skill, and had used his left for the trickier business of cutting up his food.

And if his luck continued to hold out he was certain he was going to get away with the rest of the evening.

He filled the cafetiere with Sainsbury's Colombian coffee, placed it on the tray with the cups and saucers, along with a box of mint chocolates, and took it through to the sitting-room, where he found Jessica standing in front of the bookcase. She turned to look at him when she heard him come into the room.

'What's the interest in multiple sclerosis?' she asked. She showed him the book in her hands, *Multiple Sclerosis – And How to Get the Better of It.*

He gripped the edges of the tray and carefully moved across the room; all his euphoria instantly gone. He lowered the tray on to the glass-topped table, sank into the sofa and swallowed back his shock. He racked his brain for something convincing to say.

She came over and joined him, the book still in her hands. 'It's an illness I know nothing about,' she said.

'The majority of people don't need to know anything about it,' he said flatly.

'I suppose not. But do you know somebody with MS, then? Is that why you've got this?'

He swallowed and hoped that Charlie would forgive him. 'Yes,' he said, 'my brother Charlie.'

She put down the book on the table. 'Oh, I'm sorry.'

Aware that he could still save the situation, he poured out the coffee with his good hand and began the not so subtle web of lies that he hoped would satisfy Jessica and get him off the hook. 'Charlie's not got it too badly,' he said, trying to sound casual, 'it's just every now and again that he gets caught out, he gets tired easily. But most of the time you'd never know there was anything wrong.'

'When did it start?'

'A few years back. It was quite out of the blue.' He paused, then said, 'Do you think we could drop the subject of my brother?'

'Of course,' she said, 'I'm sorry, I was being nosy.' Jessica had already concluded that Josh and his brother were close, but going by the tone of Josh's voice, it was clear that he was also extremely concerned about Charlie. She felt annoyed with herself for her insensitivity.

'How about some music?' Josh asked, already on his feet and going over to the CD player. 'What do you fancy?'

She was tipsy enough to say 'You,' but sober enough to refrain. 'You choose,' she said.

He put on *The Best of Chris Rea* and 'The Road to Hell' started up. The irony was not lost on him. He went back to the sofa and poured out two glasses of Southern Comfort.

They sat in silence for a while listening to the music and, conscious that they were only a few inches apart, Josh decided it was now or never. It was time to make a move on Jessica. He turned and faced her, and found that she was staring at him. He reached out to her hand on her lap, but was cheated of the touch of her; his fingers were completely numb. He raised his good hand to stroke her face and when she made no attempt to push him away, he kissed her, slowly and lingeringly, and for the first time that night he felt his entire body relax. It was wonderful. He hadn't realised just how uptight he'd been. He gently pushed her along the length of the sofa and began parting the front of her skirt. It was going to be easier than he'd thought.

Dead easy.

He was home and dry.

She was as keen as he was.

But from nowhere he experienced a bolt of self-revulsion; it caught him like a punch in the stomach. He saw what he was doing for what it really was – he was using Jessica as a means to boost his self-esteem. By bedding her, he hoped to chalk up a point of victory over his illness.

And with this clarity of thought came a wave of nausea. He wanted to put it down to the overpowering smell coming from the lilies on the mantelpiece, but he knew deep down that it was something more. He felt cheap and shabby, and knew he couldn't go through the motions of seducing Jessica in the contrived manner he had planned so exactly. It was all wrong. With a shock he realised that instead of the desire for a mindless easy lay upstairs on the clean sheets, he was overcome with the need for something more.

But what?

Charlie's words came into his head – *Wouldn't you rather have something more meaningful?*

No! he wanted to shout.

No. No. *No!* I'm not capable of anything more. What the hell can I offer anyone in a long-term relationship?

23

It was the first wet day in over three weeks and as Alec drove past Capesthorne Hall the rain came down even harder. He switched the windscreen wipers on to full and dropped his speed as he joined the queue of cars which stretched back almost two hundred yards from the traffic lights at the junction ahead. It was always busy at this time in the morning and every day as he waited in this same stream of traffic he promised himself to leave the house earlier in order to avoid the rush.

He thought the same now.

But as the wipers tump-tumped across the windscreen he suddenly thought, why? Why should he?

Why should he deprive himself of a few precious minutes at home with Kate just so that he could reach the office at eight thirty instead of eight forty? What possible difference would it make?

None.

None whatsoever. He would still get exactly the same amount of work done. So why bother?

Because the old Alec McLaren had spent a lifetime on the treadmill convinced that the only way to be was to adhere to the puritanical work ethic that his father had drilled into him – a busy mind is a pure mind.

He smiled and not for the first time wondered what his poor father would have made of his relationship with Kate. The old man's verdict would probably have been that Alec hadn't kept himself busy enough. 'Your mind has wandered,' he'd have said, 'and wandered badly into the mire of evil.'

Alec had been terrified of his father as a child and had never attached himself to any of the religious views he propounded, finding the commitment to such an apparently cold and unforgiving deity too austere a concept to consider as having any value or relevance.

He preferred his mother's God. While his father had frightened him with his tales of hell and purgatory, his mother had told him reassuring stories of a merciful God who was more interested in seeing a smile on Alec's face, rather than a grim expression of servitude.

His mother had been a quiet, affectionate woman whom Alec had adored. Being her only child she had spoilt him as much as she dared and, without ever defying her husband or the strict code of conduct by which he expected them all to live, she had managed to ensure that Alec's childhood was a happy one.

He wasn't quite sure that it was something he should admit, or ever explore in any depth, but there were definitely times when Kate reminded him of his mother. Physically the two women were quite different – his mother had been a tiny dark-haired woman – but they both had the same ability to give him a sense of true well-being. Often, when he left work and drove home to Kate, he experienced the same degree of comfort and anchorage as when he'd been a ten-year-old boy arriving home from school on a cold, wintry afternoon to find his mother pulling a tray of freshly baked oatcakes out of the oven.

If he wanted to offer up a superficial analysis of any of this, he supposed it was possible that he loved Kate as much as he did because, like his mother who had eased the severity of his father's treatment of him, Kate had wiped away the shock and pain of what Melissa had done.

In the end, time had helped him to resolve the difficult relationship with his father. As an adult, Alec had grown to understand, and on occasion almost respect, the strong will and reserved manner that had kept them apart. To this day, though, it saddened Alec that they hadn't been closer. When his father was dying and he and his mother had spent so many hours by his hospital bedside there had still been that impenetrable barrier of stiff formality between them. What would have seemed the most natural thing in the world to have done was to have hugged his father and said that he loved him. But it hadn't happened. Even at so poignant a moment to have shown the slightest flicker of emotion in front of this formidable man was unthinkable. And perhaps that's the way it should have been. It was probably what his father would have wanted. No emotion. Just a quiet acceptance that his life was over.

Except it wasn't.

No life was ever over. It could never be that clear-cut. There was always a legacy that kept the deceased well and truly alive. And in his father's case he had bequeathed Alec a confusion of conflicting attitudes that was hard to shake off. It was frightening just how good a job his father had done, because sure enough, the work-till-you-drop ethic was clearly ingrained in Alec, which was why from time to time he had to force himself to stand firm and veto this edict from the grave.

So, no, he now said as the lights changed to green and he turned left on to the Chelford Road. No, he would not leave the house any earlier to avoid the traffic just so that he could gain an extra ten minutes at his desk.

He reached the office at the same time as Melissa and parked alongside her MR2. She let them into the redbrick building that had once been the local village school. With its distinctive Victorian arched windows, it still looked exactly like a school from the outside, but inside it was completely different, with many of the walls knocked down to open up what had originally been small cramped classrooms into large areas of creative working space. The windows were perfect for letting in plenty of natural light so that the three artists they currently employed could work at their best. Where the light wasn't quite so good, Melissa and Alec had their offices, along with other members of the team who carried out the administrative side of the business.

Many of the people whom they employed had been with them since Thistle Cards had moved to these premises back in 1981. Before those days the business had been little more than a dream, consisting of him and Melissa putting in a full day's work for a small advertising agency where they were both employed as designers, then taking it in turns to look after Ruth or spend an evening inhaling the fumes of turpentine-based ink in a rented basement room beneath Squeaky Clean, a dog parlour that was a local harbouring ground for fleas, ticks and any other ghastly canine parasite you'd care to think of. Alec didn't know which was worse, the stink of the turpentine in that tiny dank room as they worked until gone midnight producing a limited range of cards, or the permanent smell of wet dog seeping through the rotten floorboards above their heads.

'What are you smiling about?' Melissa said, catching the expression on his face as she looked up from sorting through the mail in her hands.

'Sorry,' he said, 'I didn't realise I was. I was just reminiscing.'

She followed him through to his office. 'Reminiscing about anything in particular?'

'I was thinking about Squeaky Clean.'

Melissa shuddered. 'I gave up thinking about those awful days a long time ago. I much prefer to think of the present.'

He sat in his swivel chair and considered what she'd just said. 'In all ways?' he asked.

The question hung in the air while Melissa returned his gaze. She thought about answering it, but decided not to – cheap shots at an ex-husband were two a penny. Instead she said, 'I want to check a few things with you about Birmingham.'

At this time of the year the Birmingham trade fair was their biggest concern. There was a colossal amount of work involved in order to be ready for the September event. But despite the organisational headache both he and Melissa thrived on it. They always had. It was where the bulk of their business was done and where, most importantly, they found their entrée into the export markets; a third of their money was made in the USA, Japan, Australia and more recently Iceland had been added to their order books. The trade fairs were a fundamental part of the greetings card industry, without them they might just as well pack up and go home.

'What is it?' he asked. 'A problem?'

She sat in the chair opposite him. 'Of course not, stop thinking the worst.'

He was reminded of Kate on Monday evening when he'd got back from work and found her eager to share some news with him. 'Sit down,' she'd said, 'I've got something to tell you, and don't go jumping to conclusions and thinking the worst.'

'What is it?' he'd asked warily. The awful thought had gone through his mind that Kate was about to tell him that she was pregnant. He'd sat awkwardly in the armchair petrified that his expression would betray him. He knew that Kate would love to have a baby and knew too how she would want him to react to such a piece of news. But when she'd told him that she'd decided that she wanted to retrain and become a teacher he had pulled her on to his lap and hugged her.

'That's a brilliant idea,' he'd said, kissing her. 'That's fantastic.'

Thinking now about his relief that Kate wasn't pregnant it struck him how utterly selfish he was. It wasn't a pleasant realisation. In fact, it was a rather unpalatable conclusion that spoke volumes about their relationship. Without doubt he loved Kate more than he'd loved anyone, but it was all too clear that he didn't love her sufficiently to give her complete happiness. Whereas Kate loved him selflessly. Because of her love for him she was prepared to deny herself something she desperately wanted – a family of her own.

What was he prepared to sacrifice for Kate? Good God, he hadn't even had the decency to marry her.

When he and Melissa had finished discussing the Birmingham trade fair Alec phoned Kate. He suddenly wanted to hear her gentle, loving voice. He needed confirmation that he wasn't a complete heel.

Kate put down the phone and went back to pouring out a small mug of Ribena for Oscar.

'Was that Gramps?' he asked from the table where he was busy painting.

'Yes,' she said, handing him his drink.

He put down his paintbrush, taking care to keep it on the newspaper that Kate had partially covered the table with.

'Would you like a rice cake?'

He shook his head.

'A biscuit?'

His face lit up. 'Yes please.'

Kate fetched the biscuit tin from the cupboard and came back and sat next to him. She prised the lid off and offered him the tin. He took a custard cream and began nibbling on one of its corners. He stared at her thoughtfully. 'If you were married to Gramps, would that make you my grandma?'

Kate smiled. 'I don't think so,' she said, amused at the notion of being a grandmother.

'Good,' he said. 'I don't want you to be like Grandma Melissa.'

Much as a good bitching session about Melissa would intrigue her, Kate knew better than to draw Oscar on the subject. 'Grandma Melissa and I are very different,' she said tactfully.

'I don't like her,' he confessed, his eyes lowered. 'She tells me off.'

'Well,' Kate said slowly, 'if you've been naughty then she has every right to tell you off.'

He raised his eyes and looked indignant. 'But I wasn't naughty. I only said that I liked you better than her.'

'Oh, Oscar,' Kate said, 'you mustn't say things like that.'

'Why not?'

'Because . . . because you must have hurt Grandma Melissa by saying what you did and that's something you mustn't do, you mustn't go around hurting people. It's not nice.'

'I didn't mean to hurt her,' he said, his face full of concern. 'Mummy says I mustn't tell lies . . . I was telling the truth. I only told Grandma Melissa that I liked you better than anyone else. What was wrong with that?'

Nothing, thought Kate, if you were a four-and-a-half-year-old boy. 'Come on,' she said by way of distraction, 'how's this picture coming along?'

Oscar drained his mug of Ribena, set it down next to the jam jar of greeny-grey water and picked up his paintbrush. 'I'm going to do the sky next. Will you help me?'

'If you want. But you go first and I'll do a tiny bit at the end.'

Kate watched Oscar dip his brush into the jar of water and select his colour from the plastic tray of paints. He covered the stumpy bristles in blue and started stroking the brush across the top two inches of his picture. He worked carefully and slowly, and Kate watched his face closely. It was rigid with concentration, his tongue poking out of the corner of his mouth, his smudgy little eyebrows furrowed lest he make a mistake.

This was Oscar's first day with Kate – and Ruth's first day working alongside Adam. She had arrived late, having told Kate on the phone last night to expect her at eight o'clock. She'd eventually turned up at a quarter to nine. 'The roads are a nightmare,' she'd said to Kate, bundling Oscar out of the car as the rain had lashed down on them, 'I can't believe how selfish people are all travelling in separate cars. Haven't they heard of public transport, or car pools for that matter?'

Kate would have liked to suggest that maybe Ruth ought to travel to work with Adam and save yet another car from adding to the congestion, but she hadn't; instead she had taken Oscar's hand and led him through to the kitchen.

'I've brought his jacket and boots so that you can take him for a walk,' Ruth had added, throwing the things down on the floor in the hall, 'he must have at least half an hour of fresh air.' She made him sound like a dog. 'And here are some rice cakes for him to eat instead of biscuits. I don't want you filling him up with rubbish. I'll see you at about six.'

She'd flown out of the house without so much as a kiss for Oscar and together he and Kate had waved goodbye from the doorstep.

'There,' Oscar said, turning to face Kate and handing her the paintbrush. 'I've left you the bit in the corner.'

'Thank you. But tell you what, why don't we put a bright jolly sun in that space? What do you think?'

He turned away and looked out of the kitchen window to the scene of the courtyard that he'd been painting. 'But there isn't a sun today, it's still raining,' he said.

She smiled. 'But we're using our imaginations to do this, aren't we? Let's paint a sun in, then maybe if we're really lucky it might make the rain go away and we could go for a walk.'

'I'll need some clean water.'

She got up and took the jam jar over to the sink. She refilled it and cleaned the brush under the tap. When she went back to Oscar the phone rang.

It was Caroline. 'Hi,' she said, 'have you got a minute?'

'Of course, but not too many, I've got Oscar here with me.'

'Oscar? Who's he? Some gorgeous hunk?'

'Gorgeous, but not a hunk. He's Alec's grandson.'

'Oh, yes, I remember you saying something about a child. But never mind all that. You're not going to believe this, but I've taken your advice.'

'You're right, I don't believe you. You never listen to anything I say, never mind act on it.'

'Well, this time I have. I've joined an introductions agency.' These last two words were whispered into the phone. 'And if you breathe a word about this to anyone I'll kill you. Got that?'

Kate smiled. 'Don't worry, I shan't say a word to anyone. So tell me all about it.'

'I won't bore you with all the details now, but hopefully by this time next week I shall be fixed up with my first date. I just hope it isn't somebody I know. Can you imagine the shame?'

'Well, don't forget, it will be the same for him. He'll be just as embarrassed.'

'That would be impossible.'

'But it's true. The men are bound to feel as awkward as you.' She recalled Alec telling her how anxious he'd been about meeting her. 'I very nearly bottled out,' he'd admitted. 'I parked the car and as I walked to the wine bar I thought I was going to be sick with nerves.'

'So how come you're suddenly such an expert on the matter?' Caroline demanded.

'I'm not,' Kate said quickly, 'I'm just imagining how it must be, that's all.'

'Look, I'm going to have to go now, the place is swarming with creepy old men in macs with nothing better to do than make a nuisance of themselves in the library. First drop of rain in weeks and they bloody well come in here dripping wet umbrellas on the carpet. By the way, when will you be in for that teacher training info?'

'How about first thing next week?'

'Come in on Tuesday morning and we can have lunch afterwards.'

'I might have Oscar with me.'

'He can come so long as you put a muzzle on him. Bye.'

Kate put down the phone and when she looked up she saw two figures hurrying across the courtyard in the rain. Amanda and Hattie.

Oh, heavens, what did Amanda want now?

24

Amanda removed the heated rollers from her hair and carefully began brushing it. She framed her face with her full bob of hair in the way that she normally wore it. Then she looked critically at herself in the mirror and changed her mind. She decided to go for a completely different look and, sweeping back her hair, she tucked it behind her ears, and before it had a chance to flop forward she quickly fixed it into place with some maximum-hold hair spray. When she'd finished she stared at her reflection and smiled at herself. Not bad, she thought. Not bad at all.

But then, at that precise moment she was feeling particularly pleased with herself anyway.

Not only had she finally decided on the fabric and wallpaper for the sitting-room – and found a decorator who wasn't fully booked up until Christmas – but she had managed to off-load Hattie on to Cholmford's very own equivalent to Maria von Trapp for that evening, leaving her and Tony free to take her mother out to dinner. And if all went well tonight, and there was no reason to suspect that it wouldn't, the outcome would be that her mother would baby-sit Hattie next month, enabling her and Tony to go away for an all-expenses-paid weekend that Arc was putting on.

'It's nothing special,' Tony had said at breakfast that morning, 'it's just the usual Arc "do" to encourage the team.'

Tony might not think that a long weekend spent at Gleneagles was special, but she had other ideas. Compared with what she was used to, three days of pampering would be bliss and she had every intention of indulging herself to the full. The first thing she planned to do, once Tony and his boring colleagues had gone off to the golf course, or whatever it was they were expected to do, was to hit the hotel fitness centre, followed by the beauty salon where she would gratify herself for as long as she wanted. And after three days of being steamed, covered in seaweed, plucked, waxed, massaged and manicured she would emerge a new woman. It would be fantastic. She couldn't wait.

The only thing that could conceivably get in the way of this wonderful weekend was Rita refusing to do her bit.

Downstairs she heard the sound of the doorbell. Good. That meant the ever reliable, ever sweet Kate had arrived.

Tony let Kate in. He took her through to the kitchen where he was in the middle of tidying up Hattie's tea things. 'This is very good of you,' he said, 'I hope you don't think we're taking advantage.'

She smiled and shook her head. 'Of course I don't.'

He tried not to stare at her, but he couldn't help himself and as he watched her push her wonderful hair away from her face he experienced a wave of something he hadn't felt in a long time.

It was a wave of desire.

And not some piddly ebb and flow of desire.

This was a roller.

A breaker.

A torrent.

A ruddy great tidal wave.

To hell with that, it was the Niagara Falls of desire.

He cleared his throat and went back to scraping the remains of Hattie's tea into the bin. Watch it, Tony, he said to himself as he dolloped tomato ketchup on to a half-eaten apple, you're imagining things. Nobody could have that effect on anyone.

Wrong!

Eve had. Eve had bowled him over the second they'd met.

He swallowed. Why was it that every time he was in Kate's company he was reminded of Eve? Was it because she had the same effect on him?

'Hello Kate.' It was Hattie. She was not long out of the bath and as she came into the kitchen Tony could smell the sweetness of her; a combination of bubble bath and talc. He watched her approach Kate and envied the warm hug she received. 'Will you read to me like you did last time?' she asked Kate.

'I should think so,' Kate answered. 'Why don't you go upstairs and choose which books you'd like.'

Hattie smiled. 'I've done that already.'

Tony laughed, went over to Hattie and lifted her up into his arms. 'What a terrible little opportunist you are,' he said, holding her aloft. He kissed her cheek and she kissed him back, smack on the lips, her hands clasped tightly around his neck.

'Will you come up and say good-night to me before you go out?' she asked him, her eyes wide and appealing.

'Try and stop me.' He gently lowered her to the floor. 'Go on, off you go, I'll be up in a minute.' He watched her leave the kitchen, then turned to Kate. 'Would you like a drink?' he asked.

'No thank you,' she said.

'Sure?'

'Yes.'

'How about something to eat?'

She smiled. 'I had a sandwich earlier.'

'Is that all?'

'I'm fine, really.'

'So there's nothing I can offer you?' Bloody hell! What did he sound like? – *So there's nothing I can offer you?* Why didn't he have done with it and start wearing a chunky gold bracelet and a fake tan, and take a crash course in *doubles entendres* for the intellectually challenged?

'*Kate,*' came a voice from the landing, 'are you coming up now?'

But before Kate could answer, Amanda made her appearance in the kitchen, her high heels clickety-clicking across the tiled floor. 'You really mustn't let Hattie boss you about, Kate,' she said, opening her small leather purse and slipping a tissue inside, then snapping it shut.

Hattie isn't bossing Kate about, Tony wanted to snipe back at Amanda, and without meaning to he ran a critical eye over what his wife was wearing.

She was smartly dressed in a pair of oatmeal-coloured linen trousers with a navy blazer and she had on just the right amount of gold jewellery – she'd got the balance exactly right, any more and she would have looked ostentatious. Her make-up had been carefully applied and enhanced her high cheek-bones, as well as smoothing away the fine lines round her eyes. He sensed that there was something different about her hair, but he couldn't put his finger on what exactly. He also sensed that anyone meeting Amanda for the first time, dressed as she was, would say that she was a most poised and elegant woman, that she was the epitome of a woman in her mid-thirties who knew what she was about – a no-nonsense woman who was completely in control of her life. Which was what had attracted him to her in the first place. He had recognised in her an ability to take charge of his disorganised life. He had seen in her someone to resolve all his problems.

But she hadn't, he now realised, she had only added to them.

He risked a sideways glance at Kate. The contrast between the two women couldn't have been greater. Kate was dressed in faded blue jeans with a tiny sort of misshapen cotton cardigan that was not only low-necked but also so short it didn't quite meet the top of her jeans and revealed about an inch of tantalising waistline. She wore no jewellery and as far as Tony could see, no make-up either. She was delightfully natural and fresh-faced, and standing beside Amanda she made her look overdressed and starchy.

'I'll just go and say good-night to Hattie,' he said, hastily retreating from the kitchen before the expression on his face gave him away. He wasn't imagining it, he told himself as he climbed the stairs. What he felt for Kate was no trick of the mind. His feelings for her were as real as those he'd felt for Eve. So why the bloody hell had fate done this to him? Why had it let him marry the wrong woman, then taunted him with exactly the kind of woman whom he could have loved and been happy with?

Back in the kitchen, Amanda was saying, 'Now you know where everything is. Just help yourself to teas and coffees and anything else you might need. We shan't be that late, about eleven-thirty I should think.'

'That's fine,' said Kate, 'please don't worry about the time.'

'I hope Alec doesn't mind you doing this for us.'

'He doesn't mind at all. He's working late tonight anyway, but he might join me when he gets back. Is that okay?'

'Of course.'

Uncomfortable in Amanda's presence and anxious not to prolong their conversation, Kate said, 'I think I'll go up and start reading to Hattie. Have a good evening.'

When she reached Hattie's bedroom door she paused, suddenly unsure whether to go in or not. She felt as if she might be barging in on Hattie and her father. She could hear them talking, their voices low and confiding. She thought about going back downstairs, but as she turned to go the floor betrayed her presence and gave off a loud creak.

'Is that you, Kate?' asked Hattie.

She pushed open the door and went in. Tony was sitting on the bed beside Hattie. He had one of his arms around her shoulders and from nowhere Kate was reminded of what she'd missed out on as a child. She couldn't ever recall being tucked into bed when she'd been little. Her mother had always been too busy arranging her own life to be bothered with sitting on the edge of a bed to kiss her good-night. Even now her mother was too busy to bother about Kate. The only contact between them was a Christmas card enclosing a cheque each year and the occasional birthday card sent from her latest home, which she shared with her third husband in Sydney, Australia. It had been like that for years. Kate didn't hold it against her mother, there was no point, some people just weren't designed to be parents.

Kate looked at Tony and realised that he was openly staring at her in a way that made her feel unaccountably confused.

The meal was dreadful and the company diabolical.

Bloody Rita was the last person on earth with whom Tony wanted to spend an evening. And as he picked out the artificially red cherries from the enormous slice of black forest gateau in front of him he found himself wishing that Amanda's father was there with them instead of taking the minutes at the AGM of his local history group – Roy might be one of the most boring men on the planet, in fact he could bore for the entire universe on the subject of ancient burial sites in the area, but his company would at least have had a sedative effect.

Tony forced himself to listen with half an ear to what his wife and mother-in-law were rattling on about. But he had no interest in their conversation – what did he care that some neighbour of Bloody Rita's was applying for planning permission to extend his house? With a more than willing mind he turned his thoughts to Kate.

He was trying to work out how he was ever going to see her alone. He knew he was playing with fire, but he couldn't help himself. He wanted to be with her. He wanted, just once, to be able to touch her, maybe even kiss her. Because perhaps then the spell she had cast on him would be lifted. He was trying to convince himself that what he felt for her had to be little more than infatuation and that no harm would come to either of them if he could just touch her and make the fantasy disappear.

'Isn't that right, Tony?'

'Sorry,' he said, suddenly alert to having been caught out not listening to the conversation.

Amanda frowned at him. 'I was just telling Mum about the important weekend away that Arc have asked us to host.'

It was his turn to frown. It was news to him that they were supposed to be hosting the event. But a kick under the table told him that Amanda was deliberately exaggerating the importance of the weekend in order to enlist her mother's help.

'Yes,' he lied, 'it should be quite an interesting weekend.' Hell's teeth, it would be the usual boring routine of trying to rally the troops – such as they were – to keep them working themselves into the ground in order to please Arc. He couldn't imagine anything worse.

No. That wasn't true. A weekend with Bloody Rita would win hands down.

He didn't know what it was about the woman, but she had an uncanny knack for metaphorically disembowelling him each time they met. He prided himself on getting on with most people, but here was somebody he'd failed to impress. She made it very clear to him that he didn't match her expectations for her only daughter. If he'd been a doctor or a barrister, or even an accountant, he might have given her something to be pleased about, but in her opinion being a sales director was nothing short of making a living out of knocking on doors with a suitcase of polishing cloths to peddle.

It was a class thing, of course. In her eyes he was nothing but a cloth-capped lad in clogs from Rochdale. 'Rochdale?' she'd said in a disappointed tone of voice, at their first meeting when she'd asked 'And from where do you hail?' – *from where do you hail?* – did any normal human being talk like that these days? He had no obvious accent to speak of, but her cross-examination of his upbringing had made him want to return to his roots and stretch out his vowels.

Rita's dislike of him was set in stone from that day on.

Even on the phone she couldn't bring herself to communicate with him more than was necessary. 'Is my daughter there?' would be her opening gambit if he ever picked up the phone when she called – she made no pretence at small talk.

Her generosity was as abundant as her conversation. Her Christmas present to them last year had been a pair of salt and pepper pots. Except they weren't a pair. They didn't match.

A bit like him and Amanda really.

Maybe Bloody Rita had known this right from the outset and had been trying to tell him something.

He tuned in again to what Amanda was saying. It sounded as if she was getting to the crucial bit.

'So we thought that perhaps you might like to help us out.'

'How exactly?' said Bloody Rita, her eyes narrowing, her lips tightening to a point.

How do you think, you stupid woman! Tony wanted to yell across the table.

'With Hattie,' Amanda carried on bravely, 'we wondered whether you could come and look after her for us. There's nobody else we can ask.'

The eyes had almost disappeared, as had the lips, which had been sucked in, in an expression of wary mistrust. 'For how long?' she asked, when a few seconds had passed.

'It'll only be a couple of days.'

Rita stared at her daughter. 'Be more specific, please.'

'From Friday morning through till Sunday evening,' interceded Tony, who could be as specific as the next person when he chose.

'I don't know,' Rita said, without even bothering to look at Tony, 'I haven't brought my diary with me. I'm away on a bowling trip during August.'

'Yes I know,' said Amanda, 'you're going the first weekend, our weekend is the second.'

Tony had to admire Amanda's persistence, but he didn't hold out much hope of Bloody Rita being persuaded into any kind of agreement. He understood her well enough to know that they were a long way from clinching the deal. But to be honest he didn't care. He wasn't fussed about a ra-ra weekend of team bonding, not when he was so disillusioned with the whole show. It had been different last year; company morale had been good and he'd gone to great lengths to organise a nanny to take care of Hattie so that he could join in with the fun, but what would be the point this time? With Bradley Hurst's blood-stained butcher's knife hanging over everybody, what fun would there be for any of them?

On top of all that, he wasn't keen on the idea of Hattie being looked after by Bloody Rita. In fact, the more he thought about it, the less he liked the prospect of his daughter having to put up with this witch of a woman.

'Perhaps we've been too presumptuous,' he heard himself say, 'we shouldn't have put you on the spot like this, Rita. Forget we ever mentioned it.'

He got a sharp kick from Amanda and a look that would have withered the strongest of men. He also received a sceptical lifting of an over-plucked eyebrow from his mother-in-law.

The atmosphere in the car after they'd dropped Rita off at home was deadly. Tony had no intention of speaking. He knew Amanda was cross with him, so it was just a matter of waiting until she'd calmed down enough to spit out the words in the right order.

Inevitably she did. 'What the hell did you think you were doing back there?' she hissed. 'After all the softening up I'd done you just waded in and blew it all away.'

He decided to be honest, which was a dangerous thing to do, but he was past caring. 'I don't want your mother looking after Hattie. If you really want to know, I don't ever want her to take care of my daughter.'

'What!'

'You heard.'

'I don't believe I'm hearing this.'

'You did ask. And you'd better believe it.'

They drove on in silence for a further mile and as they approached the small bridge over the canal Amanda found her voice once more. 'Are you serious, or are you just annoyed with her? I know the pair of you don't exactly get on.'

What an understatement! 'I'm serious. I want Hattie to be with someone who is genuinely fond of her. Your mother clearly isn't. She would only be doing it out of a sense of duty, which is never the right motivation to do anything.' He of all people knew how true that was.

Amanda was stunned. 'Well, that's that then. We shan't be able to go. Unless . . .'

'Unless what?'

'Unless Maria von Trapp would do it.'

'Who?'

'Kate, of course, who else.'

'No,' he said firmly. 'Absolutely not. We've imposed on her enough. You're not to ask her, it wouldn't be fair.'

They remained silent for the remainder of the journey.

161

Amanda stared out into the blackened fields. She was furious with Tony, but was determined not to be cheated out of her weekend of indulgence; she knew very well that she *would* ask Kate. Probably tomorrow. She would buy some flowers and pop over as she had this morning.

When they reached home they found Kate in the sitting-room reading. She was alone.

'Alec didn't show, then?' Tony said, his spirits lifted by the sight of Kate.

She stood up. 'No, he had some work he wanted to do on the computer at home.'

Amanda flopped into a chair. 'These shoes are killing me,' she said bad-temperedly. She kicked them off and rubbed her aching feet.

'Everything all right with Hattie?' Tony asked.

'No problem. She was fine.'

'Good. That's great. I'll see you out.'

He led her to the hall and as she reached to open the door he did exactly what he'd planned to do while sitting in the restaurant – he placed his hand over hers. 'Here, let me get that for you, it can be awkward at times.'

For a fraction of a second their hands were together and knowing that he had no more than a moment to ensure the final part of his plan was carried out he opened the door, said good-night and quickly kissed her cheek.

– A kiss that was as innocent as a neighbourly debt of gratitude.

– A kiss that was as guilty as a lover's act of adultery.

He watched her cross the courtyard in the darkness and as she let herself into number five she turned and glanced back at him.

He gave her a little wave and knew that he had to touch her again. Once wasn't enough.

But then he'd known it wouldn't be. He'd merely been fooling himself that the fantasy could be disarmed so easily.

25

Dear Cara,

Synopsis of A Casual Affair
The story so far!

Our heroine, Clare (aged twenty-eight and as feisty as a Tabasco sandwich) is bored with her going-nowhere job with a large insurance company and on the point of handing in her notice when her boss obligingly drops down dead. A replacement is quickly found who turns out to be Miles – thirty-something, attractive-ish but shy, unmarried and, according to the office gossip on the third floor from where he's been plucked, sexually inexperienced, with a preference for putting all his energy into his work rather than chasing women. Clare immediately sees the potential her new boss can offer her and, into scheming overdrive and with designs not just on promotion but on Miles, she decides that a casual affair with him would be as good a way as any to relieve her current boredom and further her career. But attracting Miles's attention proves to be more difficult than she imagined.

Hope this meets with your approval, Cara.

Best wishes,

Copy to Piers Lambert.

Jessica printed three copies of the letter – one for Cara, one for Piers and one for her file – and when she'd signed them and addressed the envelopes she looked out of her study window, over to Josh's house and wondered if she was using the wrong deodorant.

It was now a week since Tuesday night and she had the sneaky feeling that, like Clare's new boss in *A Casual Affair*, Crawford – the slimy toe-rag – was ignoring her; there hadn't been so much as a call or a visit from him.

Well, let him ignore her.

What did she care if he had decided that she was the last person on earth with whom he wanted to spend any time?

Unfortunately – and this was the annoying part – she did care. Oh boy, she cared. Josh Crawford, she had come to the conclusion, with his sexy smile and neat bum, had seemed an ideal antidote to the malaise that Gavin had left her with.

Put like that, it did seem a bit calculating to have viewed Josh in such a way, so perhaps it served her right that things had turned out the way they had. But what the heck, it was all hypothetical now anyway. Clearly Josh wasn't the slightest bit interested in her.

She lowered her gaze from his house and let it rest on the card on her window-sill. It was a familiar picturesque view of the harbour at Kassiopi: fishing boats and pleasure crafts were neatly lined up around the small quay, and in the background shops and tavernas with stripy awnings were bustling with sun-tanned tourists, and above the jumble of pastel-painted buildings the sky was an unbelievable shade of blue.

But then the card itself was pretty unbelievable.

It was from Gavin. And all that was written overleaf, apart from her address, were the words – *Wish you were here, missing you something rotten. Come back!*

Yeah right! And just who did he think he was kidding? had been her initial response to this unexpected communication.

Did he really think that a few scribbled words would have her leaping on the next available flight to Corfu?

Did he truly imagine her sitting in England, sad and lonely, strumming her fingers to the beat of her aching heart?

She looked down and caught sight of her fingers playing over the desk. She snatched up her hand and frowned.

She was not sad.

She was not lonely.

And she certainly wasn't longing for Gavin – any more than he was longing for her.

Not in her wildest dreams did she think it remotely possible that if she were to go back to Corfu she would find a heart-broken Gavin wasting away, yearning for her.

Fat chance of that! More likely she'd find him busy rubbing sun-tan oil all over the sleek, man-made body of Silicone Sal. And if not her, then some other beach babe.

But deep down, somewhere deep in the dark, romantically candle-lit recesses of her childlike gullibility, where she still wanted to believe in fairies and Father Christmas, she also wanted to believe in Gavin. She wanted him to be missing her, for him to have come crashing to his senses and realise what he'd lost.

At the sound of a car she glanced out of the window and saw Josh's midnight-blue Shogun sweep into the courtyard, followed by a flashy open-top sports car, the engine of which gave off an impressive and satisfying throaty roar as it came to a stop. Very nice, thought Jessica. She watched Josh get out of his car, then the other driver as he emerged from his. He held a briefcase in one hand and a small brown paper carrier bag in the other – which, with its tell-tale splodges of grease, made it look suspiciously like a take-away. Whoever it was who was dining at 1 Cholmford Hall Mews that night, he was slightly shorter than Josh, but equally good-looking and as well-dressed, but in marked contrast to Josh's usual black attire he was wearing a vivid orange-and-green check shirt with a light-coloured suede jacket hanging off one of his shoulders.

The thought of the tasty meal that Josh and his friend were about to tuck into made Jessica leave her study and go in search of something to eat for herself.

She suddenly realised that she was famished and as she began rooting through the near empty fridge for some kind of culinary inspiration – she really must get into the habit of shopping more regularly – she thought of the supper Josh had cooked for her.

He really had gone to a lot of trouble that evening – and not just in the kitchen. In her experience single men rarely reached for the Pine-O-Fresh without there being an ulterior motive behind such an out-of-character activity, namely that of luring a woman upstairs and into their beds.

So why the sudden red light that night?

One minute they had been on the verge of a repeat performance of their *après* Tony and Amanda dinner-party session – except this time she had planned on being a willing participant – and the next Josh had been up on his feet saying it was late and that he had an early start the next day.

It didn't make sense.

Unless it had all been a deliberate ploy to get his own back on her for having messed him around previously. Had he played dirty to prove a point with her? No girl teases Josh Crawford and gets away with it. Had that been his game?

Could he really be that proud and petty?

Charlie was worried about Josh. Which was why when they had finished work he had suggested that they pick up a take-away and spend the evening together.

Not since Josh's illness had been diagnosed had Charlie seen his brother so low and despondent. There was an awful emptiness to him that concerned Charlie. The past few days had been particularly bad, with Josh seemingly distancing himself from those around him. He had become morose and deeply withdrawn, punctuating his moody silences with a level of cynicism that was cruel and barbed, and aimed at anyone who got in his way.

Yesterday at work, Charlie had found Mo in a full-blown tearful strop. 'I only asked him if he was okay when I took him in a cup of coffee,' she'd told Charlie, 'and he bit my head off. He can make his own coffee in future.'

Charlie knew that not only did Mo have a soft spot for Josh, but that under normal circumstances she wouldn't have thought twice about blasting off at him for treating her in such a way, but since his illness had become general knowledge at work she, like everybody else, had tended to shy away from speaking her mind. 'What's got into him?' she'd asked Charlie, when Josh had gone to Failsworth to check on a lost delivery and had given everybody the chance to come out from hiding for a couple of hours.

'I wish I knew,' he'd said in answer to Mo's question.

More than anything, Charlie wished he knew exactly what was going on inside his brother's head. Which was why he was here now. He had no intention of leaving until he'd got to the bottom of what was making Josh so unbearable at work.

'Another beer?'

Charlie looked up from his lamb korma. 'I'll get them,' he said.

He was almost on his feet when Josh said, 'Sit down. This is my sodding house and if I'm offering you a drink I'll bloody well get it myself. Okay?'

Charlie watched Josh limp across the kitchen and open the fridge. When he came back to the island unit he handed him a can of Budweiser. Charlie took it and experienced the urge to smash the can into his brother's face. Appalled at the level of anger he felt for Josh, he wondered if their lives would ever be the way they used to be. But then they couldn't be, could they? Josh could never be the man he had been. It was unfair and selfish to expect that of him. Charlie wasn't proud of himself for thinking it, but he didn't know how much longer he could put up with his brother's mood-swings.

They continued their meal without speaking, each forking up his food and washing it down with the occasional mouthful of beer. Charlie couldn't bear it and in the end he pushed his unfinished plate away. 'I've had enough of this,' he said.

Josh raised his eyes. 'I hope you're referring to your meal because if you're about to start on one of your bloody lectures you might just as well leave now. I'm not in the mood.'

'That's just the point. What kind of mood are you in? You seem to be going out of your way to upset everyone.'

Josh gave an indifferent shrug of his shoulders. 'Can't say I'd noticed.'

Charlie silently counted to five before saying in as calm a voice as he could, 'What the hell's got into you, Josh? Why are you acting like this?'

Josh stood up and went over to the window, which looked out over the courtyard. He saw Jessica moving about in her kitchen. He turned away. 'You just don't get it, do you?'

'All I can see is you intent on punishing everyone else for your MS and if you want my honest opinion on that, I think it sucks.'

'Maybe you're right,' Josh said flatly, 'but you should try having all your dreams taken away from you. Imagine . . . imagine wanting something and knowing you couldn't have it . . . that all that was on offer to you was something so second-rate it wasn't worth having.'

Charlie didn't know what to say. Who was he to make a comment on what Josh had just said? He hadn't had his dreams taken away. He didn't know what it felt like. He hoped he never would. 'Are we talking generally or specifically?' he asked.

'What the hell do you think?'

Charlie had no idea. 'Josh, I'm not a mind-reader, so just cut the crap and tell me what's going on.'

Josh came and sat down. He picked up his can of beer and began turning it round in his hands. 'I'm not sure I understand it myself,' he said. He badly wanted to say what he'd been feeling all this week, but each time he tried to put it into words, even to himself, it only served to fuel his anger and bitter frustration. Ever since that evening with Jessica, when the realisation had hit him that he wanted much more from her than he'd bargained for, he'd felt confused, depressed and demoralised. His low sense of self-worth told him that he couldn't expect a woman like Jessica to be the slightest bit interested in him when he had so little to offer. And supposing she did allow herself to become involved with him, when she knew the truth, how long would it last? How long would it be before she decided she wanted to be with a man who wasn't going to become a burden?

He looked up and saw that Charlie was waiting for him to speak. He suddenly felt sorry for him. Poor Charlie, so keen to help and so clearly out of his depth. Not unlike himself really. 'Do you remember at Mum and Dad's the other Sunday,' he said, 'when you asked me if I wouldn't prefer a relationship that was a touch more meaningful than a one-night stand?'

'Yes,' Charlie said cautiously.

'Well, you were right . . . and that's the problem.'

'Is this to do with your neighbour Jessica?'

Josh nodded and slipping off the stool, began slowly prowling round the kitchen. When his leg started to ache he stopped in front of the window and stared out across the courtyard. Charlie came and joined him.

'So what's the problem?' he asked. He now had a pretty good idea what was going through Josh's mind, but he wanted his brother to go through the process of actually explaining it to him.

'Like I said to you that day, what's the point in me getting into a serious relationship, or even considering one? What could I offer Jessica?'

'Quite a lot, I should think.'

Josh shook his head. 'Maybe a few good years . . . and when my health really starts to deteriorate, what then? I'm hardly the pull of the decade, am I?'

'Isn't that for her to decide?'

'I wouldn't want her pity.'

'Is she the pitying kind?'

Josh considered this. He thought of the way Jessica called him Crawford and accused him of having a manner smooth enough to charm the devil. He also thought of her vibrant face and slightly mocking eyes. There was an energy to her that he found exciting. Each time he had been with her he'd been aware of her vitality and her strength of character. 'No,' he said with a hint of a smile. 'No, she's not the pitying kind.'

'Well then, why not give it a go and see what happens? And if it doesn't work out, I guarantee it's because she catches on to what a pillock you are.'

'You reckon?'

Charlie smiled. 'I reckon. Now, when do I get to meet her?'

It was just gone ten o'clock when Josh watched Charlie's car disappear through the archway and for a few moments he stayed where he was on the doorstep, contemplating his brother's pep talk.

Was Charlie right? Was Jessica worth pursuing?

With an evening's worth of beer inside him he decided that there was no better time to find out. He'd go over now and ask her out to dinner later in the week. What's more, he'd be honest with her and to hell with the consequences. If she didn't like the idea of him being a potential cripple, then tough. Humiliation was something he was going to have to learn to deal with.

He put his front door on the latch and started walking across the courtyard, but with each step he took his confidence began to wane.

He was mad. Mad to think that Jessica would be remotely interested in him. He glanced at his watch. Surely it was too late to call on her? But as he looked up, all set to do a quick turn-about, he saw her gazing at him from her kitchen window. *Hell!* Now what? What excuse could he give for going across to see her?

But there was no time to think of anything, her front door suddenly opened and there she was, staring straight at him. She looked as if she was dressed ready for bed. All she had on was a T-shirt emblazoned with the slogan *Wind Surfers Do It Wet And Standing Up*. It was difficult not to stare at her long legs.

'Hi,' she said, aware of his gaze, 'and what brings you here at this time of night?'

'I . . .' He paused, ran a hand through his hair, shifted a little to the right, then back to the left. 'I was just wondering –'

'You were just passing and wondered if I had any sugar, is that it?'

'Not exactly.'

'Coffee, then?'

He shook his head. Oh shit, why was he so nervous? And where the hell was his alcohol-induced confidence when he needed it?

'Well, Crawford, I know I'm a writer, but I'm running out of lines here; you're going to have to help me out.'

He swallowed. Or rather he would have if his throat hadn't dried up – was it from desire at the sight of Jessica's legs, or just plain nerves? 'I wondered whether you'd like to come for a walk,' he said. *A walk!* He couldn't believe he was hearing himself. Was he completely out of his mind? He'd be suggesting a quick jog around the block next.

She stared at him, then up at the night sky. 'Mm . . .' she said, 'the moon and stars look pretty enough. Why not? Give me a couple of minutes and I'll put something on. Come in while you wait.'

He stood in the hall and listened to Jessica moving about upstairs. He stupidly hoped she wasn't putting on too much. Within minutes she was back with him – the T-shirt had been exchanged for a baggy sweat-shirt and her lovely legs had been covered with a pair of jeans.

'You've put your legs away,' he said, disappointed.

'And you've been ignoring me all this week.' She shut the door behind them and led the way across the courtyard. He struggled to keep up. She turned and faced him. 'Sorry, was I going too fast?'

'Yes,' he admitted, 'and I haven't been ignoring you.'

'So where have you been? I tried several times to thank you for dinner last week, but each time I knocked on your door there was no answer. In the end I shoved a note through your letter-box.'

'I got it, thanks. There was no need, though.'

'Yes there was. You went to a lot of trouble.'

'Not really.'

'Are you going to dispute everything I say?'

He didn't answer and they carried on without speaking. The night was warm and very still, and as they approached the copse, bone-dry twigs crackled noisily beneath their feet and the moon shone down on them, intermittently lighting their way as it filtered its silvery brightness through the leafy branches of the trees. It wasn't long before Josh's leg was giving out on him. He needed to rest and, spying a fallen oak, he grabbed Jessica's hand and pulled her towards it.

'So,' she said, sitting beside him on the moss-covered trunk and drawing up a knee to rest her chin on.

'So?'

'So, why are we here, Josh?'

He shrugged. 'I fancied a walk and thought you might like to join me.'

'And is this something you do a lot of, nocturnal wanderings?'

'Not really. I just wanted the opportunity to talk to you.'

'Aha, in that case, I'm all ears.' She lowered her leg and turned to face him, her eyes flashing with that mocking humour he had come to know. 'Fire away.'

He cleared his throat, ready to launch himself into what he had to say. *See, here's the situation: I'm thirty-seven, not unattractive – so I'm told – I'm financially solvent. I have my own home and car, and a more than healthy interest in sex – especially with the right partner. The only downside is that there's a strong possibility that I'll be a dead weight hanging round your neck within a few years. So how about it? How about you and me getting it together?* Oh sod it! He couldn't do it. 'Will you have dinner with me again?'

A slow smile crept over her face. 'Yes. But on one condition.'

'What's that?'

'That you stop messing about and make full use of the romantic opportunity offered here beneath the stars and kiss me. I've waited long enough.'

He laughed out loud, and as his laughter drifted away into the darkness, it was as if all the tension of the past week went with it, as though if he watched closely, he would see the bits of himself he hated and despised being cast into the night sky. If there was one thing he had come to realise in the short time he'd known Jessica it was that when he was with her, she had a fantastic effect on him. Her sense of fun was wonderfully recuperative.

'I'm waiting.'

'Are you coming on to me, Jessica?' he asked with a smile.

'Certainly not. I just want a kiss.'

'And would this be for research purposes?'

'It might be.'

'Well, we'd better get it right, then, hadn't we? What kind of kiss did you have in mind, exactly?'

'Let me see what you've got to offer.'

He gave her a chaste peck on the cheek.

'Sorry, but I don't write that kind of novel. My readers expect a little more from my romantic heroes.'

He moved closer and kissed her lightly on the lips.

'Better, but I was hoping for something a little more melt-in-the-mouth, like the other night.'

'You should have said.' He held her face in his hands and gave her a long, deep kiss. 'Now was that more what you had in mind?'

'I'm not sure,' she said breathlessly. 'Could you run it by me one more time?'

He did, and as their mouths came together, he slipped one of his hands under her sweat-shirt. He felt the tremor in her body as he found her breast and her instant response to his touch exploded within him. With only one thought in his mind, he very gently began pushing her backwards. But he'd forgotten what they were sitting on and the next moment they were lying in a heap on the soft bedding of leaves and ferns the other side of the fallen tree. Their happy laughter filled the dark copse and after they'd disentangled themselves they sat down again.

Jessica rested her head against Josh's shoulder. 'Why did you give me the brush-off at your place last week?' she asked.

He reached out for her hand and wondered what to say. Was this the bit when he told her the truth?

No. No, he couldn't. Not yet. He couldn't face it right now. He didn't want anything to spoil what he was feeling. 'I didn't give you the brush-off,' he lied.

She raised her head and looked at him. Straight at him. 'You did. You couldn't wait to get me out of your house, my feet didn't touch.'

He flinched at the strength of her directness. 'Okay,' he said, 'you're right.' And determined to give at least part of the truth, he tried to explain his actions. 'I wasn't very subtle that night, was I? I'd planned to get you into bed and suddenly I felt ashamed of myself in the way I'd gone about it. It seemed too contrived ... and I didn't want it to be like that. I'm not sure I really understand it myself, but I suddenly realised that I wanted something more than what I'd intended to make happen ... and it had to be something that you wanted as well.' He watched her closely while she took in his words. 'I'm sorry,' he added.

She regarded him with a steady gaze. Then she smiled. 'Crawford,' she said, 'you're a man of surprises.'

Aren't I just, he thought. 'Come on,' he said, 'let's go back, it's getting cold.'

When they reached Jessica's house she let them in. 'Would you like a drink?' she asked. 'Wine, coffee, brandy, or ...' But her voice broke off as Josh, with unexpected force, took her in his arms, pressed her against the wall and kissed her.

'Or tea?' she managed to say when he finally let her come up for air.

'I'm not thirsty,' he whispered.

'Me neither,' she whispered back. 'Josh, why are we whispering?'

He smiled. 'It's supposed to be romantic.'

'I must remember that.'

'Isn't that what romantic heroes get up to? I thought they only spoke in hoarse whispers.'

'Not in my books, they don't.'

'Oh well, never mind ... Jessica?'

'Yes.'

He looked deep, deep into her eyes and she felt herself go limp with longing. She watched his Adam's apple bob about as he swallowed.

'Do you think there's any chance that –'

'You've stopped whispering,' she interrupted him, 'does that mean the romantic interlude has passed?'

'No, it means we're on to the serious stuff now.'

'Serious stuff?'

'Yes. I'm about to ask if you'd like to go upstairs.'

'To do what?'

'I thought I could slowly undress that beautiful body of yours and make love to you. But only if you wanted me to.'

'I'd need to think about that.'

'Take your time. I'm in no hurry.'

'Would there be much kissing, like just now?'

'Comes as standard.'

'Caresses?'

'Lots.'

'All over?'

'Definitely.'

'Of the light-as-a-butterfly's-wing variety?'

'Lighter.'

'Pounding hearts?'

'Like steam hammers.'

'Gasps of pleasure?'

'Loud enough to wake the neighbours.'

'Bodies as one?'

'A perfect synthesis of intimacy.'

'Soaring high as a bird?'

'Spinning into orbit.'

'The "Hallelujah Chorus"? I would have to insist on that.'

'It's yours, followed by the *1812 Overture.*'

'With cannons?'

'Fireworks as well.'

She smiled. 'You paint a tempting picture.'

'And your answer?'

'Oh, the answer was always going to be yes.'

The Middle

26

Kate stared and stared at the small white stick in her hand. What she had suspected since the August Bank Holiday, just over a week ago, was now confirmed. She was pregnant.

Pregnant!

She hugged the secret to her. She hadn't shared with anyone the thought that she might be pregnant; not Caroline, not Jessica, not even Alec.

Definitely not Alec.

But now she would have to. Tonight, Alec would be arriving back from his week away at the Birmingham trade fair. He had wanted her to go down with him, but knowing that Melissa was going to be there, too, she had cried off – staying in the same hotel as Melissa for a whole week was not something she had any desire to do. Instead, she had stayed at home and mentally ticked off the days on the calendar waiting for the first possible opportunity to use the pregnancy test kit that she had already sneaked into the house.

She continued to gaze at the little white stick and despite the sense of foreboding about breaking the news to Alec, a warm feeling of euphoric happiness crept over her. Her greatest wish had been granted. She wanted to leap in the air, clap her hands, even dance a little jig round the kitchen, and she would have done exactly that if the phone hadn't rung. She skipped across to it and snatched up the receiver. 'Hello,' she said, hoping that it was Alec – while he'd been away he had called her at least twice a day.

But it wasn't, it was Melissa. 'Kate, I haven't got long, it's unbelievably busy here, but over breakfast I spoke to Alec and he suggested I talk to you. Have you got your diary to hand?'

'It's in the study, hang on a minute.' Light-headed with happiness, Kate went through to the study. *I'm going to have a baby*, she chanted delightedly to herself. She found the diary Alec always kept on his desk and picked up the phone extension. *I'm going to have a baby!*

'Melissa, are you there?' *I'm going to have a baby.* How wonderful it would be to let the words trip off her tongue.

175

'Yes, I'm still here. Now flick through to 22 November. It's a Saturday, are you both free?'

A baby! Her very own baby! 'Yes we are.'

'Good. I'm giving a dinner party for Alec that night, seeing as it's a special year for him.'

Kate froze. 'Special,' she repeated. 'What do you mean?'

'Good Lord, Kate, don't tell me you've forgotten that it's Alec's fiftieth birthday on 15 November. Surely you're doing something for him? I deliberately chose the following weekend because I thought you would be organising some kind of party on the actual day.'

Kate was mortified. Alec's fiftieth! How could she have made such an oversight?

'Clearly you had forgotten. Anyway, I must go, Alec and I are having lunch with some Japanese distributors.'

Kate replaced the receiver and sank into the chair in front of the desk. She was devastated, not because she hadn't given Alec's birthday any thought, but because Melissa had. The ex-wife of the man she loved – *the father of her child* – had shown her up, had pipped her to the post good and proper.

And what was more, she hated the idea of *Alec and I are having lunch.* Breakfast, too.

She should have gone with Alec to the trade fair. He had wanted her to go and she had let him down, preferring instead to stay selfishly at home nursing the possible gestation of her greatest desire.

So now what? What was she to do? Pretend that she'd arranged a party all along? And if so, whom should she invite?

She decided to go next door and see Jessica. She would know what to do.

Throughout the summer, she and Jessica had formed a strong friendship and when her writing wasn't going well they would go for long walks. Some days it was just the two of them, occasionally it would be Oscar. When he was with them they would put a picnic together and Jessica would tell him they were going exploring. She knew the surrounding area well and had taken them on some wonderful walks, but her favourite route was along the banks of the canal. It had become Oscar's favourite place to potter as well, especially if there were any passing boats to watch. Invariably he would be too tired to walk all the way back to the house and they would take it in turns to carry him home.

But it wasn't just during the day that she and Jessica got together. Now and again, they would go out as a foursome; she and Alec, and Jessica and Josh. Only the other week, Alec had commented to Kate that he thought their neighbours made a great couple. Kate thought so too. Jessica's sharp wit, which might have threatened and undermined another man, was always met with an equal measure of mercurial humour from Josh. But there were times when Kate felt there was another side to Josh's character: a more intense facet of his make-up that she suspected was only glimpsed when his guard was down. On one of their recent evenings out together she had noticed that Josh had been unusually quiet and that his normally handsome face had borne an expression of painful weariness. At the time she had put it down to tiredness, knowing that he had just spent a hectic week down in London, but a few days later when they'd all been having a drink at Jessica's she had seen the same exhausted countenance. She wondered if he was working too hard, was maybe under a lot of pressure.

But Josh's problems were not hers to solve. She had enough of her own.

She went back to the kitchen, tidied away the pregnancy test kit and called on Jessica. 'Is it a bad moment?' she asked, when Jessica let her in. She was always wary of disturbing her when she was working.

'Your timing couldn't be better. I'm getting nowhere with chapter eleven so a distraction is perfect. Fancy some fresh air?'

They took the path towards the copse, then set off in a south-easterly direction between recently harvested fields of corn. Though it was September and the midday sun wasn't as high in the cloud-dotted sky as it had been a few weeks ago, it was still warm enough to make Jessica strip off her sweat-shirt and tie it round her waist. 'So what's eating you?' she suddenly asked.

Kate looked up. 'Oh dear, is it that obvious?'

'Sure is. The long face is a dead give-away.'

'I've just let Alec's ex-wife get one over me,' Kate said miserably.

'Go on.'

'And what's worse, it was through my own selfishness. I've been so preoccupied with myself these past weeks I'd forgotten all about Alec's birthday.'

'And Melissa remembered?'

Kate nodded.

'Oh dear, well that certainly sounds like a life-threatening situation. I mean to say, you forgot and she remembered. Wow! Sorry, but I can't see what the fuss is all about. She was married to the man for goodness knows how long, she's going to have the date permanently etched on her brain.'

'It gets worse. It's his fiftieth.'

'So?'

'It's special. Melissa's doing a dinner party for him to mark the occasion.'

'Mark the occasion, my foot! She wants to rub his nose in the fact that he's getting on.'

'He's not getting on,' Kate said defensively.

'Sorry, I could have put that better, but you know what I mean.'

'I think she's done it to make it look as if I don't care about Alec. That I'm not up to the job.'

Jessica could see the distress in Kate's face and knew that it was real enough, but in all honesty she doubted whether there were many women who would go to so much trouble just to undermine their ex-husband's new partner. Over the summer, she had got to know Kate sufficiently to realise that at times she allowed her insecurity to get the better of her. 'Alec knows how you feel about him and that's all that matters,' she said.

'But it's not enough, is it? It's not just a case of pleasing Alec, I've got to prove myself to Melissa.'

'Oh come on, Kate, think about what you've just said; it's ridiculous.'

'No it's not and I have thought about it – there are times when I think of nothing else. Proving ourselves is what all second wives and girlfriends have to do. We're constantly having to compete with the wretched person we've replaced; it's all part of the bloody awful triangle.'

Jessica had never heard Kate swear before. The mild-mannered Kate whom she knew rarely broke into anything more vitriolic than a sneeze. Clearly something was wrong. 'Ever thought that it might be the other way around?' she suggested.

'You mean Melissa competing with me?' Kate shook her head. 'You've never met her, she's not the type to need to prove herself. She's so confident and together.'

'You sound like you're frightened of her.'

'I'm terrified of her ... and jealous. I'm convinced that if she ever wanted to make a play for Alec she could do so.'

'And so what if she did? From what I've seen of you and Alec he's potty about you, his eyes barely leave your face and I've noticed how he struggles to keep his hands off you when we've been out together. It's like being with a couple of teenagers.'

Kate blushed. 'But supposing Alec's only infatuated with me, supposing it's not love at all?'

Jessica needed time to think about this. Were Kate and Alec having problems? Was that why Kate was so edgy? And if so, what sort of advice should she be offering?

They had come to the end of the footpath that crossed the open fields and they now had to climb over a stile and join another path, which led down to the canal and would eventually wend its way to Willow Cottage.

'You haven't answered my question,' Kate said, as she stepped over the wooden stile.

'I haven't because I'm trying to work out what's behind this sudden loss of confidence in your relationship. It can't just be that Melissa has decided to treat her ex to a meal; you've told me yourself there are endless family get-togethers, so why is this one any different? You sure there isn't something else that's bothering you?'

Bothering was not the word for it. Kate could hardly believe that only an hour ago she had been thrilled to bits knowing that she was expecting a baby, but then Melissa, straight out of the blue, had phoned and like a bird of prey had swooped down on her and plucked her happiness right out of her hands.

Except she knew in her heart that wasn't really what had happened. Melissa's call had simply tugged on one of the slippery silk ribbons that held her and Alec's relationship together. With startling clarity she now saw that it wasn't, as she'd always thought, Melissa who held the key to her happiness, it was Alec. How would he react when she told him about the baby? If he was only infatuated with her then their relationship was over – he had made it very clear that he wasn't interested in having any more children. Only a man who truly loved her would stick with her in the circumstances.

'I've just found out that I'm pregnant,' she said, 'and I know that Alec is going to hate the idea of being a father again.'

'Ah,' Jessica said, 'well, cheer up, just think, that's one hell of a birthday present Melissa can't give him.'

Kate tried to laugh, but she couldn't. 'I was so happy when I found out, but now I'm frightened how Alec will react when I tell him. He'll be furious. He might even want me to get rid –'

'I doubt that very much,' cut in Jessica. 'Most men hate the idea of babies littering the house, but when confronted with the reality of the fruits of their loins they usually manage to step into the role of proud father without too much persuasion. Mark my words, Alec will be as proud as anything. There's great kudos involved when an older man starts begetting wee ones. There's nothing like an offspring to prove a man's virility.'

Kate looked up hopefully. 'Do you really think so?'

Jessica smiled. 'Not for sure, but it sounds about right, doesn't it?'

They were now walking along the tow-path of the canal. It had rained the day before and the ground, in parts, was damp and slightly soft underfoot. Everything looked lush and green. Tall, upright stems of ragwort leant casually over the bank as if, while nobody was looking, the vibrant yellow flower-heads were trying to catch their reflection in the still water. Red clover speckled the long tufts of grass and the occasional bee staggered from flower to flower with its heavy load of nectar. Seeing a straggly bush of blackberries, Jessica came to a stop and helped herself to a handful of fat juicy berries. 'Mm ... beautiful,' she said, when she'd tasted one. She offered her hand to Kate. 'Eat up, you'll need all the vitamin C you can get from now on.'

'I'm going to need more than vitamin C to get me through the ordeal of telling Alec about the baby,' Kate said despondently. She started to cry. 'Oh dear, you must think me very silly.'

'Nonsense, you're at the mercy of your hormones, you're allowed to cry over the slightest of things, spilt milk even. Dare I ask how it happened? I assume at least one of you was doing something to prevent this happy event ever taking place.'

'I've never liked taking the pill and the idea of a coil makes me cross my legs, so it was down to Alec. I guess something just went wrong.'

'Well, at least he can't accuse you of being deliberately careless, not unless he thinks you're not above sabotage, you know, sticking pins into certain things behind his back.'

Kate wiped her eyes and almost smiled. 'But you do see the problem, don't you? Alec is so against us having a family, he's had one ghastly child and the thought of another like Ruth must terrify him. How do you think Josh would react if you were to tell him you were pregnant?'

Jessica gave a loud snort of laughter. 'Josh and I don't have that kind of relationship.'

Kate frowned. 'You mean you don't ... you don't ...'

'Oh we have sex right enough. No, I just meant that our relationship is very different from what you and Alec have.'

'What do you mean?'

'Good question,' Jessica said thoughtfully. What exactly did she and Josh mean to each other? There was no doubt that they got on well together, more than that, there were times when she felt so close to him it was as if she'd always known him. He was fun to be with and she respected his quick and alert mind. He was urbane and erudite, and had rapidly gained her respect. And since that day in July when they'd gone for a late-night walk in the copse, he had proved to be as good in bed as he was in the kitchen – two qualities, in her opinion, no woman should ever underestimate when choosing a partner. It amused her to think of Josh on that unforgettable night when they'd first made love. He had been so nervous when she'd opened the door to him – she'd seen less nerves in a dentist's waiting-room. His awkwardness had touched her and had made him utterly irresistible, prompting her in the woods to demand a kiss from him. But by the time they'd made it to the bedroom his nervousness had vanished and he'd made love to her with a gentle skill that made Gavin's technique seem more like a Grand Prix driver racing round the track of her body, hell-bent on clocking up as many erogenous zones as possible on his way to the finishing line – which at the time had been breathtakingly exhilarating, but which now appeared to be a little lacking compared with Josh's more loving approach. In short, sex with Gavin had left her wanting more, whereas sex with Josh left her feeling wonderfully content.

And quite apart from any physical compatibility between them, she had come to value Josh's opinion, to such a degree that she had actually allowed him to read a few chapters of *A Casual Affair*, something she had never done in the past with anyone – an unfinished manuscript was such a fragile and vulnerable thing. But Josh had been awarded special status in this respect. The question was, why?

Especially when, just recently, she had begun to feel a little uneasy about their relationship. He rarely invited her over to his house these days, saying that he preferred to come to her, and often he would arrive straight from work and cook them supper while she finished off what she was doing. And whenever they made love – and they did frequently – it was strange, but he never stayed the night.

If she wanted to be objective about his behaviour she would say that Josh was a man who had to compartmentalise his life, as though anything he did with her had to be completely isolated from anything else he chose to do, which probably meant that no matter how close they became, there would always be a part of Josh that would remain shut to her.

But if she wanted to be subjective she would say that Josh was turning out to be just like Gavin – allergic to commitment.

And like Gavin, Josh was showing signs of being unreliable. On several occasions in the past couple of weeks when they had arranged to go out, he had backed out at the last minute. On one particular evening somebody from work, possibly a secretary, had called to say that he was sorry, but he'd been held up in a meeting, which was likely to go on for quite a few hours yet.

It didn't take a fool to wonder if Josh was leading a double life. Heaven forbid, but the situation had the signs of a Gavin and Silicone Sal scenario stamped all over it.

What was it with men? Why did they always have this need to cheat and double-cross?

And why hadn't she kicked Josh into touch yet?

Well, because if she was honest she was intrigued to see how long he thought he could go on fooling her, and so long as she didn't get herself too emotionally involved – whatever that might mean – she was sure that he wouldn't be able to hurt her in the way Gavin had.

And, so much for the lying, cheating wretch in Corfu who was supposedly *missing her something rotten*, she'd not heard another peep out of him since that postcard back in July.

Realising that Kate was still waiting for an answer, she said, 'Josh and I are nothing like you and Alec. Commitment is written all over Alec's face. As the old line goes, Josh and I are just good friends.'

'Do you think it will stay that way?'

Jessica laughed. 'With my track record, yes. I know it's a corny thing to say, but I long for the day when a man will be sufficiently nuts about me to want to spend his every waking moment in my company. The nearest I ever get to being with my ideal man is writing about him. You don't know how lucky you are with Alec.'

But it was the wrong thing to say.

Kate's face crumpled and she started to cry again. 'I know exactly how lucky I am ... that's why I'm convinced that I'm going to lose him.'

27

Josh took off his glasses and flung them down on to the desk. He ran a hand over his face, then rubbed his eyes. He felt dreadful. Like death.

It was only four o'clock and normally he wouldn't dream of leaving work at this time of day, not when he still had so much to get through, but today he would have to – if he left it much later there was a very real danger that he might not be able to drive himself home.

Both his legs felt as though they were on fire; the heat was radiating through his trousers as if he had a fever. It had been going on like this for a few days now, the mornings would start off okay, but by the afternoon the tingling would kick in and the excruciating burning sensation would follow. He'd experienced something similar last year, but nowhere near as bad as this, and certainly not in both legs. Which probably meant his MS was getting a firmer hold on him.

For a short while during the summer he had thought he was on top of the illness. The symptoms had lessened and his energy levels had definitely increased; even his leg had shown signs of loosening up. And certainly his relationship with Jessica had gone a long way to revitalising him, bringing about a resurgence in his confidence as well as a general sense of well-being. For a few wonderful weeks it was as if the clock had been turned back and he was his old self.

But the period of remission – if that was indeed what it was – had been cruelly short-lived. The only warning he got that the holiday was over was a feeling of extreme tiredness creeping over him as he and Charlie had driven back from London after their week at the Earls Court trade show. By the time Charlie had dropped him off at Cholmford his arms and legs had felt heavy and sluggish. He'd gone out that night with Jessica and Kate and Alec, but had been far from good company for them – just trying to join in with the conversation had taken all his concentration. By the time he'd reached the safety of his own house, having fobbed off Jessica with some lame excuse about being tired, he'd crashed out in bed and woken up the following afternoon to find that his co-ordination was all over the place, as was his balance, and when he'd eventually mastered the art of walking upright and without falling over, his feet, which were virtually numb, gave him the sensation that he was walking on thick cotton wool. It had been a grim weekend.

He put his glasses back on and tried to focus his mind on the design specifications for their summer range for the following year. But it was no good. He couldn't concentrate. All he could think of was the agonising pain in his legs and the desire to immerse himself in a bath of icy cold water. He had to get home. He slapped the pile of papers into his briefcase, in the hope of working on them later that night, and got to his feet, then suddenly found himself plunged into darkness.

When he opened his eyes, Charlie was kneeling on the floor beside him. He couldn't see Mo, but he could hear her anxious voice in the background.

'Is he okay? Shall I get a doctor or something?'

He wondered in the confused fog of his mind what a 'something' could possibly be. He tried to sit up, but a hammering immediately set off inside his head. He tentatively touched his left temple where the worst of the hammering seemed to be located and when he looked at his hand it was covered in blood.

'It looks worse than it actually is,' Charlie said at once, handing him his handkerchief. 'Mo, will you go and get the first-aid kit, please?'

When Mo had discreetly shut the door behind her Charlie said, 'What happened?'

'How the hell should I know,' Josh snapped. He pushed Charlie's hands away and got determinedly to his feet. 'One minute I was packing up to go home and the next you're in here acting like Florence frigging Nightingale.'

There was a knock at the door. Mo stepped into the office and handed Charlie the first-aid kit. She tried not to stare at Josh and at the amount of blood trickling down his face. 'I'll put all calls on hold, shall I?' she asked.

'Yes,' said Charlie, 'whoever it is, say we'll get back to them tomorrow.'

When they were alone, Charlie made Josh sit down so that he could assess the damage. 'Like I said, it looks worse than it really is. I don't think you need stitches, but I'm going to put a dressing on it.'

While his brother fussed with antiseptic, squares of lint and plasters, Josh rummaged in the red plastic box for some pain-killers. There was nothing stronger than Paracetamol, so he swallowed four and hoped they might take the edge off not just the pain in his head but the burning sensation in his legs. He tried to reason what could have happened. He must have caught his foot on something and tripped, and head-butted his desk. It was the only logical explanation.

It had to be.

Oh God, please let it be that, he thought desperately. Not black-outs. He couldn't take that. He wouldn't be allowed to drive. It would mean the end of his independence, of everything.

'There,' Charlie said when he'd finished. 'Now what?'

'I want to go home,' Josh said bleakly.

'Okay. I'll drive you.'

Josh felt too awful to argue that he was capable of driving himself. He knew he couldn't, that he was beaten. He even doubted his ability to walk out of his office, never mind make it to the car-park.

They waited until everybody else had gone home, then Charlie helped Josh to the lift and took him down to the ground floor. He went and fetched his car, and brought it round to the front of the building where Josh was waiting for him. They drove out of Manchester, through the rush-hour traffic and down the A34. Neither of them spoke. Josh's head was back against the head-rest, his eyes closed.

When they reached Cholmford Hall Mews, Charlie parked as near to the house as he could. 'Don't try and help me,' Josh said, opening the car door, 'I don't want —'

'Don't be so bloody stupid!'

Too weak to fight back, Josh found himself willingly putting his arm round his brother's neck as he helped him into the house. Just once he looked over his shoulder to see if Jessica had seen him. But there was no sign of her.

Charlie took him through to the sitting-room, where he collapsed, exhausted, on to the sofa. Every bit of him ached, particularly the joints in his legs. The burning sensation had now spread to the rest of his body. He started kicking off his shoes, pulling at his jacket, then the buttons on his shirt.

'What do you need? What can I get you?' Charlie asked, suddenly aware just how ill his brother looked. His face was flushed and tiny beads of sweat were forming on his forehead, his lips were pale and drawn. He looked terrible.

'Run me a bath,' Josh murmured, leaning back on the sofa, his eyes tightly closed, 'a cold one, I'm burning up.'

Charlie went over and touched him. 'Shit!' he said, 'you're right. You sure you haven't got flu?'

'I wish!'

Charlie went upstairs and began running a bath. He stood over it, watching the water gush out from the taps, wishing he could do more for Josh. Perhaps Mo had been right earlier, maybe they should have called a doctor.

When he went back downstairs he found Josh in the kitchen. He was stripped down to his boxer shorts, lying stretched out on the tiled floor, a bag of frozen peas on one knee, a frozen loaf of bread balanced on the other. It was reminiscent of years gone by when at a party they'd both ended up so drunk that they'd crashed out on their friend's kitchen floor, surrounded by a knocked-over vegetable rack. But that had been fun. This was different. This was Josh suffering God knows what.

'It's bliss,' Josh said, when he realised Charlie was there, 'better than sex.'

'You'd better not let Jessica hear you say that.'

'She's a very understanding woman,' Josh said, shifting the bag of peas to his ankle.

'And why, if she's so understanding, haven't you told her about your MS?'

Josh scowled. 'How do you know I haven't?'

'Don't bullshit me! I saw the way you were peering over your shoulder when I helped you into the house. You were terrified she'd see you . . . that she'd see the real you.'

Very slowly, Josh got to his feet. He returned the peas and loaf of bread to the freezer and walked stiffly out of the kitchen, every now and again reaching out to the wall to support himself.

Charlie followed him to the hall and up the stairs. 'Well?' he said, when Josh had immersed himself in the bath. 'Have you told her the truth?'

Josh continued to ignore his brother. He slipped under the cool water. He opened his eyes and through the ripples could make out Charlie's distorted face staring down at him. How easy it would be to finish it all like this one day, he thought. All it would take would be some pills and a bottle of Scotch, and for him to let himself simply sink beneath the surface of what was left of his life.

He closed his eyes and stayed where he was, feeling nothing beyond the stabbing pressure on his lungs. But then he was suddenly being hauled out of the water and Charlie's face, a picture of fury, was glaring at him. 'Don't even think about it, you bastard!' he yelled. 'Just don't even think about it!' There was real anger in his face . . . and tears in his eyes.

Bowing his head in shame, Josh coughed and spluttered as his chest heaved at the sudden intake of oxygen. When his breathing had steadied he said, 'I'm sorry. Let's just say it's been a bad week.'

Charlie grabbed a towel and dried his hands and arms, then settled himself on the loo seat. 'With your fondness for irony, I assume that has to be a colossal understatement.'

Josh rested his head back against the bath. 'Look,' he said wearily, 'I've told you before, I don't have any spare energy to try and help you understand what I'm going through. I've barely enough for myself. I'm just trying to learn to cope with this on my own, that's all. I can't keep dumping on you.'

'Well, you just have, big time. How do you think it makes me feel realising you're going through hell knows what and you won't let me help?

You can't go on shutting us all out; me, Mum, Dad . . . even Jessica for that matter.'

'She doesn't need to know,' Josh said sharply.

'Why? What makes you think you have the right to go round operating on some stupid need-to-know basis?'

'She doesn't need to know because . . . because I'm probably going to stop seeing her.'

'What?' Charlie was bewildered. He had yet to meet Jessica, but from what Josh had shared with him he got the impression that she was good for him. Certainly up until the past couple of weeks Josh's mood-swings had levelled out and he'd seemed much better in himself.

'Don't look at me like that,' Josh said, reaching for the plug. He was shivering now and wrapping himself in a large towel he carefully stepped out of the bath, his movements awkward and clumsy. 'Why don't you do something useful like make us some supper? There's a lasagne in the fridge, bung it in the microwave. I'll be down soon.'

On his own, Josh lay on his bed and stared up at the ceiling. His body had miraculously cooled down, but his head still ached. He touched Charlie's dressing. It was sopping wet and fresh blood was beginning to seep out. He breathed in deeply, then exhaled slowly. What was he going to do? And not just about coping with what was happening to him, but with Jessica. Was he really going to stop seeing her?

No, he wasn't. He'd only said that as a knee-jerk reaction to what Charlie was saying.

He had no idea how he'd managed to hide the truth from Jessica for as long as he had. He hated the deception – and himself for what he was doing – and had lost track of the number of lies he'd told her. Not once had she questioned him, not even when he'd let her down. He was ashamed of his selfishness, that by hiding the truth from her he'd tried to ensure their relationship could continue. He covered his face with his hands in an agony of shame, appalled at the depth of his deceit as he recalled the catalogue of lies he'd devised: getting Mo to ring Jessica to say that he was held up in a meeting, when the truth was he'd been having a bad-speech day and had been unable to string more than two words together; backing out of dinner dates at the last minute because some bit of his body had given up on him; and worst of the lot, refusing to spend one single night with her.

That bit of deception seemed particularly hurtful. After making love he would immediately start pulling on his clothes and get ready to leave her. 'Crawford,' she'd said once, 'is my bed not good for anything more than a bonk?' And he had laughed, kissed her good-night and slowly made his way across the courtyard in the dark to the loneliness of his own bed, when all the time he'd wanted to lie next to Jessica and hear the steady rhythm of her breathing and feel the warmth of her arms around him. But he couldn't take the risk of enjoying that particular pleasure because he never knew what he would wake up to. If he had woken beside her and found he was unable to walk properly, or that his speech was slurred, or his hands refused to grip anything, she would have wanted to know what was wrong and the game would have been up.

Not that he saw their relationship as a game, far from it. He was dangerously close to admitting that he cared deeply for Jessica, in a way he'd never experienced before. And to make matters worse, because he'd been so adroit at keeping her at arm's length he had no idea what she really felt for him.

He wished now that he had told her about his MS in the first place. If he'd had the courage at the outset, he wouldn't be in the mess he was in now. But he'd been so terrified of losing her that he'd kept quiet, living each day as it came, hoping that by some miracle there would never be the need to tell her the truth. For he knew that when she did find out the truth it would destroy their relationship. Much as he hated the lies, he had no choice but to carry on with them ... it was the only way he could be sure of seeing Jessica.

In the kitchen, the microwave hummed its tuneless tune, then pinged intrusively. Charlie finished setting the table for supper and went upstairs to see if Josh was ready. He found him asleep on the bed, still wrapped in the damp towel. Carefully, he manoeuvred it away and covered his brother with the duvet.

Downstairs again, he helped himself to a plate of lasagne. It was only when he'd finished eating that he remembered he was supposed to be somewhere else – having dinner with Rachel. Rachel had joined the firm of solicitors below Crawford's a few weeks ago. She wasn't really his type, but these days it seemed he couldn't be choosy. He reached for his jacket hanging on the back of the chair and pulled out his mobile phone.

Rachel wasn't impressed when he made his apologies and explained that something had come up. He didn't blame her, he wasn't exactly chuffed with the way things had worked out either.

But then, nor was Josh, he suspected.

28

While preparing supper, Kate could hear Alec running the shower upstairs. He was just back from Birmingham. The M6 had been a nightmare and having contended with roadworks and an accident just north of Stafford, he'd finally made it home an hour and a half later than he'd originally told her to expect him. He'd spoken to her several times on his mobile to warn her that he was held up, as well as wanting to pass the time by talking to her.

'What are you doing now?' he'd asked, when he'd called her twenty minutes after their first conversation.

'Talking to you,' she'd said evasively. She couldn't tell him that she was actually standing in front of the hall mirror, sideways on, foolishly checking to see if there was any discernible change in her shape. She had also been trying to work out how best to break the news to Alec.

As she was now.

There were any number of ways of going about it, but she had yet to decide on the right one.

Darling, she could say, *I've got some news.* But that sounded awful, like some trite piece of sit-com dialogue.

Or there was: *Alec, you'll never believe it but I'm –*

That sounded horribly flippant.

Almost as bad as *Guess what, Alec?*

She carried on chopping up pieces of bacon for the carbonara and flung them into the frying pan. She gave them a half-hearted prod with a wooden spatula. Oh, how she sympathised with poor Mary! What must the poor girl have gone through after the Angel Gabriel had paid his little visit and she'd had to wait for Joseph to appear after a hard day's toiling with his chisels – Joseph, trust me, and doubt me not, but behold, I am with child. Joseph, why dost thou look at me with eyes of disbelieving scorn?

She prodded the bacon again and let out a sigh.

'What's that for?'

She spun round at the sound of Alec's voice and forgetting the wooden spatula in her hand, whacked him smack on the chest with it. She reached for the dishcloth but he caught her hand and raised it to his lips.

'I've missed you so much,' he said. He drew her into his arms. 'Promise you'll come with me to the Harrogate fair in February; a week's too long to be without you.'

'I'll do my best,' she said and slipping out of his arms she quickly turned her attention to the pan of spaghetti that was threatening to boil over.

Alec watched Kate moving about the kitchen. Something was wrong. He could see it in her body; the lovely fluidity of her movements was gone. She looked stiff and awkward, like she did whenever Melissa was in the same room as her.

'Did Melissa ring you?' he asked, knowing full well that she had. He helped himself to a handful of grated cheese from the dish next to the cooker, wondering if his ex-wife, with her blunt way of speaking, had upset Kate in some way. He should have phoned Kate himself and not suggested Melissa speak to her.

'Yes, she did,' Kate said, hoping that she could hide behind the conversation she'd had with Melissa until she'd finally summoned up sufficient courage to tell Alec her news.

But as the evening wore on she realised that she was no nearer to making her confession. They ate their meal in the sitting-room with trays on their laps, while watching a Channel Four programme on the changing face of the British work-force. Kate had no interest in it, but Alec was engrossed, occasionally shaking his head and pointing his fork at the television screen in disagreement. 'It's all hyperbole, jingoistic rhetoric of the day. It's common sense that if you pay a man a decent wage he'll do a better job.' He turned to Kate. 'These idiots don't have a clue . . . Kate, are you okay? You haven't eaten a thing.'

She pushed her untouched meal away from her. 'I'm just tired,' she said, 'take no notice.'

Alec put his tray on the floor, reached for the remote control and switched off a fat-cat industrialist expounding on the lack of motivation in your average Brit. 'Kate,' he said gently, 'I know there's something wrong. Is it . . . are you still upset about not doing the teacher training?'

Kate shook her head guiltily. Guiltily because she had lied to Alec. She had been all set to make her formal application to the college when she had begun to suspect that she was pregnant. She had then decided against the course. There seemed no point, not when she would soon have a baby to take care of. She had told Alec that her application had been turned down by the college because she had missed the last date for enrolment.

'You're not upset about Melissa organising that dinner party, are you?' Alec persisted.

She shook her head again, desperately hoping that the right words would magically pop into her head. But they didn't. Instead she blurted out, 'Would you like me to do a party for your birthday? I didn't go ahead and organise anything because I wanted to know what you'd like to do. Not everyone wants a party, do they? And I know that you don't like a lot of fuss. Oh ... I'm sorry, Alec, but the truth is I forgot all about your birthday. I'm sorry.'

Alec smiled at her kindly, relieved to know at last what had caused Kate to be so unhappy. 'It's okay,' he said, 'I don't particularly want to be reminded of how old I'm going to be.'

'But you're not old,' Kate said vehemently, 'and I love the way you are.' She suddenly threw her arms around him and hugged him tightly. 'I don't ever want things to change between us.'

'They won't,' he whispered into her ear, 'I won't ever let anything change between us.' Then, pulling back from her, he said, 'And anyway, I've decided what I'm doing for my birthday, I'm taking you away for a romantic weekend. Just the two of us, no family or friends to worry about. Just us.'

Kate buried her face in his neck and clung to him. *Just us.* She couldn't tell him now, not now.

Alec smiled to himself, thinking of his plan to take Kate to Venice, where to mark the occasion of his fiftieth birthday he intended to ask her to marry him, something he should have done months ago. He just hoped she'd say yes.

29

Late that night Tony brought the car to a slow and steady stop. He didn't want to jolt Hattie awake. She was fast asleep in the back and had been so since they'd joined the motorway at Exeter. Amanda was also asleep with her head lolling to one side, but as he opened his door and activated the interior light she stirred. She stretched her legs. 'Good,' she said, 'we're home. At last.'

Her words didn't come anywhere near his own thoughts. He was more than glad to be home. Never before had home been such an attraction. Their last-minute booked holiday – a cottage in Devon – had been nothing short of a lifetime in Purgatory and he'd spent most of the week wishing he were back in Cholmford. The thatched cottage that they had rented had been advertised as being idyllically situated, quaint and cosy. It had been none of these things. It had been cramped, damp and dismal, and had made the tiny terraced house in which he'd grown up seem like a palace in comparison. And with the rain that had poured down almost every day they had been forced either to stay indoors and risk cabin fever, or go out and join the other miserable holiday-makers wandering wretchedly around butterfly farms, cheese-making factories and any other lucrative enterprise that had been set up to entertain bored and depressed tourists too bedraggled to fight back and say to hell with your so-called attractions, I'm off! He suspected that if some local had stuck up a sign outside his garage and declared it to be a Museum of Post-War Horticultural Implements, he and hoards of other suicidally depressed holiday-makers would willingly have got in line to stare at a bench of B & Q garden tools. What was it with people on holiday that made them put up with being taken for such a monumental ride?

He'd expected Amanda to be the first to say she wanted none of it, but some perversity must have taken hold of her because she'd actually admitted to enjoying herself. Extraordinary.

He reached into the back of the car for Hattie. He carried her indoors, up to her bedroom where he carefully removed her sandals and snuggled her into bed. He kissed her forehead. In response she turned on to her side. He kissed her again, unable to resist her warm little cheek.

Downstairs, he found Amanda going through the mail that Kate had thoughtfully placed on the breakfast bar for their return. 'Anything urgent?' he asked, thinking of the present he and Hattie had picked out specially for Kate.

It had been Amanda's suggestion that they go away and also her idea that they ask Kate to keep an eye on things in their absence. 'She won't mind watering a few plants,' Amanda had said. 'After all, what else has she to do all day while Alec's at work?'

In return for Kate watering the patio tubs of geraniums and trailing lobelia, Amanda had suggested that they reward her with a half-pound tin of Devonshire cream toffees. But Tony had had other ideas and had gone shopping with Hattie, and between them they had settled on a hand-painted silk scarf for Kate. They found it in a smart little shop selling quality-produced arts and crafts. He didn't tell Amanda how much he'd paid for the scarf and hoped that Hattie wouldn't attach any significance to his using his Barclaycard rather than cash.

It was picturing the smile on Kate's face when she opened the present that had mainly kept him going during the week. There had been other thoughts that had gone through his head as well during the interminable days of rain and boredom, but he had tried to dismiss them as nothing more than the wild imaginings of a desperate man.

Wild imaginings or not, they had come to him in the long empty nights in that poky cottage where he had no escape from Amanda. Initially he'd tried to resist the powerful images in his head of him and Kate together – whichever way he tried to justify it, lying next to Amanda and wishing that she were Kate was wrong – but in the end, and because it was the only way he could get to sleep, he had given in to the fantasy.

And now he was doing it again, but not in that hole of a bedroom that had mould-spotted wallpaper held up in places with drawing-pins and Sellotape, but lying in their own comfortable bed.

Here it felt even more wrong.

This was their marital bed. This wasn't some anonymous cheap plywood divan and damp mattress that a thousand other unfortunate couples had shared.

Guiltily, he turned his thoughts to something altogether less shameful.

It was Hattie's first day at her new school tomorrow and to surprise her he had specially taken an extra day off work to drive her in himself. He wouldn't hang around, he'd just help her find her new classroom and leave quietly. Once that was done, he planned to take the silk scarf over to Kate, when ... when Alec would be out of the way and Amanda at the supermarket stocking up for the week ahead.

193

The house was wonderfully quiet and Amanda was revelling in it.

Having taken Hattie to school, Tony was now in the sitting-room reading the newspaper and she was in the kitchen – her lovely, spacious, airy kitchen, at least four times the size of that hateful kitchenette she'd suffered in Devon. She was putting a shopping list together: *Lurpak. Olio Spread. Fromage frais.* But her thoughts soon strayed from Sainsbury's dairy produce to their week in Devon.

It had been an unmitigated disaster. She had never seen Tony so fed-up and she was glad of it. He deserved to be miserable. It served him right for the humiliating weekend he'd put her through last month.

The Arc weekend at Gleneagles – the jolly that she had been so looking forward to – had turned out to be nothing of the kind. There had been none of the manicures and massages that she had imagined, nor any of the elegant dinners enjoying excellent food and interesting company set amid stylish surroundings.

What she'd got instead was a shambles of a doss-house that couldn't provide sufficient hot water for a bath after she'd spent most of each day being drenched and covered in mud – and not the expensive stuff that was so good for the skin.

She shuddered at the memory.

It had been humiliating.

And downright unfair.

Having dumped Hattie on Kate and Alec, much against Tony's wishes but very much in line with Hattie's, they had arrived at the hotel in the depths of the Shropshire countryside, only to find that everyone else had got there at least three hours ahead of them and, judging from their boisterous behaviour, must have settled themselves into the Anne Boleyn bar for most of that time.

The owner of the hotel, not in evidence himself – he was away on holiday in Marbella – was a fan of Henry VIII, and had gone out of his way to share his love of the man with his guests and had named all the rooms accordingly. She and Tony were staying in the Sir Thomas More suite and after they'd unpacked they joined everyone in the bar. Tony introduced her to the other wives, then abandoned her and went and chatted with his colleagues. The women all knew one another and it soon became clear that in the current climate of job insecurity at Arc she was, as Tony's wife, classed as the enemy. One of the wives, a tiny woman with a strong Mancunian accent and the longest nail extensions Amanda had ever seen, asked her which of Agatha Christie's novels she thought most resembled Arc's attitude to its employees. Amanda had said, 'I'm sorry, I've no idea.'

'*Ten Little Niggers*, of course . . . *and then there were none.*'

She had laughed politely, but then realised that she was laughing alone. It wasn't a joke.

Embarrassed, she had struggled through the rest of the evening, picking out ominous curly brown hairs from her coq au vin in the Thomas Cranmer dining-room and trying very hard to ingratiate herself with the two men either side of her. She gave up when one of them, no doubt rendered brain-dead from the amount of beer he'd earlier chucked down his throat and which he was now topping up with Piesporter plonk, kept referring to her as Eve.

'Well, Eve,' he said, 'how's that sweet little daughter of yours that Tony's always on about?' He repeated the question a further five times, despite the looks others were throwing him.

She barely slept that night, due to the Thomas More suite being situated directly above the Anne Boleyn bar, the staff of which couldn't have been acquainted with the phrase 'last orders', and in the morning, as they dressed for breakfast, Tony told her what they would be doing that day.

'What?' she'd cried, looking out of the dirty window at the rain beating down on the weed-infested tennis court, making it resemble a large rectangular pond. 'Orienteering? But I haven't brought anything to wear to go tramping through woods.'

'You don't need to worry about that, the hotel specialises in these kinds of activities; they provide boots, waterproofs, everything you could possibly need.'

'The hell they do! I haven't seen anything here that remotely resembles a beauty salon or a personal fitness centre.'

'I did warn you,' he'd said, 'I told you that it wasn't going to be the normal event. In view of the downsizing going on at work, Marty decided that the usual extravagant do at Gleneagles would be inappropriate.'

'And this is appropriate?'

He'd shrugged his shoulders in that pathetic way he did sometimes – you wouldn't catch a man like Bradley Hurst shrugging his shoulders.

'Why didn't you tell me exactly what it was going to be like?'

'I didn't know anything about it. Marty organised the whole thing. It was to be a surprise.'

It was a surprise all right.

She was put into a group with the woman with the nail extensions, whose name was Wendy, along with Marty – the one who had kept calling her Eve the previous evening.

'Right then, Wend and Mand,' Marty said, rubbing his hands together and obviously deciding that in their group he was the only one qualified to take charge. 'This isn't a race exactly, but I want us to get back to base at least twenty minutes ahead of the others. Remember, there are no winners, only losers. Mand, sweetheart, you ever done this kind of thing before? Any good with a compass?'

They'd finished last, which probably was due to the sit-down row she'd had with Marty. Not that he'd seemed to notice. The man had a skin thicker than tarmac and with about as much sensitivity.

'I'm not going any further,' she'd screamed at him, after she'd slipped in the mud for the third time. The rain was pouring off her ill-fitting sou'wester, cascading into her face and streaking what wasn't already streaked of the make-up she'd applied before Tony had broken the news to her. 'I've been out here in this bloody awful rain for over five hours, I'm not taking another step. I've had enough.' And she'd thrown herself down on the muddy ground and added, 'You'll have to carry me back.'

'Hey, Mand, sweetheart,' Marty had said, adopting a let's-be-reasonable tone of voice and squatting down beside her, 'this is the bit where you have to apply your mind. Your body's tired and is attempting a mental coup of your brain, you've gotta step right in there and put a stop to it.'

'Balls!'

Wendy had laughed out loud. 'That's what I like to hear, a bit of plain speaking.'

'And you can shut up as well!'

Wendy ignored her. 'When the going gets tough, it's time for a bevvy.' She leant against a tree, pulled out a hip flask from a pocket and began swigging on it. The forethought of the woman had incensed Amanda even more.

The weekend didn't get any better and by the time they were safely heading for home Amanda had promised herself that, if it was the last thing she would do, it would be to teach Tony a lesson. Of course he'd known what Marty would organise. Wasn't it his job to know what was going on?

So when they'd arrived in Devon last weekend, to find that the cottage they'd booked through the small ads in the *Sunday Times* was little more than a thatched coal shed, she had been delighted. The expression on Tony's face as they'd let themselves in was one to savour.

'It's disgusting,' he'd said, after taking one look at the grimy sofa and coffee-cup-ringed table in the sitting-room that measured less than their *en suite* bathroom. 'We can't stay here. The place stinks.'

'Oh, do you think so?' she'd said, 'I think it's rather quaint.'

As the days slowly went by and the rain came down, she could see that Tony was becoming more and more depressed. Now you know what it feels like, she thought maliciously. This is nothing compared with what you put me through in Shropshire.

Amanda looked down at her shopping list. She hadn't got very far with it.

Which was how she felt about her marriage. Her attempts back in June to try and inject some kind of purpose into her life with Tony had fallen foul of the realisation that Tony was never going to be another Bradley Hurst. He didn't have the killer instinct. All he seemed to care about was Hattie.

Was Hattie happy?

Would Hattie cope with her new school?

Of course she would. That girl, with her uncanny knack for manipulating people, was one of life's great survivors. Just look at the way she could get Kate drooling over her. And as for the way she wound Tony round her little finger, well, that was plain sickening – a day off work just to take her to school! Pathetic. Surely he had more important things to be doing. Bradley Hurst hadn't got to where he was by fussing over a devious child.

She finished her shopping list and as she underlined the last entry, she forced herself to swallow the unpalatable truth that the way things were going between her and Tony, their marriage was heading for a fall. What had seemed at the outset to be a marriage of happy convenience on both sides was now proving to be a battleground of silent dissatisfaction. She had accepted for some time that Hattie resented her, and equally so, she resented Hattie. But now she was beginning to feel the same for Tony.

In fact, she felt little else for him.

Tony thought Amanda would never go off to the supermarket. How long did it take to put a shopping list together, for heaven's sake?

He checked himself one more time in the hall mirror. His hair was newly washed, he was wearing fresh clean clothes – he'd spent ages deciding what to put on – and had poured enough aftershave all over himself to knock 'em dead in John o'Groats.

But was it enough to make an impression on Kate?

Well, it was time to find out.

He locked up the house, straightened his collar, cleared his throat and strode across the courtyard. He knocked lightly – in view of what was on his mind, anything louder would have been a flagrant announcement of his intentions.

He waited for her to come to the door.

And waited.

He knocked again, this time slightly louder.

Still no answer.

He looked over his shoulder at the staring windows behind him. His guilt was so palpable he was convinced that if anyone was watching him they would know exactly what he was up to. He was about to give up and accept that maybe Kate was out when he heard a movement from within.

Very slowly the door opened and Kate appeared. She was crying. More than that, her whole body was shaking as tears streamed down her pale face. Something terrible must have happened.

Overcome with concern at the sight of her distress, Tony stepped over the threshold, took her in his arms and closed the door behind him.

30

Jessica was in her study where she was trying to heighten the tension between Clare and Miles. She'd got to the tricky bit in the middle of her first draft of *A Casual Affair*, the bit where there had to be some kind of romantic action going on between her two main characters, and if Clare didn't get Miles to surrender to her charms in the next few pages then the reader was going to get bored and give up on the book – and on Jessica Lloyd.

Jessica knew as well as the next novelist that a loyal reader is the best friend an author can have and that they should always be treated with respect. As Piers had once said to her, 'To short-change a loyal reader is an act of gross stupidity, Jessica. Take care that you're never foolish enough to make that mistake.' It was as basic as knowing that every story had to have a beginning, a middle and an end.

So come on, she told herself as she stared at the blank screen in front of her, it was time for Clare to get tough with Miles. So far Clare had been pussy-footing about with him – casually dropping hints over the photocopier along the lines of there being more to her than met the eye was never going to crash through Miles's shy reserve. She was going to have to come up with something infinitely more to the point, like ... like cornering him in his office and grabbing him by his insurance bonds.

Jessica laughed, suddenly recollecting the scene in Piers's office when her vivid imagination had run riot and had wondered what it would be like to have its wicked way with her agent across his desk.

Mm ... she wondered. What if ... what if Clare tries that?

And what if Miles responds? Unbridled passion across the spread-sheets would certainly hot up the pace.

She started tapping away at the laptop, the scenario in her mind rapidly taking shape.

'Jessica,' came a voice from somewhere beyond the study.

'Yes,' answered Jessica absent-mindedly. In her ability totally to absorb herself in her writing she had forgotten that Anna was spending the day with her and that she was making a start on redecorating the kitchen.

'Isn't it about time for a coffee break?'

Clare and Miles's big moment was put on hold as Jessica left the study and went and joined her mother in the kitchen. Anna was half-way up a pair of aluminium step-ladders and was stripping wallpaper from around the window that faced the courtyard. Jessica watched her pull at a piece of wallpaper; it came away in one long, satisfying piece. She made some coffee and they sat at the kitchen table. It was covered with colour charts and several back issues of *Ideal Home*, which Anna had brought with her to help Jessica choose a new look for her kitchen. Between them they had decided on 'clotted cream' for the walls and 'summer blue' for the skirting and kitchen cupboards – Anna had assured her that sanding down the expensive units and repainting them would be simplicity itself. 'I've seen them doing it on the television, it looks straightforward enough. We'll change the doorknobs as well while we're about it.' Jessica had had no idea how expert at DIY her mother had become. She watched her now as she picked over the biscuit tin hunting for one of the few remaining chocolate bickies.

She was enjoying having her mother around. Since the rockery argument, when Anna had made her feelings about her independence very clear, she had managed to curb the desire to watch over her too zealously. It wasn't always easy, as Anna at times seemed to have a death-wish. She'd recently taken up going to the local swimming baths first thing in the morning and after she'd been boasting about the number of lengths she could notch up in an hour Jessica occasionally made the effort to join her so that she could keep a surreptitious eye on her and make sure she didn't overdo it, especially as her mother had recently bought a black Speedo costume, an obscene-looking rubber hat and a pair of goggles.

Breaking into her thoughts, Anna said, 'I should have the rest of the wallpaper off by tomorrow, then I can make a start on rubbing down the units.'

'There's no need to rush things.'

'No point in not.'

That was the trouble, thought Jessica. Every minute counted to Anna, not a single second was to be wasted. She doubted whether she would ever view life in the same way. It wasn't that Jessica was idle, well, she didn't think she was, it was more a case of having lived such a happy-go-lucky existence for so many years – Corfiotes were not people to rush things – that she tended to take a more relaxed approach to getting things done. Her mother on the other hand was a human dynamo and didn't know how to slow down.

'So how's the writing going?' Anna asked, digging around in the biscuit tin again.

'Not bad, I was having trouble getting the main character and her love interest together, but just before you called me through I found a way round the problem.'

Anna raised her eyes from the biscuit that she was dunking in her coffee. 'And how's Josh? I've not heard you mention him recently.'

Jessica laughed. 'So subtle, Mother dear. I don't know how you do it.'

'Well? How is he?'

'Good question, I haven't seen him for a few days.'

'How many days?'

'Over a week.'

'Mm . . . that doesn't sound good.'

'Thanks!'

'You must face up to these things, Jessica. If he were seriously interested in you he'd be banging that front door down and pulling you by the hair across to his place and . . . well, I think I can safely leave the rest to you. I wonder if he'd consider a more mature woman?'

'Forget it, there's mature and there's downright gone off.'

But Jessica knew that her mother was right. The way Josh had vanished from her life so suddenly hardly gave a girl cause to hope. And yes, she was well aware that she could quite easily go over and see him herself. Or for that matter, she could phone him. But that wasn't the point. It was *she* who had phoned him last, it was now down to him to make the next move. No way in the world was she going to go crawling to him. Her begging days were over. Fool that she'd been, she'd done enough of that with Gavin.

From his bed, Josh gazed out of the window, across the fields and towards the distant lumpy shapes of the Peak District. It didn't seem that long ago since he and Charlie used to go off to Derbyshire for walking weekends – weekends which usually had a habit of turning into long-distance pub crawls. But wallowing in memories never did him any good.

He pushed back the duvet, slowly slid his legs out of the bed and placed his feet firmly on the floor. So far so good. Then, holding his breath, he stood up. That was good, too. Okay, now it was time to move. Still holding his breath, he took a couple of paces.

Yesss! He was mobile.

When he'd lain on the bed last night, his head aching from where he'd struck it at work, the rest of his body had felt as though it would never move again. It was a huge relief to him now to know that this was not the case.

Spurred on, he shuffled over to the wardrobe and knowing there was no chance of him making it in to work that day, he pulled out a pair of black jeans. He considered a shirt, but thought of the buttons and instantly dismissed the idea – his fingers had all the dexterity of a bunch of bananas. He chose a T-shirt instead. Next it was over to the chest of drawers for some socks and boxer shorts, followed by the staggering journey right across the bedroom to the adjoining bathroom. He was exhausted by the time he reached it and leant against the basin for support. But at least he'd made it. By shit he'd made it!

He didn't bother with shaving, but once he'd washed and dressed he stood at the top of the stairs and geared himself up for what today, for him, was his very own equivalent to the downward climb of the north face of the Eiger.

As he'd suspected, when he finally entered the kitchen Charlie was already there and was making breakfast. He'd known that his brother would stay the night, that he would never have left him alone. He was grateful, touched by Charlie's concern, but too much of him was angry at the circumstances in which he found himself to be able to thank him in the way he ought.

'You look better than you did last night,' was Charlie's only comment when he saw him.

'Thanks. So do you.'

They ate in the kitchen. Josh would have liked to have had breakfast outside on the patio in the warm morning sun, but the thought of traversing the entire length of the hall, sitting-room and the two steps down to reach the garden made him settle for where they were.

'I thought I'd hang around here for the day,' Charlie said, 'if that's okay with you?'

Josh shrugged. 'Sure.'

'I've phoned Mo and explained we won't be in. I thought if you were feeling up to it we could go for a pub lunch later on?'

'And maybe a walk afterwards?' The sarcasm in Josh's voice made Charlie throw down his knife.

'Sod it, Josh! I'm just trying to help, that's all.'

Josh buried his head in his hands. 'I know,' he said, 'I know.' He looked up. 'I can't help myself at times. It's like there's more anger in me than I know what to do with. I'm ... I'm sorry.'

'Will you promise me one thing,' Charlie said, his face suddenly earnest. 'What went through your mind in the bath last night ... you ... you wouldn't ever ...'

'What, top myself?'

Charlie nodded.

'I don't think that's a promise I can make ... or perhaps anyone is capable of making. The dark demons of the mind leap out on you when you're least expecting them, a bit like Jehovah's Witnesses really.'

'That's hardly the reassuring response I need, though.'

'Yeah, well, right now it's the best I can do.'

'But you've got so much going for you.'

'Have I?' Josh's voice was expressionless.

'Yes!' Charlie was defiantly adamant. 'There are so many people who care about you and apart from anything else, how the hell would I run the business on my own?'

'You'd manage.' Again the same flat voice.

'But I don't want to run it alone, I want you there with me, or ... or there'd be no point.'

Josh turned away. He couldn't cope with Charlie's honesty. 'Look, can we drop this?' he muttered. 'It's really not helping either of us.'

'And what about Jessica?' Charlie had the bit between his teeth now. Josh looked up sharply. 'What about her?'

'Last night you said you weren't going to carry on seeing her. Why? Isn't she someone who'd be worth living for?'

'Don't you think I haven't thought of that!' Josh rounded on him.

'Then stop bloody well pissing about and do something. Go over there and tell her the truth. Give her time to think about it and start treating her with the respect she deserves instead of palming her off with all those lies you've been dishing out. Yes, Mo told me about the phone call you asked her to make. I dread to think what else you've been up to.'

Josh stared angrily at his brother. 'Have you quite finished?'

'No!' Charlie retorted, 'no, I haven't.' But as he tried to think of what else he wanted verbally to throw at his brother, he realised that his fury at Josh's stubbornness had suddenly rendered him impotent. He could think of nothing else to say. Nothing that would be of any help. He stood up. 'This is no good,' he said, 'I can't cope with you when you're like this. I'll be at work if you need me.'

Unable to get to his feet fast enough to go after his brother, Josh listened to the sound of the front door shutting, then the unmistakable rumble of Charlie's TVR starting up.

He slowly lowered his head into his hands, saddened beyond measure that he continually treated Charlie so badly.

31

Acting as a shoulder to cry on wasn't exactly what Tony had had in mind when he'd knocked on Kate's door half an hour ago, but it was all he could do in the circumstances.

She had stopped crying now, but was still sitting hunched on the bottom step of the stairs – she'd been there since she'd let him in. In front of her was a half-empty box of Kleenex, beside it, a pile of soggy screwed-up tissues. His present for her was lying unopened on the hall table next to the phone, which she kept glancing at. She was doing so now. 'When he's calmed down, he'll ring, won't he?' she said, her bloodshot eyes filling with tears once more as she hugged her knees to her.

'Maybe,' Tony said softly beside her. From what Kate had told him it seemed pretty unlikely that Alec would call for a few hours yet. 'He needs time to cool off,' he added. He had to admit, though, that Alec's reaction to Kate telling him that she was pregnant did seem a bit extreme. He remembered how he had felt when Eve had told him she was expecting Hattie. It had come as a complete surprise to them both as they hadn't planned on having children so soon. But his reaction had been one of amazement rather than shock. 'How come?' had been his first astonished words. 'Because you've impregnated my body with your sperm, dummy,' had been Eve's response, followed by a smile that had shown him how pleased she was. They had gone out for a meal to celebrate and later they'd made love. 'It won't harm the baby, will it?' he'd asked afterwards, suddenly concerned. She'd laughed and rolled on top of him. 'Honestly,' she'd said, 'men, they know nothing!'

'It takes time for a man to adjust to the idea of being a father,' he said kindly to Kate. He slipped his hand over hers and squeezed it. 'It took me a while really to get to grips with the idea of Eve being pregnant. I was frightened that a baby might come between us. Men can be very insecure when it comes to sharing the woman they love.'

Kate looked down at Tony's hand holding her own. He had nice hands, she suddenly thought. 'How long did it take for you to come round?'

The truthful answer was less than a few days, but the truth wouldn't help Kate right now. 'A couple of weeks,' he lied. 'It might even have been longer.'

'But Alec might never come round to the idea,' she said, staring into the middle distance. In her mind's eye she could see Alec's face earlier that morning; first the shock in it, then the disappointment and finally the anger.

Over breakfast she had summoned up the courage to tell him about the baby. He had been listening to Sue MacGregor and John Humphrys bringing to the nation's attention that inflation was up – or was it down? – and that as a result home-owners would be worse off, but investors would be happier. And I don't give a damn, she'd thought as she'd got up from the table and switched off the radio and faced Alec. She didn't wrap her announcement in any kind of fancy packaging. She simply stood before him and in a matter-of-fact voice that was vaguely reminiscent of Sue MacGregor reading the news she said, 'Alec, I'm pregnant. I know this isn't what you wanted, but I'm afraid it's definitely something I want.'

His eyes were what she noticed first – they suddenly seemed to grow larger; it was the shock, she supposed. Then it was his hands that caught her attention; they stopped what they were doing and came to rest either side of his plate of half-buttered toast, the palms face down as though feeling for some levitational force that was about to start making the table bounce about.

Very slowly he had begun to move. He stood up. Then he spoke. 'You knew I didn't want this. You knew.' The disappointment in his voice was heart-breaking.

But worse was to come when he walked out of the kitchen. He paused in the doorway, turned back to her and said, 'You've used me. Ruth said you would. She warned me, but I wouldn't listen.'

And that was the anger. Scalding, accusative anger, as though she had planned the whole thing.

Within seconds he was gone, the door closing quietly behind him – Alec wasn't a dramatic man, slamming the door would have been too hackneyed. She watched him get into his car and drive away to work.

To Melissa.

She had started to cry then, tears of sobbing heartache that she had been storing up over the weekend. Or was it longer? Had she always known that it would end like this?

It was while she was trying to pull herself together, at the same time clearing up the breakfast things, that she had heard the sound of knocking. At first she'd ignored it. She didn't want to see anybody. But then she'd wondered if it was Jessica and realising that she was the only other person who knew her predicament and that she might be able to help her, she went to the door. But it had been Tony. The details of what happened next were hazy, but she could remember the sense of relief as he'd held her – she hated crying alone and to be able to cry while somebody held her somehow made the hurt seem slightly more bearable. He'd sat with her on the stairs, handed her tissues and listened while she told him what had happened.

'It's over,' she now whispered. 'I know it is. Alec thinks I've done this deliberately.'

Tony put his arm around her shoulders. How easy it would be to manipulate the situation to his own advantage, he thought, to write off Alec and claim Kate for his own. But he couldn't. Kate's distress touched him too much even to consider what had earlier been in his mind. 'Come on,' he said gently, 'let's get you somewhere more comfortable to sit.'

They went into the sitting-room. Kate curled herself up in one of the armchairs in the bay window. He took the chair opposite. He handed her the present which he'd picked up from the hall table. 'Here,' he said, hoping it would provide a temporary diversion, 'open this, it's a thank-you for looking after the house while we were away.'

She carefully unwrapped the layers of cream tissue paper. 'It's beautiful,' she exclaimed, when she saw what was inside, 'but I don't deserve it, I only watered a few plants.'

'Nonsense, of course you deserve it. Hattie and I chose it together. Are the colours okay? We hoped all those different shades of pale green would suit you.' He was conscious that he was speaking too quickly. He so wanted her to like the present.

She nodded and lovingly stroked the silk scarf. 'It's perfect. Thank you. And will you thank Hattie for me? How is she?'

Brief as the diversion might be, Tony was glad that the scarf had brought about a respite in Kate's unhappiness. 'She's fine. Or rather she was when I left her a few hours ago. It's her first day at her new school. I think I was the more nervous of the two of us when it was time to say goodbye. Do you think you'd be up to a visit later when she comes home? She'd love to see you. Children are wonderful for taking your mind off things.' He saw immediately the pained expression on her face. 'I'm sorry,' he said, 'that was insensitive of me.'

She blinked away the threat of fresh tears. 'I've always wanted children,' she said wistfully. 'I'd love a little Hattie of my own . . . you're very lucky.'

'Yes,' he said softly, 'I know I am.' Then before he could stop himself, he added, 'But it didn't always seem that way, not when . . . not when Eve died.' He clenched his hands in his lap. 'I've never told anyone this before, but . . . but I would have willingly swapped them over.' He leapt to his feet. 'Oh God, what does that make me sound like?' He leant against the window, resting his hands on the sill and, needing time to compose himself, he stared through the glass, concentrating his gaze on the jutting shape of Bosley Cloud in the far-away distance.

After a few seconds he slowly turned round and faced Kate. 'I didn't mean that I wanted Hattie dead, it wasn't like that, I just wanted Eve. I wanted her so desperately . . . I would have done anything to have her alive again.' But as he spoke those last terrible words he felt his composure going again. He had to fight hard to overcome the terrible pain that always threatened to engulf him when he thought of Eve's senseless death. 'I've no idea why I'm telling you all this,' he said, his voice low and shaky, 'but I love Hattie more than I thought possible. Maybe it's guilt. Maybe I'm overcompensating for what I once felt.' He cleared his throat and willed himself to finish what he'd started. 'And as a result I know I've made the biggest mistake of my life. I made the error of thinking that Hattie needed a mother more than . . . more than I needed a woman I could love.'

They stared at one another, the room suddenly still with a taut silence. 'I thought so,' Kate said at last.

He was stunned. He sat down again. 'Is it that obvious?'

She didn't answer his question, but said simply, 'What will you do?'

He shook his head and let out his breath. 'I've no idea.'

207

32

Alec wasn't interested in what Susan Ashton from the warehouse in Oxford had to say. It didn't bother him that the hand-finishing on one of the Christmas card lines was taking longer than originally estimated; for all he cared Susan could have phoned with the news that the entire factory had burnt down and there were no survivors.

All he could think of was Kate.

Why, oh why had this happened?

They'd been fine as they were. Now everything would be different. All the plans he'd had in mind were ruined. There'd be no more romantic dinners together. And there'd certainly be no chance of any romantic weekends away. In fact, experience told him that there'd be no bloody romance at all.

He could remember all too vividly what it had been like when Ruth was born; the whole house had been given over to her. It was the smell he'd disliked most; whichever way he turned there was the smell of drying nappies, sour milk and sickly talcum powder. There was no escape from it.

He'd become a stranger in his own home, unable to walk into any room for fear of disturbing Ruth who might be sleeping there in her Moses basket – it had always seemed absurd to him that such a tiny being not only possessed its own mini-empire within hours of its birth, but was actually given the power to rule and dominate it.

But the trouble had started way before Ruth's arrival in the world: it had begun when Melissa discovered that she was pregnant. Pregnancy hadn't suited her and from day one it had made her tired and crotchety, and she'd been in bed by eight thirty most nights, with sex clearly no longer a viable proposition. After Ruth was born he'd waited patiently for Melissa to wave the green flag. But there was still no sign of affection between them. By the time Ruth was five months old he was beginning to lose hope of them ever having any kind of sex life again. If he gave so much as a hint that he desired her in bed, Melissa would turn away from him. It was only after she had stopped breast-feeding that things improved. But it was never the same.

It had always been his opinion that it was Ruth's conception that had created the first crack in their marriage.

And exactly the same would happen between him and Kate. A child would come between them. He just knew it.

Kate would, of course, deny that anything would change between them, but he knew better. It was all down to nature. Nature dictated that a woman behaved differently the moment she became pregnant. She didn't realise what was going on herself, but very gradually all her thoughts became wrapped up in that small being that was fast taking her over, allowing no room for anything else in her life, or anyone else for that matter. And when the baby was actually born, nature stepped in to ensure it survived by putting its needs first and foremost in its mother's brain. There was no room for any other thought, all nature allowed the mother to think of was providing nourishment, warmth and a safe environment for her child.

And that was another thing nature did – the child was never *their* child, it was only ever *her* child.

Ruth had never been his. His initial clumsy attempts at bathing or dressing her had been mocked and devalued, and had reduced him to the position of onlooker, where his services were only required in the middle of the night when Melissa was too exhausted to soothe a teething Ruth.

He could imagine Kate saying she would never be like Melissa, that she would never make the same mistakes, but in his heart he suspected that she would be worse – she was so very desperate for a child of her own that she probably wouldn't let him have a single look-in. He would be squeezed out. Surplus to requirements.

It had been just like that when Hattie had stayed with them that weekend last month. Kate had spent nearly all her time entertaining the child. Thinking that he mustn't let his jealousy get the better of him he had left her to it and spent most of Saturday and Sunday at work.

'So what do you want me to do, Alec? Give it one more try?'

Susan's insistent voice at the other end of the line forced Alec back to what she was saying. 'I'm sorry,' he said curtly, 'I've got to go. Speak to Melissa about the problem.'

He replaced the receiver and sank back into his chair. Almost immediately the phone rang again. He snatched it up. 'I'm busy,' he barked at the receptionist who'd put the call through. 'I don't want to be disturbed.'

Was there to be no peace for him?

The answer was obviously no, as at that moment his door opened and in walked the very last person with whom he wanted to speak. Hell, she'd love every minute of this, he thought. He watched Melissa drop a batch of sample cards on his desk and for the first time since Tim had arrived on the scene he experienced a wave of angry jealousy about the relationship she had with him. How simple it must be for the pair of them, he thought enviously, there was no danger of a pregnancy to bugger things up because very conveniently Melissa had had a hysterectomy six years ago. And unable to stomach the idea of her gloating, he stood up quickly and pulled on his jacket. 'Whatever it is, it'll have to wait,' he said. He moved towards the door. 'I'm going for an early lunch.'

Melissa stared after him. Something was wrong. Very wrong. In all the years she had known Alec she had only twice seen such a distraught look on his face – when his mother had died and when she'd told him she wanted a divorce. She had never forgotten that sad, wounded expression. She had hurt him so badly and it had taken all her strength to carry out what she had instigated. He had never known how near she'd come to changing her mind that night.

But it had been the right thing to do. She had never since doubted the decision she'd made. She and Alec got on much better as friends and business partners than they had as husband and wife. She still loved him – she always had – and that was perhaps why she had divorced him; if they'd stayed together they might have ended up hating each other and she'd never have wanted that; it had been a case of being cruel to be kind. It had been difficult at times, though, she'd had to adopt a tough veneer to convince Alec that she no longer cared for him in the way she once had. In the early days after she'd moved out, when he'd taken to drinking the lonely evenings away, she'd had to fight back the urge to comfort him. Instead, she had put on what she called her tough bitch act and bossed him about, ordering him to pull himself together. Little did he know that she had spent many a lonesome night worrying about him.

Still, that was all in the past. She now had Tim and Alec seemed to have found genuine happiness with Kate.

Alec was driving much too fast for his car to cope with the country lanes and after coming within an inch of his life on a tight bend and almost smashing his Saab into the back of a tractor he lowered his speed.

He had been driving recklessly and mindlessly for the past hour, but now as he approached the village of Swettenham he decided he needed a break, as well as something to eat. He headed towards the Swettenham Arms. The car-park was large and not very full, and he easily found himself a space.

Inside the pub he was met by the comforting smell of real ale. He ordered a pint of bitter and a steak and kidney pudding, and took his drink over to the only available table. It was in the window, where not so long ago he and Kate had sat. They had been celebrating some kind of anniversary – five months of knowing one another, or was it six? Whatever it was, happiness and contentment had flowed between them as they'd sat wrapped in each other's love that warm, sunny spring afternoon. There had been a small vase on the wooden table containing a single carnation which he had taken out and tucked into her hair – a silly, sentimental gesture which had made them both laugh, as well as the couple sitting close by.

There was no flower on the table today, just a solitary squashed chip left over from somebody else's lunch.

He drank his beer and when his food arrived he found he wasn't hungry. He managed to force a mouthful of boiled potato down but gave up after a feeling of nausea spread over him.

Eating wasn't going to solve his problem. Nor was drinking. He looked reproachfully at the almost empty glass in his hand. He'd already been down that particular road when Melissa had left him. It hadn't worked then. It wouldn't work now.

So what was the answer?

Go home and talk to Kate?

But what good would that do? Talking would only lead to one of them compromising. And again, what good would that do?

If it was he who compromised there was a danger he would always hold it against Kate, that the slightest disagreement between them would be blown out of proportion because he would feel he'd conceded so much to her already.

And if it was she who compromised – could he really expect her to have an abortion? – then he would never be able to look her in the eye again for fear of seeing the most profound bitter regret in her face. And worse would come – her bitterness would turn to pure hatred for what he'd made her do.

Either way, they couldn't win.

He drained his beer, pushed his uneaten lunch away and made himself accept that because of his selfish love for Kate he had almost certainly lost her. There could be no hope for their relationship now.

Caroline was full of fighting talk. 'The bastard! How dare he say that to you? It's he who's used you.'

'Caroline,' hissed Kate, 'keep your voice down, people are looking.'

'Let them,' Caroline said even louder, staring defiantly round at the faces now glancing their way. 'Let them know what a pig he's been.'

'Caroline, if you don't shut up I'll walk out of here.'

Caroline stared at her friend, mystified. 'Well I must say, you seem to be taking this very calmly. Don't you feel angry at the way he's treating you?'

'I'm too confused and upset to feel angry,' Kate said. 'Now please, can we order what we're going to eat and talk rationally.'

When Tony had left her that morning – having made sure that she was over the worst of the tears – she had phoned Caroline to see if she was free for lunch. She had been in luck: Caroline was enjoying a few days off work. The really good thing about her friendship with Caroline was that she never failed to focus Kate's thoughts and make her feel level-headed, and as she'd driven to the wine bar in Knutsford to meet her she had known that within minutes of listening to her friend's over-the-top reaction to her news she would feel composed and empowered.

A good-looking waiter came and took their order, and when he walked away, after Caroline had tried a bit of small talk with him, she said, 'Now, Kate, he's much more what you should have gone after, not some old duffer who's not prepared to take on his responsibilities.'

Kate frowned. 'Alec is not an old duffer, Caroline, how many times do I have to tell you, he's only forty-nine?'

Caroline snorted. 'Whatever you say. So what are you going to do?'

'I think that depends on what Alec is going to do.'

'Well, as to that, I think you'll find he's had his bit of fun, now he'll be off. Mark my words, he'll have you out of that house before you've had your first antenatal appointment. He'll have some kind of legal document drawn up, stating he knows he's the father and here's the dosh for the next X years, then it'll be a case of it's been nice knowing you, ta ta.'

'He might change his mind,' Kate said, ignoring her friend's damning indictment of Alec, and determined to give him the benefit of the doubt she added, 'Tony says lots of men over-react when they hear they're going to be a father.'

Caroline looked up, interested. 'Who's Tony?'

'He's a neighbour and he . . .'

'And he what?'

'He came over this morning when I was doing my hysterical bit. He was very kind.'

'Was he indeed?' smirked Caroline.

'Don't be ridiculous,' said Kate, but despite herself she couldn't prevent her face from colouring as she thought of Tony. She recalled his hand on hers and the way he'd comforted her. When he'd started talking about his problems she had felt so sorry for him that for a few minutes she had forgotten her own worries and had been concerned only for a man who in the midst of his troubles had shown her such kindness. It was strange that without having acknowledged it to herself she had known all along that Tony wasn't happy with Amanda. Or maybe it wasn't strange; after all, Amanda wasn't a particularly lovable person. There was a coldness to her that was at odds with Tony's naturally warm personality. Perhaps anybody who got to know Tony and Amanda as a couple would quickly realise that he couldn't possibly have married her for love. Equally so, she suspected, they would guess that Amanda's readiness to marry Tony had also had very little to do with love.

'So what's he like?' asked Caroline.

Kate smiled. 'You're impossible, you really are.'

'Answer the question. I want to know what kind of men you're keeping in with. Tell me all.'

'There's nothing to tell.'

'Not much, there isn't. You've gone the colour of my nail varnish.'

Kate gave in. 'He's quite tall.'

'How tall?'

'Five foot ten-ish.'

'Hair?'

'Yes.'

'Don't get clever. What colour?'

'Fair-ish.'

'Eyes?'

'Blue-ish.'

'Age?'

'Mid-thirties-ish.'

'And I suppose if I were to ask what kind of car he drove you'd say it was fast-ish. Are you being deliberately vague?'

Kate smiled. 'He drives a Porsche and it's silvery grey –'

'Don't tell me,' interrupted Caroline, 'it's silvery grey-*ish*.'

They both laughed.

'Well, with or without the babe-catching machine he sounds distinctly eligible. How would he feel about taking on somebody else's child?'

'He's married and has one of his own. So end of story.'

'There's always something to spoil it, isn't there? Oh, good, here's lunch.'

After the waiter had left them alone again, Kate said, 'Caroline, I want to talk seriously with you now.'

'Do you have to? I was just beginning to enjoy myself.'

'I want to ask a favour of you. If Alec . . . if I do have to move out, can I come and stay with you, just until I've got myself sorted?'

Caroline inwardly groaned. The picture of her lovely little house messed up with crate-loads of Pampers and sicked-on Babygros did not appeal, but realising that her attitude was sympathising with the enemy – namely Alec – she said cheerfully, 'Of course you can, so long as we have an understanding; if I'm lucky enough to bring a man back to the house you're to keep out of sight, one look at you and they won't be interested in me. Hey, you're not about to start blubbing, are you?'

Kate swallowed and blinked away the threat of tears. 'I'm just really grateful, that's all. It probably won't come to it. Alec and I will sort everything out, but if I do need a place to go to, it's nice to know there is one.' And, keen to change the subject, she said, 'Tell me how the dating's going.'

Caroline knew that she was one of the least sensitive people around – she knew this because Kate was always quick to tell her that it was the case – but today she could see only too clearly that Kate needed her to distract her and she was more than ready to comply with her friend's wishes. 'You won't believe some of the dorks I've met,' she said. 'It beggars belief that there are so many weirdos out there. There was this one guy who wittered on for hours about his collection of purple ceramic dragons. Well, it would have been for hours if I hadn't pretended to feel violently ill and excused myself. There was one guy who kept going on about all his previous girlfriends. And there was another who was a Buddy Holly freak; he turned up in a fifties suit with those hideous specs and asked if I minded being called Peggy Sue for the evening. I just did a runner, straight out the door, down the high street and to my car. I went home and drooled over my George Clooney scrapbook with a cup of hot chocolate. It's a nightmare, a total nightmare. They sound sane enough on the phone, but believe me they all turn out as dorky as Woody Allen and with twice as many hang-ups.'

'But you must have met at least one decent man,' said Kate.

'If I did, I must have missed him among all the dross.'

They carried on eating for a while, then Kate said in a low voice, 'I've a confession to make.'

'You do fancy that Tony guy? I knew it!'

'I wish I'd never mentioned him now,' Kate said crossly. 'I was going to tell you that it was through an agency that I met Alec.'

Caroline lowered her knife and fork and stared at Kate, then gradually a small, wry smile appeared on her lips. 'Well,' she said, raising her glass of wine, 'I rest my case, m'lud, not a decent man among the lot of them.'

It was late afternoon when Kate drove through the archway of Cholmford Hall Mews. The first thing she saw was Alec's car parked outside the house. She was tempted to reverse straight back out through the arch, but several hours of being in Caroline's company had prepared her for the inevitable confrontation with Alec. 'I will not fall apart,' she told herself firmly as she parked alongside his Saab. 'I am in control of the situation,' she went on, as she locked her car door, 'I will hold my ground.'

She let herself into the house.

He was in the study, bent over his desk, flicking through some letters he must have brought home with him from work. He turned round when she entered the room.

'I think we should get this over with,' she said, her hands gripping her keys behind her back.

'You're right,' he said. He followed her through to the kitchen.

Why was it that so many of life's big decisions were made in the kitchen? Kate wondered as they stood facing each other, the table between them acting like a barrier. So this is it, she thought. This is really it. This is when I make my choice and stand by it. She marvelled at how calm she felt. I've aged about ten years today, she reflected.

All his emotions petrified, Alec stared down at his shoes. He was waiting for Kate to speak. He didn't think he had the courage to go first. But when she didn't say anything he slowly raised his eyes. Not directly at her, but to the window, then to the fridge where Kate had stuck one of Oscar's paintings – it was a picture of him and Kate holding hands, beneath their feet was a thin green strip of grass and above their heads a wobbly stripe of blue sky, and written in pencil in Oscar's four-and-a-half-year-old shaky handwriting were the words, *Grampa Alec and Kate.*

'I'm sorry,' he blurted out, unable to take the silence a moment longer. But still he didn't look at her. He kept his eyes on Oscar's picture – Kate with her impossibly long, matchstick-thin legs and he with a round barrel of a stomach and tiny stumps for legs. 'I'm sorry,' he repeated.

'What are you sorry for, Alec?' she said.

He tore his gaze away from Oscar's artwork and looked at her. The late afternoon sun was pouring in through the window and her hair was glowing a vibrant shade of golden chestnut. It was tied up with a silk scarf he didn't recognise and the colours in the fabric brought out the exquisite shade of green in her eyes – large, sad eyes that were fixed on him. He thought he'd never seen her look more beautiful. And as he thought this, the awful strain and horror of the day suddenly lifted from him and he knew what he had to do.

He went to her, wrapped her in his arms, needing to undo all the harm he'd done – desperate for her forgiveness. 'Oh, Kate,' he whispered, 'I didn't mean what I said this morning. It was the shock. Just give me time to adjust and I promise everything will be all right. I promise.'

33

By Monday evening Josh was feeling a lot better. The burning sensation that had plagued him for most of the previous week had gradually receded over the weekend and other than coping with the usual stiffness in his leg he had felt relatively normal today.

He'd gone in to work for a couple of hours that morning and, after making his peace with Charlie and sorting out a few things that had been left pending since Thursday, he'd come home after lunch with his briefcase stuffed full of faxes to deal with, from their suppliers in Hong Kong. He'd decided – before Charlie had had a chance to suggest it – to take things easy on his first day back.

He'd spent most of the weekend taking it easy. In fact, he'd slept through the best part of it, finding it difficult to stay awake for much of the time. He hated to admit it, but maybe in the future he ought to take more notice of his body. Perhaps if he hadn't struggled on trying to ignore the pain in his legs last week he wouldn't have ended up so exhausted ... or head-butting his desk. He was now fully convinced that what he'd experienced in his office on Thursday afternoon hadn't been the start of him suffering from black-outs, but had been a one-off case of him collapsing through exhaustion. His body had simply had enough.

The only disturbance to his weekend of recovery was a call on Saturday morning from his mother – he suspected that Charlie had been at work in the background and had prompted her to ring him.

'Everything all right for Sunday lunch next week?' she'd asked. 'You'll be able to make it, won't you?' He had heard the tense wariness in her voice, knowing that she was torn between wanting to rush over and make sure he was all right – but knowing that it would be the last thing he'd want – and pretending that she knew nothing of his latest MS attack.

'Yes, as far as I can tell,' he'd replied, feeling genuinely sorry for her. Ever since he had lost his temper with his mother, the day after he'd been diagnosed as having multiple sclerosis and when he'd felt smothered by everyone's concern, she had been wary of him. She had been so hurt by his lashing out at her that she had never wanted to repeat the episode and had tiptoed round him, scared of saying the wrong thing. He kept meaning to talk to her about it, but somehow the right moment had never presented itself.

Their conversation hadn't lasted long. But using as much tact as she could, she had asked him how he was and in a by-the-way tone of voice had added that Charlie had spoken to her, and in order to circumvent the painful process of her drawing out the grisly details from him he'd said, 'I'm fine, Mum, please don't worry. I'll see you next week. I'll be there as usual.'

As he'd put down the phone he'd made himself promise to find time to speak to his mother, to talk to her properly.

Now as he finished dealing with the last of the faxes that he'd brought home with him he took off his glasses and sat back in his chair. He gazed across the courtyard, through the sash window of his study, and wondered if now was the right time to stop hiding from Jessica and talk to her. He didn't hold out much hope that she'd want to say very much to him, though. It was ages since they'd last spoken – it was when she'd called him and he'd been feeling rotten, and the resulting conversation had been as lively and interesting as a party political broadcast. No wonder she hadn't bothered to ring him again.

He turned away from the window and looked at the bookshelf to the left of his desk. There, in pride of place between a framed photograph of him and Charlie on the slopes at Val d'Isère and another of the pair of them up at Victoria Peak in Hong Kong, were copies of Jessica's books. He'd read them both and much to his surprise – he'd never read a romantic comedy in his life before – had laughed out loud. Her style of writing was incisive, pacey and sardonic – just as she was herself – and he was conscious that given his behaviour towards her of late, she could make short work of him if she so chose. God knows, she was entitled.

He returned his attention to looking out of the window and twirling his glasses round in his hand, and thinking just how much he'd missed Jessica's company he caught sight of her in the room directly opposite. She had just walked into her study.

Without giving himself time to change his mind he leaned forwards, picked up the phone and dialled her number from the piece of paper he had propped against the halogen desk lamp – a piece of paper that had stared reproachfully at him for nearly two weeks now.

He watched her pick up her phone. 'Hi,' he said, 'it's Josh.'

There was a pause, then the sound of her voice. 'Mm . . . now let me see, would that be Josh Reynolds the painter chappie, or that other well-known Josh, the man who led the Israelites to the Promised Land?'

'Neither. It's Josh the pain in the bum who hasn't spoken to you for . . . for quite a while.'

'Oh, that one. Well I have a sketchy picture of him in my mind, but you'll have to help me out, he's little more than a vague memory these days.'

'If you look out of your window you might catch a glimpse of something that could help.'

There was a slight pause. 'Good heavens, there's a mad man out there waving back at me. Fancy that. But hang on, I think you're right, there is something familiar about him. It's beginning to come to me now.'

'How are you, Jessica? I've missed you.'

'Have you?'

'Yes.'

'Really?'

'Really.'

'Like hell you have!'

'But it's true, I have.'

'So why haven't you been in touch?'

'I've been busy.'

'Crawford, save me the bull. Get off the phone and get your butt over here and make your apologies in person.'

'I . . . I can't.'

'Why not?'

'Because . . . because I'm just getting over flu.' Oh hell! He was off again. More lies.

'Why didn't you let me know you'd been ill? I could have come over and made broth, and mopped your brow for you and stood prettily at the end of your bed.'

'Nice idea, but I'm afraid I make a lousy patient.'

'Believe me, most men make lousy patients. So why are you ringing me?'

'I'd like to see you.'

'I'm not sure I want to see you.'

'Jessica, I said I'm sorry. I've been busy, work's been crazy –'

'And don't forget how ill you've been with the flu.'

'Can I see you tomorrow evening?'

'You sure you'll be well enough?'

'I'll make sure I am.'

'Okay. Be here for half past seven. And Crawford –'

'Yes?'

'No excuses this time, okay?'

'As if.'

Josh spent most of Tuesday praying that he'd make it through the day. If something went wrong with him and he didn't get to Jessica's that evening she was never going to believe another word he said.

And as it was the truth he wanted to speak tonight, it was important that nothing prevented him from seeing her.

Speaking to Jessica on the phone yesterday evening, it couldn't have been further from his mind to own up to her about his MS. When she'd suggested he call on her there and then, he'd suddenly lost his nerve and had been terrified that he might get half-way across the courtyard and keel over. So rather than take the risk, he'd backed out and given her some crap about recovering from flu.

How pathetic.

And how cowardly.

It was after he'd put down the phone and he'd made himself some supper that he'd known that he couldn't go on as he was. It was time to come clean with Jessica. He would rather she knew the truth about him than have her condemn him as a complete shyster.

At half past five he gathered up his things and switched off the lights in his office. Out in the reception area Mo was chatting to Charlie. When she saw Josh she handed him a small card. It was an invitation.

'It's my birthday on Friday, I'm having a party, will you come?'

'Of course he will,' Charlie said.

'I'm not sure,' Josh said hesitantly.

'Oh, please,' said Mo. Reluctantly she added, 'You can bring Jessica if you want. Charlie's going to try and persuade Rachel to come.'

'I'll think about it.'

'You're an ungracious bugger,' Charlie said as he and Josh walked to their cars. 'You could have just said yes to Mo.'

'I don't like making promises I might not be able to keep.'

Charlie let it go. He was tired of reasoning with his brother. 'Doing anything tonight?'

'Yes. I'm seeing Jessica. I'm ... I'm going to tell her.'

Charlie came to a stop. 'About your MS?'

Josh nodded.

Charlie wasn't sure what to say. If he said anything glib like: 'It'll be fine, don't worry,' it would be an insult to Josh's intelligence. And though he himself had urged his brother on many occasions to be honest with Jessica, he didn't for one minute underestimate the risk Josh was taking. His last girl-friend's sudden departure from his life was proof enough that love didn't always conquer all.

'Good luck,' was all he could think to say. 'Give me a ring if ... well, you know.'

'What, if things don't turn out well?'

However Josh had thought the evening might turn out, he couldn't have predicted the way it did.

He called on Jessica, spot on seven-thirty as she'd instructed, but when she didn't let him into the house as he'd expected, his plan of quietly explaining things to her immediately went on hold.

She led him towards her car and said, 'Get in and don't argue. It's time for you to loosen up. You're going to sit for two whole hours in my company whether you want to or not, and what's more, you're going to do it in the dark and you're going to laugh. I might even let you have some popcorn if you're good.'

The film was billed as a knockabout comedy with Steve Martin playing a love-struck oil tycoon.

'This really isn't my kind of thing,' Josh said petulantly as they took up their seats in the crowded cinema.

'Yeah, I know, this is far too unsophisticated for you, isn't it. But then, that's your trouble, you've let yourself go. You're old before your time and have forgotten how to enjoy yourself. Now, why don't you sit back and let the child within come out to play?'

'I'd rather be an adult at home playing with you.'

'Ssh! The film's about to start. Have some popcorn. And don't look like that, sulking won't get you anywhere with me.'

When the credits began to roll at the end of the film, to the sound of Aretha Franklin singing 'What Now My Love', they joined the stream of people queuing for the exit and left the cinema. It was dark outside and soft rain was beginning to fall.

Jessica unlocked the car and they climbed in. 'Well,' she said, 'it wasn't such a bad film, was it? I distinctly heard you laughing back there.'

'I was laughing to please you,' he conceded.

She threw him a look and for the first time noticed the cut to his temple. 'You've hurt yourself,' she said. 'How did you do that?'

He hesitated. Was this the opening he needed? Was this the perfectly timed moment for him to tell her the truth? That he suffered from MS and it had got the better of him last week at work. 'It's nothing,' he said, turning away from her, 'nothing at all.'

Jessica started up the engine, drove out of the car-park and, as she waited for the traffic lights on the main road to change, she said, 'Josh?'

'Yes?'

'I don't believe you.'

'What don't you believe?'

'That you would want to please me.'

There was an awkward pause between them.

'Well, you're wrong,' Josh said at last. 'Nothing would give me more pleasure than to please you, only –'

'*But* alert! *But* alert!' Jessica said, shifting into first gear and moving off. 'As clear as daylight I sense one looming large on the horizon.'

He frowned and reached out and gently stroked her neck, just in the bit where he knew she liked it. 'The *but* is I don't think I'm up to the task.'

'And if that isn't the sound of a man back-pedalling his way out of a relationship I don't know what is. You'd better take your hand away or we'll smash into the car in front.'

Josh did as she said and decided to wait until they were home before telling her what he had to say. He wanted to be able to see her face when she realised the truth about him, to read her expression. It was crucial.

When they finally drew up alongside her house, Jessica snatched on the handbrake and switched off the engine. Without looking at him and keeping her eyes straight ahead she suddenly said, 'Is there somebody else? Because if there is, do us both a favour and tell me. All I want to know is where I stand. I don't think I'm being unreasonable.'

Oh hell! she thought, I'm sounding like a paranoid middle-aged wife. Any minute and I'll be telling him to consider the children and the effect it will have on them. But much as she disliked the sound of the words coming out of her mouth, she knew that now that she had started, in true *Mastermind* fashion, she was going to bloody well finish and have her say. He was going to get the full force of her anger for the way he'd treated her. In fact, he was probably going to get Gavin's share as well!

'If there is somebody else I think I have the right to be told,' she went on. 'One minute you're there in my life and the next you're not. I'm not a possessive woman, I just don't like being mucked about. I had enough of that with Gavin and I'm not about to start accepting that kind of situation all over again. And of course, if it's the perennial problem of a man being scared of commitment, then –'

'I'm not scared of commitment,' he interrupted her, magically stemming the flow of her anger, 'at least not in the way you mean.' She felt a hand on her shoulder and he slowly turned her round. 'And there's no one else,' he said firmly. 'I'm appalled that you should think there is. Now be quiet long enough for me to kiss you. And when I've done that, can we go inside? There's something I want to discuss with you.'

She swallowed back her relief. *There wasn't anybody else! Oh, thank you, God!*

'So what do you want to talk about? Devolution? Unification? Or global warming?'

Oh, heaven help her, she was rambling again. What was it about him tonight that was making her so nervous?

He shook his head. 'Nothing as trivial as that.'

Another swallow. 'Oh. Something serious then? In that case it must be the escalating cost of the Millennium Dome.'

'More serious than that.'

'Come off it, nothing's more serious than the greatest white elephant this side of Lord Irvine's pad. Not unless you . . . but surely you can't mean the Charles and Camilla conundrum. We're not going to discuss that, are we?'

Somebody stop me!

'For pity's sake, Jessica, shut up.' He silenced her with a long kiss. 'Now please, can we go inside before I lose my nerve?'

34

The house was in darkness as Jessica unlocked the front door and let them in.

'*What now my love,*' she sang happily, à la Ms Franklin – there was nothing like a good kiss to calm the nerves. She switched on the hall light. '*Now that you've left me –*'

'Please don't sing that,' Josh said abruptly.

'Why?' She laughed. 'Don't you like my singing?'

He followed her into the half-decorated kitchen and watched her throw her bag and keys on to the table. 'It's not that,' he said.

She came towards him and put her arms around his shoulders. 'What, then?'

'It's the lyrics, they're too sentimental ... too melancholic.' They were also too close for comfort. Particularly the lines that came next – *How can I live through another day watching my dreams turning into ashes and all of my hopes into bits of clay* – and with what he was about to say to Jessica and her possible reaction, these were sentiments he didn't want to hear.

She smiled. 'There's nothing wrong with a good dose of schmaltzy melancholy, it's good for the heart.'

He didn't return her smile and as he stared down into her eyes Jessica was shocked to realise how changed he was since she'd last seen him. The youthful, handsome face that had come to be so familiar to her was gone and in its place was the expression of a deeply troubled man. He looked pale. His eyes were sad and sombre, and conveyed an impression of intense dread within him, and as her body rested against his she sensed that he was tense and unyielding. 'What did you want to talk to me about?' she asked nervously, suddenly concluding that the change that had come over him had to be connected with what he wanted to discuss with her. Immediately she'd reached this conclusion her mind began stacking up a set of possible explanations for his apprehension – he had lied earlier in the car about not seeing anyone else, or worse ...

But what could be worse?

What terrible revelation did he have to throw at her that was causing him so much consternation? Come off it, his face didn't so much betray consternation as downright fear.

Oh, my grandfathers, she thought. What was the current nightmare for anyone not in a long-term relationship? What was the spectre at the feast when it came to sex these days?

She slowly released herself from his arms and stepped away from him. No wonder he'd been absent from her life recently. He'd probably been ill ... and not with flu. 'You've got AIDS, haven't you?'

A mixture of horror and incredulous disbelief swept over Josh's face, but before he had a chance to speak the phone rang. It made them both jump.

'I'm letting it ring until you answer me,' Jessica whispered. She was motionless with shock. Rigid with fear. *If he had AIDS then so might she.* Above the insistent shrill of the phone she racked her brain, trying to think if they'd ever had unprotected sex. But they'd always been careful. Even the first time they'd made love, when Josh had been unprepared for the way the night had turned out, she had managed to produce a remnant of her old love life. They had joked about it and pretended to blow the dust away from the small packet. 'Well?' she demanded of him. 'What have you got to say?'

'Please, Jessica, stop being so dramatic and just answer the bloody phone.'

'No! Not until you've told me the truth.'

He shook his head, and went over and picked up the receiver. A few seconds passed before he put it down. 'Jessica,' he said, his face even more anxious than it had been before. 'It's your mother, she's had an accident.'

'Not serious!' Jessica roared at Josh as he sat in the passenger seat of her car once more. 'How the bloody hell do you know it's not serious?'

'Because she said so,' he said calmly. 'She said that she was okay and that you weren't to worry or think the worst.' When he'd answered the phone in Jessica's kitchen, Josh had been surprised to hear a faint voice at the other end of the line saying, 'I've no idea to whom I'm speaking, but don't whatever you do put Jessica on. Just tell her that her mother has had a slight accident and if she'd like to pop over, I'm at home. Be sure to explain that I'm okay and that it's nothing serious.'

He could see now why Jessica's mother had specifically asked not to speak to her daughter. Frantic with worry, Jessica had just rocketed her car through the archway of the development and with her foot jammed down on the accelerator they were speeding along the avenue of chestnut trees.

It was raining harder than when they'd driven back from the cinema and Josh watched her fumble for the switch for the windscreen wipers. 'Some lights might be a good idea,' he suggested.

Jessica flashed him a look of fury. 'Nothing to worry about, my foot,' she muttered while flicking on the headlights. 'Let me tell you, my mother was taken into hospital for what she said was a routine operation and that there was nothing for me to worry about. When I arrived at the hospital I discovered that she was having a triple heart bypass operation. I've since learnt to ignore anything she says.'

'Perhaps you shouldn't. Perhaps it isn't fair to treat her like Cassandra.'

'Like who?'

'Cassandra, the Greek prophetess who was cursed never to be believed.'

'I don't believe I'm hearing this. My mother could well be dying and you're giving me a lecture on Greek mythology? She's my concern, so if I want to worry about her, I bloody well will.'

'Fine, if that's the way you want it.'

'I do. It's exactly how I want it.'

'And by the way, I don't have AIDS, so you needn't worry about that as well. I haven't infected you with anything.'

'Right now I couldn't give a damn whether you have or not,' she fired back. 'All I care about is what in heaven's name my mother's done to herself.' She gripped the steering wheel knowing that she was behaving atrociously, that Josh didn't deserve this, but so long as she was able to take out her anger on somebody it meant that she was just about in control of the situation.

She pulled up in front of Willow Cottage and before Josh had even climbed out of the car was letting herself into the house with the key that she'd insisted Anna give her some weeks ago. She called out to her mother.

'I'm up here,' came a faint reply.

Jessica took the stairs two at a time.

She found Anna on the floor in her bedroom. A pair of step-ladders and the contents of an upturned box of tools lay all around her, as well as the phone from the bedside table.

'I'm sorry, Jessica, but I'm afraid I've broken it.' Her mother nodded towards a decapitated china statue that Jessica had given her when she was a child, the head of which had rolled across the room and now lay with its nose tucked into the carpet pile in front of the dressing-table. 'I caught it with my foot on the window-sill,' Anna added, as though this made everything clear. 'I think I may also have broken my arm,' she said as Jessica crouched beside her, 'and my ribs don't feel so good. Oh, you must be Josh.'

Josh came into the room. 'Hi,' he said with an easy smile and, joining them on the floor, he started to pick up the scattered tools, 'you look like you've been busy.'

'I do my best,' Anna said. She returned his smile and passed him a screwdriver that was clutched in her hand.

'Any chance of making it to the bed?'

'Well you're a fast one, I must say. But I'm not sure Jessica would approve. She looks furious as it is.'

'Of course I'm furious,' exploded Jessica, her anxiety now given rein to turn into full-blown angry relief. 'How many times have I told you to be careful? How could you do this!'

Anna smiled at Josh. 'How long do you give her before she says I told you so?'

'And I'd have every right to say that. This is serious, Mum, you could have killed yourself.'

'What, and missed the opportunity to meet this delightful young man?' Anna said with a wink at Josh. 'No fear.'

Jessica looked even more enraged and opened her mouth to remonstrate further, but Josh intervened. 'Jessica,' he said firmly, 'this isn't helping. Now, Mrs Lloyd, do you think you can manage the stairs? From what I can see of your wrist it most certainly is broken and I think we should drive you straight to a hospital.'

Tony was in no mood to speak to Bloody Rita. He didn't make any effort to be polite to her, but handed the phone over to Amanda and went upstairs for a shower. He'd had a tedious day that had got him nowhere. Bradley-Dewhurst-the-Butcher's-Boy had set up a tele-conference late in the afternoon and it had served no purpose other than to delay everybody from getting off home.

On his way to the bathroom he hovered outside Hattie's door. He pushed it open a crack, just to see if she was asleep.

'Is that you, Daddy?'

He smiled and went in. 'Come on, you little pixie, you should have been fast asleep hours ago.'

'I can't get to sleep.'

He smoothed out the rumpled duvet, then sat on the edge of the bed. 'And why's that?' He was instantly worried that maybe her new school was bothering her. He knew that Hattie was by nature a confident child, but it was a dangerous thing to overestimate her ability to accept change. It seemed pretty unlikely, however, that there was anything wrong at school as only yesterday her teacher had told Amanda how well Hattie was fitting in.

'You're not worried about anything, are you?' he asked.

She nodded.

He stroked her hair. 'Is it school?'

She shook her head.

'What, then?'

She pulled him down to her and whispered into his ear, 'It's Grandma Rita.'

'What about Grandma Rita?' he whispered back.

'Amanda says she might be coming to stay with us.'

Tony sat upright. 'That's news to me,' he said.

'Amanda said you wouldn't mind.'

'And when did Amanda discuss this with you?'

'In the car coming home from school. She said it was a surprise, though. It's not a very nice surprise, is it?'

Tony smiled.

'Does she have to come?'

'We'll see. Now off to sleep with you.' He kissed her forehead, then squeezed her hand.

'You won't tell Amanda I said anything, will you? I think she might be cross with me.'

'Of course not. Now go to sleep.'

He was almost out of the room when she sat up and said, 'Daddy, what's a boarding-school?'

He frowned and came back to the bed. 'What do you mean?'

'I heard Amanda talking to Grandma Rita on the phone about something called a boarding-school.'

'Did you indeed?'

'Would I like it?'

He shook his head. 'No,' he said grimly, 'no, you wouldn't. And nor would I.'

'Amanda told Grandma Rita that it would be best for me.'

'Well, she's wrong. Very, very wrong.'

'So what is a boarding-school?'

'It's not something you ever need to think about. Now, it really is time for you to go to sleep. Good-night.' He kissed her again and wondered at the ruthlessness of his wife, that she could plot and scheme about his daughter's future behind his back.

Later, when Tony came out of the shower, he found Amanda in their bedroom sorting through a large plastic laundry basket of ironing. She was a meticulous ironer, everything was steamed and pressed, even his socks. 'How's your mother?' he fished.

'Fine. She sends her love.'

Like hell she does! Bloody Rita would no more send him her love than she would dance naked through the streets of Alderley Edge where she lived. 'That's nice of her,' he said, totally convinced that Hattie must have been right and that Amanda was now switching on to 'softening-up mode' before announcing that Rita was coming to stay. 'We haven't seen her for a while,' he added, 'what's she been up to?' – *something sweet and innocent like evenings out with the Ku-Klux-Klan?*

227

'Oh, just the usual; bridge and bowling. The bowling club's hoping to go off on tour again.'

'Sounds good.' *Especially if it were a six-month tour of Australia! The further away the better.*

He didn't trust himself to cross-examine Amanda about the boarding-school issue and so got into bed. Well, she could forget that little scheme. He would never allow it to happen.

He closed his eyes and listened to Amanda moving about the room, tidying away clothes into cupboards and drawers. He wondered what Kate was doing. He had no way of knowing what had happened to her since he'd seen her yesterday morning. He didn't know whether she and Alec had resolved things between them, or if Alec was still refusing to accept his child. He hadn't mentioned any of this to Amanda – the thought of her gossiping about Kate was too much for him. He hoped, though, that if Kate needed any help she would feel able to come to him. He'd given her his work number, just in case, and throughout today he had stupidly hoped it was her each time his phone had rung. What kind of help he thought he'd be able to give he wasn't sure. Possibly what he wanted to offer Kate would only complicate matters.

And what exactly was he offering?

He was a married man with a child; the sort of man who would never have imagined himself capable of cheating on his wife. But that was exactly what he'd planned to do, wasn't it? When he'd gone to see Kate yesterday morning he had knocked on her door with the sole expectation of tempting her into an affair with him.

And given half a chance he still would.

He turned on to his side and pulled the duvet up over his head. He wanted the world to disappear.

No, that wasn't true.

He just wanted Amanda and Alec to disappear.

35

A Casual Affair was getting nowhere – Clare and Miles had spent the past week locked in one another's arms and as passionate embraces went, theirs was proving to be the longest in history.

Following Anna's accident on Tuesday night, Jessica had moved into Willow Cottage to look after her mother. She had brought Clare and Miles along with her on her laptop, but much as she cared about their will-they-won't-they relationship, she had found she didn't have a spare minute to devote to them, or if she were honest, the inclination. Her heart just wasn't in it. She was too preoccupied with her mother.

She had thought that Anna's wilfulness would be dramatically reduced by having an arm in a sling, but if anything, the plaster cast was proving a challenge to her obstinate mother – she had even threatened Jessica with it.

'Ask me one more time if I'm comfortable, Jessica, and I shall bring this wretched cast down on your head.'

It wasn't an easy situation, but as Jessica prodded another log into place in the grate with a pair of old brass tongs, she knew that it was down to her to make her mother see sense and keep her from straying from the safe confines of her armchair by the fire.

She put down the tongs and glanced out of the window. The weather, she reflected, was as jittery as she was. Yesterday had been clear and bright, with a warm September sun drying away the early-morning dew and mist, but today a north-easterly wind had chilled the air and there was no sign of the sun as it hid behind the thick banks of grey clouds that threw down the occasional downpour. It was a cold, wet, miserable day. It felt more like winter than autumn and just before lunch Jessica had lit the fire in the sitting-room and insisted Anna sit beside it. But Anna hadn't wanted to and had accused Jessica of treating her like a child. 'That's because you're behaving like one,' Jessica had retorted, 'now please, do as I say.'

Jessica moved away from the fire. She sat in the chair opposite her mother and began pouring out their tea.

It was Friday afternoon and so far they'd been cooped up together at Willow Cottage for three whole days. Jessica didn't know how much longer she could cope. She was exhausted and irritable with worry. The thought that Anna's accident could have ended so differently was never far from her mind. But it hadn't been fatal, she had to keep reminding herself; a broken arm and a cracked rib weren't life-threatening; her mother would be all right. She leant forward and placed a cup of tea on the little table beside her mother's chair.

Anna put down the magazine Jessica had bought for her, which she wasn't really reading, and added it to the pile that had been thoughtfully placed within arm's reach. 'Thank you,' she said, wishing that she actually meant the words. She felt as grateful to Jessica as a blind man would if somebody had helpfully switched on the light for him. She really didn't know how much more of her daughter she could put up with.

What she regretted most about her little mishap – which had happened while she had been trying to fix a window lock in her bedroom – was that it had brought out the worst in both herself and Jessica. In her desire to help, Jessica had turned into a monstrous gaoler and she herself had become a dispirited prisoner with only one aim in her life: to escape.

She raised her cup to her lips, stared across the mahogany table in front of the fire and looked at her daughter's unhappy face. She looked ragged and worn-out. Clearly the situation was doing neither of them any good. They resembled a middle-aged couple who'd been together for a thousand years and now had nothing to say to one another. You saw them all the time, glum-faced people mindlessly stirring cups of over-brewed tea in British Home Stores restaurants all over the country.

Something had to be done.

And soon.

'You know, I'm beginning to feel much better,' Anna said brightly.

The immediate look of scorn on Jessica's face silenced her from trying her luck with suggesting that she could now manage on her own and wasn't it time Jessica went back to her own home?

She stared forlornly out of the window at her deserted garden. How she longed to roll up her sleeves and get her hands dirty. It was most frustrating, especially when there was so much to do. Plums were dropping like manna from heaven from the fruit trees; the stakes and ties for the dahlias needed checking in case the wind got up; the roses were in need of deadheading and it was more than two weeks since she'd last sprayed them for mildew, and goodness only knew what the greenfly were up to while her back was turned. And there were all those dwarf daffodil and tulip bulbs waiting to be planted in the rockery she'd built earlier in the summer. Dermot was all very well, and the lad did his best, but it was her garden and nobody loved it as she did.

If only Jessica were green-fingered, at least then there might have been a chance of her putting something of her over-zealous caring energy into looking after the garden instead of plaguing her.

No, that wasn't fair, she thought, Jessica was only doing what she thought was best.

'Are you sure you shouldn't be working?' Anna tried again – the prisoner had her eye on the imaginary set of keys dangling from her gaoler's belt.

Jessica lowered her cup and looked at her mother. 'You're more important,' she said simply.

The keys were once again moved out of the prisoner's grasp.

'But what about your deadline? You know how much you worry about delivering a manuscript on time.' Desperate now, the prisoner was considering a swift blow to the gaoler's Achilles heel – Jessica's obsession with meeting her publisher's deadline.

'That's not for ages, not until next year, and anyway I can give Piers and Cara a ring, they'll understand.'

Anna frowned, then a tiny idea took hold. An idea that made her realise that she had hit upon a means of tunnelling her way out of her prison cell ... and all she would need was a sneaky peep at Jessica's address book. But how could she get Jessica out of the way long enough to do that?

Her question was answered sooner than she'd thought possible when the sound of the doorbell broke the dreadful silence that had cloaked the house since her well-meaning daughter had moved in.

Jessica put down her cup and quickly went to answer it. Anna listened to find out who it was – if only it could be a passing member of the SAS expertly trained in dealing with hostage situations. It was a few seconds before she recognised the voice: Josh. A smile spread over her face. Her immediate thought was to leap out of her chair and invite him in, thereby providing a distraction so that she could slip upstairs to Jessica's room and snoop through her things for the precious address book. But she knew it was more than her life was worth even to move from the chair and anyway, if she were painfully honest, the only leaping she was capable of doing was a leap of the imagination.

'If that's Josh, don't keep him on the doorstep, bring him in,' she called out to Jessica. 'It'll be nice to have a visitor' – *yes, it would break the suffocating monotony.*

'Hello, Mrs Lloyd,' Josh said when Jessica brought him into the sitting-room. He held out a pot of white chrysanthemums. 'I saw these on the way home from work and thought you might like them. How are you feeling?'

'Please, you must call me Anna, and I'm feeling much better, thank you.'

Jessica tutted loudly and took the flowers from Josh. She placed them on the oak dresser, alongside the half-eaten box of Thornton's Continental chocolates that Josh had brought earlier in the week. 'She'd be a darn sight better if she kept still for two minutes,' she scolded.

Anna winked at Josh and he smiled back at her.

'Jessica, why don't you make a fresh pot of tea? I'm sure Josh must be thirsty.'

Jessica looked at Josh, her expression clearly indicating that she expected him to refuse any such hospitality.

'That would be great,' he said.

Anna smiled triumphantly and watched her gaoler pick up the tray from the table and retreat from the room. When they were alone she carefully leant forward and whispered to Josh, 'You've got to help me, she's driving me mad.'

'Earl Grey or ordinary?'

Anna jerked her head towards the doorway where Jessica was standing with a grim scowl on her face.

'Ordinary will be fine,' Josh said smoothly. 'What's the problem?' he asked, when he and Anna were sure they were alone.

'She won't leave me be, not even for a few minutes. It's not so much a case of mother's little helper as mother's little tormentor.'

He laughed.

'I'm serious, Josh, she's turned into a monster. I can't do anything without her fussing. She watches me the whole time.'

'So what do you want me to do?'

'I need you to get her out of the house for a few minutes, take her for a walk, anything, so long as it gives me an opportunity to make a call to somebody who'll come to my rescue. Will you do that?'

'I'll try, though I'm not sure it'll work. I'm not exactly her favourite person at the moment.'

'Mm ... I noticed that the other day when you called. What have you done? You've not two-timed her, have you? She's not very keen on men who do that.'

He shook his head. 'No, nothing like that.'

'What, then?'

Josh hesitated. 'I've ... I've hidden something from her, something important which I was about to explain to her on the night of your accident.'

'How intriguing. What is it? Are you really a world-famous drug baron lying low here in Cholmford?'

'Who's a drug baron lying low?' asked Jessica, coming in with a tray and banging it down on the table between Josh and her mother.

'Nobody,' Josh answered, sitting back in his chair. He watched Jessica drop on to the sofa. She looked tired and there was no denying the coldness she was displaying towards him. She had been the same when he'd called on Wednesday on his way home after work. Ostensibly he'd dropped in to see how her mother was, but mainly because he wanted a chance to talk to Jessica. She had made it impossible for him to do so, busying herself in the kitchen with cooking supper for herself and Anna. Even when he'd started to say that he wanted to finish the conversation they'd started on Tuesday night she had pushed past him saying that she didn't have time to listen. She had been close to crying and, sensing that his presence was adding to her distress and the apparent antagonism between them, he had said goodbye and left. He couldn't help feeling confused. It was as if she were blaming him for her mother's accident.

He'd called again today, fool that he was, because he had decided to ask Jessica if she'd go with him to Mo's party that evening. He didn't hold out much hope that she'd say yes, and if the look on her face as she poured out his tea was anything to go by he'd be lucky to escape without having his ears boxed.

'Thank you,' he said when she handed him his cup. 'How's the book going?' He hoped the question would place him on firmer ground than he'd been on previously. He soon found it did no such thing.

'Hah!' she said scornfully, 'as if I've got time for writing.'

He exchanged the briefest of looks with Anna and wondered how he could now suggest that Jessica had time for an evening out. Feet first seemed the only way. He took a fortifying sip of his tea and said, 'I know it's short notice, but I don't suppose you'd like to come to a party with me tonight, would you?'

Anna marvelled at Josh. In the face of her daughter's open hostility towards him the man had real courage. She held her breath and waited for Jessica's reply.

It came in the form of a tut of derision. 'How can you expect me to leave Anna all alone?'

'Oh, what nonsense,' Anna chipped in smartly — *just think of it, a whole evening to herself!* 'I think it's a wonderful idea and just what you need to perk you up.'

'Perk me up?' Jessica said indignantly. 'Who says I need perking up?'

'Not perking up *per se*,' Anna said quickly, 'but it'll give you something to think about other than worrying over me.' *Oh what bliss, to be allowed to settle down to an evening of telly without being interrupted by Jessica continually suggesting that what she really needed was an early night. She'd stretch out on the sofa with a great big martini, at the same time plundering Josh's box of chocolates.* 'I really think you should go,' she added wishfully.

'I'm sure you do,' muttered Jessica, 'so that you can get up to heaven knows what mischief in my absence. I wouldn't put it past you to knock up a quick loft extension while I'm out.'

Anna feigned horror at such an idea. 'Cross my heart and hope to die, I wouldn't get in to any mischief. I've learnt my lesson.'

'And I promise not to keep you out too late, Jessica,' Josh said. He turned to Anna. 'I'll make sure she's back in time to help you into bed.'

'Well, that all seems to be arranged to everybody's satisfaction then,' Anna said happily, secretly hoping that Josh wouldn't stick to his bargain too literally. It was Friday night and there was bound to be a good late-night film on one of the channels.

Jessica stared suspiciously at Anna, then at Josh. 'Yes,' she said slowly, 'it does seem to be arranged to your satisfaction, doesn't it? Anyone would think you'd cooked this up between the pair of you.'

At eight o'clock Josh returned to Willow Cottage. As Jessica climbed into the Shogun he felt the coolness of her manner towards him increase. Once he'd negotiated the narrow bridge over the canal and was driving along the dark lane he said, 'Your mother will be fine, and if there is any problem she's got the number for my mobile.'

'I know that,' Jessica said stiffly.

Without a word Josh suddenly brought the car to a stop. He switched off the engine, turned and faced Jessica. 'Okay,' he said, 'what's this all about? What terrible thing have I done that's caused you to be so cold and rude? You were warmer to me that night when you thought I was the mad axeman of Cholmford.'

Jessica refused to look at him. She didn't say anything either.

'Look, Jessica, a few days ago you were a different woman. Then you were sexy and sarky and made me laugh, now . . . well, now you're moody and miserable; what's got into you?'

'I would have thought it was perfectly obvious. I've got more important things on my mind than providing you with a non-stop twenty-four-hour programme of entertainment. And for your information, unless used with care, alliteration is best avoided.'

He smiled. 'I'll bear that in mind in the future.'

'Good. You do that.'

'Any more advice for me?'

'Yes. You can stop encouraging my mother to flirt with you. She doesn't need a toy boy and I'd hate to read about her in the *Sun*. I can see the headlines now: *Senior Citizen in Sleazy Sex Scandal!*'

'I thought you said alliteration was best avoided.'

She turned and looked at him and he saw that there was a glimmer of a smile on her face, and hoping that maybe he had broken the ice between them he reached out and touched her hands in her lap. 'You love your mother very much, don't you?'

The unexpected frankness of his words cut through Jessica's defences and the pain of the past few days rose up and engulfed her. From nowhere a tiny tear appeared in the corner of her left eye. She lowered her head and bit her lip to stop it from betraying the fact that she was so close to crying. She felt angry with herself. Angry, because crying wasn't something she went in for. It was an emotion she had managed without for as long as she could remember. Crying equalled weakness and she wasn't weak. She was strong, always had been. Just like her mother. It was what had held them together when her father died. 'I need you to be strong,' her mother had said that night after the funeral. It was her only real memory of the day; her mother sitting on the edge of her bed, holding her hand, telling her everything would be all right, they just had to be strong.

She heard Josh unbuckle his seat-belt and when he moved nearer and held her in his arms she knew she couldn't hold back the tears any longer.

'I love her so much,' she sobbed into his shoulder, 'and I'm terrified of losing her. I haven't been a good daughter to her, I've never been there for her.'

He held her tenderly and gently stroked her hair.

'I'm all she's got,' Jessica continued, 'it's down to me to take care of her.'

'But you are.'

She pulled away from him and fumbled for a tissue in her bag. 'No, I'm not,' she said, 'I'm making it worse for her. I'm no good at this saintly caring stuff, I know I'm not.'

'You just need to relax, that's all.'

'But how? I try, but I end up behaving like some ghastly fifties-style matron and bossing Mum about, and biting everyone else's head off . . . you included.'

'Me in particular,' he said.

She smiled. 'I'm sorry. I've been horrible to you, haven't I?'

'Yes,' he agreed.

'I was particularly horrid to you the other night, I'm sorry that I shouted and said all those things. What was it you wanted to talk to me about?'

He ran his hand through her hair and let it linger on the nape of her neck. *Now, tell her now*, he willed himself. *Go on. Just say it. Get it over and done with. Just open your mouth and say, Jessica, I've got MS and I'm sorry that I've lied to you.* 'It'll keep,' he said. He'd tell her tomorrow. Tomorrow, when she wasn't so upset about her mother. He slowly moved away from her, then turned the key in the ignition. 'What you need is a party to cheer you up,' he said.

'Don't you mean to perk me up?'

'That too.'

But once again Josh was to find that the best-laid plans have a habit of going entirely their own way.

36

Back at Willow Cottage, Anna was busy putting her own plan into operation.

Earlier, while Jessica had been in the bathroom getting ready to go out, she had sneaked into her daughter's bedroom and had found what she needed. She was now tapping the number from Jessica's address book into the phone, hardly daring to hope that it would be answered.

It was, almost immediately, which gave her no time to consider what she was going to say.

'Yes,' barked out a cross voice at the other end of the line.

'Good evening, is that Piers Lambert?'

'Of course it is, who else would be answering my private line at this time of night?'

'My word, you're just as Jessica described you.'

'I beg your pardon? Who is this?'

'My name is Anna Lloyd, I'm Jessica's mother.'

'Are you indeed? And what precisely can I do for you?'

Anna told him.

Mo shared a large Victorian house in Rusholme with two female engineering students, a hairdresser – who frequently carried out ground-breaking experiments on Mo's hair, often with hair-raising results – and a night-club bouncer. Josh had been to the house just once before. He'd driven Mo home from work one day when she'd been ill and had come away thinking that its colourful inhabitants made the characters of *This Life* look like wooden extras from *Crossroads*.

There was nowhere to park directly outside Mo's place, but further up the road there was a parking space between an electric-blue VW Beetle and a wreck of a Fiat Panda. Josh squeezed his Shogun into the space and noticed his brother's car across the road where it was parked in front of a house that looked like it had been burnt out; all the windows were boarded up. He wondered if Charlie had persuaded Rachel to come. It probably wasn't Rachel's kind of party. She struck Josh as being more of a canapé-and-spritzer partygoer.

'Am I going to feel very old and out of it here?' Jessica broke into his thoughts. 'You did say Mo was only twenty-five. Won't all her friends be horribly young and trendy?'

Josh smiled. 'Horribly young and trendy.'

Jessica groaned. 'I knew it. It'll be wall-to-wall global hip-hop, oversized jeans with crotches dragging on the floor, drugs in your face and everyone punctuating their sentences with the word shag.'

Josh smiled again and got out of the car. When Jessica joined him on the pavement and he'd activated the alarm, he said, 'You wouldn't be judging others by your own twenty-something behaviour, would you?'

'Certainly not. When I was Mo's age I needed a clear head to chase all those hunks up and down the slopes of Colorado.'

He put his arm around her. 'I'm not sure I like the sound of that.'

She looked up at him with a smile. 'Why's that?'

He returned her gaze. 'Why do you think?'

'I must be particularly dense tonight, I need it spelling out for me.'

'I've always believed that actions speak louder than words.' And manoeuvring her back against the side of the car, Josh pressed his body against hers and kissed her for the longest of moments. 'Now does that give you any kind of a clue?' he asked.

'It was a bit cryptic in places.'

He kissed her again. Longer and deeper. 'We don't have to go to this party,' he said, after they'd been disturbed by an elderly woman passing with her dog, 'we could go back to your place and –'

She laughed. 'Crawford, get your desire in check and lead me on to the party.'

The hum and thud of a thousand decibels spilled out across the untidy front garden as the door was opened to them by a young black man who was wearing a Jimi Hendrix hairdo and a magenta-coloured velvet suit. He ushered them through the house to a large kitchen where a crowd of people were gathered round a selection of bottles that could have stocked a small off-licence.

'Help yourself, man,' Jimi Hendrix said to Josh. He left them to it.

'What do you fancy?' Josh asked Jessica.

'Some kind of white wine would be nice … *man*.'

Josh smiled and began opening a new bottle of wine – he'd heard enough morning-after stories from Mo to know that it wouldn't be wise to trust any of the opened bottles. When he'd poured out two plastic cups of plonk, he said, 'Come on, let's go and find the birthday girl.'

They found her outside in the long thin back garden, where some of the trees and bushes had been decorated with fairy lights. There were flaming torches pushed into the ground and candles flickering on all the window-sills of the house. Mo was easy to spot and Josh burst out laughing when he saw her. She was bouncing on a trampoline and showing off a pair of frilly patriotic knickers to a delighted crowd of onlookers. She saw Josh and waved at him mid-bounce. He waved back and caught sight of his brother in the crowd gathered round the trampoline, and surprise, surprise, there didn't seem to be any sign of Rachel. Holding Jessica by the arm, he took her over to meet Charlie.

'At long last we meet,' Charlie said warmly, 'I've heard a lot about you.'

'Not as much as I've heard about you.' Jessica laughed, realising that this was the good-looking man she'd seen with the suspected take-away and the flashy sports car. As brothers went, the resemblance wasn't that strong between them. If she had to guess which was the elder, she'd say it was Charlie. She wondered if he was envious of Josh's youthful looks and the complete absence of grey from his thick dark-brown hair – Charlie's, she noticed, was speckled with grey and was showing signs of receding.

'What's with the trampoline?' asked Josh.

'It's a present from her parents,' Charlie said, 'apparently she always wanted a trampoline as a child, but it's only now that they thought they could trust her with one.'

'How wrong could they be.' Josh smiled.

Jessica turned her attention back to Mo. She'd been joined on the trampoline by a beautiful-looking Asian man, with a long plait of silky black hair swishing behind him like the tail of a frisky pony.

'Who's the guy with her?' asked Jessica.

'That's Sid,' Josh said, 'he's our designer. His parents are from Hong Kong and he's invaluable on any of our buying trips to the Far East.'

'He's also mad about Mo,' Charlie added.

'They look like they'd make a great couple,' Jessica said as she observed the antics going on in front of her.

'And so they would, but unfortunately Mo carries the torch of love for somebody –'

'Give it a rest, Charlie,' Josh interrupted. 'Jessica doesn't want to hear about that.' And draining his plastic cup he said, 'Anyone for another drink?'

'No thanks,' Jessica said – she'd barely touched hers.

'If you're going that way, you can get me something non-alcoholic.' Charlie handed Josh his empty cup.

'So who's Mo carrying a torch for?' Jessica asked Charlie, as soon as Josh was out of earshot.

'Yonder brother, of course.'

Jessica raised an eyebrow. 'And he's never ... you know ...'

'Good Lord, no. Mo's been with us since she was seventeen. I guess we both look on her as a kid sister.'

'Which she probably hates.'

'If she does, she's never shown it.'

'But then, as we all know, men are not the most perceptive or sensitive of beings.'

'So how's your mother?'

Jessica laughed out loud. 'Now you're scaring me. In that one simple question you hope to prove that not only do you and Josh communicate with one another, but that you can be sensitive enough to a complete stranger to enquire after a relative's well-being. I like it, the Crawford brothers are the exception to the rule, they have finer feelings just like women.'

'So, how *is* your mother?' Charlie pursued, entertained by Jessica's forthright manner.

Jessica frowned. 'I don't know is the honest answer. She's got a broken arm and a cracked rib, and tries to make out that she's as fit as a fiddle. If she had her way, she'd dispense with her cast and sling, wrap a bit of sticking plaster round her wrist, pull on her gardening gloves and dig up half of Cheshire.'

'Poor you. It's not easy caring for people, is it?'

'You're not kidding,' but then, catching the reflective tone in Charlie's voice and remembering what Josh had told her about his brother, she said, 'I'm sure you'd be easy to look after.'

He gave her a puzzled look. 'Let's hope I'm never in that situation.'

'Ooh, my legs feel all wobbly, like I've been on a boat.' It was Mo and she was breathless and perspiring from all the bouncing. She reached out to Charlie to steady herself.

'Happy birthday,' he said, propping her up and kissing her cheek.

'Where's Josh?'

'Doing what he's best at, fetching drinks. This is Jessica, by the way.'

'Hi,' Jessica said. As Mo turned to face her she was conscious that the young girl was sizing her up. Jessica was surprised how antagonistic she felt towards Mo. When Charlie had said that Mo had a bit of a thing for Josh, her stomach had done silly things like lurch about. It had reminded her of days gone by when she had discovered Gavin had been seeing other women. She glanced around her, suddenly wanting Josh back by her side, where she could see him ... where she could keep an eye on him.

She saw him making his way through the crowd of guests and experienced a wave of relief. No, it wasn't relief, it was something else. But what? She stared at his limping figure as he approached and tried to assimilate what her response to the sight of him really meant. Could the combination of that handsome face and those intense brown eyes really be held responsible for making her feel so extraordinarily weak at the knees? Could that tall slim body truly hold so much attraction for her? Could the thought of those hands that were so gentle and instinctive when they caressed her body actually cause her mouth to go so dry? And while they were on the subject, that mouth of his had a charm all of its own. As kissers went, he was the best. Definitely in a class of his own. When God had been handing out the attributes guaranteed to make a man physically irresistible to a woman, he'd given Josh the top-drawer stuff. There'd been no stinting. Josh, my lad, God would have said when he'd seen what he'd created, with you I am well pleased.

Jessica smiled to herself and suddenly realised that she'd stopped breathing, that her throat was tight with desire. She gulped back her wine, draining the plastic cup in one go. And as she did, she found herself admitting that it wasn't a mere physical desire that she felt for Josh. It was much more. And it scared her.

'Hello, Mo,' he said, when he finally drew level. He handed Charlie his drink, then put his hand in his jacket pocket. He pulled out a small package. 'Happy birthday, it's from Charlie and me.'

Mo's face broke into a smile as her eager fingers slipped off the wrapping paper to reveal a box. She opened it hurriedly and lifted away a layer of cotton wool. 'It's beautiful,' she cried, holding up a silver bangle. 'I love it! Thank you so much.' She kissed Charlie without thinking, but approached Josh more shyly.

Once again Jessica's stomach gave a sharp involuntary lurch.

At eleven o'clock, when it was too chilly to stay outside in the garden – unless you were prepared to keep warm by flinging yourself about on the trampoline – Jessica and Josh went inside, to a room that on his previous visit Josh was convinced had been the sitting-room. Now it was empty of most of its furniture, the lights had been lowered and people were dancing to boppy music blaring from two enormous loudspeakers.

'We ought to be thinking about going,' Josh said. The last thing he needed was Jessica wanting him to dance with her. He'd been standing for most of the night and his leg was good for nothing now; his knee ached and every now and again a stab of pain seared through him. 'I did promise your mother I wouldn't get you home too late,' he added.

'Oh,' said Jessica, disappointed. 'Couldn't we have one quick boogie?' She'd drunk just enough wine to think that maybe her mother could manage a short while longer without her.

Josh hesitated. 'I ... I'm not very good at dancing.'

Jessica laughed. 'You don't have to be.' And when the record abruptly changed to a slow, smoochy number she said, 'Come on, I actually recognise this, it's Elton John, isn't it?'

'George Michael, you idiot.'

'I knew that.' She took his hands and pulled him towards the other couples.

He held her close as they came together and hoped that she wouldn't notice the lack of movement on his part.

'You feel tense,' she remarked.

'Just tired,' he said and, looking for a way to distract her, he asked, 'Any chance of a kiss?'

'Only the one?'

'Quality, not quantity, that's what I always say.'

'Here goes then.'

And by the time they'd kissed their way through 'You Have Been Loved', Jessica no longer felt scared by her earlier realisation.

After all, what possible harm could she come to by falling in love with Josh Crawford?

While Josh looked for Mo to say goodbye, Jessica went in search of the bathroom. There were numerous bodies to pick her way over as she climbed the stairs and when she reached the landing she found Mo all alone and slumped on the floor. She looked ghastly and was holding a wet flannel to her forehead. 'I don't think Bacardi should be so vigorously shaken,' she moaned.

'Can I get you anything?' Jessica asked, crouching beside her. Suddenly Mo didn't seem like a rival any more. In fact, she seemed more like a poor sick child.

'It was probably the pizza I had afterwards that did it,' Mo whimpered. 'Anchovies don't agree with me. I never learn. The five triple vodkas and Cokes was pushing it a bit, I guess.'

Jessica tried not to laugh. 'Do you think some cold water might be in order?'

Mo groaned. 'Death. That's what I need. Nothing heroic, mind. Just a small affair, me and the grim reaper, face to face. I'd go quietly, I'd be no trouble.'

'And what about the funeral? Any ideas on that?'

'Yes. I want a Princess Di do, lots of flowers and fuss. And I'd like Josh to follow the coffin if that's okay with you.'

'I'm sure he'd oblige.'

Mo lowered the flannel from her face and looked at Jessica. 'You're a lucky bitch. I'd give anything to be in your shoes. You will take care of him, won't you?'

Jessica frowned. 'He doesn't seem to be the sort who needs taking care of.'

Mo tried to smile knowingly, but it came out as a sickly grimace. She returned the wet flannel to her forehead and groaned. 'He pretends he doesn't, but really he does. It's what makes him so bloody moody at times. But then you must have noticed that, one minute he's up and the next he's down.'

Jessica shook her head. 'I'm not sure what you're talking about.'

'It's what MS does to you. And before you jump to the wrong conclusion, I don't love him out of sympathy, I loved him way before his illness was diagnosed. I just hope you're not going to dump him like the last girlfriend did. Oh, bugger, I'm going to be sick again.'

Jessica watched Mo stagger into the bathroom just in time. She slowly went back downstairs and with each body she climbed over she asked herself a question.

Why had he lied?

Why had he wanted to keep it from her?

Was this what he had been trying to talk to her about?

And if it was, why had he turned it into such a big deal?

And what the hell was multiple sclerosis anyway?

She suddenly felt angry, as if Josh had been cheating on her.

When she reached the bottom of the stairs she found him waiting for her by the front door. Charlie was with him.

'We couldn't find Mo,' Josh said, when he saw her, 'somebody said she wasn't feeling well.'

'I've just been talking to her,' Jessica said coolly. 'In fact, we had a surprisingly interesting conversation. Revealing is perhaps the word I'd use. Josh, why did you make me believe that your brother suffered from multiple sclerosis? Why didn't you tell me the truth?'

37

Somebody had turned up the volume of the music and above the sonic-boom effect of Oasis's 'Roll With It' coming at them down the narrow length of the hallway Charlie said, 'I think this is best sorted out between the pair of you.' And without another word, or a backward glance, he opened the front door and shot out into the night.

'Well?' said Jessica, 'I'm waiting for an explanation.'

Josh leant against the wall behind him and lowered his head. 'Not here,' was all he said.

They drove in brooding silence through the streets of Rusholme and only when they joined the A34 did Josh say anything. 'I'll explain it all when we get home.' His face was dark and sombre. He passed her his mobile phone. 'Perhaps you'd better ring your mother and check that she's okay and tell her that you'll be later than you thought.'

When they reached Cholmford Hall Mews, he parked alongside his house and let them in. He went straight to the kitchen where he poured out two large glasses of Southern Comfort. He added some ice and passed one to Jessica. He took her through to the sitting-room. 'Sit down,' he said, gesturing towards the sofa. He didn't join her, but walked stiffly over to a chair and sank gratefully into it, all his energy now gone. He knocked back half his drink in one quick mouthful. 'So what's your first question?' he said, his eyes fixed firmly on the glass in his hand.

Jessica stared thoughtfully across the room at him. 'I'm not sure,' she said. As they'd driven away from the party she'd had all sorts of questions in mind to fire at Josh, but his uncommunicative manner in the car had made it very clear to her that he didn't want to talk to her then and she'd respected his wishes. But now that she was being given the opportunity to speak she found that she couldn't. It was the sight of his obvious discomfort that was unnerving her. He looked so downcast. So defeated. She'd never seen him like this before.

'Don't you want to know why I concealed it from you?' he asked. 'I would have thought you were dying to know that.' There was a hardness to his voice that made his question sound like an accusation. He still didn't look at her.

'Again I'm not sure,' she said. 'I don't understand why you've turned your illness into such a big deal.'

Now he did look up and straight at her. 'Because for me it is a big deal. Don't you know *anything* about MS?'

She shook her head. 'I told you that the night of my migraine attack, don't you remember –?'

'Yes,' he snapped loudly, 'I remember that perfectly well, there's nothing wrong with my memory. I'm not that far gone.' He lowered his eyes and ran a hand through his hair. 'I'm sorry, I didn't mean to . . .' He drained his glass and banged it down on the table in front of him. 'I'm really sorry, Jessica. This is so bloody important to me and I just seem to be making a hash of it.'

She gave him a tiny smile of encouragement. 'Why don't you tell me why you felt the need to hide your illness from me? When we've dealt with that you can explain what MS is. How does that sound?'

He let out his breath, surprised how reasonable she was being. 'How about another drink?'

'Just get on with it,' she said gently.

He ran a hand over his chin. 'Okay, here goes. But first, I want you to know that I did try telling you . . . it was the night your mother had her accident.'

'I guessed that.'

'I'd spent the best part of the day planning what to say.' He paused, then got to his feet. 'It's no good, I definitely need another drink. You sure you won't join me?'

She shook her head. When he came back into the room he sat down again and she watched him nervously turn the glass round in his hands. The room was so quiet she could hear the cubes of ice chinking against the sides of the glass. She wanted to prompt him, but knew she mustn't – whatever it was he had to say, he had to say it in his own time.

At last he spoke. 'The reason I felt so compelled to hide my MS from you,' he said in a low voice, 'is because my last girlfriend beat a hasty retreat the moment I explained it to her and . . . and I thought that so long as you didn't know there was anything wrong with me I could carry on seeing you.'

'And is that what you expect me to do now,' she asked quietly, 'to run off at the double?'

He shrugged. 'Maybe not right away, but in time, yes.'

'Then you have a very poor opinion of people, Josh. What gives you the right to put a ceiling on my feelings for you?'

He looked up. 'But you said yourself that you don't know anything about MS. You don't know the implications.'

'We'll get on to that in a minute. But first I want to know how far your deception went. Did it include avoiding me at times?'

He nodded guiltily. 'More times than I care to think of.'

She smiled, relieved. 'And there was I convinced that you were doing a Gavin on me.'

'Believe me, Jessica, that would have taken more energy than I possess ... and even if I had the energy I would never do that to you.'

She went to him and knelt on the floor at his feet. She rested her head against his legs.

'Can I ask *you* a question now?' he asked.

'Of course.'

'When you came down the stairs at Mo's and you said that you'd just been talking to her, you seemed angry. Were you?'

She turned and looked at him. 'I was furious, if you must know, I was spitting bricks.'

'Why?'

'The situation reminded me of Gavin. I know it sounds crazy, but from where I was standing I'd suddenly found out something about you and it was like discovering you'd been lying and cheating on me.'

He stroked her hair. 'I'm so very sorry.'

'Don't be.' She lifted his hand from her head and gently squeezed it within her own. 'Now I want you to tell me what's wrong with you. And no glossing over anything. I want the truth. Tell me everything.'

He sighed. 'Where do I start?'

'In true story-telling tradition, try the beginning.'

'Okay. I have what is known as relapsing-remitting multiple sclerosis.' His voice sounded flat and uninteresting, as if he were reading from a script. 'Which means the symptoms I experience come and go as they please. I have no control over them, I'm at the mercy of whatever my body decides to chuck at me.'

'Such as?'

He let go of her hand and stroked her hair again. 'You name it,' he said. 'The most obvious and frequent symptom I have is the lack of mobility in my leg, which seems to be getting steadily worse ... I'm afraid I blatantly lied about that, by the way.'

She smiled cautiously. 'Not a heroic skiing injury then?'

''Fraid not.' He then went on to describe the catalogue of symptoms he'd experienced over the past few years; the slurred speech, the numbness, the tingling, the acute fatigue, the lack of control over his limbs and the most frightening of the lot, the momentary loss of sight in one of his eyes.

When he finished Jessica said, 'But what about a cure?'

He shook his head. 'Nothing. Not even a wonder drug that puts the illness on hold.'

She frowned. 'How bloody unfair! And how bloody awful for you.'

'It isn't always awful,' he said, surprised to hear himself admitting this, 'the symptoms vary in severity, there are some good days.'

'And today?'

He smiled. 'Today's been okay, which was why I plucked up the courage to ask you to come to Mo's party.'

She thought about this. 'Does that mean I've only ever seen you on your good days?'

He nodded. 'Apart from when I moved in and burst in on you and your mother. My speech was all over the place, I could barely get the words out.'

Jessica recalled the day with shame, seeing now his apparently ill-mannered behaviour in a completely different light. 'I'm sorry I thought you'd been rude and even sorrier that I told you so to your face. That was terrible of me.'

'Forget it,' he said lightly. 'You weren't to know. And anyway, that's nothing compared with what I've done to you. I can't begin to think what you must have thought of me each time I deserted you after we'd made love. I hated doing that.'

'I hated it as well. What were you so frightened of?'

'Of the morning ... of you waking to the truth about me and discovering that I wasn't the man you thought I was.'

'And I suppose you didn't really have flu the other week.'

'No. I ... I'd been feeling particularly ill that week and I collapsed at work ... Charlie had to bring me home.'

She looked up at him, full of concern. 'Oh, Josh, I wish you'd told me, I could have helped. I could have been there for you.'

'It's bad enough having to face up to MS oneself without admitting to other people what's going on. Half the time I don't even tell Charlie what's happening, I'm afraid I make his life hell.'

'He strikes me as being able to cope.'

'I'm not sure at times whether he is,' Josh said reflectively, 'he's had to put up with a lot of crap from me. My parents too. Even Mo.'

Jessica smiled. 'Talking of Mo, you do realise that she's completely and utterly in love with you, don't you?'

He didn't answer her. Instead he pulled her on to his lap. 'But more to the point,' he said, 'do you realise that I've gone and let myself fall in love with you?'

'Hang on a moment,' she said with a nervous little laugh, 'it's me who's supposed to write the romantic lines.'

'I'm not kidding, Jessica. God help you, but it's the truth.'

'I'm delighted to hear it, because I reached the same decision about you earlier this evening.'

'You did? My God! When?'

'When I thought that Mo might be a threat, I was so mad with jealousy I could have torn the sweet girl limb from limb.'

He laughed happily and held her close. He couldn't believe the way the evening had turned out. 'I don't suppose there's any chance of you staying the night with me, is there?'

'Mm ... that's a tempting offer, Crawford.' And relaxing into his embrace, she settled herself in for a good long kiss. But suddenly she sat bolt upright. 'I've forgotten all about my mother! What time is it?'

He looked at his watch. 'One o'clock.'

'*What!*' She sprang out of his lap.

'Calm down. If there'd been a problem she would have phoned. Now let me get my keys and I'll drive you back.'

'You sure you're safe to drive,' she asked when they were outside and he was locking his front door. 'You haven't had too much to drink, have you?'

'I'm fine,' he said. He opened her side of the car and just as she was about to climb in he took her in his arms. 'I'm claiming my good-night kiss now,' he said, 'I might not get another chance.'

38

Jessica started buttering a piece of toast for her mother. She spread the low-fat butter substitute evenly, right to the darkened edges of the crusts, then added some of Anna's home-made whisky-spiked marmalade; this too was pressed into place with careful precision, ensuring an equal distribution of finely shredded orange peel. And all the time she was doing this Jessica was thinking of Josh.

Last night he had shared with her two vital pieces of information: first, that he suffered from some illness which he'd gone to great lengths to hide from her, and second ... and second, that he loved her.

He actually loved her.

Amazing!

Getting anybody to fall in love with her in the past had always been such a mighty uphill struggle – in fact, she doubted whether it had ever happened. Certainly Gavin had never loved her.

But Josh did!

And she loved him.

Oh, yes. She loved him right enough. Falling in love with Josh Crawford had been effortless, it had been as easy, as the silly cliché goes, as falling off a log – just like they had that night in the copse.

In a funny way it almost seemed unfair that it had been so easy to fall in love with Josh and he with her, when for more than a year she had tried to make Gavin do the same – or at least care for her exclusively. But it had never happened. It was strange that so much hard work had gone into that particular relationship and it had all gone to waste.

It was very confusing.

As was Josh's illness.

She wasn't quite sure what to make of it. She knew that Josh had found last night an ordeal and that he'd done his best to explain what multiple sclerosis was all about, but when she'd woken up this morning she had realised that not once had he referred to the future.

What was his future?

Would he stay as he was?

Or was he likely to get worse?

And if so, what did that mean precisely?

And could MS be life-threatening?

Oh God! Why didn't she know? Why was she so ignorant?

And another thing. Why hadn't she sensed that there was something wrong with Josh? How blind and insensitive could a person be? For goodness sake, she was a writer, she was supposed to be a keen observer of her fellow human beings.

How damning it was to realise that she had been so shallow. Always, always, her response to Josh had been to consider the effect he had on her. How could she have viewed him in such a two-dimensional manner?

The answer, she suspected, lay in her relationship with Gavin. Determined never to allow another man to hurt her again she had probably been so preoccupied with self-protection that she had become introverted and unaware of those around her, only thinking what the consequences of anything would be to herself.

How selfish she had been.

Which was what she'd felt last night after Josh had dropped her off. When she had found Anna stretched out on the sofa, fast asleep with a throw-over covering her, she had been appalled. The fire had all but gone out and the faintly glowing embers had stared back at her accusingly as though reprimanding her for having neglected her mother that evening. Guilt had overwhelmed her. How could she have left Anna for so long? How could she have abandoned her mother when she needed her most? What kind of daughter was she that could behave so reprehensibly?

She cut the piece of toast diagonally in half and passed it across the table.

'A work of art,' Anna said, having spent the last five minutes watching her daughter closely, 'thank you.'

It was patently clear to Anna that Jessica had something on her mind. But then for that matter so did she.

Although it was only eight-thirty, Anna was willing the phone to ring; it was making her jumpy with nervous expectation. Piers Lambert had said he'd help and ridiculously she was sitting at the breakfast table waiting for him instantly to come to her aid. She had imagined him late last night bursting into action like some mighty Cape Crusader bringing forth with the dawn some way of getting Jessica off her back.

'What do you suggest?' had been his immediate response on the phone, when she'd told him what was going on.

'I don't know, that's why I'm ringing you.'

'You must have had some idea in mind or you wouldn't have called me.'

Jessica had told Anna many times that her agent was direct to the point of rudeness, but she was still taken by surprise at the severity of his manner which, instead of irritating her as she might have expected, did the opposite, it instilled within her a sense of hope – here was somebody who really would get her daughter to step in line and keep her there.

'I want you to crack the whip over Jessica,' Anna had said, 'make her believe that she's got to get on with writing this novel. Can't you make out that the deadline has been brought forward and that she's got to get back to work?'

'That wouldn't be for me to tell Jessica, that would have to come from her publishers. And I'm afraid Jessica's publishers aren't going to start switching round launch dates just to suit you.'

'But surely there must be something you can do.'

'When did she last do any writing?'

'Over a week ago.'

'That's not very long. I think you're exaggerating the case.'

'Look, Mr Lambert, my arm's going to be in plaster for at least another five weeks, maybe longer. Can she afford to take that much time off?'

'Mm ... perhaps you're right. Leave it with me. Good-night.'

Abrupt and to the point Piers Lambert certainly seemed to be, and Anna wished whole-heartedly that his actions would be as forceful and as effective as his behaviour implied.

Tony knew that he was becoming openly hostile towards Bloody Rita – any day now and he'd be lobbing ruddy great grenades at her. He didn't know what it was about her that got his back up most, her haughtiness, or her coldness towards him. He deliberately banged the phone down on the kitchen worktop so as to give his mother-in-law's eardrums a damn good jolt. He called out to Amanda. 'It's your mum,' he yelled at the top of his voice, knowing that such a breach of etiquette would have Bloody Rita blanching into her *Daily Mail* – it could have been worse, he could have referred to her as *mam*.

When Amanda appeared in the kitchen he said, 'I'm off out with Hattie to her ballet lesson, see you about a quarter past eleven.' He was tempted to hang about and eavesdrop on his wife's conversation – he still didn't know what she and her mother were up to – but with Hattie hovering at the front door dressed in her little pink leotard and white tights and her ballet shoes in her hands there was no time for loitering with intent. The thought crossed his mind that it wouldn't be a bad idea to make enquiries into obtaining a few bits and pieces of surveillance equipment, just some useful devices for tapping phones, that kind of thing. He smiled to himself, imagining what might follow if he went down that particular road of madness – he'd end up in a false beard and nose, darting about the streets in a raincoat shadowing Amanda. The idea was so ridiculous it cheered him and patting his daughter's head he said, 'Come on, Hattie, let's hit the road for *Swan Lake*.'

The hall was full of tiny girls, their hair swept back from their gleaming foreheads, their tummies and bottoms sticking out as they held on to the bar in breathless concentration as they bent their knees over their toes. When the music from a bulky ghetto blaster came to a stop, the girls relaxed, curtsied to their teacher and chanted '*Mercy M'dame*', then they stampeded to the back of the hall and their waiting parents, who were on hand with life-saving cartons of juice, bags of crisps and KitKats. Tony gave Hattie a quick kiss and watched her rush away on accentuated tiptoe to join her group – it was her second ever lesson and she was still in the first flourish of enthusiasm for a new-found hobby. He then slipped out of the hall and headed towards the newsagent's in the main street of Holmes Chapel.

The sun was shining and the sky was clear and bright, and it struck Tony as being the most perfect of September mornings. There was that satisfying feeling that the early chill in the air would be long gone by lunch-time and the rest of the day would be warm enough to sit outside with a glass of wine and the newspaper.

Or cut the grass, as Amanda would expect him to do.

He kept meaning to have a word with Josh, who had done the sensible thing and acquired himself a gardener. A gardener was definitely what Tony needed, somebody to take care of the grass and flower beds, leaving him free to plan his future.

In the newsagent's he bought a copy of the *Daily Mail* for Amanda – like mother like daughter – and *The Times* for himself. And while he was there, he couldn't resist scanning the shelves for a magazine aimed at the average man in the street interested in pursuing an innocent hobby of domestic espionage. Surely among the multitudinous and divers selection of magazines on offer there had to be at least one for a dim-witted husband wanting to know what his wife and mother-in-law were up to?

He paid for his papers and went back out on to the street, and weighing up whether he could be bothered to nip into the hardware store for some picture hooks that Amanda had been on at him to get, he suddenly caught sight of a flash of copper hair. It was Kate and she was walking towards the church on the opposite side of the road. Before he could stop himself he was calling out her name. 'Kate!'

She didn't hear him.

He stepped out into the road and immediately leapt back on to the pavement as a car hooted bad-temperedly at him. It was then that she noticed him. He waved over to her and when a flurry of cars had passed, he crossed the road and joined her. 'Hi,' he said. It seemed ages since their last conversation when so much had passed between them.

'Hello,' she said shyly. 'How are you?'

He nodded. 'Okay. How about you?'

'I'm fine.'

'And Alec?'

'Trying to say all the right things.' She lowered her eyes as if regretting what she'd just said.

'He'll come round. It'll be all right in the end.' Tony was surprised how sincere and genuine his voice sounded. Deep down, he didn't want Alec to 'come round'. He wanted him to be a bastard. He wanted Alec to play the Victorian baddie and be booed off the stage, so that he, wonderful, kind, considerate Tony, the young hero, could sweep the badly treated heroine off her feet and give everyone the happy ending they wanted. 'So where are you off to?' he asked, shocked at his shallowness.

She hesitated.

'Sorry, I didn't mean to pry.'

She smiled. 'No. I was just going to sit in St Luke's for a few minutes.'

He looked at the austere sandstone church behind them. He hadn't been inside a church since Eve's funeral, not since that dreadful day when he'd sat in the front pew and silently railed against a supposedly omnipotent and loving God, while all about him people prayed and sang hymns of thanksgiving and everlasting life. For him, though, it had been unthinkable to thank anybody who had seen fit to take away the woman he loved. 'Why?' he asked. 'Why do you want to go in there?'

She looked at him curiously. 'Because it usually makes me feel better.'

This was even more unfathomable to Tony. 'Better?' he repeated.

'Yes,' she said simply. 'It's the sense of peace I come away with.'

'Oh.' A sense of peace was the last thing he'd come away with after Eve's funeral service. He didn't know what else to say, so looked along the street at the determined shoppers buzzing in and out of the shops. He was surprised to feel Kate's hand on his arm and even more so to feel her guiding him towards the studded oak door.

He stood in the half-light and swallowed. It wasn't the same church he'd sat in before, but to all intents and purposes it was identical. The pervading smell of age, polish and snuffed-out candles was the same. As was the morgue-like temperature. His body stiffened as feelings of remorse and anger crept over him. Kate began to move away. He quickly followed. He didn't want to be alone. She slipped into a pew and he sat alongside her. He tried to remind himself of the warm sunshine outside, of Hattie happily prancing about in her leotard, anything so long as he didn't have to be reminded of that awful day. He fiddled with the newspapers in his hands, then glanced at Kate, unsure what was expected of him if she was going to apply herself to meaningful contemplation. But instead of finding her deep in prayer he noticed that she was observing him. And closely. 'What is it?' he whispered. 'Why are you staring at me like that?'

'I was looking at the anger in your face,' she said gently.

He turned away. But then found himself face to face with the image of a tortured Christ on the cross in the stained-glass window above the altar. To the right of this was a wooden plaque honouring local men killed in the First World War. Was there no way of getting away from all the senseless suffering in the world?

'I don't think this is a good idea,' he said. 'I ought to be going, Hattie will be waiting for me.' He stumbled out of the pew and hurried towards the escape route. Outside on the pavement he blinked in the bright sunlight and caught his breath. To his horror he realised he was shaking. He breathed out deeply, willing his emotions back into line. But it was no good, it was too reminiscent of the worst day of his life. When the service had finished he'd started shaking and had broken down and wept. He could still remember the reaction from those around him. The older members of the families had frozen in their seats, unprepared and ill-equipped to cope with such a display of loss of control. It had been his closest friends who had comforted him, bundling him out of the church and taking him to the nearest pub for a stiff drink before driving on to the crematorium.

And a stiff drink was what he could do with right now.

The sound of the church door creaking behind him made him turn.

It was Kate. 'Are you okay?' she asked, her face full of anxious concern.

'Sorry about that,' he said, his breathing now back under control. 'You don't fancy a drink, do you?'

'It's a bit early for the pub to be open,' she said, gazing along the street in the direction of the Red Lion, 'you'll probably only get morning coffee served at this time of the day. And didn't you say that Hattie was waiting for you?'

He banged his head with the newspapers in his hands. 'Yeah, of course, stupid me. I'll see you, then.'

'Yes,' she said.

Neither of them made any attempt to move.

'You are okay, aren't you?' she asked again.

'Yes. No. No, I'm not. You have a strange and wonderful effect on me, Kate. You make me remember Eve . . . and you make me want to do crazy things like kiss you.' Which he did, suddenly and intensely. It was the first time since he'd been without Eve that he'd kissed a woman and meant it. His brain told him to stop. It was madness. The consequences could be disastrous. But his heart pounded out a different message.

39

Kate drove home in a state of heart-quickening confusion. She was not in the habit of kissing men so freely. But what made it worse was that deep down she had known Tony was going to do it . . . and that she was going to let him.

Ever since Monday morning she had found it difficult to shake off the effect of not just Tony's kindness towards her, but the desperate sadness of his circumstances, which he had conveyed to her so poignantly during their conversation. When he had spoken of his first wife she had wanted to console him, to show him the compassion he had shown her, but she had been wary of doing so, fearful of the consequences, knowing that in that precise moment they were both dangerously vulnerable; made weak and defenceless by their wretchedness – a heavy heart could be implicitly treacherous.

Later, and over lunch when Caroline had questioned her about Tony, she had refused to allow herself to be drawn into giving anything more than a superficial physical description of him, but inwardly she had been thinking of the soft blue eyes that had been unable to mask his misery; of the hand that had held hers; of the thoughtfully chosen gift; and of the expression on his face that night in Hattie's bedroom when she'd interrupted him chatting with his daughter.

His countenance had puzzled her at the time because she had been unable to define it.

But now she could.

Oh yes, she now knew exactly what it had meant. His actions a few minutes ago had defined it perfectly.

And what of her actions?

How exactly could they be categorised?

And how could she be attracted to Tony when she was carrying Alec's child? It went against everything she'd ever thought herself capable of.

She sped along the road away from Holmes Chapel, as though hoping to distance herself from what had just taken place. It was only a kiss, she told herself. A single kiss, that was all. It was hardly a breach of faith.

Except it was, she knew very well it was.

Afterwards Tony had said, 'I should probably apologise for doing that, but I'm not going to, I meant every second of it. When can I see you?'

Flustered, she had checked the busy street to see if anyone was watching them. But the Saturday-morning shoppers had all seemed safely occupied with their own tasks in hand and with a shake of her head she'd murmured, 'I don't know.' She had then fled to the car-park and had driven away without risking a backward glance.

When can I see you?

The words echoed inside her head as she entered the village of Cholmford. And just as she'd known that Tony would kiss her that morning, she was certain he would do so again and that she would let him ... that she would want him to.

'Did you get the flowers?' Alec asked Kate when she let herself in.

She stared back at him, mystified.

'You know, the flowers for Ruth,' he said.

The flowers! She'd forgotten all about them. They had been one of the reasons for her visit to Holmes Chapel, she was supposed to pick up something nice from the florist to take to Ruth's for lunch that day. 'I um ... I forgot,' she said truthfully.

Alec smiled at her. 'The hormones have started blatting the little grey cells, have they?'

'Something like that,' she said uneasily, wondering if she could ever legitimately lay the responsibility of that morning's breach of faith on her mixed-up hormones.

'Don't look so worried, we'll get something on the way. Did you remember the dry-cleaning?'

'Yes,' she said with relief – thank goodness she had dropped off Alec's suit before she'd decided to cross the road to go into St Luke's.

Since moving to the area she had often visited the small sandstone church, finding herself drawn to the building that quietly dominated the square in the centre of the village. This morning she had felt the pull of its tranquil sanctuary even more keenly and had gone there in search of a few minutes of calm repose. She had wanted to think about Alec and his apparent acceptance of their child.

'Did they say when it would be ready?' he asked.

'Sorry,' she said, 'when will what be ready?'

He smiled indulgently. 'Your memory really is going, isn't it? I was asking about the dry-cleaning.'

'Oh, that. It'll be ready on Tuesday.'

'That's fine. Do you fancy some coffee? I've put the kettle on. It's such a lovely day I thought we could sit on the patio. We won't get many more chances like this. A few more weeks and it'll be autumn for real.'

'I'll have tea, please, I've gone right off coffee.' She left Alec in the kitchen and disappeared out into the garden, where she hoped to pull herself together. The sight and sound of Alec acting as he always did was too much for her. She wanted him to treat her horribly, at least then she could justify what she had done that morning. How could he treat her so courteously when she was considering . . . she swallowed hard and tried to force herself to put into words exactly what she was considering.

But she couldn't.

Alec drove them to Ruth and Adam's for lunch, stopping on the way at a petrol station to pick up a bunch of rather tired-looking carnations. 'Not as elegantly wrapped as we might have wanted,' he joked when he got back in the car, 'but it'll give Ruth something to be picky about. I swear that girl gets worse. Sometimes I'm ashamed to admit that she's my own.'

Ruth certainly seemed to be on top picky form when she opened the door to them. 'You're early,' she said, clearly annoyed by this lack of thought on their part.

'Hello to you too,' Alec said cheerily, 'have some flowers. And don't worry about us, we won't get in your way, in fact we'll hide in the car if you'd prefer.'

'Dad, you know perfectly well that sarcasm is the lowest form –'

'Of wit,' he finished for her. 'Yes, I know that and don't you just love it? Now point me in the direction of a good bottle of wine and I'll leave you well alone. Hello, Oscar, my fine young man, and how are you?'

Oscar came towards them.

'Shake hands, Oscar,' his mother said.

Oscar extended an awkward hand.

'Other one,' Ruth said sharply.

Kate intervened and stooped down to the little boy. 'I'd rather have a hug.'

Ruth tutted and led the way through to the kitchen. 'Adam!' she called out indiscriminately to some other part of the house, 'Dad and Kate are here, come and entertain them, I've got far too much to do.'

Melissa and Tim arrived late, which caused Ruth further distress. She was so preoccupied with the inconvenience thrust upon her – the pork was overdone and the potatoes were past eating – that she was blind to what was glaringly obvious to the rest of them: Tim and Melissa must have just had an almighty blazing row. Their faces were set like stone, they looked charged and ready to go off at the slightest provocation.

'It's Tim's fault we're so late,' Melissa said as Adam handed her a glass of wine, 'I told him to be ready at twelve, but would he listen?'

'And I told you first thing that I had some important phone calls to make.' Tim's voice was taut with anger, his eyes narrow and threatening.

But by the time they took their seats at the dining-room table the mood had calmed down. Whatever storm had rocked their boat, it seemed to have been lulled. Melissa was now talking about some elderly distant relative in Aberdeen who had recently married his octogenarian neighbour; a woman whom he'd known for the past fifty-five years.

'It was only a small Registry Office do,' Melissa was saying, 'that's why none of us was invited.'

'Can't say that I'd have wanted to go,' Ruth said, pulling a face and passing the first plate of carved meat to her mother. 'Just imagine all those zimmer frames cluttering up the place, to say nothing of the disgusting smell of old age. Oscar, put that book down, it's time to eat.'

'What a kindly view of the elderly you have, Ruth,' Alec said light-heartedly, 'I feel wonderfully reassured by it and can just see you selflessly taking care of me in my dotage. I look forward to that day.'

Ruth passed a plate to Kate. 'Thankfully, I shan't be called upon for that duty; you'll have Kate to swill out your false teeth and change your incontinence pads.'

All trace of the humour that had been on Alec's face was suddenly gone. Kate decided to put Ruth in her place. 'Well,' she said in a clear voice and looking straight at Ruth, 'who knows, Alec might even now end up fathering a child who would *want* to take good care of him if the situation arose.'

Ruth let out a scornful laugh. 'Well, that's the most ridiculous thing I've ever heard. Dad's well past all that, thank God. Oscar, here's your plate.'

His normal composure quickly restored, Alec gave Kate a grateful smile. Earlier in the week he had specifically asked Kate not to tell anyone in his family about the baby. 'I want to be the one who tells them and in my own time,' he'd said to her, but with a certain amount of malicious delight coming to the fore, he concluded that now was as good a time as any to break the news. Indeed, his anger at Ruth's thoughtless words convinced him there could be no better opportunity. 'Actually,' he said, raising his glass of Côte du Rhône and gazing at it intently, then twirling it round in his hand and giving off an air of easy nonchalance, 'you couldn't be more wrong, Ruth. It gives me great pleasure to tell you that Kate and I are expecting our first child.'

The silence was stupendous.

As was the expression on Ruth's face.

It was Tim who was the first to congratulate them. 'Well done, both of you,' he said, then, looking pointedly at Melissa, he added, 'and wouldn't it be a laugh if Melissa and I were to follow suit?' Melissa's eyes glittered back at him. Undaunted, he raised his glass, 'To Alec and Kate's baby, may it be the first of many!'

Half-hearted voices around the table joined in, but Kate sensed that the mood was as congratulatory as a deathbed scene.

'Are you sure?' Ruth said when the initial shock had died away.

Alec laughed. 'Well of course we are. Kate's done one of those tests from the chemist.'

Ruth laughed nastily. 'Those do-it-yourself kits aren't all they're cracked up to be,' she said dismissively, 'they can't be relied upon.'

'I've also been to the doctor,' Kate said with quiet authority as she helped Oscar to some carrots, 'and it's confirmed, it's official.'

'Oh, well, in that case you must be pregnant.'

'You don't sound very pleased, Ruth,' Alec said mischievously, at the same time holding back his surprise that Kate had been to the doctor without telling him, 'don't you like the idea of having a baby brother or sister?' He was enjoying himself now. He knew exactly how his daughter viewed him. Well, this would certainly show her.

'And why would you think that?' Ruth responded directly.

Her tight, scathing voice made Alec hesitate. They were suddenly heading into dangerous territory; sibling rivalry wasn't just for the young, it could kick in at any age. He looked at Melissa, hoping that she might diffuse the situation – she'd always been able to calm Ruth in moments of high drama – but all he got from her was an expression that clearly said, 'You've got yourself into this mess, you're on your own.'

'What kind of baby will it be?' asked Oscar, who was chasing a roast potato with his knife and fork – it was so overcooked it was taking all his concentration just to keep it from jumping off the plate.

'A perfect one,' answered Alec, quick as a flash, glad of his grandson's diversion.

Melissa groaned at the other end of the table. 'Not even being a father all over again gives you the right to start talking like that.'

'We'll have to wait and see whether it's a boy or a girl, Oscar,' Kate said. She was trying to work out why she wasn't delighted with Alec for telling his family about the baby, especially as he'd described it as their *first*.

Then it struck her what was wrong. Alec was using her pregnancy as a weapon against his charmless daughter.

Perhaps Melissa as well.

The thought chilled her.

No child of hers was ever going to be used as a weapon. She now wondered if Alec had only accepted the baby because he saw it as a way of scoring points over Ruth and his ex-wife.

40

By early Saturday evening Anna had come to terms with the knowledge that Piers was not going to come to her aid until at least Monday morning, so meanwhile there was nothing for it but to put up with Jessica's infuriating ministrations.

The only phone call they'd received was from Josh. He'd called not long after breakfast and as a consequence Jessica was now thrashing about in the kitchen putting together an unspeakably disgusting supper for the three of them to endure that evening.

When she'd heard her daughter talking to Josh on the phone she'd called out, 'Why don't you invite him for supper tonight?' She liked Josh. The truth was, she was quite taken with him and having his company at Willow Cottage did at least provide her with a welcome break from Jessica's new-found despotic behaviour. It was a shame, though, that her selfishness meant that poor Josh had to stomach one of Jessica's meals.

It was after his phone call that Jessica had explained to her why she had stayed out so late last night. 'I just don't see why he kept it from me,' Jessica had said.

But Anna could quite understand Josh's reasons for keeping quiet. 'The trouble with any serious illness or disability,' she'd told Jessica, 'is that it has a nasty habit of stripping away a person's dignity and that's what that young man is terrified of. He's intelligent and good-looking, and wants to be treated accordingly. He doesn't want shoulder-patting sympathy, no matter how well meant.'

They had then reached for the up-to-date *Family Medical Journal* that Anna had recently purchased from her book club and flicked through it looking for multiple sclerosis.

'*MS is an attack on the central nervous system, i.e. the brain and spinal cord,*' the opening paragraph began. It then went on to talk about something called myelin sheaths being destroyed and exposed nerve fibres preventing impulses from the brain being correctly transmitted. The author of the text wrote in matter-of-fact terms of the twenty per cent of extreme cases of MS sufferers who become so seriously disabled that they end up wheelchair-bound.

When they'd finished reading, Jessica had returned the book to the shelf with a worried expression on her face.

'Best not let on to Josh that we've been researching the subject,' Anna had said. 'And remember,' she'd added firmly, 'he's the same Josh you've come to know these past few months. You haven't treated him as a sick man up to this point, so there's no reason why you should start now.'

'I know that,' Jessica had said.

But Anna wasn't convinced that Jessica did. And hearing the sound of the doorbell and her daughter going to answer it, she sincerely hoped that she would heed her advice.

Josh arrived bearing almost more gifts than he could carry. He came into the sitting-room and Anna tried hard not to notice his limp – previously she'd never given it a second look, but now like a car accident on the motorway it was hard not to take her eyes off the stiffness of his leg and how it affected his gait.

'A fresh supply of chocolates for you,' he said, coming slowly over to where Anna was sitting and offering her a large flat box, 'I thought you might have finished the others by now.'

'Thank you,' she said with a smile, 'how thoughtful and intuitive of you.'

Then he turned to Jessica and handed her a beautifully arranged bouquet of red roses. He kissed her cheek. 'For being so understanding last night,' he whispered into her ear. 'And lastly, but by no means least, something for all of us, a bottle of wine.'

Jessica smiled and took that from him as well. 'Brilliant,' she said, 'it'll go a long way to disguising the awful meal I'm about to make you both eat.'

'Would you like some help?' he asked.

Anna laughed. 'Good idea, Josh. Jessica's told me what an excellent cook you are, why don't you go and see what culinary disaster she's got in store for us? I'm afraid my influence when she was growing up failed to bring out the slightest chance of any cookery expertise in her.'

'I'm sure it won't be that bad,' Josh said, already moving towards the kitchen with Jessica.

'Oh no,' she said to him, 'I'm not having you poking and prying into what I've been slaving over all afternoon and besides, you need to sit down.'

Anna bit her lip. Wrong thing to say, she wanted to shout across the room. She saw it in Josh's face only too plainly. But not in Jessica's. Oh dear, she thought, poor Josh.

When Jessica left the room, Josh came and sat by the fire with Anna. He stared into the burning logs and frowned, his face suddenly pensive, but at the same time painfully vulnerable.

Anna's heart went out to him. She decided to be honest with him. 'Jessica mentioned to me this morning what you told her last night,' she said.

He looked up morosely, his eyes dark and angry. 'What, that I love her, or that I'm a chronic invalid?'

Anna smiled kindly. 'She doesn't see you like that, Josh. Just give her time to understand. And by the way, love wasn't discussed, but I'm delighted that's the way you feel about my daughter. Now why don't you go and join her in the kitchen and help with the supper? At least then I might feel confident that we'll eat something slightly more appetising than wet newspaper.'

That night in bed, Tony lay next to Amanda unable to sleep. Like watching the winning goal in a Cup Final match being replayed over and over in slow motion he was reliving the moment when he'd kissed Kate.

And when *she'd* kissed him.

That it hadn't been a one-sided affair had surprised and delighted him. She hadn't pushed him away as he'd expected. There had been no slap in the face. No enraged 'How dare you!' or 'What the hell do you think you're doing?' None of that, just one long delicious moment of pleasure.

She had willingly kissed him, and kissed him with more passion than he'd dared to hope for. He had no idea when he would get the chance to see her alone again, but somehow he knew he would make it happen.

He got out of bed and went downstairs and looked out of the kitchen window across the moonlit courtyard. Number five was in darkness. Kate and Alec must have gone to bed. He turned away. He didn't want to imagine Kate in bed with Alec, couldn't bear the idea of another man's comforting arms around her.

So this is when the pain starts, he thought miserably.

As though he hadn't suffered enough already.

Kate wasn't lying in bed with Alec's comforting arms around her. She was staring out of the window and looking towards the copse of trees, remembering the evening she had gone there in tears when she and Alec had had their first argument. It seemed that ever since that night things had gone wrong between them.

They had very nearly argued again this afternoon when they'd driven back from Ruth and Adam's. It was only her guilt over Tony that had stopped her from challenging Alec about the way he'd announced to his family that she was pregnant. She recalled Jessica's words when she'd said that sometimes when a man became a father late in life there was an element of kudos to be revelled in. Was that what Alec was doing? Was he now hell-bent on proving his virility to Ruth and Melissa by flaunting his unborn child? She touched her stomach protectively, frightened that Alec might love their baby for all the wrong reasons.

But who was she to say what was the correct way to love a child? No two people experienced love in the same manner and anyway, it was generally agreed that fathers and mothers loved their children quite differently.

She sighed and a small misty patch of condensation appeared on the glass in front of her. She wiped it away with her fingers and wished it would be as simple to wipe away the sense of disappointment that had been steadily growing within her.

She was loved by a wonderful man and was pregnant – not so long ago this would have been all she would have wanted in life. But it was like wishing for a certain Christmas present for months and months, then opening it up on Christmas morning only to discover that it was no longer what you wanted.

So what did she want?

She turned and looked at Alec asleep in bed. He looked so peaceful, so at ease with himself. Tears pricked at her eyes and she swallowed back the painful truth that she no longer wanted Alec.

41

On Monday afternoon, just as the first of Ricki Lake's guests was within a whisker of being confronted with her worst fear in the hope of overcoming it, the phone rang – Anna's worst fear was that her lovely home would never be her own again, that Jessica would sell her house at Cholmford Hall Mews and make herself a permanent fixture at Willow Cottage.

She pointed the remote control at the television and turned down the sound on Ricki's over-excited audience, who were all now screaming and squirming as a large hairy spider was being presented to a visibly sweating, goggle-eyed Kansas mother of six, who in the interest of entertainment was giving a credible performance of a woman going to her death on national television – *you saw it here first, folks!* Out in the hall, Anna could hear Jessica speaking into the phone. From the tone of her voice it didn't sound like Josh. Was it Piers at last? She held her breath and listened in. She also quietly prayed for a small miracle.

'How on earth did you know that I was here, Piers?' Jessica asked.

'It's my job, Jessica, to know where and what you're doing. Haven't I always told you I'm supposed to make your life easier. A shame you couldn't do the same for me. I've been trying your house for days, only to get your maddening squeaky voice telling me you'll get right back to me. And as you haven't had the courtesy to do that, I've been forced into ringing this number which you gave me before you left Corfu.'

'Oh,' said Jessica, taken aback at such a long speech from Piers. Had she given him her mother's number? She couldn't remember ever doing so.

'Oh, indeed,' he said. 'So how's *A Casual Affair*?'

'Um . . .' Piers always made Jessica feel as if she were back at school when he started enquiring about her writing. The second he so much as hinted at wanting a progress report she was back in the classroom, explaining to Mr Hang'em-High-Delaney why she hadn't handed in her history essay on the Battle of Naseby. 'It's on hold for a while,' she said meekly. She took the wise precaution of backing away from the receiver.

'On hold!' roared Piers predictably. 'So that's how it is from now on, is it, Jessica? Suddenly you're earning real money and you're acting like a prima donna. You'll be expecting me to come up there and sort out your shopping next. Or maybe you've ideas of becoming another Barbra Streisand and will be wanting me to put rose petals down the loo for you!'

'I'd rather you cleaned it for me.'

'I bet you would. Now get on and explain what the hell you're playing at.'

'I've got personal problems,' she said – a comment like that to Hang'em-High-Delaney would have had him responding with *You certainly have, it's called scraping yourself off the floor after I've finished with you.* Or, *Miss Lloyd, I have no wish to know about your personal hygiene problems, kindly deal with them and get on with your work.*

'Haven't we all,' said Piers drily.

Which struck Jessica as odd. Piers wasn't the sort to have personal problems, he didn't fit the category at all; to have personal problems one had to have some kind of emotional sensitivity.

'My mother's had an accident,' she said, trying to sound as though she were in the driving seat of the conversation, 'and I'm taking care of her.' Frankly, though, it sounded too much like *Please Sir, the dog chewed up my history book.* 'She's broken her arm and cracked a rib,' she added, just in case Piers needed convincing. *Convincing!* What was she thinking of? What on earth was the matter with her? Why did she let Piers reduce her to this trembling, pathetic state? But it was a familiar question and one that she had never cared to explore too deeply. Delving into her private Pandora's box of lunacy was not a pastime she was keen to pursue. In her opinion it was best simply to nail the lid down on all that jolly psycho-babble and conclude that fathers who died before their daughters had had a chance to become an expensive millstone round their necks, had a lot to answer for.

'I'm sorry to hear about your mother,' Piers said, jolting her out of her thoughts, 'but I'm not sure I see how that prevents you from getting on with *A Casual Affair.*'

Because, you unfeeling soulless man, I can't think straight. Because all my energy's going into worrying about my mother. Surely even a Neanderthal simpleton like you can grasp that small but significant piece of information! And on top of all that I've gone and fallen in love with a man who has some bloody awful incurable disease.

Which was the stark reality of the situation in which she now found herself.

While out food shopping on Saturday afternoon and wondering what on earth she could cook for Josh that evening, she had taken a detour from the supermarket, headed for the nearest bookshop and bought their one and only book on the subject of MS. 'We don't get a lot of call for it,' the woman behind the till had said as she wiped the dust off the small paperback. 'I had an aunt who had MS,' she continued, handing over

Jessica's change, 'or maybe it was ME, I get them confused. Anyhow, whatever it was, she died. Her blood got too thick, or was it too thin? She was only young.' Which choice comments had thoroughly depressed Jessica as she'd driven back to Cholmford. It was only late that night after Josh had gone home – having bravely forced down her watery, tasteless shepherd's pie, the lumps in the mashed potato being the only substance to the meal – that she had had an opportunity to open the book. It didn't make for soothing bedtime reading. When she reached the chapter on Sexual Difficulties she had switched off the light. She didn't want to think about that. Sex with Josh was great. Better than great, it was the best she'd ever known. It was chandelier-swingingly fantastic. But would it stay that way?

'Jessica?'

'I'm sorry, Piers, what were you saying?'

'I asked why you weren't getting on with what you're paid to do?'

Jessica muttered something about Anna needing a lot of attention.

'So what am I supposed to tell Cara?'

'Nothing, I'll talk to her.'

'All this is very unprofessional, Jessica, you do realise that, don't you? Especially as I've gone to a lot of trouble to get you a slot on telly, but obviously I can see that it's now out of the question. I'll call the producer back and tell him you're unavailable.'

'Hang on a moment, what slot on telly?'

Having just signed the last two letters that Stella was waiting for, Piers pushed them towards her hovering figure in the doorway of his office and, leaning back in his chair and satisfied that Jessica had taken the bait, he began reeling her in. 'It's not much,' he said airily, 'but it would have coincided nicely with the launch of your next hardback. Cara was delighted when I told her about it this morning.'

'So tell *me* about it.'

'It's one of those new daytime life-style programmes. You know the kind of thing, yesterday's bimbos now all grown up and presenting an hour of uplifting crap. The flavour is feel-good-anything's-possible. The idea was that you would be featured as a young independent woman, attractive and well-travelled, who can rattle off the odd novel while enjoying life to the full. You were supposed to be inspirational.'

Jessica liked the sound of herself. She said modestly, 'I'm not sure about the attractive bit.'

Piers ignored this and reeled her in a few more turns. 'It would be a shame to turn it down, but I can quite see that you wouldn't have the time to fit it in. After all, they'd want to come up and spend an entire day filming with you. It would be very time-consuming.'

'When were they thinking of?'

'They've a busy schedule, Jessica, they said they could only fit you in next week, it's then or never. But don't worry, I'll make the necessary apologetic noises and –'

'It's rather a good opportunity, isn't it? I'd hate to let Cara and the team down.'

Piers had her almost out of the water now; he'd never known an author turn down an opportunity to go on television. 'But like you said, you've got a lot on your plate, they'll understand.'

Jessica was already choosing a new outfit to wear for the programme, something smart, understated, classy, probably black. She'd go to Wilmslow and treat herself. 'No,' she said decisively, 'I've got to be professional about this. Tell them I'll do it.'

Piers snapped forward in his seat, triumphant. 'So long as you're sure,' he said, affecting a casual manner and then going in for the kill. 'Now before I forget, Cara mentioned something about your next book being brought out earlier than originally agreed.'

'How much earlier?'

'May.'

'*What!*'

'You heard, Jessica. Cara said she'll ring you about it. My advice is to crack on.'

He put down the phone, pleased with himself. Jessica had always been one of his most compliant authors. She'd never given him any trouble. Not like some. One author actually expected him to make theatre and restaurant reservations whenever he was up in town. It was the older ones who were the worst; they imagined themselves to be still living in an age when writers were revered as demi-gods. They hadn't sussed that these days nobody gave a monkey's arse for their art-form and that publishers were only interested in profit margins and bestseller lists. Most of the time his job swung between appeasing the appalling egos and vanity of his authors and the ruthless commercialism of their publishers.

And relying on Jessica's vanity had paid off. He had never doubted his ability to get her back to work, but even he hadn't been prepared for the face of good fortune to smile on him so benevolently.

Dinner on Saturday night with an old friend who two years ago had left the murky waters of the publishing industry for the equally shark-infested ones of the BBC had provided him with just the carrot he needed to get Jessica off her backside, or rather on to it and back at her laptop. Max had described the new show he was producing and said they'd been let down by an author and did he have a client – a female client – who had led an ordinary but verging on the interesting life. 'We don't want the bizarre or the surreal. Everybody's sick of publishing success stories achieved on the strength of the writer's dubious background. Ex-prostitutes turned born-again missionaries are out. So are tarnished politicians. We want an ordinary woman to whom the viewer can relate, or even aspire to. Know anyone of that ilk?'

This spectacular piece of good luck was then followed by Cara phoning him first thing that morning to explain that several of their lead titles for next year had been switched about and Jessica's was being brought forward, and did he think it would be a problem for her?

And so what if it was? The amount she was being paid she could bloody well pull her finger out. Not that he'd said as much to Cara. 'I'll put it to Jessica,' he'd told her, 'but you're expecting a lot, that's three months' working time you're cutting from her schedule. She'll expect something in return, like an extra push from the publicity department.'

He clasped his hands behind his head and leant back in his chair. Not a bad day's work all in all. And it would probably please Jessica's mother into the bargain, leaving her to enjoy her broken bones in peace.

But enough of the quiet reflection, there was still work to do. He bent forward in his seat and pulled the telephone towards him. His next task was to deal with a recalcitrant mystery writer suffering from writer's block and a monumental drink problem, who was already two months late for his deadline.

If Anna hadn't had a broken wrist she would have clapped her hands delightedly. Piers had come through for her! She tried hard not to look too pleased and stared solemnly at her daughter. 'So what you're saying is that they're bringing your book out that much earlier, which means you've got to finish it sooner. That's rough on you, isn't it?' She hoped there was enough sympathy in her voice.

'But kind of convenient for you, wouldn't you say?' Jessica said. 'You're thinking, yippee, Jessica won't have time to take care of me now, aren't you?'

'Nonsense, you know how much I've enjoyed having you here – why, it's what's kept me going these long dreary days.'

'Hah! You hate having me around.'

Anna smiled. 'On a permanent basis, yes. A lot of you goes a long way when you're trying to be nice, Jessica; you're a bit like saccharin.'

'Thanks for the recommendation, I'm flattered.'

'In the circumstances, it's the best I can do. When are you leaving?'

Jessica frowned. 'I'm not,' she said stubbornly. 'You need looking after. There are things you can't manage.'

'Such as?'

'A whole load.' Jessica looked helplessly about her. 'For a start, you can't clear out the ashes from the fire and re-lay it, and you certainly can't bring in the logs –'

'Only because you haven't let me. If I take it slowly –'

'No. It's out of the question.' Jessica began pacing the room. 'I can't leave you all alone, I shall have to work from here. I'll set myself up in the dining-room. Just because Cara has changed the goalposts it doesn't mean that I have to leave you.'

Disappointment made Anna want to cry. 'But Jessica, you're driving me mad,' she shouted angrily. 'I want some time on my own, why do you think I never remarried? Why do you think I've always lived in Cholmford where there aren't any neighbours to pester me? Can't you get it into your thick head? *I like being alone.*'

Jessica came to a stop behind the sofa. She rested her hands on the back of it and stared at her mother, amazed at her outburst.

'We've got to reach a compromise,' Anna said more calmly, but wondering whether it was physically possible to throttle her daughter with one hand.

Jessica continued to stare at her mother. Then very slowly she moved across the room and sat in the chair opposite her. 'You're right,' she said. Her voice suddenly sounded dragged down with resignation. 'It's just that I don't know how to compromise where you're concerned; you've done so much for me all my life.'

'I was only doing my job,' Anna said lightly, 'and I'm not sure I've done that much for you.'

'But you have. And now that it's my turn to look after you, you won't let me. You're not being fair.'

Anna smiled. 'When I really need your help I'll let you know. Let's just accept that now isn't that time.'

Jessica frowned, far from convinced that this was the case. She thought of her mother's angry outburst a few moments ago. 'Did you really mean what you just said, about not remarrying because you wanted to be on your own?'

'Absolutely. I've always enjoyed my freedom. Granted it's probably what's made me selfish and difficult to get on with, but it's my life and I'll live it exactly how I want to.'

'So you want me out?'

'Yes, please.'

'But what if something happens?'

'Why don't we do what Josh suggested?'

'What was that?'

'We'll get me a mobile phone and that way, should something go wrong, you know, like I collapse in the bathroom, I'll be able to call you at the flick of a switch.'

'Knowing you, you'll leave the wretched thing somewhere and forget where you've put it.'

'Do you mind! I'm not as daft as all that.'

'Or you'll run the batteries down and for that crucial phone call you won't be able to ring me.'

'Your over-active imagination is running away with you, dear.'

'Don't call me dear, it makes me deeply suspicious. Gavin started calling me *dear* and *darling* before I found out about Silicone Sal. And I don't care what you say, I should sleep here with you every night.'

Anna sighed. 'No,' she said firmly. 'You can pop in for a short while every day, just to make sure I haven't pegged out, but that's as far as it goes. Anyway, wouldn't you rather spend more time with Josh?'

Jessica opened her mouth to refute this, but found she couldn't. The truth was she did want to see more of Josh. Lots more of him. And now that he had nothing to hide from her they could actually spend a whole night together.

Seeing the hesitation in her daughter's face and knowing that the last of her resolve had been weakened, Anna pressed on: 'And as Piers has just told you, you have to concentrate on your writing. He and Cara are relying on you. Now tell me again about the BBC coming to film us.'

'*Us?* It's me, your young, attractive, independent daughter they're interested in,' Jessica said, aware that a feeling very much like relief was creeping over her.

'Really? I didn't know I had one of those. But they'll want to film a snippet or two of where you grew up, won't they?' Anna was thinking about getting the garden into shape ready for the cameras. She and Dermot could sweep up the leaves that were already beginning to fall and they could put them in a neat, tidy pile ready for a bonfire on the day the film crew came; bonfires with a thin trail of smoke hanging in the damp autumn air always looked so atmospheric on the television, she thought. What fun it would be.

42

Mo had spent most of the day in hiding. As soon as she'd caught sight of Josh entering the building earlier that morning she'd made herself scarce by disappearing to the loo. She even conned Sid into taking Josh's coffee to him. Sid knew all about what had happened at the party because after she'd finally made it back downstairs he'd told her what had gone on between Josh and Jessica. 'You're in it deep, Mo,' he'd said, 'about as deep as it gets. The look on the guy's face was awesome. I've never seen anything like it.'

'Oh shit,' she'd cried, realising with horror what she'd done, 'oh shit, oh shit, oh *shit*!'

'Yeah, that's the stuff you're knee-deep in,' Sid had said and, taking her through to the kitchen and pushing everyone out of the way, he'd started making her several gallons of black coffee.

'I don't need that,' she'd wailed hysterically. 'What you've just told me is sobering enough.'

'You're going to drink it,' he'd insisted.

Between forcing down several mugs of Turkish-strength coffee she'd kept saying, 'But I thought she knew. I really thought he must have told her. How was I to know he hadn't?'

'Come on,' Sid had said when she'd refused to drink any more, 'come and dance with me. You need cheering up.'

'No I don't,' she'd said miserably.

'Yes you do and while we dance we can work out what you're going to say to Josh on Monday morning.'

And here they were, half past five on Monday afternoon and still she hadn't plucked up the courage to speak to Josh. Sid had been great to her all day and had taken her out for a sandwich at lunch-time to try and calm her down. She knew that he fancied her and really he was quite cute, with that cool hair of his, and maybe she ought to think about him more seriously . . . now that Josh was probably never going to speak to her again.

She bent down beneath the reception desk and began getting her stuff ready to go home. She slipped a bundle of essay notes into her bag, along with a magazine, both of which she'd been too sick with nerves to so much as glance at during the day. When she stood upright she let out a sudden gasp – Josh was standing straight in front of her.

'Got time for a chat?' he asked.

There was no avoiding him now and with a leaden step she followed him slowly to his office, aware that everybody was staring at them – word had soon gone round that she'd blown her future with Crawford's. She was conscious, too, of the chunky heels of her knee-high PVC boots reverberating loudly on the wooden floor as if beating out a painfully slow death march. It made her remember what she'd said to Jessica about wanting Josh to follow behind her coffin when she was dead. Yes, she thought, he'd follow it all right and then stamp on her grave afterwards. How he must hate her. And with every right. She had committed the one act guaranteed to get up his nose: she had gossiped about his illness behind his back.

As she entered Josh's office she caught sight of Sid giving her an encouraging smile over the top of his computer. Then the door closed ominously behind her.

'How are you feeling?' Josh asked.

She watched him loosen his tie and undo the top button of his Paul Smith shirt; it was one of her favourites and it was attractively crumpled from its day's work. And as he rolled up his sleeves and leant back against his desk she thought, *God, I fancy him.* She then thought, *Jeez, girl, pull yourself together! This is no time for lust. This is the moment you get fired. You're history, kid. You're outta here.* 'I'm fine,' she muttered, suddenly remembering that Josh had asked her a question.

'You sure?'

She gave a little nod and twisted her hands nervously behind her back. Her fingers touched the silver bangle Josh and Charlie had given her. How she wished she could turn the clock back to that lovely precious moment in the garden when she'd opened their present.

He went and sat down and, still regarding her, removed his glasses and added them to a pile of sample T-shirts. 'I haven't been able to thank you for Friday evening,' he said. 'Whenever I went to look for you I couldn't find you.'

She swallowed and wished he'd just get on with it. Why put her through all this agony? Did he want her to suffer? And hadn't she suffered enough all weekend, dreading coming in to work? She moved a little nearer to his desk. It was time to get it over with. 'Look,' she said, 'I'm really sorry about the other night. I'd had too much to drink and I was feeling wretched and I shot my big mouth off and I'm really –'

'Yes,' he interrupted, 'Jessica said you weren't well when she spoke to you.'

'I am sorry, honestly.'

He looked at her fondly. 'In a way you did me a favour.'

It was a few seconds before Mo registered that there was a hint of a smile playing at the corners of his tempting mouth. 'A favour?' she repeated.

'Yes, but I don't particularly want to go into that now.' He picked up his glasses and began fiddling with them. The hint of a smile was gone.

'Does that mean you're not going to sack me?'

He frowned. 'Why would I want to do that?'

'Because ... because of what I told Jessica,' Mo said, wishing he wouldn't frown – didn't he know that it made him even more attractive?

He shook his head tiredly. 'Forget it. At the moment what really concerns me is that you've spent the day hiding from me.'

She lowered her eyes.

'And don't look like that, I'm not a tyrant.'

She didn't know what to say, so she stood staring blankly down at her shiny boots. After a while she said, 'Can I go now? I think I'm going to cry.'

He stood up and went to her.

'It must be the relief,' she sniffed. 'You and Charlie have always been so good to me and then I go and do the worst possible thing to upset you.'

'Come on, Mo,' he said gently, 'I've told you it's all right. It was all my fault anyway, it's me who should be sorry for putting you in such a difficult position.'

She looked up at him. 'Do you really mean that?'

He nodded.

'You're not just saying it to make me feel better?'

'Come on,' he said, 'stop giving yourself such a hard time.'

She managed a small smile.

'Now go home and cheer yourself up on that trampoline of yours. Or better still, make Sid's day and get him to take you out for a drink.'

When he was alone Josh dialled the number for Willow Cottage. He wanted to see if he could make his own day by seeing Jessica that evening.

It was some time before the phone was answered and when it was he was surprised to hear Anna's voice at the other end of the line. 'Hello, Josh,' she said, 'if it's Jessica you want, she's not here, she's gone to one of those late-night-opening stores to buy me a mobile phone, just like you suggested. She's moving back to her own place, isn't that wonderful news?'

'I guess so,' he said, 'you sure you'll be okay?'

'Now don't you start, Josh. I thought if there was one person I could rely on it would be you.'

'Point taken. But ...' He hesitated. Would Anna accept his help? he wondered.

'But what?' she asked.

'I was just thinking if there was ever something you needed and you didn't want Jessica concerned you could always give me a ring, you know that, don't you?'

'That's very kind of you, Josh, and I promise to bear it in mind.'

When he'd finished his call with Anna, Josh caught sight of Mo through his open office door. She had her large Moschino bag slung over her shoulder and was chatting to Sid while he switched off his computer. Josh smiled, hoping that Mo might at last transfer the affection she had for him to poor patient Sid. He put on his glasses and returned his attention to what he'd been dealing with before he'd finally tracked down Mo. But it was no good. He couldn't concentrate. He couldn't shake off the uncomfortable image of himself that Mo had left him with. Did she really think him capable of sacking her, just like that?

First thing that morning when they were going through the post Charlie had said, 'Go easy on Mo, won't you, she looks sick with worry.'

But he'd had no intention of laying into Mo for what she'd done. It was his own fault that it had happened. He should never have played such a potentially dangerous game. It had been unfair of him to expect Mo to be a mind-reader. How was she supposed to know that he hadn't told Jessica the truth?

'How'd it go?'

He looked up to see his brother peering round the door.

'What, when I finally got to speak to Mo?'

Charlie came in. 'Precisely that.'

'She's fine, it's all sorted.'

'Thank heavens.'

'She thought I was going to fire her,' Josh said, a troubled expression on his face.

'So did everybody else.'

'But that's crazy. Why? Why would I do that?'

Charlie shrugged.

'I'm not some wacko jackboot bully.'

But you give a damned good impression of one at times, thought Charlie. 'If you say so,' he said tactfully. 'Any chance of cadging a meal off you tonight?' he added. 'I'm getting bored of solitary take-aways.'

'Sorry, I'm hoping to see Jessica.'

'Oh.'

'How about you and Rachel?'

Charlie shook his head. 'Nothing doing there. Looks like I failed at the first gate ... unlike you and Jessica.'

Josh leant back in his chair and slowly tapped a pencil on the keyboard by his hand. 'I wouldn't say it's going to be plain sailing from now on,' he said thoughtfully.

'Why do you say that? When I phoned you on Saturday, you said it was all straight between the two of you, that you'd explained everything and she was okay. Sounded to me like she'd taken it pretty well. Better than you could have hoped for in the circumstances.'

'I know. It's just . . .' He let go of the pencil and flicked it across the desk. 'I can't get it out of my head that she's going to over-react.'

'What do you mean?'

He told Charlie about the way Jessica had been driving her mother round the bend with her constant fussing. 'And she started doing it with me on Saturday when I had supper with them. She wouldn't let me help with anything because, to use her words, "*you need to sit down*". She kept watching me, as if she was worried I'd collapse any second.'

'Well maybe *you're* over-reacting,' Charlie said. 'Personally I thought Jessica was great when I met her at Mo's; I just hope you don't go and ruin things by acting like a real lulu. Give her time.'

'Yeah, that's what her mother said.'

Charlie smiled. 'So if nothing else, it sounds like you're well in with the future mother-in-law.'

Tony was doing a Reggie Perrin, he was imagining his mother-in-law as a hippopotamus. It was a pleasing picture and took his mind off Bradley-Dewhurst-the-Butcher's-Boy who was jawing into the phone about last month's spectacularly good sales figures.

'I just want you to know how much we appreciate what you're doing, Tony. You've really turned things around.'

'There's no reason why this month shouldn't be as good, or the next,' Tony said, wrenching his mind away from Bloody Rita half submerged in a pool of mud. He decided to go on the attack. 'Do we really need to go through with the downsizing we discussed when you were over here?'

'Sure we do, Tony. I know it's tough for those men, but I'm certain I don't have to convince you that these are tough times for us all, we gotta do all we can to concentrate the focus –'

Tony drifted back to the pool of mud. Except now there were two enormous wallowing hippos: Bradley Hurst had joined Bloody Rita.

Later he drove home listening to Dire Straits' *Love Over Gold*. Away from the office he allowed himself the treat of letting his thoughts linger on Kate. There had to be a way of seeing her. But how could he do that when Alec was usually around most evenings? Not to mention the continuous presence of Amanda. Could he suggest that she take up a hobby? Cake icing or something equally fascinating. Anything. Just so long as it got her out of the house one evening a week. But there was still Alec to deal with. Admittedly he was away on business sometimes, but those occasions seemed to be pretty few and far between. He had wanted to ring Kate at home today, but each time he'd got out her number somebody had come into his office. Tomorrow he would definitely do it. He'd get to work early and ring her before anyone else arrived. But not too early, or Alec would still be there.

He wondered if he could prompt Amanda to invite Alec and Kate to dinner.

No!

That was not a good idea.

It would be awful. How did he think he could sit for an entire evening in the same room as Kate without actually touching her?

But a dinner party was exactly what was on Amanda's mind, which was odd because it shouldn't have been, not really.

At nine thirty that morning her mother had arrived on the doorstep and had set the strangest of days in motion. 'There's something you should know,' she'd said, taking off her coat and handing it to Amanda. 'You'd better prepare yourself for a shock. Tony's having an affair.'

But shock is relative and while Amanda wasn't exactly consigning her mother's early-morning revelation to the level of mild irritation caused by a snagged nail, she was not sufficiently shocked to be rendered speechless. She led her mother through to the sitting-room, waited for her to sit down, then said very calmly, 'Are you quite sure?'

'Quite sure. Your father was driving through Holmes Chapel on Saturday morning and he saw Tony kissing her in broad daylight. Bold as you like. The street full of people and the pair of them wrapped in –'

'Yes,' Amanda cut in quickly. 'I think I get the picture.' She was surprised how hurt she felt. Then she realised it wasn't hurt she was experiencing, but anger. She was furious. Tony's betrayal had jeopardised everything. If their marriage could be likened to a business partnership – and it was a fair analogy in her opinion – she had just discovered her co-managing director with his hands in the till, wilfully destroying the company's future. Clamping down on her anger and determining to put it to good use at a later date she said, 'Is Daddy absolutely sure it was Tony?'

'I know he's not the most observant of men, Amanda, but credit him with sufficient sense to recognise his own son-in-law.'

'So why didn't you tell me sooner?'

'Your father didn't want to upset you. He didn't even tell me until late last night. You know what a coward he can be.'

Amanda didn't say anything for a few minutes. Nor did Rita. Amanda went over to the window and looked out to the garden and at the fields beyond. She thought back to Saturday morning. What had they been doing? Or more to the point, what had Tony been doing? Then she remembered – Tony had taken Hattie to her ballet class. It must have been then. While his daughter was tripping the light fantastic he was with somebody. But who?

Unable to take the silence any longer, or restrain herself from blurting out what she'd obviously wanted to say from the moment she'd arrived, Rita said, 'I warned you. I warned you on your wedding day, but would you listen? I told you that you hadn't put enough thought into what you were doing.'

Amanda turned back to her mother. 'This is not the time for a lesson in I-told-you-so. Did Daddy say what the woman looked like?'

'Yes, but I hardly think that's the point right now. We need to discuss what you're going to do. We need to –'

'Please, I want to know.' A sixth sense told Amanda that she knew exactly who Tony had been with.

'Why? Do you think it's somebody you might know? Somebody from the office? Some slip of a secretary who's been making eyes at him?'

Amanda shook her head. 'No. Not somebody from work. Somebody closer to home.' *Very close to home.*

'Your father mentioned something about a lot of red hair.'

Yes! Who else but sweet Kate? That vision of innocent loveliness. Dear, sweet Kate.

Being a practical woman with no time or need for emotional outpourings – what possible use would such a waste of energy be to anyone? – Amanda quickly got rid of her mother, then set her mind to what to do next. She was determined to salvage as much as she could from her marriage and by late afternoon she had worked out a plan of strategy. A whacking great divorce settlement was her objective, but before that she would have some fun ... and at Tony's expense.

A little dinner party was required.

She would suggest that they invite Alec and Kate to dinner during the week. It would be better, she knew, and much more convenient no doubt for everyone concerned to wait until the weekend, but she really didn't think she could hold out that long – and what the hell did she care for anyone else's convenience anyway? It would be rather amusing to watch the happy lovers passing the salt to one another, maybe even to catch a glimpse of eyes meeting and fingers touching. Perhaps she might drop a few hints, subtle hints, but sharp enough to make them fidget in their seats.

Did she know? they'd ask themselves guiltily.

How did she know?

Oh, yes, she would make them sweat.

She would make them suffer.

Then, when she was sure that she had her own future neatly buttoned up, she would pounce on them.

43

By Friday afternoon Jessica was well into her stride with *A Casual Affair*, another five or six chapters and the first draft would be in the bag.

Since she'd returned to Cholmford Hall Mews – straight after breakfast on Tuesday morning and very much at her mother's insistence – she had set to on her laptop with a vengeance, rattling the keys for hours on end, only pausing for breath to make herself drinks, go to the loo and phone Anna, just as she'd promised she would. But it didn't seem to be improving matters between them.

'You're doing it again, Jessica,' Anna had shouted at her on Wednesday. 'You've phoned me a total of twelve times since you left. Now get on with your work and leave me alone. I'm fine and am doing nothing more energetic than turning the pages of my newspaper.'

'I don't believe you,' Jessica had said, 'you're probably back up that blasted ladder fixing something or other. Prove to me that you're in the sitting-room, put the telly on.'

'I can't do that, because I'm in the bathroom.'

'What are you doing in there?' Jessica had asked suspiciously, 're-tiling?'

'Goodbye, Jessica. Speak to you soon, no doubt.'

Her frustration with her mother was making her vent her feelings on her characters in *A Casual Affair*. Miles was getting it in the neck from Clare, who was wondering if the shy, handsome Miles was worth all the trouble. Jessica knew better than anyone that happy endings were her speciality, but in her current frame of mind she was tempted to split Clare and Miles asunder and be damned. Let Clare be a woman empowered by her own actions. Let her discover that she needed a man as much as she needed . . . as much as she needed a recalcitrant mother.

Damn her mother!

No. She didn't mean that. She loved Anna and wanted desperately to help her. But how to go about it was the thing. How did all these caring and compassionate doctors and nurses get the strength to do what they did? Or maybe they'd never come up against somebody as stubborn as Anna?

She returned her attention to chapter thirty-two and when she was satisfied with its ending she set the printer in motion and looked out of the window. After a short while she saw Josh's Shogun drive into the courtyard.

She smiled. And there was somebody else she loved.

But like the love she felt for her mother, her feelings for Josh were beginning to be made all the more poignant by her anxiety for him. Over the past few days she had noticed a change in him. He was quieter. More tired as well. And, at times, slightly introverted. From what she had come to understand of MS from the book she'd bought, it was possible that these were signs that a relapse was on the cards. But amateur armchair diagnosis was a dangerous occupation and not one that she ought to risk.

It was just gone seven o'clock and the light was already fading outside and with her desk lamp switched on she knew that Josh would be able to see her clearly through her study window. He parked his car and as he locked it he looked over and waved at her. She waved back and he started towards her house.

She watched his progress with concern. Even in the half-light she could see that he was exhausted. His steps were slow and awkward, and greatly exaggerated; his briefcase gave the impression of being much too heavy for him to carry. He looked wrung-out. Her heart ached for him. She went to the door to let him in. 'Good day at the office, darling?' she said mockingly, taking his case from his hand and kissing him. She felt the burnt-out heaviness in his body as he leant against her, but there was nothing burnt-out in the way he kissed her.

'Do we have to go to Tony and Amanda's this evening?' he asked, holding her tight.

'Why, are you too tired?'

He pulled away from her. 'No, I just don't feel like it.'

Conscious that she'd said the wrong thing, she offered him a drink. 'I've just finished work, so your timing is perfect. I'm having a glass of wine, just to put me in the right frame of mind for tonight.'

'I'll have the same,' he said, following her into the kitchen, 'I need something to dull the effect of Amanda. Are you sure we can't lie low and simply not turn up?'

Jessica smiled. 'She'd come and get us; there'd be nowhere for us to hide. And anyway, I promised Kate we'd go. Safety in numbers, etc. The poor girl's terrified of Amanda.'

'Whereas we just loathe the dreadful woman.'

'Something like that.'

Jessica pulled a bottle of wine out of the fridge, but before she had a chance to do anything with it the phone rang. She handed Josh the bottle and said, 'Corkscrew's in the right-hand drawer next to the cooker, glasses are in the dishwasher.'

She took the call in the study and was stunned to hear Helen's voice. 'Helen!' she yelped loudly.

'Is that horror or delight that's making you squeal like a pig?'

'Delight, of course, where are you?'

'Would you believe in Huddersfield?'

'No!'

'Yes. We're over for our usual health and dental checks. Any chance of seeing you?'

'Still not trusting the Corfiotes with your body, then?'

'Oh, I trust the Corfiotes with my body, just not the bones of me. Anyway, when can Jack and I come to see you?'

'How about tomorrow? You could come for lunch and spend the rest of the day here.'

'That'll be fine. I'll hand you over to Jack and you can give him directions.'

After a brief conversation with Jack, Jessica went back into the kitchen, happy at the prospect of seeing her old friends again, but she was met with a crash and the sound of breaking glass.

'Bugger it!' Josh muttered under his breath, then seeing Jessica in the doorway he said, 'It slipped out of my hands.' He stooped down to the floor and started picking up the pieces.

'Not to worry, butter-fingers,' she said brightly. 'Here, let me do that.' She made to push him out of the way.

'Leave it,' he snapped back at her. 'I'm quite capable of clearing it up.'

She looked at him, stung by the fierceness in his voice. 'I know you are, I just ... I just don't want you cutting yourself, that's all.'

He got to his feet. 'Meaning I'm more likely to cut myself than you, is that it?'

'Don't be silly,' she said, forcing a lightness into her words. But his face told her he wasn't taken in and he walked away. She wanted to shout at his retreating figure, to tell him he was being unreasonable. But she didn't trust herself. On top of her mother, Josh acting like a sulky child was the last thing she needed. She cleared up the mess, found another bottle of wine, opened it and when she'd calmed down sufficiently took two glasses through to the sitting-room where she found Josh in the dark staring out into the twilight. She switched on a lamp and cautiously approached him by the window.

He turned round. 'I'm sorry,' he said.

'I'm sorry too.' She passed him his wine. He took it from her awkwardly and catching sight of his hand she suddenly realised why he'd dropped the bottle. His fingers were cruelly distorted and were curled into the palm of his hand.

Shocked, she raised her eyes to his and saw the angry frustration in his face. 'Will we be doing a lot of that?'

'What?' he asked. He knew what Jessica had just been staring at and, uncomfortable with her unspoken concern, switched the glass of wine from his right to his left hand.

'Apologising to one another,' she said.

He shrugged. 'Probably.'

They sat down. 'You need to be more honest with me, Josh,' she said. 'If you had told me that you couldn't open —'

'Believe me,' he cut in, 'it's not as simple as that.'

She put down her glass and took his hand in hers. She stroked it gently. 'What does it feel like right now?' she asked.

He tried to remove his hand from her lap, but she wouldn't let him. 'Tell me,' she said, 'please, I want to know. Does it hurt?'

'A bit.'

'Does this make it worse?'

He shook his head and let out his breath, wanting to be able to admit that what she was doing was good, that it helped. But he couldn't. Instead he said, 'What I hate most is that it makes me so bloody clumsy.'

'And bad-tempered?' she ventured.

'That too.'

She continued stroking the back of his hand, then turned it over and began caressing the palm. Very slowly he flexed and straightened his fingers, and one by one, she stroked those as well, but then like a flower closing at night his hand gradually curled back into the rigid position of before, except now her own hand was held firmly within his.

Kate wished she'd been honest with Amanda earlier in the week. 'No, Amanda,' she should have said, 'Alec and I can't come for dinner on Friday night because your husband is the most physically attractive man I've ever met and I'm worried that if I sit in the same room as him I shall burn up with desire for him.'

Powerful stuff.

Shocking, too.

Was it her hormones again? Or was this what love was really like?

With Alec she had always felt safe. Safe and reassured. Comforted. Protected.

But Tony had a different effect on her. The thought of him made her bold. Tacky though it sounded, he made her want to throw caution to the wind.

And she was certainly doing that!

He had phoned her on Tuesday morning, not long after Ruth had dropped off Oscar, and at the sound of his voice she had experienced a rush of something wonderfully exhilarating flow through her.

'Are you alone?' he'd asked.

'No,' she'd said.

'Is Alec still with you?'

'No. I've got Oscar here with me.'

'Who's Oscar?'

'He's Alec's grandson, I look after him during the week.'

'Does that mean I can't see you for lunch?'

Her heart had pounded. 'No. He goes to nursery school in the afternoons.'

'Tomorrow?'

'I could be free from just after one.'

'Where shall we meet?'

'Somewhere a million miles away from here.'

'It's a bit short notice for lunch on Mars.'

In the end they had decided to meet at John Lewis's in Cheadle. It wasn't a very likely venue for a romantic assignation, but it was at least safe; if they were seen, they could pretend they'd simply bumped into each other while shopping.

'I know you don't approve of what we're doing,' he'd said, as they'd roamed the display shelves of china looking for all the world like a normal married couple, 'and I'm not sure that I do either, all I know is that I have to see you.'

She'd echoed his words, but added what she hoped was a well-grounded warning: 'It'll only last a short while. It's probably a case of caprice. It'll pass and you'll return to Amanda and I'll go back to my life with Alec.'

'I don't believe that for a minute,' he'd said.

In her heart, nor did she.

Nor did she think she had the strength to carry off tonight. Surely the moment she and Tony looked at each other everyone in the room would realise what was going on between them?

She finished dressing and went downstairs to Alec, who had already changed out of his work suit and was wearing a peach-coloured shirt with chinos. He looked younger than his approaching fiftieth birthday.

He looked up from his newspaper when he saw her and gave an appreciative whistle. 'Very nice,' he said, taking in the new dress she'd bought when Tony had left her to go back to his office, 'pregnancy obviously suits you, you look lovely. A regular glowing beauty.'

She turned away guiltily, convinced that it wasn't her pregnancy that was making her glow, but the thought of spending an evening with Tony.

Tony still couldn't believe what was happening. It was like some crazy nightmare from which he couldn't wake himself. There was something horribly different about Amanda. He wished he knew what had got into her. From the minute she'd suggested this dinner party she'd been acting strangely. He'd tried his damnedest to dissuade her from going ahead, but she'd have none of it.

It was on Tuesday evening – the day that he'd seen Kate – that Amanda had announced she was inviting the neighbours to supper again. He'd been horrified and had said the first thing that came into his head, 'I shan't be able to make it, I'm working late that night.'

'But you don't know which night I'm talking about,' she'd said in response, 'and anyway I've checked with your secretary and you're definitely free on Friday evening. I've spoken to everybody else, they're all available. I had a lovely long chat with Alec on the phone, he's such a pleasant man. Did you know that Kate was pregnant? I had no idea. Alec sounded as if he was really looking forward to being a father again.'

'That's not what I'd heard.' Which had been a silly slip on his part, for Amanda had seized on it straight away, probably hoping for some nice juicy gossip to mull over.

'What do you mean?' she'd said.

'Oh nothing, it's just that I'm sure I remember Alec saying that he wasn't keen on having any more children.'

He'd phoned Kate the following morning to see what her reaction was. Half of him wanted her to say that she'd back out at the last minute claiming that she wasn't well, but that was tempting fate and he didn't want her to be ill. The other half of him wanted her to be there, at least that way they would see one another. Her thoughts had been the same as his.

And here they all were. Apart from Alec, who seemed to be as easygoing as ever, the rest of them appeared to be on edge.

Josh and Jessica were certainly quieter than usual, with Josh looking well below par. He'd dropped his fork earlier, as well as knocking over a glass, and he was making slow progress with his meal. He'd also noticed Jessica occasionally casting anxious glances in his direction. Perhaps he was coming down with something.

And, as ever, Kate was looking radiantly beautiful, but again, like Josh and Jessica, she was quiet and only added to the conversation when prompted by Amanda.

As for Amanda, well quite frankly, if he didn't know better he would say that each time she darted out to the kitchen she was having a snort of something. She seemed totally wired and was freaking the hell out of him.

At the other end of the table he suddenly heard her asking Kate when she thought she and Alec would get married. He froze. What would Kate say?

'Because you will, won't you,' Amanda persisted, 'especially now that you're pregnant, such a *sweet* couple as yourselves should do the right thing and tie the knot. I've never seen a couple more in love, isn't that right, Tony?'

'Apart from you and me,' he said silkily.

'Ah, ah, ah.' Amanda's laugh was high-pitched and chilling. 'He's full of talk, just listen to him. But back to you, Kate, you haven't answered my question.'

'I'm ... I'm not really sure,' Kate said hesitantly.

Alec intervened, aware of Kate's discomfort opposite him. 'Maybe that's for me to decide,' he said jovially.

Jessica laughed. 'Dangerous words, Alec, in this day and age of equality. There's no reason why Kate shouldn't pop the question.'

Amanda turned to Josh. 'And how would you feel, Josh, if Jessica proposed to you, pleased or emasculated?'

Josh swallowed his wine and looked thoughtfully across the table. He contemplated Jessica's face through the flickering candle-light. Her eyes were dark and compelling and so very sure, and she was smiling at him in that challenging way she did. 'I'd be pleased,' he said softly, 'and ... and I'd say yes.'

The room suddenly went very quiet as Jessica and Josh continued to stare at each other.

Until Amanda, who Tony was convinced had all the sensitivity of a rhinoceros – no, second thoughts, make that a hippopotamus along with her mother and Bradley Hurst – jumped up from the table and said, 'Time for cheese, and why don't we be terribly sophisticated and change seats and swap partners, so to speak.'

Tony stared at her. 'What?' he demanded. He'd have been less surprised if she'd suggested a game of strip poker.

'It's what people do at dinner parties,' she said, 'it makes for better interaction between guests.' She ignored his look of bewilderment and began clearing up the dishes. When she came to Josh's she said, 'You've hardly touched your profiteroles, we can't have you wasting away, you'll have to get Jessica to help feed you in the future and teach you not to be so clumsy.'

Jessica had never wilfully struck another person, not if you discounted the incident at infant school when she hit a girl over the head with her satchel, but she was very tempted to leap up from her chair and smash Josh's bowl into Amanda's face. She'd grind it so hard into that artful countenance that the glaze would come clean off the dish. How dare she speak to Josh in that condescending manner.

But if Josh was riled by what the dinner-party hostess from hell had said he gave no outward sign of it. Jessica was proud of him. As they'd walked across the courtyard earlier that evening he had told her that he didn't want any of their neighbours knowing about his MS. 'Can you imagine what that dreadful woman would say to me?' he'd said, 'she'd probably tell me it's all in my mind and advise me to pull myself together.'

Amanda finished gathering up the dishes, took them through to the kitchen and quietly marvelled at herself. The look on Tony's face when she was asking Kate about getting married, oh, it was priceless. Absolutely priceless.

The shock.

The horror.

The jealousy!

It had all been there in his expression. What a slow-witted fool to have given himself away so easily.

Oh, yes, the evening was definitely a success. And it wasn't over yet. Not by a long way.

She had no idea whether that sharp-tongued Jessica and old limping misery guts knew about Tony and Kate, but she had decided to invite them tonight to find out. She wished she hadn't bothered. Witnessing that excruciating little scene between the pair of them just now had been enough to make her violently sick.

But then, if that didn't make her sick, odds on Kate would. Sitting there like Little Miss Dumb Muffet, convincing everyone that she was the last word in angelic sweetness, was too much. What an act! It would serve the bitch right if she walked straight back into the dining-room and announced that she knew what was going on. 'So Kate,' she could say, 'just who exactly is your baby's father? Alec or Tony? Or maybe you've sampled Josh as well?' That would sure as hell take the smug look off Jessica's face.

It was a tempting thought to stir things up so agreeably, but she wasn't ready yet for such a direct confrontation. She had a much better plan in mind. Since her mother had put her so clearly in the picture she had had plenty of time to consider her options. When her anger had eventually subsided she had wondered – for all of a split second – about doing a Hillary Clinton and turning a blind eye to what Tony was up to; it was one way of ensuring the reins of power stayed firmly within her own grip. But it wasn't in her nature to play the part of forgiving wife and besides, Tony simply wasn't worth it.

What intrigued her most was how she had guessed right away who the 'other woman' was. Funny, that. Without realising it she must have absorbed the connection Tony had made with Kate. And since her subconscious had been forced into a state of acknowledgement she had come face to face with what could only be described as incriminating evidence. Tony's Barclaycard statement, showing the cost of that silk scarf he'd insisted on buying Kate in Devon, was a dead give-away. No wonder he had kicked up such a fuss about a tin of toffees. A bit of overcooked sugar was never going to be good enough to impress a lover. But perhaps the real hard evidence of their affair was the fact that Kate was expecting a baby. Truth would certainly tell on that score.

Hearing a sudden burst of laughter coming from the dining-room, Amanda picked up the plate of cheese that she'd put together earlier along with a basket of oatmeal and Bath Oliver biscuits and went back into the fray for some more fun. 'Well, look at this,' she said, 'you've all moved and yet somehow the shuffling hasn't quite worked. Jessica and Josh are fine, I'll allow that, but Kate, why don't you change places with Alec and sit next to Tony, yes, that's a much better idea. There now, let's see how that improves our intercourse.' She laughed, 'No *double entendre* intended.'

'None taken,' Tony said sharply. Had she been doing a line of Jif out there in the kitchen, or what? And so what if she had? He was past caring. So long as she left him to enjoy the illicit sensation of sitting in such close proximity to Kate, she could do as she pleased. He was now so near her that he hardly dared to move for fear of actually touching her and, the way he was feeling, if he did touch even the tiniest bit of her he was in danger of turning into a freak case of spontaneous combustion.

'Now Jessica,' Amanda said as she passed her the plate of cheese, 'why don't you tell us how your latest book is coming along.'

Jessica helped herself to a piece of Stilton. 'Sorry, Amanda, I'm afraid I can't oblige you. I *never* discuss my work while it's still in progress.'

'How boring. But tell me, do you often write about infidelity?'

'I –'

'Something stuck in your throat, Tony? Kate, you'd better pass Tony that bottle of water, he looks ready to choke to death. Sorry, Jessica, carry on, you were saying...'

'I was just going to say that I covered the subject quite extensively in *Caught in the Act.*'

'Really. You'll have to lend me a copy.'

'And that's something else I never do. You'll have to buy your own, I need the royalties.'

Amanda gave Jessica a hard stare.

In return Jessica yawned and looked pointedly at her watch.

44

When Jessica opened her eyes she felt unaccountably guilty. Then she realised why. She had just been dreaming of Gavin.

She'd been lying in bed with him. Well, more than that, but she didn't want to think about having sex with a man she no longer loved.

She turned over and immediately Gavin was gone and he was replaced with the man she did love.

Josh.

She gazed at his face – a face that at times could be vulnerably sensitive and open, but at other times closed and drawn. She lovingly traced the outline of his jaw with her finger, down his neck, then to his bare chest. She'd never been into hairy men and Josh's sprinkling of fine hair was just perfect. He stirred slightly at her touch, but not enough to wake, and watching him shift position she thought of what he'd said at Tony and Amanda's last night – *'I'd say yes.'*

Would he indeed?

She couldn't have written the scene any better herself. It had been a few seconds of pure magic. The look in his eyes had been so utterly spellbinding that she could have thrown herself down on one knee there and then. But Amanda had put paid to any chance of that.

Honestly, the woman had no soul.

But there again sensitivity was hardly a phenomenon that Amanda was best friends with, it seemed.

Jessica could handle Amanda's snotty comments about her writing – she'd get even one day with her by using her as a character in a future novel – but her manner towards Josh was altogether another matter. The thoughtlessness of the woman had made Jessica want to take her by the throat and shake her till her teeth rattled and her eyes popped out. It was only out of respect for Josh's amazing ability to ignore Amanda that she had restrained herself and kept her anger in check.

When they'd left the scene of what had been the most extraordinary of evenings, Josh had come back with her and they'd gone straight to bed. He was knackered and it was just beginning to dawn on Jessica what life must be like for him. He'd slowly climbed the stairs, collapsed into bed and had fallen asleep almost immediately, leaving her with no opportunity to enquire about tantalising little details such as what he had really meant by 'I'd say yes.'

But more important, would *she* ever want to pop the question?

Too soon to tell, she told herself. They hadn't known one another long enough.

So how long would it take?

And did his illness have anything to do with her hesitation?

Now look here, what is this? she asked herself defensively, of course Josh's MS had nothing to do with her hesitation. Why, that would make her an *ist* of some kind and she'd never been prejudiced against anything in her life.

No, the truth was they were still in the early stages of their relationship and only time would tell if they had a future together.

Sure, she wrote about people falling madly in love and knowing within a few chapters that they were made for one another, but that was fiction. Real life wasn't like that. Real people took ages dithering about trying to decide whether they would be able to put up with one another for the next five minutes, never mind the next fifty years. And if they weren't doing that they were wondering if it wouldn't be a bad idea to wait and see if somebody better came along.

Well, didn't they?

Wasn't that what Gavin had been doing?

Damn, now she was back to Gavin.

So why exactly had she been dreaming of him?

That was easy – no Freudian worries on that score! – his presence in her subconscious was all down to her seeing Jack and Helen today and their imminent visit had stirred up all sorts of memories.

Thinking about Jack and Helen's impending arrival had her carefully slipping out of bed and tiptoeing downstairs. They would be here in four hours and she really ought to do something about getting the house into some sort of order.

She also needed to think what she could give them to eat.

She opened the fridge for inspiration.

Mm ... not too promising.

The freezer was no greater source of creativity either. Not unless she could get away with serving a deep pan pizza followed by a Magnum – one between them all.

Hell! Now she'd have to go to the supermarket. She groaned. Food shopping and cooking were her two most hated chores in the world. She'd rather spend a fortnight cleaning out an Egyptian public toilet. Okay. Maybe she was exaggerating, make that a week, but who in their right mind enjoyed spending their time browsing along aisle upon aisle searching for yet another way to satiate their stomach? What was happening to them all? Were they turning into a nation of Belly Worshippers? *Oh Great Belly God, unto whom all shopping lists be prepared, receive this miserable sacrifice, a trial special offer of a lime and coriander quorn curry.* There were times when she seriously longed for the simplicity of the small family-run supermarkets in Kassiopi. The less choice, the easier the task. And she was all for an easy life.

She made herself a cup of tea and sat down with a cookery book – her only cookery book and one which Anna had given her years ago. So what was it to be? Could she be crass enough to make moussaka for Jack and Helen? Or should she be equally silly and cook them roast beef and Yorkshire pudding?

No. Helen was mad enough as it was.

Roast lamb, then. That was easy to do, surely? She could do new potatoes, they wouldn't take too much fiddling about with. But hang on, she was now entering the danger zone of being a hypocrite. It was late September and she was considering new potatoes because the very supermarket she had just condemned for offering too much choice would indeed supply this out-of-season vegetable. Stick to your principles, she told herself. Roast potatoes would have to do instead, a little more work involved, but worth it all the same. And they'd have runner beans and courgettes, they were very much in season.

Her brief shopping list completed, she drank her tea, then poured herself another, as well as one for Josh. She took the mugs upstairs. As she slipped back into bed he awoke.

'Hi,' she said. She bent down to him and kissed the top of his head. 'I've brought you some tea.'

He sat up slowly. 'What time is it?'

'Time I was scurrying around with the Hoover. Jack and Helen will be here at one.'

He glanced at his watch. 'Plenty of time.'

She passed him his mug.

He reached out for it, but then hesitated. She looked at his hand, it was tightly clenched, much worse than last night. 'Still bad?' she asked.

'Yep.' He took the cup with his other hand. 'What time do you want me out of here?'

'Sorry?'

'Well, you won't want me around when your friends are here.'

'Says who?'

'I just assumed.'

'You assumed wrong, Crawford. I'd like you to meet them. I ought to invite Mum for lunch as well, she always got on with Jack and Helen when she used to come and stay.'

'In that case, would you like me to cook for you?'

'Would the Pope like us all to be Catholics?'

He smiled. 'I'll take that as a yes, shall I?'

'A resounding yes.'

'What do you fancy?'

'Apart from you?'

'I think you'll find I won't fit in the oven, Jessica.'

'Spoil-sport. I thought of having a crack at roast lamb, but you're the chef, you decide. Tell me what you want and I'll go shopping for it.'

'That's okay, we'll go together.'

'Wouldn't you rather stay here and . . .?' Her voice trailed away.

'What?' he said, regarding her levelly. 'Rest? Is that what you were going to say?'

'Heavens no. I was going to get you on cleaning duty.'

He let it go. He could see it wasn't easy for Jessica. 'I'd prefer to go shopping,' he said, 'you can be in charge of the cleaning.'

'There,' Jessica said, coming into the kitchen, her hands full of dusters, empty coffee mugs and several weeks' worth of the *Sunday Times* rounded up from all corners of the house, 'I defy anyone to find so much as a speck of dust in this place. Mm . . . that smells good.'

'It's the garlic and rosemary with the lamb,' Josh said, glancing up from the chopping board where he was slowly working his way through a mound of carrots, potatoes, courgettes and baby turnips.

'And what fate awaits them?' she asked, coming over to take a closer look at what he was doing.

'They'll be roasted in olive oil with sprigs of thyme.'

'Delicious. You're a man in a million, Crawford. Anything I can do to help?'

He watched her throw the old newspapers into the bin, store the cleaning things in the cupboard under the sink and wash her hands. He tried hard to overcome his natural desire to struggle on, but though the fingers in his right hand were beginning to straighten he knew they didn't have the strength or the dexterity to enable him to get through the pile of vegetables in front of him. 'You could help with the chopping, if you want.'

Jessica dried her hands and came back to him. She wanted to say, 'Now that wasn't too difficult, was it?' But she didn't dare. She guessed that what had just passed between them was a tiny milestone. Josh had actually swallowed a minuscule piece of his pride. But would it be something he would be prepared to keep on doing?

'Now show me how you want them,' she said, 'big chunks or little chunks?'

'Medium-sized chunks.'

'You would.' She began chopping.

'No, not like that, make the shapes more even or some will be cooked while others will still be raw.'

'Show me then, clever dick.'

He stood behind her and placed his hands over hers. 'Here, this is how you do it.'

His breath tickled her neck and as his warm body pressed against hers she thought of the film *Ghost* and the bit when Demi Moore gets an extra pair of helping hands during her late-night pottery session. She started to giggle.

'What's so funny?' he asked.

'It's you, you're distracting me.'

He nibbled her ear and she laughed some more. 'Stop it,' she said, 'or I'll have one of your fingers off.'

He took the knife from her, put it down and turned her round to face him. She gazed into his eyes and saw that they were dark with desire. It suddenly seemed the perfect time to ask him what he'd meant last night by '*I'd say yes*'.

'Josh,' she said, 'you know at Tony and Amanda's when you –' But she got no further. The sound of a car coming slowly into the courtyard announced the untimely arrival of Jack and Helen.

'I must say you're looking extremely well,' Jack said as he helped himself to another glass of wine from the bottle he and Helen had brought with them.

They were in the kitchen and Jessica was doing her best to finish chopping all the vegetables that Josh had left her in charge of while he went to fetch Anna.

'No guesses for why that's the case,' Helen said with a smile. 'You never mentioned anything in your letters about a new man in your life, not that you've written much to us.' She put on an air of hurt.

Jessica laughed. 'If I spent all my free time writing letters to you I wouldn't have had the opportunity to catch myself such a fine-looking man, now would I?'

'How right you are,' Helen agreed, 'they don't come much finer. So why isn't he already snapped up?'

'Same reason as me I suppose,' Jessica said with a smug smile, 'he's been waiting for that special person.'

Helen stuck her fingers in her mouth. 'Please, somebody pass me the bucket.'

Jack smiled at Jessica. 'She's becoming very cynical in her old age. Ready for some wine yet?'

'Yes,' Jessica said. She flung down the vegetable knife and took the proffered glass. 'Though what Josh wants to do next with this little lot is anybody's guess.'

Helen's eyes opened wide. 'Don't tell me he can cook as well?'

Jessica gave Helen another smug smile. 'He sure can. This is *his* meal.'

Helen gave Jack one of her look-learn-and-take-note looks. Then she said, 'Well, I suppose that really does put the tin lid on Gavin's chances.'

'Helen,' warned Jack in a low voice, 'definitely not the time.'

'What?' asked Jessica, noticing the exchange between her friends.

'Oh, nothing,' said Helen. She reached over to pinch a piece of raw carrot.

'Come on, you're holding back on me. What is it? Jack, you tell me.'

But Jack ignored Jessica. He stared awkwardly at his shoes.

Helen crunched on the carrot. 'Oh, what the hell? It's not much, it's just that we promised Gavin while we were over that we'd try and put a word in for him.'

Jessica gaped. 'What kind of word?'

'Look, Jessica, he's really sorry for what he did.'

'*Hah!*'

'No, let me finish. A more contrite man you could never hope to come across. Silicone Sal is way out of the picture and Gavin ...'

'And Gavin what?' Jessica prompted her friend.

'And Gavin wanted us to see if there was any chance of a reconciliation.'

'You make it sound as if we were married.'

'Perhaps if you hadn't gone rushing off in such a sulk you might have been.'

'Helen, I don't believe you. He was two-timing me. Probably three-timing if the truth be known. And you know jolly well I didn't leave Corfu because of him.'

'Just as you say, Jessica, but as I said, Gavin's old ways are behind him, he wants to make up with you. He wants to –'

'Well, you can tell him he's too late. Whatever he thinks he's offering, it wouldn't be enough.'

'And what would be enough?'

Jessica picked up the small vegetable knife and drove it through the heart of a piece of potato. 'I want commitment. I want to be really needed. I want to feel that I belong to that person and that he belongs to me ... that he couldn't live without me.'

Helen banged her empty glass of wine down on the work surface. 'Oh, for heaven's sake, Jessica, that's the stuff of fiction!'

'I don't care. It's what I want. I'm simply not interested in anything less.'

45

Alec had long since gone to work and Kate was alone. She lay on their bed and waited for the feeling of nausea to pass. She closed her eyes and concentrated her mind on what she had resolved to do later that day; what she had concluded at five o'clock that morning as being the only way to resolve matters.

Unable to sleep, she had left Alec slumbering soundly and gone downstairs to the sitting-room where she had sat in one of the armchairs in the bay window and watched the dawn break. Staring out at the dramatically changing sky with its swathes of cobalt-blue darkness giving way to bursts of soft pink light, a diffraction of clarity had suddenly cut through her own confused darkness and with it came the knowledge that today she would bring about an end to the muddle that she had created of her life. It was time to be honest with Alec. She couldn't go on treating him so badly. It wasn't fair. She had to tell him that whatever it was that had brought them together in the first place was not enough to keep them together. She wouldn't tell him about Tony, there was no need for that. Tony wasn't the reason she was leaving him. He had been a symptom of their failing relationship. He was not the cause.

But it wasn't just Alec who had to be told the truth. There was Tony as well.

After that dreadful night last week at Tony and Amanda's, when she came away convinced that Amanda was on to them – all that talk of infidelity and swapping partners had to be for a reason – she had known that what she was doing was wrong. She had gone to bed that night shocked and ashamed. Her duplicity appalled her. All those lies she had told. She hated the woman she had let herself become.

She had no idea how Tony was going to react when she told him she wouldn't be seeing him again, but he had to realise that her leaving Alec didn't mean that she was simply making the way clear to be with him. Tony was a married man. No matter what his feelings were for Kate, or hers for him, he had a wife who could not be ignored.

And like Tony, she too had her own responsibility; that of doing the right thing for the baby she was carrying. She wanted her child's tiny fragile beginnings to be founded on love and honesty. Not on deception. Not on depravity. She didn't want her child to have a mother who could be found culpable for wrecking another person's marriage.

She opened her eyes. The nausea of morning sickness still hadn't passed. But she couldn't stay lying on the bed all day, she was meeting Tony in less than an hour. She got to her feet, determined to ignore her threatening stomach, and went downstairs. As she glanced at her reflection in the hall mirror she caught sight of her pale, tired face in the glass. Guilt, she told herself. Guilt and shame. It serves you right.

As arranged, Kate met Tony in the car-park of a pub neither of them had been to before – anonymity was, after all, the essence of a perfect assignation.

The first thing Tony said was, 'Are you okay? You look as white as a sheet.'

'I'm fine,' she said, though she knew she wasn't. It's nerves, she told herself. Nerves at what she had to tell Tony.

Though the day was warm, the inside of the pub was dismally cold, so they ordered their drinks and chose a small table in an alcove a few feet away from a gently smouldering log fire where a large, thickset man of indefinable age was jammed into a chair that looked much too small for him. He had tufts of hair sticking out from under a woolly hat and he was nursing a near empty pint glass in a pair of big, strong hands. He nodded at them. 'A fair day, wouldn't you say?'

'Very fair,' Tony responded with a smile.

'Set to continue, I heard this morning on the radio.'

'That's good.'

The man shifted in his seat. 'Well, it's good and it's not good. A splash more rain would do no harm. No harm at all. In fact, we could do a lot worse than have a bloody great lashing.'

Kate inwardly groaned. How could this happen? How could they have ended up, today of all days, with the pub bore chuntering on to them about the weather? She raised her eyes and met Tony's. She could see he was trying not to laugh and her response to his smiling face was to think how much she would miss seeing him. She pushed this dangerous thought aside. She mustn't weaken. Not now.

'Shall I order us something to eat?' he asked.

She shook her head. She felt too sick to eat.

'The ploughman's not up to much,' the pub bore interjected. 'Too much wet green stuff on the plate for my liking. I shouldn't bother with the trout neither. It's never fresh. Nor's the salmon.'

'Kate, are you sure you're all right?'

'Chicken curry's not bad.'

293

'Kate?'

'Take my word for it, your best bet is the chicken curry.'

Tony's patience was wearing thin. He flashed a look of annoyance at the man in the hope of shutting him up. He turned his attention back to Kate. 'What is it?' he whispered. 'You look dreadful.'

'I'm not sure,' she answered faintly. She rose slowly to her feet. 'I'll be a few minutes.'

He watched her cross the carpeted floor and remembered how Eve had suffered with morning sickness. But even Eve had never looked as ghastly as Kate did just now. He drank from his glass of mineral water and thought about what he had planned to tell Kate over their lunch.

After Amanda's bizarre behaviour on Friday night he had spent the weekend facing up to the truth that he'd been pushed as far as he was ever going to be pushed. He wanted a divorce. He would be generous to Amanda. More than generous. He would give her everything she wanted. He had the feeling, though, that she wouldn't be slow in defining the parameters of a settlement heavily weighted in her favour, but just so long as she gave him his freedom she could demand as much as she wanted. It would be difficult coping with Hattie on his own again, but he would find a way round the problem. He would have to. Whichever way he looked at it, the situation would be preferable to the madness he'd experienced of late.

And perhaps, just perhaps, his freedom would give him the opportunity to offer Kate something more worthwhile than he was currently able to give her.

'Looks like your lady friend has legged it,' the pub bore said. He gave off a throaty laugh. 'Maybe she got wind of the kitchen and thought better of having lunch here.'

Tony forced a smile to his lips. He glanced down at his watch. He'd been on his own for nearly twenty minutes. He began to worry. He was just wondering what he should do when a woman approached him.

'Are you Tony?' she asked.

'Yes.'

'Your girlfriend told me to tell you that she's waiting for you outside. I think you need to get her to a doctor. She doesn't look at all well.'

Tony raced out of the pub. He found Kate leaning against his car. 'It's the baby,' she whispered, her eyes wide and frightened, 'I think I'm losing it.'

He drove to the nearest hospital. He knew next to nothing about miscarriages, but instinct told him that there would be no chance of saving Kate's child.

While he waited to be told what was happening, he phoned directory enquiries for Alec's work number. When he got through to Thistle Cards he left a message explaining where Kate was. No matter what he felt for Kate, or Alec for that matter, it was only right that Alec should know what was going on; he was the father after all.

A few seconds after Tony had finished his call a nurse came and told him what he'd already suspected. He sat by the side of Kate's bed and held her hand. But she wouldn't speak to him.

'I've left a message for Alec,' he told her, 'I expect he'll be here soon.'

She nodded dumbly.

'Do you want me to stay?'

She shook her head and closed her eyes. Tears trickled down her pale cheeks and splashed on to the crisp white pillowcase. She turned from him and let go of his hand.

He walked quietly away.

He couldn't face going back to the office.

Not yet.

He needed to be on his own, so he drove up the A34 and headed towards the motorway. There was surprisingly little traffic and at the speed he was driving Greater Manchester was soon behind him, while ahead the first sighting of open moorland drew him further on. Seeing the sign for junction 21 he pulled in behind a large haulage wagon. He drove through the familiar roads of Milnrow and when he came to Hollingworth Lake he stopped. Other than a shiny red Nissan Micra, whose elderly occupants were enjoying the view and a flask of something hot, he was alone.

He had often come here as a boy. On a Saturday morning he and his friends would cycle over from Rochdale. It seemed quite a distance now, but in those days he hadn't given the journey a second thought. His mum would put together a parcel of jam sandwiches for him and his mates, and the minute they reached the lake they'd eat the sandwiches while throwing stones into the water. They got told off once by a fierce old lady who came out of her house and accused them of frightening the ducks. They'd called her Old Ma Quackers after that.

How big they thought they were.

And how smart.

They presumed so much.

Little did they know how bloody complicated life could be.

He stared at the rippling surface of the lake and thought of Kate and the loss of her badly wanted child. And because he knew that her loss would be so great to her he was convinced that she was going to shut him out.

If she hadn't already.

He wished now that he'd had the opportunity at the pub to explain to Kate that he was going to ask Amanda for a divorce. If she'd known that she might not have turned away from him in the hospital.

His solitary musings were brought to an abrupt end by the sudden trill of his mobile.

It was Vicki, his secretary. 'Tony, where on earth are you? You're supposed to be in a meeting in ten minutes.'

Damn! He'd forgotten all about that. 'Cancel it,' he said.

'Any reason I can give?'

'No.'

'I've also got a message from your wife,' Vicki went on. 'She says she can't collect Hattie from school today.'

'*What!*'

'I'm sorry, Tony, that's the message.'

'Didn't she give any reason? Any explanation?'

'It seems to be the day for people not wanting to explain things,' she said archly. 'Will you be in later?'

'No. I'll see you tomorrow.'

He looked at his watch. Hattie would be coming out of school in thirty minutes. He phoned home to see what was wrong with Amanda. There was no answer. Next he phoned school and asked them to keep Hattie there until he arrived.

He drove faster than he ought, zigzagging his speeding Porsche through the lanes of traffic and all the time wondering what the hell Amanda was up to.

When he and Hattie finally made it home, the answer was waiting for him.

Amanda had gone.

And so had all their furniture.

'Have we been burgled?' asked Hattie, taking a step closer to her father and reaching for his hand as they stood in the middle of the empty sitting-room. Everything had vanished, the furniture, the hi-fi, the television, the video, the pictures from the walls, the knick-knacks, even the pot plants.

Tony finished reading Amanda's letter, which he had found on the floor of their empty bedroom. He screwed it into a tight hard ball and threw it down at his feet – at least she'd left the carpets!

'No, we haven't been burgled,' he said, suddenly realising that his daughter needed his reassurance. He scooped her up in his arms and smiled. Then he threw back his head and laughed. It echoed horribly in the bare room. Seeing Hattie's uncertain little face, he hugged her tightly and kissed her. 'I'm starving,' he said, 'let's go into town and have ourselves a McDonald's.'

'Really?'

'You bet! You can have whatever you want. Gherkins, fries, the lot.'

'Won't Amanda be cross?'

'Amanda will never *ever* know.'

Tony might have felt that for the first time in months he could breathe properly as he sat in the ultra-clean air-conditioned environment of McDonald's, but he was well aware that there was no getting away from the fact that the swift kick in the groin that Amanda had given him – much as it pleased him in the long term – had precipitated his number-one problem: looking after Hattie.

He stared at his daughter across the small table and for a brief moment she took her lips away from the thick gunky milkshake that she was sucking up with a straw. She didn't seem at all put out by what he had just told her in the car. 'Amanda's decided that she doesn't want to be with us any more,' he had explained, which had been a more elegant way of putting what Amanda had written in her letter.

I've taken only what I think I deserve [the letter had begun]. *You can try and fight me if you want, but really I wouldn't advise it. I'm divorcing you on the grounds of adultery – I know all about you and Kate – and you shan't be hearing from me again, except through my solicitor. I'd just like you to know that marrying you was the biggest mistake I ever made.*

'But why did she take all the furniture?' Hattie had asked, adding quite reasonably, 'It doesn't seem fair.'

'Maybe she liked it a lot,' he'd said. With hindsight, if he'd thought it would have got rid of Amanda sooner he'd have given it to her long ago. He couldn't deny that she had a perfect right to be bitter, she had after all discovered that he was on the verge of having a full-blown affair with Kate – in truth, what had passed between him and Kate could not technically be described as adultery, but nevertheless, the intent was there; if the circumstances had been right he didn't doubt for a single moment that he would have taken Kate to bed. Just thinking about it made him long for her.

He wondered how she was. He hoped that Alec was taking good care of her. He felt no jealousy or animosity towards Alec, only a wish that he would be able to comfort Kate when she needed it most.

'Your chips are getting cold,' Hattie said, pointing at him with one of her own. She tickled the end of his nose with it.

He smiled and resumed eating, marvelling at his daughter. She really didn't have a care in the world.

Just like him as a child when he'd thrown stones into the water at Hollingworth Lake and laughed at Old Ma Quackers behind her back.

By six-thirty that evening Kate had swapped one bed for another. She was back at home, with Alec fussing around her, straightening and smoothing the duvet, patting her hands, fiddling with her pillows.

She didn't need to be in bed, but Alec had insisted. 'I'm not listening to you, Kate,' he'd said when he'd brought her home from the hospital and she'd told him she wanted to be in the sitting-room, 'I'm in charge and I want you to go to bed and rest.'

And how did he think she could rest if he was going to spend all his time fussing over her?

She knew what he was doing. He was busying himself so that she couldn't see the relief in his face. But she could hear it in his voice. With each gentle and cajoling word he spoke she could hear how relieved he was that she was no longer pregnant.

'We'll go away,' he was saying, as once again he smoothed and patted the duvet, 'just the two of us, to a nice quiet little hotel, where you can be pampered and thoroughly spoilt.'

Did he have to say *just the two of us*?

'I'll take you to that wonderful hotel in Bath I told you about. We'll go for long country walks and in the evening we'll sit by a log fire and drink champagne. Do you like the sound of that?'

No, she didn't like the sound of it. She had no desire to go anywhere. But she wished Alec would go away, that he would leave her alone.

But still he rambled on about all the wonderful things they would do together.

'We'll have a four-poster bed and a jacuzzi the size of a small swimming pool, you'll love it.'

Was there no way to stop him?

Yes. Yes, there was.

'Alec,' she said finally, staring him straight in the eye, 'I'm very sorry . . . and I wish there were a better way to put this, but I think we both know in our hearts that it's over between us.'

46

Josh recognised Tony's car straight away, as well as Hattie's small figure sitting in the back. Within seconds Tony saw Josh in his rear-view mirror and held up his hand in acknowledgement. They drove the remaining distance to Cholmford Hall Mews in convoy and when Josh had parked in front of his house he went over to Tony to thank him for the other night, not out of any genuine desire to pass on his thanks to Amanda, but out of a sense of solidarity – hell, the man needed some kind of support for putting up with such a weird wife.

'How's it going?' he asked when he drew level with Tony and Hattie.
'Come in and see for yourself.'

Inside, Josh stared round at the empty walls. 'What the –?'

'Amanda's left us,' Hattie said with a big smile on her face. She then went upstairs to her bedroom.

'She's cleared me out,' Tony said, when they were alone. 'Fancy a drink to celebrate?'

Confounded, Josh watched Tony take out a bottle of Scotch from one of the kitchen cupboards. 'She left you that, then?' he said.

'Yes, she left me the cheap and nasty booze and took the decent stuff.' He poured two generous measures into a matching pair of plastic cups that were decorated with Walt Disney characters. 'Sorry about the lack of crystal ware,' he said, passing a cup to Josh, 'but she took that as well, china too, but credit where credit's due, she left all of Hattie's things.'

'I hate to pry, Tony, but did she give a reason why? Did you have any kind of clue that this was on the cards?'

'She found out that I was seeing Kate.'

If Josh had been stunned a few moments ago, he was even more taken aback now. He took a large gulp of Scotch. 'You and Kate,' he said, astonished, 'you mean you were –?'

Tony nodded. 'Though nothing had actually happened between us.' He explained about him and Kate. He then told Josh about Kate losing the baby that afternoon. 'I think she's going to push me away. Guilt will make her want to blame somebody for what happened and I guess I'm the obvious target.'

'It's been quite a day for you,' Josh said, 'I don't know what to say. Were you the father?'

Tony looked shocked. 'No. Absolutely not. I told you, nothing really happened between us.'

'And does Alec know about you and Kate?'

'I don't think so. But then I didn't think Amanda knew. But she obviously did.'

Josh looked round at the empty kitchen. 'Obviously,' he repeated. 'So what happens next?'

Tony drained his cup. '*Next* is my big problem. I'm going to have to organise a child-minder to take care of Hattie after school each day.' He ran his hand through his hair. 'Though at such short notice I don't hold out much hope of getting fixed up this week. I'll just have to take the time off work.'

'Isn't there anyone you can ask for help? Grandparents?'

'All dead.'

'What about the other mothers at Hattie's school?'

'She's only been there a short while. I couldn't tell you who any of her friends are, never mind their mothers' names.'

Josh thought for a moment. 'How about Jessica? You could ask her, just until you've got yourself properly sorted.'

Jessica and Josh gave Tony a wave and drove through the archway.

They'd both just spent the past hour giving Tony a hand. This was after he and Josh had called on Jessica to tell her what had happened and to enlist her services for collecting Hattie from school. 'Do you mind?' Tony had asked. 'I hate to land this on you.'

'It's not a problem,' Jessica had said. 'But what can we do right now for you? If you've not got a stick of furniture you'd better borrow some of mine.'

And though Tony had said he and Hattie would be fine, Jessica had insisted and between the three of them they'd carted Jessica's barely used dining-table and three chairs over to Tony's and from Josh's house they'd put together a basic selection of crockery. When Jessica had pointed out that Tony didn't have a bed to sleep on he'd refused her offer of dragging one of her mattresses across the courtyard and said that he could make do with an old camp-bed he had in the garage.

Which was what they'd just left him searching for. Amanda might have stripped the house from top to bottom, save for Hattie's bedroom, but she'd either forgotten the things in the garage or had felt kind-hearted enough to let Tony keep the lawn-mower, step-ladders and Boy Scout odds and ends of camping gear – somehow Jessica didn't think Amanda would have much use for an old tent and box of billycans; she didn't strike one as being happy-camper material.

'You didn't mind me suggesting to Tony that you might look after Hattie, did you?' Josh asked Jessica as they drove through the avenue of chestnut trees.

'No. Not at all. Why do you ask?'

'You just seemed ... well, a bit quiet at Tony's.'

'I think the word you're searching for is gobsmacked. I still can't believe the Kate and Tony thing. I knew Kate was worried about Alec's reaction to being a father again, but I honestly thought they'd sort that out between them and everything would be sweet. Did you have any idea what was going on?'

'Not a clue. Do you think that's what Friday night was all about?'

'Almost certainly. Amanda must have known what was going on and decided to put Tony and Kate through their paces. All that stuff about *when are you and Alec getting married?* – she mimicked Amanda's voice with unerring accuracy – 'it was just a ploy for twisting the knife in Tony's back and making Kate squirm.'

'But how on earth did Amanda get all the stuff out of the house without any of us seeing?'

'If you think about it that wasn't too tricky. She knew you and Alec would be at work and if you remember back to Friday night she asked both Kate and me what we'd be doing this week. I thought at the time it was odd that she asked specifically about today.'

'You're right, she did rather press the point. Kate said something about seeing a friend for lunch –'

'Who turned out to be Tony.'

'And you said you were going shopping in Wilmslow. I suppose that's what you were up to,' he said with a grin.

She smiled. 'Crawford, you've rumbled me. Guilty as charged. Lock me up and throw away the key.' But suddenly her smile was gone. '*Bloody hell!*'

'What? What is it?'

Jessica slammed on the brakes and brought the car to a shuddering halt just before the brow of the bridge over the canal. 'Look! Just look at that! What the hell does she think she's doing?'

Josh followed Jessica's gaze. In the semi-darkness, sweeping the steps that led from the garden of Willow Cottage down to the tow-path, was Anna. He smiled to himself. Poor woman, she must have thought she was safe from Jessica's ever-watchful eye, having had her daily visit from her daughter a couple of hours ago.

But before Josh could say anything, Jessica was out of the car and running towards the gate of Willow Cottage. She stormed over to her mother and even from where he was Josh could hear her shouting at Anna.

'What do you think you're doing?' she yelled. 'Have you gone completely mad? I thought I'd told you to take it easy.'

Josh opened his door and slowly limped after Jessica. It had been a long day and his leg had given him nothing but trouble for most of it; to-ing and fro-ing to Tony's hadn't helped either. By the time he had managed to drag his worn-out body after Jessica, who was now snatching the broom out of Anna's grasp, he could scarcely feel the ground beneath his left foot. He was ill prepared to put up with one of Jessica's bossy moods. 'Jessica!' he shouted, 'for God's sake, leave your mother alone.' In the dusky lull of early evening his voice bounced off the still water of the canal, ringing out harsh and discordant.

Jessica stared back at him and for a split second he thought she was going to hit him with the broom. To be on the safe side of self-preservation he took it from her and propped it against Anna's wheelbarrow.

'This is none of your business,' she hissed, her eyes wide with astonished anger.

'Oh, stop being such a bloody pain and give your mother some space.' He turned to Anna. 'Shall we go inside for a moment, just the two of us? I said just the two of us, Jessica,' he added firmly, when she started to move with them.

When he and Anna reached the cottage and they stepped into the kitchen his leg finally gave way and he staggered and fell back against the door.

'Josh!' cried Anna, 'are you all right?' She fetched him a chair. 'What can I do?'

'Nothing,' he gasped. He sat down and rubbed at the numb, aching pain in his knee. 'Please ... don't fuss.'

'I wouldn't dream of it, not when we're such good allies.'

He managed a small smile.

'You looked very cross out there with Jessica,' Anna said, as she hovered anxiously round him, 'you won't hold it against her, will you?'

He stared at her. 'What do you mean?'

'I mean, don't judge her too harshly. Her loss of temper is her way of showing how much she cares.'

'I know that,' he said solemnly, 'I just can't bear to see her treating you as though you don't have any say in what you do ... it's too close to home.'

She touched his shoulder and gently squeezed it. 'Don't worry about me, Josh. I can handle Jessica. I'm up to speed with her tantrums.'

'Good. So tell me where your mobile phone is.'

She turned away guiltily.

302

He sighed. 'Come on, Anna. The deal was Jessica leaves you alone so that you can get up to whatever you want, but you have your mobile permanently with you. Remember, it was my idea for you to have a phone. If something serious ever happened to you and you weren't able to call for help, Jessica would never forgive me. And that's certainly something I can do without.'

'It's over there,' Anna admitted sheepishly. She pointed to the cluttered window-sill. 'I keep forgetting about it. It's not a habit with me yet.'

Josh suddenly tilted his head towards the back door. 'Quick,' he said, 'she's coming, put the damn thing in your sling.'

Anna moved nimbly across the kitchen. She was just in time.

'Well?' said Jessica, coming into the kitchen and casting her eyes first on Josh, then on Anna.

'Well what, dear?' Anna asked innocently.

'I've told you before, don't call me dear or darling, it makes me incredibly suspicious. What have you two been up to in here?'

With the greatest of effort, Josh got stiffly to his feet. 'It's all been taken care of, Jessica,' he said. 'Anna had only been outside for a few minutes and she had her phone with her anyway, so if there had been a problem she would have been fine. Isn't that right, Anna?'

Anna smiled and obligingly pulled out the corroborative evidence from her sling. 'See,' she said.

Jessica scowled. She wasn't convinced that anything was fine. How dare Josh railroad her in that appalling fashion. Who did he think he was? Taking care of Anna was her responsibility, not his. What right did he think he had to barge his way in like that?

'Off somewhere nice?' Anna asked, keen to change the subject and aware now that Jessica wasn't cross only with her but also with Josh.

'I'm taking Jessica to meet my parents,' he said.

'Oh,' said Anna, 'well, don't let me keep you.' Given her daughter's mood, heaven help Mr and Mrs Crawford, she thought as she waved them off.

Jessica was all set to be furious with Josh after her mother had closed the front door on them, but as soon as she saw how difficult it was for him to walk her anger changed to concern. 'Josh, we shouldn't be going anywhere but home. You said earlier that your leg was a bit stiff and that I ought to drive, but look at you, you can barely walk.'

'Like I really need to be told that, Jessica. Now shut up and give me your arm.'

She helped him to the car. 'Now what?' she asked when she'd settled him in his seat. 'Home?'

'No,' he said, 'to my parents as originally planned. And please don't think you can boss me about as you do your mother.'

Jessica didn't trust herself to retaliate and wanting to make the right impression on Josh's parents, she concentrated on improving her temper. Think of something nice, she told herself as she switched on the engine. She immediately thought of Corfu; of swimming in the crystal-clear water below her little house and of enjoying a perfect sunset while having drinks on the terrace with Helen and Jack. She then recalled Helen and Jack's visit at the weekend. Despite the conversation about Gavin – and not for a single minute did she believe a word of what Helen had said on that particular subject – the day had gone really well. Helen had been on fine form and had started flirting with Josh. To her surprise, and no doubt delight, Josh had flirted back and before he knew where he was Anna had joined in and was declaring him a dirty dog. 'I don't mind sharing you with my daughter,' she'd said, 'but sharing you with a married woman is going too far!' In the end Jessica and Jack had left Josh to defend himself against Anna and Helen, and had disappeared to the kitchen to tidy up.

'My advice is to forget about Gavin,' Jack had said when they were both stacking the dishwasher. 'Josh is by far the better bet.'

'Thanks, Jack,' she'd said, 'I think so too.' She'd given him a big kiss, only to be caught in the act by Helen who had gone straight back into the sitting-room to tell Josh that she was now a free agent and did he fancy a life in the sun with an older woman? He'd told her he'd be five minutes packing his bag, but could Anna join them?

It had been a day of fun and laughter.

Unlike now, thought Jessica miserably. Just what kind of evening lay ahead?

Before setting eyes on Jessica, William and Constance Crawford had long since made up their minds about the woman their younger son was seeing. They very much liked the sound of her. Charlie was, of course, responsible for influencing his parents in this way, for he had told them in considerable detail what he thought about Josh's latest girlfriend. He was at the house when Josh and Jessica arrived and it was he who greeted them at the door. He saw immediately the state his brother was in and did his best not to react.

'Hi,' he said to Jessica. He kissed her cheek. 'All ready to be put under the spotlight?' he asked with a smile.

He took them through to the sitting-room where William and Constance were standing either side of the fireplace. Constance came forward first. She gave Josh a motherly kiss, chided him lightly for looking tired and offered her hand to Jessica. 'I'm Constance and this is my husband William. Ignore most of what he says, it comes of not knowing the right thing to say.'

Jessica shook hands with Constance and instantly felt at ease. She guessed that Josh's mother was younger than Anna, probably in her early sixties. There was an enviable air of charm and grace about her. She was quite tall and was clearly a woman who knew how to dress. Though Jessica was no expert and didn't know one designer outfit from another, she surmised that the stylish taupe-coloured shift dress Constance was wearing was no knock-down high street bargain. The cream cardigan draped over her shoulders was probably cashmere and the buttons were exquisite mother-of-pearl beauties. Her softly greying hair was elegantly pushed away from her face and seemed to be held in place by nothing more elaborate than sheer will-power. Jessica wondered why she could never get her hair to behave like that.

She then shook hands with William and was immediately aware of the similarity between the two Crawford boys – it was as if their father were the missing link between the pair of them. He was a handsome man and must have been as drop-dead gorgeous as his two sons when he was their age. He insisted that Jessica sit next to him and she didn't refuse.

From across the room, where he was pouring drinks, Charlie winked at her. 'The oldies are having sherry,' he said, 'but what would you like, Jessica?'

'I'll have the same, please.'

He brought the drinks over and handed them round.

Then he turned to Josh, who so far hadn't uttered a word. He was slumped in a chair with his head tilted back. He looked shattered, with deep shadows now showing under his eyes, which were tightly closed. 'Beer, Josh?' asked Charlie.

He opened his eyes and nodded.

'Would you rather sit on the sofa, Joshua?' asked Constance.

He looked at her as if considering her words. 'Why?' was all he said.

Constance turned nervously to her husband, then back to Josh. 'I . . . I just thought that maybe you'd be more comfortable there,' she said in a small voice.

'I'm fine where I am,' he said.

But it was obvious he wasn't and after he'd taken a sip of his beer he put it down and closed his eyes again.

'Well, Jessica, we hear that you're a writer.'

Jessica smiled at William, recognising that with or without Josh's contribution, there was an accepted amount of small talk to get through.

She did her best. So did Charlie. And between them they held the evening together. Every now and then she would look over to Josh and will him to feel better. She also stole a glance or two at the many framed family photographs that adorned the furniture around the large, beautifully decorated room. Constance and William Crawford were rightly proud of their offspring and every stage of their development was there to be seen;

from toothless baby grins to formal school portraits to grown men. On a small pedestal table beside Jessica was a lone picture. It was of Josh. She put him at about seventeen or eighteen. He was wearing a baggy sweat-shirt and a pair of John Lennon sunglasses, and looked every inch like a young baby-faced pop star. His hair was much the same as it was now, thick and swept back – and held in place, she now realised, by the same force that Constance applied to hers. He looked just as attractive at that young age as he did now and Jessica knew that if she'd known him then, as a silly, giggling teenager at school, she would have been madly in love with him – his name would have been scribbled all over her books.

As the conversation continued, Jessica could see that both Constance and William were trying hard not to stare at their younger son, though their concern was clearly visible in their anxious faces. And the question that came into her mind was how did they cope with seeing Josh like this? Jessica had no idea what it felt like to be a mother and she could only guess what it was to experience that strong bond of love between parent and child. She didn't doubt for a minute that more than anything Constance was looking at her son, wanting to wrap him in her love and wish away all his pain.

Because as a lover that was certainly what Jessica wanted to do. In the past couple of weeks since she had been allowed to see the real Josh, her love for him had turned fierce and protective, breathtakingly so at times – that monstrous Amanda had been lucky to have survived the other night when she had been so rude to Josh.

Until recently she'd never been aware of what a temper she had, but what with Anna, and now Josh, to worry over, she realised that it was something she was going to have to get the better of.

Josh had been right in the car when he'd warned her not to boss him as she did her mother. It frightened her that he had been so right. But what scared her more was that she had no way of knowing how to stop it. She also knew that if she didn't find a way, and soon, it was probably what was going to come between them.

Alec was determined to convince himself that what Kate had told him a few hours ago was brought on by the shock of her miscarriage.

He was downstairs in his study, the door shut, the lights out, with a near empty bottle of Glenlivet for company. He poured another glass and told himself yet again what he needed to hear. Kate was just upset and confused. Tomorrow she'd wake up and say that she was sorry, that she hadn't meant any of what she'd said. And he would tell her that he understood and that it was behind them.

He drained his glass and pushed it away from him. He could go on telling himself this until he was blue in the face, but deep down he knew what Kate had said was perfectly true.

She had seen right through him. Of course he hadn't really accepted the baby she was carrying as a child he would love and nurture.

Yes, he was relieved that it was over and was that really such a sin? Was it so bad of him to want a partner all to himself?

Damn it! He was going to be fifty in a few weeks' time, what the hell did he want with fatherhood all over again?

He poured himself another drink, swallowed it down in one, lowered his head on to the desk and fell into a heavy drunken sleep.

Kate was awake by five o'clock and by half past six she had packed the bulk of her clothes into two large suitcases. The rest of her things she would have to come back for at a later date.

She sat on the edge of the bed and wondered what to do next. She wanted to go right away, to get this part over with as painlessly as she could, but she didn't want to leave Alec without saying goodbye. To creep away without a final word would be too cruel. She couldn't do that to him; he deserved better.

She crept quietly downstairs, unsure where Alec had slept the night. As she walked past the study she heard a noise. She took her courage in both hands and opened the door. The small room stank of stale alcohol. Alec was on his feet and was opening the sash window above his desk. He turned and stared at her. He looked dreadful: eyes horribly bloodshot, face mottled with a ghastly grey pallor.

'Shall I make us both some coffee?' she asked.

'I'll do it,' he said.

She bit her lip. Even at their parting he was still being the same considerate Alec.

They sat in the kitchen, in their usual seats, directly opposite each other. Kate was reminded of the morning she had told him she was pregnant.

'I don't suppose there's any point in asking you to change your mind, is there?'

'I'm sorry,' she said, 'I really am.'

He nodded. 'So am I.'

'You've always been so wonderful to me, Alec, I'll always –'

'No,' he said, holding up his hand to stop her. 'Please don't, this is bad enough without you telling me something like you love me, but you're not *in* love with me.'

She caught her breath and watched him blink away his tears. He couldn't have put it better. For that was exactly what she felt for him. She wanted to reach across the table and take his hand, but she knew that would only add insult to injury.

'Where will you go?' he asked gruffly.

'To Caroline.'

'Of course.' He looked up at her. 'She never really approved of me, did she?'

'No.' There was no point in lying to him.

They finished their coffee in silence. She made to get up and said, 'I think I'll get going now. I need to call for a taxi.'

He shook his head. 'A last request from a condemned man,' he said.

She frowned. 'You're not a condemned man, Alec.'

'I'll be the judge of that.'

She slipped back into her chair. 'What, then?'

'I don't actually want to see you go, wait until I've gone to work ... please.'

47

Jessica was not the most organised of people and this morning was proving to be more than usually chaotic. It was the day the BBC were coming to make their film and in an hour's time the luvvies would be arriving, and if she didn't get a move on she would appear on daytime telly with nothing but a towel and a look of panic to cover her modesty.

After an early start she'd washed and dried her hair, and after several attempts at trying to persuade it into something a little more stylish than it was used to she'd given up and let it have its own way. Which meant she looked no different from the way she normally did: a mess!

She now tried to decide what to wear. Spread out on the bed were a variety of clothes, along with more packets of tights than she'd possessed in the whole of her life. On one pillow was a selection of opaque tights; they varied in their opaqueness, ranging from so thick they were bullet proof, down to merely wind resistant. They came in black or barely black; matt or shiny. On the adjacent pillow was a selection of sheer tights in all the different shades of black currently available on the market, as well as barley, beige and natural for that *au naturel* look.

It was a bewildering choice.

If it had been for any other occasion Jessica would simply have bought the first available pair, but because today was important she was doing her best to look the part of a successful novelist – whatever that looked like when it was at home. Prior to her visit to Wilmslow, she'd had the quaint notion that tights were just tights – living in Corfu, she hadn't had much call for them: in summer her legs were always bare and in winter they were covered by jeans. But after yesterday she had come to realise just how wrong she'd been; during her absence from England the buying of the silly things had apparently become an exact science. There were probably obscure universities offering postgraduate courses on the subject.

She hadn't expected to derive any pleasure from her shopping trip, but she had hoped to experience, at the very least, an element of cheap satisfaction. After all, it wasn't everybody who was out that day to spruce themselves up for their fifteen minutes of fame on telly. But as was so often the way with any of her expectations, she was wildly off beam. Cheap satisfaction was not to be had. Only the expensive brand was on offer.

She'd favoured a smart black no-nonsense suit when she'd entered the posh clothes department at Hooper's, but had instantly been pounced upon by an eager assistant who had other ideas and had tried to steer her towards a display of acid-green outfits. After she'd managed to give the girl the slip she made a beeline for the undertaker's rail of funereal black.

The prices were enough to make Jessica drop down dead from shock, but the little voice of temptation inside her head said, *Go on, treat yourself, it is in the line of work, after all.* Trouble came when she couldn't choose between trousers or a skirt. Both fitted her like a dream. Temptation whispered that further television appearances might follow and a second outfit would come in handy. Then it was downstairs to the shoe department. And naturally what went with the trousers didn't go with the skirt. Two pairs of shoes later, with the voice of reason asking her if she was feeling all right and wouldn't she like to sit down, she pressed on to the hosiery department. In the end it was just easiest to take as many pairs as she could carry and choose what to wear at home.

Except it wasn't. She was no nearer deciding what to put on this morning than she'd been yesterday.

She should have asked Josh for his opinion. He had such good taste when it came to clothes, but then he would, wouldn't he, it was his trade. She suspected, though, that in the rag trade or not, he would always have had a knack for making the most of his appearance. It didn't matter what he wore – black jeans and a T-shirt, or one of his trendy suits like the one he'd had on at Mo's party with the little stand-up collar – he always looked as if he'd just been posing for the front cover of *GQ*. She wondered if he was ever disappointed in her abysmal lack of interest in her clothes. If so, he'd never shown it. She looked at the stuff on the bed and wondered whether he'd approve of her choice. It was a shame it was too late to ask him for his advice – she'd heard his Shogun driving out through the courtyard over half an hour ago.

But seeking Josh's guidance on something as trivial as what she should wear seemed in very poor taste after last night. Poor Josh, he must have been in such agony at his parents'.

As the evening had drawn on and she had seen the pain in Josh's face intensify she had twice very nearly suggested that perhaps they should be going, but each time she had opened her mouth to say something she had stopped herself, frightened that her concern to get Josh home would annoy him. She noticed that while she was being careful not to cause Josh any annoyance, so too were his parents. Charlie as well. At no stage in the evening did anybody ask him how he was. Nobody offered to help him as he struggled to his feet when he decided it was time to go. Nobody said anything when he stumbled in the hall. And it wasn't because they didn't care. It was clear that they all cared very deeply about Josh, but they were simply taking their lead from him – if he didn't want to talk about how he felt, then it wasn't their place to refer to it either.

So was that how it was to be?

Was a long-term relationship with Josh going to comprise nervously tiptoeing around him for fear of upsetting him?

And was that really what she wanted? Surely, after being messed about by Gavin, what she needed was an uncomplicated relationship that would allow her to be herself. She thought of Gavin and what Helen had told her. Could he really have changed? And if he had, why hadn't he let her know this himself?

Wondering if Gavin had changed made her remember the first time she'd caught sight of him. She'd been on the beach with Helen, who for once was quiet, as she concentrated hard on the painting she was working on. Very slowly, a small sailing boat had come into view and as the craft had neared the shore Jessica could make out a head of sun-bleached blond hair and a magnificent bronzed body. Helen had seen him too. 'Jessica,' she'd said, 'you're drooling, put your tongue away.'

They'd watched him jump out of the small boat and pull it up on to the hot white sand. There was nobody else on the beach so it was only to be expected that a conversation would ensue. He came over, pushed his sunglasses up on to his head and took a closer look at what Helen was painting. 'Very nice,' he said. And then as if they'd been expecting him, he settled himself on the sand next to Jessica. 'My name's Gavin, do you fancy a turn around the bay so that we can get better acquainted?'

God, but he'd been sweet. His carefree manner had made it so easy for her to fall for him.

But then everything about Gavin was carefree. Just as her own life had once been. She was shocked to realise that there was a tiny bit of her that was hungry for that way of life again. Since coming back to Cholmford everything she had anything to do with seemed to be so intense – her mother, her writing, and Josh.

Most of all Josh.

There was an intensity to him that Jessica doubted she was capable of handling.

This doubt about Josh had crept over her last night when she had driven them home from Prestbury. He had made it very clear as they approached Cholmford that he wanted to be alone and she had parked outside his house, as close to his front door as was possible, and had helped him inside by offering her arm as support. She had stayed with him for just a few awkward minutes, frightened of doing or saying the wrong thing – having seen his anger once already that evening she had no desire to provoke a repeat performance. She had gone home confused and uncertain as to what she felt for Josh. She had then phoned her mother to check that she was all right.

And to apologise. 'I'm sorry,' she'd said. 'I went at you a bit, didn't I?'

'You most certainly did,' Anna had replied. 'How's Josh and how was your evening?'

'Mixed. I'll tell you about it another time. I'm going to bed now.'

'Yes, you'll want your beauty sleep for the big day tomorrow. You will come and fetch me, won't you? I don't want to miss out on all the fun.'

The sound of the doorbell downstairs jolted Jessica out of her thoughts. She tightened the towel around her and hurried to see who it was, praying like mad that the luvvies hadn't arrived early.

But it wasn't the film crew, it was Kate.

Jessica stared at Kate's pale face and the two suitcases either side of her. 'Oh dear,' she said, weighing up the situation at once. She stood back so that Kate could come in. 'Life has suddenly become very complicated for us all, hasn't it?'

'It's all gone wrong between Alec and me,' Kate said. 'I've left him.'

'I know. Or rather I thought that's what would happen.'

'You did?'

'Josh and I spoke to Tony last night,' Jessica said simply. 'I'm sorry about the baby.'

Kate swallowed nervously. 'You must think I'm terrible,' she said, 'and that I've behaved very badly towards Alec.'

'I don't think anything of the kind,' Jessica said firmly. She could see that Kate was close to tears, that she was wrung out with punishing herself. 'Why don't you come upstairs and talk to me while I get ready for the film crew, they'll be here any minute.'

'Oh dear, I'd forgotten all about that. I'd better let you get on, you don't want me holding you up.'

'Oh no, you don't.' And taking Kate by the arm Jessica led her upstairs. 'I need your help. Someone has to tell me what to wear.'

And while Kate made helpful suggestions, Jessica gently probed about yesterday's events.

'It was all so fast,' Kate said quietly, 'one minute I was pregnant and the next I knew I wasn't. It wasn't particularly painful ... the real pain was knowing that I couldn't do anything to stop it. I felt so helpless.' She reached for a tissue by the side of the bed and wiped her eyes.

Jessica came over and hugged her. 'I've no idea what you've been through, Kate, so I shan't trot out a load of platitudes, but why don't you stay here for the day?'

'Won't I be in the way?'

'Probably. But it'll be a laugh and it will take your mind off things.'

Kate thought about this. She had planned to go to Caroline's and spend the day alone until her friend came home from work. But she suspected that being by herself would only make her more miserable than she already was – solitude would make her think of Alec . . . and the baby. She quickly dispelled this last thought from her mind, telling herself that she hadn't been pregnant long enough to warrant such a feeling of loss. But there was no denying what she felt. Physically her body was already recovering from what had happened yesterday – apart from feeling tired and a little weak, it seemed to be getting on with life as if there had never been a tiny baby growing within it – but her emotions were less inclined to carry on as normal and like a tearful child she wanted to shout, *It isn't fair, give me back my baby.*

When she had left the hospital she had been amazed at the ordinariness of the proceedings. The doctor and nurse who had dealt with her had both been kind, but at the same time matter of fact. But then they had to be, she supposed, they must see hundreds of women like her all the time. The doctor had described her miscarriage as being without complication. 'But just to be on the safe side,' she'd added, 'see your GP in a few days' time if you're worried about anything, it's possible that you might need a D & C if the bleeding continues for too long.'

And that was it. It was all over. She was no longer pregnant. It was as if she'd experienced nothing worse than a bad period. She looked up and saw that Jessica was waiting for her to say something. 'Okay,' she said, 'I'll spend the day here, just so long as you're sure I won't be a nuisance.'

'Great.' Jessica smiled. 'Now at least I won't have to worry about making endless cups of coffee for the luvvies; you can do it. Oh, but heavens, listen to me bossing you about. You probably need to spend time with your feet up.'

Kate shook her head. 'I'm okay. In fact I'd rather be busy.'

'Are you sure?'

'Very sure.'

'In that case, I don't suppose you'd do me a real favour and fetch my mother, would you?'

'I'm sorry but I haven't got my car.'

'No problem, you can use mine. Where is yours, by the way?'

'It's still at the pub where Tony and I were having lunch yesterday.'

'Ah,' said Jessica, 'was that where you were when you realised something was wrong?'

Kate nodded and turned, shamefaced, to look out of the window.

'Are you really sure you're doing the right thing in leaving Alec, Kate?'

Kate returned her attention to Jessica. 'I do love Alec, but not in the way . . . not in the way Tony makes me feel about him.'

'Which is?'

Kate lowered her eyes and fiddled with one of Jessica's ear-rings that lay on the bed. 'I'm not sure you'd understand.'

'Try me.'

'I suppose the difference between them is that Alec makes me feel like a young girl, whereas Tony makes me –'

'Feel like a woman?'

Kate coloured. 'Am I that transparent?'

'No.' Jessica smiled. 'I just have above-average intelligence.'

Kate smiled too. Then she said, 'I'm not leaving Alec because of Tony. Or rather, I'm not leaving him *for* Tony.'

'Did you know that Amanda left him yesterday?'

Kate looked startled. 'What?'

Jessica came and joined Kate on the bed. 'The Wicked Witch of the West must have known all about you and Tony, and some time during the day she cleared out the house.'

'I don't believe it.'

'She did. She took the lot, well, everything except Hattie's things and the stuff in the garage.'

'I don't believe it.'

'You're repeating yourself, Kate.'

'But how could she do that? And to Tony of all people.'

'I hate to state the obvious, but I would imagine her motive had something to do with him taking time out of the marriage to see you.'

Kate was horrified. What had she done? By allowing herself to become involved with Tony she had not only wrecked her relationship with Alec, but Tony's marriage. How many more people had she hurt?

As if reading her mind, Jessica said, 'You mustn't take all the blame for what Amanda has done. Tony knew the risk he was taking. I get the feeling he isn't exactly devastated by what's happened.'

Kate thought about this. If Tony's marriage was over, didn't that change things? No, she told herself firmly. She mustn't think of that. She must stop thinking of herself. 'But what about Hattie?' she said, suddenly realising that the little girl had also been affected by her reckless behaviour. 'Who's going to look after her?'

'Tell me about it! I've been roped in to picking her up from school this afternoon, though goodness knows how I'll manage if the filming hasn't finished in time.' Jessica turned her head. 'I can hear a car. It's them and I'm still not ready.' She leapt off the bed and rushed to the window. 'Oh,' she said, relieved, 'it's a taxi. Did you order one?'

'Lord yes! I'd better go down and say I don't need it for now.'

By lunch-time it appeared that the film crew had moved in permanently with Jessica. Bits of her furniture had been shoved aside and replaced with several enormous tripods bearing powerful lights. There seemed to be a ridiculous number of shiny metal cases dotted about the ground floor of the house from which had emerged an even more ridiculous amount of electricity cable and paraphernalia.

The most worrying object for Jessica was what Rodney, the producer of the programme, called a monitor. It was this that he kept his critical eye glued to throughout the proceedings. He was obviously a man who loved his work because he kept wanting to go over the same thing again and again. He was also getting along far too well with Anna for Jessica's liking – the two of them were acting like a regular pair of old buddies.

Kate was busy in the kitchen making drinks and sandwiches for the workers, and Anna and Rodney and his assistant, a young girl called Mel, were crouched over the monitor screen in the study where they and the rest of the film crew were crammed in like sardines. 'Look, Anna,' cried an animated Rodney as he replayed the last bit of the interview they'd just spent two hours filming, 'do you see how Jessica's eyes were darting about when she answered that question? That'll be dreadful on television, she'll look like Marty Feldman. We'll definitely have to redo that bit.'

Mel made a note on her clipboard and Anna said, 'She always does that with her eyes when she's nervous, she did it when she was a little girl whenever I caught her doing something she ought not to have been doing. She does it when she's cross sometimes.'

'Thanks, Mum,' Jessica said, getting up from the chair in which she'd been sitting for the duration of the interview.

The cameraman smiled at her knowingly and the sound man took off his headphones and said, 'Parents, who'd have 'em?'

'Who indeed?'

They ate their lunch in the kitchen while Rodney and Mel discussed the next few scenes they wanted to film. There was a difference of opinion, though. Mel was all in favour of showing an arty-farty Jessica wandering lonely as a cloud through the surrounding woods and fields, but Rodney had been seduced by Anna. 'I think we ought to show the viewer where it all started. Let's have a couple of scenes where Jessica grew up, maybe even have her mother in a shot or two.'

'Oh, do you really think so?' said a delighted Anna.

Jessica rolled her eyes. Then she remembered Marty Feldman.

Rodney was enraptured with Willow Cottage. 'It's perfect,' he crooned, 'just look at the wonderful reflections in the water from those willow trees.' But when he saw the old swing with the last of the summer roses climbing all over it, his artistic cup began to run over in a maelstrom of ecstasy. 'Jessica, Jessica, quick, here, sit on the swing for me.'

'He'll have you looking like something out of a Fragonard painting if you're not careful.' Mel laughed from behind her clipboard. There was more than a hint of cattiness to her voice. She was clearly put out that she hadn't got her way with the woods and fields.

'Something's not right,' Rodney said, disappointed, when Jessica took up her position on the swing.

'The clothes are all wrong,' Mel said smugly.

'Jessica, you look much too severe in that suit, could you be a real sweetheart and go home and change?'

'*Change!*' she squawked. Didn't this man have any idea how much this outfit had cost? And as for severe, well he'd get a dose of that in a minute if he didn't watch his step!

'Yes,' he carried on undaunted, 'slip into something soft and floaty for me, something summery. I know it's autumn, but we'll take a bit of licence with the seasons on this one. Mel, you go with Jessica and help her choose the right look. A long, wafty scarf would be a nice touch.'

Mel drove Jessica the short journey home in the hire car in which the crew had driven up from London. Kate opened the door to them. It was then that Jessica remembered Hattie. 'Hell's bells!' she said, 'what are we going to do? Hattie needs picking up in half an hour and Cecil B. DeMille is nowhere near finished.'

'I could fetch her for you,' Kate said.

'You're a life saver, Kate, truly you are. I'll dedicate the next book to you.'

Suitably attired in a simple cotton top and her longest and most revealing skirt – not her choice, but Mel's – Jessica was driven back to Willow Cottage. She found her mother artfully posing with a rake for the camera, there was even a small bonfire of smoking leaves in the background. Jessica noticed that Anna had removed her sling and was standing so as to disguise the fact that her arm was in a cast.

'Your mother's a natural,' Rodney announced as Jessica stomped her way across the lawn – *whose fifteen minutes of fame was this anyway?*

They filmed the swing scene next. It took nearly forty minutes to get it just the way Rodney had in mind and by the time he was satisfied with what his faithful monitor was showing him Jessica was shivering with cold. Floaty was all very well in the height of summer, but on a sharp autumnal day it was bloody freezing! Piers, she decided, would pay for this.

The filming went on.

And on.

Jessica's childhood was revisited in every shape, form and manner that Rodney could come up with. They filmed her sitting in her old bedroom. They filmed her studying her school reports, which Anna magically unearthed from some overstuffed drawer in the kitchen. She was made to read out her English teacher's comments about her appalling spelling and grammar – 'we want to show the viewer that anyone can be a writer,' Rodney not so tactfully enthused. They filmed her looking at her infant school photograph and had her point out, from the line-up of black and white faces, the smallest and ugliest and skinniest child as herself.

And only when all these avenues of humiliation had been thoroughly explored and Rodney was convinced that Willow Cottage had been fully exploited did he suggest that maybe they could call it a day and head back to London.

There wasn't even a single mention of it being a wrap. It was most disappointing.

After the film crew had packed up and gone, Jessica borrowed an old coat from Anna and walked home. It was nearly half past six when she let herself in. She found Kate in the sitting-room with Hattie; they looked very cosy on the sofa together with Hattie tucked under Kate's arm.

'I'm shattered,' Jessica said, flopping into the nearest chair. 'Remind me never *ever* to be so vain as to want to do anything like this again.'

Kate smiled. 'Cup of tea?'

'Please. That would be lovely. I'll go upstairs and change, I'm nithered to death in these summer rags.'

But she didn't make it as far as the stairs when the doorbell rang. 'Oh, Lord, what now?'

It was Tony. 'Was everything all right with Hattie?' he asked anxiously. 'I'm sorry I couldn't get here sooner. I've been in a meeting all afternoon.'

'Don't worry, she's fine and has been in more than capable hands.'

Hattie came running into the hall. 'Daddy, Daddy, guess who came for me at school.'

He picked her up and swung her round. 'I know who did, it was Jessica and wasn't she kind to do that? We're lucky to have such helpful neighbours.'

'Oh, no, it wasn't Jessica, it was Kate.'

'Kate?' repeated Tony. He turned at the sound of footsteps and as Kate appeared in the doorway he slowly lowered Hattie to the floor. He couldn't think what to say.

But Jessica did. She had written this kind of scene before and knew the score exactly. 'Hattie,' she said, 'why don't you and I go out for some fish and chips for everybody's supper tonight while Kate makes a drink for your father? He looks as though he could do with one.'

48

With Jessica and Hattie's sudden departure, the house fell eerily quiet.

'How are you . . . how are you feeling?' Tony's words were hesitant and barely audible, and magnified the uneasy atmosphere between them.

'I'm fine,' Kate said.

He nodded, then looked down at his shoes. 'That's good. I'm glad. I'm glad you're all right.' He took off his jacket and carefully laid it on the back of a sofa. This was awful. Why couldn't he talk to her? Why was he so terrified? But the answer was simple. One wrong word from him now and he was sure he'd lose Kate for ever.

'How about you?' she asked.

'Me?'

'Yes, you.'

He shrugged. 'I'm okay.' He went over to the patio doors and pretended to look outside into the darkness, but all he could see was his own nervous reflection in the glass staring back at him. He turned away from himself. 'No,' he said abruptly, swinging round to face Kate, 'that's a lie, I'm far from okay.'

She looked concerned. 'Jessica told me about Amanda. I'm sorry, I never meant for anything like this to happen.'

Tony stared at her, then realised the mistake she'd made. 'No,' he said, 'no, you don't understand. Amanda taking things into her own hands is the best thing that could have happened.'

'So why –'

He took a few tentative steps towards her. 'So why am I not okay?'

'Yes.'

A few more steps. 'Yesterday at the hospital I thought you would blame me . . . blame *us*, for what happened . . . that you might not want to see me again.'

She lowered her eyes.

'I'm right, aren't I? That is what you thought.'

'Not entirely,' she said softly.

He was so close now he was almost touching her, could smell her light, fragrant perfume.

'I've left Alec,' she said, suddenly lifting her head and looking at him.

Nothing could have surprised Tony more. He stepped back from her and said the first thing that came into his head: 'Why?'

'Because, without meaning to, I changed. I wasn't right for Alec any more . . . and he was no longer right for me.'

He looked away, hardly daring to think of the consequences of what Kate had just told him. Did he have a chance? Was it possible that they could start all over again? And would she want that? Did she think they could be right for one another? An unlikely wave of sympathy for Alec swept over him. What must he be going through? He turned back to Kate and found that she was studying him in the same way she had that day in St Luke's.

'What is it,' he asked uncomfortably, 'why are you looking at me like that?'

'I was wondering if I would ever see you smile again, you look so earnest.'

He shook his head. 'Is it any wonder I feel earnest, Kate?' And with a sudden rush of nervous energy he moved away from her. He began pacing the room. 'Look,' he said, bringing his hands down with a bang on the back of one of Jessica's cream sofas. 'I'm just a simple guy. I'm not clever with words. I can't dress this up. But I'll say it anyway. I need to know where I stand with you. I'm not going to push you into anything and . . . and I know you need time to get over Alec, but . . . but can I see you from time to time? I'd like to do things properly with you.'

'Properly?'

'Yes. We didn't meet in the right circumstances. I want us to have a fresh start. I want to take you out for dinner and flirt outrageously with you, then drop you off at home and spend the next twenty-four hours ringing you up and agonising over when I'm going to see you again. How does that sound?'

'For a man who can't dress things up it sounds heavenly.'

He came to a standstill and stared at her. 'It does?'

She nodded and went to him. She raised one of her hands and let her fingers drift the length of his jaw, then she kissed him.

'Please don't stop,' he said, when at last he felt her pulling away.

She smiled. 'I'm afraid I need the oxygen,' she said.

He drew her further into his arms. 'By the way, where will home be?'

She lifted her head from his shoulder to answer his question. 'Knutsford. I'm going to stay with a friend until I've got myself sorted. The first thing I need to do is find a job. I don't suppose you'd consider employing me meanwhile, would you?'

319

'What, at Arc?'

'No, silly. You're going to need somebody to look after Hattie after school, it might just as well be me.'

To her surprise he shook his head. 'No,' he said firmly. 'It's out of the question.'

'But why? It would be perfect.'

'I can't do that. Everyone would say that I was using you.'

'And who's everyone?'

He shook his head again. 'Just people.'

'Well I don't have a problem with it.'

'But I do. I don't want you to be the hired help.'

'Then don't pay me.'

'Now you're being silly.'

She smiled. 'And you're not?'

He let go of her and walked away. He went and sat down. 'I just want it to be right between us, Kate,' he said. 'I did everything wrong with Amanda and I'm not inclined to repeat any past mistakes.'

'Good, so that's settled then. I'll pick Hattie up from school tomorrow.'

'Didn't you hear me?'

'I heard you, Tony. I heard you loud and clear, making life unnecessarily difficult for yourself.' She joined him on the sofa. 'I'm offering to look after Hattie because I'm very fond of her and it just so happens that she's the daughter of the man I'm even more fond of.' She kissed him and as Tony gave himself up to her embrace he realised that there really wasn't any point in disagreeing with Kate. Her mind was obviously made up.

Jessica crawled into bed like a woman suffering from sleep deprivation. She was shattered. Stardom wasn't all it was cracked up to be, especially when it was compounded by a star-struck mother and an evening of running to earth a fish-and-chip shop that was actually open. She and Hattie must have tried nearly half a dozen, only to find they didn't open until eight o'clock, which was no good when they were starving hungry at seven. In the end they'd tracked one down and had then headed for home and found Kate and Tony smiling contentedly like a couple of chipmunks on the sofa.

Love's young dream was written all over their faces and Jessica had felt pleased for them. They'd all sat in the kitchen with their plates of fish and chips, and cracked open a bottle of wine. When they'd finished eating, Tony had driven Kate to her friend's house in Knutsford.

The only downside to the evening for Jessica was that Josh wasn't there to join in. She had tried ringing him several times to see if he wanted to come over, but there was no answer, not even from his mobile. His house, like Alec's, was in darkness and with no sign of his car, she could only assume that he was working late, or was with Charlie.

She lay back on the pillow ready for a good night's sleep – boy, had she earned it. But sleep was to be denied her. The phone rang almost the second she closed her eyes. It was only ten forty-five, but rarely did anyone call her so late. She snatched up the receiver, a vision instantly in her mind of her mother in trouble.

But it wasn't Anna.

'Gavin!' she yelled into the phone, jerking herself into an upright position.

'Yeah, that's the fella. You knew him once. Alas, poor Gavin, I knew him well. And in this case very well.'

'Have you been drinking?'

'Just the merest, teensiest, weensiest bottle or two of Metaxa.'

'What do you want, Gavin?'

'Oh, Jess, don't you know?'

'No, Gavin, I don't.'

'It's you, Jess. I want *you.*'

'You had your chance and you threw it away,' she said nastily.

'But I've changed, Jess.'

'Prove it to me.'

'I've grown a beard.'

'A what?'

'You know, one of those hairy things men wear on their chins.'

'*Yugh!* Why?'

'I thought it would keep the women away.'

'And does it?'

'No.'

'Good-night, Gavin.'

'You're a hard woman, Jessie Lloyd.'

'Thank you. Any other compliments for me?'

'Oh, come on, Jess. I'm trying to tell you that I've changed, that I'm ready to settle down.'

'And I suppose you really expect me to believe that?'

'And why wouldn't you?'

'So let's get this straight. You're telling me you're ready for children and slippers and a Ford Mondeo?'

'Steady on, Jess, I only meant I was ready to settle down for a life of regular sex and a clean pair of trollies every day.'

'*Hah!*'

'Would it help if I sang to you? You used to like me singing to you when we were in bed together.'

'Well, we're not in bed together now, are we?' she snapped back at him.

'Oh, Jess, you've turned into a bitter woman.'

'I'm not bitter!'

'Well that new fella's obviously not treating you right, or you wouldn't be sounding so hard.'

'What do you know about Josh? Oh, don't tell me, Helen told you all about him.'

There was a long pause.

'Well?' demanded Jessica, 'answer me, Gavin.'

'I'm trying to look sheepish down the line, that's why I'm not saying anything.'

Jessica suddenly laughed. 'Gavin, go to bed. If you want to ring me, do so when you're sober.'

'But I'm more romantic when I'm a little the worse for drink, the words come easier.'

'That's a matter for debate.'

'Jess?'

'Yes.'

'I love you, Jess.'

'No you don't, Gavin. Good-night.'

49

'I can't see that you've any choice,' Charlie said bravely.

They were having breakfast and as a consequence of what Charlie had just said a deathly hush had settled on them, but Josh's anger as he continued obstinately to read the front page of the *Financial Times* was as palpable as the strong smell of the coffee Charlie had just made.

It was also as manifestly real as the black cloud of depression that had descended on Josh and it was at times like this that Charlie knew he was way out of his depth. As far as he was concerned, before MS had booted its way into his life Josh had never suffered from depression; the moodiest he'd ever been was when he'd been recovering from a hangover.

But this was different. A glass of Alka-Seltzer was no remedy for what Josh was experiencing. Charlie knew that once the grip of depression was on him there was no instant cure. Sometimes it would only last for a few hours, at others it could be days. He'd read an article once in a magazine about a guy who could never shake off his depression, it was always with him. The poor fellow had likened it to having a parasite in his stomach eating away at the guts of him.

Thank God Josh didn't have it as badly as that.

Charlie poured out the coffee from the cafetiere and pushed his brother's mug across the table. He deliberately placed it next to Josh's left hand – he could see that his right was too clenched to get a proper grip on anything.

Still Josh didn't raise his eyes from the newspaper.

'You've got to face up to it, Josh,' Charlie said, determined to pursue the point and to make Josh admit to what was so glaringly obvious. 'You've reached the stage where you need a stick. It would help you.'

But still Josh didn't say anything.

And he didn't need to. Charlie could see well enough what was going through his brother's mind. He knew that this whole MS thing was the most humiliating ordeal for Josh, that it was steadily eroding away his self-esteem, stripping him of his sense of worth. Resorting to a walking stick at his age was bound to be a hell of a blow to his pride. He probably viewed it as giving in to his MS rather than keeping up the fight against it.

But his attitude would have to change. He had no choice.

After work last night when everyone had gone home, Charlie had gone into Josh's office to go over a couple of ideas he'd had on one of their new lines and had found him inching his way round the room for a sample garment hanging on a rail some six yards away from him. Charlie had seen the strain in his face as he completed what to anybody else would have been a few easy steps, but what to Josh at that precise moment was the equivalent of running a half-marathon on one leg.

Much against Josh's wishes, Charlie had insisted he spend the night with him at his house in Hale. As he'd driven them home he had asked Josh when was the last time he'd seen a doctor. But all Josh had said was, 'I know how I feel, I don't need some bloody doctor telling me what I already know.'

And now, as he stared at Josh's sullen face, he decided the silence had gone on for long enough. Josh would have to listen to him. And act on it.

'I just think it would help you,' he said.

Josh lowered his mug of coffee. 'And how the hell would you know?' His words were slow and accusing.

'I'm making an assumption,' Charlie battled on, 'it makes sense, that's all, a stick would give you the support you need. It would stop you from –'

Josh threw down his paper. 'Well, why don't we just get straight to it? Let's not mess about with a stick, let's get me a wheelchair. Would that make you feel better?'

'It's not a question of how it would make *me* feel.'

'Oh, yes it bloody well is! You don't like the sight of me crawling round the office. It embarrasses the hell out of you.'

'That's not true.'

Charlie made a point of staying out of Josh's way that day at work. He knew that if he ventured into his brother's office another argument would ensue. There didn't seem any way of helping him. He appeared determined to ignore what was staring him right in the face. Something, or someone, had to explain to Josh that there were certain things he could do to make his life easier. The thought crossed his mind that perhaps Jessica could help. Could she be the one to get through to Josh?

He didn't have Jessica's phone number so he went in search of Mo. Josh had got her to ring Jessica once and with a bit of luck she might still have a note of the number.

Mo was an obsessive hoarder of bits of paper. Her desk was always a mess, as was the large drawer where she kept everything stashed away. 'I'm pretty sure I've still got it,' she told Charlie as she began taking out her pile of essay notes for that week's homework. At the back of the drawer she found a thick wodge of telephone messages and after sorting through them she finally came up with the one Charlie wanted. 'Why didn't you just ask Josh for it?' she asked.

'Because I'm going behind his back, so not a word, okay?'

'Hey, you're not trying to pinch Jessica, are you? Because if that's your game you can hand that over. I've done enough harm in that department without aiding and abetting you.' She tried to snatch the slip of paper out of his hand.

'Of course I'm not. I just need her help. Now remember, nothing about this to Josh.'

Jessica wasn't in when Charlie phoned her, so he left a message on her answerphone.

Jessica was at Willow Cottage. She'd just taken Anna shopping and now they were filling the cupboards and fridge with enough food to ensure that Anna wouldn't go hungry for the next six months. This was partially due to Jessica's desire to appease her conscience over her mother's welfare and also because first thing that morning George and Emily, just back from a holiday touring the west coast of Ireland, had phoned and when they'd heard about Anna's accident had immediately invited themselves to come and stay for a few days.

The arrangement suited Jessica perfectly. At least now there would be somebody keeping a keen eye on Anna. Not Emily, who was as irresponsible as Anna, but George, who was rock solid – forty years as a barrister specialising in Personal Injury had made him reliably cautious. Jessica was more than happy to entrust her mother's well-being to the capable hands of a man who would no more stand for her DIY antics than he would allow her to go bungee jumping.

'Right,' said Jessica. 'That's about everything stored away, do you want me to throw something together for your supper tonight with George and Emily?'

'Heavens no!' cried Anna, 'what have they ever done to you to deserve such a punishment?'

'You're all sweetness, Mum.'

'I know. I do my best. Now off you go and leave me alone. I've got things to do and you've certainly got a book to get on with. Kissy, kissy, bye, bye, and all that.'

Jessica drove home in a despondent mood. She would have liked to have lingered a little longer with her mother. It was silly, but she wanted to talk to her about Gavin's phone call last night. Silly because there really wasn't anything to discuss.

Or was there?

Hadn't she spent most of the night tossing and turning, thinking about

Gavin and what he'd said? He'd never before said he loved her. Drunk or sober, the word love had never been a part of his vocabulary. So why, oh why, did he have to go and say it now? Why couldn't he have said it months ago when she wanted him to?

There were two messages waiting for her on the answerphone when she let herself in. She hoped that one of them was from Josh, but she was disappointed. The first was from Charlie asking her to ring him back and the second was ... was from Gavin.

'I'm not drunk now, Jess, honestly,' he said, sounding hollow and tinny as the machine amplified and distorted his voice. 'And guess what, I meant what I said last night. Not the bit about you being a bitter woman, or being hard, but the other thing. You know, the bit when I said that, well you know, when I said that I –'

But the technology hadn't allowed Gavin time to finish what he was saying and Jessica felt slightly relieved. To have heard Gavin, without the aid of a gallon of Metaxa inside him, saying that he loved her was too much.

She replayed Charlie's message, then phoned him back. She listened to what he had to say. 'I'll try, Charlie,' she said when she'd taken in what he wanted her to do, 'but to be honest I don't think he'll listen to me.'

'But you'll have a go?'

'Of course, but just don't put all your hopes on me. I can't help but think that if you've failed to get through to him there's no chance of me succeeding.'

'It's got to be worth a try, Jessica. But whatever you say to him, don't let on that I put you up to it.'

'Okay.'

'And look, I don't wish to sound alarmist, but I'm convinced he's getting worse. Last night he could barely manage it to the car. If I hadn't been around I don't know how he'd have coped. And another word of warning –'

'Charlie, don't go on, you're making Josh sound like a minefield.'

'That's not a bad way of describing him in his current mood.'

'What do you mean?'

'Put it this way, his mood hasn't improved since the other night at Mum and Dad's.'

'Is he worse?'

'I'd say so.'

'Poor Josh.'

'I've seen it before. It's like he gets caught in a downward spiral and sucked into the darkness. All you can do is go with him and accept that you can't say or do the right thing. You just have to be there for him, a silent support act, you could call it. I only wish I could remember to do it myself. Unfortunately I managed to antagonise him thoroughly this morning.'

'Who's to say I won't?'

'But he feels differently towards you, Jessica. I'm just his boring old brother.'

After they'd finished their conversation Jessica tried to psych herself up for an afternoon of writing, but not surprisingly she found that she couldn't concentrate on *A Casual Affair*. Her thoughts alternated between Gavin, who had been so free and easy with her emotions, and Josh, who even though he was such a troubled person had made her feel like no other man had.

She had only known him for a short while, but within that time he had touched her in an exceptional way. When he wasn't battling with his MS he was all the things Gavin wasn't: gentle and sensitive, thoughtful and astute, and so very loving. She had found him to be the perfect foil to her own personality, which tended to be a little abrasive. She was aware, too, that what she felt for him didn't hinge on what he felt for her. It was almost as if loving him was fulfilment enough. Was this what selfless love meant?

If so, it was the antithesis of what she'd experienced with Gavin. The more she thought she'd loved Gavin, the more she'd wanted him to love her. But he never had.

Until now, apparently.

If he was to be believed.

But she didn't want to think any more about Gavin. He'd taken up far too much of her thoughts today as it was.

She reached for the phone and dialled Josh's mobile, a number which she knew by heart.

He sounded distant when he answered.

'Is it a bad time to talk?' she asked, thinking that maybe he had someone in his office with him.

'I'm a bit busy,' he said.

'Oh.' She wasn't prepared for such a lack of response from him. 'I tried ringing you yesterday evening.'

'I spent the night at Charlie's.'

'Oh.' She cringed. What was happening to her? She was a woman who made her living from words and here she was unable to utter anything more scintillating than *oh*. 'There was a lot of excitement going on last night,' she said, trying to inject some life into their joyless banter. *Why hadn't he asked her about her big day being filmed?*

'Oh?'

Oh great! Now he was at it as well.

She told him about Tony and Kate.

'Good for them,' Josh said uninterestedly.

His lack of enthusiasm annoyed her. He's tired, she told herself when she put down the phone. As Charlie said, this is a definite low period for him.

And just how on earth did Charlie think she was going to be able to broach the subject of Josh seeing a doctor, never mind the other thing she was supposed to bring up casually in conversation that evening – oh, and by the way, Josh, ever thought that a walking stick might come in handy?

So far there had been little conversation passing between them. There hadn't been so much as a kiss or a cuddle.

Nothing.

Zilch.

The atmosphere was distinctly chilly. Any cooler and they'd be chipping the ice off one another.

Jessica had resorted to switching on the television to provide a diversion. But yet another interminable medical drama was not what was required, especially when it was about a small child dying of some muscle-wasting disease. She quickly zapped the telly with the remote control.

Josh turned and gave her an odd look. 'What was wrong with that?' he asked.

Instantly she saw the trap he was setting her. 'Men in masks and gowns give me the willies,' she said. 'Another drink?' Hellfire, he was touchy tonight and obviously just waiting for her to put a foot wrong. Charlie was right. In his current frame of mind Josh really was a minefield.

She fetched the bottle of wine from the kitchen and poured the remains into their glasses. She put the empty bottle under the table and sat down next to Josh. Somehow she had to get him to talk. In the past she'd found it effortless to be light-hearted and flippant with him, but this evening she seemed incapable of the most basic small talk. What had happened to her?

Then she realised what it was. It was her reaction to what Charlie had described as Josh's downward spiral – it was destroying her confidence, making her fearful of him. She had to snap out of it. She might not be able to do anything about Josh's mood, but she had to work on her own.

Tentatively, she touched his hand. 'Josh,' she said, 'talk to me. You've hardly opened your mouth since you got here.'

'What do you want me to say?'

'I ... I'm not sure.'

'Well, in that case, neither am I.' He removed his hand from hers and reached for his wineglass. He drained it in one go, but when he went to replace it on the table he misjudged the distance and the glass dropped with a soft thud on to the carpet by his feet.

Jessica made no move to pick it up – she'd learnt that much from being with him. Instead, she watched him retrieve the glass and place it with extreme care on the table in front of him.

'See,' he said, 'I managed it all on my own. How about that? Not bad for a disabled person, wouldn't you say?'

Jessica was either going to lose her temper or cry. And deciding that tears were for wimps, she resorted to her old standby. She leapt to her feet. 'Right, that's it!' she shouted at him. 'I've had enough. I've tried to be considerate. I've tried to humour you. I've even tried to do your brother's bidding, but enough is enough. I'm not a patient woman, I've a temper on me like a . . . like a, oh God, I give up, I'm hopeless at similes, but just hear this good and proper, I'm not going to stand here and let you use me like a punchbag. Have you got that?'

He stared at her, his eyes dark and narrowed, his lips drawn in a tight line. 'What do you mean, my brother's bidding?' His voice was frighteningly low.

Jessica's anger was suddenly checked. Damn, she'd given Charlie away. 'Did Charlie put you up to something?'

She swallowed nervously. 'No.'

'Liar.'

She swallowed again, her anger now straining to unleash itself. 'Okay then,' she said, 'you're right. And what of it?'

He continued to stare at her. 'I thought as much,' he said coolly. 'So the pair of you had a little confab behind my back, did you?'

Jessica's anger had fully returned now. And in triple strength. 'God, you're so self-obsessed,' she let rip at him, 'you're so full of self-pity you really can't see what you're doing to those who love you. Your poor parents live in constant fear of saying the wrong thing and as for Charlie, he's so desperate to help he'd chop off one of his own legs if he thought it would be of any use to you. And yes,' she continued, 'Charlie was worried enough to ask if I would talk to you. And what of it? Is that really such a crime? Doesn't it just prove how much he cares about you?'

A cruel smile came over Josh's face. 'Don't tell me, you were supposed to convince me that it was time to put up a neat little sticker in my car window and persuade me to buy the latest in disability accessories? Was that it?'

'If you had a broken leg you'd be more than happy to use a pair of crutches,' she blasted back at him, 'just tell me what the difference is.'

'The difference, Jessica, in case you hadn't cottoned on, is that I've got some fucking disease that is slowly killing me.'

'The only thing that's killing you is your bloody pride, you pig-headed, arrogant bastard!'

His jaw tightened and cold fury sprang into his eyes. 'Well, thanks for informing me of that, Jessica. I'll bear it in mind on the days when I can't put one foot in front of the other. Oh, that's all right, I'll tell myself, Jessica says it's only pride that's preventing me from being able to walk, it's got nothing to do with the gradual breakdown of my central nervous system.'

He began hauling himself to his feet. His movements were heartachingly clumsy. Jessica turned away. She couldn't watch him. It was too painful.

'I think we've said enough,' he said, when he was fully upright. 'In fact, we've probably said all that we ever need to say to one another. Good-night, Jessica. Or perhaps I mean goodbye, but there again that sounds too trite and clichéd even for a romantic novelist.' The bitterness in his voice was total. So was the contempt.

When he'd gone, Jessica threw herself on the sofa and buried her face in the cushion that he'd been leaning against. She could smell his aftershave on the fabric, the redolence of which brought forth the first of the tears; small, pitiful tears that quickly turned into painful sobs of remorse.

How could she have shouted at him like that?

How could she have hurt him when she loved him so much?

And how could she have let him walk away from her?

Why hadn't she tried to stop him? He was so weak, so worn down that she could have stopped him with her little finger.

The answer was ironically clear. The very same thing of which she had accused Josh had stopped her from saying she was sorry. Her pride and anger at the way she felt he had mistreated her, and those closest to him, had killed his love for her.

She had lost him.

Even if he would ever listen to her, which she very much doubted, there was no going back. Those damning words could never be withdrawn.

She stumbled upstairs to bed and cried herself into a restless sleep, tormented by images of Josh reaching out to her and her turning her back on his outstretched hands.

The End

50

While the stolid and reliable George was visiting a branch of his bank in Holmes Chapel and at the same time obtaining his daily fix of *The Times*, Anna and Emily had taken the opportunity to slip in a quick hour's worth of furtive gardening. They were working on the border opposite the back door where they couldn't be seen from the road or the drive, and where Anna had assured Emily that they'd hear George's car in plenty of time so that they could skip back inside the house and pretend they'd been doing nothing more perilous than washing up the lunch things. But their enjoyment of the while-the-cat's-away-the-mice-will-play situation was being marred by Anna's concern for her daughter.

'Do you think Jessica would talk to me?' Emily asked as she pushed the fork into the soft damp earth and waited for Anna to lift out the gladioli corm.

'You could try if you want,' Anna said, taking care not to bruise the corm in her hands as she removed the soil from its surface and cut away all but the last half-inch of its stem with her secateurs, 'but to be honest, I don't think it will work. I've never seen Jessica like this. She's never blocked me out before. We've always been able to talk to one another, but this silence from her is awful.'

Emily looked at her friend's worried face. 'Are you sure you're not over-reacting?'

Anna shook her head. 'I know what you're thinking, that I've got used to having her around and now I can't cope when she's got other things on her mind, apart from me. But it's not like that. Really it isn't. I've always been used to Jessica living away from home and being independent – it was what I wanted for her – and in all that time I've never been really worried about her. I've never needed to. Whenever there was a lack of communication between us I was always confident that she was okay. Don't ask me how I knew, I just did.'

'And you're not confident now?'

'No. It's like she's closed a door on me.' Tears came into Anna's eyes. She wiped them away with the sleeve of her old gardening jacket. 'I never knew that I could miss her so much,' she said quietly, 'or feel so worried for her. Perhaps it's a just punishment for the hard time I gave her when she was doing her best to look after me.'

It was nearly a week since Jessica had informed Anna of the argument she'd had with Josh, which had brought about the end of their relationship.

'I don't want to discuss it in any detail,' Jessica had said when she'd come out for a pub lunch with George and Emily last Saturday, 'I'm just telling you what's happened so that you don't go and say something stupid.'

Later that afternoon, when they were alone in the kitchen at Willow Cottage, using all the kid-glove diplomacy she knew, Anna had drawn out of her daughter a few more details.

'It strikes me that all you need to do is apologise to one another,' Anna had suggested. She liked Josh and had entertained a very real hope that one day he might become her son-in-law. She felt strangely sad at her own loss.

But in response, Jessica had shaken her head with tears in her eyes. 'I tried ringing him this morning and he refused to speak to me. I tried to apologise, but he was so cold . . . so unforgiving. Now please, just don't talk to me about it any more. It's over and I've got work to do. I ought to go. Say goodbye to George and Emily for me.'

And she'd left, just like that, almost running out of the house. Since then, she hadn't phoned. The tables had turned and now it was Anna who was doing all the ringing to check on her daughter. Most of the time Jessica left her answerphone on and on the few occasions when Anna had spoken to her she had claimed she was either too busy to chat, or too tired.

'Shall I call on her when George gets back?' Emily pressed.

But Anna didn't get a chance to reply. 'Quick,' she said, pulling off her gardening gloves and handing her friend the box of lifted gladioli corms, 'it's George. Put those in the shed on the top shelf and I'll go and put my feet up and pretend to be having a snooze.'

'Jess, I can't sleep for thinking of you.'

'Why do you want to sleep? It's only four o'clock in the afternoon.'

'I don't mean now. I'm talking about when I'm in bed at night.'

'Then take something. Treat yourself to some chemically enhanced sleep.'

'So you've turned into a drugs dealer now, have you, Jess?'

'Look, Gavin, please, I'm just not in the mood.'

'I can't remember you ever saying that to me before. If I recall, you were always mad for it.'

'Leave me alone, Gavin.'

'You don't mean that. I know you don't.'

And he was right. These days Gavin was the only person Jessica could talk to without ending the conversation in tears. Over the past week his silly jokes and buffoonery had become a prop to her.

He'd phoned her on Saturday, the day after she'd argued with Josh, and she'd told him what had happened.

'I'm not sure I want to hear you blubbing about some other fella,' he'd said.

'Then don't ring me,' she'd told him through her tears.

'Shall I fly over and beat him up for you; would that make you feel better?'

'No.'

'What would?'

'I don't know.'

He'd phoned every day since.

On Wednesday he'd said, 'I can't hear you snivelling, does that mean you're over the awful fella or back with him?'

On Thursday he'd said, 'Why don't you give yourself a holiday? Dig out your bucket and spade and come and stay with me.'

'Don't be absurd, I've got work to do.'

'Oh, come on, Jess, you can write that penny-dreadful stuff in your sleep.'

On Friday he asked her again to go and stay with him. 'There's hardly any tourists here now, we'd have the place to ourselves. I could take you out in the boat.'

'I hate sailing, you know that.'

'We could have sex if you'd prefer. It could be good for you, you know, in a therapeutic, healing kind of way.'

'Is that your latest chat-up line?'

'Oh no, I've got a much better one than that.'

'Spare me, please.'

And now it was Tuesday and Gavin was complaining to her that he couldn't sleep. She hadn't slept much recently either.

She wondered if Josh was sleeping.

It was exactly eleven days since Josh had finished with her and for most of those days she'd seen him for the briefest of seconds. Every evening while working in her study she would wait for him to come home. Night after night she would watch him across the courtyard as he dragged his tired body from his car to his front door. Not once did he turn and look in her direction. Not once did he even acknowledge that she existed.

But he still existed for her. And each evening the painful sight of him invoked a whole series of responses in her: anger, hurt, regret, but mostly an overwhelming sense of love. Oh yes, she still loved him. She wished that she could tell him that. But he would probably never believe her. His pride and anger would stop him from accepting that she loved him unconditionally; that his MS didn't affect the way she viewed him, that in reality it was just another facet of his personality that had become so precious to her. She wouldn't have cared that their future together would have been full of uncertainty – after all, there wasn't a person alive who could rest secure in the knowledge that his or her own future was clear-cut and perfectly defined.

But there was no point in going over all this. She had to face up to the truth that Josh had no desire to see her, which was why she had taken the step of booking herself on a flight to Corfu. With the first draft of *A Casual Affair* very nearly finished, and with George and Emily staying on for another week at Willow Cottage, she felt able to go away knowing that her mother was in safe hands. Other than Helen and Jack, she had told no one of her plans. But now she told Gavin.

'Great!' he said, 'I'll clean up a bit and change the sheets.'

'No, Gavin, I'm staying with Helen and Jack.'

'You're such a tease, Jess.'

'It's true. Ask them. It's all arranged.'

'All right, then, but let me pick you up at the airport.'

'Okay, that would be nice.'

'Jess?'

'Yes.'

'I'll change the sheets anyway, shall I?'

Anna couldn't believe it.

'What is it?' Emily asked when Anna put down the phone and went and joined her friends in the sitting-room.

'It's Jessica,' she said, 'she's going back to that fool Gavin.'

'What, that chap in Corfu?' asked George, lowering his *Times* crossword and peering at Anna over the top of his glasses.

'The very one.'

'For good?' asked Emily.

'She says she's just going for a few days.'

'Oh, well, I don't suppose too much harm can come of that,' said George, returning his concentration to seven down.

But Anna was far from convinced. 'That place and that man seduced her once before. Why wouldn't the same combination work a second time . . . and keep her there for ever?'

'When does she go?'

'Tomorrow.'

Anna had never interfered in her daughter's life before, but she had absolutely no qualms over what she was about to do. It's pay-back time, she told herself as she picked up the phone. All those years when I held my tongue and let her get on with making her own mistakes have to count for something. She dialled the number and waited.

And waited.

Dammit, where was he? Why didn't he answer?

Josh ignored the ringing from his mobile phone. Whoever it was, he didn't want to speak to them. He carried on reading through the latest wad of specifications from Hong Kong.

The ringing eventually stopped. Relieved, Josh took off his glasses and rubbed his eyes. He was unbelievably tired.

Tired of work.

Tired of his failing body.

Tired of trying to banish Jessica from his thoughts.

He was also tired of Charlie.

'For God's sake, ring Jessica and say you're sorry,' Charlie had shouted at him yesterday, 'your life's bad enough without doing this to yourself.'

It was advice he didn't want or need.

Even his parents had phoned him – no guesses who had put them in the picture – 'Are you sure you know what you're doing?' his mother had asked him, 'she seemed such a lovely girl.'

But what none of them could see was that there was no point in any of it.

So much of what Jessica had flung at him he knew to be true. He had hurt his family in the past and without knowing how to stop himself he would probably go on hurting those closest to him.

I'm not going to stand here and let you use me like a punchbag, Jessica had said. It was these very words that had sealed their fate. He could never continue a relationship with Jessica because he would only end up causing her pain and he loved her too much to do that.

His mobile started ringing again. He stared at it, still not wanting to answer it.

'Are you going to let that ring all day?'

It was Charlie. He came into the office and plonked himself in the chair opposite Josh. 'Well?' he said, 'answer it, then.'

'No.'

The ringing stopped and Charlie frowned. 'Who are you afraid of?'

'Nobody,' said Josh sharply.

'Liar.'

Josh leant back in his chair. 'Not another lecture, please.'

The mobile began trilling again. Charlie snatched up the small phone from the desk and answered it. 'No, this isn't Josh, it's his brother, Charlie. Oh, hello, Mrs Lloyd. Yes, we do sound alike, don't we? Hang on and I'll hand you over.'

Josh shook his head. He waved the phone away.

'I'm sorry, Mrs Lloyd, he's rather busy, can I pass on a message or get him to call you back?'

The conversation that followed was brief and to the point, and when Charlie had said goodbye he handed the phone to his brother and said, 'I suggest you speak to Jessica before it's too late.'

'What do you mean?'

'Apparently an old boyfriend is making his presence felt and has persuaded her to go back to Corfu.'

Josh's face dropped. He quickly regained his composure. 'To live there again?' he asked calmly.

But Charlie had seen the expression of alarm in his brother's face. 'I don't know,' he said. 'Her mother just said that Jessica was catching the early-morning flight tomorrow.'

Josh said nothing. He slowly got to his feet and struggled across his office. He came to a stop in front of a large notice-board. He ran his fingers over the samples of stretch denim that were pinned to the green felt. 'So what's any of that got to do with me?' he asked.

'What the hell do you think? Go home and talk to Jessica. Tell her what you feel about her. Be honest for once.'

'It's honesty that's got me where I am.'

'I don't believe that for a single moment.'

'Suit yourself.'

Charlie banged his fist down on the desk. 'It's not a matter of what suits me.'

'Good, so keep out of my life.'

Charlie leapt to his feet. 'I wish I bloody well could! I also wish I could get to the bottom of what's gone wrong between you and Jessica. She's the first woman who's made any real impression on you and you seem absurdly content to let her go. I don't know the full ins and outs of what you and Jessica argued about, you didn't tell me the whole story, but I bet your bloody pride is involved somewhere.'

Josh turned on him. 'The only reason you're so keen for there to be a neat package of Jessica and Josh is that you hope it'll let you off the hook!'

'*What!*' exploded Charlie.

'That's right. You want me to be conveniently hitched up with Jessica so that you won't have to worry about me any more, you'll have somebody else to do it for you.'

An anger that was raw and violent swept over Charlie. The blood drained from his face. He felt sick with rage. 'Don't ever, ever accuse me again of something as despicable as that.' He spat the words out and turned to walk away, but he changed his mind, and suddenly and without warning he slammed his fist into Josh's face.

Charlie stared in horror at his brother as he lay on the floor. It was a couple of seconds before he took in what he'd done and it took a further split second for him to come to terms with how easy it had been to knock Josh clean off his feet.

Josh's head was spinning. He could taste blood. He gingerly touched his mouth, then looked up to see Charlie offering him his hand.

'I'm not even going to say sorry for doing that,' Charlie said when he was up on his feet, 'you deserved it too much.'

Josh took out a handkerchief from his pocket and pressed it against his lower lip. 'I can't recall you ever hitting me,' he said in a shocked voice. Holding the hanky to his mouth, he went and sat down. 'Do I really get up your nose that much?' he asked.

Charlie pushed his hands into his trouser pockets. 'Yes,' he said simply. 'There've been more times than I'd care to admit when all I've wanted to do is thump the living daylights out of you.'

'So what's stopped you in the past?'

Charlie shrugged. 'Hitting somebody when they're down doesn't seem to be the decent thing to do, I suppose.'

'You mean until now it was pity that was keeping your fists off me.'

Charlie paced the room. 'Why do you have to make pity sound so derogatory? Look it up in the dictionary, it means sadness and compassion felt for another's suffering. I can't help feeling that way about you. You're my brother.'

Josh closed his eyes. His head was still spinning. The shock of Charlie actually hitting him was still with him too. Knowing that he'd pushed his brother to such an extreme appalled him. What had he become? What kind of monster had his illness turned him into? Whoever or whatever he was, he was no longer recognisable to himself.

'There's nothing wrong with people having a genuine concern for you, Josh,' he heard Charlie say. 'It's called love. And it's what Jessica feels for you.'

He flicked his eyes open. 'Yeah well, maybe you're right,' he said matter-of-factly. 'But it's over. We've said our goodbyes. And that's my final word on the subject.'

But Charlie was determined to prove his brother wrong.

Jessica's taxi came for her at the unearthly hour of twenty to six in the morning. It was pitch dark when she was driven away from Cholmford Hall Mews, and as the car negotiated the small bridge over the canal and she looked back at Willow Cottage she was reminded of the night she'd returned to England. It seemed an age since then, so much had happened.

But in reality, it wasn't the case.

It was just that what had gone on during the past few months had been so all-consuming. Love was like that, though. Once it got a hold of you it held you in its grip, giving you the impression it would never let you go.

But sometimes it did.

And this was one of those occasions.

At the airport she paid the taxi driver and made her way to the long row of check-in desks in the departure hall. After queuing for a short while she checked in her luggage and went in search of a café where she hoped to force down some breakfast. But the way she was feeling it was unlikely that she would manage it. Her churning stomach was leaving her in no doubt that it wasn't happy at being disturbed so early.

Josh opened his front door. 'What the hell are you doing here?' he asked, bleary-eyed and disorientated – it was six o'clock in the morning and his brother was on his doorstep. *Why?*

Charlie ignored Josh's question. He stepped in and closed the door behind him. 'Get washed, shaved and dressed, you're coming with me.'

Josh opened his mouth to speak, but Charlie raised his hand and pointed a forefinger at him. 'Not a word. Got it?'

Upstairs in Josh's bathroom, Charlie stood over him. 'You've missed a bit,' he said, watching his brother shave, then realising that Josh's hands were shaking and were too stiff to do a proper job he added, 'here, give it to me.'

'I know exactly what you're doing, Charlie,' Josh said above the sound of the razor.

'Good, so let's get on with it.'

'It won't work. I know it won't. It's gone beyond that.'

'Right now, I can't be arsed with your pessimism. Okay, that's the shaving done. Clean your teeth, then splash on something irresistible while I get your clothes. What do you think Jessica would like to see you in?'

'After the way I've treated her a coffin, probably.'

'Would that be teak or mahogany?'

When Charlie parked his car he switched off the engine and reached through to the back seat. He handed Josh a Jiffy bag. 'A present,' he said, 'open it and don't argue.'

'You bastard,' Josh said, when he saw what it was. But instead of there being anger in his face as Charlie had dreaded, there was a look of resigned acceptance as Josh inspected the specially designed fold-away walking stick.

'I got it through one of Dad's catalogues. At least it's black and matches your image.'

'Some bloody image.'

'There's also a slip of paper there for you ... with some addresses you might like to follow up.'

Josh looked inside the Jiffy bag and pulled out the piece of paper. He read what was written on it and, without saying anything, pushed it into his jeans pocket.

They locked the car and slowly made their way to the lift as Josh tried out the new stick. Charlie pressed the button and the doors opened immediately. They stepped inside and as they dropped to the fifth floor Josh alternated between chewing the inside of his mouth and looking at his watch.

'Relax, we'll make it,' Charlie said, 'I checked earlier, the flight won't be called for at least another half-hour.'

'But what if she's gone through passport control already?'

'It never happens that way in all the films,' Charlie said lightly, needing to take the edge off his own apprehension.

The lift stopped, the doors opened and Josh froze. 'I can't go through with this,' he said, suddenly rooted to the spot. 'What if she won't talk to me?'

Charlie took him by the elbow and helped him out. He couldn't answer his brother's question because even he was frightened that Jessica would turn her back on them and simply get on her plane.

They looked everywhere for her, but couldn't find her. They checked out W. H. Smith, searching for her among the shelves of magazines and bestsellers. They moved on to Boots. Then across to the Body Shop. But there was no sign of her anywhere.

Miserable and depressed, Josh was all for giving up, but Charlie wasn't. 'I've got an idea,' he said, 'come on.'

Jessica's stomach was threatening to do its worst. For any normal person there was no decision to be made. It had already been made. The flight was booked. She was at the airport. She was all set for Corfu.

But was she? Was she really?

If she got on that plane there were certain things that would happen as a consequence. She just knew it.

She wiped the sweat from her palms and from her top lip. Lord, she was nervous! She hadn't felt this sick with indecision since that awful day in London with Piers. And as on that surreal day, she was now prepared to let her future be decided by a toilet.

A bloody toilet! I ask you!

To flush or not to flush, that was the question.

This is no time for joking, she told herself severely, just consider the facts, calmly and rationally.

If the toilet flushed first go, she would stay where she was – and that's Cholmford, not Manchester airport, she added for clarification – and she'd talk to Josh. She'd force him to listen to her; he had to realise she was sorry.

And if the toilet didn't flush then she would get on that flight for Corfu. Well, that seemed clear enough, didn't it?

She reached out to the handle, knowing that she was seconds away from a decision. A crucial one.

Whoa! Just a cotton-picking moment. Was there to be no clarification on the second option? No definition of what Corfu actually stood for? Was the jury to be denied the full facts of the matter? Were the members of the jury not to be told that a few days spent languishing in Corfu licking her wounds was in actual fact an excuse for bailing out at the first sign of difficulty and running straight back into the arms of a previous lover?

She looked round guiltily. So what if it was? What was wrong in doing that? The situation was quite clear. Josh didn't want her. Gavin did.

And besides, a little comforting wouldn't do any harm. Because that's all it would be. She knew how to handle Gavin now. She wouldn't be taken in by those pouty, hurt, little-boy lips whenever he couldn't get his own way with her. Oh, no, those days were gone. She was a much stronger woman than the one who had left Corfu in the summer.

Yes, she thought sarcastically, you're a thoroughly empowered woman, so much so that you're letting a toilet decide your future.

No need to get nasty.

Then get on with it!

She took a deep breath and reached out to the handle.

'Would Miss Jessica Lloyd please go at once to the special assembly area opposite the Lufthansa ticket desk.' The tight nasal voice that came over the PA system threw Jessica into an immediate state of alarm. Something had happened to her mother. She'd had a heart attack and George and Emily were trying to get hold of her. Panic-stricken, she spun round in the small cubicle and head-butted the door.

'Miss Jessica Lloyd to the special assembly area. Thank you.'

'Be quiet you stupid woman!' Jessica muttered under her breath as she fumbled to unlock the door, and with an egg-sized lump already forming on her forehead, she belted out of the Ladies and raced across the arrival hall. Oh God, how could she have thought of leaving her mother? How selfish she'd been.

'Where's the Lufthansa ticket desk?' she shouted at one of the girls on the British Airways check-in desks.

'Straight on and to the right.'

Jessica ran, turned the corner, then stopped dead in her tracks.

She saw Charlie first, then Josh. All at once she realised that her mother was quite safe and that the only heart in trouble was her own. It was pounding so fast it was likely to burst out of her chest.

Charlie smiled at her. He said something to his brother, then walked away.

Josh came slowly towards her. Which was just as well as she was in such a state of shock she didn't think she'd ever move again – a shock that was compounded by the sight of him having its normal effect on her. Her mouth was instantly chalk dry; she thought he'd never looked more desirable. He was dressed in his usual black jeans and with a baggy V-neck sweater over a white T-shirt he reminded her of the teenage heartbreaker in the photograph at his parents' house.

She then noticed that he was using a stick.

A stick? Had Charlie finally got through to him?

She noticed, too, how terrified he looked.

He was standing in front of her now, so close she could see all the dazzling flecks of colour in his wonderful brown eyes and her stomach twisted itself into the kind of knot she'd learnt as a Girl Guide. *But why was he here? To wave her off? Or . . .*

'You've cut yourself,' she said, lowering her gaze from his eyes to his mouth.

'Charlie hit me.'

'He did what?'

'He said I deserved it.'

'And did you?'

'I think so, yes.'

'That's all right, then. I was brought up to believe that we always get what we deserve.'

'Sound advice. So what have *you* been up to?'

'Me?'

'You've hurt your head.'

She raised her hand and felt the bump on her forehead. 'Nothing gets past you, does it, Crawford?'

'I sincerely hope you're right.'

His voice was suddenly low, which in turn increased the pounding in Jessica's rib-cage. Hardly daring to ask, she said, 'Why are you here, Josh?'

'I would have thought that was obvious.'

She swallowed hard. 'A girl likes to have it properly explained, especially if she's a writer.'

He suddenly smiled. It was the first real smile she'd seen on him for what felt like for ever. Much more of this and she'd be the one needing that stick for support!

'Just my luck that I go and fall in love with a writer,' he said.

Love! He'd mentioned the word love. Was there hope? 'Hey, it could be worse. I could be a civil servant and want it in triplicate.'

He shook his head. 'Believe me, Jessica, nothing could be worse than falling in love with you.'

'I'm not sure how to take that.'

He took a deep breath. 'Look, I'm sorry for the way I've treated you, for all those things I said, please ... I don't want you to go.'

'Not even for a holiday?'

'No. I hate the thought of you being with that Gavin character. Or any other man for that matter. I love you. And ... and I need you more than anyone else ever could. Perhaps I ...' But his voice trailed away and he lowered his gaze.

'Perhaps what?'

'Perhaps I need you too much.'

Hot, stinging tears pricked at her eyes. *He loved her ... he needed her.* Nobody had ever said that to her before. Nobody. It was all she'd ever wanted to hear. 'You could never want me too much,' she said, and throwing her arms round his neck she kissed him.

When they finally parted he said, 'I'm completely knackered, do you mind if we sit down?'

51

It was a cold, wintry evening in the middle of November and everyone had gathered in Josh's house to enjoy Jessica's fifteen minutes of fame.

Except for Jessica.

She was there with them all, but unlike the others, she held no expectation of deriving a single second of pleasure from watching herself on the television. And determined to put the dreaded moment off for as long as possible she was now opening the first of the bottles of champagne that Josh had specially bought to mark the occasion.

'I think a few toasts are in order,' she announced as she passed the glasses round.

'Oh?' said Anna, 'anything in particular?'

Jessica caught the hopeful glance her mother gave her left hand. 'Yes,' she said, 'for a start I think we should celebrate the removal of your plaster cast this morning and that, despite your worst endeavours, you've been given a clean bill of health.'

'Any chance of having that in writing from you, Jessica, dear?'

'Don't push it, Mum!'

Josh laughed and raised his glass. 'To Anna and her clean bill of health.'

'What's a clean bill of health?' whispered Hattie to her father after she'd taken a gulp from her own tiny glass and had felt the bubbles fizzing up her nose.

'I'll tell you later,' he whispered back. Then putting his arm round Kate, he said, 'I think we should also congratulate Kate on being offered a part-time job where she used to work.'

'That's brilliant news,' said Jessica. 'When did you hear?'

'Yesterday,' Kate answered.

'And after the way they treated you before, you weren't tempted to tell them to shove their job straight up their Dewey System?'

Kate laughed at Jessica. 'No,' she said, 'I'm much too practical for that.'

'You mean you're too nice,' said Jessica.

'Not really. I need the work and besides, for now, the hours are perfect. This way I'll still be able to carry on taking care of Hattie.'

Jessica smiled at Kate, then at Tony and Hattie. 'Well, here's to all three of you and your perfect arrangement.'

They raised their glasses one more time.

'I'm sorry,' Anna suddenly said when the room went quiet, 'but I really can't take the suspense any longer. I'm dying to see a bestselling author's mother on TV. How about it?'

Jessica cringed. 'Do we have to? Can't we have another toast?'

Anna groaned. 'What to this time? The weather?'

Jessica looked thoughtful. 'I know,' she said. 'To the new people moving into number three next week. May they be as —'

'As mad as you,' said Josh. 'At least then there'll be a chance of them fitting in around here.'

Jessica pulled a face at him. 'I was going to say, may they be as sweet-natured as you, lover boy.'

'Please!' cried a thoroughly exasperated Anna, 'before we all die of old age, can we just sit down and watch the video?'

'Okay,' Jessica demurred, 'but only on the condition that I'm in charge of the remote control and I'm allowed to have all the cushions to hide behind.'

'You could always go behind the sofa like you did as a child when you were scared,' Anna said. 'Now come on, I want to see how my garden turned out.'

They settled themselves down: Anna in the armchair nearest the television, Kate and Tony on the floor with Hattie on her father's lap, and Jessica and Josh on the sofa together.

Jessica pointed the remote control at the video, wishing that she hadn't made such a ridiculous pact with her mother and Josh last night – because Josh would be at work when the programme went out, he and Anna had insisted that none of them watched it until they could all be together that evening. 'Now if anybody laughs,' she said, 'I'm warning you, I'll switch it off.'

'Get on with it!'

Amanda was getting ready to go out to a party. As she switched off her hair-drier she could hear her mother arguing with her father downstairs. It was a familiar scene, but one which she had forgotten about until she'd left Tony. Living with her parents for a few months had seemed a good idea, but now it didn't. No wonder her father spent all his time with his head in the past. He had all her sympathy. And just as soon as she'd found herself a job she would be off.

Over the coming weeks she had several interviews arranged, one of which was a follow-up interview, and she was confident that she'd soon be back in full-time employment.

Meanwhile, there was the divorce to organise. Tony had so far acted very decently and had given in to all her requests – no more than he should after everything she'd done for him. Half the house was to be hers, just as soon as it could be sold, as well as a suitable sum of money, part of which was to compensate her for loss of earnings while being stuck at home looking after Hattie. And, of course, she had all that furniture in store just waiting for her to set herself up somewhere new.

When she'd asked her solicitor if it wasn't worth their while pushing for more, the woman's response had been a little disappointing. 'My advice to you, Mrs Fergusson, is to quit while you're ahead,' she'd said.

Well, maybe her solicitor was right. It wouldn't do to be seen as greedy. Not that she thought she was being greedy. In her opinion Tony had been prepared to hand over as much as he had because his conscience had made him do so. He had put no effort into making a go of their marriage and had been only too quick to stray into the arms of another woman. And if it hadn't been for her father catching Tony and Kate red-handed that day in Holmes Chapel, goodness knows how long it would have been before she'd have discovered what he was up to.

She finished applying her make-up and went downstairs. There was no sign of her father, but she found her mother in the sitting-room watching a wildlife programme. Amanda's stomach turned as she caught sight of a panther feasting on a gazelle. She shuddered. Predatory animals, weren't they just the worst?

It was Alec's fiftieth birthday. He wasn't celebrating it in the way he had imagined – in Venice with Kate – but he was enjoying himself. His dinner companion was proving to be good company, but then he wouldn't have expected anything less.

Getting over Kate hadn't been as bad as he'd thought it would be. Initially he had felt sorry for himself and had wanted her back. Unable to stop what he was doing, he had been rather pathetic and pestered poor Jessica and Josh about Kate. They had been very patient with him. And very tactful. When he'd discovered that Kate had been seeing Tony behind his back he had been mortified, distraught with jealousy. But in a way all that deception had helped him to get over her. There was nothing like a little anger to harden one's resolve.

As time wore on, and from the little he could glean from Jessica, his reaction to what had happened between him and Kate changed. It shook him that he actually wished Kate and Tony well. He hoped that one day she would have the children she so badly craved. He was even thankful that it had been Tony who had taken Kate to the hospital that day when she'd lost the baby. He was glad that it hadn't been, as Kate had told him, a stranger who had helped her, but someone who really cared about her.

He saw now that he had fallen for Kate because he'd been unbelievably flattered by her being interested in him. What man wouldn't be? She had stroked and pampered his battered ego – Melissa's departure had left him more devastated than he'd realised at the time – and Kate had made him feel as though he wasn't such a disaster area after all. When it came down to it, it wasn't love that he'd felt for Kate, but gratitude. And feeling grateful to another person leaves you vulnerable – it makes you feel beholden to that person, that you could never be worthy of their love.

He now looked at the person sitting opposite him. Gratitude was something he'd never felt for Melissa – he'd felt a lot of other things for her, but a sense of obligation had never been one of them. Perhaps this was because they'd always viewed one another as equals. Since they'd formed Thistle Cards there had never been a time when they hadn't worked well together – even during their divorce the company had been rock steady under their equal partnership. When it came to business they were of one mind, with an uncanny knack for second-guessing what the other was thinking.

But they weren't conducting business tonight, which meant he had no idea what his ex-wife was thinking. Melissa was one of the most private people he knew and when it came to anything of a personal nature she played things close to the chest. Last week he had spoken to Ruth on the phone and when his daughter had taken a break from complaining about Kate – 'I feel very let down, Dad, decent child-minders are hard to come by' – she had told him that Tim was now history. 'Don't say I said anything,' she went on, 'but Mum sent him packing. She said she couldn't stand him any longer. Something about him having too high an opinion of himself and too low an opinion of others.'

It was certainly news to Alec. Melissa hadn't said a word about any of this at work. But then he wouldn't have expected her to confide in him.

And as they read their menus Alec decided to give Melissa an opportunity to put him in the picture. 'So how's things with you and Tim?' he said as directly as he dared, but at the same time hiding behind his menu.

'Tim who?'

Alec raised his eyes and smiled. 'Like that, is it?'

She didn't return his smile, but kept her gaze on her menu. 'I think I'll have the Dover sole.'

'No starter?'

'No. But you go ahead, I'll pick something from your plate.'

Alec was tempted to say 'like in the old days', but a comment like that deserved to be treated to the derision she would most certainly fling back at him – he and Melissa might spend their days constantly immersed in greetings card sentiment, but there were limits to what either of them would put up with after office hours.

They ordered their food and Alec poured their wine.

'Will you stay in Cholmford?' she asked him.

'I haven't decided yet.' Which was true. At first he'd thought he'd have to move, that he wouldn't be able to cope with seeing Kate's car parked outside Tony's, but when he'd seen the 'for sale' board go up at number two he'd decided to sit tight for a while. There was no point in running away when very soon there wouldn't be anything to run away from. And despite everything that had happened, he liked his house; it was home to him now.

Melissa raised her glass to him. 'Happy fiftieth, by the way,' she said. Then she reached down to her handbag on the floor and pulled out a small parcel for him.

'For me?'

'Who else?'

'You shouldn't have.'

'Save the self-effacing touch and get on and open it.'

He unwrapped the parcel. It was an uninspiring cheaply made notebook, the sort with which the Chinese continually flooded the market. 'Um ... thank you,' he said.

She laughed. 'I know exactly what you're thinking, Alec.'

'You do?'

'You're wondering how to thank me for such a cheap and nasty present, aren't you?'

'Of course not.' Then he smiled. 'Okay, then, you're right. Have you bought me an expensive pen to go with it?'

She shook her head. 'That's the present, take it or leave it.'

'Oh, I shall definitely take it,' he said, 'gift horses and all that.'

'It's up to you what you use it for, but it's meant to be symbolic.'

'Of what?'

She reached for her glass of wine. 'Do you remember when I left you, I said I was tired of reading the same book?'

'Yes,' he said, 'I remember very well. I was extremely hurt by what you said.'

'I'm sorry I hurt you, Alec, but I said it because it was true ... at the time.'

Alec had an uncomfortable feeling that he knew what Melissa was going to say next and he wasn't sure what to make of it. 'And now?'

'Well, let's just say that since then, and after what we've been through, both of us must be quite different.'

'You mean improved, like a good wine?'

'Let's not overdo the metaphors.' She smiled. 'What I'm saying is that

349

you're a different book now and one I'd be interested in taking off the shelf. I'm prepared to take the risk ... are you?'

He leant back in his chair and contemplated her. 'I think you've got a bloody nerve, Melissa,' he said slowly.

'But that's what you always liked about me,' she countered. 'You used to say that you admired my strength of character.'

'And what makes you think, after what you did to me, that I'd even consider taking a risk on you again?'

'It was *you* who invited me to dinner tonight.'

'For something called old times' sake.'

'Well, it could be a start.'

'Are you serious, Melissa?'

'We could see if it works.'

Alec shook his head. 'I don't know. We're not the people we used to be, it would be –'

'That's the whole point. It would be different.'

'I still don't know. What about sex?'

'What, right now?'

'*Melissa!*'

She smiled. 'That, too, would be different. I assume you've learnt a new trick or two from Kate. I know I have from Tim. Alec, I don't believe it, you're blushing.'

'Look,' he said, reaching for her hand across the table, 'I'm just an old-fashioned bloke who's beginning to feel his age. I'm not sure I'm up to all this.'

'Nonsense. You'll pick it up as we go along.'

He smiled at her, then laughed. 'You're quite amazing, you know that?'

'It's often been said. And while we're on the subject, you're not so bad yourself. Now, where's my sole? I'm hungry.'

He laughed again. 'There must be some wise-cracking response to that question, but I'm too stunned to come up with anything.'

'Good. Now pour me another glass of wine and let's drink to the future.'

'No, I've a better toast. Here's to better the devil you know.'

'You silly old fool, you.'

'You can come out now,' Josh said as Jessica's face disappeared from the television screen and the presenter of the programme moved on to discuss the relative merits of a home confinement.

Jessica lowered the cushions and emerged. 'I swear that wasn't me,' she said. 'I didn't say half of those things, they've dubbed stuff on afterwards. Nobody could sound that ridiculous.'

'You did say those things,' Anna said. 'I was there; I saw and heard all of it. I was rather good, wasn't I? That bit with the bonfire came across well, I thought.'

'You were both wonderful,' Kate said generously.

'Yes,' agreed Tony, 'quite the double act.'

Jessica groaned. 'My claim to fame, the unfunny half of a double act; the stooge.'

Josh squeezed her hand. 'You were fine, honestly.'

'But what about that bit on the swing?'

He grinned. 'It was the best bit. I'm going to watch it again later.'

She pulled a face. 'For that, you can go and get us all something to eat. And as a real punishment I'll come and help you.'

'Anything I can do?' offered Kate.

'No,' said Jessica, 'I want to bully Josh alone.'

He got to his feet and Jessica slowly followed behind him. When they reached the kitchen they could hear the others replaying the video and laughing out loud.

'Mum was pretty good, wasn't she?' Jessica said as she watched Josh open the oven and pull out a large dish of Cajun-style chicken wings. He placed the hot dish on the hob and gave the pieces of chicken a prod with a sharp knife.

'Perfect,' he said.

'Oh, come on, she wasn't that good.'

'I was talking about the chicken, but you're right, Anna played her part beautifully. So did you.'

'Really? Do you mean that?'

He glanced over at her and frowned. 'I've never seen you in unsure mode before. You okay?'

'Mm . . . I don't know, I think I need a hug.'

He put the chicken back in the oven, took off the oven gloves and held out his arms. She went to him like a small child needing to be comforted. He held her tightly. 'That better?' he asked.

'Nearly.'

He stroked her hair, suddenly worried. With shame he realised that lately life had been so good for him he'd hardly bothered to wonder if the same was true for Jessica. She always appeared so strong, so confident and positive, and had been such a support to him over the weeks that he had come to rely on her vitality to help him through any of his low periods. But had it been too much for her? Was he sapping her of her energy? And was she beginning to regret moving in with him?

A week after he'd stopped her getting on that plane for Corfu he had suggested that they live together and it had been her idea that she move in with him, rather than the other way around. 'Your house is bigger than mine and has the best views,' she'd said in her typically frank manner, 'let's see how it goes, shall we?' He'd thought that the arrangement was working perfectly. Jessica would work in her study in her own house during the day and when she had finished writing, not long after he arrived home, she would come across the courtyard to him. It had seemed an ideal set-up.

But maybe it wasn't. Perhaps she had seen too much of the real him. It was possible that she had found his problems too much to cope with, and he could hardly blame her for that, sometimes they seemed too much for him.

No, that wasn't strictly true these days. Having Jessica in his life and feeling secure in their love for one another had gone a long way to altering his perspective. Though not completely, there were still times when he panicked when he thought of the future, which was reasonable enough – Jessica's love could never be turned into a miracle cure, but it was certainly palliative. She had boosted his self-esteem, which in turn had put him on better terms with his brother and parents, and everyone at work including Mo. They were less cautious of him now. He suspected that this was because they had always taken their cue from him and now that he was more at ease, they were too.

He'd taken his mother out to lunch one day to try and apologise to her, to bridge the gap he had so ruthlessly forced between them. It had been difficult at first to find the right words to express himself because he had become so used to concealing the truth from her. In the end he had resorted to saying that he was sorry and to ask if she would forgive him. 'Nothing to forgive,' she'd said, but the tears in her eyes had told him that this wasn't the case. It also told him just how much he had hurt her.

Undeniably, his mental capacity to cope with his MS was stronger than it had been, which was just as well because it was showing no sign of easing up – but to be positive, it wasn't showing any sign of worsening. The stiffness in his leg was as bad as ever and sometimes it really got to him, but with the help of a physiotherapist whom he'd started seeing recently – and not forgetting the wretched stick Charlie had given him – he was now able to move about more freely. With regard to the wretched stick, his brother hadn't ever said the words 'I told you so', but Josh knew they were there for the prompting, which amused him.

It also amused him when Jessica tried to play the role of Florence Nightingale on speed. He'd found the perfect way to stop her. Instead of over-reacting and blowing up at her, he simply took her in his arms and kissed her till she couldn't breathe. 'A shame I can't do that to her myself,' Anna had said when he'd told her how he had got round Jessica's bossiness.

But it was Jessica's forthright manner that had helped him to take an important step, one that he now saw as being crucial for them both. That day at the airport when Charlie had presented him with the walking stick his brother had also given him the address of the MS Society, as well as the name and phone number of a man who belonged to a self-help group for MS sufferers in the area. His first reaction was that he would have none of it – what would he have in common with a bunch of people who wanted to sit around discussing how ill they were? But he hadn't bargained on Jessica taking things into her own hands. Without him knowing it she phoned the number Charlie had given him and asked the man if he would agree to meet them for a drink.

He came to the house late one evening. His name was Chris Perry and it was only when Jessica had made the necessary introductions that Josh realised what she'd done behind his back. But it was impossible for him to be cross, for two reasons. First, he found he loved Jessica too much to be furious with her and second, the man who had gone to such trouble to meet him was wearing an item of clothing that invariably caused most people to be on their best behaviour, including Josh.

'Sorry, I'm late,' he'd said, settling himself in a chair and taking the glass of wine Jessica was offering him. He knocked back the drink and began removing his dog-collar. 'Do you mind?' he asked, tossing it on the table, 'I hate wearing the damn thing, but I've just been dealing with a woman who thought her house was haunted. She needed the reassurance of a bit of Popery, 'course there wasn't a ghost in sight, just a case of noisy neighbours. Anyway, less of me, more of you, Josh. How's it hanging?'

The Reverend Chris Perry was in his early forties, an Anglican minister, married, with a young son, and before MS – in a relatively mild form – had entered his life, he'd been a compulsive potholer. 'Of course, these days the only hole I get near is the one I've dug myself into from the pulpit,' he told them. 'There's nothing like a controversial vicar to stir up the mob.'

On the face of it he and Chris had nothing in common, but the more the conversation progressed, the more similarities Josh could see between them. Despite the bravado Chris showed, Josh sensed that he was just as concerned for his own future as Josh was. 'I don't mind the possibility of one day being in a wheelchair,' he had said, while driving Josh to meet the rest of the group for the first time two weeks ago, 'it's the crap that goes with it I can't hack. If you can't walk, people assume that you're brain-dead.'

It was a view that was shared by everyone to whom Josh was introduced at the group that evening. If he'd thought the only common thread that would hold these people together would be their depressing list of aches and pains he was proved wrong – it was actually their spirited sense of humour that kept them afloat, offering each other support and under-standing. Josh had come away impressed.

And a little humbled. He had a lot to learn.

Which was what Chris said to him in the car on the way home

afterwards. 'It's not just about learning to confront the illness,' he'd said, 'it's learning to laugh at yourself. An illness like MS tends to bring out the worst in us, the challenge is to overcome that and dig out the best in ourselves. No matter how deep you have to go, Josh, just keep on digging.'

On reflection, it was quite a challenge and Josh wasn't entirely sure that he was up for it. But on the other hand, he was aware that in the past few days he'd actually caught himself thinking how happy he was. A milestone in itself.

But suddenly he wasn't so sure.

If Jessica wasn't happy, where did that leave him? Was it possible that she was still hankering for her old way of life in Corfu? Was that where she believed she really belonged? With Gavin . . . a man who didn't have half the problems he had? 'There's nothing wrong, is there?' he finally dared to ask Jessica.

She raised her head from his shoulder. 'No, not really. What made you say that?'

'I was just wondering if you thought that moving in with me wasn't such a good idea.'

'What an extraordinary thing to say. I love being here with you. I wouldn't have it any other way.'

'So why the long face?'

She sighed. 'It's called seeing yourself as others see you. I'm in shock. I looked and sounded dreadful on that programme.'

Relief flooded through him. Nothing had changed between them. Everything was all right. He kissed her. 'Now you know what I have to put up with every morning when I see you lying next to me.'

'You're all charm, now get back to your oven gloves.'

'No,' he said, still holding her in his arms and deciding that now was as good a time as any to let Jessica know what she meant to him, 'there's something I'd like you to ask me.'

'Mm . . .' she said, 'something you want *me* to ask *you*? Sounds a bit tricksy. Any clues?'

He nodded. 'You already know the answer to the question because I gave it to you that awful night at Tony and Amanda's. Do you remember?'

She stared at him, unsure. Then it slowly dawned on her – the flickering candle-light, the way he'd gazed at her and the heart-stopping moment when he'd said *I'd say yes*. She swallowed. 'You mean –?'

'I know I'm not much of a catch, a man who hobbles about with a stick and –'

'Don't go selling yourself short, Crawford,' she said with a smile. 'I know the score.'

He smiled too. 'So, is there any chance that you might ever want to ask me that particular question?'

'Do rabbits like hot-cross buns?'

He raised a puzzled eyebrow. 'Don't you mean carrots?'

'Hey, who's asking the questions? Now tell me, has this got to be a down-on-the-one-knee job?'

He laughed. 'I would think so. Properly or not at all.'

'Like this?'

'Yes, that looks about right.'

'Well, here goes then.' She looked up at him and cleared her throat. 'Joshua, will you –' But she got no further. The phone rang out, loud and shrill.

'I hope that's got nothing to do with fate,' Josh said, disappointed as Jessica got to her feet. 'I'll get it while you serve up the supper for the others,' he added.

He answered the phone, then covered the mouthpiece with his hand. 'It's Piers,' he said, 'do you want to take it in the study while I finish off here?'

Wishing she'd never been so stupid as to give Josh's number to her agent, Jessica picked up the extension in Josh's study. 'Hello, Piers,' she said grumpily, 'this had better be good because your timing is absolutely bloody awful.'

'And good-evening to you, too, Jessica.'

'Don't be sarcastic with me, you've just ruined the greatest moment of my life.'

'Well, if I can tear you away for a little longer, I was ringing to say that you weren't bad on the television this afternoon. Not bad at all. In fact, almost good. A shame you had to go and spoil it by showing your knickers on the swing.'

'How kind of you to share that with me, Piers.' *Argh!* Would he never change? Would he never pay her a clear-cut compliment?

'I'll be in touch.'

'No hurry. Good-night.'

She went back to the kitchen and found everybody helping themselves to something to eat. Another bottle of bubbly had been opened and they all seemed very merry. She wondered if they would miss her and Josh for a while. He came over to her. 'Everything okay?' he asked quietly.

'How's your leg?' she whispered.

'Pardon?'

'Could you manage a short walk?'

'Where to?'

'Just to the woods.'

'Any reason why?'

'I want to get you alone and finish what we started a few minutes ago.'

They sat on what they now referred to as 'their' fallen oak tree. It was a cold and blustery night, and thick black clouds scudded over a full moon; branches swayed, leaves rustled.

'It's like something out of a Hammer House of Horror film, isn't it?' said Jessica with a shiver as she stared up at the restless sky. 'All we need is a howling wolf to complete the scene.'

'And some swirling mist.'

'Vincent Price in a black cloak with blood-red silk lining would be a nice touch.'

'So would Peter Cushing.'

'We shouldn't leave out Christopher Lee.'

'You're right. We'd have to have all three.'

'But what about Boris Karloff?'

'Him, too, if you want.' Josh put his arm around Jessica's shoulder and drew her inside his thick overcoat. He wondered if she was beginning to change her mind. 'You're not getting cold feet, are you?'

She turned her head and smiled up at him. 'You wouldn't be trying to talk me out of proposing to you, would you?'

He suddenly looked serious. 'I wouldn't blame you. We can't pretend my problems won't affect –'

She silenced him by placing a finger on his lips.

'And what about Gavin?' he mumbled against her finger.

She removed her hand. 'I don't believe you. Now you really are getting desperate.'

'He was very upset when you didn't turn up in Corfu. How many times did he ring you?'

'Too many, that's how many. Now please, can we put all the prevaricating aside and get on with what we're here to do? And to put us in the right frame of mind, we'll kick off with a kiss.'

'You sound like you've done this before.'

She laughed and kissed him. And when they stopped, she stared up into his face. 'I'm sorry,' she said in a low voice, 'it's no good, I really can't go through with it. I've changed my mind.'

He looked at her with a horrified gaze. 'But –'

'Don't panic.' She smiled. 'It turns out I'm a traditionalist at heart. In my book the romantic hero has to do the proposing.'

He let out his breath in one long sigh of relief. 'In that case, there's nothing else for it. Miss Jessica Lloyd –'

'Yes!'

'I haven't finished. Would you –'

'Yes!'

'Do me –'

'Yes!'

'The honour –'

'*Yes?*'

'Of marrying me?'

'Yes, yes, yes, yes, yes!'

'Thank goodness for that.'

'Now what do we do?'

'We go home. I'm frozen to death sitting here.'

'You're such a romantic, Crawford.'

'But cute with it, wouldn't you say?'

She helped him to his feet and passed him his stick. 'And as we walk, we'll plan the wedding. St Paul's would be a good choice. We ought to think big.'

'Yes. But if it's booked, we'll make do with Westminster Abbey.'

'And Charlie can be best man.'

'Naturally. And Helen could be your matron of honour.'

'How about Chris to officiate?'

'Good idea. And to hell with convention, Anna can give you away.'

'Brilliant. She'll love doing that.'

'I can hardly wait.'

'Me neither.'

'Jessica?'

'Yes?'

'Where will we live?'

'Your house, of course. Why move again? I've a feeling it's exactly where we both belong.'

THE END

Or to put it another way

THE BEGINNING

Dancing in the Dark

For Yvette Goulden

Acknowledgement

I am grateful to the authors of the following books which were of great assistance when writing *Dancing in the Dark*. *The Admiralty Regrets* by C. E. T. Warren and James Benson, published by White Lion Publishers, provided a thorough and detailed description of the *Thetis* tragedy. David M. Whale's fascinating series, *Lost Villages of Liverpool*, published by T. Stephenson & Sons, told me all I needed to know about old Toxteth.

Prologue

It always began with the sound of the footsteps, the soft, slithering footsteps on the stairs, the unshod feet in their well-darned socks lifting steadily from one step to the next. He wasn't the sort of man to wear slippers. Listening, I would picture him in my mind's eye, just his feet, coming up the narrow beige carpet with the red border, the cheapest you could buy, worn away to threads in the middle and secured to the stairs with triangular-shaped varnished rods that slid into bronze brackets at the side. I saw everything very, very clearly, in precise detail.

Even on the nights when there were no footsteps, I never went asleep before Mam came home from work at ten o'clock. Then I would feel relatively safe, but not completely. Mam had never been able to offer much protection. But even he must have realised that a child's screams at dead of night might have alerted someone; a neighbour, a passer-by.

I still dream about it frequently, always the footsteps, never the violence, the terror that was to come. Because in my dreams I am not there when he enters the room. My bed is empty. Yet I can see him, as though an invisible me is present, the tall figure of my father, an expression on his dark, handsome face and in his dark eyes that I could never quite fathom. Was it excitement? Anticipation? Behind the glitter of the main emotion, whatever it might have been, I sensed something else, mysterious, sad, as if deep within him he regretted what he was about to do. But he couldn't help it. The excitement, the anticipation, gripped him like a drug, stifling any other, kinder, feelings he might have had.

In my dream I would watch him slowly undo his belt buckle, hear its tiny click, the feathery smooth sound the leather made as he pulled it through the loops of his trousers until it dangled from his hand like a snake.

Then he would reach down to drag me out of bed, but this was a dream *and I wasn't there!*

Oh, the look on his face then! I savoured it. I felt triumphant.

At this point, I usually woke up bathed in perspiration, my heart beating fiercely, still triumphant, but at the same time slightly sick.

I'd escaped!

Sometimes, though, the dream continued, just as life had continued in the days when the dream wasn't a dream but real.

I knew that when he came back from the pub, always drunk, he would scratch around downstairs, poking here and there, in the dirty washing, through the toys, searching for something that would give him an excuse to let rip with a thrashing. He liked to have an excuse. He'd find the mark of a felt-tipped pen on a tablecloth that Mam hadn't had time to wash, paint dropped on a frock at school, the arm off a doll, or toys not put away properly. Anything could trigger the sound of those slithering footsteps on the stairs.

There were other nights, the best ones, when he would fall asleep in the chair – according to Mam, he worked hard – or he might watch television. Looking back, my memory softened slightly by time, this probably happened more often than I used to think.

In the extended dream I still wasn't there, but now my little sister was in the other bed, and it was she who bore the brunt of our father's anger, or frustration, or excitement, or self-loathing, or whatever it was that made him want to beat the life out of his wife and children, so that his dark shadow lay heavily over our house, even when he wasn't there.

There would be no feeling of triumph when I woke up, just desolation and despair. Would the dreams never end? Would I ever forget? For the rest of my life, would I, Millie Cameron, never stop wishing that I was invisible?

Millie

1

The sun spilled under the curtains, seeping on to the polished window-sill like thick cream. The wine bottle that Trudy had painted and given me for Christmas dazzled, a brilliant flame of light.

Sunday!

I sat up and stretched my arms. I was free to do whatsoever I pleased. In the bed beside me, James grunted and turned over. I slid carefully from under the bedclothes so as not to disturb him, put on a towelling robe and went into the living room, closing the door quietly behind me.

With a sigh of satisfaction at the thought that it was all mine and mine alone, I surveyed the room, its dark pink walls and off-white upholstered sofa, old pine furniture and glass-shaded lamps. Then, I switched on the computer and the television and reversed the answering-machine. In the kitchen, I paused momentarily to admire the effect of the sun on the Aztec-patterned tiles before filling the kettle. Back in the living room, I opened the door to the balcony and stepped outside.

What a glorious day, unseasonably hot for late September. The roses bordering the communal garden were overblown red and yellow cabbages, the dew-drenched grass glistened like wet silk. In the furthest corner, the biggest tree had already begun to shed its tiny, almost white leaves, which scattered the lawn like snow.

I loved my flat, but the thing I loved most was the balcony. It was tiny, just big enough for two black wrought-iron chairs and a large plant-pot in between. I knew nothing about gardening and had been thrilled when the squiggly green things I'd been given last spring had turned out to be geraniums. I enjoyed sitting outside early in the morning with a cup of tea, savouring the salty Liverpool air; the river Mersey was less than a mile away. Occasionally, just before bed on warm evenings, I would sit with the light from the living room falling on to the darkness of the garden, reliving the day.

Most of the curtains in the three-storey block of flats that ran at right angles to my own were still drawn. I glanced at my watch – just gone seven. From the corner of my eye, I became aware of activity in a kitchen on the ground floor. The old lady who lived there was opening a window. I kept my head turned away. If she saw me looking she would wave, I would feel obliged to wave back, and one day I might find myself invited in for coffee, which I would hate. I was glad I'd managed to get a top-floor corner flat. It meant I was cut off from the other residents.

The kettle clicked and I went to make the tea. There was a political programme on television, so I switched it off and turned up the sound on the answering-machine. I nearly turned it down again when I heard my mother's voice. A shadow fell over the day when I remembered it was the last Sunday of the month; my family would be expecting me for lunch.

'... this is the third time I've called, Millicent,' my mother was saying shrilly. 'Don't you ever listen to that machine of yours? Ring back straight away, there's bad news. And I don't see why I should always have to remind you about dinner ...'

I groaned. I could tell from the tone of my mother's voice that the news wasn't seriously bad. Possibly Scotty had been on one of his regular sexual rampages and other dog owners had complained, or Declan, my brother, had lost his twentieth job.

Just as I was about to take my tea on to the balcony, the bedroom door opened and James came out. He wore a pair of dark blue boxer shorts and his straw blond hair was tousled. He grinned. 'Hi!'

'Hi, yourself.' I eyed his tanned body enviously and wished I could turn such a lovely golden brown in the sun.

'Been up long?'

'Fifteen, twenty minutes. It's a lovely day.'

'The best.' He enveloped me in his muscular arms and nuzzled my neck. 'Know what today is?'

'Sunday?'

'True, but it's also our anniversary. It's a year today since we met.' He kissed me softly on the lips. 'I went into a wine bar in Castle Street and there was this gorgeous leggy ash-blonde with the most amazing green eyes – who was that guy you were with? I knew him slightly – that's how I managed to get introduced.'

'I forget.' I felt uneasy. Remembering anniversaries seemed a sign of ... well, that the relationship *meant* something, when we had always maintained stoutly that it didn't.

'Rodney!' he said triumphantly. 'Rod. I met him at a Young Conservatives' do.'

I moved out of his arms and went to the computer. 'I didn't think you were interested in politics.'

'I'm not, but Pa maintains it's good for business. He makes lots of useful contacts in the Party. Is there more tea?'

'The pot's full. Don't forget to put the cosy back on.'

He saluted. 'No, ma'am.'

When he came back, I was seated at my desk. He stood behind me, his arm resting lightly on my shoulder. 'This your report?'

'Uh-huh.' I pressed the mouse and the words rolled down the screen. I read them quickly. Despite night school and the subsequent A level in English, I worried that my terrible education might be obvious when I wrote at length. I hoped I hadn't split any infinitives or put an apostrophe in the wrong place.

'You've spelt "feasible" wrong,' James said. 'It's "-ible" not "-able".'

'I did that bit when I was tired. I probably wasn't thinking straight.' He'd gone to one of the best public schools in the country, followed by a good university.

'Shall we go somewhere special for lunch to celebrate? How about that new place in Formby?'

'Sorry, duty calls. Today I'm lunching with my parents.' I wished I had a more pleasant excuse.

'Of course, the last Sunday...' To my irritation, he knelt down and twisted the chair round until we were facing each other. 'When am I going to meet your folks?'

'What point is there in you meeting them?' I said coldly.

'You've met mine.'

'You invited me, I didn't ask.' I disliked going to see his family in the converted, centuries-old farmhouse in its own grounds three miles from Southport. I felt out of place, uncomfortably aware of the stark contrast between it and my own family's home on a council estate in Kirkby. His mother, with her expensive clothes and beautifully coiffured hair, was always patronising. His father was polite, but in the main ignored me. A businessman to the core, he spent most of the time on the phone or ensconced in his study plying fellow businessmen with drink. Phillip Atherton owned three garages on Merseyside, which sold high-class sports cars to 'fools who've got more money than sense', according to my own father. Atherton's rarely dealt in cars worth less than twenty thousand pounds. James was nominally in charge of the Southport garage, but his father kept a close eye on all three.

The phone went. James was still kneeling, his arms around my waist. After three rings, the answering-machine came on, with the sound still turned up. My mother again. 'Millicent. You've not been out all night, surely. Why don't you call back?'

James's eyes sparkled. 'Millicent! I thought it was Mildred.'

'I would have hated being Mildred even more.' I got up quickly to pick up the receiver. I didn't want him hearing any more of the whining voice with its strong, adenoidal Liverpool accent, one of the reasons I'd told my mother never to call me at the office. 'Hello, Mum.'

'There you are!' She sounded relieved. 'Can we expect to see you today?'

'Of course.'

'Sometimes I worry you'll forget.'

I rolled my eyes. 'As if!'

'Don't be sarcastic, Millicent. After all, it's only once a month you visit. You'd never think you only lived a few miles away in Blundellsands. Mrs Mole's Sybil comes every week from Manchester to see her mam.'

'Perhaps Mrs Mole's Sybil's got nothing else to do.'

'You might like to know she's got two kids and a husband.' There was a pause. 'You've become awfully hard, luv.'

'Don't be silly, Mum.' With an effort, I made my voice softer. Mum set great store by the regular family gatherings now that only Declan was left at home. 'What's the bad news?' I enquired.

'Eh? Oh, I nearly forgot. Your auntie Flo's dead. The poor old soul was knocked down by a car or something. But the thing is, luv,' her voice throbbed with indignation, 'she was already six feet under by the time some woman rang to let your gran know.'

'Why should Gran care? She had nothing to do with Flo.' Auntie Flo had, in fact, been a great-aunt, and the black sheep of the family, I had no idea why. Gran never mentioned her name. It was only when Auntie Sally had died ten years ago that I first set eyes on Flo, at the funeral. She was the youngest of the three Clancy sisters, then in her sixties, had never married, and seemed to me an exceptionally mild old woman.

'Blood's thicker than water,' my mother said meaninglessly.

'What did Auntie Flo do that was so awful?' I asked curiously.

'I think there was a row, but I've no idea what it was about. Your gran would never talk about it.'

I was about to ring off, when Mum said, 'Have you been to Mass?'

To save an argument, I told her I was going to the eleven o'clock. I had no intention of going to Mass.

I replaced the receiver and looked at James. There was a strange, intense expression in his light blue eyes, and I realised he'd been watching me like that throughout the entire conversation with my mother. 'You're very beautiful,' he said.

'You're not so bad yourself.' I tried to sound jokey. Something about his expression disturbed me.

'You know, marriage isn't such a bad thing.'

Alarm bells sounded in my head. Was this a roundabout way of proposing? 'That's not what you've said before.'

'I've changed my mind.'

'Well, I haven't.' He came towards me, but I avoided him by going on to the balcony. 'I've tried it before, remember?'

James was standing just inside the window. 'You didn't keep his name. Were things really so awful?'

'I didn't want his name once we were no longer a couple. And it wasn't awful with Gary, just deadly dull.'

'It wouldn't be dull with me.'

So it *was* a proposal. I stuffed my hands in my dressing-gown pockets to hide my agitation and sat down. Why did he have to spoil things? We'd made it plain to each other from the start that there was to be no commitment. I liked him – no, more than that, I was very fond of him. He was good to be with, extraordinarily handsome in a rugged open-air way. We got on famously, always had loads to talk about, and were great together in bed. But I didn't want to spend the rest of my life with him or with anybody else. I'd struggled hard to get where I was and wanted to get further, without having a husband questioning my every decision, interfering.

I remembered Gary's astonishment when I said I wanted to take an A level. We'd been married two years. 'What on earth d'you want that for?' I recalled his round pleasant face, his round moist eyes. We'd first gone out together at school and had married at eighteen. I'd realised, far too late, that he'd been my escape route from home.

Why did I want an A level? Perhaps to prove to myself that I wasn't as stupid as my teachers had claimed, for self-respect, to gain the enjoyment from books that I'd only briefly experienced before my father had put a brutal stop to it.

'I'd like to get a better job,' is what I said to Gary. I was bored rigid working at Peterssen's packing chocolates. 'I'd like to learn to type as well, use a computer.'

Gary had laughed. 'What good will all that stuff be when we have kids?'

We were living in Kirkby with his widowed mother, not far from my parents. Although we'd put our name down for a council house, one would not be forthcoming until we had a family – not just one child but two or three. I visualised the future, trailing to the shops with a baby, more kids hanging on to the pram, getting a part-time job in another factory because Gary's wages as a storeman would never be enough to live on. It was why we'd never even considered buying a place of our own.

Two years later we were divorced. A bewildered Gary wanted to know what he'd done wrong. 'Nothing,' I told him. I regretted hurting him, but he was devoid of ambition, content to spend the rest of his life in a dead-end job wondering where the next penny would come from.

My father was disgusted, my mother horrified: a Catholic, getting divorced! Even so, Mum did her utmost to persuade me to come back home. My younger sister, Trudy, had found her own escape route via Colin Daley and had also married at eighteen, though Colin had been a better bet than Gary. After ten years they were still happily together.

Wild horses couldn't have dragged me back to Kirkby and my family. Instead, I rented a bedsit. I had my English A level by then, and until I bought my flat, nothing in life had given me more pleasure than the certificate to say I'd achieved a grade C. Armed with a dictionary, I'd *made* myself read the books I'd been set, struggled for hours to understand them in the bedroom at my mother-in-law's, while downstairs Gary watched football and game-shows on television. It seemed no time before the words started to make sense, as if I'd always known them, as if they'd been stored in my head waiting to be used. I shall never forget the day I finished reading *Pride and Prejudice*. I'd understood it. I'd enjoyed it. It was like discovering you could sing or play the piano.

Once settled in the bedsit, I took courses in typing and computing at night school, left Peterssen's, and began to wonder if it had all been worth it as I drifted from one dead-end office job to another – until three years ago, when I became a receptionist/typist with Stock Masterton, an estate agent's in the city centre. Of course, I had to tell George Masterton I'd worked in a factory until I was twenty-four, but he had been impressed. 'Ah, a self-made woman. I like that.'

George and I hit it off immediately. I was promoted to 'property negotiator'. Me! Now George was contemplating opening a branch in Woolton, a relatively middle-class area of Liverpool, and I was determined to be appointed manager, which was why I was writing the report. I'd driven round Woolton, taking in the number of superior properties, the roads of substantial semi-detacheds, the terraced period cottages that could be hyped and sold for a bomb. I'd noted how often the buses ran to town, listed the schools, the supermarkets ... The report would help George make up his mind and show him how keen I was to have the job.

It was through Stock Masterton that I'd found my flat. The builders had gone bankrupt and the units were being sold for a song, which was unfair on the people already there who'd paid thousands more but the bank wanted its money and wasn't prepared to wait.

'I've not done bad for someone not quite thirty,' I murmured to myself. 'I've got my own place, a job with prospects and a car. I earn twice as much as Gary.'

No, I'd not done badly at all.

Yet I wasn't happy.

I leaned on the iron rail and rested my chin on my arms. Somewhere deep within I felt a deadness, and I wondered if I would ever be happy. There were times when I felt like a skater going across the thinnest of ice. It was bound to crack some time, and I would disappear for ever into the freezing, murky water beneath. I shook myself. It was too lovely a morning for such morbid thoughts.

I'd forgotten about James. He appeared on the balcony tucking a black shirt into his jeans. Even in casual clothes, he always looked crisp, neat, tidy. I turned away when he fastened the buckle of his wide leather belt.

He frowned. 'What's the matter?'

'Nothing. Why?'

'You shuddered. Have you gone off me all of a sudden?'

'Don't be silly!' I laughed.

James sat in the other chair. I swung up my bare feet so they rested between his legs and wriggled my toes.

'Cor!' he gasped.

'Don't look like that. People will realise what I'm doing.'

'Would you like to do it inside where no one can see?'

'In a minute. I want to take a shower.'

He smacked his lips. 'I'll take it with you.'

'You've just got dressed!'

'I can get undressed pretty damn quick.' He looked at me quizzically. 'Does this mean I'm forgiven?'

'For what?' I was being deliberately vague.

'For proposing. I'd forgotten you modern women take an offer of marriage as an insult.' He took my feet in his hands. I was conscious of how large and warm and comforting they felt. 'As an alternative, how about if I moved in with you?'

I tried to pull away my feet, but he held them firmly. 'The flat's only small,' I muttered. 'There's only one bedroom.'

'I wasn't contemplating occupying the other if there were two.'

No! I valued my privacy as much as my independence. I didn't want someone suggesting it was time I went to bed or asking why I was late home – and did I really want the living room painted such a dark pink? I wished I could start the day again and stop him proposing. I had been quite enjoying things as they were.

James put my feet down carefully on the balcony floor. 'Between us we could get somewhere bigger.'

'You've changed the rules,' I said.

He sighed. 'I know, but it's not the rules that have changed, it's me. I think I'm in love with you, Millie Cameron. In fact, I know I am.' He tried to catch my eyes. 'I take it the feeling isn't reciprocated?'

I bit my lip and shook my head. James turned away and I contemplated his perfect profile: straight nose, broad mouth, pale, stubby lashes. His hair lay in a flattering corn-coloured quiff on his broad, tanned forehead. He didn't look as if it was the end of the world that I'd turned him down. According to his mother, who never failed to mention it, there'd been an army of girls before me. How many had he fallen in love with? On reflection, I didn't know him all that well. True, we talked a lot, but never about anything serious; the conversation rarely strayed from films, plays, mutual acquaintances and clothes. Oh, and football. I sensed he was shallow and also rather weak, always anxious still to do his father's bidding, even though he, too, was twenty-nine. I felt irritated again that he'd spoiled things: I didn't want to give him up. Nor did I want to hurt him, but I couldn't be expected to fall in love with him just because he had decided he was in love with me.

'Perhaps we can talk about it some other time?' I ventured. In a year, two years, ten.

He closed his eyes briefly and gave a sigh of relief. 'I was worried you might dump me.'

'I wouldn't dream of it!' I jumped to my feet and ran inside. James followed. Outside the bathroom, I removed my dressing-gown and posed tauntingly before opening the door and going in. I stepped into the shower and turned on the water. It felt freezing . . . but it had warmed up nicely by the time James drew the curtain back and joined me.

2

'Hello, luv. You look pale.'

'Hi, Mum.' I made a kissing noise two inches from my mother's plump, sagging cheek. Whenever I turned up in Kirkby, she claimed I looked pale or tired or on the verge of coming down with something.

'Say hello to your dad. He's in the garden with his tomaters.'

My father – I couldn't even *think* of him as Dad – had always been a keen if unimaginative gardener. Dutifully, I opened the kitchen door and called, 'Hello.'

The greenhouse was just beyond the neat lawn, the door open. 'Hello there, luv.' My father was inside, a cigarette hanging from his bottom lip. His dark, sombre expression brightened at the sound of my voice. He threw away the cigarette, wiped his hands on the hips of his trousers and came inside. 'How's the estate-agency business?'

'Okay.' I managed to keep the loathing out of my voice. He told everyone I was a property negotiator. Nowadays he claimed to be proud of his girls. 'Where's Declan?'

'Gone to the pub.' Mum couldn't have looked more harassed if she had been preparing a meal for royalty. She took a casserole out of the oven, then put it back. 'What have I done with the spuds? Oh, I know, they're in the top oven. Declan's promised to be back by one.'

'Will the grub be ready on time, luv?'

'Yes, Norman. Oh, yes.' Mum jumped at her husband's apparently mild question, though it was years since he'd beaten her. 'It'll be ready the minute our Trudy and Declan come.'

'Good. I'll have another ciggie while I'm waiting.' He disappeared into the lounge.

'Why don't you have a talk with your dad and I'll get on with this?' Mum said, as she stirred something in a pan.

As if I would! She'd always tried to pretend we were a perfectly normal family. 'I'd sooner stay and talk to you.'

She flushed with pleasure. 'What have you been up to lately?'

I shrugged. 'Nothing much. Went to a club last night, the theatre on Wednesday. I'm going out to dinner tonight.'

'With that James chap?'

'Yes,' I said shortly. I regretted telling them about James. It was when Declan had jokingly remarked he was thinking of trading in his bike for a Ferrari that I'd told him about Atherton Cars where several could be had. The following Sunday, my father had driven over to Southport to take a look and I was terrified that one day he'd introduce himself to James.

Mum was poised anxiously over the ancient cooker, which had been there when we moved into the council house in 1969. I was three and Trudy just a baby; Declan and Alison had yet to arrive. These days, Mum wasn't just stout but shapelessly stout. Her shabby skirt, with no waist to fix on, was down at the front and up at the rear, revealing the backs of her surprisingly well-shaped but heavily veined legs. I always thought it would have been better if they had grown fat with the rest of her. As it was, she looked like some sort of strange insect: a huge, round body stuck on pins. Her worried, good-natured face was colourless, her skin the texture of putty. The once beautiful hair, the same ash-blonde as her children's, she cut herself with no regard for fashion. She wore no makeup, hadn't for years, as if she was going out of her way to make herself unattractive, or perhaps she just didn't care any more. She was fifty-five but looked ten years older.

Yet she'd been so lovely! I recalled the wedding photo on the mantelpiece in the lounge, the bride tall, willowy and girlish, the fitted lace dress clinging to her slim, perfect figure, though her face was wistful, rather sad, as if she'd been able to see into the future and knew what fate had in store for her. Her hair was long and straight, gleaming in the sunshine of her wedding day, turning under slightly at the ends as mine and Trudy's did. Declan and Alison had curly hair. None of us had taken after our father, with his swarthy good looks and bitter chocolate eyes. Perhaps that's why he'd never liked us much; four children and not one in his image.

The back door opened and my brother came in. 'Hi, Sis. Long time no see.' He aimed a pretend punch at my stomach and I aimed one back. 'That's a nice frock. Dark colours suit you.' He fingered the material. 'What would you call that green?'

Declan had always been interested in his sisters' clothes, which infuriated our father who called him a cissy, and had done his brutal best to make a man out of him.

'Olive, I think. It was terribly cheap.'

' "It was terribly cheap!" ' Declan repeated, with an impish grin. 'You don't half talk posh these days, Mill. I'd be ashamed to take you to the pub.'

A shout came from the lounge. 'Is that you, Declan?'

'Yes, Dad.'

'You're only just in time,' the voice said pointedly.

Declan winked at me. He was twenty, a tall, lanky boy with a sensitive face and an infectious smile, always cheerful. He was currently working as a labourer on a demolition site, which seemed an entirely unsuitable job for someone who looked as if a feather would knock him down. I often wondered why he still lived at home and assumed it was for Mum's sake. He shouted, 'Scotty met this smashing bitch. I had a job getting him home. I forgot to take his lead.'

'Where is Scotty?'

'In the garden.'

I went outside to say hello to the little black dog that vaguely resembled a Scotch terrier. 'You're an oversexed ruffian.' I laughed as the rough hairy body bounced up and down to greet me.

A car stopped outside, and seconds later two small children came hurtling down the side of the house. I picked up Scotty and held him like a shield as Melanie and Jake launched themselves at me.

'Leave your aunt Millie alone!' Trudy shouted. 'I've told you before, she doesn't like kids.' She beamed. 'Hi, Sis. I've painted you another bottle.'

'Hi, Trude. I'd love another bottle. Hello, Colin.'

Colin Daley was a stocky, quiet man, who worked long into the night six days a week in his one-man engineering company. He was doing well: he and Trudy had already sold their first house and bought a bigger one in Orrell Park. I sensed he didn't like me much. He'd got on well with Gary and perhaps he thought I neglected my family, left too much to Trudy. During the week, she often came over to Kirkby with the children. He nodded in my direction. 'Hello, there.'

'Do you really not like kids?' Jake enquired gravely. He was six, two years older than his sister, a happy little boy with Colin's blue eyes. Both Trudy's children were happy – she'd made sure of that.

'I like you two,' I lied. As kids went they weren't bad, but talking to them got on my nerves. I hugged Scotty, who was licking my ear. I would have had a dog of my own if I hadn't spent so much time at work.

Jake looked at me doubtfully. 'Honest?'

'Cross my heart.'

We all went indoors. Mum shrieked, 'C'mon, you little rascals, and give your gran a hug.' The children allowed themselves to be kissed, then they cried, 'Where's Grandad?'

'In the lounge.'

Mum looked wistful as Melanie and Jake whooped their way into the other room. She said, 'They've got a thing about their grandad.'

'I know.' It was strange that Trudy's children adored the man who'd once nearly killed their mother. She still bore a scar from his belt buckle above her left eyebrow.

When I went in Trudy was standing in the lounge, hovering near her children who were sitting on their grandad's knee. I noticed her eyes flicker to the big hands, one resting on each child's waist. We looked at each other in mutual understanding.

As usual, the meal was revolting. The mound of mashed potatoes, watery cabbage and stewing steak on my plate made me feel nauseous. 'I'll never eat all this, Mum,' I protested. 'I asked you not to give me much.'

'You look as if you need a decent meal, luv. There's a nice apple charlotte for afters.'

'It's a sin to waste good food,' my father said jovially.

I caught Trudy's eye and Declan hid a grin. The final Sunday of the month was a day for catching eyes and making faces. Odd phrases brought back bitter memories: 'It's a sin to waste good food,' was not said so lightly in those days.

On the surface, it was a civilised gathering, occasionally merry, a family united for Sunday lunch, except for Alison, of course. But I always felt on tenterhooks, as if I were watching someone blowing up a balloon, bigger and bigger until it was about to burst. Perhaps it was just me. Perhaps no one else remembered how Colin detested his father-in-law, how nervous Mum was, what Sunday dinner used to be like when we were little. Even now, I was still terrified that I would drop food on the tablecloth and that a nicotine-stained hand would reach across and slap my face, so hard that tears would come to my eyes, even though I'd sworn at an early age never to let him see me cry.

The conversation had turned to Auntie Flo. 'We were friendly for a while before I married your dad,' Mum said. 'I went to her flat in Toxteth a few times, though your gran never knew.' She turned to me. 'Actually, Millicent, that's where you come in.'

'What's Auntie Flo got to do with me?'

'Your gran wants her place cleared before the rent runs out, otherwise the landlord might chuck everything away.'

'Why ask me?' I could think of few less welcome things to do than clear out the belongings of an old lady I hadn't known. 'Why not you or Gran or Trudy? What about that woman you mentioned, the one who rang?'

Mum looked hurt. 'It's not much to ask, luv. I can't do it because . . .' she paused uncomfortably '. . . well, your dad's not very keen on the idea. Gran's too upset, she's taken Flo's death hard. Anyroad, she never goes out nowadays.'

'And Trudy's already got enough to do,' Colin growled.

'As for the woman who rang, she's just someone who lives upstairs. We don't want a stranger going through Auntie Flo's precious things, do we?'

'What precious things?' I noticed my father's fists clench. I reminded myself that he could do nothing to me now. I could say what I liked. 'I don't know what she did for a living, but I can't imagine Auntie Flo having acquired many precious things.'

'She worked in a launderette till she retired.' For a moment, Mum looked nonplussed. Then she went on eagerly, 'But there'll be papers, luv, letters perhaps, odds and ends of jewellery your gran would like. The clothes can go to one of those charity shops, Oxfam. I'm sure you'll find someone to take the furniture, and if there's anything nice, I wouldn't mind it meself. Declan knows a lad who has a van.'

I tried to think of a way of getting out of it. My mother was looking at me pleadingly, her pasty face slightly moist. *She* would probably thoroughly enjoy going through the flat, but Dad had put his foot down for some reason, not that he'd ever needed a reason in the past. The mere fact that Mum *wanted* to do something was enough. Maybe I could get it done in a few hours if I went armed with several cardboard boxes. I had one last try. 'I've always avoided Toxteth like the plague. It's full of drugs and crime. People get murdered there, shot.'

Mum looked concerned. 'Oh, well, if that's –' she began, but my father butted in, 'Your auntie Flo lived there for over fifty years without coming to any harm.'

It seemed I had no choice. 'Oh, all right,' I said reluctantly. 'When's the rent due?'

'I've no idea.' Mum looked relieved. 'The woman upstairs will know. Mrs Smith, her name is, Charmian Smith.'

'Don't forget to give me the address before I go.'

'I won't, luv. I'll ring and tell Gran later. She'll be pleased.'

After the meal was over and the dishes washed, Trudy produced the bottle she'd painted for me. It was exquisite, an empty wine bottle transformed into a work of art. The glass was covered with roses and dark green leaves edged with gold.

'It's beautiful!' I breathed, holding it up to the light. 'I'm not sure where to put it. The other one's in the bedroom.'

'I'll do you another,' Trudy offered. 'I'm running out of people to give them to.'

'I suggested she have a stall in a craft market,' Colin said proudly. 'I could look after the kids if it was a Sunday.'

I waved the bottle in support. 'That's a great idea, Trude. You'd pay ten pounds for this in a shop.'

'Millicent.' Mum came sidling up. 'Have you got much to do this afternoon?'

I was immediately wary. 'I'm in the middle of a report.'

'It's just I'd like to go and see Alison.'

'Can't you go yourself?' The only reason she'd learned to drive was so she could visit Alison in the home.

'There's something wrong with the car. Your dad promised to get it fixed but he never got round to it.'

He'd probably not got round to it deliberately. He would prefer to think his youngest child didn't exist. 'Sorry, Mum. As I said, I've got this report to write.'

'We'll take you, luv.' Colin must have overheard. 'It's a couple of weeks since we saw Alison.'

Mum looked grateful. 'That's nice of you, Colin, but there's nothing for Melanie and Jake to do. They get fed up within the first five minutes.'

'You can leave the kids here with me,' my father offered.

'No, thanks,' Trudy said, much too quickly.

'I'll take them for a walk once we get there, and you and Trudy can stay with Alison,' Colin said.

In the midst of this discussion, I went upstairs to the lavatory. The bathroom, like everywhere else in the house, reeked of poverty, the linoleum cracked and crumbling, the plastic curtains faded. I was well into my teens before I discovered we were relatively well-off – or should have been. My father's wages as a toolmaker were high, but the family saw little of the money. He'd been a betting man all his life and a consistent loser.

As usual, I couldn't wait to be back in my own place. I felt guilty for refusing to visit Alison, pity for my mother, angry that the pity made me turn up for the monthly get-togethers then guilty again, knowing that I would get out of coming if I could. When Stock Masterton had begun to open on Sundays, I'd hoped that would provide a good excuse, but George, a workaholic, insisted on looking after the office himself with the help of a part-timer.

After saying goodbye, I went outside to the car. Several boys were playing football in the road, and someone had written 'Fuck off' in black felt pen on the side of my yellow Polo. I was rubbing it off with my handkerchief when Trudy came out with the children. She ushered them into the back of the family's old Sierra and came over to me. 'Thank the Lord that's over for another month.'

'You can say that again!'

'I can't get me head round this kindly old grandfather shit.' Absent-mindedly she rubbed the scar over her left eyebrow.

'I suppose we should be thankful for small mercies.'

Trudy regarded me keenly. 'You okay, Sis? You look a bit pale.'

'Mum said that. I'm fine, been working hard, that's all.' I eyed the car. I'd got most of it off and what was left wasn't legible. 'Look, Sis, I'm sorry about Alison,' I said in a rush, 'but I really have got work to do.'

Trudy pressed my arm. She glanced at the house where we'd grown up. 'I feel as if I'd like to drive away and never have to see another member of me family again, but we're trapped, aren't we? I don't know if I could bear it without Colin.'

As I started the car, I noticed that the house opposite had been boarded up, although children had broken down the door and were playing in the hallway. There was a rusty car without wheels in the front garden. As I drove away, the sun seemed to darken, although there wasn't a cloud to be seen. Unexpectedly, I felt overwhelmed by a sense of alienation. Where do I belong? I wondered, frightened. Not here, please not here! Yet I'd been born in a tower block less than a mile from this spot, where nowadays Gran lived like a prisoner: Martha Colquitt rarely left home since she'd been mugged for her pension five years ago. My own flat in Blundellsands was a pretence, more like a stage set than a proper home, and I was a fake. I couldn't understand what James saw in me, or why George Masterton was my friend. I was putting on an act, I wasn't real.

And what would James think if he met my slovenly mother and chain-smoking father, and if I told him about my brutal childhood? What would he say if he knew I had a sister with severe learning difficulties who'd been in a home since she was three, safely out of my father's way? A scene flashed through my mind, of my father slapping Alison, knocking her pretty little face first one way then the other, trying to make her stop saying that same word over and over again. 'Slippers,' Alison would mutter, in her dull monotone. 'Slippers, slippers, slippers.' She said it still, when agitated, although she was seventeen now.

Even if I were in love with James, we could never marry, not with all the family baggage I had in tow. I reminded myself that I didn't want to get married again, that I wasn't capable of falling in love. I belonged nowhere and to nobody.

Nevertheless, I had an urgent desire to see James. He was calling for me at seven. I looked forward to losing myself in empty talk, good food, wine.

He would bring me home and we would make love and all that business with my family would be forgotten, until the time came for me to go again. Except, that is, for the dreams, from which I would never escape.

3

It wasn't until Thursday that I managed to get to Toxteth. James had tickets for a jazz concert at the Philharmonic Hall on Monday night, which I had forgotten about. Tuesday, I'd promised to go to dinner with Diana Riddick, a colleague from the office whom I'd never particularly got on with, but then few people did. Diana was thirty-five, single, and lived with her elderly father, who was a 'pain', she claimed, particularly now that his health was failing. She was a small, slight woman, permanently discontented, with a garishly painted face, a degree in land and property management, and an eye on the position of manager of the Woolton office. She didn't realise that I nursed the same ambition and when we were alone together she openly discussed it. I'd suspected she had an ulterior motive in inviting me that evening and it turned out she wanted to pump me about George's plans.

'Has he ever talked to you about it?' she asked, over the Italian meal. There were red and white gingham cloths on the tables and candles in green bottles dripping wax. The walls were hung with plastic vines.

'Hardly ever,' I replied truthfully.

'I bet you anything he gives the job to Oliver.' She pouted. Oliver Brett, solid and dependable, was the assistant manager, in charge when George was away, which was rare.

'I doubt it. Oliver's nice, but he's proved more than once he couldn't handle the responsibility.' I sipped my wine. On nights like this, Kirkby seemed a million miles away. 'Remember last Christmas when he rang George in the Seychelles to ask his advice?'

'Hmm!' Diana looked dubious. 'Yes, but he's a man. The world is prejudiced in favour of men. I shall be very cross if it's Tweedledum or Tweedledee.'

'That's most unlikely.' I laughed. Apart from June, who'd taken my old job as receptionist, the only other permanent members of staff were two young men in their mid-twenties, Darren and Elliot, startlingly alike in looks and manner, which accounted for their nicknames. Both were too immature for promotion. 'George has never struck me as being prejudiced against women,' I added.

'I might do a survey of Woolton, see how the land lies.' Diana's rather heavy eyebrows drew together in a frown and the discontented lines between her eyes deepened further. 'I'll type up some notes for George.'

'What a good idea,' I murmured. I hadn't added to my own report since last week.

It was late on Wednesday when I returned to the office in Castle Street. I'd taken a couple, the Naughtons, to see a property in Lydiate. It was the sixth house they'd viewed. As usual, they walked round several times, wondering aloud whether their present furniture would fit, asking if I would measure the windows so they could check if the curtains they had now would do. George insisted that keys were returned, no matter how late, and it was almost eight when I hung them on the rack. George was still working in his glass-partitioned office and Oliver was about to go home. His good-natured face creased into a smile as he said, 'Goodnight.'

I was wondering if there was time to drive to Blundellsands, collect the cardboard boxes I'd acquired from a supermarket, return to town and start on Auntie Flo's flat. I couldn't bring the car to work with boxes on the back seat when I had to take clients to view.

Before I'd made up my mind George came out of his cubicle. 'Millie! Please say you're not doing anything special tonight. I'm longing for a drink and desperately in need of company.'

'I'm not, doing anything special that is.' I would have said the same whatever the case. At the moment it was essential to keep in George's good books.

We went to a wine bar, the one where I'd met James. George ordered a roast-beef sandwich and a bottle of Chablis. I refused anything to eat. 'You should get some food down you.' He patted my hand in a fatherly way. 'You look pale.'

'That's what everyone keeps telling me. I'll wear blusher tomorrow.'

'You mean rouge. My old mother used to go to town with the rouge.' His mother had died only a year ago and he missed her badly, just as he missed the children his ex-wife and her new husband had taken to live in France. He was alone, hated it, and buried himself in work to compensate. George Masterton was fifty, tall and thin to the point of emaciation although he ate like a horse. He wore expensive suits that hung badly from his narrow, stooped shoulders. Despite this, he had an air of drooping elegance, enhanced by his deceptively laid-back, languid manner. Only those who knew him well were aware that behind the lazy charm George was an irascible, unpredictable man, who suffered from severe bouts of depression and panic attacks.

'Why the desperate need for company?' I asked lightly. I always felt at my oddest with George, as if one day he would see what a fake I was, and never speak to me again.

'Oh, I dunno.' He shrugged. 'It was Annabel's birthday on Monday. She was sixteen. Thought about whizzing over to France on Eurostar but told myself Stock Masterton would collapse without me. Really, I was scared I wouldn't be welcome. I'm supposed to be having her and Bill for Christmas, but I shan't be at all surprised if they don't come.'

It was my turn to pat his hand. 'I bet Annabel would have been thrilled to see you. As for Christmas, it's months off. Try not to start worrying yet.'

'Families, eh!' He chuckled. 'They're a pain in the arse when you've got them, and a pain when they're not there. Diana calls her old dad everything but now he's ill she's terrified he'll die. Poor chap, it sounds like cancer. Anyway, how's your lot over in Kirkby?'

'Same as usual.' I told him about Auntie Flo's flat, and he said bring the boxes in tomorrow and put them in the stationery cupboard until I found time to go. He asked where the flat was.

'Toxteth, William Square. I don't know round there all that well.'

His sandwich arrived. Between mouthfuls, he explained that William Square had once been very beautiful. 'They're five-storeyed properties, including the basement where the skivvies used to work. Lovely stately houses, massive pillars, intricate wrought-iron balconies like bloody lace, bay windows at least twelve feet high. It's where the nobs used to live at the turn of the century, though it's gone seriously downhill since the war.' He paused over the last of the sandwich. 'Sure you'll be safe? Wasn't there a chap shot in that area a few weeks ago?'

'I'll go in daylight. Trouble is, finding the time. Things keep coming up.'

George grinned. 'Such as me demanding your company! Sorry about that. Look, take tomorrow afternoon off. I'd feel happier about you going then. Don't forget to take your mobile and you can call for help if you get in trouble.'

'For goodness sake, George, you'd think I was going to a war zone!'

'Toxteth's been compared to one before now. As far as I'm concerned, it's as bad as Bosnia used to be.'

At two o'clock on a brilliantly sunny afternoon, William Square still looked beautiful when I drove in. I found an empty parking space some distance past the house I wanted, number one, and sat in the car for several minutes, taking in the big, gracious houses on all four sides. On close inspection, they appeared anything but beautiful. The elaborate stucco decorating the fronts had dropped off leaving bare patches like sores. Most of the front doors were a mass of peeling paint, and some houses were without a knocker, the letterbox a gaping hole. Several windows were broken and had been repaired with cardboard.

The big oblong garden in the centre of the square was now, according to George, maintained by the council. Evergreen trees with thick rubbery leaves were clumped densely behind high black railings. I thought it gloomy, and the square depressed me.

With a sigh, I got out of the car, collected some boxes and trudged along to number one. Two small boys, playing cricket on the pavement, watched me curiously.

The house looked clean, but shabby. Someone had brushed the wide steps leading up to the front door recently. There was a row of four buzzers with a name beside each, so faded they were unreadable. I ignored these and used the knocker – Charmian Smith lived on the ground floor.

A few seconds later the door was opened by a statuesque black woman not much older than me, wearing a lime green T-shirt and a wrap-round skirt patterned with tropical fruit. Her midriff was bare, revealing satin smooth skin. She held a baby in one arm. Two small children, a boy and a girl, stood either side of her, clutching her skirt. They stared at me shyly, and the little girl began audibly to suck her thumb.

'Mrs Smith?'

'Yes?' The woman regarded me aggressively.

'I've come for the key to Flo Clancy's flat.'

Her expression changed. 'I thought you were selling something! I should have known from the boxes. Not only that, you're awful like Flo. Come in, luv, and I'll get the key.'

The magnificent hallway had a black-and-white mosaic tiled floor and a broad, sweeping staircase with an intricately carved balustrade. The ornate ceiling was at least fourteen feet high. But whatever grand effect the architect had planned was spoilt by crumbling plaster on the coving and cornices, hanging cobwebs and bare wooden stairs worn to a curve. Several sections of balustrade were missing.

I stayed in the hall when Charmian Smith went into the ground-floor room, the children still clinging to her skirt. Through the open door, I could see that her flat was comfortably furnished, the walls covered with maroon flock paper. Everywhere was very clean, even the massive bay window, which must have taken hours to polish.

'Here you are, girl.'

'Thanks.' I took the proffered key and wondered if the children stayed attached to their mother like that all day. 'Which floor is it?'

'Basement. Give us a shout if you need anything.'

'Thanks.' I returned outside. The basement was situated behind railings down a narrow well of steep concrete steps. Little light reached the small window. I struggled down with the boxes to a tiny area full of old chip papers and other debris. To my consternation, there were several used condoms. I wondered what on earth I'd let myself in for.

A plastic mac and an umbrella were hanging from a hook inside the tiny lobby, and a brass horseshoe was attached to the inner door, which opened when I turned the knob.

The first thing I noticed when I stepped inside was the smell of musty dampness, and the cold, which made me shiver. Although it was broad daylight, I could see nothing. I fumbled for a light switch just inside the door and turned it on. My heart sank. The room was crammed with furniture, and every surface was equally crammed with ornaments. There were two sideboards, one very old and huge, six feet high at least, with little cupboards in the upper half. The other was more modern, but still large. Beneath the window was a chest covered with a red fringed shawl and a pretty lace cloth. On top of that a vase stood filled with silk flowers; poppies. I touched them. The effect was striking, as if they'd been bought to echo the colour of the shawl. It was the sort of thing I might have done myself.

I walked slowly down the room, which ran the length of the house. Halfway along, two massive beams had been built into the walls to support an equally massive lintel, all painted black, and covered with little brass plaques. An elderly gas fire was fitted in the green-tiled fireplace, and on each side of it, more cupboards reached to the ceiling, one of which I opened. Every shelf was stuffed to capacity: clothes, crockery, books, bedding, more ornaments stored in boxes . . .

'I can't do this all on my own,' I said aloud. I had no idea where to start, and I would need more like a hundred cardboard boxes than ten.

A window at the far end overlooked a tiny yard, which was level with the rear of the flat. It contained a wooden bench, a table and plant-holders full of limp pansies. The wall had been painted almost the same pink as my lounge – another indication that Auntie Flo and I had shared similar taste. The woman upstairs had said I was like Flo, and I wondered if there was a photograph somewhere.

I turned and surveyed the room, and supposed that, in its way, it had charm. Very little matched, yet everything seemed to gel together nicely. There was a large brown plush settee and a matching chair with crocheted patchwork covers on the backs and arms. Obviously Flo hadn't believed in leaving an inch of space bare. There were numerous pictures and several tiny tables, all with bowls of silk flowers. Linoleum, with a pattern of blue and red tiles, covered the floor, and there was a handmade rag rug on the hearth. A large-screen television stood next to an up-to-date music centre, a record visible on the turntable beneath the smoky plastic lid.

If only it wasn't so cold! On the hearth next to the fire I saw a box of matches. I struck one, shoved it between the bars and turned the knob at the side. There was a mini explosion and the gas jets roared briefly before settling down into a steady flame.

I held out my hands to warm them and remembered I'd been looking for a photo of Flo. After a while, I got up and moved round the room again until I found some on a gate-leg table, which had been folded to its narrowest against the wall. The photos, about a dozen in all, were spread each side of a glass jar of anemones.

The first was a coloured snap of two women taken in what looked like a fairground. I recognised Flo from Auntie Sally's funeral. Despite her age, it was obvious that she'd once been pretty. She was smiling at the camera, a calm, sweet smile. Her companion wore a leopardskin coat and black leggings, and her hair was a violent unnatural red. I turned the photo over: 'Me and Bel at Blackpool Lights, October 1993'.

There was a picture of Auntie Sally's wartime wedding, which I'd seen before at Gran's. The bride, in her pin-striped suit and white felt hat, looked like a character out of *Guys and Dolls*. Another wedding photo, the couple in Army uniform. Despite the unflattering clothes, the woman was startlingly lovely. On the back was written, 'Bel & Bob's wedding, December, 1940'. Flo and Bel must have been friends all their lives.

I found two more photos of Bel getting married; 'Bel & Ivor's wedding, 1945,' in what looked like a foreign setting, and 'Bel & Edward's wedding, 1974' showed a glamorous Bel with a decrepit-looking old man.

At last I held a picture of a young Flo, a snapshot turning white at the edges. It was taken outside a ramshackle building with 'Fritz's Laundry' above the door. A man in a dark suit and wire-rimmed glasses – Fritz? – stood in the middle of six women all wearing aprons and turbans. Flo was recognisable immediately because she was so like me, except that she was smiling and I had never smiled like that in all my life. She looked about eighteen, and seemed to be bursting with happiness, you could see it in her eyes, her dimples, and the curve of her lovely wide mouth.

As I replaced the silver-framed photo on the table, I sighed. More than half a century spanned the images of my great-aunt, the one in Blackpool, the other outside Fritz's Laundry, yet little seemed to have happened over the years to make her expression change.

I was turning away with the intention of getting on with what I'd come for, when I noticed a studio portrait, in sepia tones, of a woman with a baby. There was something familiar about her grim yet good-looking face. I knew nothing about babies and couldn't tell the child's age – it was a boy in an old-fashioned romper suit with a sailor collar – but he was adorable. I looked at the back, and read, 'Elsa Cameron with Norman (Martha's godson), on his first birthday, May, 1939'.

The baby was my father! His mother had died long before I was born.

I slammed the photo face down on the table. I was shivering again. I was about to kneel in front of the fire once more, when I saw the sherry on the sideboard, the modern one. My jangling nerves needed calming. In the cupboard underneath, where I looked for a glass, I found five more bottles of sherry, and several glasses hanging by their stems from a circular wooden stand. I filled a glass, drank the sherry, filled it again, took it over to the settee, and sank into the cushions. My head was buzzing. How could such a beautiful child grow up to become such a *monster?*

The sherry took effect quickly and I began to relax. There seemed to be a sagging hole in the middle cushion of the settee into which my bottom fitted perfectly. Perhaps it was where Flo had always sat. Outside, cars drove past occasionally and I could hear children playing in the square. People walked by, heels clicking on the pavement, only their legs visible from the knees down through the small window by the door.

I put down the empty glass and promptly fell asleep.

When I woke up it was nearly half past five. There was a throbbing between my eyes, which I supposed was the result of the sherry, though it didn't feel particularly unpleasant. I would have given anything for a cup of tea or coffee and remembered I hadn't seen the kitchen yet, or the bedroom.

I got to my feet, and staggered towards the door at the back of the room, where I found myself in a little dark inner hall with a tiled floor and two more doors, left and right. The left led to a tiny Spartan kitchen with a deep porcelain sink, a cooker older than Mum's, a digitally operated microwave oven but no fridge. In the wall cupboard, behind several packets of biscuits, there was coffee and, to my relief, a jar of Coffeemate. I put a spoonful of each with water in a flowered mug and stuck it in the microwave to heat.

Whilst I was waiting, I went back to the inner hall, opened the other door, and switched on the light. The bedroom was mainly white, curtains, walls, bedspread. A pair of pink furry slippers were set neatly side by side under the bed. A large crucifix hung from the wall and there was a statue of Our Lord on the six-drawer chest, surrounded by smaller statues. The walls were covered with holy pictures: Our Lord again, Baby Jesus, the Virgin Mary, and an assortment of saints. Otherwise, the room was sparsely furnished: apart from the chest, there was only a matching wardrobe with a narrow, full-length mirror on the door, and a little cane bedside table, which held an old-fashioned alarm clock, a white-shaded lamp, and a Mills & Boon novel with an embroidered bookmark. An old brown foolscap envelope was propped against the lamp. I picked it up and put it in the pocket of my linen jacket. It might contain Flo's pension book, which would need to be cancelled.

I admired the wardrobe and the chest-of-drawers. They looked like stained oak and had been polished to satin smoothness. They'd look lovely in my flat, I thought. I wouldn't have minded the brass bedstead either. My own bedroom furniture had been bought in kits and had taken weeks to put together.

In the kitchen, the microwave beeped. I sat on the bed, which was like sitting on a cloud it felt so soft, and bounced up and down, but stopped when I caught sight of my reflection in the mirror. I saw a tall, graceful young woman who looked years younger than her age, dressed in white and pink, with long slim legs and hair that shone like silver under Auntie Flo's bedroom light. Her wide, generous mouth was turned up slightly – she'd been childishly enjoying bouncing on the bed. At school, she had been regarded as stuck up because of her straight, slightly patrician nose, but James's mother had said once, 'What fine bone structure you have, Millie. Some women would pay a plastic surgeon a fortune for cheekbones like that.'

The young woman had forgotten to use blusher and she *did* look pale, as everyone had been saying, but it was the deadness in the green eyes that shocked me.

I took the coffee and a packet of custard creams into the lounge, switched on the television and watched *Neighbours*, then an old cowboy film on BBC2.

Just as the film was finishing, I glimpsed through the window the majestic figure of Charmian Smith descending the concrete stairs. I kicked the boxes aside and opened the door, feeling slightly uncomfortable when she gave me a warm smile, as if we were the greatest friends.

'I'd forgotten all about you until our Minola, that's me daughter, collected her kids and said there was a light on in Flo's flat. Me feller's just got home and I wondered if you'd like a bite to eat with us.' She came into the room without waiting to be asked, as if it was something she was used to doing.

'What does your daughter do?' I was astonished to learn that Charmian was grandmother to the children I'd seen earlier.

'She's learning to use a computer. It was when Jay, that's me son, went to university last year, she decided it was time she used her brain.' Charmian's brown eyes danced. 'I told her she'd regret getting married at sixteen. I said, "There's more things to life than a husband and a family, luv," but kids never listen, do they? I didn't listen to me own mam when I got married at the same age.'

'I suppose not.'

'Are you married? Y'know, I don't know your name.'

'Millie Cameron, and no, I'm not married.' I wished the woman would leave so I could get down to work. It seemed imperative suddenly that I take at least half a dozen boxes of stuff to Oxfam tomorrow. To my dismay, she sank gracefully into the armchair, her long bead earrings swinging against her gleaming neck.

'I didn't know Flo had any relatives left after her sister Sally died,' she said, 'apart from Sally's daughter who went to live in Australia. It wasn't until Bel gave me a number to ring after the funeral that I knew there was another sister.'

Bel, the woman in the photographs. '*After* the funeral?'

'That's right, Martha Colquitt. Is she your gran?' I nodded. 'I felt terrible when the poor woman burst into tears, but Bel said that was the way Flo wanted it.' Charmian glanced sadly round the room. 'I can't get used to her not being here. I used to come and see her several times a day over the last year when she was stuck indoors with her terrible headaches.'

'That was very kind of you,' I said stiffly.

'Lord, girl, it was nothing to do with kindness. It was no more than she deserved. Flo was there for me when I needed her – she got me a job in the launderette when me kids were little. It changed me life.' She leaned against the crocheted cover and, for a moment, looked as if she might cry. Then, once again, her eyes swept the room. 'It's like a museum, isn't it? Such a shame everything's got to go. People always fetched her ornaments back from their holidays.' She indicated the brass plaques on the beams. 'We brought her the key and the little dog from Clacton. This was Flo's favourite, though – and mine.' She eased herself smoothly out of the chair and switched on the lamp on top of the television.

I had already noticed the cut-out parchment lamp with its wooden base and thought it tasteless. It reminded me of a cheap Christmas card: a line of laughing children dressed as they might have been in this very square a hundred years ago, fur hats, fur muffs, lace-up boots.

'I'll switch the main light off so you can see the effect once the bulb warms up,' Charmian said.

To my surprise, the shade slowly began to revolve. I hadn't realised there was another behind it that turned in the opposite direction. The children passed a toyshop, a sweetshop, a church, a Christmas tree decorated with coloured lights. Shadows flitted across the ceiling of the long, low room. Hazy, almost lifesize figures passed over my head.

'Tom brought her that from Austria of all places.'

I felt almost hypnotised by the moving lamp. 'Tom?'

'Flo's friend. She loved sitting watching her lamp and listening to her record. The lamp was still on when I came down the day they found her dead in the park. Did you know she got run over?'

'My mother said.'

'They never found who did it. Oh dear!' Now Charmian did begin to cry. 'I don't half miss her. I hate the thought of her dying all alone.'

'I'm terribly sorry.' I went over and awkwardly touched the woman's arm. I hadn't the faintest notion how you were supposed to comfort a stranger. Perhaps another person, someone who didn't have dead eyes, might have taken the weeping woman in their arms, but I could no more have done that than I could have sprouted wings and flown.

Charmian sniffed and wiped her eyes. 'Anyroad, I'd better go. Herbie's waiting for his tea – which reminds me, luv, would you care to join us?'

'Thanks all the same, but I'd better not. There's so much to do.' I gestured at the room, which was exactly the same as when I'd come six hours before.

Charmian squeezed my hand. 'Perhaps next time, eh? It'll take you weeks to sort this lot out. I'd offer to help, but I couldn't bear to see Flo's lovely stuff being packed away.'

I watched her climb the steps outside. I had meant to ask when the rent was due, so that I could pay a few weeks if necessary. I hadn't realised that dusk had fallen and it was rapidly growing dark. The streetlights were on, and it was time to draw the curtains. It was then that I noticed someone standing motionless outside. I pressed my face against the glass and peered upwards. It was a girl of about sixteen, wearing a tight red mini-dress that barely covered her behind and emphasised the curves of her slight body. There was something about her stance, the way she leaned against the railings, one foot slightly in front of the other, the way she held her cigarette, left hand supporting the right elbow, that made me guess immediately what she was. I pressed my face the other way, and saw two more girls outside the house next door.

'Oh, lord!' I felt scared. Perhaps I should let someone know where I was – James or my mother – but I couldn't recall seeing a phone in the flat and, despite what George had said, I'd left my mobile in the office. As soon as I'd had another cup of coffee, I'd go home and come back on Sunday to start packing.

The kitchen was like a fridge. No wonder Flo didn't have one – she didn't need it. I returned, shivering, to the settee, my hands wrapped round a mug of coffee. It was odd, but the room seemed even more cosy and charming now I knew about the girl outside. I no longer felt scared, but safe and secure, as if there was no chance of coming to any harm inside Auntie Flo's four walls.

I became aware of something stiff against my hip and remembered the envelope that I'd found in the bedroom. It didn't contain a pension book, but several newspaper cuttings, yellow and crisp with age, held together with a paper clip. They'd mainly been taken from the *Liverpool Daily Post* and the *Echo*. I looked at the top one for a date – Friday, 2 June 1939 – then skimmed through the words underneath.

THETIS TRAPPED UNDERWATER was the main headline, followed by a sub-heading. *Submarine Fails to Re-surface in Liverpool Bay – Admiralty Assures Relatives All Those On Board Will Be Rescued.*

I turned to the next cutting dated the following day. *Hope Fading For*

Men Trapped On The Thetis. Stunned Relatives Wait Outside Cammell Laird Offices in Birkenhead. The news had been worse when the *Echo* came out that afternoon: *Hope Virtually Abandoned for 99* men on Thetis, and by Sunday, *All Hope Abandoned . . .*

Why had Flo kept them?

On the television, the lamp swirled and the children did their Christmas shopping. I found myself waiting for a girl in a red coat and brown fur bonnet to come round. She was waving at someone, but the someone never appeared.

Flo had sat in this very spot hundreds, no, thousands of times, watching the girl in red, listening to her record. Curious, I went over to the record player and studied the controls. I pressed Play, and beneath the plastic lid, the arm lifted and swung across to the record.

There was crackling, then the strains of a vaguely familiar tune filled the room, silent until then except for the hiss of the gas fire. After a while, a man's voice, also vaguely familiar, began to sing. He'd been in a film on television recently – Bing Crosby. 'Dancing in the dark,' a voice like melting chocolate crooned.

What had Flo Clancy done to make her the black sheep of the family? Why had Gran refused to mention her name? Bel, Flo's old friend, had asked Charmian Smith to ring Gran *after* the funeral because 'that's the way Flo wanted it'. What had happened between the sisters to make them dislike each other so much? And why had Flo kept cuttings of a submarine disaster beside her bed?

I would almost certainly never know the truth about Auntie Flo, but what did it matter? As the lamp slowly turned and dark shadows swept the ceiling of the room and the music reached a crescendo, filling every nook and corner, I took a long, deep breath and allowed myself to be sucked into the enchantment of it all. A quite unexpected thing had happened, something quite wonderful. I had never felt so much at peace with myself before.

Flo

1

Flo Clancy opened her eyes, saw that the fingers on the brass alarm clock on the tallboy were pointing to half past seven, and nearly screamed. She'd be late for work! She was about to leap out of bed when she remembered it was Whit Monday and she could lie in.

Whew! She peeped over the covers at her sisters, both fast asleep in the double bed only a few feet away. Martha would have done her nut if she'd been woken early. Flo pursed her lips and blew gently at Sally who was sleeping on the outside, but Sal's brown eyelashes merely flickered before she turned over, dead to the world.

But Flo was wide awake and it was a sin to stay in bed on such a lovely morning. She sat up carefully – the springs of the single bed creaked like blazes – and stretched her arms. The sun streamed through the thin curtains making the roses on the floorcloth seem almost real. She poked her feet out and wriggled her white toes. As usual, the bedclothes were a mess – her sisters refused to sleep with her, claiming she fidgeted non-stop the whole night long.

Shall I get up and risk disturbing our Martha? Flo mused. She'd have to get dressed in the little space between the wardrobe and the tallboy. Since their dear dad, a railwayman, had died two years ago – struck by a train on the lines near Edge Hill station – and they'd had to take in a lodger, the girls could no longer wander round the little house in Burnett Street half dressed.

The frock Martha had worn last night when she'd gone with Albert Colquitt, their lodger, to see Bette Davis in *The Little Foxes* was hanging outside the wardrobe. Flo glared at it. What a miserable garment, dark grey with grey buttons, more suitable for a funeral than a night out with the man you hoped to marry. She transferred her gaze to her sister's head, which could just be seen above the green eiderdown. How on earth could she sleep with her hair screwed up in a million metal curlers? And did

someone of o.
cold cream so s.

Oh dear! She wa.
loved her just as mu.
owned the laundry wher.
Mam not feeling too well, .
eldest to be In Charge and ke.
been strict – he'd been a soft ou.
was still hard to get used to him i.

She couldn't stand being in bed a i.
and got dressed quickly in her best pin.
collar and the cuffs of the short puffed sleev.
were off to New Brighton on the ferry.

As she crept downstairs, she could hear Ma.
bedroom. There was no sound from the parlour. N.   .ave
gone to work, poor man. Flo felt for him. As a tick.   on the
trams, he had to work on days most people had off.

In the living room, she automatically kissed the feet of the porcelain
figure of Christ on the crucifix over the mantelpiece, then skipped into the
back kitchen where she washed her face and cleaned her teeth. She combed
her silvery blonde hair before the mirror over the sink. As an experiment,
she twisted it into two long plaits and pinned them together on top of her
head with a slide. Irene Dunne had worn her hair like that in a picture
she'd seen recently. Flo had been meaning to try it ever since. It looked
dead elegant.

She made a face at herself and was about to burst into song, when she
remembered the superstition, 'Sing before breakfast, cry before tea.'
Anyroad, everyone upstairs was still asleep. She'd make a pot of tea and
take them a cup when she heard them stir. Martha and Sally enjoyed sitting
up in bed, pillows tucked behind them, gossiping, on days they didn't have
to get up for work. Unlike Flo, they both had horrible jobs: Martha was a
bottle topper in Goodlad's Brewery, and Sally worked behind the counter
of the butcher's on the corner of Smithdown Road and Tunstall Street.

Oh, but it was difficult not to sing on such a glorious day. The sun must
be splitting the flags outside, and the whitewashed walls in the backyard
dazzled so brightly it hurt her eyes to look. Flo filled the kettle, put it on
the hob over the fire in the living room, releasing the flue so the embers
from the night before began to sizzle and glow, and decided to dance
instead. She took a deep breath and was twirling across the room like a
ballerina, when she came to a sudden halt in the arms of their lodger.

'Mr Colquitt! I thought you'd gone.' Flo felt as if she'd blushed right
down to her toes. He was wearing his regulation navy blue uniform with
red piping, and grinning from ear to ear.

...e sight of a fairy dancing

...o stammered, conscious of his arms still

...you, Flo. How many times have I told you to call me

...n't remember.' To her relief, he removed his hands, came into the room and sat in the easy chair that used to be Dad's. Flo didn't mind, because she liked Mr Colquitt – Albert – though couldn't for the life of her understand why Martha was so keen on capturing for a husband a widower more than twice her age. Since her best friend, Elsa, had married Eugene Cameron, Martha was terrified of being left on the shelf. Like Flo, she took after Mam's side of the family, with her slim figure, pale blonde hair and unusual green eyes, but had unfortunately inherited Dad's poor eyesight: she had worn glasses since she was nine and had never come to terms with it. She thought herself the unluckiest girl in the world, whose chances of finding a decent husband were doomed.

Martha had been setting her cap at Albert ever since he arrived on the scene. He was a tall, ungainly man with a round pot belly like a football. Although he was not handsome, his face was pleasant and his grey eyes shone with good humour. His wispy hair grew in sideboards to way below his ears, which Flo thought looked a bit daft. The main thing wrong with Albert, though, was that he didn't get his uniform cleaned often enough, so it ponged something dreadful, particularly in summer. It was ponging now, and she would have opened the window if it hadn't meant climbing on his knee.

'Would you like a bite to eat?' she enquired. Breakfast and an evening meal were supposed to be included in his rent, but he usually left too early for anyone to make breakfast, so compensated by eating a thundering great tea when he came home.

'I wouldn't say no to a couple of slices of toast, and is that water boiling for tea?'

'It is so.' Flo cut two slices of bread and managed to get both on the toasting fork. She knelt in front of the fire and toasted her arm at the same time.

'You've done your hair different,' Albert said suddenly. 'It's very nice. You look like a snow princess.'

'Ta.' Flo had never mentioned it to a living soul, but she sometimes wondered if he liked her better than he did Martha, though not in a romantic way, of course. She also thought that maybe he wasn't too keen to allow pretty, bespectacled Martha Clancy to get her claws into him. He might be twice her age and smell awful, but he didn't want to get married again. Flo hoped Martha wouldn't try too hard so that he'd feel obliged to leave. His thirty bob a week made all the difference to the housekeeping nowadays. It meant they could buy scented soap and decent cuts of meat, luxuries that they could never afford otherwise. Although there were three wages coming in, women earned much less than men.

He ate his toast, drank his tea, made several more flattering remarks about her appearance, then left for work. Flo returned to the living room, poured a cup of tea, and curled up in Dad's chair. She wanted to think about Tommy O'Mara before anyone got up. If Martha was in the room, it was impossible – her sister's mere presence made Flo feel guilty. For a second, a shadow fell over her face. Tommy was married to Nancy, but he'd explained the strange circumstances to Flo's satisfaction. Next year, sooner if possible, he and Flo would be married. Her face cleared. Until the magic day occurred, it was perfectly all right to meet Tommy O'Mara twice a week outside the Mystery.

Upstairs, Mam coughed and Flo held her breath until the house was quiet again. She'd met Tommy on the Tuesday after Easter when he'd come into the laundry by the side door. Customers were supposed to use the front, which led to the office where Mr Fritz was usually behind the counter. It was a dull day, slightly chilly, but the side door was left open, except in the iciest of weather, because when all the boilers, presses and irons were working at full pelt, the laundry got hotter than a Turkish bath.

Flo was pressing sheets in the giant new electric contraption Mr Fritz had only recently bought. She was nearest to the door, wreathed in steam, only vaguely aware of someone approaching through the mist until a voice with a strong Irish accent said, 'Do you do dry-cleaning, luv?'

'Sorry, no, just laundry.' As the steam cleared, she saw a young man with a brown suit over his arm. He wore a grey, collarless shirt and, despite the cold, the sleeves were rolled up to his armpits, showing off his strong, brown arms – there was a tattoo of a tiger on the right. A tweed cap was set jauntily on the back of his untidy brown curls. His waist was as slim as a girl's, something he must have been proud of as his baggy corduroy trousers were held up with a leather belt pulled as tight as it would go. A red hanky was tied carelessly around his neck, emphasising the devil-may-care expression on his handsome, sunburnt face.

'The nearest dry-cleaner's is Thompson's, that's along Gainsborough Road on the first corner,' she said. There was a peculiar feeling in the pit of her tummy as she watched him over the pressing machine. He was staring at her boldly, making no attempt to conceal the admiration in his dark eyes. She wanted to tear off her white turban and let him see she looked even prettier with her blonde hair loose.

'What's your name?' he asked.

Flo felt as flustered as if he'd asked to borrow a pound note. 'Flo Clancy,' she stammered.

'I'm Tommy O'Mara.'

'Are you now!' You'd think she was the only one there the way he kept his eyes locked on hers, and seemed unaware that the other five women had stopped work for a good look – Josie Driver was leering at him provocatively over the shirts she was supposed to be ironing.

'I suppose I'd better make me way round to Thompson's,' he said.

'I suppose you had.'

He winked. 'Tara, Flo.' With a swagger, he was gone.

'Tara,' Flo whispered. Her legs felt weak and her heart was thumping madly.

'Who was that?' Josie called eagerly. 'Jaysus, he could have me for sixpence!'

Before Flo could reply, Olive Knott shouted, 'His name's Tommy O'Mara. He lives in the next street to us, and before you young 'uns get too excited, you might like to know he's well and truly married.'

Flo's thumping heart sank to her boots. Married!

Mr Fritz came out of the office to ask what all the fuss was about.

'We've just had Franchot Tone, Clark Gable and Ronald Colman all rolled into one asking if we did dry-cleaning,' Olive said cuttingly.

'Why, Flo, you've gone all pink.' Mr Fritz beamed at her through his wire-rimmed spectacles. He was a plump, comfortable little man with a round face and lots of frizzy brown hair. He was wearing a brown coat overall, which meant he was about to go out in the van to deliver clean laundry and collect dirty items in return. Olive, who'd been there the longest and was vaguely considered next in command, would take over the office and answer the telephone.

'I didn't mean to,' Flo said stupidly.

'It must be nice to be young and impressionable.' He sighed gloomily, as if he already had one foot in the grave though he wasn't quite forty. For some reason, Mr Fritz was forever trying to make out he was dead miserable, when everyone knew he was the happiest man alive – and the nicest, kindest employer in the whole wide world. His surname was Austrian, a bit of a mouthful and difficult to spell, so everyone called him by his first name, Fritz, and referred to his equally plump little Irish wife, Stella, as Mrs Fritz, and their eight children – three girls and five boys – as the little Fritzes.

He departed, and the women returned to their work, happy in the knowledge that on Tuesdays he called at Sinclair's, the confectioner's, to collect the overalls and would bring them back a cream cake each.

Try as she might, Flo was unable to get Tommy O'Mara out of her mind. Twice before, she'd thought she was in love, the first time with Frank McGee, then Kevin Kelly – she'd actually let Kevin kiss her on the way home from the Rialto where they'd been to a St Patrick's Day dance – but the feelings she had for them paled to nothing when she thought about the man who'd looked at her so boldly. Was it possible she was properly in love with someone she'd exchanged scarcely more than half a dozen words with?

When they were having their tea that night Martha asked sharply, 'What's the matter with you?'

Flo emerged from the daydream in which an unmarried Tommy O'Mara had just proposed. 'Nowt!' she answered, just as sharply.

'I've asked three times if you want pudding. It's apple pie.'

'For goodness sake, Martha, leave the girl alone.' Mam was having one of her good days, which meant she resented Martha acting as if she owned the place. At other times she was too worn out and listless to open her mouth. More and more often, Flo found her in bed when she arrived home from work. Mam patted her youngest daughter's arm. 'She was in a lovely little world of her own, weren't you, luv? I could tell. Your eyes were sparkling as if you were thinking of something dead nice.'

'I was so.' Flo stuck out her tongue at Martha as she disappeared into the back kitchen.

'Can I borrow your pink frock tonight, Flo?' Sally enquired. 'I'm going to the Grand with Brian Maloney.'

'Isn't he a Protestant?' Martha shouted from the kitchen.

'I've no idea,' Sally yelled back.

Martha appeared, grim-faced, in the doorway. 'I'd sooner you didn't go out with Protestants, Sal.'

'It's none of your bloody business,' Flo said indignantly.

Mam shook her head. 'Don't swear, luv.'

Sally wriggled uncomfortably in the chair. 'We're only going to the pictures.'

'You can never tell how things develop with a feller. It's best not to get involved with a Protestant from the start.'

'I'll tell him I won't see him again after tonight.'

'In that case, you won't need our Flo's best frock. Go in something old. He might get ideas if you arrive all dolled up.'

Flo felt cross with both her sisters, one for being so bossy and the other for allowing herself to be bossed.

'What are you doing with yourself tonight, luv?' Mam asked.

'I thought I'd stay in and read a book – but I'll play cards with you if you like.' When Dad was alive, the two of them used to play cards for hours.

'No, ta, luv. I feel a bit tired. I might go to bed after I've had a cup of tea. I'll not bother with the apple pie, Martha.'

'I wish you'd go to the doctor's, Mam,' Flo said worriedly. Kate Clancy had never been a strong woman, and since the sudden, violent death of her beloved husband, she seemed to have lost the will to live, becoming thinner and more frail by the day.

'So do I.' Martha stroked Mam's hair, which had changed from ash-blonde to genuine silver almost overnight.

'Me, too,' echoed Sally.

But Mam screwed her thin face into the stubborn expression they'd seen many times before. 'Now, don't you girls start on that again,' she said tightly. 'I've told you, I'm not seeing a doctor. He might find something wrong with me, and there's no way I'm letting them cut me open. I'm just run down, that's all. I'll feel better when the warm weather comes.'

'Are you taking the bile beans I bought?' Martha demanded.

'They're beside me bed and I take them every morning.'

The girls glanced at each other with concern. If Mam died so soon after Dad, they didn't think they could bear it.

Mam went to bed and Sally got ready to meet Brian Maloney. Martha made her remove her earrings before she left, as if sixpenny pearl earrings from Woolworths would drive a man so wild with desire that he'd propose on the spot and Sally would feel obliged to accept!

It was Flo's turn to wash and dry the dishes. She cleared the table, shook the white cloth in the yard, straightened the green chenille cloth underneath and folded one leaf of the table down, before putting the white cloth on again for when their lodger came home. A meal fit for a giant was in the oven keeping warm. Flo set his place: knife, fork and spoon, condiments to the right, mustard to the left. As soon as she'd finished, she sank into the armchair with the novel she was halfway through, *Shattered Love, Shattered Dreams*.

Martha came in and adjusted everything on the table as if it had been crooked. 'You've always got your head buried in a book, Flo Clancy,' she remarked.

'You moan when I go out and you moan when I stay in.' Flo made a face at her sister. 'What do you expect me to do all night? Sit and twiddle me thumbs?'

'I wasn't moaning, I was merely stating a fact.' Martha gave the table a critical glance. 'Will you look after Albert when he comes?'

'Of course.' There was nothing to be done except move the plate from the oven to the table, which Albert could no doubt manage alone if no help was available.

'I'd stay meself, but I promised to go and see Elsa Cameron. That baby's getting her down something awful. I'm sure she smacks him, yet the little lad's not even twelve months old.'

'Norman? He's a lovely baby. I wouldn't mind having him meself.'

'Nor I.' Martha shoved a hatpin into a little veiled cocked hat, then sighed as she adjusted her glasses in the mirror. She was smartly dressed, although she was only going around the corner, in a long grey skirt with a cardigan to match. The whole outfit had cost ten bob in Paddy's Market. 'Trouble is, Flo, I'm beginning to think Elsa's not quite right in the head. She's been acting dead peculiar since Norman arrived. The other day when I turned up she was undoing her knitting, but when I asked why, she'd no idea. She mightn't be so bad if Eugene was there, but him being in the Merchant Navy, like, it means he's hardly ever home.'

'It's a terrible shame,' Flo said sincerely. Norman Cameron was Martha's godson and the most delightful baby she'd ever known. It was terrible to think he was getting his mam down. 'Can't Eugene get a different job?'

'Not with a million men already out of work,' Martha said. 'Mind you, that'll soon change if there's a war.'

'There won't be a war,' Flo said quickly. She looked at her sister, scared. 'Will there?'

'Oh, I don't know, luv. According to the papers, that Hitler's getting far too big for his boots.'

Like Mam dying, war was something best not thought about. After Martha left, Flo tried to bury herself in her book, but the man over whom the heroine was pining was a pale, insipid creature compared to Tommy O'Mara, and instead of words, she kept seeing *him* on the page: his dark, shameless eyes, his reckless face, the cheeky way he wore his cap. She reckoned it was a good job she wouldn't be seeing him again. If he'd been as knocked sideways by her as she'd been by him, he might ask her out, and although a good Catholic girl should never, never go out with a married man, Flo wasn't convinced she'd be capable of resisting Tommy O'Mara.

She *did* see him again, only two days later. He came into the laundry, this time bearing two white shirts that already looked perfectly clean. She looked up from the press and found him smiling at her intently as if she was the only woman in the world, never mind the laundry.

'I'd like these laundered, please.'

Flo had to swallow several times before she could answer. 'You need to take them round the front and Mr Fritz will give you a ticket,' she said, in a voice that sounded as if it belonged to someone else.

He frowned. 'Does that mean I won't see you when I collect them?'

'I'm afraid not,' she said, still in someone else's voice.

He flung the shirts over his shoulder, stuck his thumbs in his belt and rocked back on his heels. 'In that case, I'll not beat about the bush. Would you like to come for a walk with me one night, Flo? We can have a bevy on the way – you're old enough to go in boozers, aren't you?'

'I'll be nineteen in May,' Flo said faintly. 'Though I've never been in a booz – a pub before.'

'Well, there's a first time for everything.' He winked. 'See you tomorrer night then, eight o'clock outside the Mystery gates, the Smithdown Road end.'

'Rightio.' She watched him leave, knowing that she'd done something terribly wrong. She felt very adult and worldly wise, as if she was much older than Sally and Martha. Tomorrow night she was going out with a married man and the thing was *she didn't care!*

'What did he want?' Olive Knott brought her down to earth with a sharp nudge in the ribs.

'He brought his shirts to the wrong place. I sent him round the front.'

Olive's brow creased worriedly. 'He didn't ask you out, did he?'

For the first time in her life Flo lied. 'No.'

'He's got his eye on you, that's plain to see. Oh, he has a way with him, there's no denying it, but it's best for nice girls like you to stay clear of men like Tommy O'Mara, Flo.'

But Flo was lost. She would have gone out with Tommy O'Mara if Olive had declared him to be the divil himself.

Friday was another dull day and there was drizzle on and off until early evening when a late sun appeared. It looked as soft as a jelly in the dusky blue sky, and its gentle rays filled the air with gold dust.

Flo felt very odd as she made her way to the Mystery. Every step that took her nearer seemed of momentous significance, as if she was walking towards her destiny, and that after tonight nothing would ever be the same again. She thought of the lie she'd told at home – that she was calling on Josie Driver who'd been off sick and Mr Fritz wanted to know how she was, which had been all she could think of when Martha demanded to know where she was going.

When she arrived Tommy was already there. He was standing outside the gates, whistling, wearing a dark blue suit that looked a bit too big, a white and blue striped shirt with a high stiff collar, and a grey tie. A slightly more respectable tweed cap was set at the same jaunty angle on the back of his curly head. The mere sight of the swaggering, audacious figure made Flo feel quite faint.

'There you are!' He smiled. 'You're late. I was worried you might have changed your mind.'

The thought had never entered her head. She smiled nervously and said, 'Hello.'

'You look nice,' he said appreciatively. 'Green suits you. It sets off your eyes. That was the first thing I noticed when I came into the laundry, those green eyes. I bet you have stacks of fellers chasing after you.'

'Not exactly,' Flo mumbled.

'In that case, the fellers round here must be mad!' When he linked her arm Flo could smell a mixture of strong tobacco and carbolic soap. She got the peculiar feeling in her tummy again as they began to stroll through the park, though the Mystery was more like a playing-field: a vast expanse of grass surrounded by trees. The Liverpool-to-London railway line ran along one side. The trees were bursting into life, ready for summer, and pale sunlight filtered through the branches, making dappled patterns on the green grass underneath.

Without any prompting, Tommy briefly told her the story of his life. He'd been born in Ireland, in the county of Limerick, and had come to Liverpool ten years ago when he was twenty. 'I've got fourteen brothers and sisters, half of 'em still at home. I send me mam a few bob when I've got it to spare.'

Flo said she thought that very generous. She asked where he worked.

'I'm a fitter at Cammell Laird's in Birkenhead,' he said boastfully. 'You should see this ship we're building at the moment. It's a T-class submarine, the *Thetis*. Guess how much it's costing?'

She confessed she had absolutely no idea.

'Three hundred thousand smackeroos!'

'Three hundred thousand!' Flo gasped. 'Is it made of gold or something?'

He laughed and squeezed her arm. 'No, but it's the very latest design. You should see the instruments in the conning tower! *And* it's got ten torpedo tubes. I don't envy any German ships that come near the *Thetis* if there's a war.'

'There won't be a war,' Flo said stubbornly.

'That's what women always say.' He chuckled.

She realised he'd omitted to tell her about one important aspect of his life – his wife. There was silence for a while, except for his whistling, as they strolled across the grass and the April sun began to disappear behind the trees.

Perhaps Tommy had read her thoughts, because he said suddenly, 'I should have told you this before, Flo. I'm married.'

'I know,' Flo said.

He raised his finely drawn eyebrows in surprise. 'Who told you?'

'A woman at work, Olive Knott. She lives in the next street to you.'

'Does she now.' He made a face. 'I'm surprised you came, knowing, like.'

Flo wasn't in the least surprised: she'd have come even if she'd been told he had ten wives.

They'd arrived at the other side of the Mystery and emerged into Gainsborough Road. Tommy steered her inside the first pub they came to. 'What would you like to drink?' he asked.

'I've no idea.' The only alcohol that ever crossed Flo's lips was a small glass of sherry at Christmas.

'I'll get you a port and lemon. That's what women usually like.'

The pub was crowded. Flo glanced round when Tommy went to be served, worried someone might recognise her, but there were no familiar faces. She noticed that quite a few women were eyeing Tommy up and down as he waited at the bar, legs crossed nonchalantly at the ankles. Without doubt he was the best-looking man there – and he was with *her*! Flo gasped at the sheer magic of it all, just as Tommy turned round and winked.

Her eyes flickered as she tried to wink back, but couldn't quite manage it. Tommy laughed at her efforts as he came over with the drinks. 'You know,' he whispered, 'you're the most beautiful girl here, Flo Clancy, perhaps the most beautiful in the whole of Liverpool. There's something special between us, isn't there? I recognised it the minute I set eyes on you. It's something that doesn't happen often between a man and a woman, but it's happened between you and me.'

Flo felt as if she wanted to cry. She also wanted to say something meaningful, but all she could think of was, 'I suppose it has.'

Tommy swallowed half his beer in one go, then returned the pint glass to the table with a thump. He took a tin of tobacco from his pocket and deftly rolled a ciggie out of the thick dark shreds that smelt of tar. He shoved the tin in Flo's direction, but she shook her head. 'It's time I explained about Nancy,' he said grandly.

'Nancy?'

'Me wife. It's not a genuine marriage, Flo, not in any respects.' He looked at her knowingly. 'I met Nancy in Spain when I was fighting in the Civil War. She's a gypsy. I won't deny I fell for her hook, line and sinker. I would have married her proper, given the opportunity, but 'stead, I did it Nancy's way.' The way he told it it sounded like the most romantic novel ever written. He and Nancy had 'plighted their troth', as he put it, at a gypsy ceremony in a wood near Barcelona. 'It means nowt in the eyes of British law or the Roman Catholic Church,' he said contemptuously. He'd been meaning to leave for a long time, and as soon as Nancy got better he'd be off like a shot. 'Then I'll be free to marry an English girl, proper, like, this time.' He clasped Flo's hand and gazed deep into her eyes. 'And you know who that'll be, don't you?'

Flo felt the blood run hot through her body. She gulped. 'What's wrong with Nancy?'

Tommy sighed. 'It's a bit embarrassing to explain, luv. It's what's called a woman's complaint. She's been to Smithdown Road ozzie and the doctors said it'll all be cleared up in about six months. I don't like to leave till she gets better,' he added virtuously.

The guilt that had been lurking in a little corner of Flo's mind about going out with a married man disappeared, along with the suspicion that he'd only told her about Nancy in case someone else did. Why, he was almost single! It seemed wise, though, not to mention him and his peculiar circumstances to her family. Martha, in particular, would never understand. She'd say nothing until they got engaged.

'I trust you'll keep what I've just said under your hat for now, luv,' Tommy said conspiratorially. 'I don't want people knowing me private business, like, till the time comes to tell them.'

'I won't breathe a word,' Flo assured him. 'I'd already decided to keep you a secret.'

'A secret! I like the idea of being the secret man in Flo Clancy's life.' His brown eyes sparkled. 'How about another drink before we go?'

'No, ta.' The port and lemon had already gone to her head.

'I'll just have another quick pint, then we'll be off.'

It was dark when they went outside. The sky glowed hazy orange where the sun had set, but was otherwise dark blue, almost black. They wandered hand in hand through the Mystery, the noise of the traffic behind growing fainter, until nothing could be heard except their feet on the grass, the slight rustle of the trees, and Tommy's musical whistle.

'What's that tune?' Flo enquired. 'I can't quite place it.'

'"Dancing in the Dark." Have you never heard it before?'

'I couldn't remember what it was called.'

He began to sing. '"Dancing in the dark..." C'mon, Flo.' He grabbed her by the waist and twirled her around. Flo threw back her head and laughed. '"Dancing in the dark,"' they sang together.

They stopped when two men walked past and Flo shivered. 'I forgot to bring a cardy.'

Tommy put his arm around her shoulders. 'You don't feel cold.' He placed his hand on the back of her neck. 'You feel hot. Your neck's sweating.'

She wasn't sure if she was hot or cold. Her body felt as if it was on fire, yet she shivered again. Tommy's hand pressed harder on her neck as he began to lead her towards a tree not far away. He pushed her against the broad trunk and took her in his arms. 'I've been thinking of nothing else but this for days.'

A train roared past on the furthest side of the park, the engine puffing eerie clouds of smoke. Flo thought about Dad, who'd been knocked down on that very same railway line, but not for long: Tommy's lips were pressed against hers and she felt as if she was being sucked into a whirlpool. Her head spun and she seemed to be slipping down and down and down. She came to briefly and found herself lying on the damp grass with Tommy bent over her. He'd undone the front of her dress and his lips were seeking her breasts, his tongue tenderly touching her nipples. Flo arched her back and almost screamed because the sensation was so wonderful. She knew what was to come, she knew it was a bad thing, but she could no more have stopped him than she could have stopped the sun from rising the next morning.

Tommy was pushing up her skirt, pulling away her underthings. There was the sound of her stockings tearing and she felt his callused hand between her legs. He was groaning, murmuring over and over, 'I love you, Flo,' and she could hear other little breathless cries that she realised came from her own throat. All the while, she was running her fingers through his thick dark curls, kissing his ears, his neck . . .

He felt so *big* when he entered her, and it hurt, but the hurt soon faded and turned into something else, something that no words had been invented to describe.

It all ended in a wild, feverish explosion that left them shaken and exhausted, and with Flo convinced that the only reason she'd been born was to make love with Tommy O'Mara.

'Jaysus, Flo!' he said hoarsely. 'That was the best I've ever known.' After a while, he began to pull her clothes back on. 'Get dressed, luv, else you'll catch cold.'

Flo touched his sensually curved lips with her finger, feeling the love flow from her heart right down her arm. 'I love you, Tommy.'

'I love you, girl.'

There was the faint murmur of voices upstairs: Martha and Sally were awake. Flo leaped out of the chair to take them up a cup of tea. On the way to the back kitchen, she did a pirouette. She'd always been happy, but nowadays she was so happy she could bust – and it had all begun that night in the Mystery when she'd danced in the dark with Tommy.

She and Sally had a wonderful day in New Brighton. They went on every single ride in the fairground, even the children's ones. Sally complained afterwards she felt quite sick, though it was more likely caused by the fish and chips followed by a giant ice-cream cornet with strawberry topping. She recovered swiftly on the ferry back when they clicked with two sailors who invited them to the pictures. 'Why did you turn them down?' she grumbled, on the tram home to Wavertree.

'I didn't fancy that Peter,' Flo replied. In fact, both sailors had been quite nice, but she was meeting Tommy at eight o'clock. Even if she wasn't, she would have felt disloyal going out with another man.

'I quite fancied Jock.' Her sister sighed. Sally was neither plain nor pretty, a bit like Dad with her neat brown hair and hazel eyes. She hadn't had a date since the one with Brian Maloney, almost two months ago.

Flo felt bad about the sailors. If it hadn't been for Tommy she'd have gone like a shot. 'You gave Jock your address, Sal. He might write,' she said hopefully.

'And where are you off to?' Martha demanded that night when Flo came downstairs ready to go out.

'I'm going to see Josie.' Unknown to Josie Driver, she and Flo had become the greatest of friends since Tommy had appeared on the scene. She met Josie twice a week, Mondays and Fridays. Josie would have been surprised to learn she was thinking of becoming a nun and needed someone in whom she could confide her deepest, most intimate thoughts while coming to such a major decision.

Martha's eyes looked suspicious behind her thick glasses. 'Why do you need a red bow in your hair just to see Josie?'

'I bought the ribbon in New Brighton,' Flo replied haughtily.

'It looks very nice,' Albert Colquitt said, from the table where he was having his tea.

'I think so, too,' Mam concurred.

Martha gave up. 'Don't be too late.'

'Have a nice time,' Flo called, as she slammed the door. Albert had just bought a wireless and everyone was staying in to listen to a play, Mam armed with two bottles of Guinness to 'build her up', although she'd been feeling better since the weather had improved. Flo shuddered to think of her sisters sitting in the parlour on Albert's bed-settee. What a way for two young women to spend a bank-holiday evening!

'I like your bow,' said Tommy.

'I like your tie,' Flo sang.

'I like your face, your eyes, your lips. I like every single little thing about you!' He picked her up and spun her around until they both felt dizzy and fell, laughing, on to the grass, whereupon he began to kiss her passionately.

'It's still broad daylight,' Flo murmured.

'So it is.' He kissed her again and caressed her breasts.

'We might get arrested and it'd be in the *Echo*.'

'Would that matter?'

'Not to me it wouldn't,' Flo giggled, 'but me mam wouldn't be pleased and our Martha'd have a fit. Nancy wouldn't like it either.'

'Nancy would just have to lump it.' Nevertheless, he sat up and smoothed his unruly curls.

Flo had never told him she'd seen Nancy. One day when she knew he was at work she'd set out for Clement Street, off Smithdown Road. It was a respectable street of small two-up, two-down houses. The windows shone, the steps had been scrubbed that morning. Flo paused across the road opposite number eighteen.

So this was where he lived. Nancy must take pride in her house. The curtains were maroon cretonne, upstairs and down, and there were paper flowers in the parlour window. The front door and the window-sills were dark green, freshly painted. Flo's heart missed a beat – had *he* painted them? She'd never ask because she didn't want him to know she'd spied on his house.

She walked up and down the street several times, keeping a close eye on number eighteen in case Nancy came out to clean the windows or brush the step. After about half an hour, when she was about to give up, a woman carrying a shopping basket came towards her from the direction of Smithdown Road. Flo knew it was Nancy because she looked exactly like the gypsy Tommy had said she was. She was outstanding in her way, the sort of woman that would be described as handsome. Her skin was the colour of cinnamon, her eyes as black as night, and she had a big beaked nose and glossy black hair drawn back in a cushiony bun at the nape of her thin neck.

'Mercy me!' Flo muttered. She wasn't sure why, but something about the woman disturbed her. And what peculiar clothes she wore to go shopping! A flowing black skirt, red satin blouse and a brightly embroidered garment that wasn't quite a jacket and wasn't quite a shawl.

The two women passed. Flo had no idea if Nancy glanced in her direction because she kept her own eyes fixed firmly on the ground. After a few seconds, she turned and saw the colourful figure cross the road and go into number eighteen.

In the Mystery, Tommy got to his feet and reached down to pull her up. 'We'll come back later when it's dark. And then . . .' His dark eyes smouldered and Flo's tummy did a cartwheel.

'And then . . .' she whispered. Then they would come as close to heaven as it was possible to get on earth.

She told him about the sailors because she wanted to make him jealous and he duly was. 'You belong to me, Flo Clancy,' he said angrily. 'We belong to each other till the end of time.'

'I know, I know!' she cried. 'I wouldn't dream of going out with another man when I've got you.'

He looked sulky. 'I should hope not!'

In the pub, he informed her that the submarine he'd been working on, the *Thetis*, was taking its first diving exercise on Thursday. 'Some of the shipyard workers are sailing with it, but my name wasn't on the list. You get extra pay, at least ten bob.' He looked wistful. 'I would have gone for nothing.'

'Never mind.' Flo was keeping a close eye on the sky outside. She wasn't bothered about the *Thetis.* All her concentration was centred on how swiftly night would fall so they could go to the Mystery and make love.

2

The Fritz family had been to Anglesey for Whit, a regular haunt, and Mr Fritz didn't return to the laundry till Thursday when the children were due back at school. He'd bought a camera, there was one exposure left on the roll, and he wanted a snapshot taken of him with his girls. Later that morning, Mrs Fritz came bustling along to take it. It was the first of June and a perfect day for taking photographs. The weather had been brilliantly sunny all week.

The six women trooped outside, excited. 'You stand by me, Flo,' Mr Fritz hissed. 'It's an excuse to put my arm around you. I want a record of that smile. It's always been enough to dazzle the strongest eyes, but lately it's not just a smile, it's a miracle.'

Mrs Fritz stationed her plump body in the middle of the street. 'Try and get the sign in over the door, Stella,' her husband shouted, as everyone shuffled into position.

'Say cheese!' Mrs Fritz called.

'*Cheese!*'

There was a click. 'All done!'

'If it turns out all right, I'll order a copy each.' Mr Fritz squeezed Flo's waist and whispered, 'I enjoyed that.'

Flo knew he was only joking, because he adored his sweet little wife and eight children, but she hoped no one had noticed – Josie was always complaining that Flo was Mr Fritz's favourite.

The rest of the day passed in a dream, as the days did since she'd met Tommy. She lived for Monday, lived for Friday, then lived for Monday again. They would have met more often, but he didn't like to leave Nancy while she felt so poorly.

Six o'clock came and she made her way home, still immersed in her dream, and scarcely noticed the crowd that had gathered on the corner of the street next to hers until she reached it.

'What's up?' she asked.

A woman grabbed her arm. 'There's been a terrible accident, girl. Haven't you heard?'

'What sort of accident?'

'It's some ship, a submarine called the *Thetis* – it's trapped underwater in Liverpool Bay and they can't find its position. There's over a hundred men on board.'

'Holy Mary, Mother of God!' Flo crossed herself. At first she felt relieved that Tommy hadn't been on board, but concern followed quickly for the men who were. She could think of nothing more horrific than to be trapped beneath the sea in a vessel she imagined being shaped like a big black fish. 'They'll be rescued, won't they?' she said anxiously.

An elderly man butted in. 'Of course they will, luv. I'm an ould salt meself, so I know Liverpool Bay's no more than twenty-five fathoms deep. They'll have them men up in no time.'

When she got home Mam and her sisters had already heard the bad news. Martha was wondering if they dared invade Albert's room and turn on the wireless.

'It's not been declared official yet,' Mam said. 'So far it's just rumour.'

'You mean it might not have happened?' Sally looked hopeful.

'Oh, it's happened all right.' Mam shook her head sadly. 'Mrs Cox's nephew works in Cammell Laird where everyone knows full well there's been an accident. Women have already started to collect outside to wait for news of their men. It's just that nothing's been confirmed, so the news won't have reached the wireless.'

It wasn't until ten o'clock that the plight of the *Thetis* was conveyed to the nation by the BBC. One hundred and three men were on board, fifty of them civilians. The Admiralty assured everyone concerned that rescue ships were on their way and there was every hope the men would be saved.

'I should think so!' Flo said indignantly. 'It's only twenty-five fathoms deep.'

'How much is that in feet?' Martha asked Albert, as if men automatically knew everything. Albert confessed he had no idea.

There was a search for Dad's dictionary, which had conversion tables at the back. Twenty-five fathoms was 150 feet.

In bed that night, Flo was unable to get the trapped men out of her mind. She tossed and turned restlessly.

'Are you awake, Flo?' Sally whispered.

'Yes. I can't stop thinking of those men in the *Thetis*.'

'Me neither.'

Martha's voice surprised them because she usually slept like a log, despite the metal curlers. 'Let's say a silent prayer. Remember that one we learned at school for shipwrecked mariners?'

Eventually the sisters fell asleep, the words of the prayer on their lips.

When they woke next morning the *Thetis* came straight to mind. The weather was lovely, gloriously sunny, and it seemed incongruous and unfair that those safe on land should be blessed with such a perfect day in view of the disaster unfolding beneath the sea.

Albert had given them permission to listen to his wireless, from which they learned there'd been no developments overnight. Ships and aircraft were still trying to pinpoint the position of the stricken submarine.

On her way to work, Flo passed several groups of people gravely discussing the tragedy, which had touched the hearts of everyone in Liverpool. Twice she was asked, 'Have you heard any fresh news, luv?' All she could do was shake her head.

She bought a *Daily Herald*. Everyone in the laundry had bought a paper and the *Thetis* was the main headline on them all, as well as the sole topic of conversation all morning. Betty Bryant knew a woman who knew a woman whose cousin's husband was on board.

'I know someone on board even better than that,' Olive Knott said smugly. 'In fact, we all do. Remember that feller who brought his suit in for dry-cleaning a couple of months ago, Tommy O'Mara? He's a fitter with Cammell Laird. His poor ould wife wasn't half making a scene last night! Running up and down the street she was, screaming her head off. It took half a dozen neighbours to calm her. Mind you, Nancy O'Mara's always had a couple of screws loose.'

'But he wasn't supposed to go!' Flo's horrified words were lost in the chorus of dismay.

'Such a dead handsome feller, what a shame!'

'He was a cheeky-looking bugger, but I liked him.' Josie Driver looked close to tears.

Olive made a sour face. 'I don't wish him any harm, but Nancy'll be better off without the bugger. He drove the poor woman doo-lally with his philandering. No woman, married or single, was safe near Tommy O'Mara.'

That's not true! Flo wanted to scream that Olive was talking nonsense. Tommy may have been a bit of a blade in the past – in fact, he'd hinted so more than once – but it was only because Nancy hadn't been a proper wife in a long time. Since he'd met Flo, he wouldn't have given another woman a second glance. Oh, if only she could tell them! But why on earth was she thinking like this when it didn't matter a jot what Olive thought? What mattered was that Tommy might die! If he did, Flo wanted to die, too.

In her agitation she nearly scorched a shirt. Then Betty made things worse by reading out something from the newspaper. There was only enough oxygen on board to last thirty-six hours. Once the supply dried up, the men would die from carbon-dioxide poisoning. 'It means there's not much time left.' Betty clasped her hands together as if she were praying. 'Holy Mary, Mother of God, please save those poor men!'

Then Mr Fritz came hurrying in, panting for breath. 'The *Thetis* has been spotted with its stern sticking out of the water fourteen miles from Great Ormes Head. It was on the wireless just before I left.'

'Thank the Lord!' Josie shouted. 'They're bound to save them now.'

Relief swept through Flo's body so forcefully that, for a moment, she felt sick. She swayed, and Mr Fritz snatched the gas iron from her hand. 'Are you all right, Flo?'

'I hardly slept last night. I feel a bit ragged, that's all.'

'You go home, girl, if you don't feel better soon,' he said concernedly. 'I don't want you on your feet all day if you've got problems.'

'Problems' meant he thought she had a period. Standing for ten hours in the equivalent of a steambath was hard on women who had trouble with their monthlies, and Mr Fritz was always sympathetic if someone needed a day off. Flo, however, had always sailed through hers without so much as a twinge. Apart from a week's holiday each year, she hadn't had a single day off since she'd started five years ago straight from school.

'I'll see how I feel,' she told him gratefully.

The feeling of sickness soon left her, but for the first time the noise in the laundry began to get on her nerves: the churning of the washing in the boilers, the clatter of the belt-driven wringers, the hiss of the irons. Flo knew she couldn't work all day with the sounds pressing against her brain while she remained ignorant of the fate of the *Thetis*.

At midday, she went into the office and told Mr Fritz she felt no better. 'I wouldn't mind going home, after all.' She felt slightly ashamed of how good she'd become at lying over the last two months.

He fussed around, patted her cheek, and said she didn't look anything like her usual glowing self. He even offered to take her to Burnett Street in the van.

'No, ta,' she said. 'I might walk around a bit to clear me head. I'll go to bed this avvy.'

'Good idea, Flo, I hope you feel better tomorrow.'

Several hundred men and women had congregated in front of the gates of Cammell Laird. Some of the women held babies in their arms with slightly older children clutching their skirts. Some faces were hopeful, others blank with despair. A woman she couldn't see was shouting for her man. Flo's heart sank. It would seem there hadn't been more good news.

A girl with a glorious head of red hair, about the same age as herself, was standing at the back. 'What's happening?' Flo asked.

'Four men got out through the escape hatches, otherwise nowt.' The girl's face was extraordinarily colourful: pink lips, rosy cheeks, black-lashed eyes the colour of violets, all framed in the cloud of red waves.

'But someone at work said the stern was sticking out the water,' Flo groaned. 'I'd have thought they'd have hauled it up by now.'

The girl shrugged. 'I'd have thought so, too, but they haven't.' She looked at Flo sympathetically. 'Have you got someone on board?'

Flo bit her lip. 'Me feller.'

'Aye, so's mine. Well, he's only a sort of feller.' She didn't look the least bit upset. 'I only came out of curiosity. I'm always looking for an excuse to get off work. I suppose it's about time I went – I called in and said I had to see the doctor.'

'I told a lie to get away meself,' Flo confessed.

The girl made a face as if implying they were partners in a crime. 'Are you from Liverpool or Birkenhead?' She spoke in a loud, musical voice that rose and fell as if she was singing.

'Liverpool. I came on the ferry.'

'Me, too. I'll catch the next one back. Are you coming?'

'I only just got here. I'd sooner stay and see if anything happens.' Flo wished the girl didn't have to go. She rather liked her friendly, down-to-earth manner.

'I might go to the pics tonight. It'll be all about the *Thetis* on the Pathé News. Tara, then.' She clattered away on her high heels.

'Tara.' Flo sighed. If the submarine hadn't been brought up by tonight, it would be cutting things fine for those on board.

She turned her attention to the crowd. 'What I'd like to know,' a man muttered aggressively, 'is why they don't bore a hole through the hull and get everyone out that way, or at least pass in a hose of oxygen.'

Somewhere a woman was still shouting: 'What have you done with my man?' Flo edged her way through the throng.

'There's no need for that carry-on,' an elderly woman remarked acidly. 'Most of us are feared for our lads, but we're not reduced to weeping and wailing like a bloody banshee. Just look at the way she's throwing herself about an' all!'

Flo didn't answer. She had almost reached the front when she froze. Nancy O'Mara was kneeling on the ground, her hands clasped imploringly towards the closed gates of the ship-builder's. Her crow-black eyes burned unnaturally bright, as if with fever. Long strands of hair had escaped from the big bun coiled on her neck, and writhed like little snakes as she rocked to and fro. She looked almost insane with grief. Every now and then she turned her tragic face towards the men and women standing silently each side of her. 'Why?' she pleaded. 'Why, oh, why?'

Nobody answered, the faces remained impassive. They had no idea why. At that moment, there wasn't a person on earth who knew why ninety-nine human beings still remained on the stricken vessel when it was surrounded by rescue ships and the stern was visible for all to see.

Flo stood stock-still as she watched Tommy's wife throw herself back and forth on the pavement. Nancy paused to seek succour from those around her yet again. 'Why?' Then she caught sight of Flo, who stood transfixed as the burning eyes bored into hers, so full of hate that she felt her blood turn to ice.

Nancy knew!

With a cry that almost choked her, Flo turned and pushed her way through the crowd. She ran, faster than she'd ever run before, past the docks, the half-built ships, the vessels waiting to be loaded or unloaded. She ran until she reached the ferry, where a seaman was just about to raise the gangplank, and launched herself on to the deck. 'Just made it, luv.' He grinned.

Flo hardly heard. She climbed the stairs until she reached the top deck where she leaned on the hand-rail and stared into the calm greeny-brown waters of the Mersey. A warm breeze fanned her face, and her mind was blank, devoid of emotion or thought.

'Hello, there,' said a familiar voice. 'I thought you were going to stay and see what happened?'

'I decided not to.' Flo turned. The red-haired girl was the only person she didn't mind seeing at the moment. 'I felt too upset.'

'You shouldn't get upset over a feller.' The girl leaned on the rail beside her. She wore a smart emerald-green frock that accentuated her vividly coloured face. At any other time Flo would have felt ashamed of the shabby blouse and skirt she wore for work. 'There's plenty more where he came from. Someone with your looks will soon get fixed up again.'

'I don't want to get fixed up again,' Flo whispered. 'I'll never go out with anyone else. Never!'

'Don't tell me you're in love?' The girl sounded faintly disgusted.

Flo nodded numbly. For the first time since she'd heard the news about Tommy, she began to cry. The tears flowed freely down her cheeks and fell silently on to the smooth waters below.

'Come on, girl.' Flo felt her shoulders being painfully squeezed. 'What's your name?'

'Flo Clancy.'

'I'm Isobel MacIntyre, but everyone calls me Bel.' She gave Flo a little shake. 'Look, the ferry's about to dock. Shall we find somewhere and have a cup of tea?'

'I'd love to, but what about your job?'

'Sod me job! I'll tell them the doctor said I was run down and I needed a day off to put me feet up. Anyroad, it says almost half past two on the Liver building clock, so it's not worth going in.'

Flo couldn't help but smile through her tears. 'You're the healthiest-looking person I've ever seen.'

There was a café a short way along Water Street, almost empty after the dinner-time rush. They were about to enter, when Flo remembered she had only enough money for her tram fare home.

'Don't worry,' Bel said, when she told her. 'I'm flush so it can be my treat.'

As they drank their tea and Flo nibbled at a sticky bun, Bel informed her that she worked as a waitress at La Porte Rouge, a restaurant in Bold Street. 'That's French for the Red Door. It's dead posh and I get good tips, particularly off the fellers. Last week, I got fifteen bob altogether.'

'Just in tips! Gosh, I don't get much more than that in wages.'

Bel asked where she worked and where she lived and all about her family. Flo could tell she was trying to keep her mind off the events taking place above and below the sea not too many miles away. She gladly told her all about Fritz's Laundry, about Mam and her sisters, and how they'd had to take in a lodger when Dad died. 'He's dead nice, Albert. The thing is, our Martha's determined to marry him. I can't think why, 'cos though he's nice, he's no oil painting, and he's forty-five. She wears glasses, though, and she thinks she'll never catch a feller. You should hear the way she bosses me and our Sal around, just 'cos she's the oldest,' Flo said indignantly.

'She couldn't be any worse than me auntie Mabel,' Bel said flatly. 'She's an ould cow if there ever was one.' She explained that her mam had died when she was only four and she'd been dumped on Auntie Mabel who lived in Everton Valley. 'Me dad's away at sea most of the time. I can't wait to get away meself. I'm eighteen, and the very second the war starts, I'm going to join the Army.'

'But the Army only take men!'

'Of course they don't, soft girl! They take women an' all. They're called the ATS, which stands for Auxiliary Territorial Service.'

Just then, two men came in, talking volubly, and sat at the next table. After they had given the waitress their order, they continued their conversation.

'It's bloody disgraceful!' one said angrily. 'If I had a son on board, I'd kick up a stink all the way to Parliament. Why was she allowed to dive with twice the normal complement on board? Why was the Navy so long finding her position? And I'll never understand why cutting gear hasn't been brought by now and a hole made in her stern. The men would be free if the powers-that-be had any sense of urgency.'

'If someone doesn't get their finger out pretty soon, it'll be too late,' the other man said.

'If it isn't already! That business about there being enough oxygen for thirty-six hours, I'd like to know if that takes account of the extra men as well as the crew.'

'Do you ever go dancing, Flo?' Bel asked brightly.

But Flo's mind had been distracted long enough. 'I wonder if anything's happened,' she whispered.

'Don't sound like it. But try not to lose heart, Flo. There's still hope.'

Flo gave a deep, shuddering sigh. It was strange, but she couldn't help thinking about Nancy.

'Your chap's married, isn't he?' Bel said knowingly.

'How did you guess?' Flo gasped.

'If he was a proper boyfriend, this Mr Fritz would have let you off like a shot. Instead, you had to tell a lie to get away.'

'So did you,' Flo pointed out. 'Your chap must be married, too.'

Bel made a face. 'It so happens he's not. Tuesday was only the second time I'd seen him. That's when he told me he was sailing with the *Thetis* because some other feller had been taken poorly. When I saw the headlines in this morning's papers, it seemed a good excuse for a ride on the ferry – I often go on me own. In fact, that's where I met my chap, on the Birkenhead ferry.' She pursed her red lips primly. 'I'm not the sort of girl who goes out with married men, thanks all the same. Mind you, Flo, you don't look the sort, either, particularly with you being a Catholic an' all, not like me.'

Flo felt it was important to explain the nature of her relationship with Tommy. 'My chap wasn't married proper. We were going to get married next year.' She paused, frowning. 'His wife – I mean, his sort-of-wife – was outside Cammell Laird's. You never heard such a carry-on.'

'Was she the one who was shouting?'

'That's right, Nancy. The thing is, I'm sure she recognised me.'

'Maybe she's been following you and your bloke around?'

Flo shuddered. 'Oh, don't! Tommy would have a fit at the very idea.'

'Who?'

'Tommy. Tommy O'Mara. What's your chap's name?'

Bel was scowling at the teapot as she poured more water in. Her cheeks were flaming. 'Er, Jack Smith,' she said shortly. Despite having refilled the pot, she leaped to her feet and paid the bill. Outside, she began to walk quickly, for no reason that a rather confused Flo could see, back towards the river.

They arrived at the Pier Head just as a ferry returning from New Brighton was docking. Children came running off the boat on to the landing-stage carrying buckets and spades, their hair full of sand, faces brown from the sun. Flo remembered going to New Brighton with Mam and Dad and her sisters. It seemed a hundred lifetimes ago. The area was unusually crowded for a weekday. People were staring out to sea, as if hoping to see signs of the attempts being made to rescue the ill-fated submarine. The girls wandered across to join them.

They stood for a long while in silence, until Flo said dully, 'I don't know what I'm going to do if Tommy's dead. I'll never love another man the way I loved him. If they don't fetch the *Thetis* up, me life's over.'

'I've never heard such nonsense!' Bel's expressive face conveyed a mixture of sympathy and impatience. 'No one's life's over when they're only nineteen. What about all the proper wives? Are their lives over, too? You're dead stupid you are, Flo Clancy, letting yourself get all worked up over a chap who's not worth twopence.'

The criticism was rather blunt and scathing coming from someone she'd only just met, but Flo was too upset to take offence. She began to cry again. 'How would you know what he's worth?' she sobbed. 'Tommy O'Mara's worth a million pounds to me.'

'I've never met a chap worth twopence meself,' Bel said brusquely. 'When I meet a threepenny one, I'll marry him like a shot. The trouble with you is you're dead soft. I'm as hard as nails, me. You'll never see me cry over a man, not even a threepenny one.' She seemed unable to grasp the extent of Flo's despair. 'C'mon, let's walk into town. It might take your mind off things, though we'd best steer clear of Bold Street case someone from work sees me.'

It wasn't until half past five that Flo and Bel parted. They exchanged addresses and promised to keep in touch. Flo wanted to arrive home as she usually did from work. She wouldn't tell anyone where she'd been that afternoon.

'Good heavens, Flo!' Mam remarked, when she went in. 'You're as white as a ghost and you're shivering. I hope you're not coming down with a cold. Summer colds are the worst to shake off.'

'Has anything happened?' Flo demanded abruptly.

Mam knew exactly what she meant. 'No, luv,' she said sadly. 'According to Mrs Cox, they managed to get a hawser to the hull, but it snapped and the ship sank underwater. I went to church today to say prayers with the Legion of Mary, but they don't seem to have done much good.'

Flo refused anything to eat. At Mam's insistence, she went to bed after a cup of tea. She felt uncomfortable when Martha came up later with a hot-water bottle and tucked her in. Martha wouldn't be so sympathetic if she knew the reason why her sister felt so out of sorts.

That night, she slept fitfully. Each time she woke, she was left with the memory of the same dream: she'd been wandering alone through the Mystery when an orchestra wearing full evening dress appeared before her, the sort she'd seen in films. But these were hollow, insubstantial figures – she could see right through them. They were playing 'Dancing in the Dark', and equally shadowy couples began to waltz in a circle around her. Instead of staring at each other, they gazed at Flo, unpleasant, gloating expressions on their faces. They were sneering because she was the only person without a partner. Her sense of isolation was so acute that she felt as if she was encased in a block of ice. Then the couples disappeared, the music stopped, and all that could be heard was the rustle of the trees. Flo was alone with only the moon for company.

Next morning, Mam came up with a cup of tea. 'To save you asking, I just listened to the BBC and there's no news, I'm afraid.'

Flo sat up. To her amazement there was no sign of Martha and Sally, and their bed was neatly made.

'They've gone to work,' Mam explained. 'We decided not to wake you. It wouldn't hurt to have the day off, it being Saturday, like, and you'd only be there till one. I'm sure Mr Fritz won't mind – you've never been off before.'

Flo was only too willing to comply. After Mam had gone, she pulled the bedclothes over her head and sobbed her heart out. She wasn't sure what time it was when she heard a knock on the front door, followed by Mr Fritz's voice asking how she was. 'We're all worried about her. It's not like Flo to be sick.' She hoped he wouldn't say she'd been off yesterday. It seemed he didn't, because Mam came up shortly afterwards and didn't mention it.

'He's a lovely man,' she said warmly. 'I'm very fond of him. You're ever so lucky, Flo, working in such a nice place.'

By late afternoon everyone was home, including Albert. Flo got up, and after tea they all trooped into the parlour to listen to the six o'clock news. In a chilling voice the announcer read a statement: 'The Admiralty regrets that hope of saving lives in the *Thetis* must be abandoned.'

Liverpool, the entire country, was stunned. A cablegram arrived from King George VI in Canada. His mother, Queen Mary conveyed her sympathies to the grieving relatives, and Adolf Hitler sent condolences from the citizens of Germany. When this was announced in the cinema, the audience set up a chorus of boos. A fund was set up for relatives of the dead; within days it had reached thousands of pounds. The Clancy family clubbed together and managed to raise a pound between them. Albert Colquitt added another pound and promised to take it to the collection point in the town hall.

The following Tuesday was a day of mourning. Birkenhead Cenotaph was said to be a mass of wreaths. Fifteen thousand attended the service and five thousand workers marched in honour of the memory of those who had died.

While the country mourned and salvage work began on the *Thetis*, the press were asking questions. It was impossible to grasp that so many lives had been lost when only a few feet had separated the men from their rescuers. Why hadn't experienced divers been rushed to the scene? Where was the oxyacetyline gear? A tribunal was appointed to investigate.

It wasn't until November that the *Thetis* was salvaged and able to deliver her dead for proper burial. The ship was pronounced sound enough to return by sea to its place of birth in Birkenhead. At any other time, this would have been headline news, but by now the country was already in the grip of a tragedy that would result in far greater loss of life than on a single submarine. The unthinkable had happened: Great Britain was at war with Germany and immersed in the struggle to survive.

Flo Clancy drifted through the months after Tommy O'Mara died. Everyone wanted to know what had happened to her lovely smile. Mr Fritz gave her the lightest jobs, much to the chagrin of Josie Driver who turned quite nasty. Mam bought an iron tonic, which Flo took dutifully three times a day, though she knew it wouldn't do any good. Only Bel MacIntyre, whom she saw regularly, knew why Flo no longer smiled. But Bel knew only the half of it. Flo had more things than the loss of Tommy to worry about.

On the first Sunday in September, a day blessed with shimmering sunshine and an atmosphere as heady as wine, Flo sat in the parlour listening to Albert's wireless. She heard Neville Chamberlain, the Prime Minister, announce that the country was at war and wished it mattered as much to her as it did to the rest of her family. Sally had burst into tears. 'What's going to happen to Jock?' she wept.

Jock Wilson had been writing to Sally ever since Whit Monday when they'd met on the New Brighton ferry. He'd been back to Liverpool to see her whenever he could manage a few days' leave.

Albert turned off the wireless. He looked grim. Martha reached across and self-consciously took his hand. Poor Mam's face seemed to collapse before their eyes. 'Oh, I don't half wish your dad was here!' she cried.

But Flo was too concerned with her own luckless state to care. She'd scarcely noticed missing the first period, and it wasn't until July that she had become alarmed. By the time July had given way to August and there was still no sign, she realised, with increasing horror, that she was pregnant with Tommy O'Mara's child.

Millie

1

Sharp fingers of light strobed the dark ceiling of the nightclub, interlocking briefly; blue, red, green, then yellow, followed by blue again. The disc jockey's overwrought, grating voice announced a change of record, though his words could scarcely be heard above the music booming from the huge speakers on either side of him.

In the centre of the large room, which was mainly painted black, the dancers gyrated, faces blank. Only their bodies reacted to the pounding rhythm of Joey Negro's 'Can't Take it With You', the sound bouncing off the ceiling and the walls.

I could feel the noise vibrating through the plastic seat and the soles of my shoes. It throbbed through the table and up my arms. Although I hadn't danced so far, the heat felt tremendous and my neck was damp with perspiration.

Beside me, James didn't look bored exactly, but definitely fed up. He'd been like that since we met earlier, which wasn't a bit like him. I felt put out. After a stressful week, I'd been looking forward to Saturday and his relaxing company. The friends we'd come with, Julie and Gavin, had got up to dance about half an hour ago, though I could see no sign of them on the floor.

I put my mouth against James's ear and shouted, 'Enjoying yourself?'

'Oh, I'm having a wonderful time.' He spoke with a sarcasm I'd never heard before. 'Want another drink?'

I shook my head just as Julie and Gavin returned. Gavin was an old schoolfriend of James, a massively built yet graceful man who played amateur rugby. He surreptitiously removed a piece of folded paper from the breast pocket of his silk jacket and emptied the contents on to the table. Three pink tablets rolled out.

'Eleven quid each,' he shouted. He pushed one towards James. 'Have this on me.'

'Not tonight, thanks,' James said stiffly.

'Come on, James,' Julie coaxed. She was a pretty girl with a cascade of blonde curly hair. 'You look way down in the dumps. An E will put a different perspective on things.'

'I said no, thanks.'

Gavin shrugged. 'How about you, Millie? Does Miss Morality fancy changing the habit of a lifetime and popping a pill for once?'

I was tired of explaining that refusing Ecstasy had nothing to do with morality, but that the thought of not having full control of my faculties frightened me. Before I could refuse, James said angrily, 'No, she doesn't.' He looked at me, irritated at his own impatience, because he knew I would resent his answering on my behalf. 'Aw, shit!' He groaned. 'I can't stand it here. I'm going out for some fresh air.'

'He's not himself,' I said in excuse. I collected my coat and bag and James's jacket. 'We might see you later, but don't wait.'

I pushed my way through the crowded tables and found James outside in the car park. He was already shivering without his coat. October had brought an end to the beautiful Indian summer and the temperature must have dropped twenty degrees. I handed him the jacket. 'Put this on or you'll catch cold.'

'Yes, ma'am.' He forced a smile. 'Sorry about that, but I'm getting too old for clubbing.'

I linked his arm as we strolled through the car park towards the rear of the club. I had no idea where the place was situated; over the water, somewhere between Birkenhead and Rock Ferry. 'You'd think you were ready to collect your pension.'

'Seriously, Millie, once you reach a certain age, life has to have more to it than the non-stop pursuit of a so-called "good time". Life's got to mean something.' There was a tinge of desperation in his voice. 'Oh, hell! I'm no good at explaining. It's just that, at twenty-nine, I feel I should be doing something rather more worthwhile than prancing round a nightclub, taking happy pills.'

'Such as?' To my surprise, I found we'd reached a stretch of lumpy sand and the Mersey glinted blackly in the distance, reflecting a wobbly quarter-moon. We climbed the chain-link fence and walked towards the water.

'You'll be annoyed if I tell you.'

'I promise, on my heart, not to be.'

'I'd like us to get married and have kids,' James said flatly. 'And I'd prefer to do a job that made some sort of contribution towards society.'

Astonished, I came to a standstill on the sand. 'You'd give up the garage? What would your father have to say?' The business was to be his one day.

'Sod Pa, and sod the garage,' James said, even more astonishingly. 'I'm sick to death of selling poncy, overpowered cars to idiots like myself. The job's as worthless as my life. It's useless, I'm useless.' He kicked moodily at a stone. 'I took today off and went to Liverpool. There was a march, hundreds of dockers who've been turfed out by Mersey Docks and Harbour Board because they refused to sign contracts that meant worse conditions and less pay. They've been out of work a year. There were fathers and sons among them. Men like that are the salt of the earth. I feel so . . . so *inadequate* compared to them.'

We reached the water. James released my arm and stuffed his hands in his pockets. He stared into the black waves. 'I've led a charmed life, Millie. I've never had to struggle for anything. Everything I've wanted has just dropped into my lap without my needing to ask. We're very lucky, the pair of us.'

I wanted to laugh out loud and say, 'You speak for yourself! Nothing has ever dropped into *my* lap. I've worked very hard for what I've got.' But what did he know about it? I'd told him virtually nothing about myself. Instead, I muttered, almost inaudibly, 'Marriage may not be the answer, James. It sounds to me like you're going through some sort of crisis.'

'Oh, God, Millie!' He pulled me into his arms, so tightly I could hardly breathe. 'Then help me through, darling. I've been going out of my mind over the last week.'

Only a week, I thought wryly. It was only during the past two or three years that I'd vaguely begun to feel an acceptable member of the human race. I put my arms around his neck and laid my head on his shoulder, not sure what to say. A dredger, barely lit, was moving silently down the river. The music from the nightclub was a muted throb. A memory returned, as it so often did, of one of the worst beatings. Mam had been out, working evenings to make ends meet. I didn't hear him come in. I heard nothing until the slithering footsteps sounded on the stairs and my body froze with fear. *I was reading in bed with a torch!* I was six and had only just learned to read. The teacher was amazed at how quickly I'd taken to it, but books offered undreamed-of pleasures, as well as escape from grim reality. I read in the lavatory, at breaktimes, and in the canteen. I had no idea why my father should detest the idea of my reading. It was as if he couldn't stand his children, or his wife, getting enjoyment from something, being happy.

So I'd been ordered not to read in bed. At the sound of the footsteps, I fumbled frantically with the torch, but it wouldn't go off. My hands were clammy with terror and I dropped it on the floor. The book followed. Two little thuds that sounded like thunderclaps in the quiet house.

'I thought I told yer not ter read in bed.' His voice was low and quiet, full of menace. The words travelled the years, as if they'd been spoken only a few minutes ago.

'I'm sorry, Dad.' I quaked with fright. I could feel my insides tearing apart, the way the ground erupts in an earthquake.

'I'll give yer summat to be sorry for. Gerrout!'

But I was still frozen, terrified, under the covers. I couldn't move. He pulled them back, roughly dragged me on to the floor, and began to undo the buckle of his wide leather belt. 'Kneel down,' he ordered. 'Kneel down against the bed and pull yer nightie up.'

'I didn't mean it, Dad. I won't read again, I promise,' I wailed. This was before I vowed never to let him see me cry. In her bed on the other side of the room, our Trudy stirred. 'Whassa matter?'

'Get back ter sleep,' our father snarled.

With my face buried in the bedclothes, I began to whimper. 'I won't do it again, Dad, honest.'

'Yer can bet yer life on that, yer little bitch! Bend over further.'

My arms tightened around James's neck as I remembered and felt the blows rain down on my bare bottom for the millionth time. The hard leather cut into my soft, childish flesh and I felt blood trickle down my legs. I heard my screams of pain, my pleas for mercy. 'I won't read again, Dad, I promise.'

I never did, not for a long time. The teacher was mystified as to why words no longer meant anything to her best pupil. 'It must have been a flash in the pan,' she said.

Perhaps it was Trudy, sobbing hysterically, that made him stop or perhaps he was exhausted. I was never sure. My face was still pressed against the bed, when I heard him going downstairs, the most welcome sound on earth. 'Thank you, God!' I breathed.

I broke free of James's arms and began to walk along the sands. My heart was beating rapidly and my legs were shaking. The tide rippled in over my shoes, but I didn't notice.

James caught up and grabbed my arm. 'Darling, what's wrong? What did you just say? Thank you, God, for what?'

'Nothing.' I hadn't realised I'd spoken aloud.

'You're trembling. How can it be nothing?' He regarded me sadly. 'Why are you keeping things from me?'

'Because there are things I don't want you to know.'

'If we're to be married, we should know everything about each other.'

I put my hands over my ears to shut him – everything – out, I shouted, 'Who said we're to be married? *I* didn't. When you brought the subject up last Sunday I said I'd sooner talk about it some other time. I didn't mean a few days later.'

'Darling, your feet are getting soaked.' Before I knew what was happening, he'd picked me up in his arms and carried me back to where the sand was dry. He crouched down beside me and started to take off my wet shoes. 'We're a mixed-up pair, Millie,' he said.

'You were perfectly well adjusted when we met. If you're mixed up now, it must be my fault.'

He stroked my hair. 'That's probably true. You're driving me nuts, Millie Cameron.'

I relaxed against him. Perhaps marrying James wouldn't be such a bad thing, though I'd have to think long and hard before having children. He was so comfortable to be with, so nice. But, then, no one could have been nicer than Gary, who'd bored me silly, and presumably Dad had been as nice as pie when he was courting Mum.

He was hurt when I insisted that he leave immediately after lunch next day. 'I thought we'd be spending Sunday together,' he said forlornly.

But I was firm. 'I'm clearing out my auntie's flat. I told you about it, remember? This is my only free day.'

'Why can't I go with you?' he pleaded. 'I could help. I could carry stuff out to the car. Anyway, it isn't safe for a woman on her own round there. Isn't William Square a red-light area?'

'Don't be silly,' I said dismissively. I couldn't wait to get to Flo's flat and had no intention of taking anyone with me. Mum had telephoned on Friday night and offered to lend a hand after she'd finished in the newsagent's shop where she worked till noon. 'You could meet me off the bus in town and let me have the key – I'll leave it with the woman upstairs. As long as I'm home before your dad, he'd never know I'd been.'

'It's quite all right, Mum,' I assured her. 'I can manage on my own.' I felt as if the flat was mine.

'Are you sure, luv? Last Sunday I got the impression you didn't want to be bothered.'

'I don't know where you got that idea from,' I said innocently. 'I don't mind a bit.'

After James had gone, I dressed in jeans and sweatshirt, and was brushing my hair when the phone rang. I ignored it, and heard the answering-machine click on. It was Mum. I sat on the off-white settee with a sigh and listened to the whining voice.

'Millicent, it's Mam. Your dad and Declan are out. Are you there, luv? It's just that I got this letter yesterday from the charity that runs our Alison's home. They can only keep her till she's eighteen. Next April she'll be transferred to this adult place in Oxford. Is that far, luv? I daren't show the letter to your dad – you know how he feels about Alison – and I can't find the atlas anywhere . . .'

My mother rambled on, as if the answering-machine itself was enough to talk to. I felt tears prickle my eyes as I listened. Mum loved her youngest child to distraction. She spent any spare money saved from the housekeeping on little presents for Alison, and had never stopped pining for her lost daughter. I couldn't bear to think how she would feel if Alison was placed out of reach of her weekly visits.

Oh, if only I could get shot of my family as easily as I'd got shot of Gary! If only I could divorce them and never see them again! By now, tears were pouring down my cheeks and I couldn't stand my mother's pain another second. I stumbled across the room and picked up the receiver.

'Mam!' But she had hung up. I had neither the strength nor the courage to ring back.

I breathed a sigh of relief as I closed the door of Flo's flat behind me. It felt like coming home. There were letters on the mat. As I lit the fire I scanned through them quickly, then turned on the lamp and went into the kitchen to put the kettle on. Nothing important; circulars, a market-research survey, a reminder that the TV licence was due. I put them aside and made a cup of tea. This time, I'd brought teabags, fresh milk and sandwiches. Still dunking a teabag, I returned to the living room and sank into the middle of the settee.

After a few minutes, I got up and put on Flo's record. Listening to Bing Crosby's soothing voice, I relaxed even more. The newspaper cuttings about the lost submarine, the *Thetis*, were still on the coffee table. I'd meant to ask someone about it, but the only elderly person I knew was Gran.

For almost an hour, I breathed in the peaceful atmosphere of the room, and the tension flowed from my body. I would have been quite happy to stay there for ever, but after a while I got up and began to wander round, poking in cupboards and drawers. Flo had been only superficially tidy. One sideboard drawer was full of gloves, another full of scarves, all in a mess. Another contained balls of string, a tangle of old shoelaces, an assortment of electric plugs, and a wad of money-off coupons held together with a rusty paperclip, which were years out of date.

For some reason, I found it necessary to untangle the laces, and was concentrating hard on undoing knots and trying to find pairs when there was a knock at the door. It would be Charmian I thought, and went to answer it. An elderly woman, very thin, with a huge cloud of unnatural mahogany-coloured hair and a still lovely though deeply wrinkled face, was standing outside. She wore a fake leopardskin jacket over a purple mohair jumper and black leggings, and appeared to be in the middle of a conversation with someone.

'Can't you wear a jacket or something?' she demanded angrily. There was a mumbled reply I couldn't catch, then the woman said, 'You'll do even less business if you catch the flu.' She turned and smiled at me ruefully, revealing a set of over-large false teeth. 'That bloody Fiona! She's wearing a dress with no sleeves that barely covers her arse. She'll perish in this weather. Hello, luv.'

No one waited for an invitation into Flo's, it seemed: the woman bounced into the room with the vitality of a teenager, although she must have been well into her seventies, followed by a waft of expensive perfume. 'I'm Bel Eddison, Flo's friend,' she said loudly. 'I know who you are – Millicent Cameron. I asked Charmian to give me a ring next time you came. She was right. You're the spitting image of Flo, and it's even more obvious to me 'cos I knew her when she was a girl. It gave me quite a turn when you opened the door.'

I'd already recognised the woman from the snapshot taken in Blackpool. It felt strange shaking hands with Flo's best friend, as if I was stepping back into the past, yet Bel was very much part of the present. 'How do you do?' I murmured. 'Please call me Millie.' I don't think I had ever seen such lovely eyes before, genuine violet. They were heavily made up, though, far too much for someone so old. The purple shadow had seeped into the crêpey lids, giving the effect of cracked eggshells.

'I'm tip-top, luv. How are you?' Bel didn't wait for an answer. Instead, she put her hands on her hips and regarded the room with exaggerated surprise. 'You haven't touched a thing,' she remarked. 'I was expecting to see the place stripped bare by now.'

'I was working out a plan of action,' I said guiltily, pushing the laces back into the drawer and closing it. 'Would you like a cup of tea?' I asked, when the newcomer removed her coat and threw herself on to the settee as if she'd come to stay. The springs squeaked in protest.

'No, ta, but I wouldn't mind a glass of Flo's sherry,' she said. Not only did she speak loudly, but also very quickly, in a strong, melodic voice that gave no hint of her age. 'Me and Flo sat here getting pissed on sherry more times than you've had hot dinners.'

Flo pissed didn't quite fit the image I'd built up in my mind, and I said as much to Bel when I gave her a glass. I poured one for myself too.

'It was her only vice,' Bel said. 'That's if you could call sherry a vice. Otherwise she led the life of a saint. For a long while, she went on retreat once a month to some convent in Wales. What's these?' She picked up the newspaper cuttings. 'Oh, you found them.' She grimaced.

'They were by the bed. Why did she keep them?' I asked.

'Draw your own conclusions, luv. It should be obvious.'

'She was in love with someone and he died on the *Thetis*?' I did a quick calculation: Flo would have been nineteen at the time.

'I said, draw your own conclusions.' Bel pursed her lips. I got the impression she enjoyed being mysterious. 'I'm not confirming or denying anything. I'd be betraying Flo's memory if I told things she kept to herself all her life.' She regarded me with her bright violet eyes. 'So, you're Kate Colquitt's eldest girl?'

'You know my mother?' I said, surprised.

'I did once. She used to come and see Flo a long time ago, but not since she married your dad. She was a lovely girl, Kate Colquitt. How is she these days?'

'She's okay,' I said abruptly.

Bel wriggled contentedly on the settee. Her expressive face displayed even the most fleeting emotion. 'This is nice! I never thought I'd sup sherry in Flo's again – pass us the bottle, there's a good girl. Ta!' she said comfortably. 'I'll top your glass up, shall I? We used to do this regular every Sunday. Sometimes Charmian joined us. It's uncanny, what with Flo dead, but you looking so much like her. Actually,' she continued with a frown, 'I'm racking me brains trying to bring to mind your husband's name. Was it Harry? You'd only been married a couple of years when Sally died – can you remember me at the funeral? Sally was the only contact Flo had with your family. When she died, Flo had no way of knowing how you were all getting on.'

'I'm sorry I don't remember you. I looked out for Flo, wondering what she was like. She disappeared before anyone could speak to her.'

'And how's Harry getting on?' Bel probed.

'Actually, it was Gary. We're divorced.'

'Really!' Bel sipped her sherry, clearly interested. 'What's your position now?' She looked all set for a long jangle. I felt less annoyed than I'd expected that the afternoon I'd anticipated having to myself had been interrupted. In fact, I *wasn't* annoyed. I liked Bel: she was so cheerfully vivid and alive. I wondered if we could trade information. If I told her a few things about myself, would she provide some details about Flo?

'I've got a boyfriend,' I explained. 'His name's James Atherton and we've been going out for a year. He's twenty-nine, and his father owns three garages on Merseyside. James manages the Southport one.'

'Is it serious?' Bel enquired gravely.

'On his side, not mine.' I thought about what James had said last night on the sands outside the nightclub. 'He's been going through some sort of crisis for an entire week.'

'Poor bugger,' Bel said laconically. 'Fellers wouldn't recognise a crisis if it crept up behind and threw them to the ground.'

'It's all my fault.' I wrinkled my nose.

'It shouldn't do him any harm. Men generally have it too easy in relationships with women.'

'Where did you meet Flo?' It was time she answered a few questions.

'Birkenhead, luv, a few months before the war began. She was a year older than me. She lived in Wavertree in those days.'

'Did Flo join the forces like you?'

'How did you know . . . ?' Bel began, then nodded at the photographs on the table. 'Of course, the photo of yours truly getting hitched to dear ould Bob. That was me in the ATS. No, Flo stayed working in the laundry during the war. I was posted to Egypt and it was years before I saw her again.' She glanced sadly around the room. For the first time she looked her age as her face grew sober and her eyes darkened with sadness. She appeared to be slightly drunk. 'She was such a lovely girl. You should have seen her smile – it was like a ray of sunshine, yet she buried herself in this place for most of her life. It's a dead rotten shame.'

'Would you like more sherry?' I asked. I much preferred the cheerful Bel, even if it meant her getting even drunker.

'I wouldn't say no.' She perked up. 'The bottle's nearly gone, but there'll be more in the sideboard. Flo always had half a dozen in. She said it helped with her headaches. Is there anything to eat, luv? Me stomach's rumbling something awful. I would have had summat before I left, but I never thought I'd be out so long.'

In the kitchen, I found several tins of soup in a cupboard. I opened a tin of pea and ham, poured it into two mugs and put them in the microwave to heat, then unwrapped the ham sandwiches I'd brought with me. I didn't realise I was singing until Bel shouted, 'Someone sounds happy! You've been listening to Flo's record.'

It was totally different from how I'd spent Sunday afternoons before and I wasn't doing anything that could remotely be considered exciting, yet I felt contented as I watched the red figures count down on the microwave. I wondered if Flo had bought the microwave and other things like the record player and the television on hire purchase. During my rather pathetic forays into drawers and cupboards, I hadn't come across any papers. Flo must have a pension book somewhere, possibly an insurance policy, and there were bound to be other matters that had to be dealt with; electricity and gas bills, council tax, water rates. I was being negligent in dealing with her affairs. This was the second time I'd come and the flat was no different now than it was when Flo died, except that there was less sherry and less food. As soon as Bel went, I'd get down to work, clear a few drawers or something.

I searched for a tray and discovered one in the cupboard under the sink. There was salt and pepper in pretty porcelain containers – 'A Gift from Margate'. I put everything on the tray and took it into the living room where Bel was half asleep.

'Who paid for the funeral?' I asked.

Bel came awake with a furious blinking of her thickly mascaraed lashes and immediately attacked a sandwich. 'Both me and Flo took out special funeral policies. She showed me where hers was kept and I showed her where to find mine. We used to wonder which of us would go first. Flo swore it would be her. I never said anything but I thought the same.' She made one of her outrageous faces. 'I'll have to show someone else where me policy is, won't I?'

'Haven't you got any children?'

'No, luv.' For a moment, Bel looked desolate. 'I was in the club three times but never able to bring a baby to term. Nowadays, they can do something about it, but not then.'

'I'm sorry,' I said softly. In fact, I was so sorry that a lump came to my throat.

Unexpectedly Bel smiled. 'That's all right, luv. I used to joke with Flo sometimes that we were a barren pair of bitches but, as she'd say, kids don't automatically bring happiness. Some you'd be better off without.' She went on tactlessly, 'How's that sister of yours, the sick one? I can't remember her name.'

'Alison. She's not sick, she's autistic.' I shrugged. 'She's the same as ever.'

'And what about your other sister? And you've got a brother, haven't you?'

I was being cross-questioned again, I told her about Trudy. 'As for Declan, he just drifts from job to job. He's getting nowhere.'

Bel screwed up her face in an expression of disgust. 'There's not much hope for young people nowadays.' She sipped her soup for a while, then said casually, 'How's your gran?'

I had the definite feeling that Bel had been leading up to this question from the start. 'She's fine. She was eighty in June.'

'Is she still in the same place in Kirkby?'

'Yes.'

Bel stared at her ultra-fashionable boots: lace-ups with thick soles and heels, not quite Dr Marten's, but almost. 'I don't suppose,' she said wistfully, 'you know what that row was all about?'

'What row?'

'The one all them years ago between your gran and Flo.'

'I don't know anything about it,' I said. 'We were always led to believe Flo had done something terrible, and Gran never spoke to her again.'

Bel pulled one of her peculiar faces. 'I heard it the other way round, that it was Martha who'd done wrong and Flo who'd taken umbrage. More than once she said to me, 'Bel, under no circumstances must our Martha be told if I go to meet me Maker before she does – at least not till the funeral's over,' but she'd never tell me why, although she wasn't one to keep secrets from her best friend. We knew everything about each other except for that.'

At six o'clock, Bel announced that she was going home, but changed her mind when Charmian arrived with a plate of chicken legs and a wedge of home-made fruitcake. By then I was a bit drunk and gladly opened another bottle of sherry. At half past seven we watched *Coronation Street*. It was hours later that my visitors left, and I was sorry to see them go. Charmian was natural and outgoing, with a sharp wit, and I felt completely at ease, as if I'd known them both all my life. It was as though I had inherited two good friends from Flo.

'I've had a great time today,' Bel said, with a satisfied chuckle when she was leaving. 'It's almost as if Flo's still with us. We must do this again next Sunday. I don't live far away in Maynard Street.'

I was already looking forward to it, forgetting that I was there to sort out Flo's possessions, not enjoy myself.

Charmian said, 'Our Jay's twenty-one this week, Millie, and we're having a party on Saturday. You're invited if you're free – bring a boyfriend if you've got one.'

'Of course she's got a boyfriend, a lovely girl like her!' Bel exclaimed. 'A party might be just the thing to help your James through his crisis.'

Charmian rolled her eyes. 'It's a party, not a counselling session.'

'I'll ask him, but I'm sure he's already got something arranged.' I was convinced that James would hate the idea.

The flat felt unusually still and quiet without Bel and her loud voice, though it still smelt strongly of her perfume. A police car came screeching round the corner, the flashing blue light sweeping across the room through the thin curtains. It made me realise that I'd had more glasses of sherry than I could count. If I was stopped and breathalysed, I would lose my licence, and I couldn't afford that: a car was essential to my job. I'll have to stay here tonight, I thought.

The idea of sleeping in the soft, springy bed was appealing. I made coffee, put it in the microwave and went into the bedroom to take stock. There were nightdresses in the bottom drawer of the chest. I picked out a pretty blue cotton one with short puffed sleeves and white lace trimming on the hem. A dramatic quilted black dressing-gown, patterned with swirling pink roses, was hanging behind the door, and I remembered the pink furry slippers under the bed. I undressed quickly and put on the nightie. It felt crisp and cold, but the dressing-gown was lined with something fleecy and in no time I was warm. I shoved my cold feet into Flo's slippers. Everything smelt slightly of that lovely scent from the Body Shop, Dewberry! It seemed odd, because I kept thinking of Flo as belonging to another age, not someone who frequented the Body Shop.

It didn't seem the least bit odd or unpleasant to be wearing a dead woman's clothes. In fact, it seemed as if Flo had left everything in place especially for me.

There wouldn't be time in the morning to go home and change, and George disapproved of jeans in the office. A quick glance in the wardrobe showed it to be so tightly packed with clothes that I could barely get my fingers between them. There was bound to be something I could wear.

I collected the coffee, took it into the bedroom and climbed into bed. I switched on the bedside lamp and picked up the book Flo had been reading before she died, turning to the first page. I was deeply involved when my eyes started to close, although it wasn't yet ten o'clock, hours before I usually went to bed. I turned off the lamp, slid under the bedclothes and lay in the cool darkness, vaguely aware of the saints staring down at me from the walls, and the crucifix above my head.

There were shouts in the distance, followed by a crashing sound, as if someone had broken a window. A car's brakes shrieked, there were more shouts, but I scarcely noticed. I thought about James. Perhaps I was too hard on him. I resolved to be nicer in future. My thoughts drifted briefly to Bel, but she had scarcely occupied my mind for more than a few seconds before I fell into a deep, restful and dreamless sleep.

2

'That's a charming dress,' said George. 'You look exceptionally sweet and demure this morning.'

'So do you,' I replied tartly. I always resent men considering it their prerogative to make comments on a woman's appearance. 'The dress belonged to my aunt. I stayed the night in her flat.'

George looked at me askance. 'That's a bit risky, isn't it? I hope you weren't alone.'

'I was, but seem to have survived the experience.'

The extension rang on my desk and George disappeared into his office. It was James. 'Where on earth were you last night?' he demanded crossly. 'I rang and rang and left increasingly desperate messages on your answering-machine. Then I called early this morning and you still weren't there.'

I frowned in annoyance. What right had he to know my whereabouts for twenty-four hours a day? 'I had visitors at my aunt's flat and we drank a bottle of sherry between us. It didn't seem safe to drive.'

'If I'd known what number your aunt had lived at, I'd have come to William Square in search of you.'

'If you had, I'd have been very cross,' I said coldly.

James groaned. 'Darling, I've been out of my head with worry. I thought you might have come to some harm.'

I remembered that I'd vowed to be nicer to him, so bit back another sharp reply. 'I'm perfectly all right,' I said pleasantly. 'In fact, I had the best night's sleep in years.' Even Diana had remarked on how well I looked. 'Sparkling' was how she had put it. 'You never usually have much colour, but your cheeks today are a lovely pink.'

'Shall we meet tonight, catch a movie, have dinner? *Leaving Las Vegas* is on at the Odeon.'

'Not tonight, James. I really need to get on with some work at home. I haven't touched my report in ages.' George had muttered something earlier about having found an ideal site in Woolton for the new office. 'Perhaps Wednesday or Thursday.'

'Okay, darling.' He sighed. 'I'll call you tomorrow.'

I hadn't time to worry if I'd hurt him because the phone rang again immediately I put the receiver down. The Naughtons wished to view a house in Ormskirk; they'd received the details that morning. This time they'd make their own way there, and I arranged to meet them outside the property at two o'clock.

The phone scarcely stopped ringing for the rest of the morning. I ate lunch at my desk, and remembered my appointment with the Naughtons just in time to avoid being late. Snatching the keys off the wall, I told George I'd probably be gone for hours. 'They take for ever, wandering around discussing curtains and stuff.'

'Humour them, Millie, even if it takes all day,' George said affably. He grinned. 'I must say you look a picture in that dress.'

I stuck out my tongue at him because I knew he was teasing. Flo's dress was a pale blue and pink check with a white Peter Pan collar, long sleeves and a wide, stiff belt. The material was a mixture of wool and cotton. It fitted perfectly and didn't look in the least old-fashioned. Neither did the short pink swagger coat that had been tucked at the back of the wardrobe, though I'd had an awful job pressing out the creases with a damp tea-towel. Even Flo's narrow, size seven shoes could have been bought with me in mind: the clumpy-heeled cream slingbacks went perfectly with everything.

Until I reached the countryside, I hadn't noticed how miserable the weather was. Mist hung over the fields, drifting in and out of the dank wet hedges. The sky was a dreary grey with blotches of black.

When I drew up outside the house the Naughtons were waiting in their car. It was a compact detached property on a small but very smart estate that had been built only five years ago.

I got out and shook hands with the rather homely middle-aged couple. Their children had left home and they were looking for something smaller and easier to clean. The trouble was, they were unwilling to give up a single item of furniture and seemed unable to visualise life without their present curtains. 'Let's hope this is it!' I smiled. They were registered with several other agents and had been viewing properties for months. 'The vendors are both at work, so we'll have the place to ourselves.'

The house was owned by schoolteachers who were moving south. It had been very untidy when I had called to take details a few days before, but I'd assumed they would tidy up when they knew prospective purchasers were coming – I'd never known a seller yet who hadn't. However, when we went in, the place was a tip. Heaps of clothes lay on the stairs to be taken up, the remains of breakfast was still on the kitchen table and there were years of ground-in dirt on the tiled floor.

'This is disgusting,' Mrs Naughton expostulated indignantly. Her husband nudged her, embarrassed, but she refused to be silenced. 'It smells!' she claimed.

After a brief glance in the lounge, which looked as if a hurricane had swept through it, Mrs Naughton refused to go upstairs. 'I dread to think what the bathroom must be like. I couldn't possibly live here.' She made for the door.

Seconds later, I found myself shaking hands again and apologising for the state of the house. They drove away, Mrs Naughton in high dudgeon, and I returned to my car. I had expected the view to take at least an hour but it had been over within a few minutes.

I drove out of the estate and was about to turn right towards Liverpool when I remembered that the St Osyth Trust, where Alison lived, was only about five miles away. On impulse, I turned left in the direction of Skelmersdale. I'd tell George the Naughtons had taken their usual lengthy time. 'I'm normally very conscientious,' I told myself virtuously. 'I rarely take time off. I'm never ill.'

It was months since I'd seen my sister. I preferred to go without Mum, who frequently made a big emotional scene, patting and kissing a mystified Alison who had no idea what all the fuss was about.

The sky was growing darker and it began to drizzle. I hated driving with the windscreen wipers on, and it was with relief that I turned off the narrow, isolated road into the circular drive of the gloomy red-brick mansion.

The big oak trees bordering the grounds at the front had shed their leaves and a gardener was leisurely raking them into little heaps on the lawn. Round the side of the house, a bonfire smouldered reluctantly. I parked in the area reserved for visitors. Perhaps because it was Monday, I appeared to be the only one there.

The heels of Flo's shoes clicked loudly on the polished wooden floor as I went over to Reception where a woman was typing. She looked up questioningly. 'Can I help you?'

'I've come to see Alison Cameron. I'm her sister.' I felt uncomfortable. The woman, Evelyn Porter, had worked there for as long as I could remember, yet she didn't recognise me because I came so rarely.

'Of course. I should have known. Alison's in the lounge. She's already got a visitor. You know the way, don't you?'

I nodded and turned to go, when Evelyn Porter said, 'I should warn you that Alison's a little upset today. We had to have the upstairs redecorated – it was in a terrible state, and the painters are in her room. Alison can't stand her precious things being disturbed and you'll find her rather agitated.'

The lounge was built on to the rear of the house, a sturdy conservatory that went its entire width, filled with brightly cushioned cane furniture. I paused before going in, praying it would be Trudy who was visiting, not Mum. Trudy's car hadn't been outside, though, and Mum couldn't fit in the bus journey to Skelmersdale between finishing work and being home in time to make my father's tea. During the week he monopolised the car – it would have been fixed quick enough when he needed it himself, assuming there'd been anything wrong in the first place.

To my pleased surprise, when I opened the door I found Declan, who was supposed to be at work, alone in the lounge with Alison. 'What on earth are you doing here?'

He stood up and hugged me. 'Hi, Sis. You're the last person I expected to see.'

We stayed in each other's arms for several seconds. It was only when I saw him that I remembered just how much I loved my little brother, though he was several inches taller than me now. 'Declan, love, you're thinner than ever,' I said. I could feel the bones protruding from his neck and shoulders, and I remembered the violence meted out to his puny body by our father. I gave him an affectionate push and turned to my sister. 'Hallo, Alison. It's Millie. I've come to see you.'

Over the last few years, Alison Cameron had grown into a beautiful young woman. She'd always been the prettiest of us three sisters, but now she was breathtaking. Her eyes were large and very green, like a luminous sea in sunlight, the lashes long and thick, several shades darker than her abundant ash-blonde hair, emphasising the creamy whiteness of her flawless skin. Her condition was only evident in the movements of her lovely body: stiff, clumsy, lacking grace.

'Hallo, hallo, hallo.' Alison flicked her long fingers in front of her eyes. 'You want to go upstairs.'

She meant, 'I'. 'I want to go upstairs.'

'Sorry, luv. You can't,' Declan said gently. 'Your room's being painted a nice new colour.'

I kissed the smooth, porcelain cheek, but Alison didn't seem aware of the gesture. 'It will look very pretty when it's done, darling. Then you can spread all your lovely things out again.' She kept her talcum powder, hairslides, toys and other odds and ends in neat rows on the bedside table and window-sill, and was always deeply distressed if anything was put in the wrong place.

'You want to go upstairs.'

'Later, darling, later.'

Alison looked at the floor, avoiding eye-contact. 'Come in thing with wheels?'

'I came in my car, yes.'

'You go in thing with wheels.'

'You've been in a car? Whose car, darling?'

'I think Trudy and Colin took her for a drive yesterday,' Declan whispered, when Alison shook herself irritably and began to flick her fingers again.

I had never been able to comprehend what went on in my sister's mind, although one of the doctors had once tried to explain it to Mum. It was something to do with mind blindness, the inability to perceive another person's emotions, which was why she sometimes laughed when our mother cried. Poor Mum was unable to accept that Alison wasn't laughing at *her*. My sister just wasn't aware of tears.

'Would you like to do a jigsaw puzzle, luv?' Declan suggested. 'The woman brought some in before,' he said. 'Thought they might calm her down, like.'

But Alison was looking out of the window, where a narrow line of smoke was drifting upwards from the bonfire. She had an uncanny, inexplicable ability to do the most complicated jigsaws in a fraction of the time it would have taken most people.

Declan and I looked at each other. As far as Alison was concerned, we might as well not be there.

'You know,' Declan said softly, 'I used to think me dad was responsible for the way Alison is. I thought he shook and slapped her so hard it damaged her brain. I envied her something rotten. I always hoped he'd do the same to me so I'd be sent here, too.'

'He did more than shake and slap you, Dec. He leathered the three of us regularly.'

'You had it the worst, Mill. You were the oldest, and he seemed to have it in for you more than the rest of us.'

I made a face. I seemed to have caught the habit from Bel. 'Maybe there was something about me that drove him over the edge,' I suggested lightly.

'Still, it didn't damage our brains. We all stayed quite normal.' Declan grinned. 'Least, relatively normal. Mind you,' the grin disappeared, 'there's still time for one of us to snap. I'll end up behind bars if I stay in that house much longer. I swear one day I'll kill the bastard because of the way he treats Mam. He hasn't given her any money in weeks. It used to be the horses, now it's that bloody lottery. Yet you should hear him moan if the food isn't up to scratch. He nearly hit the roof when we got a reminder for the electricity bill, as if she could pay everything out of the fifty quid a week she earns and what I hand over for me keep. He called her a lazy bitch and said it was about time she got a full-time job. If she did, there'd be hell to pay if his meals weren't ready on time.'

Declan's soft, rather feminine voice was rising, and I noticed that his hands, long and white like Alison's were gripping the arms of the chair, the knuckles taut. His gentle face was drawn and tired. I leaned back in the chair and sighed. My brother's unhappiness was painful to watch and it was to avoid that pain that I kept as far away from my family as I could. I almost wished I hadn't come or that Declan hadn't been there. 'Why don't you leave, Dec?' I pleaded. Then there'd only be Mum for me to worry about.

'As if I could leave Mam on her own with that bastard.'

'You can't stay for ever, love.'

'I'll stay as long as I have to.'

I got up and walked down the long room to the coffee machine provided for visitors. The light was on, which meant the machine was working. 'Fancy a coffee, Dec?' I called. Alison remained fascinated by the smoke.

'Please.'

'What are you doing here, anyway?' I asked, when I returned with the drinks. 'You're supposed to be at work.'

Declan recovered his good humour swiftly. His knack of making a joke of things that would have driven another person to despair was impressive. Dad's belt had broken once in the middle of a thrashing. 'Never mind, Dad,' he had said chirpily. 'I'll get you another for Christmas.'

'I lost me job.' He smiled. 'I got the sack three weeks ago.'

'Mum never said!'

He shrugged his delicate shoulders. 'That's because she doesn't know. She gets dead upset every time I get the shove. No one knows except our Trudy. I've looked for other work, Millie, honest, but I can't get anything. I've got no references because I've never held a job down long enough. The thing is, all I know is labouring and I'm not up to it.'

'Oh, Dec! What do you do with yourself all day?' I felt hurt that he had confided in Trudy and not in me. I was his sister, too. I wanted, reluctantly, to help.

'I wander the streets, go to the Job Centre, call on Trudy, then go home for six o'clock so Mam thinks I've been to work. This is the third time I've come to see Alison, but it means hitching lifts and last time I had to walk all the way back.'

'You should have told me.' I would have given him the key to my flat, where he could watch TV and help himself to food.

'I didn't think you'd be interested,' Declan said, which hurt more.

'I'll have to go soon,' I said. 'They'll be expecting me at the office. We don't seem to be doing much good here.' I made a quick decision. 'Look, I'll take you into town and you can go to the cinema – *Leaving Las Vegas* is on at the Odeon. When I finish work, we'll go back to my place for a meal. I've got pizza in the freezer.'

Declan's big green eyes sparkled. 'Great idea, Sis. I'll ring Mam and tell her I'm working late or she'll want to know how I met you. The pictures are out 'cos I'm skint. I give Mam all I get off the social, but it'll be nice to look round the shops. I haven't been to town in ages.'

It was even worse than I'd thought. 'What have you been doing for money all this time?' I asked, dismayed.

'Trudy gives me the odd few quid, but she doesn't want Colin to know what's happened. She reckons he's had enough of the Camerons.'

Despite Declan's protests that he didn't want to scrounge, I insisted he take all the money I had with me, twenty pounds.

A woman in a white overall came in to ask how Alison was. 'She doesn't want to know us today, do you, Sis?' Declan chucked his beautiful sister under the chin, but she remained as unaware of the gesture as she'd been of my kiss. 'Slippers,' she muttered. 'Slippers, slippers, slippers.'

'The builders are just packing up for the day so we can put her things back in place. They've only got the ceiling to do tomorrow. Would you mind if I took her upstairs? I think she'll feel happier once she knows everything's back to normal. Next time you come she'll be fine.'

Well, as fine as she'll ever be, I thought sadly. I watched Alison being led away, oblivious to the presence of her brother and sister.

When it came down to it, I was no good at telling blatant lies. I couldn't bring myself to tell George that the Naughtons had taken ages viewing the house when it wasn't true. 'I hope you don't mind, but I went to see my sister. She only lives a few miles away. It was a spur-of-the-moment thing.'

'The one in the home?'

'That's right.' Sometimes I forgot George knew things about me that no one outside my family did.

'No problem,' George said easily.

'I should have let you know on the mobile.'

George laughed. 'I said, no problem. You could get away with murder in that dress, Ms Millicent Cameron. What prompted your folks to call you that, by the way?'

'It's after a singer my mother liked, Millicent Martin.'

'Oh, Lord!' he groaned. 'I liked her, too. Does that show my age?'

'Very much so, George,' I said gravely, getting my own back for his comments on Flo's frock.

We grinned at each other amiably, and George said, 'I was wondering where you were. Mrs Naughton telephoned to complain to a higher authority about the state of that house. I'll give the vendors a ring tonight, suggest they tidy up, but be prepared to warn people in future, just in case.'

I hung up the keys and went over to my desk, aware of how close I'd come to blotting my copybook with George.

It was my job to prepare a list of properties to advertise in the local press and I was gathering together details to feed into the computer when I became aware that Diana, whose desk was next to mine, was crying quietly. Tweedledum and Tweedledee were out, and Oliver Brett was in George's office. June, the receptionist, was on the phone, her back to us.

'What's the matter?' I asked. The woman's eyes were red with weeping.

'It's my father. I don't know if I told you he was ill. It's cancer of the stomach. A neighbour's just called to say she found him unconscious on the kitchen floor. He's been taken to hospital.'

'Then go and see him straight away. George won't mind.'

'Why should I?' Diana looked at me mutinously. 'I've got work to do – I'm just finishing off those notes on Woolton. It could affect my prospects of promotion.'

I said nothing, but wondered where my priorities would lie in the same situation.

'Parents are a pain,' Diana said, in a hard voice. 'When they grow old, it's worse than having children.' She blew her nose, wiped her eyes, and began to cry again. 'I don't know what I'll do if Daddy dies!'

'I think you should go to the hospital.'

Diana didn't reply. She typed furiously for a while, then said, 'No. I'm too busy. I wish that bloody neighbour hadn't phoned. There comes a time when you've got to put yourself first.'

'If you say so.' I tried to ignore her as I finished off the adverts then faxed them through to the press, by which time it had gone six o'clock. I was meeting Declan in a pub in Water Street close to where I'd parked the car. When I left Diana was still typing, her brow creased in concentration, her eyes still red. I stood for a moment, looking at her and wondering what to say. Eventually, all I could think of was, 'Goodnight, Diana.'

'Night,' Diana replied, in a clipped voice.

Declan had thoroughly enjoyed the film. 'Dad would be in his element in Las Vegas,' he said, chuckling, on the way to Blundellsands.

'Only if he had a few thousand pounds to play with,' I said drily, 'and he'd probably lose that within a day.' I patted his knee. 'Try to forget about him and enjoy yourself for a change. We can watch a video later, if you like.'

'That'd be the gear, Sis.' Declan sighed blissfully as I drove into the parking area at the side of my flat. 'I feel dead honoured. I've only been here once before.' His voice rose an octave and became a squeak. 'Jaysus, look at that car! It's only a Maserati!'

A low-slung black sports car was parked against the boundary wall. It wasn't possible to see through the dark-tinted windows who was inside it, but a terrible suspicion entered my mind.

'I'd sell me soul for a car like that!' Declan murmured reverently. He leaped out of the Polo as soon as it stopped and went over to the black car with the deference of a pilgrim approaching the Pope. My suspicions were confirmed when the car door opened and James climbed out. He frequently turned up in strange cars belonging to the garage.

'Millie?' His voice contained a great deal of anger and hurt. It even sounded slightly querulous. 'Millie?' he said again.

I realised he thought that Declan was a boyfriend. He'd asked me out that night and I'd refused, saying I had work to do. Instead I was seeing someone else. I felt irritated. Why shouldn't I go out with another man if I wanted? I was cross that James had turned up uninvited. Now I would have to introduce him to Declan, and I wanted the Camerons and the Athertons kept apart for as long as possible. For ever would be even better.

'This is my brother, Declan,' I said stiffly. 'Declan, this is James.'

James's broad shoulders sagged with relief. 'Declan!' he said jovially, as he shook hands. 'I've heard a lot about you.' He was being polite: he knew nothing about my brother other than that he existed.

'Is this your car?' Declan's jaw dropped in disbelief: he had a sister who had a boyfriend who drove a Maserati.

'No, I just borrowed it for tonight. My own car is an Aston Martin.'

'Jaysus! Can I look under the bonnet? Would you mind if I sat behind the wheel, only for a minute, like?'

James was happy to oblige. He got back into the car and pulled the lever to raise the bonnet. Seconds later the pair were bent over the engine and James was explaining how things worked. I trudged upstairs, dreading the evening ahead.

I put the kettle and the oven on, and began to prepare a salad. James would probably expect to stay to dinner and fortunately the pizza was a large one. I opened a bottle of wine and drank a glass to steady my nerves. By the time James and Declan arrived, almost half an hour later, I'd drunk half the bottle and had to open another to have with the meal. I blamed Flo. It wouldn't have crossed my mind to drink alone if I hadn't come face to face with all that sherry.

The two men were getting on famously. The conversation had turned to football. 'There's a match on TV later, Liverpool versus Newcastle.' James rubbed his hands. 'You don't mind if we watch it, do you, Millie?'

'Not at all.' By now, I was terrified Declan would say something, give the

435

game away, and the whole respectable edifice I'd built around myself would come tumbling down.

It wasn't until they had finished their meal that he revealed the smallest of my secrets. 'That was great, Sis. I haven't had such decent grub in ages.' He turned to James. 'Our mam does her best, but everything comes with mashed spuds and cabbage.' He patted his stomach. 'I'm not half glad I went to see Alison in Skem, else I wouldn't have met our Millie.'

'I thought Alison lived in Kirkby with you,' James said, puzzled.

'Oh, no. Alison's autistic. She's in a home. Hasn't Millie told you?'

'Who'd like coffee?' I said brightly. I went into the kitchen, bringing that line of conversation to an abrupt end. When I returned with the coffee, Declan had just rung home. 'I forgot to tell Mam I'm supposed to be working late. I lost me job the other week,' he explained to James, 'and I still haven't got round to telling our mam and dad.'

James looked sympathetic. 'What sort of work do you do?'

I gritted my teeth as Declan replied, 'Only labouring. I was working on this demolition site, but it seemed to be me who got demolished more often than the building.'

'You're wasted as a labourer. Why don't you take a college course like Millie did?'

To my surprise, Declan's face turned bright red. He blinked his long lashes rapidly and said, 'It's never entered me head.'

Fortunately, it was time for the match to start. I switched on the television, then the computer. I wanted to finish my report, but my brain was incapable of competing with the sound of the television and James and Declan's bellows of support alternated with groans of despair whenever Newcastle went near the Liverpool goal. I tried to read a book, gave up, and went into the kitchen where I caught up with the ironing and prayed the match wouldn't go into extra time. The minute it was over, I'd take Declan home. It was imperative that my brother and my boyfriend were separated before any more of the Camerons' dirty linen was aired.

To my dismay, James had already offered Declan a lift. I thought of the burnt-out car abandoned opposite my parents' house – hopefully James wouldn't notice in the dark – of the lads who'd still be playing outside and might not feel too charitably towards the driver of a Maserati.

'Tara, Sis.' Declan punched me lightly on the shoulder. 'It's been a smashing evening.'

'We must do it again soon. Perhaps next time there's a match, eh?' James kissed me on the lips. 'I'll call later.'

'Oh, no, you won't,' I cried as soon as I'd closed the door. I took the phone off the hook, ran a bath, and finished off the wine while I soaked in the warm, scented water. The events of the day swirled through my mind:

the Naughtons and that filthy house, Alison, Declan, Diana and her father, James.

James! What was Declan saying to him? It wasn't that I cared about him loving me less, I only cared about him – anybody – *knowing*. And when it came down to it, it was nothing to do with the house in Kirkby, or being poor, or Mum letting herself go, or Alison. It was the terror of my childhood that I wanted to keep to myself: the beatings, the fear, the sheer indignity of it all. I'd felt as if my body didn't belong to me, that it could be used by someone else whenever the whim took them. What I wanted more than anything was to put the past behind me so that the dreams would stop. I wanted to forget everything and become a person not a victim. But this would never happen while my family remained a haunting reminder, always there to ensure that the past was part of the present and, possibly, the future. The only solution would be to go far away, start a new life elsewhere – but although my mother set my teeth on edge, I loved her so much that it hurt. I could never desert her.

The water in the bath had gone cold. I climbed out, reached for a towel, and was almost dry when the doorbell rang.

'Blast!' I struggled into a bathrobe.

'I tried to call you on the car phone,' James said, as he came breezing in, 'but you seemed to be incommunicado.' He noticed the receiver was off the hook. 'Is this deliberate or accidental?'

'Deliberate,' I said irritably. 'I want some peace. I want to be left alone.' He tried to take me in his arms, but I pushed him away. 'Please, James.'

He threw himself on to the settee with a sigh. 'Why didn't you tell me all that stuff before?'

My heart missed a beat. 'What stuff?'

'You know what I mean. About Alison, and about Declan being gay.'

'Declan's not gay!' I gasped.

'Of course he is, Millie. It's obvious.'

'You're talking utter rubbish,' I said half-heartedly, remembering how Declan had blushed when James paid him a compliment. Then I remembered all sorts of other things about my brother. He was girlish, no doubt about it, but gay?

'Darling, I guessed straight away.'

I shook my reeling head. It was too much, coming after such an eventful day. 'What did you and Declan talk about on the way to Kirkby?'

'Cars, mainly, football a bit. Why?'

'I just wondered.'

'After I dropped him off, I gave some kids a ride around the block. They were very impressed with the Maserati.'

'That was nice of you.'

I made him a coffee, then insisted he went home. Before going to bed, I took three aspirins. Even so, unlike last night at Flo's, it was several hours before I eventually fell asleep, a restless, jerky sleep, full of unwelcome, unpleasant dreams.

Diana's father was kept in hospital overnight. The fall had nothing to do with his illness; he had had a dizzy spell. Next morning she said that a neighbour had offered to bring him home. 'I suppose you think I'm awful, not going myself,' she went on.

'Why should I?'

'Well, I think I'm awful. Daddy's being incredibly brave. At times, I wish he'd have a good old moan and I'd really have something to complain about. I'd feel less of a louse.' She wrinkled her nose. 'I'm all mixed up.'

'Who isn't?' I snorted.

3

James had been told bluntly that I needed time to myself, time to think. If he turned up uninvited again, I would be very cross. He agreed meekly that we wouldn't meet again until Saturday. 'Will you be very cross if I call you?' he asked, in a little-boy voice.

'Of course not, but if I'm not around I don't want anguished messages left on my answering-machine.'

'No, ma'am. Thank you very much, ma'am.'

I kissed his nose, because he was so patient and understanding. I couldn't imagine allowing a man to mess me about as much as I did him. Nor could I understand why he put up with it from someone like me.

Throughout the week, I did my utmost to get to the flat in William Square, but the estate-agency business, while not exactly booming, was picking up. On Wednesday and Thursday I was still hard at work in the office until well past seven o'clock.

On Friday night, I finished off the report and stapled together the eight pages. I decided to read through it again and give it to George on Monday: he'd begun negotiations for the empty shop, which he hoped to have open by Christmas. Even if Diana got her 'notes' in first, it would show that I was equally keen.

Afterwards, I phoned home, which I'd been meaning to do all week, and was relieved when Declan answered.

'Where's Mum?' I asked.

'Out. Dad went to the pub, so I gave her five quid of that twenty I got off you on condition she went to bingo.' He chuckled. 'She was dead chuffed.'

'Declan?'

'Yes, luv?'

'That suggestion James made, about you going to college, why don't you do it? You could learn car mechanics or something, get a job in a garage.' Unlike me, he had left school with two reasonable O levels.

'Oh, I dunno, Millie. Me dad would blow his top.'

'You're twenty, Declan. It's nothing to do with him what you do with your life.'

'That's easy for you to say. It's not you who'd face the consequences when he finds out I've given up work for college.' He sounded peevish, as if he thought I'd forgotten the way my father's powerful presence still dominated the house in Kirkby.

'You've already given up work, Declan – or, rather, work's given up on you.' He was too soft, too unselfish, not like me and Trudy, who couldn't wait to get away. He was also weak. In a strange way, the horror had made my sister and me stronger, but our father had beaten all of the stuffing out of his only son. Declan's sole ambition seemed to be to exist from day to day with as little effort as possible.

'I suppose it wouldn't hurt to make a few enquiries,' he said grudgingly. 'What I've always fancied is learning about fashion – y'know, designing dresses or material, that sort of thing.'

'In that case, go for it, Dec,' I urged, and tried to imagine what our father would say when told his son was training to be a dress designer. Even worse, how would he react if James was right and he, too, realised that Declan was gay? I would have liked to discuss it with Declan there and then, but it was up to him to out himself. Until he did, I would never breathe a word to a soul.

I had expected James to claim he'd missed me dreadfully, but when he picked me up on Saturday night he said 'I've had a great week. I've joined the SWP.'

'The what?' I felt a trifle put out, particularly when he didn't even notice my new outfit, a short black satin shift, nor that I'd parted my hair in the middle and smoothed it back behind my ears for a change.

'The Socialist Workers' Party.'

'Good heavens, James!' I gasped. 'Isn't that a bit over the top? What's wrong with the Labour Party?'

'Everything!' he said crisply. 'This chap, Ed, said that they're all a shower of wankers. This morning I helped collect money for those dockers I told you about. I nearly brought my placard into Stock Masterton to show you.'

'I'm glad you didn't!' I hid a smile. 'Does this mean you're over your crisis?'

'I'm not sure, but for the first time in my life, I feel as if I have some

439

connection with the real world, real people. I've learned an awful lot this week. You wouldn't believe the tiny amount single mothers have to live on, and I never knew the National Health Service was in such a state.'

All the way into town, he reeled off statistics that most people, me included, already knew. Only a tiny percentage of the population owned a huge percentage of the country's wealth; revenue from North Sea oil had disappeared into thin air; privatisation had created hundreds of million-aires.

In the restaurant, a favourite one in the basement of a renovated warehouse, with bare brick walls and a Continental atmosphere, he didn't show his usual interest in the food. 'I went to Ed's place on Wednesday to watch a video. Did you know that in the Spanish Civil War the Communists fought on the side of the legally elected government? I'd always thought it was the other way round, that the Communists were the revolutionaries.'

I stared at him, aghast: he'd been to public school, followed by three years at university during which he'd studied history, for God's sake, and he hadn't known that! 'What does your father have to say about your miraculous conversion?' I asked. 'A couple of weeks ago, you were in the Young Conservatives.'

He frowned and looked annoyed. 'My folks think it jolly amusing. Pop said he's glad I've started to use my brain at last. My sister got involved with a group of anarchists at university, and he thinks I'll grow out of it, like Anna did.'

Anna was married with two children and lived in London. So far, we'd not met. I sipped my coffee thoughtfully. I wasn't sure if I wanted him to grow out of it. The trouble was, like his folks, I found the whole thing rather amusing. Although, no doubt, he felt sincerely about his newly found beliefs, he didn't sound sincere, more like a little boy who'd discovered a rare stamp for his collection.

'Where shall we go?' He looked at his watch. 'It's only half past ten.'

All I could think of was a club, but James reminded me he'd gone off them. 'I've just remembered,' I said, 'We're invited to a party in William Square.' It was Charmian's son's twenty-first.

'Great,' James said eagerly. 'Let's go.'

'But you'd hate it,' I laughed. 'They're not at all your sort of people.'

He looked hurt. 'What do you mean, not my sort of people? You'd think I came from a different planet. I quite fancy partying with a new crowd. Wherever we go it's always the same old faces.'

The same old middle-class professionals; bankers and farmers, stock-brokers and chaps who were something in insurance. Some of the women had careers, and those who'd given up their jobs to have children complained bitterly about the horrendous cost of employing cleaners and au pairs. I always felt out of place, just as I probably would at Charmian's. I wondered if there was anywhere I'd feel right.

'We'll go to the party if you like,' I said, but only to please James. After all, now he'd joined the SWP he'd have to get used to mixing with the hoi polloi.

Charmian looked exotic in a cerise robe with a turban wound round her majestic head. 'Lovely to see you, girl,' she murmured, and kissed me.

Rather to my own surprise, I kissed her back as I handed over the wine James had bought in the restaurant for a ludicrous price because he couldn't be bothered to search for an off-licence. I introduced him to Charmian, who seemed taken aback when he shook her hand and said, in his beautifully cultured voice, 'How lovely to meet you.'

The Smiths' big living room was packed, though several couples in the middle were managing somehow to dance to the almost deafening sound of Take That's 'Relight My Fire'. I met Herbie, Charmian's husband, a mild, good-humoured man with greying hair who was circulating with a bottle of wine in each hand. 'Our Jay's around somewhere.' Charmian peered over the crowd. 'You must meet the birthday boy.' With that, she plunged into the fray.

I found a bedroom and left my coat. When I returned, there was no sign of James so I helped myself to a glass of wine and leaned against the wall, hoping Bel had been invited so that I would have someone to talk to.

A young man with a wild head of shaggy black curls and a fluffy beard came and stood beside me, his dark eyes smiling through heavy horn-rimmed glasses. 'You look like the proverbial wallflower.'

'I'm waiting for my boyfriend,' I explained.

'Fancy a dance in the meantime?'

'I wouldn't mind.' I felt rather conspicuous on my own.

He took my hand and led the way through to the dancers. There wasn't room to do anything other than shuffle round on the spot.

'Do you live round here?' I asked politely. I'd never been much good at small talk.

'Next door, basement flat. Do you still live in Kirkby?'

'You know me!' I never liked coming across people from the past.

'We were in the same class together at school. You're Millie Cameron, aren't you?'

I nodded. 'I'm at a disadvantage compared to you,' I said. 'I don't recall anyone in class with a beard.'

'I'm Peter Maxwell, in those days known as Weedy. You can't have forgotten me. I usually had a black eye, sometimes two, and an inordinate amount of cuts and bruises. The other lads used to wallop me because I was no good at games. Me mam wasn't slow at walloping me either but she didn't need a reason.'

'I remember.' He'd been a frail, pathetic little boy, the smallest in the class, smaller even than the girls. There never seemed to be a time when he wasn't crying. Rumour had it that his father had been killed during a fight outside a pub in Huyton. I envied his ability to talk about things so openly: there'd been no need for him to tell me who he was. Maybe he knew my own history. It had been no secret that Millie and Trudy Cameron's father hit his girls.

'How come you grew so big?' I asked. He was only as tall as I was, about five feet eight, but his shoulders were broad and I could sense the strength in his arms.

'Turned sixteen, left home, found work, spent all my spare time in a gym, where I grew massively, but mainly sideways.' He grinned engagingly. 'Having developed the brawn, it was time to develop the brain, so I went to university and got a degree in economics. I teach at a comprehensive a mile from here.'

'That's a tough job!' I admired him enormously, particularly his lack of hang-ups.

'It helps to have muscles like Arnold Schwarzenegger,' he conceded, 'particularly when dealing with bullies, but most kids want to learn, not cause trouble. Now, that's enough about me, Millie. What are you up to these days? If I remember rightly, you married Gary Bennett.'

'I did, yes, but we're divorced. I'm a property negotiator with Stock –'

Before I could say another word, a young woman in a red velvet trouser suit pushed through the dancers and seized his arm. 'There you are! I've been looking everywhere for you.' She dragged him away, and he turned to me, mouthing, 'Sorry.'

I was just as sorry to see him go – it had been interesting to talk to someone with a background similar to my own. I spotted James, deep in conversation with a middle-aged couple. He seemed to have forgotten about me. I felt a bit lost and made my way to the kitchen where I offered to help wash dishes. Herbie shooed me away with an indignant, 'You're here to enjoy yourself, girl.'

By now, the party had spilled out into the hall. I went out in the hope of finding Bel, but there was no sign of her so I sat on the stairs and was immediately drawn into an argument over the acting ability, or lack of it, of John Travolta.

'He was great in *Pulp Fiction*,' a woman maintained hotly.

'He stank in *Saturday Night Fever*,' someone else said.

'That was years ago.' The woman waved her arms in disgust. 'Anyroad, no one expected him to act in *Saturday Night Fever*. It was a musical and his dancing was superb.'

The front door opened and a man came in, a tall, slim man in his twenties with a pale, hard face and brown hair drawn back in a ponytail. He wore small gold gypsy earrings and was simply dressed in jeans, white T-shirt, and black leather jacket. There was something sensual about the way he moved, smoothly and effortlessly, like a panther, that made me shiver. At the same time, his lean body was taut, on edge. Despite his hard expression, his features were gentle: a thin nose, flaring wide at the nostrils, full lips, high, moulded cheekbones. I shivered again.

The man closed the door and leaned against it. His eyes flickered over the guests congregated in the hall. I held my breath when our eyes met and his widened slightly, as if he recognised me. Then he turned away, almost contemptuously, and went into the living room.

'What do you think? What did you say your name was?' The woman who had been defending John Travolta was speaking to me.

'Millie. What do I think about what?'

'Didn't you think he was fantastic in *Get Shorty*?'

'Amazing,' I agreed, still preoccupied with the man who'd just come in.

For the next hour I barely listened as the discussion moved on to other Hollywood stars. Someone brought me another glass of wine, then James appeared, gave a thumbs-up, and vanished again. I contemplated looking for the man with the ponytail to find out who he was – but I had left it too late: the front door opened and through the crowd I glimpsed him leaving.

At one o'clock, the party was still going strong. There were sounds of a fight from the living room, and Herbie emerged holding two young men by the scruff of the neck and flung them out of the door.

By now, I was tired of Hollywood and longed to go home. I searched for James and found him sitting on the floor with half a dozen people who were all bellowing at each other about politics. He'd removed his jacket and was drinking beer from a can. I didn't like to disturb him when he appeared to be enjoying himself so much. Nevertheless, I fancied some peace and quiet and knew exactly where I could find it.

William Square, bathed in the light of a brilliant full moon, was quiet when I went outside, though the silence was deceptive. Women, barely clothed, leaned idly against the railings, smoking and waiting for their next customer. A car crawled past, then stopped, and the driver rolled down the window. A girl in white shorts went over and spoke to him. She got in, the driver revved the engine and drove away. Two dogs roamed the pavements, casually sniffing each other. In the distance, the wail of a siren could be heard, and in the even further distance, someone screamed. A cat rubbed itself against my legs, but ran away when I bent to stroke it.

Suddenly, a police helicopter roared into the sky, like a monstrous, brilliantly lit bird. The noise was almost deafening. It really was a war zone, as George had said. I ran down the steps to Flo's flat. To my consternation,

I saw that the curtains were drawn and the light was on, yet I could distinctly remember switching off the light and pulling back the curtains the last time I was there. Perhaps someone, Charmian or Bel, had decided it would be wise to make the place look lived in. But there was only one key, the one I held in my hand right now.

Cautiously I unlocked the door. It was unlikely I'd come to any harm with fifty or sixty people upstairs. I opened the inner door and gasped in surprise. The man with the ponytail was lounging on Flo's settee, his feet on the coffee table, watching the swirling lamp and listening to her record.

'Who are you? What are you doing here?' I snapped.

He turned and regarded me lazily, and I saw that his eyes were green, like mine. His face seemed softer than when I'd seen him upstairs, as if he, too, was under the spell of the blurred shadows flitting around the room and the enchanting music.

'I never thought I'd do this again,' he said. 'I came to leave me key on the mantelpiece and found Flo's place no different than it's always been.'

'Where did you get the key?'

'Off Flo, of course. Who else?' His voice was coarse, his Liverpool accent thick and nasal. He was the sort of man from whom I'd normally run a mile, and yet, and yet . . . I did my level best to hide another shiver.

'You still haven't told me who you are.'

'No, but I've told you why I'm here.' He swung his feet off the table with obvious reluctance, as if he wasn't used to being polite, and stood up. 'I was a friend of Flo's. Me name is Tom O'Mara.'

Flo

1

'Tommy O'Mara!' Martha's voice was raw with a mixture of hysteria and horror. 'You're having a baby by Tommy O'Mara! Didn't he go down on the *Thetis*?'

Flo didn't answer. Sally, sitting at the table, pale and shocked, muttered, 'That's right.'

'You mean you've been with a married man?' Martha screeched. Her face had gone puffy and her eyes were two beads of shock behind her round glasses. 'Have you no shame, girl? I'll never be able to hold up me head in Burnett Street again. We'll have to start using a different church. And they're bound to find out at work. Everybody will be laughing at me behind me back.'

'It's Flo who's having the baby, Martha, not you,' Sally said gently.

Flo was grateful that Sally appeared to be on her side or, at least, sympathetic to her plight. A few minutes ago when she had announced that she was pregnant, Martha had exploded but Mam had said quietly, 'I can't stand this,' and had gone straight upstairs, leaving Flo to Martha's rage and disgust. The statement had been made after tea deliberately, just before Albert Colquitt was due when Martha would feel bound to shut up. After Albert had been seen to, she might have calmed down a bit, but Flo knew that she would be at the receiving end of many more lashings from her sister's sharp tongue.

'It might be Flo having the baby, but it's the whole family that'll bear the shame,' Martha said cuttingly. She turned to her youngest sister, 'How could you, Flo?'

'I was in love with him,' Flo said simply. 'We were going to get wed when Nancy got better.'

'Nancy! Of course, he married that Nancy Evans, didn't he? Everyone used to call her the Welsh witch.' Martha scowled. 'What do you mean,

445

you were going to get wed when she got better? She's never been sick, as far as I know. Anyroad, what's that got to do with it?'

As Martha was unlikely to know the intimate details of Nancy O'Mara's medical history, Flo ignored the comment, but she was disconcerted to learn that Nancy was Welsh when she was supposed to have been Spanish. In a faltering voice she said, 'He wasn't married proper to Nancy.' She didn't mention the gypsy ceremony in a wood near Barcelona because it sounded ridiculous. In her heart of hearts, she'd never truly believed it. It was too far-fetched. She wondered bleakly if Tommy had ever been to Spain, and realised that everything of which Martha accused her was true: she was a fallen woman, lacking in morals, who'd brought disgrace upon her family.

It wasn't surprising to hear Martha say that there was no question of Tommy O'Mara not being married proper to Nancy Evans, because she had been in church when the banns were called. 'He used to lodge with the family of this girl I met at Sunday school,' she said, and added spitefully, 'She said her mam couldn't wait to get shot of him because she had a terrible job getting the money off him for his bed and board.'

Sally gasped. 'Shush, Martha. There's no need for that.'

'I'm sorry,' Flo said brokenly. 'I'm so sorry.'

'There, there, Sis.' Sally slipped off the chair and put her arms around her sister, but Martha wasn't to be swayed easily by expressions of regret.

'And so you should be sorry,' she blasted. 'You realise everyone will call the kid a bastard? No one will speak to it at school. It'll be spat upon and kicked wherever it goes.'

'Martha!' Mam said sharply, from the doorway. 'That's enough.'

Flo burst into tears and ran upstairs, just as the front door opened and Albert Colquitt arrived.

A few minutes later, Sally came in and sat on the bed where Flo was lying face down, sobbing.

'You should have taken precautions, luv,' she whispered. 'I know what it's like when you're in love. It's hard to stop if things get out of hand.'

'You mean, you and Jock . . .' Flo raised her head and looked tearfully at her sister. Jock Wilson continued to descend on Liverpool whenever he could wangle a few days' leave.

Sally nodded. 'Don't tell Martha, whatever you do.'

The idea was so preposterous, that Flo actually laughed. 'As if I would!'

'She doesn't mean everything she says, you know. I don't know why she's so bitter and twisted. You'd think she was jealous that you'd been with a man.' Sally sighed. 'Poor Martha. Lord knows what she'll say when she finds out me and Jock are getting married at Christmas, if he can get away. She'd have expected to go first, being the eldest, like.'

'Sally, Oh, Sal, I'm so pleased for you.' Flo forgot her own troubles and hugged her sister. Sally made her promise to keep the news to herself: she didn't want anyone to know until it was definite.

After a while, Sally went downstairs because it was her turn to do the dishes and she didn't want Martha getting in a further twist.

Flo sat up, leaned against the headboard, and rested her hands on her swelling tummy. She'd put off breaking the dreadful news for as long as possible, but it was October, she was four and a half months' pregnant, and it was beginning to show. One or two women in the laundry had been eyeing her suspiciously, and the other day when she'd been hanging out sheets in the drying room she'd turned to find Mrs Fritz at the door, watching keenly. Then Mrs Fritz had spent quite a long time in the office with Mr Fritz.

At first Flo had considered not telling a soul, running away and having the baby somewhere else. But she didn't want to stay away for ever and there'd be a baby to explain when she came back. Anyroad, where would she run to and how would she support herself? She had no money and wouldn't be able to get a job. She realised, sadly, that she would have to leave the laundry and it would be dreadful saying goodbye to Mr Fritz.

The door opened and Mam came in. 'I'm sorry I walked out, girl, but I couldn't stand our Martha's screaming. Perhaps it would have been best if you'd told your mam first and left me to deal with Martha.' She looked at her daughter reproachfully. 'How could you, Flo?'

'Please, Mam, don't go on at me.' Flo began to cry again at the sight of her mother's drawn face. Mam had seemed much better since the war began, as if she'd pulled herself together and was determined to see her family through the conflict to its bitter end. 'I'll leave home if you want. I never wanted to bring shame on me family.' Getting pregnant had been far from her mind when she'd lain under the trees in the Mystery with Tommy O'Mara.

'The man, this Tommy O'Mara, he should have known better. Martha says he was at least thirty. He was wrong to take advantage of a naïve young girl.' Mam pursed her lips disapprovingly.

'Oh, no, Mam,' Flo cried. 'He didn't take advantage. He loved me, and I loved him.' The lies he'd told meant nothing and neither did the promises. It was only because he was worried she might not go out with him that he'd said the things he had. 'If Tommy hadn't died, he'd have left Nancy by now and we'd be together.'

This was altogether too much for her mother. 'Don't be ridiculous, girl,' she said heatedly. 'You're talking like a scarlet woman.'

Perhaps she *was* a scarlet woman, because Flo had meant every word she said. Perhaps other couples didn't love each other as much as she and Tommy had. To appease her mother, she said meekly, 'I'm sorry.'

'Anyroad, that part's over and done with,' Mam sighed. 'What we have to deal with now are the consequences. I've had a word with Martha and Sal, and we think the best thing is for you to stay indoors until you've had the baby, then have it adopted. No one in the street will have known a thing. I'll go round and see Mr Fritz tomorrer and tell him you've been taken ill and won't be coming back. I hate to deceive him, he's such a nice feller, but what else can I do?'

'Nothing, Mam,' Flo said calmly. She was quite agreeable to the first part of the suggestion, that she stay indoors until the baby was born, but there was no way she intended giving up Tommy O'Mara's child, which was the next best thing to having Tommy himself. She wouldn't tell Mam that, otherwise there would be non-stop rows for months. Once it was born, she would move to another part of Liverpool, a place where no one knew her, but not too far for her family to come and visit. She'd say she was a widow who had lost her husband in the war, which meant there was no reason for anyone to call her child a bastard. She would support them both by taking in laundry and possibly a bit of mending – Mr Fritz often declared that no one else could darn a sheet as neatly as Flo.

War had made little impact so far on the country and people had begun to refer to it as 'phoney'. Lots of lads had been called up and ships were sunk frequently, with enormous loss of life, but it all seemed very far away. There was no sign of the dreaded air-raids and food was still plentiful.

Flo passed the days knitting clothes for the baby: lacy matinée coats and bonnets, unbelievably tiny booties and mittens, and dreaming about how things would be when her child was born. Occasionally, she could hear Mam and her sisters having whispered conversations in the kitchen, and the word adoption would be mentioned. It seemed that Martha already had the matter in hand. Flo didn't bother to disillusion them – anything for a quiet life. When she wasn't knitting, she read the books that Sally got her from the library. Once a month, she wrote to Bel McIntyre, who'd joined the ATS and was stationed up in the wilds of Scotland where she was having a wonderful time. 'There's a girl for every fifteen men,' she wrote. 'But there's one chap in particular I really like. Remember I said once I'd never met a chap worth twopence? Well, I've come across one worth at least a hundred quid. His name is Bob Knox and he comes from Edinburgh like me dad.' Flo didn't mention the baby in her letters. Bel had thought her daft to become involved with a married man, and she didn't want her to know just how involved and completely daft she'd been.

Often, she wished she could go for a walk, particularly when it was sunny, and as the time crawled by, she ached to go out even in the pouring rain. The worst time was when visitors came or their lodger was at home and she had to spend hours shut in the bedroom. According to Martha, of all the people in the world, Albert Colquitt was the one who must remain most ignorant of Flo's dark secret. If he knew what sort of family he was living with he might leave, and that would be disastrous, 'seeing as you're no longer bringing in a wage.' She sniffed. Sally thought Martha was mainly worried that he wouldn't want to marry her, a goal she was still working towards with all her might.

'How do you explain that I'm never there?' asked Flo.

'He's been told you're run down, anaemic, and have to stay in bed and rest.'

'I've never felt so healthy in me life.'

She was blooming, her cheeks the colour and texture of peaches, her eyes bright, and her hair unusually thick and glossy. She wondered why she should look so well when she felt so miserable without Tommy, but perhaps it was because she couldn't wait to have the baby. Also, Mam had ordered extra milk especially for her, and Martha, for all her carping comments and sniffs of disapproval, often brought home a pound of apples and made sure there was cod-liver oil in the house, which was what Elsa Cameron had taken when she was pregnant. 'And look what a lovely baby Norman turned out to be.' Flo knew she was lucky: another family might have thrown her out on to the street.

It was on a black dreary morning in December that the Clancys' lodger discovered the secret he was never supposed to know. Mam had gone Christmas shopping and Flo was in the living room, knitting, when the key turned in the front door. It wasn't often anyone used the front door apart from Albert. She assumed Mam's shopping bags were too heavy to carry round the back, and hurried out to help. To her horror, she came face to face with Albert.

'I forgot me wallet,' he beamed, 'least I hope I did, and it's not lost. It's not just the ten-bob note I had, but there's me identity card, and some photos I'd hate to lose, as well as . . .' His voice faded and his eyes widened in surprise as he took in Flo's condition. 'I didn't know, luv,' he whispered. 'Jaysus, I didn't know.'

Flo was stumbling up the stairs. Halfway, she turned, 'Don't tell our Martha you've seen me,' she implored. 'Please!'

'Of course not, luv.' He looked stunned. 'Flo!' he called, but by then Flo was in the bedroom and had slammed the door.

She heard him go into the parlour, and a few minutes later Mam returned from the shops. 'Are you all right, girl?' she called.

'I'm just having a little lie-down, Mam.'

'I'll bring a cup of tea up in a minute, then I'm going round to St Theresa's to do the flowers for Sunday.'

Mam was obviously unaware that Albert was in the parlour and remained unaware for the whole time she was at home. After she'd gone, Albert didn't stir or make even the smallest of sounds. Flo wondered if he was still searching for his wallet. Perhaps he was contemplating handing in a week's notice and finding somewhere more respectable to live.

Another half-hour passed, and still no sound. Then the parlour door opened and heavy footsteps could be heard coming upstairs. There was a tap on the door and a voice said hesitantly, 'Flo?'

'Yes?'

'Would you come downstairs a minute, luv? I'd like to talk to you.'

'What about?' Flo said warily.

'Come down and see.'

A few minutes later she and Albert were sitting stiffly in the living room. She felt over-conscious of her enormous stomach and hoped Albert wasn't intent on giving her a lecture, because she'd tell him it was none of his business. She felt deeply ashamed when, instead of a lecture, Albert mumbled, 'I've missed you, Flo. The house doesn't seem as bright and cheery without you.'

'I've been . . . upstairs,' she said lamely.

He shifted uncomfortably in the chair, then, without looking at her directly, said, 'I hope you don't mind me seeming personal, luv, but what's happened to the feller who . . . ?' Words failed him.

'He's dead,' said Flo.

'I thought he might be in the forces, like, and one day he'd turn up and you'd get married.'

'There's no chance of that, not when he's dead.'

'Of course not.' His face was cherry red, and she could see beads of perspiration glistening on his forehead. That he was sweating so profusely made his uniform pong even more strongly than it normally did. She wondered why on earth he was so embarrassed, when if anyone should be it was her. 'It'll be hard, bringing up a kiddie without a husband,' he said awkwardly.

'I'll manage. I'll have to, won't I?'

'It'll still be hard, and the thing is, I'd like to make it easier if you'll let me.' He paused and his face grew even redder before he plunged on. 'I'd like to marry you, Flo, and provide you and the little 'un with a home. I earn decent money as an inspector on the trams, and it's a good, secure job with prospects of promotion to depot superintendent. We could get a nice little house between us, and I've enough put away to buy the furniture we'd need. What do you say, luv?'

Flo hoped the distaste she felt didn't show on her face: the last thing in the world she wanted was to hurt him, but the idea of sharing a bed with a middle-aged man with a pot belly and a dreadful smell made her feel sick.

'It's kind of you, Albert –' she began, but he interrupted, as if he wanted to get everything off his chest.

'Of course, I wouldn't expect to be a proper husband, luv. We'd have separate rooms, and if you ever wanted to leave, it'd be up to you. There'd be no strings. To make it easier, we could get wed in one of those register-office places. I'd just be getting you out of a temporary hole, as it were. You'd have marriage lines, and if we did it quick enough, the baby'd have a dad, at least on paper.'

He was incredibly unselfish, and Flo was angry with herself for finding his proposal so disagreeable. But she'd once dreamed of sharing her life with Tommy O'Mara, beside whom Albert Colquitt was – well, there wasn't any comparison. On the other hand, she thought, as she leaned back in the chair and stared into the fire, would it really be so disagreeable? It would be getting her out of a hole, as he put it. No one would call the baby names if it had a father, and Flo wouldn't have to take in laundry but would have a nice, newly furnished house in which to live. She wouldn't be taking advantage of him, not in a mean way, because it was his idea. Of course, everyone would kick up hell at the idea of a Clancy getting married in a register office but, under the circumstances, Flo didn't care. And Martha would be livid, claiming Flo had stolen Albert from right under her nose.

She was still wondering how to respond when Albert said wistfully, 'Me wife died in childbirth, you know, along with the baby. It was a girl. We were going to call her Patricia, Patsy, if we had a girl. I've always wanted a kiddie of me own.'

If he hadn't said that she might have agreed to marry him, if only on a temporary basis – he'd made it clear that she could leave whenever she wanted. But she knew she could never be so cruel as to walk out once he'd grown to love the baby he'd always wanted. She would feel trapped. It would be like a second bereavement and he would lose another wife and child. No, best turn him down now.

So Flo told him, very nicely and very gently, that she couldn't possibly marry him but that she would never forget his kind gesture. She never dreamed that this decision would haunt her for the rest of her days.

Much to Martha's disappointment, Albert took himself off to stay with a cousin in Macclesfield over Christmas, though Flo was glad because it meant she could remain downstairs except when the occasional visitor came. She wondered if he'd gone for that very reason, and said a little prayer that he would enjoy himself in Macclesfield and that the scarf she'd knitted him would keep him warm – the weather throughout the country was freezing cold with snow several feet deep. Before Albert went, he gave the girls a present each: a gold-plated chain bracelet with a tiny charm. Martha's charm was a monkey, Sally's a key and Flo's a heart.

'I bet he meant to give me the heart,' Martha said.

'We'll swop if you like,' Flo offered.

'It doesn't matter now.'

On Christmas Eve, a package arrived from Bel containing a card and a pretty tapestry purse. When Flo opened the card, a photograph fell out. 'Bel's married!' she cried. 'She's married someone called Bob Knox, he's a Scot.'

'I only met her the once, but she seemed a nice young lady,' Mam said, pleased. 'You must pass on our congratulations, Flo, next time you write. Why not send her one of those Irish cotton doilies as a little present?'

'I wanted those doilies for me bottom drawer, Mam,' Martha pouted.

Flo shook her head. 'Thanks all the same, Mam, but she won't want a doily in the Army. She'd prefer a bottle of scent or a nice pair of stockings.'

'And have you got the wherewithal to buy scent and nice stockings?' Martha asked nastily.

'I'll get a present when I'm earning money of me own,' Flo snapped.

Their mother clapped her hands impatiently. 'Now, girls, stop bickering. It's Christmas, the season of goodwill.'

'Sorry, Flo.' Martha smiled for once. 'I love you, really.'

'I love you too, Sis.'

Later, Martha said to Flo, 'How old is Bel?'

'Eighteen.'

'Only eighteen!' Martha removed her glasses and polished them agitatedly. 'I'll be twenty-four next year.'

Flo wished with all her heart that she could buy a husband for her unhappy sister and hang him on the tree. It didn't help when, on Boxing Day, a telegram arrived for Sally. GOT LICENCE STOP GOT LEAVE STOP BOOK CHURCH MONDAY STOP JOCK.

'I'm getting married on Monday,' Sally sang, starry-eyed.

Flo whooped with joy, and Mam began to cry. 'Sally, luv! This is awful sudden.'

'It's wartime, Mam. It's the way things happen nowadays.'

'Does it mean you'll be leaving home, luv?' Mam sobbed.

'Jock doesn't have a regular port. I'll stay with me family till the war's over, then we'll get a house of our own.'

At this, Mam's tears stopped and she became practical. She'd call on Father Haughey that very day and book the church. Monday afternoon would be best, just in case Jock was late. Even trains had a job getting through the snow. At this, Sally blanched: she had forgotten that the entire country was snowbound. 'He's coming from Solway Firth. Is that far?' No one had the faintest idea so Dad's atlas was brought out and Solway Firth was discovered to be two counties away.

'I'll die if he doesn't get here!' Sally looked as if she might die there and then.

'Surely he'll be coming by ship.' Martha hadn't spoken until then. Her face was as white as the snow outside and her eyes were bleak. She was the eldest, she was being left behind, and she couldn't stand it.

'Of course!' Sally breathed a sigh of relief.

Mam continued to be practical. Did Sally want a white wedding? No? Well, in that case, tomorrow she'd meet her outside the butcher's at dinner-time, and they'd tour the dress shops in Smithdown Road for a nice costume, her wedding present to her daughter. 'It's no use getting pots and pans yet. And we'll have to have a taxi on the day. It's impossible to set foot outside the house in ordinary shoes in this weather, and you can't very well get married in Wellies. As for the reception, I wonder if it's too late to book a room?'

'I don't want a reception, Mam. I'd prefer tea in a café afterwards. Jock's mate will be best man. All I want is me family, you, Martha and Flo.'

'Our Flo can't go,' Martha pointed out. 'Not in her condition.'

Everyone turned to look at Flo, who dropped her eyes, shame-faced. 'I hate the idea of missing your wedding, Sal,' she mumbled.

'I'll be thinking of you, Flo,' Sally said affectionately. 'You'll be there in spirit, if not in the flesh.'

Flo summoned up every charitable instinct in her body. 'Albert will be back from Macclesfield by then,' she said. 'Perhaps he could go instead of me. He'd be a partner for our Martha.'

Albert declared himself supremely honoured to be invited to the wedding. 'He likes to feel part of the family,' Sally said. 'I suspect he's lonely.'

On the day of her sister's wedding, Flo sat alone in the quiet house, thinking how much things had changed over the last twelve months. A year ago Mam was ill, and the sisters' lives had been jogging along uneventfully. Now, Mam had bucked up out of all recognition, Flo had found, and lost, Tommy O'Mara, and was carrying his child, and at this very minute Sally, wearing an ugly pinstriped costume and a white felt hat that made her look like an American gangster, was in the process of becoming Mrs Jock Wilson. Martha was the only one for whom everything was still the same.

She laid her hands contentedly on her stomach. It was odd, but nowadays she scarcely thought about Tommy O'Mara, as if all her love had been transferred to the baby, who chose that moment to give her a vicious kick. She felt a spark of fear. It wasn't due for another six weeks, on St Valentine's Day, exactly nine months and one week since the date of her last period – Mam had worked it out – but what if it arrived early while she was in the house by herself? Martha had booked a midwife under a 'vow of confidentiality', as she put it, who would deliver the baby when the time came. Flo couldn't wait for everything to be over, when her life would change even more.

Snow continued to fall throughout January, and February brought no respite from the Arctic weather. By now Flo was huge, although she remained nimble on her feet. As the days crept by, though, she lost her appetite and felt increasingly sick. Martha left instructions that she was to be fetched immediately if the baby started to arrive when she was at work.

'Surely it would be best to fetch the midwife first?' cried Mam. 'If you'll tell me where she lives, I'll get her.'

'I'd sooner get her meself,' Martha said testily. 'There'll be no need to panic. First babies take ages to arrive. Elsa Cameron was twenty-four hours in labour.'

'Jaysus!' Flo screamed. 'Twenty-four whole hours! Did it hurt much?'

Martha looked away. 'Only a bit.'

The phosphorous fingers on the alarm clock showed twenty past two as Flo twisted restlessly in bed – it was such a palaver turning over. St Valentine's Day had been and gone and still the baby showed no sign of arriving. She lifted the curtain and looked outside. More snow, falling silently and relentlessly in lumps as big as golf balls. The roads would be impassable again tomorrow.

Suddenly, without warning, pain tore through her belly, so forcefully, that she gasped aloud. The sound must have disturbed her sisters, because Martha stopped snoring and Sally stirred.

Flo waited, her heart in her mouth, glad that the time had come but praying that she wouldn't have a pain like that again. She screamed when another pain, far worse, gripped her from head to toe.

'What's the matter?' Sally leaped out of bed, followed by Martha. 'Has it started, luv?'

'Oh, Lord, yes!' Flo groaned. 'Fetch the midwife, Martha, quick.'

'Where does she live?' demanded Sally. 'I'll go.'

'There isn't time for a midwife,' Martha said shortly, 'not if the pains are this strong. Wake Mam up, if she's not awake already, and put water on to boil – two big pans and the kettle. Once you've done that, fetch those old sheets off the top shelf of the airing cupboard.'

'I still think I should get the midwife, Martha. You and Mam can see to Flo while I'm gone.'

'I said there isn't time!' Martha slapped her hand over Flo's mouth when another pain began. 'Don't scream, Flo, we don't want the neighbours hearing. It would happen the night Albert's not out fire-watching,' she added irritably.

'I can't help screaming,' Flo gasped, pushing Martha's hand away. 'I've got to scream.'

Mam came into the room in her nightdress. 'Help me pull the bed round a bit so's I can get on the other side,' she commanded. When it had been moved, she knelt beside her daughter. 'I know it hurts, luv,' she whispered, 'but try and keep a bit quiet, like.'

'I'll try, Mam. Oh, God!' Flo flung her arms into the air and grasped the wooden headboard.

'Keep her arms like that,' Martha instructed. 'I read a book about it in the library.'

Sally brought the sheets, and Flo felt herself being lifted, her nightie pulled up, and the old bedding was slipped beneath her.

'You didn't book a midwife, did you, our Martha?' Sally said in a low, accusing voice. 'It was all a lie. God, you make me sick, you do. You're too bloody respectable by a mile. You'd let our poor Flo suffer just to protect your own miserable reputation. I don't give a sod if me sister has a baby out of wedlock. You're not human, you.'

'Is it true about the midwife, Martha?' Mam said, in a shocked voice.

'Yes!' Martha spat. 'There's not a single one I'd trust to keep her lip buttoned. It's all right for Sal, she's married. I bet Jock wouldn't have been so keen if he'd known what her sister had been up to.'

'It so happens, Jock's known about Flo for months, but it was me he wanted to marry, not me family.'

'Stoppit!' Flo screamed. 'Stoppit!'

'Girls! Girls! This isn't the time to have a fight.' Mam stroked Flo's brow distractedly. 'Do try to keep quiet, there's a good girl.'

'I'm trying, Mam, honest, but it don't half hurt.'

'I know, luv, I know, but we've kept it to ourselves all these months, there's only a short while to go.'

'Can I go for a walk once it's over?'

'Yes, luv. As soon as you're fit, we'll go for a walk together.'

In her agony, Flo forgot that by the time she was fit again she would be gone from the house in Burnett Street. She would be living somewhere else with her baby.

Afterwards, she never thought to ask how long the torment lasted: one hour, two hours, three. All she could remember were the agonising spasms that seized her body regularly and which wouldn't have felt quite so bad if only she could have screamed. But every time she opened her mouth, Martha's hand would slam down on her face and Mam would shake her arm and whisper, 'Try not to make a noise, there's a good girl.'

She was only vaguely aware of the argument raging furiously over her head. 'This is cruel,' Sally hissed. 'You're both being dead cruel. It's only what I'd expect from our Martha, but I'm surprised at you, Mam.'

Then Mam replied, in a strange, cold voice, 'I'm sorry about the midwife, naturally, but one of these days, you'll leave this house, girl, all three of you will. I don't want to be known for the rest of me life as the woman who's daughter had an illegitimate baby, because that's how they'll think of me in the street and in the Legion of Mary, and I'd never be able to hold me head up in front of Father Haughey again.'

Later, Sally demanded, 'What happens if she tears? She'll need stitches. For Christ's sake, at least get the doctor to sew her up.'

'Women didn't have stitches in the past,' Martha said tersely. 'Flo's a healthy girl. She'll mend by herself.'

'I want to go to the lavatory,' Flo wailed. 'Fetch the chamber, quick, or I'll do it in the bed.'

'It's coming!' Mam said urgently.

'Push, Flo,' Martha hissed. 'Push hard.'

'I need the chamber!'

'No, you don't, Flo. It's the baby. *Push!*'

Flo felt sure her body was going to burst and the hurt was so tremendous that the room turned black and little stars appeared, dancing on the ceiling. ' "Dancing in the dark," she bellowed. "Dancing in the dark. Dancing . . ." '

'Oh, Lord!' Sally was almost sobbing. 'She's lost her mind. Now see what you've done!'

Which was the last thing Flo heard until she woke up with a peculiar taste in her mouth. She opened her eyes very, very slowly, because the lids felt too heavy to lift. It was broad daylight outside. Every ounce of strength had drained from her body, and she could barely raise her arms. Unbelievably, for several seconds she forgot about the baby. It wasn't until she noticed her almost flat tummy that she remembered. Despite her all-out weariness, she was gripped by shivers of excitement. She forced herself on to her elbows and looked around the room, but the only strange thing there was a bottle of brandy on the dressing-table which accounted for the funny taste in her mouth, though she couldn't remember drinking it. There was no sign of a baby.

'Mam,' she called weakly. 'Martha, Sal.'

Mam came into the room looking exhausted, but relieved. 'How do you feel, luv?'

'Tired, that's all. Where's the baby?'

'Why, luv, he's gone. Martha took him round to the woman who arranged the adoption. Apparently a very nice couple have been waiting anxiously for him to arrive, not that they cared whether it was a boy or a girl, like. They'll have him by now. He'll be one of the best-loved babies in the whole world.'

It was a boy *and he'd been given away!* Flo's heart leaped to her throat and pounded as loudly as a drum. 'I want my baby,' she croaked. 'I want him this very minute.' She struggled out of bed, but her legs gave way and she fell to the floor. 'Tell me where Martha took him, and I'll fetch him back.'

'Flo, luv.' Mam came over and tried to help her to her feet, but Flo pushed her away and crawled towards the door. If necessary, she'd crawl in her nightdress through the snow to find her son, Tommy's lad, their baby.

'Oh, Flo, my dear, sweet girl,' Mam cried, 'can't you see this is the best possible way? It's what we decided ages ago. You're only nineteen, you've got your whole life ahead of you. You don't want to be burdened with a child at your age!'

'He's not a burden. I want him.' Flo collapsed, weeping on to the floor. 'I want my baby.'

Martha came in. 'It's all over, Flo,' she said gently. 'Now's the time to put the whole thing behind you.'

Between them, they picked her up and helped her back to bed. 'C'mon, luv,' Martha said, 'Have another few spoons of brandy, it'll help you sleep and you need to get your strength back. You'll be pleased to know none of the neighbours have been round wanting to know what all the racket was last night, which means we got away with it, didn't we?'

Why, oh, why hadn't she just taken a chance, run away and hoped everything would turn out all right? Why hadn't she made it plain that she wanted to keep the baby? Why hadn't she married Albert Colquitt?

In the fevered, nightmarish days that followed, Flo remained in bed and tortured herself with the same questions over and over again. She cursed her lack of courage: she'd been too frightened to run away, preferring to remain in the comfort of her home with her family around her, letting them think she was agreeable to the adoption to avoid the inevitable rows. She cursed her ignorance in assuming that she'd have the baby, leap out of bed, and carry him off into the unknown. Finally, she cursed her soft heart for turning down Albert's proposal because she didn't want him hurt at some time in the far-distant future.

All the time, her arms ached to hold her little son. The unwanted milk dried up, her breasts turned to concrete, and her insides felt as if they were shrivelling to nothing. She didn't cry, she was beyond tears.

'What did he look like?' she asked Sally one day.

'He was a dear little thing. I'm sure Mam wished we could have kept him. She cried when Martha made her give him up.'

'At least Mam held him, which is more than I did,' Flo said bitterly. 'I never even saw him.'

'That's what happens when women give their babies up for adoption. They're not allowed to see them, let alone hold them, least so Martha says. It's what's called being cruel to be kind.' Sally's eyes were full of sympathy, but even she thought that what had happened was for the best.

'Our Martha seems to know everything.' Flo had refused to speak to Martha until she revealed the whereabouts of her son.

'That's something I'll just have to get used to,' Martha said blithely, 'I couldn't tell you even if I wanted to because the names of adoptive parents are kept confidential. All I've been told is the baby's got a mam and dad who love him. That should make you happy, not sad. They'll be able to give him all the things that you never could.'

Flo gripped her painful breasts and glared contemptuously at her sister. 'They can't give him his mother's milk, can they? There'll be no bond between him and some strange woman who didn't carry him in *her* belly for nine whole months.'

'Don't be silly, Flo.' For once, Martha was unable to meet her sister's eyes. She turned away, her face strangely flushed.

March came, and a few days later the weather changed dramatically. The snow that had lain on the ground for months melted swiftly as the temperature soared.

Spring had arrived!

Flo couldn't resist the bright yellow sunshine that poured into the bedroom, caressing her face with its gentle warmth. She threw back the bedclothes, and got up for the first time in a fortnight. Her legs were still weak, her stomach hurt, her head felt as if it had been stuffed with old rags, but she had to go for a walk.

She walked further every day. Gradually, her young body recovered its strength and vigour. When she met people she knew, they remarked on how fit and well she looked. 'You're a picture of health, Flo. No one would guess you'd been so ill.'

But Flo knew that, no matter how well she looked, she would never be the same person again. She would never stop mourning her lost baby, a month old by now. There was an ache in her chest, as if a little piece of her heart had been removed when her son was taken away.

2

Sally had left the butcher's to take up war work at Rootes Securities, an aircraft factory in Speke, for three times the wages. She was coping well in the machine shop in what used to be a man's job. Even Mam was talking about looking for part-time work. 'After all, there's a war on. We've all got to do our bit.' Albert was out most nights fire-watching, though so far there hadn't been a fire for him to watch.

Flo realised it was time she got back to work. Sally suggested she apply to Rootes Securities. 'If we got on the same shift we could go together on the bus. You'll find it peculiar, working nights, but it's the gear there, Sis. All we do the whole time is laugh.'

Laugh! Flo couldn't imagine smiling again, let alone laughing. Sally fetched an application form for her to fill in and took it back next morning. Later, as Flo roamed the streets of Liverpool, she thought wistfully of Fritz's Laundry. She'd sooner work there than in a factory, even if the pay was a pittance compared to what Sal earned.

Since emerging from her long confinement, she'd passed the laundry numerous times. The side door was always open, but she hadn't had the nerve to peek inside. She felt sure the women, including Mrs Fritz, had guessed the real reason why she'd left.

On her way home the same day, she passed the laundry again. Smoke was pouring from the chimneys, and a cloud of steam floated out the door.

'I'll pop in and say hello,' she decided. 'If they're rude, then I'll never go again. But I'd like to thank Mr Fritz for the lovely necklace he sent at Christmas.'

She crossed the street, wondering what sort of reception she would get. To her astonishment, when she presented herself at the door, the only person there was Mr Fritz, his shirtsleeves rolled up, working away furiously on the big pressing machine that Flo had come to regard as her own.

'Mr Fritz!'

'Flo!' He stopped work and came over to kiss her warmly on the cheek. 'Why, it's good to see you. It's as if the sun has come out twice today. What are you doing here?'

'I just came to say hello, like, and thank you for the necklace. Where is everyone?'

He spread his arms dramatically. 'Gone! Olive was the first, then Josie, then the others. Once they discovered they could earn twice as much in a factory they upped and went. Not that I blame them. I can't compete with those sort of wages, and why should they make sacrifices on behalf of Mr and Mrs Fritz and their eight children when they have families of their own?'

Mrs Fritz came hurrying out of the drying room with a pile of bedding. Her face hardened when she saw Flo. 'Hello,' she said shortly. She scooped clean washing out of a boiler and disappeared again.

Her husband wrinkled his stubby little nose in embarrassment. 'Don't take any notice of Stella. She's worn out. Her mother is over from Ireland to look after the children, as we work all the hours God sends, including weekends. You see, Flo,' he went on earnestly, 'lots of hotels and restaurants have lost staff to the war and they send us the washing they used to do themselves. Business has soared, and I hate to turn it away, so

459

Stella and I are trying to cope on our own. I've hired a lad, Jimmy Cromer, to collect and deliver on a bike with a sidecart. He's a right scally, but very reliable for a fourteen-year-old.' He managed to chuckle and look gloomy at the same time. 'One of these days, Stella and I will find ourselves buried under a mountain of sheets and pillowcases, and no one will find us again.'

'Would you like a hand?' Flo blurted. 'Permanent, like.'

'Would I!' He beamed, then bit his lip and glanced uneasily towards the drying room. 'Just a minute, Flo.'

He was gone a long time. Flo couldn't hear what was said, but sensed from the sound of the muffled voices that he and Stella were arguing. She supposed she might as well get on with a bit of pressing rather than stand around doing nothing, so folded several tablecloths and was wreathed in a cloud of hissing steam when he returned.

'We'd love to have you, Flo,' he said, rubbing his hands together happily, though she guessed he was putting it on a bit. Mrs Fritz had probably agreed because they were desperate. As if to prove this, he went on, 'You'll have to make allowances for Stella. As I said, she's worn out. The children daren't look at her in case she snaps their heads off. As for me, I'm very much in her bad books. She regards me as personally responsible for the war and our present difficulties.'

As the profit from the laundry had provided the Fritz family with a high standard of living and a big house in William Square, one of the best addresses in Liverpool, Flo thought it unfair of Stella to complain. She said nothing, but offered to go home, change into old clothes and start work that afternoon.

Mr Fritz accepted her suggestion gratefully. 'But are you sure you're up to it, Flo? Your mother said you were very ill each time I called.' He looked into her eyes and she could tell he knew why she'd been 'ill' but, unlike his wife, he didn't care. 'There'll be three of us doing the work of six.'

'Does that mean the wages will be more?' She was glad to be coming back, but it seemed only fair that if she was doing the work of two women, she should get an increase in wages. He might not be able to compete with a factory, but if business was soaring he should be able to manage a few extra bob.

He blinked, as if the thought hadn't entered his head. Just in case it hadn't, Flo said, 'I've applied for a job in Rootes Securities where our Sally works. She's paid time and a half if she works Saturdays.'

Mr Fritz's shoulders shook with laughter. 'Don't worry, my dear. I promise your pocket won't suffer if you work for me. I'll pay you by the hour from now on, including time and a half on Saturdays.'

Flo blushed. 'I didn't mean to sound greedy, like.'

He pecked both her cheeks and chucked her under the chin. 'I haven't seen you smile yet. Come on, Flo, brighten up my day even further and give me one of your lovely smiles.'

And to Flo's never-ending astonishment, she managed to smile.

Stella Fritz had seemed such a sweet, uncomplaining person in the days when Flo hardly knew her, but after they'd worked side by side for a short while, she turned out to be a sour little woman who complained all the time. Perhaps she was worn out and missed being with her children, but there was no need to be quite so nasty to Mr Fritz, who was blamed for every single thing, from exceptionally dirty sheets that needed boiling twice to food rationing, which had just been introduced.

'Bloody hell! She was only a farm girl back in Ireland,' Martha said indignantly, when Flo brought up the subject at home – Flo's vow never to speak to her eldest sister had been forgotten. 'She's dead lucky to have hooked someone like Mr Fritz. Have you seen their house in William Square?'

'I hope she's not nasty to you,' Mam remarked. 'If she is I'll go round there and give her a piece of me mind.'

'Oh, she just ignores me, thank goodness.' It was a relief to be beneath the woman's contempt. It meant she could get on with things without expecting the wrath of Cain to fall on her because the chain in the lavatory had stopped working or the soap powder hadn't arrived.

Mr Fritz said privately that he'd never felt so pleased about anything in his life as he was to have Flo back. She told him he was exaggerating, but he maintained stoutly that he meant every word. 'I love my wife, Flo, but she was beginning to get me down. The atmosphere has improved enormously since you reappeared on the scene. Things don't seem so bad if you can make a joke of them. Until you came, it all seemed rather tragic.' Every time Stella went into the drying room, or outside for some fresh air, he would make a peculiar face and sing, 'The dragon lady's gone, oh, the dragon lady's gone. What shall we do now the dragon lady's gone?'

When the dragon lady returned, he would cry, 'Ah, there you are, my love!' Stella would throw him a murderous look and Flo would do her best to stifle a giggle. She thought Mr Fritz was incredibly patient. A less kind-hearted person might have dumped Stella in one of the boilers.

She scarcely noticed spring turn into summer because she was working so hard, sometimes till eight or nine o'clock at night, arriving home bone weary, with feet swollen to twice their normal size, ready to fall into bed where she went to sleep immediately. Sally was equally tired and Martha's brewery was short-staffed, which meant she often had to work late. In order to hang on to their remaining staff, the brewery increased the wages, or the pubs might run out of beer, a situation too horrendous even to

461

contemplate. Mam got a part-time job in a greengrocer's in Park Road. The Clancy family had never been so wealthy, but there was nothing to spend the money on. Rationing meant food was strictly limited, and the girls hadn't time to wander round the shops looking at clothes. They all started post-office accounts, and began to save for the day when the war would be over, though that day seemed a long way off.

By now, the war could no longer be described as 'phoney'. Adolf Hitler had conquered most of Europe; in June, he took France, and although thousands of British and French soldiers were rescued in the great evacuation of Dunkirk, thousands more lost their lives or were taken prisoner. The British Isles was separated from the massed German troops by only a narrow strip of water. People shivered in their beds, because invasion seemed inevitable, although the government did all it could to make an invasion as hazardous as possible. Road signs and the names of stations were removed, barricades were erected, aliens were sent to detention camps all over the country, including nice Mr and Mrs Gabrielli who owned the fish-and-chip shop in Earl Road.

One Monday, Flo arrived at work to find Mrs Fritz all on her own, ironing a white shirt with unnecessary force. Her eyes were red, as if she had been weeping. The two women rarely spoke, but Flo felt bound to ask, 'What's the matter? Is Mr Fritz all right?'

'No, he isn't,' Stella said, in a thin voice. 'He's been rounded up like a common criminal and sent to a detention camp on the Isle of Man. Oh, I said he should have taken British nationality years ago but he was proud of being Austrian, the fool. Not only that, we've lost two of our biggest customers. It seems hotels would sooner have dirty sheets than have them washed in a laundry with a foreign name.' Her Irish accent, scarcely noticeable before, had returned in full force with the power of her anger.

'Oh, no!' Flo was sorry about the lost orders, naturally, but devastated at the thought of dear Mr Fritz, who wouldn't have hurt a fly and loathed Hitler every bit as much as she did, being confined behind bars or barbed wire, like a thief or a murderer. 'How long are they keeping him?' she asked.

'For the duration of the bloody war.'

'Oh, no,' Flo said again.

'I suppose I'll just have to close this place down,' Mrs Fritz said bleakly. 'I can't manage on me own. Anyroad, those cancellations could be the start of an avalanche. Soon, there mightn't be any customers left. I suppose we're lucky the building hasn't been attacked. The German pork butcher's in Lodge Lane had all its winders broken.'

'But you can't close down!' Flo cried. 'You've got to keep going for when Mr Fritz comes home. The laundry is his life. And his old customers won't desert him, not the ones who know him personally. We can cope, just the two of us, if there's going to be less work.'

Mrs Fritz attacked the shirt again and didn't answer. Flo took a load of washing into the drying room and was hanging it on the line when Stella Fritz appeared at the door.

'All right, we'll keep the laundry going between us,' she said, in a cold voice, 'but I'd like it made plain from the start, Flo Clancy, that I don't like you. I know full well what you've been up to, and just because I've agreed we should work together, it doesn't mean that I approve.'

Flo tried to look indifferent. 'I don't care if you approve or not. I'm only doing it for Mr Fritz.'

'As long as we know where we stand.'

'Rightio. There's just one thing. What about changing the name from Fritz's Laundry to something else?'

'Such as?'

'Oh, I dunno.' Flo pondered hard. 'What's your maiden name?'

'McGonegal.'

'McGonegal's Laundry is a bit of a mouthful. What about White? White's Laundry. It's got the same number of letters as Fritz, so it'll be easy to change the sign outside. Of course, it won't fool the old customers but it'll certainly fool the new.' It seemed rather traitorous because no one could have been more patriotic than dear Mr Fritz, but if his foreign name was a hindrance to his business, she felt sure he wouldn't mind it being changed.

After a few hiccups – another two big customers withdrew – by August, White's Laundry was back on its feet. More large hotels sent enormous bundles of washing, including one who'd used the laundry before and seemed content to use it again now the name had been changed.

'That was a good idea you had,' Stella Fritz said grudgingly, the day she heard their old customer had returned.

'Ta,' Flo said.

'Though it means we'll be even more snowed under with work than ever,' she muttered, half to herself.

'Hmm,' Flo muttered back. The two women still rarely spoke. There wasn't the time and they had nothing to say to each other. Occasionally Flo asked if Stella had heard from her husband, and was told he'd written and sounded depressed. It was hard to make out whether Stella was upset or angry that Mr Fritz had gone.

Mam had been discussing with her friends at the Legion of Mary the long hours her youngest daughter worked. One night she said, 'There's these two spinsters in the Legion, twins, Jennifer and Joanna Holbrook.

They're in their late seventies, but as spry and fit as women half their age. They want to know if you'd like a hand in the laundry.'

'We're desperate. Stella's tried, but there's better jobs around for women these days. I doubt if two old ladies in their seventies would be much good, though, Mam.'

'I told them to pop in sometime and have a word with Mrs Fritz, anyroad.'

Two days later the Holbrook twins presented themselves to an astonished Stella Fritz. They were nearly six feet tall, stick thin, with narrow, animated faces, and identical to each other in every detail, right down to each item of their clothing. Papa had been in shipping, they explained between them, in their breathless, posh voices, and they'd never done a day's work in their lives, apart from in a voluntary capacity in the other great war.

'Of course, we've been knitting squares for the Red Cross . . .' said one – Flo was never able to recognise one twin from the other.

'. . . and rolling bandages . . .'

'. . . and collecting silver paper . . .'

'. . . but we'd far sooner go *out* to work . . .'

'. . . it would be almost as good as joining up.'

Mrs Fritz looked flummoxed. She glanced at Flo, who rolled her eyes helplessly.

'We wrote to the Army and offered our services . . .'

'. . . but they turned us down . . .'

'. . . even though we explained we could speak French and German fluently.'

'I don't know what to say.' Normally blunt, often rude, Mrs Fritz was stuck for words before the two women towering over her.

'What about a week's trial?' Flo suggested.

One twin clapped her hands and cried, 'That would be marvellous!'

'Absolutely wonderful!' cried the other.

'The money isn't important . . .'

'. . . we'd work for peanuts . . .'

'. . . and regard it as our contribution towards the war.'

Stella Fritz offered them peanuts and agreed that they should start tomorrow.

The twins turned up next day in uniforms that had once been worn by their maids: identical white ankle-length pinafores and gathered caps that covered their eyebrows. They were undoubtedly fit, but not quite as spry as Mam had claimed. Every now and then, they required a 'little sit-down', and would produce silver cigarette cases from the pockets of their pinnies and light each other's cigarette with a silver lighter. Then they would take long, deep puffs, as if they had been deprived for months.

'I needed that, Jen.'

'Same here, Jo.'

When their first week was up, there was no suggestion of them leaving, and once again the atmosphere in the laundry improved. Observing the Holbrook twins at close quarters was like having the front seat in a theatre, because they were as good as a top-class variety act. Even Stella Fritz seemed happier, particularly as they didn't have to work so hard and could leave at a civilised hour. It was nice to have a proper break at dinner-time instead of trying to eat a butty and iron a shirt at the same time. Flo didn't bother going home for dinner, and continued to take butties, which she sometimes ate as she wandered along Smithdown Road peering in shop windows. Once or twice, she ventured into the Mystery, but that part of her life no longer seemed real. It was impossible to believe that eighteen months ago she hadn't even met Tommy O'Mara. She felt like a very old woman trying to recall events that had happened more than half a century before. Flo had once had a lover, then she'd had a baby, but now both were gone, she was back at work in the laundry, and it was as if nothing had ever happened. Nothing at all.

Perhaps Hitler felt too daunted by the English Channel, because the threat of invasion faded, to be replaced by a more immediate terror: air raids. Liverpudlians dreaded the ominous wail of the siren warning them that enemy planes were on their way, while the sweetest sound on earth was the single-pitched tone of the all-clear to announce that the raid was over.

Over tea, Mrs Clancy would reel off the places that had been hit: the Customs House, the Dunlop rubber works, Tunnel Road picture house and Central Station. Edge Hill goods station, where Dad had worked, was seriously damaged. Then Albert Colquitt would come home and reel off a different list.

Sally came home from work one morning to report that Rootes Securities had been narrowly missed, and did Flo know that Josie Driver, who used to work in the laundry, had been killed last week when Ullet Road was bombed? 'I thought she'd gone in a convent.'

Flo was wandering along Smithdown Road in her dinner hour, thinking about last night's raid, when she saw the frock and the war was promptly forgotten.

'Oh, it's dead smart!' She stood in front of the window of Elaine's, Ladies' and Children's Fashions, eyeing the frock longingly. It was mauve, with long sleeves, a black velvet collar and velvet buttons down the front. 'It's dead smart, and only two pounds, nine and eleven. I could wear it for church, or to go dancing in. It's ages since I've been to a dance. And I've enough money saved.' She caught sight of her reflection in the window.

She looked a fright. It was about time she smartened herself up, did something with her hair, started to wear powder and lipstick again. She couldn't mope for ever. 'If I bought that frock, perhaps Sally would come dancing with me. I bet Jock wouldn't mind.' It was no use asking Martha because she was convinced that no one would ask a girl with glasses to dance, even though Flo assured her there were plenty of men in glasses who didn't hesitate to ask girls up.

'I'll buy it – least, I'll try it on. If it fits, I'll ask them to put it on one side and come back tomorrer with the money.' Excited, she was about to enter the shop when she saw Nancy O'Mara coming towards her pushing a big black pram.

Nancy was dressed less flamboyantly than the last time Flo had seen her, outside the gates of Cammell Laird, in a plain brown coat that looked rather old. Her hair was in the same plump bun on the back of her thin yellow neck. Long earrings with amber-coloured stones dangled from her ears, dragging the lobes so that they looked elongated and deformed. She stopped at the butcher's shop next door, nudged the brake of the pram with her foot, and went inside.

Curious, Flo temporarily put aside her longing for the mauve frock, and walked along to the butcher's. Nancy had joined the small queue inside and her back was to the window. The hood of the pram was half up. Inside, a pretty baby, about seven or eight months old, with fair hair and a dead perfect little face, half sat, half lay against a frilly white pillow, playing sleepily with a rattle. She supposed it was a boy, because he wore blue: blue bonnet and matinée coat, both hand-knitted. Nancy must be minding him for someone. Flo thought of all the baby clothes she'd knitted which had been left behind when her son had been taken away. She'd asked Sally to hide them, because she hadn't wanted ever to see them again. For the first time, she wondered what her little boy had been wearing when Martha took him out into the snow to give to the couple who'd been so anxiously waiting for him to be born.

One of the baby's mittens had come off. 'You've lost a mitt, love,' she said softly.

At the sound of her voice, the baby turned his head. He smiled straight at her, shook the rattle, and uttered a contented little gurgle. As Flo stared into the two huge pools of green that were the baby's eyes, she felt a tingling creep down her spine, and knew that he was hers. *Martha had given her baby to Nancy O'Mara!*

'Aaah!' she breathed. Her arms reached down to pick her son out of the pram, when a scrawny yellow hand appeared from nowhere and gripped her right arm like a vice.

'Stay away from him!' Nancy O'Mara hissed. 'Don't think you'll ever get him back because I'll kill him first. He's mine. D'you hear?' Her voice rose hysterically and became a shriek. *'He's mine!'*

3

Flo's feet scarcely touched the pavement as she flew along the narrow streets, her mind in turmoil. It would always hurt, but she'd more or less got used to the idea that her baby was with someone else, but she would never get used to him being with Nancy O'Mara. She'd get him back, she'd claim him as her own.

Her face was on fire, and there were waves of pain like contractions in her belly. She had no idea where she was going, but when she found herself in Clement Street, where Nancy O'Mara lived, she realised she'd known all along. Without even thinking what she was going to say, she knocked at the house next door. A woman in a flowered overall answered almost immediately. She wore a scarf over a head crammed with metal curlers. A cigarette was poking out of the corner of her mouth.

The words, the lies, seem to come to Flo quite naturally. 'I'm looking for me friend, Nancy O'Mara, but she doesn't seem to be in. I haven't seen her in ages and thought I'd check if she still lived in the same place before I came all the way back.'

'She's out shopping with the baby, luv. I expect she'll be along any minute.'

Flo feigned surprise. 'Baby! I never knew she was expecting.'

The woman seemed amenable to an unexpected gossip on the doorstep. She folded her arms and leaned nonchalantly against the door frame. 'To tell you the truth, luv, it came as a shock to everyone. Did you know her feller died on the *Thetis*?'

'Yes. That was the last time I seen her. We went together on the ferry to Cammell Laird's. She didn't say she was in the club.'

'She wouldn't have known then, would she?' The woman took a puff of her cigarette and narrowed her eyes. 'Let's see, when was Hugh born? – February, Tommy'd been gone a few months before she told me that she'd copped one.'

Hugh! She'd called him Hugh! How can I ask if she actually saw Nancy pregnant? Flo was wondering desperately how she could frame such a question, when the woman gave a rather sardonic smile, 'It's funny,' she said, 'but Nancy O'Mara's always kept herself to herself. Hardly a soul knocks on that door, yet you're the second friend who's turned up out the blue. Actually, she looked a bit like you, 'cept she wore glasses. I don't suppose the two of you are sisters?'

'I haven't got a sister.'

'Mind you, she doesn't come so often since Hugh was born.'

'Doesn't she?' Flo said faintly.

'No. Y'see, Nancy was one of those women who hides out of sight when she's pregnant. I've a sister-in-law in Wallasey like that, me poor brother has to do all the shopping. Nancy not having a feller, like, this friend used to get her ladyship's groceries for her.'

'The friend with the glasses?'

' 'Sright, luv.'

'Did she have the baby at home or in the hospital?'

'No one's sure about that, luv. Typical of Nancy, she just appeared with him in a pram one day. Proud as punch she was, pushing him round in the snow.' She laughed coarsely. 'If she hadn't announced all those months ago that she was in the club, I'd have thought she'd pinched him.'

'You don't say.'

'Know Nancy well, do you, luv?' The woman looked quite prepared to talk all day.

'Not all that well. Me brother worked at Cammell Laird's and Nancy and Tommy came to his wedding,' Flo explained. 'I've only seen her a few times since.' She was wondering how to get away.

'Well, she certainly fell on her feet when Tommy kicked the bucket. A bob a week she used to pay in life insurance – I only know because me friend's husband's the collector and we used to joke she was planning on doing away with him one of these days, randy bugger that he was. Oh, look, here comes Nancy now.'

Nancy O'Mara had just turned the corner. She didn't notice Flo and the neighbour because all her attention was concentrated on the occupant of the pram. She was shaking her head, laughing and clucking. Then she stopped, tipped the pram towards her, and said something to the baby inside. She laughed again. Her face wore an expression Flo had rarely seen on anyone before: a radiance so intense that it was as if every wish she'd ever made had come true.

'She don't half dote on that baby,' the woman in the flowered overall murmured.

To the woman's astonishment, Flo turned on her heel and walked away.

When she returned to work more than half an hour late Stella Fritz threw her a questioning look, but Flo wasn't in the mood to make apologies or excuses. Throughout the afternoon, she worked like a madwoman, well making up for the time she'd been late. She swung wildly between sorrow, rage and loathing for the sister who had so comprehensively betrayed her. But the feeling that towered above all others was jealousy. She kept seeing

Nancy's radiantly happy face; happiness caused solely by the fact that she'd been blessed with the gift of Flo's baby. For eight months, Tommy's wife had had him all to herself, nursed him, soothed him, watched him grow; unique, wonderful experiences that had been denied his real mother. There was the oddest feeling deep within Flo, almost akin to making love with Tommy, when she imagined holding her baby to her breast.

'I'll get him back,' she swore, but remembered Nancy's face again and felt uneasy. '*Don't think you'll ever get him back, because I'll kill him first. He's mine!*' the woman had said. The way she'd looked at the baby wasn't quite natural. She loved him too much. Tommy had always claimed she wasn't quite right in the head, and even Martha had called her funny, a Welsh witch, though it hadn't stopped her from handing over her sister's child, Flo thought bitterly. As the afternoon progressed, it became easy to visualise Nancy O'Mara suffocating the tiny boy with that frilly pillow before she'd let Flo have him.

Perhaps she could snatch him from his pram, take him to another town ... but Flo knew there would never be an opportunity to steal him. She'd like to bet a hundred pounds that the baby would never be left outside a shop again. Now Nancy knew that Flo had recognised him, she would hang on to him like grim death.

When her youngest sister came storming in Martha was setting the table. Flo thought she looked furtive and immediately guessed why: Nancy O'Mara had been waiting outside the brewery to relay what had happened that afternoon.

Now that the moment had come to pour out the rage that had been mounting ever since dinner-time, scream about the terrible injustice that had been done, Flo couldn't be bothered. What was the point?

Mam was humming to herself in the back kitchen. 'Is that you, Flo?' she called.

'Yes, Mam.'

'I was just telling our Martha, I ordered a chicken today for Christmas. I couldn't believe they were taking orders so early but, as the butcher said, it's only eleven weeks off.'

'That'll be nice, won't it, Flo?' Martha said brightly. 'Maybe Albert will stay with us this year. You know, Mam,' she called, 'it might be possible to put Albert's name down for a chicken as well.'

'I suppose it might. I didn't think o' that.'

'I won't be living here by Christmas,' Flo said. The words seemed just to come out without any previous thought.

Martha's jaw dropped and she looked frightened. 'Why not?'

'You know darn well why not. Because I can't bear to live in the same house as you another minute.'

Mam came bustling in with plates of stew. 'Sal!' she yelled. 'Dinner's on

469

the table. It's blind scouse,' she explained. 'There wasn't a scrap of meat to be had in the butcher's.' She wiped her hands on her pinny. 'What was that I heard about someone not living here by Christmas?'

'Ask our Martha,' Flo said abruptly. 'I don't want any tea tonight, Mam. It's been an awful day and I feel like a lie-down.'

Sally burst into the room, full of beans because she'd had a letter from Jock that morning. She kissed her sister's cheek. 'Hello, Flo,' she sang.

Sally's evident happiness only emphasised Flo's all-embracing misery, but she gave her a long, warm hug before going upstairs. To her surprise, she only lay down for a few minutes before she fell asleep.

It was pitch dark when she woke up. Someone must have been in, because the curtains were drawn. She was collecting her thoughts, remembering the events of the day, when she became conscious of a movement in the room. As her eyes became used to the dimness, she saw that her mother was sitting on the edge of the double bed watching her sleep.

Mam must have sensed she was awake. 'I've been thinking about your uncle Seumus,' she said softly.

'I didn't know I had an uncle Seumus,' Flo said dully.

'He died long before you were born, shot by the English on the banks of the Liffey. He was smuggling arms for the IRA.'

'How old was he?' Another time Flo would have been interested to discover she'd had a romantic, if disreputable, uncle. Right now, she didn't care.

'Nineteen. I was only ten when he died, but I remember our Seumus as clearly as if he died yesterday. He was a grand lad, full of ideals, though not many people, particularly the English, would have agreed with them.' Mam sighed softly. 'I still miss him.'

'What made you think of him just now?'

'You remind me of him, that's why – hot-headed, never thinking before you act. Oh, Flo!' Mam's voice rose. 'Did it never enter your head the trouble it could cause by sleeping with a married man? God Almighty, girl, we were such a happy family before. Now everything's ruined.'

Flo didn't answer straight away. She recalled the first time she'd been on her way to meet Tommy O'Mara outside the Mystery, and the strange feeling she'd had, as if nothing would ever be the same again. It had turned out to be true, but not in the way she'd imagined. Mam was right. The Clancy family was about to break up. Flo could no longer live in the same house as Martha. 'I'm sorry, Mam,' she whispered. 'I'll leave home, like I said. Things'll be better if I'm not here.'

'Better!' Mam said hoarsely. 'Better! How will they be better without you, girl?' She reached out and stroked Flo's cheek. 'You're me daughter

470

and I love you, no matter what you've done. I just wish I could feel so charitable about our Martha.'

'Did she tell you – about Nancy O'Mara?'

Mam nodded bleakly. 'That was a terrible thing to do. I wish to God I'd known what she was up to. The thing is, I've relied too much on Martha since your dad died. I thought she was strong, but she's the weakest of us all. The only way she can feel important is by meddling in other people's lives. If anyone's going to leave home, I'd rather it be Martha, but I suppose she needs me more than you and Sal ever will, particularly if she doesn't manage to catch poor Albert.'

'Oh, Mam!' Her mother seemed to accept that she was leaving, and Flo felt the future loom up before her, dark and uncertain.

'Come on, girl.' Mam stood up with a sigh. 'There's scouse left if you feel like it. Albert's fire-watching, Sal's at work, and Martha's gone to see Elsa Cameron – Norman's had another bad fall. The little lad's only two, and every time I see him he's covered in bruises.'

'Mam?'

'Yes, luv?' Her mother paused at the door.

'D'you think I could get him back – my baby?'

'No, luv. According to Martha, the birth certificate has Nancy down as the mother and Tommy O'Mara as the dad. Everyone in the street believed she was pregnant. Legally, he's hers, fair and square.'

'But you know that's a lie, Mam,' Flo cried. 'We could go to court and swear he's mine.'

Mam's entire demeanour changed. 'Court! Don't talk soft, Florence Clancy,' she said sharply. 'I've no intention of setting foot inside a court. For one thing, we haven't got the money, and second, there'd be a terrible scandal. It'd be in all the papers and I'd never be able to hold me head up in Liverpool again.'

The raid that night was short and not too heavy. The Clancys usually stayed in bed until the last minute, then when danger seemed imminent, they would go down and sit under the stairs. That night, the all-clear sounded before anyone had stirred, but Flo remained wide awake long afterwards. Where would she live? Would Mam let her have some sheets and blankets and a few dishes? They hadn't got a suitcase, so how would she carry her few belongings?

'Are you awake, Flo?' Martha whispered.

Flo made no sign she'd heard, but Martha persisted, 'I know you're awake because you're dead restless.'

'So what if I am?' Flo snapped.

'I thought we could talk.'

'I've nothing to say to you, Martha. You're nothing but a bloody liar. All that talk about me little boy going to a nice mam and dad!'

'Just listen to me a minute. What I did was only for the best.'

'You mean giving my baby to a Welsh witch was only for the best?' Flo laughed contemptuously.

'Nancy's always longed for a child, but the good Lord didn't see fit to answer her prayers. No one could love that baby more than she does.'

'*I* could! And the good Lord had nothing to do with it. It was because Tommy hadn't touched her that way in years. He told me.'

'I was only thinking of you, luv,' Martha said piteously. 'I wish you'd change your mind about leaving home. Mam's dead upset, and I feel as if it's my fault.'

'It *is* your fault,' Flo spat. It was all she could do not to leap out of bed and beat her sister to a pulp until every ounce of frustration and anger had been spent. 'And you weren't thinking of me, you were thinking of yourself, about your stupid reputation and what people would say.' Her voice rose shrilly. 'You couldn't even arrange the adoption properly, could you? I bet you enjoyed conspiring with Nancy, doing her shopping, being her best friend.' She imagined her sister bustling round to Clement Street, eyes gleaming behind her round glasses, sounding Nancy out, skirting round the matter of Flo's pregnancy until she had established that the woman would jump at the chance of having Tommy's child. Neither had dreamed Flo would recognise her own baby, because neither had given birth to a child of their own. Flo buried her face in her hands and began to rock to and fro. 'I wish I'd had the nerve to leave once I realised I was expecting, I wish I'd married Albert, I wish –'

Martha sat up. 'What was that about Albert?' she asked tersely.

Flo blinked. She hadn't meant to mention Albert. There was still time to pretend she'd meant something else or used the wrong name, but all of a sudden she saw an opportunity to hurt her sister, not nearly so badly as she'd been hurt herself but enough to wound. Still she hesitated, because she'd never intentionally hurt anyone in her life. A hard voice inside her insisted that Martha needed to be taught a lesson. '*She took your baby and gave him to Nancy O'Mara,*' the voice reminded her.

'I've never mentioned it before,' she said lightly, 'but Albert knew about the baby. He offered to marry me there and then. He told me about his wife dying in childbirth, and his little girl, Patsy, who died at the same time. He was going to use his savings to buy furniture for our house. In view of what's happened, I'm dead sorry I turned him down.'

'I don't believe you!'

'Ask him.' Flo yawned and slid under the bedclothes. She didn't sleep another wink that night as she lay listening to her sister's sobs, unsure whether to feel glad or ashamed.

She had less trouble than she had expected in finding somewhere to live. Next day, after asking the twins if they would keep their eyes open for a room to let, Stella Fritz sidled up. 'Why are you leaving home?'

Flo resisted telling her to mind her own business. The woman was her employer and they'd been getting on much better lately. 'I just want to, that's all,' she said.

'Is it, I mean, are you . . . ?' Stella's face grew red. It was obvious she thought Flo might be in the club again.

'I'm leaving because our Martha's driving me dotty. Now our Sal's married, there's only me left to boss around. I'll be twenty-one next year, and I thought it was time I lived on me own.'

'I see. You can have our cellar, if you want. It's never used.'

'Cellar!' Flo had visions of a little dark space full of coal. 'I'm not living in a cellar, thanks all the same.'

Stella shook her head impatiently. 'I call it the cellar, but it's really a basement. It's where the housekeeper used to live in the days when William Square was full of nobs. There's a few odds and ends of furniture, and I can let you have some stuff from upstairs. The walls will need a coat of distemper. Otherwise, it's very clean.'

William Square was becoming a bit seedy, Flo thought when she went to see the basement. There was nothing you could put a finger on, but the gracious houses weren't being maintained as they used to be.

The living room was very big, only partially furnished and rather dark, but there was a separate bedroom, a kitchen, and, wonder of wonders, a bathroom with a lavatory. There was even electric light. Everywhere smelt strongly of damp, but all in all, the place was much grander than anywhere Flo had hoped to find.

'Fritz had the gas fire installed. He used to turn it on now 'n' again during the winter, case the damp spread through the house.'

Flo gazed in awe at the efficient-looking fire. Imagine not having to fetch in coal every day! Imagine just pressing a switch for the light, and sitting on the lavatory indoors!

'I'm not sure if I can afford the rent for a place like this.'

'I haven't said what the rent will be, have I? You'd make your own meals and pay your own gas and electricity – there's separate meters down here.' Stella pursed her lips. 'Five bob a week'll do.'

'But you could get as much as seven and six!'

'I could ask ten bob in this part of town, but you'd be doing me a favour if you take it.'

'What sort of favour?'

Stella ignored her and went to stand at the rear window, which overlooked a rather grubby little yard. 'Just look at that!' she said

473

tonelessly. 'Walls, bricks, dirt! Back in Ireland all we could see from our winders was green fields, trees and sky, with the lakes of Killarney sparkling in the distance. It's like living in a prison here.' She seemed to have forgotten that Flo was there. 'It was something Fritz could never understand, that there's some things more important than money, like good clean air and a sweet, blowing wind. All that concerned him was his bloody laundry.'

Flo twisted her hands together uncomfortably, not sure what to say. The Fritzes had always seemed such a happy couple.

'Oh, well.' Stella turned away. 'The palliasse for the bed's up in the loft, case it got damp. I'll fetch it down, as well as a mat for in front of the fire and a few other bits and pieces. Those chairs aren't too comfortable, but there's not much I can do about it – Fritz used to come down here sometimes for a bit of peace and quiet. Me mam'll give the place a good clean, though if you want it painting you'll have to do it yourself. There's some tins of distemper in the yard. It should be ready to move in by Monday.'

It was awful leaving Sally, but when it came to saying goodbye to her mother, Flo felt cold. Mam hadn't acted as badly as Martha, but Flo had never dreamed she could be so hard, preferring her daughter to go without her beloved baby rather than risk the faintest whiff of scandal.

When she made her departure directly after tea on Monday Albert Colquitt wasn't home. 'Give him my love, Mam,' she said. 'Tell him he's been the best lodger in the world and I'll never forget him.' She was aware of a white-faced Martha across the room. Her sister still looked stunned from their row the other night. Flo had ignored her ever since.

Mam was close to tears. 'For goodness sake, luv, you'd think you had no intention of setting foot in Burnett Street again. You can tell Albert that to his face next time you see him.'

'Tara, Mam. Tara, Sal.' Flo slung the pillowcase containing all her worldly possessions over her shoulder like a sailor. She tried to force her lips to say the words, but they refused to obey, so she left the house without speaking to Martha.

The first few months in William Square were thoroughly enjoyable. Perhaps the favour Stella had mentioned was having Flo look after the little Fritzes – not that the two eldest, Ben and Harry, were little any more. Aged thirteen and fourteen, they were almost as tall as Flo. They invaded the basement flat, all eight of them, on her first night there.

'Have you come to live with us?'

'Did you know our dad?'

'Will you read us a book, Flo?'

'Do you know how to play Strip Jack Naked?' Ben demanded.

'The answer to every question is yes,' Flo grinned. 'Yes, yes, yes, yes. Sit on me knee – what's your name? – and I'll read you the book.'

'I'm Aileen.'

'Come on, then, Aileen.'

From that night on, Flo scarcely had time to have her tea before the children would come pouring down the concrete steps. By then Stella's mother, Mrs McGonegal, had seen enough of her lively grandchildren. She was a withdrawn woman, shy, with a tight, unhappy face. According to Stella, she missed Ireland and its wide open spaces even more than her daughter and couldn't wait to get back. 'And she's petrified of the air raids. She won't come with us to the shelter but crawls under the bed and doesn't come out till the all-clear goes.'

On Sunday afternoons, Flo took the children for walks. They formed a crocodile all the way to the Pier Head and back again. Sometimes, she took the older ones to the pictures, where they saw Will Hay and Tommy Trinder and laughed till they cried. She suspected Harry had a crush on her, so treated him more tenderly than the others, which only made the crush worse.

A week after Flo moved, Sally came to see her and was startled to find the room full of little Fritzes. 'Have you started a school or something?'

'Aren't they lovely?' Flo said blissfully. 'I can't wait for Christmas. I thought I'd be spending it all by meself for the first time in me life, but Stella's invited me upstairs.' She still saw a trace of disapproval in the little Irishwoman's eyes whenever they spoke. 'I'm making decorations for the tree and it's lovely wandering round the shops at dinner-time looking for prezzies for the kids. I'm buying one a week.'

But by the time Christmas arrived, Stella Fritz, her mother, and her eight children had all gone.

After what everyone called 'the raid to end all raids' at the end of November, when for seven and a half long hours the city of Liverpool suffered a murderous attack from the air, a night when 180 people were killed in one single tragic incident, December brought blessed relief. 'I think Mr Hitler is going to let us spend the festive season in peace,' one of the twins remarked.

She spoke too soon. At twenty past six that night, all hell broke loose as wave after wave of enemy bombers unloaded their lethal cargo of incendiary and high-explosive bombs. The city was racked by explosions for nine and a half hours. Fires crackled furiously, the flames transforming the dark sky into an umbrella of crimson. Ambulances and fire engines screamed through the shattered streets.

Would the dreadful night ever end, Flo wondered, as she sat in the public shelter with the two smallest Fritzes on her knee. It hardly seemed possible that William Square could still be standing. As she tried to comfort the children, she was overcome with worry for her family and her little son.

At one point, Stella muttered, 'It's all right for Fritz, isn't it? He's safe and sound on the Isle of Man.'

At last the all-clear sounded at four o'clock in the morning; the long piercing whine had never been so welcome. Stella gathered the children together and made for home. William Square was just round the corner, and in the red glow the houses appeared miraculously intact. A small fire sizzled cheerfully in the central garden area where an incendiary bomb had fallen and several trees and bushes were alight.

'I'll help put the kids to bed,' Flo offered.

'It's all right,' Stella said tiredly, 'you see to yourself, Flo. Forget about opening up on time tomorrer. The twins have got a key – that's if they turn up themselves.' She sighed. 'I wonder how me mammy is?'

When Flo woke it was broad daylight. The birds were singing merrily. She jumped out of bed, intent on getting to work as quickly as possible – not because she was conscientious but she wanted to make sure that Clement and Burnett Streets hadn't been hit. After a cat's lick, she threw on the clothes she'd worn the day before.

Before leaving, she went upstairs to ask after Mrs McGonegal. To her astonishment, Stella Fritz opened the door wearing her best grey coat and an astrakhan hat with a matching grey bow. Her eyes were shining, and she looked happier than Flo had ever seen her, even in the days when she and Mr Fritz had seemed such an ideal married couple. 'I was about to come and see you,' she cried. 'Come in, Flo. We're off to Ireland this afternoon, to me uncle Kieran's farm in County Kerry. Me mam's over the moon. Oh, I know there's no gas or electricity, the privy's in the garden and you have to draw water from a well, but it's better than being blown to pieces in a raid.'

'I'll miss you.' Flo was devastated when she saw the row of suitcases in the hall. It was the little Fritzes she'd really miss. She looked forward to their regular invasion of her room, the walks, the visits to the pictures. Upstairs, she could hear their excited cries as they ran from room to room and supposed they were collecting their favourite possessions to take to Ireland.

'The children are dead upset you're being left behind,' Stella said, looking anything but upset herself, 'but I said to them, "Flo's going to take care of things back here. She'll look after the house." I'll leave you the keys, luv, and if you'd just take a look round once a week, like, make sure everything's all right.'

So, that was the favour. Flo had been installed downstairs so that Mrs Fritz could up and leave whenever she liked, safe in the knowledge that the house would be cared for in her absence. Flo wasn't too bothered that she'd been used. It still meant she'd got a lovely flat dead cheap. But now it appeared she'd have the flat for nothing in return for 'services'. Would she mind running the water in cold weather, save the pipes from icing up, lighting a fire now and then to keep the place aired, opening the windows occasionally so it wouldn't smell musty?

'What's happening to the laundry?' Flo asked, when Stella had finished reeling off instructions.

'You'll be in charge from now on, luv,' Stella said carelessly. 'Take on more women, if you can. I'll write and tell you how to put the money in the bank each week.'

'Right,' said Flo stoutly, as yet more responsibility was heaped on her young shoulders. 'I'll just go upstairs and say tara to the children.'

She was about to leave the room, when Stella came over and gripped her by the arms. Her good humour had evaporated and her face was hard. 'There's something I'd like cleared up before I go.'

'What's that?' Flo asked nervously.

'I know full well why you left the laundry that time. Tell me truthfully, was it my Fritz who fathered your child?'

The question was so outlandish that Flo laughed aloud. 'Of course not! What on earth gave you that idea?'

'I just wondered, that's all.' She smiled and squeezed Flo's arms. 'You're a grand girl, Flo. I'm sorry I was horrible in the past, but everything got on top of me. And I always had me suspicions about you and Fritz. Now, say tara to the kids, and tell them to come down and we'll be on our way.'

It didn't seem possible but the raid that night was even heavier than the one the night before. For more than ten hours, an endless stream of fire-bombs and explosives fell on Liverpool. Flo didn't bother with the shelter, but stayed in bed trying to read a novel she'd found upstairs. She did the same the following night when the raid was even longer. The house seemed no less safe than a brick shelter, and at least she was warm and comfortable and could make a cup of tea whenever she liked.

Each morning, she left promptly for work, although she hadn't had a wink of sleep, and on the way made sure that Clement Street and Burnett Street were still standing.

On Christmas Day she went early to Mass, then spent the morning tidying up after the Fritzes. In their excitement, the children had left clothes and toys everywhere, and there were dirty dishes in the back kitchen. Flo moved from room to room, feeling like a ghost in the big silent house, picking things up, putting them away, gathering together the dirty clothes to wash. She helped herself to a few items for downstairs; a tablecloth, a saucepan, a teapot, more books, and supposed she'd better use up the fresh food that had been left behind – the bacon looked like best back – and Mrs McGonegal had walked miles in search of dried fruit for that Christmas cake.

She went into the living room and sat in the huge bay window beside the tree that she'd helped to decorate. William Square was deserted, though there must be celebrations going on behind the blank windows. As if to confirm that this was so, a motor car drew up a few doors away and a couple with two children got out. The man opened the boot and handed the children several boxes wrapped in red paper. Flo remembered the presents she'd bought for the Fritzes, which were still hidden under her bed, away from their prying eyes. She'd take them to one of them rest centres that looked after people who'd lost everything in the blitz, let some other kids have the benefit.

The house was so quiet, you could almost sense the quietness ticking away like a bomb. They'd just be finishing dinner in Burnett Street and starting on the sherry. Sally had said that Albert would be there, and Jock. No one would be coming to see Flo because they thought she was spending Christmas with the Fritzes. Flo sniffed dejectedly. It would be easy to have a good ould cry, but the situation was entirely of her own making. If she'd turned down Tommy O'Mara when he'd asked her to go for a walk, she'd be part of the group sitting round the table in Burnett Street with Martha rationing out the sherry.

Sherry! There were half a dozen bottles on the top shelf of the larder. She went into the kitchen, collected a bottle, and was about to take everything downstairs when she noticed the wireless in an alcove beside the fireplace. Unlike Albert's battery set, this one had an electric plug. It was also far superior to Albert's. The Bakelite casing had a tortoiseshell pattern, the gold mesh shaped like a fan.

She spent the rest of the day drinking sherry, half reading a book, half listening to the wireless, and told herself she was having a good time. It wasn't until a man with a lovely deep voice began to sing 'Dancing in the Dark', that she had a good ould cry.

On Boxing Day Flo moved the furniture into the middle of the room and distempered the basement a nice fresh lemon. It needed two coats and she was exhausted by the time she had finished and stood admiring her handiwork. The room had brightened up considerably, but the blackout curtains looked dead miserable. She raided upstairs and found several sets of bronze cretonne curtains, which she hung over the blackout. The place was beginning to look like home.

Home! Flo sat on one of the lumpy chairs and put her finger thoughtfully to her chin. She had a home, yes, but she hadn't got a life. The idea of spending more nights alone listening to the wireless made her spirits wilt, and she didn't fancy going to dances or the pictures on her own. Having two sisters not much older than herself meant she'd never gone out of her way to make friends. Bel was the closest to a friend she'd ever had, but Bel wasn't much use up in Scotland. Of course, she could always change her job so that she worked with women of her own age, but she felt honour-bound to keep the business going for Mr Fritz.

'I'll take up voluntary work!' she said aloud. It would occupy the evenings, and she'd always wanted to do something towards the war effort. 'I'll join the Women's Voluntary Service, or help at a rest centre. And Albert said there's even women fire-fighters. I'll make up me mind what to do in the new year.'

Next day, Sally and Jock whizzed in and out, but Flo didn't mention that the Fritzes had gone because Sally might have felt obliged to stay – and you could tell that she and Jock couldn't wait to be by themselves. The day after, Mam came into the laundry to see how she was and Flo said she was fine. She didn't want Mam thinking she regretted leaving home, because she didn't. She might have experienced the most wretched Christmas imaginable, but she'd willingly go through the whole thing again rather than live in the same house as Martha. More than anything, she couldn't stand the idea of anyone feeling sorry for her, though by the time New Year's Eve arrived, Flo was feeling very sorry for herself.

A party was going on across the square, a pianist was thumping out all the latest tunes: 'We'll Meet Again', 'You Were Never Lovelier', 'When You Wish Upon a Star...' In Upper Parliament Street, people could be heard singing at the tops of their voices. There'd been little in the way of raids since Christmas, and no doubt everyone felt it was safe to roam the streets again. She switched on the wireless, but the disembodied voices emphasised rather than eased her sense of isolation. She contemplated going early to bed with a book and a glass of sherry – there were only two bottles left – but ever since she was a little girl she'd always been up and about when the clocks chimed in the New Year. She remembered sitting on Dad's knee, everybody kissing and hugging and wishing each other a happy new year, then singing 'Auld Lang Syne'.

I could gatecrash that party! She smiled at the thought, and a memory surfaced: Josie Driver, God rest her soul, had once mentioned ending up on St George's Plateau on New Year's Eve. 'Everyone was stewed to the eyeballs, but we had a dead good time.'

Flo threw on a coat. She'd go into town. At least there would be other human beings around, even if she didn't know them, and they could be as drunk as lords for all she cared. She hadn't been a hundred per cent sober herself since finding that sherry.

The sky was beautifully clear, lit by a half-moon and a million dazzling stars, so it was easy to see in the blackout. Music could be heard coming from the Rialto ballroom and from most of the pubs she passed. People seemed to be enjoying themselves more than ever this year, as if they had put the war to the back of their minds for this one special night.

When she arrived in the city centre it was far too early, and her heart sank when there wasn't a soul to be seen on St George's Plateau. What on earth shall I do with meself till midnight? she wondered. She began to walk slowly towards the Pier Head, aware that she was the only woman alone. The pubs were still open – they must have got an extension because it was New Year's Eve. She paused outside one. She could see nothing, because the windows had been painted black, and there was a curtain over the door, but inside a girl with a voice like an angel was singing, 'Yours Till the Stars Lose Their Glory', as it had never been sung before.

Flo stared into the black window, seeing Tommy O'Mara's reckless, impudent face gazing back at her, his cap perched on the back of his brown curly hair. Their eyes met and her insides glowed hot. She wanted him, oh, how she wanted him! 'Nobody understood how much we loved each other,' she whispered.

'D'you fancy a drink, luv?'

She turned, startled. A young soldier was standing beside her, twisting his cap nervously in his hands. Lord, he was no more than eighteen, and there was an expression on his fresh, childish face that reflected exactly how she felt herself: a look of aching, gut-wrenching loneliness. She'd like to bet he'd never tried to pick up a girl before, that this was his first time away from home, the first New Year's Eve he hadn't spent within the bosom of his family, and that he was desperate for company. She also saw fear in his eyes. Perhaps he was going overseas shortly and was afraid of being killed. Or perhaps he was just afraid she'd turn him down.

The girl inside the pub stopped singing, everyone thumped the tables, burst into enthusiastic applause, and Flo was hit with an idea that took her breath away. She knew exactly what she could do as her contribution towards the war.

'What a nice idea, luv!' she cried gaily. 'I'd love a drink. Shall we go in here?'

Millie

1

'Are you the Tom who gave her the lamp?' I'd always imagined Flo's friend being as old as Flo herself.

' 'Sright. I got it her in Austria.'

I sat in the armchair, resentful that Tom O'Mara was occupying my favourite spot on the settee, his feet back on the table. 'What were you doing in Austria?'

'Skiing,' he said abruptly.

He looked more the type to prefer a Spanish resort full of bars and fish-and-chip shops, I thought. I said, 'I've always wanted to ski.'

'I didn't know Flo had these.' He ignored my observation and picked up the newspaper cuttings. His fingers were long and slender and I imagined . . . Oh, God! I did my best to hide another shiver. 'That's how me grandad died,' he said, 'On the *Thetis*.'

'Do you know much about it?' I asked eagerly. 'I keep meaning to get a book from the library.'

'Me gran used to pin me ear back about the *Thetis*. She had a book. It's at home. You can have it, if you like. I'll send it round sometime.'

'Thanks,' I said. A pulse in my neck was beating crazily, and I covered it with my hand, worried he'd notice. What on earth was happening to me? Usually, I wouldn't give a man like Tom O'Mara the time of day. I glanced at him surreptitiously and saw that he was staring at the lamp, oblivious of me. I almost felt a nuisance for having interrupted his quiet sojourn in the flat. There was little sign that a party was going on upstairs, just a muffled thumping as people danced, and music that sounded as if it came from some distance away. 'How come you knew, Flo?' I asked.

'She was a friend of me dad's. I knew her all me life.'

'Would it be possible to meet your father? I'd love to talk to him about Flo.'

' "Would it be possible to meet your father?" ' he repeated after me, in such a false, exaggerated impersonation of my accent that I felt my face redden with anger and hurt. 'Christ, girl, you don't half talk posh, like you've got a plum in your gob or something. And you can't talk to me dad about anything. He died fourteen years ago.'

'Is there any need to be so rude?' I spluttered.

Our eyes met briefly. Despite my anger, I searched for a sign that he didn't despise me as much as he pretended, but there was none. He turned away contemptuously. 'People like you make me sick. You were born in Liverpool, yet you talk like the fucking Queen. I think it's called "denying your roots".'

'A day never goes by when I don't remember my roots,' I said shortly. 'And there are people around who could have a great deal of fun with the way you speak.' I stared at him coolly, though cool was the opposite of what I felt. 'I came down for some peace and quiet, not to be insulted. I'd be obliged if you'd go.'

Before he could reply, there was a knock on the window and James called, 'Are you there, Millie?' He must have been looking for me, and someone, Charmian or Herbie, had suggested where I might be.

'Coming!' I stood, aware that Tom O'Mara's eyes had flickered over my body, and felt exultant. My ego demanded that he found me as attractive as I found him, not that it mattered. He was an uncouth lout. Anyway, there was no likelihood of us meeting again. He could keep his book on the *Thetis*, I'd get one for myself. In my iciest voice, I said, 'I've got to go. Kindly put the key on the mantelpiece when you leave. Goodnight.'

For James's sake, I decided reluctantly to give Flo's flat a miss the next afternoon. I couldn't bring myself to ask him to leave after refusing to see him all the previous week. Bel and Charmian would be expecting me, I thought wistfully, though I really should get down to clearing things out – and I still hadn't found out about the rent. I was anxious to speak to the landlord and pay another month before the flat was let to someone else, if that hadn't happened already. One of these days I might turn up and find the place stripped bare. The rent book was bound to be among Flo's papers, but I hadn't even discovered where her papers were kept.

'This is nice.' James sighed blissfully as we lay in bed in each other's arms after making love for the third time. 'An unexpected treat. I thought I'd be sent on my way ages ago.' It was almost three o'clock.

'Mmm.' I was too exhausted to reply. I felt guilty and ashamed. James wouldn't feel quite so happy if he knew that every time I closed my eyes he turned into Tom O'Mara.

He nuzzled my breasts. 'This is heaven,' he breathed. 'Oh, darling, if only you knew how much I love you.'

I stroked his head and said dutifully, 'I think I do.'

'But you never tell me you love me back!' he said sulkily. He pulled away and threw himself on to the pillow.

'James, please,' I groaned, 'I'm not in the mood for this.'

'You're never in the mood.'

I leaped out of bed and grabbed my dressing gown. 'I wish to God you'd give me some space,' I snapped. 'Why do you keep nagging me to say things I don't want to say, to feel things I don't feel?'

'Will you ever say them? Will you ever feel them?' He stared at me forlornly.

I stormed out of the room, 'I can't stand any more. I'm going to have a shower and I'm locking the door. I expect you to be gone when I come out.'

When I emerged from the bathroom fifteen minutes later there was no sign of a contrite James begging forgiveness. No doubt he would telephone or come back later, in which case he wouldn't find me in. I got dressed quickly in jeans and an old sweatshirt and raced down to the car. It was already growing dark and I couldn't wait to be in Flo's flat where I knew I would find the tranquillity I craved.

It wasn't to be, but I didn't mind. I was unlocking the front door when Bel Eddison appeared in her leopardskin jacket. 'I thought I heard you. I've been helping Charmian clear up after the party. We were expecting you hours ago.'

'I was delayed. Come and have some sherry. Why weren't you at the party? I looked everywhere for you.'

'I had another engagement.' She smirked. 'I wouldn't say no to a glass of sherry, but me and Charmian have been finishing off the bottles left over from last night. I'm not exactly steady on me legs.' She staggered into the basement and made herself comfortable on the settee. 'Charmian can't come. Jay's going back to university in the morning and she's still sorting out his washing.'

I turned on the lamp and poured us both a drink. I noticed Tom O'Mara's key on the mantelpiece. As the lamp began slowly to revolve, I said, 'I met the man who gave her that last night.'

'Did you now.' Bel hiccuped.

'He told me how his grandad died, and you said Flo was in love with someone who was lost on the *Thetis*. I wondered if they were one and the same person.'

'I said no such thing, luv,' Bel remarked huffily. 'I said, "Draw your own conclusions," if I remember right.'

'Well, I've drawn them, and that's the conclusion I've reached.' I felt that I'd got one up on Bel for a change.

To my consternation, the old woman's face seemed to shrivel, her jaw sagged, and she whispered hoarsely, 'Flo said, "I don't know what I'm going to do if Tommy's dead. Me life's over. I'll never love another man the way I loved him." The thing is, he was a right scally, Tommy O'Mara, not fit to lick Flo's boots. It sticks in me craw to think she wasted her life on a chap like him.'

I hoped Bel wouldn't be angry, but I had to ask, 'Last night, Tom talked about his gran. Does that mean this Tommy was married when . . . ?'

Bel nodded vigorously. 'She was the last girl in the world to go out with a married man, but he spun her a tale. He was such a charmer. He told *me* he was single.'

'You mean, you went out with him, too?' I gasped.

'Yeh.' Bel grimaced. 'I never let on to Flo, it would have killed her, but I'd been out with him twice just before the *Thetis* went down. Some men aren't happy unless they've got a string of women hankering after them. Tom O'Mara's another one like that. He was a nice lad once, but he's grown up without his grandad's charm. A woman would be mad to have anything to do with him.'

'I agree about the lack of charm. I found him very rude.' I would have liked to know more about Tom O'Mara, but Bel might have thought I was interested when I definitely wasn't. Well, I told myself I wasn't. 'Would you like some tea or coffee to sober you up?' I asked instead.

'A cup of coffee would be nice, but only if it's the instant stuff. I can't stand them percolator things. Flo's got one somewhere.'

For the next few hours we chatted amiably. I told her about my job and my problems with James, and she told me about her three husbands, describing the second, Ivor, in hilarious detail. Before she left, I asked where Flo had kept her papers.

'In that pull-down section of the sideboard, the old one. Flo called it her bureau. You'll have your work cut out sorting through that lot. I think she kept every single letter she ever got.'

Bel was right. When I opened the bureau I found hundreds, possibly thousands, of pieces of paper and letters still in their envelopes, crammed in every pigeonhole and shelf. I felt tempted to close it again and snuggle on the sofa with sherry and a book, but I'd been irresponsible for far too long. I sighed and pulled out a thick wad of gas bills addressed to Miss Florence Clancy, which, to my astonishment, went back as far as 1941, when the quarterly bill was two and sevenpence.

I wondered what the flat had looked like then – and wasted ages envisaging a young Flo, living alone and pining after Tommy O'Mara. Perhaps that's what the row with Gran had been about, Flo going out with a married man. Gran was incredibly straitlaced, though it didn't seem serious enough to make them lifelong enemies.

The cardboard boxes I'd brought were in the bathroom so I fetched one and threw in the bills. Then I almost took them out again. Flo had kept them for more than half a century and it seemed a shame to chuck them away. I pulled myself together, and more than fifty years of electricity bills quickly joined them. I decided I deserved a break, made coffee and helped myself to a packet of Nice biscuits. On my way to the settee, I jumped when something clattered through the letterbox.

It was a book: *The Admiralty Regrets*. I opened the door, but whoever had delivered it had disappeared.

Fiona was leaning against the railings, smoking. 'Hi,' I said awkwardly.

She glared at me malevolently through the railings. 'Sod off,' she snarled.

Shaken, I closed the door, and put the book aside to read later. I returned to the bureau with my coffee and continued to throw out old papers. One thick wedge of receipts was intriguing. From a hotel in the Isle of Man, they were made out to a Mr and Mrs Hoffmansthal, who had stayed there for the weekend almost every month from 1949 until 1975. I decided to ask Bel about them, then changed my mind. Bel had mentioned that Flo went on retreat to a convent in Wales once a month. Perhaps Flo had kept a few secrets from her old friend and I certainly wasn't about to reveal them after all this time. I threw away the receipts with a sigh. How I'd love to know what lay behind them, and especially the identity of Mr Hoffmansthal.

The contents of the bureau were considerably diminished by the time the unimportant papers had been discarded. All that remained were letters, which I had no intention of throwing away until I'd read every one. Some looked official, big fat brown envelopes, the address typed, but most were handwritten. I tugged out a wad of letters held together with an elastic band. The top one bore a foreign stamp. It had been posted in 1942.

It dawned on me that I hadn't found the rent book that had prompted my search, or a pension book. Flo might have had them in her handbag, which, like Gran, she had kept hidden. After a fruitless search through all the cupboards, I found what I was looking for under the bed, where dust was already beginning to collect.

I took the black leather bag into the living room and emptied the contents on to the coffee table. A tapestry purse fell out, very worn and bulging with coins, followed by a set of keys on a Legs of Man keyring, a wallet, shop receipts, bus tickets, cheque book, metal compact, lipstick, comb . . . I removed a silver hair from the comb and ran it between my fingers. It was the most intimate thing belonging to Flo I'd ever touched, actually part of her. The room was very still, and I almost felt as if she was in the room with me. Yet I wasn't scared. Even when I opened the compact to compare the hair with mine in the mirror, half expecting to see Flo's face instead of my own, I didn't feel frightened, more a comfortable sensation of being watched by someone who cared about me. I knew I was being silly because Flo and I had only set eyes on each other once, and then briefly.

'One day my hair will turn that colour,' I murmured, and wondered where I would be and who I would be with, should I live to be as old as Flo. For the first time in my life, I thought it would be nice to have children, so that a strange woman I hardly knew wouldn't sort through my possessions when I died.

I came back to earth, told myself to be sensible. The cheque book meant that, like Gran since she'd been robbed, Flo's pension had probably been paid straight into the bank. I flicked through the stubs to see if cheques had been made out for rent, but most appeared to be for cash, which was no help. I would have asked Charmian for the landlord's address, but glancing at my watch, I saw it was past midnight.

Good! It was a perfect excuse to sleep in Flo's comfortable bed again.

One by one, I returned the things to the bag, glancing briefly in the wallet, which held only a bus pass, a cheque guarantee card, four five-pound notes, and a card listing a series of dental appointments two years ago. I was putting the bag away in the bureau when there was a knock on the door.

James! He'd been to my flat, waited, and when I didn't arrive he had guessed where I would be. I wouldn't let him in. If I did, he'd never keep away and this was the only place where no one could reach me. It was one of the reasons why I always seemed to forget to bring my mobile phone. I fumed at the idea of him invading what I'd come to regard as my sanctuary.

'Who is it?' I shouted.

'Tom O'Mara.'

I stood, transfixed, in the middle of the room, my stomach churning. I knew I should tell him what I'd intended to tell James, to go away, but common sense seemed to have deserted me, along with any will-power I might have had. Before I knew what I was doing, I'd opened the door.

Oh, Lord! I'd thought this only happened in books – turning weak at the knees at the sight of a man. The jacket of his black suit was hanging open, and the white collarless shirt, buttoned to the neck, gave him a priestlike air. Neither of us spoke as he followed me inside, with that sensually smooth walk I'd noticed the night before, bringing with him an atmosphere charged with electricity. I patted my hair nervously, aware that my hand was shaking. He was carrying a plastic bag that smelt of food. My mouth watered and I realised I was starving.

He held it out. 'Chinese, from the takeaway round the corner. Joe said there was someone in when he came with the book so I thought I'd see if you were still here on me way home.'

'What's this in aid of?' I gulped.

'Peace-offering,' he said abruptly. 'Flo would have slagged me off for behaving the way I did last night. No one can help the way they speak, you and me included.'

'That's charitable of you, I must say.' I'd worked hard to get rid of my accent, and felt annoyed that Tom O'Mara seemed to regard the lack of one as an affliction.

'Shall we forget about last night and start again?' He bagged my favourite spot on the settee and began to unpack the cartons of food. 'You're Millie, I'm Tom, and we're about to have some nice Chinese nosh – I don't know if you want to use these plastic forks, Flo used to fetch proper ones, and she'd warm plates up in the microwave. She didn't like eating out of boxes.'

I hurried to do as I was told, sensing that he was accustomed to giving orders, when he shouted, 'Fetch a corkscrew and some glasses while you're at it. I've got wine.'

'It's red,' he said, when I obediently brought everything in. 'I'm an ignorant bugger and I don't know if that's what you have with this sort of food.'

'Neither do I.' James always knew what sort of wine to order but I'd never taken much notice.

'I thought you'd be one of those superior sort of people who know about such things.' He shared out the food on to the plates.

'And I thought we'd made a fresh start.'

'You're right. Sorry!' His smile took my breath away. His face softened and he looked charmingly boyish. I could understand what the nineteen-year-old Flo must have seen in his grandfather.

'Did you and Flo do this often?' I asked, when he handed me my plate.

'Once a week. Mondays, usually, when I finish work early.'

'Where do you work?'

'Minerva's. It's a club.'

I'd heard of Minerva's, but had never been there. It had a terrible reputation as a hang-out for gangsters and a source of hard drugs. Scarcely a week passed when there wasn't something in the *Echo* or on local TV about the police raiding it in search of a wanted criminal or because a fight had broken out. As I sipped the rich, musky wine, I wondered what Tom O'Mara did there.

'The wine's nice,' I said.

'So it should be. It's twenty-two quid a bottle at the club.'

'Wow!' I gasped. 'All that much to have with a takeaway!'

He dismissed this with a wave of the hand. 'It didn't cost me anything, I just helped meself.'

'You mean you stole it?'

He managed to look both amused and indignant. 'I'm past the stage of nicking things, thanks all the same. Minerva's belongs to me. I can take anything I like.'

I felt a chill run through my body. He was almost certainly a criminal – he might have been in prison for all I knew. If he owned Minerva's, it meant he was involved in the drugs trade and other activities that didn't bear thinking about. But the awful thing, the really appalling thing, was that he became even more desirable in my eyes. I was horrified. I'd never dreamed it was in me to be attracted to someone like Tom O'Mara. Perhaps it was something passed down in the blood: Flo had wasted her life on a scally who, according to Bel, wasn't fit to lick her boots, Mum had fallen for my loathsome father. Now I found myself weak at the knees over possibly the most unsuitable man in the whole of Liverpool. I thought about James, who loved me and was worth ten Tom O'Maras, and for a moment wished it really had been him at the door.

I put my plate on the table and Tom said, 'You haven't eaten much.'

'I've eaten half,' I said defensively. 'I haven't a very big appetite.' He'd already finished, the plate scraped clean.

'I tell you what, let's have some music.' He went over to the record player and lifted the lid.

'Flo's only got the one record.'

'She's got a whole pile in the sideboard. Neil Diamond and Tony Bennett were her favourites. I got her this last year when she started humming it non-stop. She'd play it over and over.' The strains of 'Dancing in the Dark' began to fill the room. 'She said something once, she was half asleep, about dancing in the dark with someone in the Mystery years ago.'

'The Mystery?' I wondered if it had ever crossed his mind that the 'someone' might well have been his grandad.

'Otherwise known as Wavertree playground. There's a sports stadium there now.' He removed his jacket, saying, 'It's hot in here,' and I felt my insides quiver at the sight of his long, lean body, his slim waist.

'You were very fond of Flo?'

'I wasn't just fond of her, I loved her,' he said simply. 'I dunno why 'cos she weren't a relative, but she was more like a gran than me real one. Christ knows what I'd have done without Flo when me dad died.'

Surely he couldn't be so bad if he'd thought so much of Flo. Bing Crosby was singing and I had no idea why I should have a feeling that history was repeating itself when Tom held out his hand and said with a grin, 'Wanna dance, girl?'

I knew I should refuse. I knew I should just laugh and shrug and say, 'No, thanks, I'm not in the mood,' because I also knew what would happen when he took me in his arms. And if it did, if it did, the day might come when I would regret it. The trouble was, I had never before wanted anything so much. My body was crying out for him to touch me.

The lamp continued its steady progress, round and round, casting its dark, blurred shadows on the low ceiling of the room, and I stared at the shifting patterns, looking for the girl in the red coat. Tom O'Mara came across the room, put his hands on my waist and lifted me out of the chair. For a moment I resisted, then threw all caution to the wind. I slid my arms around his neck and kissed him. I could feel him, like a rock, pressing against me. My veins seemed to melt when our exploring tongues met, while his hard, eager hands stroked my back, my waist, my hips, burning, as if his fingers were on fire.

Still kissing, swaying together almost imperceptibly to the music, we moved slowly towards the bedroom. Outside the door, in the little cold lobby, our lips parted, and Tom cupped my face in his hands. He stared deep into my eyes, and I knew that he wanted me every bit as much as I wanted him. Then he opened the door, where the bed with its snowy white cover was waiting, and led me inside. By now, I felt weak with longing, yet once again I hesitated. There was still time to back out, to say no. But Tom O'Mara was kissing me again, touching me with those hot fingers, and I couldn't have said no to save my life. He kicked the door shut behind us.

In the living room, 'Dancing in the Dark' played through to a glorious crescendo. When it finished, I imagined, in a little corner of my mind, the needle raising itself automatically and the arm returning to nestle in the metal groove. There was silence in Flo Clancy's flat, though I knew that the lamp continued to cast its restless shadows over the walls.

I was woken by Tom O'Mara stroking my hip. 'You should have eaten the rest of that meal,' he whispered. 'You could do with a bit more flesh on you.'

Turning languorously into his arms, I began to touch him, but he caught my hand. 'I've got to go.'

'Is there nothing I can do to keep you?' I said teasingly.

'Nothing.'

He got out of bed and began to get dressed. I could have kept James in bed if the building was on fire. I lay, admiring his will-power and his slim brown limbs. His skin was as slippery as polished marble, the hollow of his neck as smooth as an egg. There was a tattoo on his chest, a heart with an arrow through it, and a woman's name I couldn't make out. I'd always thought tattoos repulsive, though it was a bit late in the day to remember that. 'What's the hurry?' I enquired.

'It's nearly seven o'clock. Me wife doesn't mind me staying out all night, but she likes me home for breakfast.'

'Mightn't it have been a good idea to mention you had a wife last night?' I said mildly. I wasn't the least bit shocked because I didn't care. We had no future together.

He paused while pulling on his trousers. 'Would it have stopped you?'

'No, but it might have stopped some women.'

'Then those sort of women should ask before leaping into bed with a bloke they hardly know.'

I made one of Bel's faces. 'You sound as if you disapprove of women who sleep with strange men.'

'It so happens that I do.'

'But you don't disapprove of men who do the same?' I laughed, pretending outrage.

'Blokes take what's on offer.' He was buttoning his shirt.

I eased myself to a sitting position. 'Do you know?' I said thoughtfully, 'I truly can't remember offering myself last night.'

'You didn't, but it's different with me and you, isn't it?'

'Is it?'

He sat on the bed. 'You know it is.' He held my face in both hands and kissed me soundly on the lips. I put my arms around his neck and kissed him back, greedy for him, and determined to keep him if I could, even if it meant I'd be late for work.

'I said I've got to go.' His voice was steely. He removed my arms none too gently and went over to the door.

'Oh, well,' I sighed exaggeratedly, 'see you around sometime, Mr O'Mara.' I was still teasing, though my heart was in my mouth, dreading he might take me at my word and say, 'See you too, Millie.'

'What the hell do you mean by that?' I was taken aback by the anger in his green eyes. The muscles were taut in his slender neck. 'Is that all it was to you, a night's shag?'

'You know it wasn't.' I blushed, remembering the night, so different from any I'd ever known. I looked at him directly. 'It was magic.'

I could have sworn he breathed a sigh of relief. 'In that case, I'll be round tonight, about twelve.' He left abruptly. A few seconds later, the front door opened and he shouted, 'It was magic for me, too.'

I got out of bed, removed the crucifix, the statues, and holy pictures off the wall, and put them in the drawer of Flo's bedside cabinet.

'You've been raiding your aunt's wardrobe again,' George said, when I arrived at Stock Masterton. 'I can tell.'

'Is it so obvious?' I stared down at the long, straight black skirt and demure white blouse with a pointed collar.

'Only because you don't usually wear those sort of clothes. You look very appealing. I could eat you for lunch.'

I tried to think of a put-down remark in reply, but couldn't.

George went on, 'That young man of yours must have had the same idea. You've got a love bite on your neck.' He sighed dolefully. 'It's called a hicky in America. I can't remember when I last gave a girl one. I must have been in my teens. Those were the days, eh?' He hooted.

Embarrassed, I went over to my desk and switched on the computer. Diana had just arrived. 'How's your father?' I asked.

'He seemed much better over the weekend,' Diana replied. Her face had lost the tense lines of the previous week. 'In fact, we had a lovely time. He told me all about his experiences during the war. I knew he'd been in Egypt in military intelligence, but I never realised he'd been in so many dangerous scrapes. He was very much a James Bond in his day.' She took an envelope from her bag. 'I managed to finish those notes I mentioned. Did George tell you his offer for the shop in Woolton has been accepted? We could be open by the new year.'

My own report was at home but didn't seem all that important any more. Nevertheless, I had to go back to the flat to collect a few things if I was going to stay at Flo's so I'd pick it up then.

'I'll give this to George.' Diana winked conspiratorially and hurried into his office. She seemed rather pathetic, I thought, yet until recently I'd wanted the job in Woolton just as much, which meant I'd been just as pathetic myself. Now, I didn't care.

The realisation surprised me. I stared at my blurred reflection in the computer screen and wondered what had changed. Me, I decided, though I had no idea why. I felt confused but, then, I'd felt confused throughout my life. Perhaps it was Flo who'd made me see things differently. Perhaps. I wish I'd known her, I thought wistfully, remembering the warm, comfortable sensation I'd had in the flat last night, as if she had been there with me. I had a feeling I could have talked to her about stuff I wouldn't dream of telling anyone else.

And there was Tom O'Mara. I cupped my chin in my hands and my reflection did the same. I'd been a married woman for four years, and there'd been other men before James, yet it was as if I'd made love for the very first time. My body had never felt so alive, so *used* in the most gratifying way. I held my breath and felt my scalp prickle when I thought about the things that Tom O'Mara and I had done to each other.

'Millie! *Millie!*'

Darren thumped my desk, and I became aware that June was shouting, 'Wake up, sleepyhead. There's a call for you.'

It was the Naughtons again. They'd had details of another house, which sounded ideal, this time in Crosby. I arranged to meet them there at noon, though felt sure it would be another waste of time. Crosby was close to Blundellsands, which meant I could call at home afterwards.

It felt strange going into my flat, as if I'd been away for weeks not merely twenty-four hours. It smelt dusty and unused, long empty. I opened the windows of the balcony to air the place, and had a shower. There was a bruise beneath my breast and another on my thigh and I wondered if Tom O'Mara also bore scars of our night together. I covered the bite on my neck with makeup. The red light was flickering on the answering-machine.

My mother's tearful voice announced that Declan had lost his job. 'He was sacked ages ago. Your dad only found out by accident off some chap in the pub. Of course he's livid, called poor Declan all the names under the sun. And, Millicent, I'd like to talk to you about Alison . . . Oh, I'll have to ring off now, luv. Your dad's on his way in.'

I waited. There was no message from James. I was glad, but thought about calling him at work to make sure he was all right. In the end, I decided not to. It might encourage him to think I cared, which I did but not nearly enough to satisfy him. I reversed the tape, packed a few clothes and toiletries in a bag, along with the folder containing the report. As I'd gone to the trouble of writing it, it wouldn't hurt to let George take a look.

He was working alone in his glass cubicle when I got back, so I took the folder in. 'You'll never guess what that bloody woman's gone and done,' he barked immediately he saw me.

I pretended to back away, frightened. 'What woman?' I couldn't recall seeing George so angry before.

'That Diana bitch. She's only given me a list of reasons why I should open the new office! I couldn't believe my eyes when I read it. Does she seriously imagine I haven't thought the whole thing through myself? Jesus Christ, Millie, I've been in the estate-agency business for over thirty years. I know it back to front, yet an idiot woman with a stupid degree thinks she knows better than I do.'

'She was only being helpful, George.'

'More likely after the boss's job,' he sneered. 'As if I'd give it her, the pushy little cow. The job's Oliver's. He never makes a decision without referring to me first, which is the way I like it.' He grinned. 'I guess I must be a control freak.'

'Did you say anything to Diana?'

'I bawled her out and she left for lunch in tears.'

'Oh, George!' I shook my head. 'You'll feel sorry about that tomorrow.' A few weeks ago I would have been as pleased as punch at Diana's fall from grace, but now, for some strange reason, I felt nothing but pity for the woman.

'I know.' He sighed. 'I'm a disagreeable sod. I'll apologise later, though it was still a stupid, tactless thing for her to do.' He nodded at the folder in my hand. 'Is that for me?'

'No. I just came to tell you about the Naughtons. Apparently, the draining board was on the wrong side.'

Later that afternoon, I fed my report into the shredder. I'd never stood the remotest chance of getting the manager's job, and it made me feel acutely embarrassed to have thought that I had.

Tom O'Mara didn't arrive at midnight as he'd promised. An hour later he still wasn't there. I lay on the settee, half watching an old film, not sure what to think. Had I been stood up? Maybe he'd had second thoughts. Maybe he'd meant tomorrow night. I tried to work out how I'd feel if I never saw him again. Hurt, I decided, hurt, insulted and angry, but definitely not heartbroken, possibly a little bit relieved. However, right now relief wasn't uppermost in my mind. I wasn't in love with Tom and never would be, yet my body ached for him and I could have sworn he felt the same. It was easy to while away the time imagining his lips touching every part of me. My pulse began to race, and I felt hot at the thought. 'Please come, Tom,' I prayed. 'Please!'

At some time during the night I fell asleep, and was woken when it was barely daylight by a kiss and the touch of a hand stroking me beneath my dressing-gown.

'How did you get in?' I whispered.

'Took me key back off the mantelpiece, didn't I?'

'You're late,' I yawned. 'Hours late.' It was delicious just lying there, feeling sleepy, yet conscious of his exploring hands.

'There was trouble at the club, and I couldn't ring. Flo always flatly refused to have a phone. How do I undo this knot?'

'I'll do it.' I unfastened the belt and he pulled the robe away.

'Anyroad, I'm here now,' he said, 'and that's all that matters.'

He was kneeling beside me, his face hard with desire. He would never say soft, tender things as James did, yet this only made me want him more. I held out my arms. 'Yes, Tom, that's all that matters.'

2

Time seemed to stand still; it had lost its meaning, all because of Tom O'Mara. I returned to my flat on Sunday morning to collect more clothes and take a shower – bathing at Flo's was like bathing in the Arctic – and found an increasingly frantic series of messages from my mother on the answering-machine. It was the last Sunday in October and it had completely slipped my mind.

'Don't forget, luv, we're expecting you for dinner on Sunday.'

'Why don't you ever ring back, Millicent? I hate these damn machines. It's like talking to the wall.'

'Have you gone away, Millicent?' the voice wailed fretfully. 'You might have told me. I'd ring your office if I didn't think it would get you into trouble.'

As usual, I felt a mixture of guilt and annoyance. I phoned home immediately. 'I'm sorry, Mum,' I said penitently. 'You were right, I've been away.' I hated lying to my mother, but how could I possibly tell her the truth? 'I know I should have called, but it was a spur-of-the-moment thing, and I was so busy when I got there, I forgot about everything. I'm sorry,' I said again, assuming this would be enough to satisfy her, but apparently not.

'When you got where?' she demanded.

I said the first place I could think of. 'Birmingham.'

'What on earth were you doing there?'

'George sent me.'

'Really!' Mum sounded so impressed that I hated myself even more. 'He must think highly of you, sending you all the way to Birmingham.'

To please her, I took particular pains with my appearance. I wore a cherry red suit with a black T-shirt underneath. To assuage my guilt, and make amends for lying, I stopped on the way to Kirkby and bought a bunch of chrysanthemums and a box of Terry's All Gold.

'You shouldn't have, luv,' Mum protested, though she looked gratifyingly pleased.

When we sat down to lunch, Flo's flat immediately became the main topic of conversation.

'I thought you'd have it well sorted by now,' Mum remarked, when I claimed there were still loads of things to do.

'I only have Sundays free, don't I?' I said defensively. 'You wouldn't believe the amount of stuff Flo had. It's taking ages.'

'Your gran keeps asking about it. I said you'd call in and see her on your way home.'

I groaned. 'Oh, Mum, you didn't!'

'She is your gran, luv. She's desperate for a little keepsake, something to remind her of Flo. A piece of jewellery would be nice.'

Flo mightn't be too pleased at the idea of anything of hers going to someone she'd specifically not wanted at her funeral. As for jewellery, I hadn't come across any so far. Everything's becoming incredibly complicated, I thought worriedly.

Things became even more complicated when Declan asked, 'How's James?'

'He's fine,' I said automatically, only then realising it was a whole week since I'd seen him, and he hadn't called once. Perhaps he'd decided being chucked out was the last straw. I dismissed him from my mind – there was already enough to think about – and said to Declan, 'Have you done anything about college?'

My father choked on his steak and kidney pudding. 'College? Him? You must be joking.'

'I think it's a very good idea,' Colin said quietly. 'If he took an engineering course, he could come and work for me. I could do with another pair of hands.'

'He'd prefer something different, wouldn't you, Declan?' I was determined to air the matter of Declan's future because I had a feeling he would never have the courage to do it himself. 'Something artistic.' I thought it wise not to mention fashion design or my father might choke to death before our very eyes.

My mother regarded him warily. 'It wouldn't hurt, would it, Norman, for our Declan to go to college? After all, Millicent went to night school and look where it got her.'

While Trudy and Colin did the dishes, I wandered down to the bottom of the garden with Scotty. The little dog jumped up and down like a yo-yo in front of me. I eased myself through the gap in the hedge that separated the main garden from the compost heap, and sat down on an enormous hump of hard soil, cuddling Scotty. This was the only place we had been allowed to play when we were little: our father wouldn't allow us on the lawn. I remembered the day when five-year-old Trudy had broken a window in the greenhouse with a tennis ball. She'd been so petrified she was literally shaking with fright and couldn't stop crying. 'He'll kill me when he gets home,' she sobbed hysterically.

Then I'd had the brilliant idea of pretending someone from the houses behind had done it. We exchanged the ball, which our father would have recognised, for a stone, and claimed ignorance when the broken pane was discovered. It was one of the few crimes we ever got away with.

'Penny for them!' Trudy murmured, as she squeezed through the hedge and sat beside me. Scotty, fast asleep, stirred and licked my knee.

'I won't say what I was thinking about. It would only depress you.'

'It was me smashing that window, I bet. I always remember when I come down here. Even now I break out in a sweat.'

I put an arm around her shoulder. 'How's things, Sis?'

Trudy shrugged. 'Okay. I'm growing a hair on me chin. See?'

'You've always had that,' I said. 'It appeared when you were about fourteen.'

'Did it? I've never noticed before. It must be the glasses.'

'What glasses?'

'I need glasses for close work, reading and painting. I've had them for months. I thought you knew.'

'No,' I said sadly. 'There was a time when we knew every single little thing about each other, but now . . .' In the darkness of our room, when our father was out, we'd whisper our innermost secrets to each other.

'Sorry, Sis.'

'Don't be.' I squeezed Trudy's shoulder. 'I'm not complaining. There's all sorts of stuff you don't know about me.'

'Such as?'

'That would be telling.' I grinned enigmatically.

Trudy pulled a face. 'Actually, there's things I can't even talk about with Colin.'

'Would you like to talk about them now?'

'No, Sis. It would take much too long.'

I watched a bee, well past its prime, buzz weakly on a dandelion. I was conscious of feeling far less fraught than I usually did on these occasions. Today hadn't been nearly as bad as other Sundays. Instead of constant reminders of the way things used to be, I was preoccupied with how things were now.

Mum appeared in the gap in the hedge, looking flustered, though she rarely looked anything else. 'You'll get your lovely clothes all dirty sitting on that soil.' She pushed her bulky frame through the sharp twigs and, ignoring her own advice, plopped down heavily beside us. Immediately Scotty jumped off my knee and on to hers. 'I wanted to talk to you both about Alison.' She began to pull at a weed. 'I found Oxford on the atlas,' she said hesitantly. 'It's almost as far as London. I was scared enough driving to Skem so I'll never make it that far in the car – that's if your dad would let me have it – and I couldn't afford to go every week by train.'

'I'll pay your fare, Mum,' I offered at the same time as Trudy said, 'Colin and me will take you.'

'No.' She shook her head. 'I don't want to be dependent on other people. Alison's me daughter. I don't love her any better than I do you and our Declan, but she needs me more than you lot ever will.'

It seemed to me that Alison didn't need anyone in particular, but perhaps the faithful figure of her mother appearing every Sunday provided a sense of security, a vague feeling that she was special in at least one person's eyes. On the other hand, perhaps the need was the other way round, and it was Mum who'd miss Alison. One day, Declan was bound to leave home and Alison, detached and indifferent, would be the only one of her children left. But, somewhat cruelly, fate had decreed she'd be miles away in Oxford.

'I want her to stay with the St Osyth Trust,' Mum was saying. 'They know and understand her. I'd have her home like a shot, but that's out the question with your dad. He's ashamed of her, for one thing, and he's no patience with her funny little ways. So I've decided to move to Oxford.'

'What!' Trudy and I cried together. It was the last thing we'd expected to hear.

'Shush!' She glanced nervously through the hedge, but the garden was empty. Her husband was inside playing with his beloved grandchildren, and Colin was on guard.

'You mean you'd actually leave him?' I gasped. Why hadn't she thought of this years ago when we were all being beaten regularly for the least little thing, and sometimes for nothing at all?

Mum said huskily, 'I should have left him a long time ago, I know, but it never crossed me mind. I always thought that if I became a better wife he'd stop hitting us, but the harder I tried, the worse he got. In the end, perhaps I was punch-drunk or something, but it all seemed quite normal.' Her voice broke. Scotty opened his eyes and looked at her curiously. 'I could never imagine things being any other way. I'm sorry, but at least I got Alison out the road, didn't I?'

'Don't rake over the past, Mum,' Trudy said softly. 'About Oxford, I don't know what to say.'

'Nor me,' I said, and then, meaning it with all my heart, 'I'll miss you, Mum.'

She dug me in the ribs with her elbow. 'Don't talk daft, Millicent. I only see you once a month as it is, and you're never there when I phone. I talk to that silly machine more than I do you.'

'I'd miss your messages,' I cried. 'Honest, Mum, I really would.' Suddenly I felt that there would be a dreadful hole in my life.

'I could still ring and leave messages.' She chuckled.

'Yes, but it wouldn't be the same if you weren't around.'

Trudy was frowning, as if she, too, was trying to contemplate a future that had so unexpectedly changed. 'Melanie and Jake would be lost without their gran,' she said, close to tears.

'They'll still have their grandad,' Mum said comfortably. Behind her back, Trudy grimaced at the idea that she'd still bring her children to Kirkby if Mum wasn't there.

'I'll get meself a full-time job,' Mum was saying, 'and look for a bedsit close to the home so's I can see Alison every day.'

'It's a big step, Mum,' Trudy said. 'Getting a job won't be easy at your age, and bedsits might cost the earth in Oxford.'

'Then I'll go on social security or whatever it's called these days,' Mum said serenely. 'I've never claimed a penny in me life, yet I've always paid me stamps.' She beamed at us. 'I feel better now I've talked to you two. Not a word about this to your dad, mind.'

Trudy shuddered. 'I wouldn't like to be in your shoes when you tell him. Would you like me and Colin to be here, give you moral support, like?'

'I don't need moral support, luv. I'll tell him to his face, and if he doesn't like it, he can lump it. Anyroad, it's months off yet.'

'Grandma,' Melanie piped, from the other side of the hedge.

'I'm here, sweetheart.' Mum scrambled to her feet, dislodging an indignant Scotty.

'Grandad said he wants a cup of tea.'

'Tell Grandad to make his own tea,' Trudy said curtly.

'No, no, don't say that, Melanie, whatever you do.' A stubby branch caught her cheek, drawing blood, as she frantically pushed her way back through the hedge.

Trudy glanced at me meaningfully. 'I wonder if she'll do it?'

I remembered the photo of Flo taken in Blackpool, the still pretty face, the lovely smile, when Gran opened the door. Age hadn't been as kind to Martha Colquitt as it had to her sister. I could never remember her smiling much, or looking anything but old. Her face was creased into a permanent scowl, and behind the severe, black-framed spectacles with their thick lenses, her eyes were unfriendly, disapproving. Her best feature was her hair, thick and silvery, which she kept in neat waves under a fine, almost invisible net.

'Oh, it's you,' she said sourly. 'Come in. I might as well not have grandchildren, I never see them.' I followed her into the spotlessly clean, over-furnished room, which stank of a mixture of cigarettes, disinfectant and the vile-smelling ointment she rubbed on her rheumatic shoulder.

'Well, I'm here now,' I said brightly. I would have come more often, or so I told myself, if the welcome was ever warm, but even my kindhearted mother found visiting Gran an ordeal, fetching her weekly shopping out of a sense of duty.

The television beside the fireplace was on without the sound. Gran turned it off. 'Nothing on nowadays but rubbish.'

I sat down in an overstuffed armchair. 'Mum said to remind you there's an old film on later that you might like. It's a musical with Beryl Grable.'

'Betty Grable,' Gran corrected irritably. Her faculties were sharper than those of most people half her age, her memory for names and faces prodigious. 'I might watch it, I'll see. It depends on how long you stay. Do you want a cup of tea?'

'Yes, please,' I said politely.

Gran disappeared into the kitchen and I went over to the window. I'd lived in this flat until I was three, and the view from the fifth floor was one of the few things I could remember clearly. It couldn't be called magnificent: a shopping precinct, the Protestant church, miles and miles of red-brick houses, with a glimpse of flat fields in the far distance, a few trees, but it seemed to change from day to day. The sky was never the same, and I always seemed to glimpse a tree or a building I hadn't noticed before. It was certainly better than no view at all, but Gran felt the need to block it out with thick lace curtains, although no one could see inside except from a passing helicopter.

The curtains had been drawn back a few inches, as if Gran had been looking out, which, apart from going to Mass on Sundays, was all she had to do: she looked out of the window, watched television and smoked – an ashtray on the sill was full of butts. Each day must seem endless.

I adjusted the curtain and returned to my seat. God, it was depressing. The room seemed much darker than Flo's basement.

'I can't remember if you take sugar.' Gran came in with tea in two fine china cups, a cigarette poking from her mouth. Because she'd been to Mass that morning she wore a neat brown woollen blouse and skirt, though Mum reported that she usually spent the day in her dressing-gown. She had no friends, no one called, so what was the point in getting dressed?

'I don't, thanks.'

'Your mam forgot to get me favourite fig biscuits. All I've got is digestives.' Poor Mum could never get the shopping right.

'I don't want a biscuit, thanks all the same.' I sipped the tea, doing my best to avoid the ash floating on the top.

The wall above the sideboard was full of photographs in identical cheap plastic frames: Grandad Colquitt, long dead, a genial-looking man with erratic facial hair, various weddings, including mine and Trudy's, lots of photos of the Cameron kids taken at school – the happy faces, grinning widely, telling a terrible lie.

'There's a photo in Flo's of my father as a baby with his mother – my other grandma,' I said. At home his parents were rarely mentioned. All I knew was that his father had been a sailor, and his mother had died when he was twenty.

'Is that so? Your other gran, Elsa, used to be me best friend.' The thin yellow lips trembled slightly. 'What's it like in Flo's place?'

'Nice.' I smiled. 'I found gas bills the other day going back to nineteen forty-one.' At least this showed I'd been making an effort to get things done.

'It was nineteen forty when she moved in,' Gran said. 'November.' Her voice was surprisingly soft, considering she was talking about her lifelong enemy. 'Just before Christmas. Mam didn't find out till later that Mrs Fritz had gone to Ireland, leaving her in that big house all by herself.'

The name seemed familiar. 'Fritz?'

'Mr Fritz owned the laundry where she worked. He was sent to an internment camp during the war.'

'There's a snap of Flo outside the laundry.' In a fit of generosity, I said,

'Would you like me to take you?' Flo might turn in her grave if she knew, but Gran looked so wretched.

'To the laundry!' The crumpled jaw fell open. 'They knocked it down years ago, girl.'

'I meant Flo's. I'm on my way there now to try to get a few more things done,' I said virtuously. 'I'll bring you home in the car.'

Gran shook her head adamantly. 'Toxteth's the last place on earth I'd go. A man was murdered there only last week, stabbed to death right on the pavement. Even the town centre isn't safe any more. A woman at church had her gold chain snatched from round her neck when she was walking through St John's precinct. She almost had a heart attack.' She looked at me with frightened eyes. 'It's a terrible world nowadays, Millicent.'

'Flo lived in Toxteth most of her life without coming to any harm.' I vaguely remembered my father saying the same thing a few weeks ago. 'And Bel lives not far away. She comes and goes all the time.'

'Bel?'

'Flo's friend.'

'I know who Bel is,' Gran said bitterly. 'I met her once when she was young. So, even she didn't bother to tell me when our Flo died!'

'Maybe she didn't know your address.'

'There aren't many Mrs M. Colquitts in the Liverpool phone book. And someone knew where to contact me, didn't they? But only when it was too late.'

'I'm sorry, Gran,' I said awkwardly. I put the cup and saucer down; the dregs were grey with ash. 'I'd better be going. Don't forget to watch that film.'

'I wish you hadn't come,' Gran said tonelessly. She fumbled in the packet for another cigarette. 'You've raked up things I'd considered long forgotten.'

'I'm sorry,' I said again. I'd only come because I'd been told she wanted to see me.

'I expect you can see yourself out.'

'Of course. 'Bye, Gran.'

There was no answer. I closed the door and flew down the stone staircase where the walls were scrawled with graffiti. As I drove towards Toxteth, it was difficult to rid myself of the memory of the stiff, unhappy woman smoking her endless cigarettes.

I parked in William Square, and as I walked back towards Flo's, Bel and Charmian must have seen me arrive for they were standing by the basement stairs. Charmian waved a bottle of wine, and my heart lifted.

'Hi!' I called, beginning to hurry. Gran was forgotten and I had the strangest feeling, as if I *was* Flo, coming home to my friends.

It would seem that the banging wasn't part of a dream. Beside me Tom O'Mara was dead to the world. I almost fell out of bed, pulled on Flo's dressing-gown and hurried towards the door before whoever was there demolished it. The noise was even louder in the living room. Any minute now Charmian or Herbie might appear, wanting to know what was going on.

'Who's there?' I shouted crossly. It must be a drunk who'd come to the wrong house. I looked blearily at my watch – ten past two – and wondered if I should have woken Tom.

The banging stopped. 'It's James. Let me in.'

James! I was wide awake in an instant, and leaned against the door. 'Go away, James, please.'

'I've no intention of going away.' He began to hammer on the door again. 'Let me in!'

'I don't want to see you,' I yelled, but he almost certainly couldn't hear me above the noise he was making. A police siren sounded in the distance, and just in case it had been alerted by a neighbour to investigate the disturbance in William Square, I opened the door.

'You're not . . .' I began, as a wild-eyed James, smelling strongly of alcohol, brushed past me into the room, '. . . coming in.' Too late. I switched on the main light. Flo's room looked so different with every corner brightly illuminated.

James stood in the middle of the room. I'd never thought him capable of such anger. I shrank before it, terrified, my heart racing. His face, his neck, his fists were swollen, as if at any minute he would explode. 'What the hell do you think you're playing at?' he demanded furiously.

'I don't know what you mean.' I kept my voice mild, stifling my own anger, not wanting to provoke him further.

He glared at me, as if I was the stupidest woman on earth. 'I've been outside your flat since five o'clock waiting for you,' he raged. 'When it got to midnight, I decided to come here, but I couldn't remember where the fucking place was. I drove round and round for ages before I found it.'

I didn't know what to say, so remained silent. Once again I thought about rousing Tom, but it seemed weak. I was determined to handle the situation on my own: with Tom there, things might turn ugly. James began to pace the floor, waving his arms, his face scarlet. 'Last week, after you threw me out, I thought, I'll give her till Sunday, then that's it. If she doesn't phone, it's over.' He thrust his red face into mine. 'You didn't phone, did you? You didn't give a fuck how I was.' He mimicked my voice, which seemed to be becoming a habit with all the men I knew. ' "I'm taking a shower and I expect you to be gone when I come out." And I went, like the good little boy I am. Then I waited for you to get in touch, but apparently you were willing to let me just walk out of your life as if I'd never existed.'

'James.' I put my hands on his arms to try to calm him. The police car screamed along the main road, William Square obviously not its destination. 'You're not making sense. You said it would be over if I didn't phone. Perhaps that would be the best thing.'

'But I love you! Can't you get into your stupid head how much I love you?' His eyes narrowed. 'You know, all my life I've had girls throw themselves at me. I've never gone short, as they say. But you, an uppity little bitch from Kirkby, you're the one I fell in love with, wanted to marry. How *dare* you turn me down?'

This wasn't happening! I closed my eyes for a second, then said quietly, 'I don't love you, James.'

At this, his hands and arms began to twitch, his blue eyes glazed. He raised his huge fist, ready to strike.

I felt myself grow dizzy. I was a little girl again, wishing I were invisible, waiting, head bowed, for a blow to fall. It was no use trying to escape, because wherever I went, wherever I hid, my father would find me and then the punishment would be even worse. I wanted to weep because this was the story of my life.

The blow I was expecting never came. The dizziness faded, reality returned. That part of my life was over. I took a step back. James was still standing, arm raised. 'Christ! What's the matter with me?' he gasped, in a horrified voice.

'What the hell's going on in here?' Tom O'Mara came out of the bedroom fastening his trousers and bare to the waist.

James's face turned ashen, his shoulders slumped. 'How could you, Millie?' he whispered.

Tom wasn't quite as tall as James, or so broad, but before I knew what was happening, he had James's right arm bent behind him with one hand, the other on his collar, and was propelling him roughly towards the door. Despite the way James had just behaved, I was shocked at the sheer brutality of it. 'There's no need for that,' I cried.

The door slammed. After a while, I could hear James stumbling up the concrete steps. I switched on the lamp, turned off the central light, and sat in the middle of Flo's settee, trembling and hugging myself tightly with both arms.

'What was that all about?' asked Tom from behind.

'Can't you guess?'

'Hadn't you told him about me?'

'It was nothing to do with you until you appeared,' I sighed.

A few seconds later, Tom sat on the settee beside me and put a glass of sherry on the coffee table. 'Drink that!' he commanded. 'It'll do you good. Flo took sherry for her nerves.'

I was actually able to smile. 'I get the impression Flo took sherry for an awful lot of things.'

He put his arm around me companionably. It was the first time he'd touched me when I didn't automatically melt. 'So, what's the story with the bloke I just chucked out? Is he the one you were with at the party?'

'Yes, and there isn't a story. He loves me and I don't love him, that's all. He'll feel worse now he's seen you.' I swallowed half the sherry in one go. Thank goodness Tom had been there. Even if James had calmed down he would have been difficult to get rid of. I thought about him driving home, drunk as a lord. The whole thing was my fault. I should have made it plain the minute he said he loved me that I didn't love him. But I did! The trouble with James is that he's spoilt, too used to having girls throw themselves at him to grasp that this one wasn't blinded by his fatal attraction. I sipped more sherry, conscious of Tom's arm, heavy on my shoulders. I would have let him hit me! I just stood there. I'd never have dreamed James had such an ugly side. He was always so gentle. I watched the lamp, waiting for the girl in the red coat, hating James for bringing ugliness into the place I loved, where I'd always felt supremely safe. I'll never see him again, I vowed.

'Better?' Tom enquired. 'You've stopped trembling.'

'Much better.' I snuggled my head against his shoulder. 'Were you happy as a child?'

'That's a funny thing to ask.' He thought for a while. 'I suppose I was. Knowing Flo helped a lot.'

'What was your dad like?'

'Me dad? Oh, he was a soft ould thing. Everyone pissed him about something rotten – Gran, me mam and me, I suppose, as well as the firm he worked for.' His voice became hard. 'That's why I swore I'd be me own boss when I grew up.'

'Where's your mother?'

He shrugged carelessly. 'No idea. She did a runner when I was five. Went off with another bloke.'

I patted his knee. 'I'm sorry.'

'Don't be,' he said carelessly. 'It were good riddance as far as I was concerned.' He kissed my ear. 'What about you?'

'What about me?'

'Were you happy – how did you put it? – as a child?'

'Sometimes I wish I could be reborn and start all over.'

'Well, you can't. You're here and that's it, you can't change anything.'

'Are these your wife's initials?' I traced the heart on his chest with my finger.

'No. Clare's always trying to persuade me to get rid of it. You can get it done with a laser.'

'Have you any children?'

'Two girls, Emma and Susanna.' He raised his eyebrows, and I sensed he was annoyed. 'What's this? The third degree?'

'I wanted to know a few things about you, that's all.'

'What's the point?' he said coldly.

Just as coldly, I replied, 'I thought it would be nice to know a little about the man I've been sleeping with for the past week.' I looked at him. 'Is there nothing you'd like to know about me?'

'You're a great fuck, that's all I care.'

I stiffened and pulled away. 'Do you have to be so coarse?'

He dragged me back against him. 'The less we know about each other the better, don't you understand that?' he whispered urgently. 'I may be coarse, but I'm not thick. I've always taken me wedding vows seriously. I love me kids, and I don't want to spoil things between me and Clare.' He twisted me around, so that I was lying on his knee, and undid the belt on my dressing-gown. 'Let's keep things the way they are. Getting to know each other could be dangerous.'

His hands were setting my body on fire. I told myself that I had no intention of falling in love with someone like him. But he aroused feelings in me that no other man had. His lips came down on mine, and we rolled on to the floor. The pleasure we gave each other was sublime, and in the midst of everything, when I was almost out of my head with delight too exquisite to describe, I could have sworn I shouted, 'I love you.'

Or perhaps it was Tom.

At some time in the early hours of the morning, he carried me into the bedroom. I pretended to be asleep when he tucked the bedclothes around me, and remained like that while he got dressed. It wasn't until the front door clicked behind him that I sat up. 'Did you ever get yourself into a mess like this, Flo?' I asked. 'If your bureau is anything to go by, you led a very neat, ordered life.'

It was ages before I had to leave for work but I got up, ran a few inches of water in the bath and splashed myself awake. I made coffee in the microwave and carried it into the living room, where I tried, unsuccessfully, to empty my mind. But as soon as I got rid of Tom O'Mara, James would take his place, followed by Mum, Alison, Declan, Trudy – what were the things my sister couldn't talk about to Colin?

I was back to Tom again when I noticed that the rising sun was shining through the rear window and the walls of the little yard were glowing a rosy pink. I'd never been up this early before, and it looked so pretty.

So far, I hadn't ventured into the yard. I went outside, wondering if Flo had sat here in the summer with her first cup of tea of the day, as I did on my balcony. A black cat regarded me benignly from the wall and graciously allowed me to stroke its back. The wooden bench was full of mould and needed scrubbing, and the pansies in the plant-holders were dead now. I nearly jumped out of my skin when a head covered with untidy black curls appeared over the neighbouring wall.

'Hi,' Peter Maxwell grinned. 'Remember me? We met the other week at Charmian's party.'

'Of course! You said you lived next door. What are you doing up so early?' I could only see him from the shoulders up and he appeared to be wearing a sleeveless T-shirt.

He flexed a bulging muscle in his arm. 'I work out every morning. I'm off for a jog in a minute.' He winked. 'You can come with me, if you like.'

'You must be joking!'

He rested his arms on the wall and said conversationally, 'Are you all right?'

'Don't I look all right?'

'You look great, even without my glasses. It's just that I heard a commotion in your place last night. I contemplated coming round, but the sounds died down.'

'It was a drunk,' I said dismissively. 'I soon got rid of him.'

'By the way, I'd like to apologise for Sharon.'

'Who's Sharon?'

'Me girlfriend – ex-girlfriend. I tore her off a strip for dragging me away when I was dancing with you at the party. She was very rude.'

'I hardly noticed.'

He looked dismayed. 'And I was quite enjoying our little chat. I thought you were, too.'

'Well, yes, I was,' I conceded.

'It means I've got a spare ticket for the school concert in December. I wondered if you'd come.'

I pulled a face. 'I hate schools.'

'So did I, but they're different when you're an adult. No one will test your spelling or demand the date of the battle of Waterloo. Come on,' he coaxed, 'it's Charles Dickens's *A Christmas Carol*. I'd love you to be there.'

'Why?'

'Because you used to know me as Weedy and I want you to see me as Peter Maxwell, MA, economics teacher, and scriptwriter of genius – I wrote the script for *A Christmas Carol* and set it in the present day. Tell you what,' he said eagerly, 'if you come to the concert, I'll let you show me round a property and we can negotiate. Then we'll have both proved to each other that we've made it.'

I smiled. 'How could I possibly refuse?'

Still smiling, I went indoors. Peter Maxwell had cheered me up. We'd both been through the mill and emerged unscathed. I paused in the act of pulling down the front of Flo's bureau, which hadn't been touched since the night Tom had arrived with a Chinese takeaway.

Unscathed? Was that true? Until that moment, I'd never thought I'd ever get over the tragedy of my childhood. I'd thought that, along with Trudy and Declan, I'd been irreparably damaged. But maybe time was fading the shadow of my father, and perhaps one day it would go away altogether. One day, the three of us would emerge, truly unscathed.

I decided not to think about it any more on such a lovely morning. I fetched a chair up to the bureau and took out the bundle of letters held together with the elastic band. It was rotten, and snapped when I pulled it off.

William Square began to wake up to the new day: cars drove away, others came to take their place; feet hurried past the basement window; children shrieked on their way to school – a football came over the railings and landed with a loud clang on the dustbin. But I was only vaguely aware of these activities. I was too engrossed in Flo's letters. It wasn't until I returned the last letter to its envelope that I remembered where I was. The letter was one of several from the same person, a Gerard Davies from Swansea, in which he implored Flo yet again to marry him. 'I love you, Flo. I always will. There'll never be another girl like you.'

Which was more or less what every other letter had said. They were love letters from a score of different men, all to Flo, and from the tone of quite a few, the relationships hadn't been platonic.

And Bel had claimed that Flo had led the life of a saint!

I remembered the mysterious receipts from the hotel in the Isle of Man. 'Oh, I bet you were a divil in your day, Flo Clancy,' I whispered.

Flo

1

1941

'Oh, Flo, you'll never guess!' Sally threw herself on to the sofa. 'Our Martha's captured Albert Colquitt at long last. They're getting married on St Patrick's Day.'

'Only two weeks off!' Flo sank beside her sister and they collapsed into giggles. 'How on earth did she manage that?'

Sally dropped her voice, though the entire house, all five floors of it, was empty and no one could have overheard. 'I think she seduced him,' she whispered dramatically.

'She what!' screamed Flo, giggling even more. 'You're joking.'

'I'm not, Flo, honest,' Sally assured her, round-eyed. 'One night after we'd gone to bed our Martha got up again. I didn't say anything, and she must have thought I was asleep. I thought she was going to the lavvy, but she sat at the dressing-table and started combing her hair. The moon was shining through the winder, so I could see her as clearly as I can see you now.' Sally frowned thoughtfully. 'I wondered why she hadn't put her curlers in or smothered herself with cold cream. Not only that, she was wearing that pink nightdress – you know, the one Elsa Cameron bought her for her twenty-first. Are you with me so far, Flo?'

'Yes, yes, I'm with you.' Flo wanted to throttle her sister for stretching the tale out so long. 'What happened then?'

'She just disappeared.'

'What d'you mean she just disappeared? You mean she vanished before your very eyes?'

'Of course not, soft girl. She left the room and was gone for ages. I was asleep by the time she got back.'

'Is that all?' Flo said, disappointed. 'I don't know how you worked out

507

she seduced Albert. She might have dozed off on the lavvy. I've nearly done it meself in the middle of the night.'

'Why didn't she put her curlers in, then? Why didn't she use her cream? And she was keeping that nightdress for her bottom drawer. Not only that,' Sally finished triumphantly, 'she wasn't wearing her glasses.'

That seemed to provide final proof of Sally's claim. It was no longer a laughing matter. 'If that's how she caught him, then she's been dead devious,' Flo said soberly. 'Not many men could resist if a girl got into bed with them. She's shamed him into getting married.'

Sally nodded knowingly, with the air of a woman of the world, well aware of men's lack of will-power when it came to sex. 'They're very weak,' she agreed. 'Anyroad, Martha and Albert are going to live at home till the war's over. Mam said she's expecting you at the wedding.'

'In that case, Mam's got another think coming.' Even if she wasn't dead set against her sister, she'd feel peculiar, knowing that Albert had asked her first and that Martha was his second choice – that's if he'd had a choice. She would, though, write him a little note. In the time she had remained in Burnett Street after his kind proposal, she'd always made sure they'd never been alone. He didn't know the truth of what had happened to her baby but it would have been a sore reminder that she shouldn't have turned him down. Last week, her son had had his first birthday. She'd sent a card, writing simply, 'To Hugh, from Flo'. But the card had come back by return of post.

Sally sighed. 'She must have been desperate. Poor Martha.'

'Poor Albert,' Flo said cynically.

The young sailor stood before her, agonisingly shy, his face red with embarrassment. She had noticed him watching her all night. 'Would you like to dance, miss?'

'Of course.' Flo lifted her arms and he clasped her awkwardly. It was the first time he'd ventured on to the floor.

'I'm not very good at this,' he stammered, when he stood on her toe.

'Then you must learn,' she chided him. 'All servicemen should learn to dance. This is a waltz, the easiest dance of all. You'll find yourself in all sorts of different towns and cities and it's the best way to meet girls.'

He swallowed, and said daringly, 'I won't meet many girls like you. I hope you don't mind me saying, but you're the prettiest one here.'

'Why on earth should I mind you saying a lovely thing like that? What's your name, luv?'

'Gerard Davies. I come from Swansea.'

'Pleased to meet you, Gerard. I'm Flo Clancy.'

'Pleased to meet you, Flo.'

It always started more or less the same. She only picked the shy ones, who were usually, though not always, very young. Gerard looked eighteen or nineteen, which meant he'd not long left home and would be missing his family.

When the waltz was over, she fanned herself with her hand and said, 'Phew! It's hot in here,' knowing that almost certainly he would offer to buy her a drink. He took the opportunity eagerly, and she chose the cheapest, a lemonade. They sat in a corner of the ballroom, and she asked him about his mum and dad, and what he'd done for a living before he was called up.

His dad ran a smallholding, he told her, and his mum worked in the shop where their vegetables were sold. He had two sisters, both older than him, and everyone had been very proud when he'd passed the scholarship and gone to grammar school. Less than three months ago, he'd gone straight from school into the Navy, and he had no idea what he wanted to do when the war was over. Flo noticed that he had the merest trace of a moustache on his upper lip, and his hands were soft and white. It was easy to believe that until recently he'd been just a schoolboy. His brown eyes were wide and guileless. He knew nothing about anything much, yet he was about to fight for his country in the worst war the world had ever known. Flo felt her heart contract at the thought.

The drink finished, they returned to the dance floor. Flo could tell that he was gaining confidence because he had a girl on his arm, and it grew as the night progressed.

At half past eleven, she said she had to be getting home. 'I have to be up for work at the crack of dawn.'

'In the laundry?'

'That's right, luv.' She'd told him quite a lot about herself. She gave a little shudder. 'I don't live far away, but I'm terrified of walking home in the blackout.'

'I'll take you home,' he said, with alacrity, which Flo had known he would. She wasn't a bit scared of the blackout.

Outside, she linked his arm in case they lost each other in the dark. 'Have you got long in Liverpool?'

'No, we're sailing tomorrow, I don't know where to. It's a secret.' She felt his thin, boyish arm tighten on her own, and reckoned he was frightened. Who wouldn't be, knowing about all the ships that had been sunk and the lives that had been lost, mainly of young men like him?

When they got to her flat she made him a cup of tea and something to eat – he appeared to be starving the way he downed the two thick cheese sarnies.

'I'd better be getting back to the ship.' He looked at her shyly. 'It's been a lovely evening, Flo. I've really enjoyed myself.'

'So've I, luv.'

509

By the door, he flushed scarlet and stammered, 'Can I kiss you, Flo?'

She didn't answer, just closed her eyes and willingly offered her lips. His mouth touched hers, softly, and his arms encircled her waist. She slid her own arms around his neck, and murmured, 'Oh, Gerard!' and he kissed her again, more firmly this time. She didn't demur when his hands fumbled awkwardly and hesitantly with her breasts. She had thought this might happen. It nearly always did.

It was another half-hour before Gerard Davies left Flo in her bed. 'Can I write to you?' he pleaded, as he got back into his uniform. 'It'd be nice to have a girl back home.'

'I'd like that very much, Gerard.'

'And can I see you if I'm in Liverpool again?'

'Of course, luv. But don't turn up unannounced, whatever you do.' She worried that more than one of her young lovers might turn up at the same time. 'Me landlady upstairs wouldn't like it a bit. I'll give you the phone number of the laundry so you can let me know beforehand, like.'

'Thanks, Flo.' Then he said, in an awestruck voice, 'This has been the most wonderful night of my life.'

Gerard Davies was the seventh young man she'd slept with. Flo told herself earnestly that it was her contribution towards the war. Tommy O'Mara had taught her that making love was the most glorious experience on earth, and she wanted to share this experience with a few bashful young men who were about to fight for their country. It made her heart swell to think that they would go into battle, perhaps even die, carrying with them the memory of the wonderful time they'd had with Flo, the pretty young woman from Liverpool, who'd made them feel so special.

It was important that she didn't get pregnant. She'd asked Sally, casual, like, what she and Jock used.

'It's something called a French letter, Flo. They're issued by the Navy. I think you can get them in the chemist's, but I'm not sure.' Sally grinned. 'Why on earth d'you want to know?'

'No reason, I just wondered.'

There was no way Flo would even consider entering a chemist's to ask for French letters, so she inserted a sponge soaked in vinegar which she'd once heard the women in the laundry say was the safest way. But Flo had the strongest feeling she would never have another baby. It was as if the productive part of her had withered away to nothing when her little boy was taken away.

Just after Martha's wedding, Bel wrote to say she was expecting. 'I'll be leaving the ATS, naturally. Bob's being posted to North Africa, so I'll be back in Liverpool soon, looking for somewhere to live. Perhaps I can help out in the laundry if there's a sitting-down job I could do.'

Flo wrote back immediately to say she'd love to have Bel stay until she found a place of her own and that, if necessary, she'd invent a sitting-down job in the laundry. She bought two ounces of white baby wool to knit a matinée jacket, but in April another letter arrived: Bel had had a miscarriage. 'You can't imagine what it's like to lose a baby, Flo. I'm staying in the ATS, though I was looking forward to living in William Square and working in this famous laundry.'

The knitting was put away, unfinished. She seemed to waste a lot of time making baby clothes that would never be worn, Flo thought sadly. She wrote to Bel. 'I wouldn't know, of course, but I can imagine how heartbreaking it must be to lose a baby.'

Flo was proud of the way she'd run the laundry since Stella Fritz had returned to Ireland four months ago. As well as the Holbrook twins, she now employed two young mothers, friends, who worked half a day each. Lottie would turn up at midday with several lusty toddlers in a big black pram, and Moira would take them home. There was also Peggy Lewis, a widow, only four and a half feet tall, who worked like a navvy. Peggy had to leave early to prepare a massive meal for her three lads who worked on the docks and arrived home famished and ready to eat the furniture if there was no food ready.

When the delivery-boy, Jimmy Cromer, a cheeky little bugger but reliable, gave in his notice, having been offered a job with a builder at five bob a week more, Flo immediately increased his wages by ten. Jimmy was thrilled. 'If I stay, can I paint "White's Laundry" on me sidecart?'

'Of course, luv. As long as you do it neat and spell it proper.'

Every Friday, Flo sat in the office working out the week's finances, putting the wages to one side, and taking the surplus to the bank. There were usually several cheques in settlement of their big customers' bills. She paid everything into the Fritzes' account, then made out a statement showing exactly what money had come in and what had gone out, to send to Stella Fritz in County Kerry. At the bottom, she usually added a little message: the laundry was doing fine, there were no problems with the house, the window-cleaner still came once a month and she assumed this was all right. She kept all her own personal bills, stamped 'paid' by the gas and electricity companies, just in case there was ever any argument.

Not once did Stella acknowledge the hard work Flo was putting in to keep the business going and looking after the house. I suppose she's too busy breathing in the good clean air and looking out the winder, Flo thought. In the absence of any authority to tell her otherwise, she promoted herself – she'd remembered a white overall in the office cupboard with Manageress embroidered in red on the breast pocket. It had been there for as long as she could remember, together with a few other odds and ends that customers had forgotten to collect.

'You look dead smart, luv,' Mam exclaimed. She often called in on her way to or from work. 'Manageress at twenty! Who'd have thought it, eh?' Flo did her utmost not to preen. 'Which reminds me,' Mam continued, 'we were talking about you the other night. It's only a fortnight off your twenty-first, May the eighth. Martha and Sal both had a party. We can't let yours go without a little celebration, drink your health an' all. What do you say, Flo?'

'Where would the party be?'

'At home, luv, where else?'

Flo shook her head stubbornly. 'I'm not coming home, Mam, not while our Martha's there.'

'Oh, luv!' Mam's face was a mixture of grief and vexation. 'How long are you going to keep up this feud with Martha? After all, the girl's expecting. I can't wait to have me first grandchild,' she added tactlessly, as if Hugh O'Mara had never existed.

'Sal told me about the baby, Mam, and it's not a feud with Martha. I'm not sure what it is.'

'You'll have to speak to her sometime.'

'No, I won't.' Flo thought about Hugh. Then she thought about Nancy O'Mara, and that no one would take Martha's baby away and give it to a Welsh witch. 'I don't have to speak to our Martha again as long as I live,' she said abruptly.

Mam gave up. 'What about your twenty-first then?'

'You and Sal can come to William Square. I'll ask the women from the laundry, get a bottle of sherry and make sarnies. You can drink me health there.'

Sally reported that Albert seemed relatively content now that he was a member of the family he'd grown so fond of. 'He's started calling Mam "Mother" and she's a bit put out – she's two years younger than him! He always asks about you, Flo. He can't understand why you never come to visit.'

'Tell him I can't stand his wife,' Flo suggested. 'How's her ladyship taken to married life, anyroad?'

'All she's ever wanted was a wedding ring and Mrs in front of her name. She goes round looking like the cat that ate the cream.'

Now that Albert was to become a father, his joy knew no bounds. Flo was pleased for him: he was a nice man who deserved happiness. But when it came to Martha, she felt only bitterness.

Frequently, in the dinner hour or on her way home, she walked down

Clement Street, but she never set eyes on Nancy and there was never a pram outside number eighteen. Once, she thought she heard a baby cry as she passed, but that might have been her imagination.

Everyone in the laundry was pleased to be invited to Flo's twenty-first. 'It won't be much,' she warned. 'There won't be any fellers, for one thing.'

'We don't mind,' Jennifer and Joanna Holbrook said together.

'Me husband wouldn't let me go if there were,' remarked Moira.

Lottie's husband was away in the Army. Nevertheless, she would have felt disloyal going to a party where there were fellers.

'I'm not bothered,' Peggy said, from somewhere within a cloud of steam. 'Anyroad, I see enough of fellers at home. You could ask Jimmy Cromer if he'd like to provide some masculine company.'

'I'm not going to a party full of ould married women,' Jimmy said in a scandalised voice.

'I'm not old and I'm not married,' Flo reminded him.

Jimmy leered at her far too maturely for a fifteen-year-old. 'Will you come out with me, then?'

'I'll do no such thing!'

'In that case, I'm not coming to your party.'

The first week of May brought air raids worse than any the city had known before. For a week, it seemed as if the Luftwaffe's intention was to blast Liverpool out of existence. Flo was convinced that her party would never take place. By the eighth no one would be left alive and there wouldn't be a building still standing. At night she stayed indoors, worried that if she went dancing a raid might start and that she really would be too scared to come home alone. In bed, with her head under the covers, she listened to the house grinding on its foundations as the bombs whistled their way down to earth and the ground shook, though it was the parachute mines, drifting silently and menacingly, that caused the greatest carnage. Bells clanged wildly as fire engines raced to put out the hundreds of fires that crackled away, turning the sky blood red.

Next morning, exhausted but still in one piece, Flo would go to work. There was rarely any sign of public transport and she had to make her way carefully along pavements carpeted with splintered glass, passing the sad, broken remains of buildings that had been the landmarks of a lifetime, and the little streets with yawning gaps where houses had been only the day before. The air was full of floating scraps of charred paper, like black confetti at a funeral.

Everyone at the laundry was miraculously still there to exclaim in horror about the events of the previous night: the narrow escapes, the bomb that had dropped in the next street killing a girl they'd gone to school with, or a chap who'd nearly married their sister. Moira lost the godmother of her youngest child. Peggy's brother-in-law, an ARP warden, was killed outright when the building he was in got a direct hit. How long, everyone wondered, would the terror continue?

'It can't go on for ever,' Peggy maintained.

It was that thought that kept them going. It had to stop sometime.

Flo arrived on the Friday of the nightmarish week to find that during the night all the mains had been fractured. There seemed little point in a laundry without electricity, gas or water so she told everyone they might as well go home. 'You'll still get paid,' she promised, not caring if Stella would approve or not. 'It's not your fault you can't work. It's that bloody Hitler's.'

'What are you going to do?' one of the twins enquired.

'I'll stay, just in case things come on again.'

'We'll stay with you.'

'Same here,' echoed Peggy.

'Me, too,' said Moira.

The next few hours always remained one of Flo's most vivid memories, proof that the human spirit obstinately refused to give in, even in the face of the worst adversity. Peggy produced a pack of cards and they played Strip Jack Naked, Rummy and Snap, and shrieked with laughter for no reason at all, though anyone listening would have thought the laughter a mite hysterical and a bit too loud. Every now and then, they'd pause for a sing-song: 'We'll Meet Again', 'Little Sir Echo', 'Run Rabbit Run'. In their quavery soprano voices, the twins entertained them with a variety of old songs, 'If You Were the Only Girl in the World', and 'Only a Bird in a Gilded Cage'.

Mid-morning, when they would normally have stopped for a cup of tea, Moira said wistfully, 'I'd give anything for a cuppa.'

As if in answer to Moira's prayer, Mrs Clancy appeared suddenly at the side door carrying a teapot. 'I expect you're all parched for a drink,' she said cheerfully. 'I always run a bucket of water before I go to bed, just in case, like, and Mrs Plunkett next door's got one of them paraffin stoves.'

There was a mad dash for cups. As usual, the twins had brought milk because they never used all their ration.

'I've got Albert at home,' Mam said to Flo. 'He hurt his leg fire-watching. He's a terrible patient. All he does is complain about people getting away without paying their fares.'

'There's hardly any trams running.'

'That's what I keep telling him. There's lines up everywhere.' She patted Flo's hand. 'I'm off to work now, luv. I'll call in for the teapot on me way home.'

'It's all right, Mam, I'll bring it. I wouldn't mind having a word with

Albert. What time will you be back?' She would take the opportunity of Martha's absence to reassure Albert, though not in words, that they would always be friends. She'd prefer him not to be alone, just in case there was a message in his eyes it would be wiser not to see.

'I'll be home about half two. Sal's on mornings, so she'll be back not long afterwards.'

Later that morning the gas supply was reconnected, and just after one o'clock water came gushing out of the tap in the lavatory, which had been left turned on. There was still no electricity, so the steam-presser remained out of use, but the boilers could be loaded with washing and the ironing done. Flo gave a sigh of relief as the laundry began to function almost normally, the women setting to work with a will. Normality seemed precious in an uncertain, dangerous world, though it didn't last for long.

Just as Flo was thinking that it was almost time to nip round to Burnett Street with the teapot, the air-raid siren began its sinister wail. She particularly hated daylight raids. They were rarely heavy and usually brief but, unlike the night raids, were impossible to ignore – or, at least, pretend to. The women groaned, but when Flo suggested they abandon work for the shelter on the corner, they flatly refused.

'The shelter's just as likely to get a direct hit as the laundry,' said Lottie, who'd recently changed shifts with Moira. 'I'd sooner stay.'

There seemed no argument to this, although the laundry was flimsy in comparison. Soon afterwards a solitary plane could be heard buzzing idly overhead. Everyone went outside to take a look. They could see the German crosses on the wings.

'Is that a Messerschmidt, Jo?'

'No, Jen. It's a Heinkel.'

Suddenly the plane went into a dive. It appeared to be coming straight for them. Peggy screamed and they ran inside and slammed the door. Almost immediately, there was a loud explosion, followed by another, then several more. The plane must have dropped a stick of bombs. From somewhere within the building, there was a thud and the crash of breaking glass.

'Jaysus! That was close!' someone gasped.

They stood still, scarcely breathing, as the plane's engine grew fainter. Then the sound disappeared and the all-clear went. The raid was over.

The laundry had suffered superficial damage. At least, Flo assumed that a shattered office window and the door blown off its hinges could be described as superficial. 'The thing is,' she said shakily, 'I'd forgotten today's the day I do the accounts, otherwise I'd have been in here sorting out the wages, or writing the statement for Mrs Fritz.' There was a small crater in the street outside, and the houses opposite had also lost their doors and windows, but thankfully, no one had been hurt.

The twins began calmly to sweep up the broken glass and restore the room to relative order. Flo decided to take the money home and leave the bank till Monday, but it was important that the women were paid. Using the presser as a desk, she counted out the money and wrote each name on a little brown envelope. She felt angry with herself because her hands were trembling and her writing was all over the place. She'd had a close shave, that was all. Some people suffered far worse without going to pieces. Her stomach was squirming. She felt uneasy, full of dread. 'Pull yourself together, Flo Clancy,' she urged.

'Flo, luv,' a voice said softly.

Flo looked up. Sally was standing at the side door and the feeling of dread grew until it almost choked her. She knew why Sally had come. 'Is it Mam?' she breathed.

Her sister nodded slowly. 'And Albert.'

Sally said, 'Promise you'll make things up with Martha.'

'Why should I?' demanded Flo.

It was almost midnight. The sisters were as yet too exhausted to grieve. They paid no heed to the raid going on outside, which was as bad as any experienced so far, decimating the beleaguered city even further. They were in William Square, the only place Sally had to go now that she'd lost her home in Burnett Street. The joint funeral would take place on Monday, the day after Flo's twenty-first birthday. There was room for Albert in his mother-in-law's grave, where she would join her beloved husband. The wreaths had been ordered, a Requiem Mass arranged, and a friend of Mam's had offered to provide refreshments after the service. Father Haughey was trying to track down Albert's cousin in Macclesfield. The address would have been in the parlour, but there was no longer a parlour, no longer a house, nothing left of the place to which Mr and Mrs Clancy had moved when they married, where they'd brought up their three girls. The bomb had gone through the roof and exploded in the living room, demolishing the houses on both sides. Martha had been safe at the brewery but Mam and Albert, sheltering under the stairs, had been killed instantly. Their shattered bodies lay in the mortuary, waiting for the funeral director to collect.

'Oh, Flo,' Sally moaned, 'how can you be so unChristian and unforgiving? Martha's pregnant and she's lost both her mam and her husband.'

Martha had been whisked from the brewery to Elsa Cameron's house. When Sally went to see her, she was fast asleep, the doctor had given her a sedative.

'I can't begin to imagine how I'd feel if I'd lost Jock and Mam at the same time,' Sally shuddered.

'But you're in love with Jock,' Flo pointed out. 'Martha was no more in love with Albert than I was – and all three of us loved Mam.'

'You're awful hard, Sis.'

'I'm only pointing out the obvious. What's hard about that?'

'Oh, I dunno. It's just that you always seemed such a soft ould thing. I never dreamed you could be so unsympathetic.'

'I feel sorry for our Martha,' Flo conceded. 'I just don't want anything more to do with her, that's all.' She felt irritated that Sally didn't seem to appreciate the enormity of what Martha had done. Maybe, because Flo's baby was a bastard, she wasn't supposed to love him the way a married mother would.

'Despite our Martha being an ould bossy-boots, she depended on Mam far more than we did.' Sally sighed. 'She'll miss her something awful. We loved Mam, but we didn't need her.' She turned to her sister and said, 'Don't think I've forgotten about Tommy O'Mara and the baby, Flo. But you're a strong person, a survivor. You've got yourself a nice little home, an important job. It's time to forgive and forget.'

'I'll never forgive Martha, and I'll never forget.' Flo's voice was like ice. 'I'll speak to her politely on Monday, but that's as far as I'm willing to go.'

But Martha was too ill to attend the funeral. And Sally had been right: Elsa Cameron reported that it was her mother Martha kept calling for. There was no mention of Albert.

2

The momentous year had flown by. Suddenly, it was Christmas again and Liverpool, though battered and badly bruised after the week-long May blitz, had survived to fight another day. The raids continued fitfully, but it was rare that the siren went nowadays. Life went on, and mid-December, Martha Colquitt gave birth to a daughter, Kate, named after the grandmother she would never know.

'She's the prettiest thing you've ever seen,' Sally told Flo. 'Ever so placid and good-humoured.'

'That's nice.' Flo did her utmost to sound generous.

'But I wish Martha'd find somewhere else to live.' Sally's brow puckered worriedly. 'I wouldn't want that Elsa Cameron anywhere near a baby of mine. She treats Norman like a punch-bag, poor bugger. He's only four, and such a lovely little chap.'

'What's happened to her husband?'

'Eugene used to come home from sea every few months, but last time he told her she was crackers and he's never been back since. I reckon he's done a bunk, permanent, like.'

'Martha said once Elsa had a sort of illness,' Flo remarked. 'She said some women go that way when they have a baby. Afterwards they're never quite right in the head.'

Sally nodded. 'There's summat wrong with the woman. By rights, Norman should be taken off her. She's not fit to be a mother.'

It seemed grotesquely unfair that Elsa Cameron, unfit to have a child, and Nancy O'Mara, unable to have one, should both have become mothers, yet Flo was childless. She changed the subject before she said something she might later regret.

'What d'you think of me decorations?' she asked. The room was festooned with paper chains and tinsel. Clusters of imitation holly hung in both windows.

'It looks like a grotto. I tried everywhere for decorations, but there's none to be had in the shops.' After living for a few months with Flo, Sally had found herself a small flat not far from Rootes Securities in Speke, which meant that she and Jock could be alone together during the precious times he was on leave.

'I got them from upstairs,' Flo said smugly. 'There's plenty more, if you'd like some. It's like having a big shop up there all to meself.'

'I wouldn't mind a few. I'm expecting Jock any minute, and it'd be nice to have the place looking Christmassy. Don't forget you're invited to Christmas dinner, will you?'

'No. And don't you forget me party the Saturday before. I feel as if I owe the girls in the laundry a party. I never had the one that was planned for me twenty-first.'

Sally twisted her lips ruefully. 'Mam was really looking forward to that. She was trying to get the ingredients for a birthday cake.'

'Was she? You've never mentioned that before.'

'I'd forgotten all about it.'

The sisters were silent for a while, thinking about Mam and Albert and how much their little world had changed over the past few years.

'Oh, well.' Sally sighed. 'I'm on early shift tomorrer. I'd better be getting home.'

It was a sad Christmas, full of bitter-sweet memories of Christmases that had gone before, made even sadder when a letter arrived from Bel to say that Bob had been killed in North Africa. 'I only wish you two had met, Flo,' she wrote. 'He was the dearest husband a woman could have. We were only married two years, almost to the day, and weren't together for a lot of that time, but I'll never stop missing him. Never.'

On New Year's Eve, Flo slipped into the Utility frock that she'd bought especially for the Rialto dance, which would go on till past midnight. It was turquoise linen, made with the minimum amount of material, short sleeves and a narrow collar. She adjusted the mirror on the mantelpiece, took a sip of sherry, and began to curl her hair into a roll.

Would she meet anyone tonight? She was glad Christmas was over and it would soon be 1942. She and Sally had both agreed that they would put the past firmly behind them and start afresh. With a wry smile, Flo glanced at the fluffy blue bunny, still in its Cellophane wrapping on the sideboard. She'd bought it for Hugh, but hadn't had the nerve to take it round to Clement Street, knowing that it would be refused. Anyroad, Hugh would be two in February and had probably grown out of fluffy bunnies. She still looked for him, walking up and down Clement Street two or three times a week. Nancy must have deliberately done her shopping when she knew Flo would be at work because there was never any sign of her out with Hugh. For a while, Flo was worried that she'd moved, but Sally said that Martha had taken Kate to see her.

She sipped more sherry, already slightly drunk and the evening hadn't even started. *She didn't even know what her son looked like!* How could she ever put the past behind her when he would still be on her mind if she lived to be a hundred? She hummed 'Auld Lang Syne', and told herself she was strong, a survivor. She wondered why she wanted to weep when she was getting ready for a dance where she was bound to have a good time. 'Because it's not really what I want,' she told herself bleakly.

When someone knocked on the door she turned, startled. Sal was spending New Year's Eve at Elsa Cameron's with Martha. 'If she's come to persuade me to go with her, she's wasting her time.'

A middle-aged man, sunburned, with hollow eyes and hollow cheeks, was standing outside the door holding a suitcase. He wore an ill-fitting tweed suit, and the collar of his frayed shirt was far too big.

'Yes?' Flo said courteously. She didn't recognise him from Adam.

'Oh, Flo! Have I changed so much?' he said tragically.

'Mr Fritz! Oh, Mr Fritz!' She grabbed his arm and pulled him inside. 'Am I pleased to see you!'

'I'm glad someone is.' He looked ready to shed the tears she'd so recently wanted to shed herself. He came into the flat and she pushed him into a chair, then stared at him as if he were a long-lost, dearly loved relative. He was much thinner than she remembered, but despite his gaunt features and the lines of strain around his jaw, he looked fit and well, as if he'd spent a lot of time working outdoors. His once chubby hands were lean and callused, but without his wire-rimmed glasses he seemed much younger. The more she stared, the less he looked like the Mr Fritz she used to know.

'Are you home for good?' she demanded. She wanted to pat him all over, make sure he was real, and had to remind herself he was only her employer.

He said drily, 'After all this time the powers-that-be decided I wasn't a danger to my adopted country. Just before Christmas they let me go.' His brown eyes grew moist. 'I've been to Ireland, Flo. Stella wasn't pleased to see me, and made it obvious she didn't want me to stay. The younger children didn't know who I was. The others were polite, but they're having such a good time on the farm I think they were scared I'd insist they come home.' He sighed. 'They're known locally as the McGonegals. Stella is ashamed of her married name.'

Flo had no idea what to say. She frowned at her hands and mumbled, 'I always thought you and Mrs Fritz were very happy together.'

'So did I!' Mr Fritz looked puzzled. 'I'm not sure what happened, but as soon as the war started Stella became a different person, bad-tempered, blaming me for things I had no control over. I couldn't produce coal or sugar out of thin air as if I were a magician. I wasn't personally responsible for the air raids. When the women left the laundry for higher wages, that was the last straw as far as Stella was concerned. It was a shock, after so many years, to discover she could be so unpleasant.'

'Perhaps,' Flo said hesitantly, 'once the war's over . . .'

'No.' He shook his head wearily. 'No, it's too late, Flo. I spent eighteen months in the camp. The other married men had letters from their families. Some wives travelled hundreds of miles to see their husbands for just a few hours. I had a single letter from Stella the whole time I was there, and that was to tell me she was back in Ireland and she'd left you in charge of the laundry and William Square.' There was a lost expression on his face. Something had happened with which he would never come to terms. 'You can't be sure of anything in this life, I hadn't realised that,' he murmured. 'I never thought it possible to feel so very alone, as if I'd never had a family. I still feel like that – alone. Do I actually have a wife and eight children? It seems absurd. It's even worse since I went to Ireland. We were like strangers to each other.'

'Oh, Lord!' Flo was horrified. He was such a dear, sweet man, who wouldn't hurt a fly. She said in her kindest voice, which seemed rather thick and emotional all of a sudden, 'You don't seem like a stranger to me.'

For the first time he smiled. 'That means a lot, Flo. It really does.' He glanced around the room and she hoped he wouldn't recognise the decorations and all the other things she'd pinched from upstairs. 'You've made this place very cosy. It's a relief to have somewhere, someone, to come back to.' He smiled again. 'But you're obviously getting ready for a night out on the town. I expect you have a date with a young man. Don't let me keep you.'

'As if I'd let you spend New Year's Eve all on your own,' Flo cried. 'I was only going to the Rialto by meself.'

Despite his protestations, she refused to leave. 'I'll pretend I got all decked up because I was expecting you,' she said, in the hope that it would make him feel less alone, more welcome.

Apparently it did. By the time she'd made a cup of tea and something to eat, he looked almost cheerful. She poured them both a glass of sherry and told him all about the laundry. 'I hope you don't mind but we changed the name to White's after we lost a lot of business.'

He already knew. Stella had given him the statements Flo had sent. 'It's all I have left now, my laundry.' He sighed, but more like the gloomy Mr Fritz of old than the joyless person who'd just landed on her doorstep.

She described the staff. 'You'll love the twins. They can only manage one person's work between them, but they only get one person's wage, so it doesn't matter.' She told him about Peggy, who had to leave early for her lads' tea, and Lottie and Moira who worked half a day each. 'And, of course, you know Jimmy Cromer, he's a treasure.'

'Jimmy will have to go now I'm back,' Mr Fritz said.

'You can't sack him!' Flo gasped. 'He's a good worker, dead reliable.'

'But there'll be nothing for him to do.' He spread his hands, palms upwards, a gesture she remembered well. 'I'll be able to collect and deliver, won't I?'

'Even so, you can't sack Jimmy for no reason,' Flo said stubbornly.

'He'll be superfluous to requirements, Flo. What better reason is there?'

'It seems very cruel.'

'It's necessary to be cruel sometimes if you run a successful business. It's what capitalism is all about. You can't employ superfluous staff and make a profit.'

'And here's me thinking you wouldn't hurt a fly,' Flo said sarcastically. 'I suppose you'll be reducing the wages next, so you make an even bigger profit. Well, you needn't think I'm working me guts out if everyone leaves.'

His eyes twinkled. 'You've changed, Flo. You would never have spoken to me like that before.'

Flo tossed her head. 'I'm not sorry.'

'Why should you be sorry for expressing an opinion? I like you better this way. But let's have more sherry and save the arguments for tomorrow. It's New Year's Eve. We'll talk about only pleasant things. Tell me, how are your family?'

'I'm afraid there's nothing pleasant to tell.' She explained about Mam and Albert being killed in the same raid that had damaged the laundry.

'So many tragedies.' Mr Fritz looked dejected. 'Hitler has a great deal to answer for. I suppose I should consider myself lucky to be alive.'

As midnight approached, he noticed the wireless and suggested they listen to Big Ben chime in the New Year. 'Is that the set from upstairs?'

'I hope you don't mind. I borrowed it,' Flo said uncomfortably, 'You can have it back tomorrer.'

'Keep it, Flo,' he said warmly. 'It will give me a good excuse to come down and listen to the news.'

'You mean I can stay?' She felt relieved. 'I thought you might prefer to have the house all to yourself, like.'

'My dear Flo,' he laughed, 'would I be silly enough to put my one and only friend out on to the street? Of course you can stay. What's more, this furniture's seen better days. There's a nice little settee and chair in Stella's sitting room that you must have. She's not likely to use it again.'

'Shush!' Flo put her finger to her lips. 'It's about to be nineteen forty-two.'

As the great clock in London chimed in the New Year, they shook hands and Mr Fritz kissed her decorously on the cheek. 'I'd expected it would be dreadful, coming back to the house without Stella and the children, Flo, but it's not been nearly as bad as I'd thought.' He squeezed her hand. 'It really is good to be home.'

He was still the same Mr Fritz, after all, who couldn't hurt a fly. Once face to face with Jimmy Cromer, he couldn't bring himself to dismiss the lad. 'I'm a hopeless capitalist,' he confessed. Instead, he gave him a job in the laundry, which Jimmy said disgustedly was women's work and got bored within a week. As a fit, able sixteen-year-old, he had no problem finding employment in war time, and he left quickly of his own accord.

While she'd been in charge Flo had got used to doing things her way. She had quite a task convincing Mr Fritz that her way was best. He got tetchy when proved wrong, she sulked when he was right, but they were always the best of friends again before the day was over. He maintained that they provided a substitute family for each other.

'Mam would be pleased,' said Flo. 'She always liked you.'

Life assumed a pleasant pattern. On Sundays, he would come to dinner, armed with a bottle of wine. On Saturday afternoons, Flo had tea upstairs, eating the thick, clumsily made sandwiches with every appearance of enjoyment.

During the week, she continued to go dancing, occasionally bringing home a young serviceman. Upstairs would be in darkness, so Mr Fritz remained ignorant of that part of her life. Not that it was any of his business, she told herself, but it was something she'd sooner keep to herself.

In July, Bel came home on five days' leave prior to being posted to

Egypt, and preferred to spend the time with her best friend, Flo, rather than with her horrible aunt Mabel.

Like virtually everyone else, Bel had changed. There was an added maturity to her lovely face, and her violet eyes were no longer quite so dazzling. Even so, she swept into the flat like a breath of fresh air, filling it with noise and laughter. She enthused over the brown plush settee and chair that had once belonged to Stella, the tall sideboard, which had so many useful drawers and cupboards, and was particularly taken with the brass bed from Mr Fritz's spare room. 'It's like a little palace, Flo, but I hate the idea of you living in a hole in the ground.'

'Don't be silly,' Flo said mildly. 'I love it.'

The two girls attracted a chorus of wolf-whistles, and many an admiring glance, as they strolled through the sunlit city streets of an evening in their summer frocks: Bel, the young widow, with her striking red hair and rosy cheeks, and green-eyed Flo, as pale and slender as a lily.

Bel and Mr Fritz took to each other straight away and pretended to flirt extravagantly. On the last night of Bel's leave, he took both girls out to dinner. 'I wonder what Stella would say if she could see me now.' He chuckled. 'Every man in this restaurant is eyeing me enviously, wondering how such an insignificant little chap managed to get the two most beautiful women in Liverpool to dine with him.'

'Insignificant!' Bel screamed. 'You're dead attractive, you. If I was on the look-out for a feller, I'd grab you like a shot.'

Flo smiled. In the past, no one would have dreamed of describing Mr Fritz as attractive, but since returning from the camp he had acquired a gaunt, melancholy charm. The twins claimed he made their old hearts flutter dangerously, and Peggy declared herself bowled over.

That night, Flo and Bel sat up in bed together drinking their final mug of cocoa. 'I won't half miss you.' Flo sighed. 'The place will seem dead quiet after you've gone.'

'I'm ever so glad I came. It's the first time I've enjoyed meself since Bob was killed.'

'Remember the day we met?' said Flo. 'You were dead impatient because I was upset over Tommy O'Mara. Now you know how I felt.'

'There's a big difference.' Bel's voice was unexpectedly tart. 'Bob was worth crying over, not like Tommy O'Mara!'

'Oh, Bel! How can you say that when you never met him?'

Bel didn't answer straight away. 'Sorry, Flo,' she said eventually. 'It was just the impression I got. But you're well over him now, aren't you?'

'I'm not sure if I ever will be. I've never met a man who comes anywhere near him.' Perhaps if Hugh hadn't always been on her mind to remind her of Tommy's existence, she might have put the memory away.

'It's about time you got yourself a proper feller, girl,' Bel snorted, 'and stopped moping over a man who died three years ago. You're twenty-two. You should be married by now, or at least courting.'

'You sound just like our Martha.' Flo laughed.

'Which reminds me,' Bel went on. 'Why haven't I been to see your Martha's little girl?'

'I thought you didn't like babies.'

'I didn't until I lost the one I was expecting.' Bel's lovely face became unbearably sad. 'You've no idea what it feels like, Flo, having this little person growing inside you. When I had the miscarriage, it was like losing part of meself. Still,' she brightened, 'that's all in the past, and as Bob said to me in his lovely Scots accent just before he was posted to North Africa and we knew he might be killed, "I know you won't forget me, girl, but don't let the memory weigh you down, like unwanted baggage. Go light into the future." ' Bel sniffed briefly. 'He was ever so clever, my Bob.'

Flo envied her friend's resilience and ability to look ahead. She spent too much time looking back.

'Anyroad,' Bel persisted, 'what's your Martha's baby like?'

'I've no idea. I haven't seen her.'

Bel's reaction was entirely predictable. 'Why ever not?' she screeched.

'Because me and our Martha had a falling out.'

'What over?'

'Mind your own business,' Flo said irritably, and although Bel pressed for ages to know why, she refused to say another word.

Next morning, the two girls left for Lime Street station, Bel trim and smart in her khaki uniform. Mr Fritz had insisted Flo see her on to the train, even though it meant she'd be hours late for work. He bade Bel a mournful farewell. 'Take care of yourself in Egypt, there's a good girl.' He put his hand over his heart. 'I think I can already feel it breaking.'

Bel flung her arms around his neck. '*You*'re the heartbreaker, Fritz, you ould rascal. Us poor girls aren't safe with chaps like you around. I'm surprised those poor women in the laundry get any work done at all.'

The station was packed with servicemen and women returning from leave or *en route* elsewhere in the British Isles. Bel found herself a seat on the London train and leaned out of the window. 'He's a lovely chap, that Fritz,' she said.

'I know.' Flo nodded.

'I think he fancies you.'

Flo was aghast. 'Don't talk daft, Bel Knox! We're friends, that's all. I'm very fond of him, but he's got a wife and eight children in Ireland.'

Bel winked. 'I think he'd sooner be more than friends. Anyroad, it's over between him and Stella. He told me.'

'Yes, but it still makes him a married man. And they'll never get divorced, they're Catholics.'

'For goodness' sake, Flo. There's a war on. Forget he's married and let yourself go for once.'

The guard blew his whistle, the carriage doors were slammed, and the train began slowly to puff out of the station, Bel still hanging out of the window. Flo walked quickly along beside her. 'One of the first things you said to me was that you didn't approve of going out with married men.'

'Under the circumstances I'd make an exception in the case of you and Mr Fritz,' Bel said. By now, the train was going too fast for Flo to keep up. Bel shouted, 'Think about it, Flo!'

'The thing is,' Flo said under her breath, waving to the red-headed figure until the face was just a blur, 'I'm not sure if I fancy *him*, not in the way Bel's on about. I'm not sure if I'll ever fancy anyone again.'

3

1945

She recognised him immediately, a thin child, delicately boned like Flo herself, hair the colour of wheat. His round, innocent eyes were a beautiful dark green flecked with gold. The other children, boys first, had come charging through the school gates whooping like savages. He came alone, separate from the rest. She could guess one reason why he wasn't part of the gang: the other lads wore shabby jerseys and baggy pants but this five-year old was neatly dressed in grey shorts with a firmly pressed crease, pullover, flannel shirt. Hugh O'Mara was the only child wearing a blazer and tie. Nancy was a good mother, but not very sensitive. Flo would never have allowed her son to stand out in such a ridiculous get-up.

Flo watched as he approached, a sensation in her gut akin to the one she'd had the first time she was on her way to meet his father. She thought of all the times when she'd glimpsed a dark-haired woman with a pushchair on the far side of the Mystery, or crossing the street leading a small boy by the hand. Either it had been someone else, or the woman and child had disappeared when she had hurried to catch up.

Now he was here, and in a few seconds he would be close enough to touch. Not that she would dare. Not just yet.

'Hello,' she said.

He looked at her, and she searched in his eyes for recognition, as if it was inevitable he would sense she wasn't a stranger but his mam, his real flesh-and-blood mam. But there was nothing, just a shy glance.

'What's that you've got there?' she asked. Like all the other children, he was carrying a large brown envelope.

'A photo. It's of all the school taken together.'

'Can I see?'

He opened the envelope and took out the photo. 'The infants are at the front. That's me there.' He pointed to the end of the row, where he was sitting, knees crossed, looking serious. 'Mr Carey said I spoilt it 'cos I'm the only one not smiling.'

'Perhaps there wasn't much to smile about that day.' Flo turned the picture over. The photographer's name was stamped on the back, which meant she could buy a copy for herself.

'I didn't like having me photo taken much,' he said as they began to walk in the direction of Smithdown Road. 'Are you a friend of me mam's?'

'No, but I know some people she knows. I knew your dad quite well.'

His eyes lit up. 'Did ya? He died on a big ship under the sea, but the other boys won't believe me when I tell them.'

'*I* believe you,' Flo declared. 'I've got newspapers at home that tell all about it.'

'Can I come and see them?' he said eagerly. 'I can read a bit.'

There was nothing Flo would have liked more, but she said, 'I live too far away. Tell you what, though, I'll come next Friday and bring the papers with me. We can sit on the grass in the Mystery and I'll read them to you.'

'Can't you come before?' The crestfallen look on his thin face was almost too much to bear. Flo wanted to snatch him up and carry him away. He was much too serious for a five-year-old. She'd like to teach him to laugh and sing, be happy. But it would be cruel to take him from the woman he thought was his mother, the woman he loved more than he would ever love Flo.

She said, 'No, luv. I only get away from work on Fridays when I go to the bank. I should have been back ages ago. Me boss'll be wondering where I am.'

'Me mam works in a sweetshop.'

'I know. Someone told me.' Martha and Nancy O'Mara still saw each other occasionally. Through Sally, Flo had learned that Nancy served in the shop till five o'clock, leaving ninety minutes during which Flo could see her son, although she could only be with him for a fraction of that time because of her own job. St Theresa's junior and infants' school was a few minutes away from the laundry.

'She brings me pear drops home sometimes, and dolly mixtures.' Unexpectedly, he reached up and put his small hand in hers. Flo could barely breathe as she touched her child for the first time. She stroked the back of his fingers with her thumb, wanting to cry as all sorts of emotions tumbled through her head. She said, knowing it sounded stupid, 'I'd like to be your friend.'

He looked at her gravely. 'Me mam doesn't like me having friends.'

'Why not?' she asked in surprise.

'She said they're a bad inf–' He stumbled over the word and rolled his eyes. 'A bad inflex, or something.'

'A bad influence?'

' 'S right,' he said.

'Perhaps I could be your secret friend.'

'Yes, please. I'd like that.'

They arrived at the laundry, where Mr Fritz was standing by the door looking concerned. He hurried towards them. 'We were worried there'd been a hold-up at the bank. Peggy thought you might have been shot.'

'Peggy's seen too many films.'

'And who's this?' He looked at Hugh benignly.

'This is my friend, Hugh O'Mara.' Flo pushed her son forward. 'Hugh, say hello to me boss, Mr Fritz.'

'Hello,' Hugh said politely.

'Pleased to meet you, Hugh, old chap,' Mr Fritz said jovially.

Flo knelt in front of the little boy and said, in a whisper, 'If ever you're in trouble, this is where you can find me. I'm here every day from eight till half past five, and till one on Sat'days.' She stroked his cheek. 'Remember that, won't you, luv?'

He nodded. 'But I don't know your name!'

'It's Flo Clancy.'

'All right, Flo.'

'Tara, now. I'll see you next Friday.'

He trotted off in his smart clothes, clutching the brown envelope. Flo watched till he turned the corner, and still watched even after he'd gone, imagining him passing the shops in Smithdown Road on his way to Clement Street, where he would remain in the house, alone and friendless, until Nancy came.

'What's the matter, Flo?' Mr Fritz said gently.

'Nothing.' Flo returned to work, and it wasn't until she was inside that she became aware of the tears that were streaming down her cheeks.

For years Gerard Davies had been imploring Flo to marry him. After they'd first met in the Rialto, he'd come to Liverpool whenever he could and he wrote to her regularly. As far as he was concerned, Flo was his girl, his sweetheart. 'We'll see once the war's over,' Flo would say, whenever the subject of marriage was raised.

The war had been over for three months, the lights were on again and the celebrations, the parties, the dancing in the streets were just memories. Gerard Davies had been demobbed and was back in Swansea. He wrote to demand that Flo keep her promise.

He wasn't the only one of her young men to propose – she could have had half a dozen husbands by now – but he was the most persistent. Flo turned down the proposals as tactfully as she could. She didn't want to hurt anyone's feelings. They would never know that things hadn't been quite so wonderful for her as they had been for them. She put the lovely letters away to keep for always.

To Gerard Davies she wrote that she'd only said, 'We'll see,' when the war was over. She hadn't promised anything. She said that she liked him very, very much, and felt honoured that he wanted her for his wife, but he deserved to marry a woman who loved him far more than she did.

Perhaps it was unfortunate that she found Gerard's letter waiting on the doormat when she arrived home the day she'd met Hugh outside school for the first time, otherwise she might have given more serious consideration to his proposal. It would be nice to have a husband, children, a proper house. Sally, who was expecting her first baby in January, had got a nice council house in Huyton with gardens front and back. Jock would complete his naval service in two years' time and they would settle down and raise their family. And Bel had got married again in Egypt to a chap called Ivor, who claimed to be descended from the Hungarian royal family. She enclosed a photo of herself dressed in a lavish lace outfit standing next to a haughty young man with an undeniably regal manner. 'Ivor lives in the land of make-believe,' Bel wrote. 'He's no more royal than my big toe, but he makes me laugh. I'll never love another man the way I loved Bob, but me and Ivor are good company for each other. I'll be back in Liverpool very soon and you can see him for yourself.' The letter was signed, 'Bel (Szerb!)' and there was a PS. 'By the way, I think I'm pregnant!'

Why can't *I* make do with second best? Flo asked herself. Why am I haunted by memories of making love with Tommy O'Mara in the Mystery all those years ago? And why am I obsessed with the son I can never have? She knew that if she married Gerard, she would be only half a wife to him and half a mother to their children. It wouldn't be fair on him or them. She stuck the stamp on the envelope containing the letter to him, thumping it angrily with her fist.

When Bel returned, it was with news of another miscarriage. 'The doctor said I'll never carry a baby to full term. I've got a weak cervix,' she said. Flo nodded sympathetically, as if she knew what it meant.

Bel was upset, but determined not to take the doctor's verdict as final. 'Me and Ivor intend to try again. At least the trying's fun.' She winked. 'It's about time you got married and tried it, Flo.'

'Perhaps, one day.'

'I take it nothing came of you and Mr Fritz?'

'You were imagining things. We're just friends.'

Flo couldn't take to Ivor, whose manner was as haughty as his appearance. He expected his wife to wait on him hand and foot. Bel had a third miscarriage, and went to work behind the handbag counter in Owen Owen's department store, while Ivor lolled around in their flat in Upper Parliament Street, refusing so much as to wash a dish.

'He won't get a job,' Bel raged. She came round to Flo's often to complain and calm her nerves with sherry. 'Whenever I point out a suitable vacancy in the *Echo*, he claims it's beneath him.'

'But it's not beneath him to live off his wife?'

'Apparently not.' Bel snorted so loudly that Flo half expected flames to shoot out of her nostrils. 'I think I'll kick him out, get a divorce.'

'You should never have married him,' Flo said, with the benefit of hindsight.

'I know.' Bel uttered an enormous sigh. 'I don't half envy your Sally. Her little girl's a proper bobby-dazzler, and that Jock seems a dead nice feller.'

'Sal's already in the club again. She's making up for lost time now that Jock'll soon be home for good.'

'Have you been seeing Hugh O'Mara, luv?' Sally asked, one stormy December Sunday when Flo went to see her in Huyton.

'How did you find out?' Flo stammered.

'Someone told Nancy and she told our Martha.' Sally's face was misty with happiness as she nursed nine-month-old Grace on her lap.

'I've been meeting him outside school every Friday for more than a year – I suppose you think I'm daft.'

'Oh, no, luv. I might have done once, but not now.' Sally glanced at her daughter. 'I can't imagine how I'd have felt if someone had taken her away before I'd even seen her, or the little one I've got in here.' She patted her bulging stomach. 'Everyone was dead cruel, Flo, me included. I thought keeping the baby would ruin your life.'

Instead, it was the other way round, Flo thought wryly. 'Is Nancy mad at me?'

'Martha couldn't make out if she was or not. She seemed more resigned than anything. I suppose she thinks it can't do much harm now.'

'I don't suppose it can,' said Flo. 'How is our Martha?' She only asked because it would please Sally, who was forever trying to reunite the sisters.

Sally grimaced and said, predictably, 'I wish you'd go and see her, Flo. She's dead miserable. Kate's starting school in January, and she'll be stuck in the house with Elsa Cameron who's completely off her rocker now. The last time I went she was singing hymns the whole time. By rights, Martha should find a place of her own, but although you'll say she only wants to interfere, Flo, she's not prepared to leave Elsa in sole charge of Norman or the woman's quite likely to kill the poor bugger. Anyroad, Norman would be lost without little Kate. They've been brought up together, and he worships the ground she walks on.'

Hugh O'Mara emerged from school wearing a woollen balaclava, a long fringed scarf, and the horrible navy-blue belted mackintosh that Flo thought made him look like a miniature gas man.

It was another terrible winter, bleaker and icier even than the notorious winter of 1940, and the fuel shortages and power cuts made it seem even worse. Food remained rationed, and in such an austere atmosphere it was hard to believe that Great Britain had won the war.

There was a little girl with Hugh, a pretty child, like a fairy, with long fair hair. She wore three-quarter-length socks and patent-leather shoes, and her winter coat was much too big. There was something familiar about her face, though Flo couldn't remember having seen her before.

'I've got another friend,' Hugh beamed happily at Flo. 'She only started last week, but I knew her before school. Me mam goes to their house sometimes. She's nearly two years younger than me, but that doesn't mean we can't be friends.'

'Of course it doesn't, luv.' He would be seven in a month's time and was shooting upwards like a vigorous sapling. Flo had already bought his present, a toy car. If you twisted the steering wheel, the four wheels turned. She was taking the risk that Nancy wouldn't object.

'Can she come with us to the Mystery?' Hugh said eagerly. 'Have you brought the ball?'

Flo was about to say the little girl should ask her mam first, when another boy came up, a dark, handsome lad of about ten, with an ugly purple and yellow bruise on his forehead. She'd noticed him before. He was a bully and most of the children kept well out of his way. He put a possessive hand on the little girl's shoulder. 'I've got to take her home,' he said, scowling. 'We live in the same house together.' He turned to Hugh and spat, 'You leave her alone, Hugh O'Mara.'

'Don't you dare speak to him like that,' Flo said angrily.

The boy ignored her and pulled the child away. 'C'mon, Kate.'

'Is that Kate Colquitt?' Flo enquired, when the children had gone.

'Yes. Do you know her?'

'I'm her auntie.'

'You never are!' Hugh's brow creased in disbelief. 'I don't understand.'

'Her mam and me are sisters,' Flo explained carefully. Then she said, 'The boy with Kate, is that Norman Cameron?'

'Yes.' Hugh wrinkled his thin shoulders. 'He's not very nice. I don't like him. No one does, not even his mam.'

'Perhaps he can't help not being very nice.' She recalled sadly what a beautiful baby Norman had been, so happy – there was a photo somewhere in the flat, taken on his first birthday, that Martha had given her at the time. She hadn't realised the three children would be at the same school – Hugh and Kate were cousins, not that they'd ever know.

Flo took a rubber ball out of her bag and began to bounce it. 'C'mon, I'll race you to the Mystery. Whoever's last has to climb to the top of the tallest tree and shout "Hallelujah" ten times.' She always won, but Hugh's legs were getting longer. As soon as he was likely to get there first, she'd have to think of a less demanding penalty.

1949

Mr Fritz was stepping out with Mrs Winters, a widow who had tightly permed black hair and wore smart, tailored suits with very short skirts, though her legs were much too thick for ankle-strap shoes – or so Bel claimed when she saw them together. 'I don't like the look of her, Flo. Once she's installed upstairs you'll be out on your arse.'

'Oh, don't!' said Flo. She felt hurt and a touch dismayed, as if Mr Fritz was letting her down. Somehow, unreasonably, she'd considered herself the only woman he wanted in his life, though their relationship had always been strictly platonic.

'It's a pity he and Stella can't get divorced,' Bel remarked. It had taken her several years to get rid of Ivor. 'Still, I suppose the poor chap's got to dip his wick somewhere. I'm glad I'm a woman and not panting for it all the time.'

Mrs Winters lasted only two months. 'I couldn't stand the way she stuck her little finger out like a flagpole when she drank her tea,' Mr Fritz confessed to Flo. 'I felt I wanted to hang something on it.' He stared at her gloomily. 'What happened to your chap from the income-tax office?'

'I gave him up. We didn't have much in common.' All Ray Meadows had wanted to talk about was figures. Bel had tried to insist that Flo encourage him. 'He's dead keen, I can tell, and a good prospect. You're not getting any younger – you'll be thirty next year.' But Flo had decided, once and for all, that she would sooner remain single than marry a man she didn't love wholeheartedly. Books and the cinema provided all the romance and excitement she needed, especially as things usually ended happily. She enjoyed the quiet of her flat, buried half under the ground, drinking sherry, and feeling pleasantly cut off from the real world. Her only regret was that she no longer had a family. She missed the love that Mam and Dad had bestowed on her, and since Sally's son, Ian, had developed muscular dystrophy at the age of two, poor little lad, Flo saw her sister rarely now. Whenever she went to Huyton, Sal and Jock seemed so wrapped up in anxiety for their son that Flo felt in the way. Of course, there was always Martha, but if it hadn't been for her, Flo would have had a son of her own for the past nine years.

'I've been invited to the Isle of Man for the weekend in July,' Mr Fritz said, with the air of a man who'd been asked to attend his own funeral. 'Some of the chaps from the camp are having a reunion. Trouble is, they're taking their wives. I've no one to take.'

By now, half of the little Fritzes were in their twenties. The previous year Mr Fritz had been invited to Ben's wedding but had refused to go. 'I'd feel most peculiar,' he said, 'like a stranger at the feast.' A few weeks ago, he'd received a card to say Ben's wife had given birth to a son. He was a grandfather, which made him feel even more peculiar, and also very old, though he was only fifty.

'I'm sure not every chap will be bringing a wife,' Flo said briskly. 'You'll probably have quite a nice time.'

Over the next few weeks, he continued to raise the subject of the reunion, saying miserably, 'I hate the idea of going by myself.' Or, 'It wouldn't have to be a wife. It would be enough to take a friend.'

'If that's the case, why not ask Mrs Winters?' Flo suggested. 'It's only a few days, and you could put up with her little finger for that long, surely.'

'No, no,' he said, distractedly. 'There's someone else I'd far sooner go with.'

Two days before he was due to leave, he came down to the basement, where he sat, sighing continuously and staring moodily into the gas fire, which wasn't even lit. After half an hour of this, Flo said, 'Bel will be round in a minute. We're going to see *The Keys of the Kingdom* at the Odeon. She's mad about Gregory Peck.'

'Gregory Peck's got everything,' he said despondently. 'I bet he wouldn't be stuck for someone to take with him to the Isle of Man.'

Flo burst out laughing. 'If you carry on like this much longer, I'll offer to go with you meself.'

To her astonishment, he jumped to his feet and caught both her hands in his. 'Oh, *would* you, Flo? I've been wanting to ask for weeks.' His brown eyes were shining in a face that had suddenly come alive. 'We'll have separate rooms, of course we will. My intentions are strictly honourable. And we'll have a lovely time. Joe Loss and his orchestra are playing at the Villa Marina. I haven't been dancing in years.'

'But ...' Flo began.

'But what, my dear girl?' he cried.

Everyone she knew, apart from Bel, would disapprove, despite the separate bedrooms and Bel would ask loads of embarrassing questions. Even so, perhaps it was the same lack of caution that had led her to accept Tommy O'Mara's invitation a decade ago, because all Flo said was, 'Oh, all right. But I don't want Bel and the women in the laundry to know. They'll only get the wrong idea.'

He put a finger to his lips. 'You can count on me not to breathe a word to a soul.'

Flo sat on the edge of the double bed and stared out of the hotel window at the choppy, green-brown waves of the Irish Sea. A large black and white ship with a red funnel was approaching Douglas, spewing white foam in its wake. It was the ship on which they would return to Liverpool.

The sky was overcast, the clouds leaden, as if about to unleash another downpour, and the pavements were still wet from the rain that had fallen all night long and the whole of the previous day. Holidaymakers wandered past forlornly in their plastic raincoats, some of the children carrying buckets and spades.

In the *en suite* bathroom, Mr Fritz could be heard humming as he shaved. At the initial gathering of the ex-internees, a man had shouted, 'Fritz Hofmannsthal, you old rascal! How are you?' and she'd been amazed when Mr Fritz went over and shook his hand.

'I didn't realise that was your name,' she whispered.

'I told you it was a mouthful,' he whispered back.

After proudly introducing her all round as 'My dear friend, Miss Florence Clancy,' Mr Fritz seemed to forget he was supposed to be at a reunion. That night, when they should have been at a special dinner, but were tangoing to 'Jealousy' in the Villa Marina, he said, 'Who wants to celebrate a miserable experience like that? It's the sort of thing I'd sooner forget.'

The first night she'd spent alone in the single bedroom he'd booked for her on the floor above. Yesterday, Sunday, they breakfasted together at a table by the window in the dining room with its cream and maroon striped Regency wallpaper. It was raining cats and dogs, and the sky was so dark that the red-shaded wall lamps had been switched on, making the large room cosy and intimate.

'This is nice,' said Mr Fritz. He touched her hand. 'This is lovely.'

They caught a taxi to Mass and back again, then read the newspapers and drank coffee in the hotel lounge until it was time for lunch. Afterwards, they battled their way through the wind and rain to an amusement arcade, then, in the afternoon, they went to the pictures to see *Notorious* with Cary Grant and Ingrid Bergman. 'I must confess,' Mr Fritz said at dinner, 'that I've always nursed a soft spot for Ingrid Bergman.'

They took their time over the meal and it was ten o'clock by the time the wine was finished. They transferred to the bar for a cocktail, and continued to talk about things of mutual interest: the laundry, the little Fritzes, Flo's family, the house in William Square.

It was an unremarkable few days, yet Flo had rarely enjoyed herself more. It was nice to be with someone she knew so much about. There were no awkward silences, no mad scrambling through her mind for what to say next. She'd known Mr Fritz for more than half her life and they were entirely comfortable with each other.

The clock was striking midnight when he offered to escort her upstairs to her room on the third floor. When they reached the second floor, he paused and looked grave. 'Flo, would you, could you . . .' He gestured along the corridor and stuttered, 'Would you consider doing me the honour of – of –'

After their lovely time together, Flo had anticipated that this might happen and was quite prepared. What harm would it do? None, she had decided. Furthermore, she had no intention of making herself out to be a shy virgin and pretending to be coy. If Stella had known she'd had a baby, then so must he. As he looked incapable of saying the words he wanted, she said them for him. 'Of sleeping with you tonight?'

He was an ardent, yet gentle lover. Flo experienced none of the passion there had been with Tommy O'Mara, but as she hadn't expected to she wasn't disappointed. When it was over, she felt cherished and satisfied. Afterwards they sat up in bed like an old married couple. 'We must do this again, Flo,' he said warmly. 'Perhaps next month, August.'

'I'd like that.' She laid her head affectionately on his shoulder.

'In that case, I'll book a double room in a different hotel, and we'll be Mr and Mrs Hofmannsthal.'

'But we'll still be Miss Clancy and Mr Fritz back in Liverpool?'

He looked at her quizzically. 'I think that would be wise, don't you? Friends at home, lovers in the Isle of Man. That way, you're less likely to tire of me. It can be our little monthly treat, our little adventure. You know,' he breathed happily, 'I've always been a tiny bit in love with you ever since the day you came to the laundry for an interview all those years ago.'

So Bel had been right, after all. Flo squeezed his arm. 'I've always been very fond of you.'

'Let's hope Stella didn't notice, eh?'

She couldn't be bothered telling him that Stella had, because it was too late to do anything about it.

'I suppose we should get some sleep,' he suggested. She slid under the covers and he bent and kissed her forehead. 'We have to be up early to catch the boat home.'

He had fallen asleep immediately, but Flo had lain wondering what she'd tell Bel when she went away again in four weeks' time. She wasn't sure why, but she preferred keeping her relationship with Mr Fritz a secret, even from her best friend. Right now, Bel thought she'd gone on retreat to a convent in Wales. I'll say I'm going on another one. It fits in with the image she's got of me. Let her go on thinking I'm as dull as ditchwater . . .

'The boat's just about to dock, Mr Fritz,' she called.

He came out of the bathroom smiling, a towel tucked under his chin, patting his cheeks. His kindly, good-natured face looked young this morning, almost boyish. 'I think we can dispense with the Mr, don't you, Flo?'

As she smiled back, she felt a surge of emotion, not real love but almost. 'I'd sooner not, if you don't mind. I'll always think of you as Mr Fritz.'

Millie

1

I'd been so engrossed in Flo's love letters that I'd forgotten about the time. I'd be late for work if I didn't hurry. I dragged on the red suit and T-shirt I'd worn the day before, and combed my hair in the car when I stopped at traffic lights. The car behind hooted angrily as I was putting on my lipstick.

Halfway through the morning I answered the phone for the umpteenth time, doing my utmost not to sound as harassed as I felt.

'It's me,' James said humbly.

If I followed my instincts and slammed down the receiver, he would only ring back. 'What do you want?' I snapped.

'To see you, to apologise.'

'I'll take the apology for granted. There's no need for us to see each other.'

'Millie, darling, I don't know what came over me. Let's have dinner tonight. Let me explain.' He sounded desperate, but I hadn't forgotten that he'd raised his fist to strike me. I wasn't interested in explanations or apologies. I could never forgive him.

'I'd sooner not.'

'Please, Millie.' He was almost sobbing. 'Please, darling, I have to see you.'

'Look, James, I'm very busy. I don't like to be rude, but I'm going to ring off. Goodbye.'

An hour later, a van drew up outside the office and a girl came in with a bouquet of red roses for Miss Millicent Cameron; two dozen, surrounded by fern, wrapped in gold paper and tied with copious amounts of scarlet ribbon. There was no card, but only one person could have sent them. I thought them ostentatious, but Diana was impressed. I dumped the flowers on her desk. 'In that case, they're yours. Your father might like them.'

'But they must cost the earth!' Diana protested.

'I don't care. I don't want them.' I changed the subject. 'How's your father?'

Diana's face brightened. 'Much improved. We think he might be in remission. It happens sometimes with cancer. Yesterday I took him to Otterspool, and we had a picnic in the car. I can't think why we've never done things like that before.'

'My mother was talking about moving away from Liverpool, and I suddenly realised how much I'd miss her.' I'd never mentioned anything about my family to Diana before, and felt that I'd made the first gesture towards friendship.

We came to the conclusion that most children took their parents too much for granted, and agreed to lunch together if we could get away at the same time. Diana hissed, 'Is George still cross with me over those notes? I suppose I've blown my chances with that job I was after.'

'The job's Oliver's. It always was. As for the notes, I bet George has forgotten all about them.'

'God, I hope so.' Diana pursed her lips. 'I made a terrible cock-up there. I envy you, Millie. You never do anything to rock the boat. You're always so meek and pliable. Men prefer women they think they can control. George doesn't like me because I'm too independent.' It might have been unintentional, but there was a strong note of spite in her voice. She touched a rose. 'No one's ever sent me flowers like this.'

Whether she meant it or not, I still felt affronted. Meek and pliable? Me? I bent my head over my work, and decided to be too busy when Diana suggested it was time for lunch.

After work, I drove to Blundellsands to do some washing and take a shower. There was a message from James on the answering-machine, which I refused to listen to. I switched off the machine and rang my mother. 'Is everything okay, Mum?'

'Everything's fine, luv. Why?'

'It's just that my answering-machine's broken, I'll be out most nights this week and I didn't want you to worry.' Nor did I want a repeat of the Birmingham episode. During the week ahead, a minor crisis of one sort or another was bound to occur in the Cameron household and Mum would need someone to talk to. 'Call me at the office if something important crops up,' I told her.

'As long as it won't get you into trouble, luv.'

It wouldn't, I assured her. 'What will you be up to the nights you're out?' she asked.

I imagined telling the truth: that I would be sleeping with the grandson of the man who'd broken Flo Clancy's heart almost sixty years ago. I said,

'I thought it was time I put in a few more hours at Auntie Flo's. I'm getting nowhere at this rate.'

'I'm sorry you were landed with it, Millicent. I never thought it'd turn out to be such a mammoth task.'

'I'm quite enjoying it.'

'Gran said you'd met Bel Szerb.'

'Bel who?'

'Szerb. At least, that's how I knew her. I think she got married again. She was a dead scream, Bel was.'

'She still is.' After impressing on her that she must nag Declan to apply for a college course, I rang off. The washing had finished its cycle so I hung it over the bath, packed a bag and made my way to William Square and Tom O'Mara.

When I got out of the car, Peter Maxwell was going down the steps to his flat with several files under his arm. He wore jeans, a thick check shirt and a donkey jacket. He grinned at me through the railings. 'Hi! Fancy a coffee and a chocolate biccy?'

'I wouldn't mind.' His laid-back, easy-going manner was welcome after James's histrionics.

His flat was completely different from next door: red-tiled floor, red curtains and white walls hung with abstract paintings. It was a man's room. Apart from the paintings and a single white-shaded lamp, there were no other ornaments and the furniture was minimal, mainly of natural wood. Two armchairs were upholstered in black and white check. The effect was cool and airy, tranquil, giving the impression that the occupant was at peace with himself, which I envied.

'This isn't a bit like Flo's,' I remarked. Another difference was that everywhere was warm due to the two large radiators, one at each end of the room.

'I know. I'll just put the kettle on.' He took off his coat, hung it behind the door and disappeared into the kitchen. When he came back, he said, 'I used to see your auntie at least once a week. It was my job to get rid of the bottles.'

'What bottles?'

He grinned. 'The sherry bottles. She didn't want Charmian, the binmen and that aged but gorgeous red-head to know how much she was drinking. Flo was knocking back more than a bottle a day over the last year. She was a nice old girl, though. I liked her.'

'I only saw her once, at another great-aunt's funeral.'

'I wish I'd known you two were related. Flo would have been tickled pink to know we'd been in the same class at school.' He disappeared into the kitchen again, returning with two mugs of coffee and a packet of Jaffa cakes. 'I'm a lousy house-husband. I'm afraid my cupboards are bare. I hope you've eaten.'

'I keep forgetting to eat.'

He ran his fingers through his beard, which already looked like an untidy bird's nest, and said thoughtfully, 'I'm sure there's a tin of corned beef and a packet of instant spuds out there. I'll knock you up a plate of corned-beef hash if you like?'

'No thanks.' I shuddered. 'That's one of my mother's favourite dishes. It would remind me too much of home.'

'I used to feel like that about *Coronation Street*,' he said. 'Me mam never missed a single episode, and the house had to be dead quiet. You daren't sneeze else you'd get a belt around the ear. For years afterwards if I passed a house and heard the music I got goosebumps.'

We stared at each other and laughed. 'Memories, eh!' he said wryly.

At the end of the room, I noticed there were french windows leading to the tiny yard.

'I had them put in last year.' He looked quite houseproud. 'It's nice to have them open in summer, brightens up the place no end. That's how I met Flo. We used to gab to each other over the garden wall.'

'Does that mean you actually own this flat? It's not rented?' I said, surprised.

'I own about a quarter, the building society has the rest.'

'I can't imagine anyone choosing to live round here if they didn't have to,' I said incredulously.

'How dare you criticise my place of abode, Miss Cameron?' he said mildly. 'I love Toxteth. I've been broken into twice, but that can happen anywhere. The people round here are the salt of the earth, including the girls who hang around the square. Okay, so it's violent, but otherwise it's a good place to live, steeped in atmosphere and history. This is the closest to how Liverpool was when it was the greatest port in the world. And did you know that, centuries ago, Toxteth was a royal park where King John used to hunt deer and wild boar?'

'I'm afraid that piece of information has been denied me until now.'

'If you like, I'll take you on a tour one day, show you precisely where his hunting lodges were situated.'

'I *would* like — it sounds fascinating.'

He looked chuffed. 'Then it's a date.'

I stayed for another cup of coffee before going next door. A scantily clad Fiona was shivering against the railings. To my surprise, she deigned to speak. 'There's been someone looking for you. She said she'd come back another time. It wasn't Bel or Charmian. It was someone else.'

'Thanks for telling me.'

Fiona yawned. 'Any time.'

As usual the air in Flo's flat smelt damp, and it was freezing cold. I turned the fire on full blast and knelt before the hissing jets, shivering and rubbing my hands, thinking enviously of Peter Maxwell's central heating. When the heat became too much, I retreated to my favourite spot on the settee and promptly fell asleep. It was nearly midnight when I woke up and my legs were covered with red blotches from the fire. Everywhere was still and quiet outside and the flat felt as if it was in a time warp, engulfed in flickering shadows and divorced from anything real.

My life's becoming more and more surreal, I thought. I scarcely ate, slept at the most peculiar times, spent hardly any time at home, and had lost interest in my job, though I still worked hard and hoped George hadn't noticed. Worst of all, I was having an affair with a man who was the epitome of everything I normally loathed about men. Things that had once seemed important, no longer mattered.

I went into the bedroom and changed into a nightdress, Flo's quilted dressing-gown, and her pink slippers, then sprayed myself with perfume ready for Tom, who might arrive at any minute. Until he came, I'd sort out a few more of Flo's papers.

With a sense of anticipation usually reserved for the start of a film or a television programme I was looking forward to, I settled in front of the bureau. The first thing I picked up was a bundle of letters from Bel sent during the war. It didn't seem proper to read them so I put them to one side in case Bel would like them back.

Next, a large, very old brown envelope with 'Wythenshaw's Photographic Studios – Portraits a Speciality' printed on the top left-hand corner. Predictably, it contained a photograph and, as I pulled it out, I wondered why Flo hadn't put it on the table with the others. It was a school photo: five rows of children, the smallest ones sitting cross-legged at the front. A boy at the end of the front row, the only child not smiling, had been circled with pencil.

What on earth was Flo doing with a photo of our Declan? I looked at the back, but there was only a stamped date, September 1945, a third of a century before Declan was born. There was something else inside the envelope, a piece of yellowing paper folded into four. It was a crude, crayon drawing of a woman with sticks for limbs, yellow hair and gooseberry green eyes. Her mouth was a huge upwards red curve, and she wore a blue dress shaped like a triangle with three buttons as big as Smarties down the front. Underneath was printed, in a careful, childish hand, 'MY FREND FLO'. There was a name at the bottom written in pencil: Hugh O'Mara.

Tom's father must have done the drawing I held in my hand. Despite the stick limbs and the mouth that stretched from ear to ear, there was something undeniably real and alive about the woman, as though the youthful artist had done his utmost to convey the inward radiance of his friend Flo. That both items had been together in the envelope meant that the child in the photograph was almost certainly Hugh O'Mara. I would have loved to have shown it to Tom, but Flo must have had a reason for keeping the photo hidden, and it seemed only right to respect it.

Tom had arrived – I could hear his light footsteps, and forgot about photographs, forgot about everything, as I waited for the sound of his key in the door. He came prowling in, a graceful, charismatic figure, despite the tasteless electric blue suit and white frilly shirt. No words were spoken as we stared at each other across the room. Then I got up and walked into his arms and we began to kiss each other hungrily. It was less than twenty-four hours since we'd parted, yet we kissed as if the gap had been much, much longer.

Another bouquet arrived at the office next morning, this time pink and white carnations. I found a vase and put them in the reception area. 'Diana's late.' June remarked. 'I thought she would have called by now.'

When she still hadn't arrived by midday, George approached me. 'Should I ring to see if she's all right? I'm still annoyed with her, but I suppose she's had it rough lately, and it wouldn't hurt to let her know we're concerned.'

'Would you like me to do it?'

'I was hoping you'd take the hint.' He looked relieved.

When I dialled Diana's home there was no reply. 'Perhaps her father's been taken to hospital again,' I suggested.

George had already lost interest. 'Can I buy you lunch?' He jingled the coins in his pocket. 'I'm desperately in need of a shoulder to cry on. I had a letter from Bill this morning. He and Annabel will stay with me over Christmas but, reading between the lines, I could tell they'd sooner not. They're only coming because their mother's off somewhere exotic with her new husband – his name's Crispin, would you believe?'

'I'm sorry, George, but I'm lunching with my sister, and I've an appointment at the Old Roan with the Naughtons at half past two. Perhaps tonight, after work?'

'You're on,' George said glumly, as he mooched into his office. 'I think I'm about to have a panic attack.'

Trudy had phoned earlier. 'Mum said you'd gone to William Square last night, but you weren't there when I called. That girl draped around the railings, is she what I suspect she is?'

I confirmed that she definitely was.

'Will you be there tonight if I come at the same time? I need to talk to someone and there's only you.'

'I'm not sure when I'll get away,' I said quickly. It was selfish, but I didn't want my sister in Flo's flat, which I regarded as my own property until the place was ready for another tenant – which seemed further away than ever. 'Are you free for lunch?' I enquired. 'My treat.'

'I thought you always worked through lunch?'

'I won't today,' I promised.

We met in Central Precinct under the high domed glass roof, where a woman was playing old familiar tunes on a white grand piano, her fingers rippling languorously up and down the keys. Trudy was already seated at a wrought-iron table, looking very smart in a dark green jacket, long black skirt and lace-up boots. We made a pretty pair, the Cameron sisters, I thought wryly: elegant, with our nice clothes, discreetly made-up faces, and lovely ash blonde hair. No one glancing at us would have guessed at our wretched childhood, though Trudy's face was rather pinched and tight, I thought.

'I've never been here before,' she said, when I sat down. 'I love the pianist.'

'Have you noticed what she's playing?' The strains of 'Moon River' came from the piano. 'Mum's favourite.'

Trudy's laugh was rather strained as she rubbed the scar above her left eyebrow. 'There's no escape, is there?'

When I returned from the counter with prawn salads and two giant cream cakes, she said, 'I've just been thinking about the way Mum used to sing it when us kids had been knocked black and blue, and Dad had probably had a go at her.'

'It was her way of coping, I suppose.' I ate several prawns with my fingers – it was my first proper meal since Sunday. 'What did you want to talk about, Sis?' I was reluctant to rush her, but I had to meet the Naughtons in an hour's time.

Trudy was shoving her food around the plate with her fork. 'I don't know where to begin,' she muttered.

'The beginning?'

'That's too far.'

I raised my eyebrows. 'I don't understand.'

My sister threw her fork on to the plate with a sigh. 'It's Colin,' she said.

A knot of fear formed in my stomach. 'What's he done?'

'Nothing,' Trudy said simply. 'He's a good, decent man. I love him, and he loves me, and he adores Melanie and Jake. He works all the hours God sends for us.'

'Then what's the problem, Trude?'

'I don't trust him.' Trudy put her elbows on the table and regarded me with abject misery.

'You mean you think he's having an affair?'

'Of course not. He wouldn't dream of it.' Trudy shook her head impatiently. 'It's nothing to do with affairs. It's to do with the children. Oh, Lord!' She dabbed her eyes with the paper napkin. 'I'm going to cry. Have I smudged my mascara?'

'A bit.' I reached out and rubbed under her eyes. A woman at the next table was watching with interest, but turned away when she saw I'd noticed.

'It's my painting, you see.' Trudy sighed. 'There must be two hundred bottles, jars, decanters and demijohns in the shed, all finished. I've painted light-bulbs, plates, tumblers, brandy glasses – we get them from car-boot sales. The children think it's great, looking for glassware for Mum to paint. And I love doing it, Millie. I get quite carried away, thinking up new ideas, new patterns, and I can't wait to see how they'll turn out. But what am I supposed to do with the damn things?' she said plaintively.

'Sell them,' I said promptly. I still hadn't grasped what the problem was. 'Didn't Colin suggest you have a stall and he'll look after the kids?'

'Yes. But I don't trust him, Mill. I feel terrible about it, but I don't trust him with me children for an entire day. I'm scared he'll hit them, and if he did I'd have to leave.'

I was beginning to make sense of things. 'Has he ever done anything to make you think he would so much as lay a finger on them?' I asked.

'No!'

'In that case, don't you think you're being a bit paranoid?' I said. 'More than a bit, in fact. Over-the-top paranoid, if you ask me.'

'I know I am. But I still can't bring meself to leave them. Colin's nagging me soft to start a stall. There's a church hall in Walton where they have a craft fair every Sunday. He can't understand why I keep putting it off.'

'Neither can I. Our father wrecked our childhood, and now you're letting him wreck your marriage. You've got to trust Colin, Trude. You've *got* to.' Even as I spoke, I recalled James, his fist raised . . . 'I think all of us are capable of violence when the chips are down, but only a very perverted person would hit children the way our father hit us.'

Trudy gnawed her bottom lip. 'I must admit I've smacked Jake's bottom once or twice. He can be a little bugger when he's in the mood.'

'Was Colin there?'

'Yes. He was ever so cross and said I must never do it again.'

'But he didn't leave!' I cried. 'And knowing your history – that children who've been abused often abuse their own children – it's *him* who should be worried about leaving Melanie and Jake with *you*! Think how upset you'd be if you thought he suspected you'd hurt them! He's always trusted you, and he deserves your trust. Start the stall now in case he guesses why you're putting it off. He might never forgive you if he does.'

Trudy began to attack her salad. 'I'm glad I talked to you, Sis. I never looked at it like that before.' She paused, a forkful of prawns halfway to her mouth. 'I wonder if Dad was hit when he was little?'

'That's something we'll never know.'

I thought about it later on the way to the Old Roan. The only feelings I'd ever had for my father were fear as a child, and loathing as I grew older. But could there have been a reason for his behaviour? For the first time in my life, I wondered if a badly damaged human being could be lurking inside the monster I'd always known.

The Naughtons found the garden of the property in Old Roan much too big, and I drove back to work irritated by the waste of time.

When I went in, George announced 'Diana's father's dead. She called earlier. He passed away peacefully in his sleep during the night.'

'How did she sound?'

'As hard as nails,' George said indignantly. 'You'd think she was calling to say her car wouldn't start.'

'She's putting it on. I reckon she's devastated.'

'You're an exceedingly charitable person, Ms Millicent Cameron. Anyway, the funeral's Friday afternoon.' He drooped. 'I suppose I'd better put in an appearance, represent the firm, as it were.'

'Do you mind if I come with you?'

'Mind? Of course not. I've rarely had a more welcome offer.'

Later, I called my mother with the news – she was always ghoulishly interested in hearing about a death. 'How old was he?'

'A good eighty,' I replied. 'Diana's parents were middle-aged when she was born.' I decided to change the subject. 'I met our Trudy for lunch.'

'That's nice, luv,' Mum said. 'I like it when you two get together.'

'Perhaps the three of us could have lunch one day, you and me and Trude. You'd love the restaurant, Mum.'

'Oh, I dunno, luv,' she said, flustered. 'I'd never get back in time to do your dad's tea.'

I assured her she'd have bags of time and my father needn't know anything.

'I'll think about it,' she promised.

'You'll have to do more than think, Mum,' I said. 'I'm going to badger you rotten till you say yes.'

There was a pause. 'You sound happy, Millicent. Has something nice happened? Has James proposed?'

'James is history, Mum. Perhaps I'm happy because I've just had lunch with my sister.'

'Whatever it is, luv, I'm glad. You were getting very hard. Not long ago, you wouldn't have dreamed of asking your mam out to lunch. Now, what's all this about James being history?'

Apart from George and me, there were only five other mourners at the funeral: Diana, stiff and unemotional, two women neighbours, and two old men who'd been friends of Diana's father.

It was a bone-chilling November day and a wind flecked with ice blew through the cemetery, whisking in and out of the gravestones, stripping the last few leaves off the trees.

'I didn't think people got buried any more,' George muttered, through chattering teeth. 'I thought they popped 'em in an oven. At least it'd be warmer for the mourners.'

I watched the coffin being lowered into the grave, then the vicar said a few respectful words, and Diana came over and thanked us for coming. I took her hand as we walked towards the cars, George trailing behind.

'I'm sorry about your father. At least he didn't suffer much pain.'

'No, and as everyone keeps saying, he had a good innings.' Diana removed her hand. 'You get over these things. From now on, I'll be able to live my life as I please.'

'If you need someone to talk to,' I said gently, 'then don't hesitate to ring. If I'm not there, I'll be at number one William Square. There's no phone, so you'll just have to turn up.'

'Thank you, Millie, but I'm fine. I can't understand people who go to pieces when somebody dies.'

2

Church bells pealed, nearby and far away, high-pitched and rippling, deep-toned and sonorous. I opened my eyes: a cold sun shimmered through the white curtains, and Tom O'Mara was leaning over me. His brown hair was loose, framing his long face. If it hadn't been for the earrings and the tattoo, he would have resembled one of the saints in the pictures I'd taken down.

'I was just wondering,' he said, 'what is it between us two?'

'I don't know what you're talking about.'

'I mean, the truth is, you're an uppity bitch, full of airs and graces, and your accent gets on me wick.'

My lips quivered as I traced the outline of the heart on his chest. 'I've always steered clear of your sort, and the way you speak sets my teeth on edge.'

He pulled the bedclothes down to my waist and buried his head in my breasts. 'So, what is it between us two?' he asked again. His lips fastened on my left breast, and I squealed in delight when his tongue touched the nipple.

'I haven't a clue,' I gasped truthfully. The deep-down feeling of intimacy was frightening, because I couldn't visualise there ever being an end. The bells were still ringing as we made love, and it wasn't until it was over that I said, 'Why are you still here?' He'd usually gone before sunrise and Flo's alarm clock showed almost half past nine.

'Me wife's taken the girls to see her mam. I thought we'd spend the day together, or at least part of it. I've got to be at the club by five.'

I was thrilled at the notion of spending the day in bed with Tom O'Mara, but he had other ideas. 'C'mon, let's have summat to eat and we'll be off.'

'Off where?' I sat up and blew the hair out of my eyes. Tom was getting dressed.

'Southport.'

'Why Southport?'

'I'll tell you later, after we've had some grub.' He pulled on a blue polo-neck sweater, and went over to the mirror, where he combed his hair and scooped it back into a ponytail with an elastic band. I watched, entranced. It was such a feminine gesture coming from such an overwhelmingly masculine man. 'Me stomach thinks me throat's been cut,' he said. 'I'm starving.'

'There isn't any "grub", as you call it, except for a few old packets of biscuits.'

He groaned. 'In that case, I'll just have a cup of tea and we'll get something to eat on the way. The pubs'll be open by then.'

The sun was as bright as a lemon, and little white clouds were chasing each other across the pale blue sky. The wind was dry and crisp and very cold. I stuffed my hands in the pockets of my tan overcoat, glad that I was wearing boots – after the funeral yesterday I'd gone home for some warm clothes.

Tom's car, a silver-blue Mercedes, was parked round the corner, a suede coat on the back seat. I remarked that he was taking a risk, leaving an expensive coat in full view. 'Someone might steal it.'

'It would be more than their life was worth.' His lips curled. 'Everyone knows whose car this is. They wouldn't dare touch it.'

'You sound like a Mafia godfather!' The words were meant as an insult, but Tom's face was impassive as he replied, 'No one's going to rip me off and get away with it, and the same goes for me friends and family. That's why Flo was always safe in her place. People round here know what's good for them, and that means not mucking around with anything belonging to Tom O'Mara.'

'I see.' The ominous message that lay beyond his words was repellent, yet I didn't hesitate to get into the car with him. I felt very aware of his closeness, the way he held the steering wheel, his long brown hand touching the gear lever.

'What are you looking at?' he asked.

'You. I haven't seen you in daylight before.'

He slid a disc into the CD player and a man with a hard, angry voice began to sing 'The Wild Rover'. 'I love Irish music,' he said. Then he looked at me in a way that made me catch my breath. 'You look great in daylight.' He started up the engine and steered aggressively into the traffic. 'But you're doing me head in, girl. I wish I'd never met you.'

We stopped at a pub in Formby, the first customers of the day. Tom demolished a mixed grill, while I forced myself to eat a slice of toast. As soon as he'd finished, I poured us a second cup of coffee, and said, 'Now will you tell me why we're going to Southport?'

'I thought you'd like to meet me gran.'

I looked at him, startled. 'Your paternal grandmother?'

'What the hell does that mean?' he almost snarled.

'Is it your father's mother?'

He banged the cup down on the saucer. 'Christ! You talk like a fuckin' encyclopaedia. It's me dad's mam, Nancy O'Mara, eighty-six years old, as fit as a fiddle, but completely gaga.'

The nursing-home was a large, detached house in a quiet road full of equally large houses, all set in spacious, well-tended grounds. The décor inside was subdued and expensive, the floors thickly carpeted in beige. The fees must have been horrendous, and I assumed it was Tom who paid.

The smiling woman in Reception toned perfectly with her surroundings: beige suit, beige shoes, beige hair. When she saw Tom, the smile became a simper. The barmaid in the pub had looked at him in the same way.

'How's me gran been?' he enquired abruptly.

'Just the same,' the woman gushed. 'Sometimes she seems very aware of what people say to her, but in the main she lives in a world of her own. We persuade her to do her exercises every day and she's in remarkably good shape for a woman of her age. She's in the garden, which is no place for an old lady on a day like today but there's no arguing with Nancy. We just wrap her up and let her go.'

Tom led the way through to the rear of the house where a door opened on to a vast lawn. On the far side, a woman was sitting ramrod stiff on a wooden bench. She looked tiny beneath the fir trees that towered over the garden on three sides, so thick that not even the faintest glimmer of sunlight could get through.

She watched our approach with interest, ebony eyes flashing brilliantly in her hawk-like, liver-spotted face. Snow-white hair, with streaks of black, was piled in a bun as big as a loaf at the nape of her stringy neck. She wore a crimson coat and fur-trimmed black boots. A black lace stole was draped around her shoulders.

'Have you come to read the meter?' she enquired, in a hoarse, deep voice, when Tom sat down beside her. He motioned to me to sit the other side.

'No, Gran. It's Tom, and I've brought a friend to see you. It's no good introducing you,' he whispered. 'She wouldn't take it in.'

'There's no need to introduce her,' Nancy said unexpectedly. 'I know who she is.' She fixed the glittering eyes in their dry brown sockets on me. 'Oh, yes! I know who she is.'

'Who am I, then?' I felt uncomfortable, slightly afraid, under the woman's piercing gaze.

Nancy cackled. 'That would be telling!' Her long face became fretful. 'The chap hasn't been to read the meter in ages. One of these days, they'll cut the 'leccy off.'

'Stop worrying about the meter, Gran. Everything's all right. It's all been seen to.' Tom's attitude to his grandmother was tolerantly offhand. He hadn't kissed her, and seemed to be there out of a sense of duty, rather than affection.

A woman in a grey cotton frock and a white apron was coming towards us with a tray of tea-things. Nancy grabbed it eagerly, apparently capable of pouring the tea, heaping sugar in all three cups. We were drinking it in silence when I noticed that one of her dangling jet earrings had caught in the stole. I leaned over to unhook it, but was shrugged away with a sharp, 'Don't touch me!'

I made a face at Tom. 'I don't think she likes me.' I was hoping we wouldn't stay long. The garden was a melancholy place, cheerless and dark, the only sound was the dew plopping from the trees on to the thick, wet grass. It was doubtful that the old woman appreciated visitors. I'd hoped to get from her a feeling of the past, of the woman who'd been married to Tommy O'Mara when he'd lost his life on the *Thetis* in 1939, but it was impossible to imagine Nancy being young.

Tom said, 'Gran's never liked anyone much. The only person she ever cared about was me dad.' He glanced at his watch. 'We'll go soon. I don't mind paying the bills, but visiting bores me rigid. I only come once a month to keep the nursing staff on their toes. I don't want them thinking they don't have to look after her proper.'

For the next quarter of an hour, I did my awkward best to engage Nancy in conversation. I admired her coat, asked who did her hair, remarked on the weather, enquired about the food. It was hard to make out whether the old woman was merely being cussed when she didn't answer, or genuinely didn't understand.

'You're wasting your time,' Tom said eventually. 'Sometimes she catches on if you talk about the things she used to know, like the war, or the shops in Smithdown Road.'

'I can't talk about either.' Of course there was the *Thetis*, but under the circumstances that mightn't be a good idea.

'C'mon let's go.' Tom squeezed Nancy's shoulder. 'Tara, Gran. See you next month.'

We were half-way across the lawn, when a hoarse voice called, 'Hey, you.' We turned to see her beckoning.

Tom gave me a little push. 'It's you she wants.'

'Are you sure? Why should she want me?' I went back reluctantly, and got a fright when a hand came out and grabbed me painfully by the arm, pulling me downwards until our faces were almost touching. I could smell the fetid breath. 'I know what you're up to, Flo Clancy,' she said, in a voice that sent shivers of ice down my spine. 'But it won't work. Your Martha gave him to me fair and square. He's mine. You'll not get him back, not ever. I've told you before, I'll kill him first.'

'She's making a hole for her own back,' said Bel.

'A rod,' corrected Charmian. 'She's making a rod for her own back, or she's digging herself into a hole. You've got your sayings mixed up.'

'Tch, tch!' Bel snorted loudly. 'She knows what I mean.'

'Would you mind not talking about me in the third person?' I said mildly. 'Furthermore, it's none of your business who I go out with. I can make a hole for my own back if I like.'

'Rod,' said Charmian

'Rod, hole, whatever.' I waved a dismissive hand. I supposed it was inevitable that Tom O'Mara's regular visits to the basement flat wouldn't go unnoticed. When he had dropped me off after we got back from Southport Bel had been watching from Charmian's window to witness my folly.

'Fiona said he'd been in and out, but I didn't believe her.' Bel made no secret of her disapproval. 'Young 'uns nowadays,' she said disgustedly, 'they hop in and out of bed with each other like rabbits. I've only slept with three men in me life, and I married 'em all first.'

'Yes, but times have changed, Bel,' Charmian reminded her. She gave me a wink as she refilled the glasses, though even Charmian looked worried. 'I hope you don't mind me saying this, Millie, but Tom O'Mara's got a terrible reputation. It's not just women but all sorts of other things – drugs, for one. I wouldn't go near that club of his. It worried me to death when our Jay invited him to his twenty-first. I don't think Flo could have known the things he was up to.'

As the evening wore on, my irritation with the pair diminished in proportion to how much I drank. By the time we'd finished a bottle of sherry and started on another, the last, I didn't give a damn what anybody thought. I lay on the rug in front of the fire staring up at the faces of my friends, feeling extraordinarily happy and without a care in the world. 'He's a scoundrel,' I agreed, 'a villain, a good-for-nothing rogue. But he's also drop-down-dead gorgeous.'

'What's happening with poor James?' Bel demanded.

I thought hard, but couldn't remember. Before I could say anything there was a knock at the door and I said, 'Perhaps that's him now.' I walked unsteadily to the door and for several seconds couldn't recognise either of the small, clearly distressed women standing outside.

'You said it was all right to come,' a familiar voice said.

'Of course.' I blinked, and the two women merged into one: Diana, a different Diana from the one I'd always known, with uncombed hair and no makeup, her face white and shrivelled, like melting wax. I asked her in, trying not to sound too drunkenly effusive, and introduced her to Bel and Charmian, adding, because it was obvious that she was in a terrible state. 'Diana's father died last week. He was only buried the day before yesterday.'

Bel, who was over-effusive even when she was sober, jumped to her feet and took the new arrival in her arms. 'You poor girl! Sit down, luv – here, have my place on the settee. Oh, I bet you're feeling dead awful. Charmian, fetch the girl summat to drink. Millie, plump that cushion up and stick it behind her.'

Diana burst into tears. 'I've felt so alone since he died. The house is like a morgue,' she cried. 'I wanted someone to talk to.'

She was eaten up with guilt and anxious to share it. The words came pouring out in a plaintive, childish voice, nothing like her usual terse, clipped tones.

She'd always blamed her father for the fact that she'd never married, she sobbed. 'He said he was sorry. He took the blame but it wasn't his fault at all. No one's ever asked me to marry them. I was using poor Daddy as an excuse for being single, for having to stay in night after night, when I only stayed in because I had nowhere else to go. I'm a total failure as a human being, and it's nobody's fault but my own.'

'Don't be silly, luv,' Bel soothed. 'You stayed with your dad, didn't you? That was very kind and unselfish.'

But Diana wailed, 'I think he wanted to be rid of me so he could have his friends round for bridge. When I came home from university, he offered to buy me a flat. I refused. I told myself it was my duty to stay but I was terrified of being on my own. Then I complained so much about his friends that he stopped asking them. It was me who ruined his life, not the other way round.'

'You're exaggerating,' I said, in what I hoped was a sober, sensible voice. 'I'm sure it wasn't as bad as that.'

'It was,' Diana insisted tearfully.

'In time, you'll see things more reasonably,' Charmian said gently. 'I felt dead guilty when me own mam died. I wished I'd been to see her more often, that I'd been a better daughter.'

Having exhausted the subject of her relationship with her father, Diana turned to her job. She was worried about losing it. George didn't like her, no one did. She'd never fitted in. 'Daddy's gone, and if my job goes, too, I think I'll kill myself.'

'George sometimes gives the impression of being an ogre, but he wouldn't dream of firing you,' I assured her, adding, though I wasn't convinced that it was true, 'He regards you as an asset to the firm.'

At ten o'clock, Herbie came down to demand the return of his wife, and Charmian went reluctantly upstairs. Bel muttered that it was time she was making tracks.

'I suppose I'd better go, too,' Diana sighed, 'though I dread the thought of spending another night on my own.'

'Come home with me,' Bel said instantly. 'I've got a spare bedroom. I can make the bed up in a jiffy.'

'Can I? Oh, Bel! You're the nicest person I've ever known.' Diana threw her arms around Bel's neck and looked as if she might easily cry again.

Nancy had said, 'I know who she is. Oh, yes, I know who she is.' She had taken me for Flo. They must have known each other, all those years ago. Was Nancy aware that Flo had been in love with her husband? And what did she mean when she said, 'Your Martha gave him to me fair and square. You're not getting him back. I'll kill him first.'

It didn't make sense, but perhaps that wasn't surprising coming from an elderly woman who'd lost her mind. Even so, Nancy must have had a reason for saying it.

I took the newspaper cuttings describing the last days of the *Thetis* over to the bureau and placed them alongside the school photo with the child who looked so much like Declan. Beside the photo, I put Hugh O'Mara's drawing of 'MY FREND FLO'. I looked thoughtfully from the cuttings to the photo to the drawing, then back again. The *Thetis* had gone down in June 1939, the photo had been taken six years later and the little boy was in the bottom class, which meant he must have been five and born in 1940. 'Your Martha gave him to me fair and square.' Flo had left instructions that Gran wasn't to be invited to her funeral. What had she done to make Flo hate her so much?

'Your Martha gave him to me fair and square.'

I felt my heart begin to race as I peered closely at the face of the little boy. He was a Clancy, no doubt about it, the same pale hair, slim build, Declan's sensitive features.

Suddenly, everything fell into place. Tommy O'Mara had been the child's father, but his real mother had been Flo. Somehow, Gran had given the baby to Nancy, against Flo's wishes, or she wouldn't have wanted him back. 'I've told you before, I'll kill him first,' Nancy had said.

It meant that Tom O'Mara and I were distant cousins. Tom had the Clancys' green eyes.

Poor Flo! I glanced around the basement room, at its fussy ordinariness, the flowers, lace cloths, abundant ornaments. When I'd first come, it had seemed typical of a place where a pleasant, but rather dull, unmarried woman had lived out most of her life. But as I'd discovered more about Flo, the atmosphere in the room had changed. There was the Flo who'd received those passionate love letters during the war; the woman who'd stayed in the Isle of Man with a man with a foreign name. The flat no longer seemed ordinary, but touched with an aura of romance and a whiff of mystery. This was where a twenty-year-old Flo had come when she was already a mother, but a mother without a child. Now, tragedy was mingled with the romance.

Yet, despite everything, Flo might have been happy. I would never know.

There was a box of drawing-pins in the bureau. I shook some out and pinned the drawing to the wall over the mantelpiece. Flo might have wanted to put it there herself fifty years ago.

The following Tuesday was unusually quiet at Stock Masterton. George went out at midday and hadn't returned by six. Darren and Elliot took the opportunity to leave early, and shortly afterwards June went home. Only Oliver and I were left.

He stretched his arms and yawned. 'I suppose one of us had better stay till George comes back.'

'Where did he go?' I asked.

'He didn't say. He got a phone call and went rushing off.'

'I'll wait,' I offered. Oliver had a long journey home through the Mersey tunnel to a remote village on the Wirral.

'Thanks, Millie.' He gave me a warm, grateful smile. 'You're a chum.'

Oliver had only been gone a few minutes when the light on the switchboard flashed to indicate there was a call. I was astonished to discover an angry Bel at the other end of the line. 'Is that woman there?' she barked.

I assumed she meant Diana, who'd been staying with her since Sunday. 'No, she hasn't been in since her father died. I thought she was with you?'

'She was until this morning,' Bel said. 'She seemed much better when she got up. I went to get us a nice chicken for tea but when I got back she'd upped and gone. Not a word of thanks, no tara, nothing!' she finished, with a high-pitched flourish.

'Perhaps she's coming back,' I suggested. 'She's gone home to collect something.'

'In that case she should have left a note – and it doesn't take five hours to get to and from Hunts Cross.' A loud indignant snort echoed round the empty office. 'Honest, Millie, me ears are numb from listening to her go on and on about bloody Daddy. I'm an ould softheart, me, and I didn't mind a bit, but I'm dead annoyed to think she's just scarpered. She ate me out of house and home. Me freezer compartment's nearly empty!'

'I'm sorry, Bel. I don't know what to say.' If Diana had been there, I could have easily strangled her for treating Bel so rudely. 'Why not come round to Flo's tonight for dinner?' I offered in an attempt to soothe her feelings. 'It'll be a takeaway, mind, from that Chinese place round the corner.'

'Me favourite's sweet and sour pork, and I really go for those little pancakes with roots in.'

'By the way, I found a bundle of letters in the bureau from you to Flo. I thought you might like them to read.'

'No, ta, luv,' Bel said firmly. 'Flo offered them to me once, but I said no to her too. I'm happy now, but I was happier when I wrote them. I'd sooner not be reminded of the ould days. Just chuck 'em out. See you later, luv.'

It was nearly seven by the time George strode into the office. 'I'd like a word with you, Millie,' he snapped, as he passed my desk and went into his cubicle.

Somewhat bemused by his tone, I followed, and was even more bemused when he nodded towards a chair, 'Sit down.' It seemed very formal. People usually sat down without waiting for an invitation.

George placed his arms on the desk and clasped his hands together, his expression grave and accusing. 'I don't think much of the way you treated Diana when she came to you for help,' he said coldly.

I heard the creak of my dropping jaw. 'I haven't the faintest idea what you're talking about.'

'Apparently she called at William Square, as you had invited her to do, desperate for someone to talk to, urgently in need of a shoulder to cry on . . .'

'That's right.' My voice shook. I was at a loss to understand what was wrong.

'But instead of help,' George went on, 'all she found was you and two other women all pissed out of your minds. Not only that, you quickly got her in the same drunken state as yourselves. Even worse, the poor girl was virtually kidnapped by a ghastly old woman who wouldn't let her go. She's been stuck in this woman's dismal little house for days. She rang just before lunch and I was forced to go and rescue her. I found her shaking, crying, and in a terrible state.'

I burst out laughing. 'Rescue her! Don't be so bloody stupid, George. Bel's anything but ghastly. In fact, Diana said she was the nicest person she'd ever met. Also, she's about seventy-five – a bit old to kidnap someone less than half her age, wouldn't you say?' It wasn't worth adding that although I'd never been in Bel's house I imagined it would be anything but dismal.

But George's face grew colder, if that was possible, and he said, 'I've never pulled rank, Millie. I've always treated my employees as equals, friends. I do, however, own this firm, and take exception to being called stupid by someone whose wages I pay.'

But he *was* being stupid! Diana had fooled him completely, putting on an act so outrageous that I marvelled at her nerve. I said nothing, just sat there, stunned, contemplating her treachery. She'd used us – me, Bel, Charmian – to rid herself of the guilt she'd felt over her father's death. Then she'd probably felt ashamed of having told so much and turned against us, possibly worried I'd tell George or the others in the office the things she'd said when she bared her soul.

'Oh, and another thing, Millie, I'd prefer it if you didn't refer to me in public as an ogre.'

'But I didn't . . .' I began, then remembered that I had. 'I didn't mean it in an offensive way.' I wanted to explain why I'd used the word, but it would probably be a waste of time at the moment. Just now George's mind was made up. It would be sensible to wait until he was able to see sense again, then put him right. 'Where is Diana now?' I asked.

'My place,' he said briefly. 'The poor girl's still very tearful. She's been through a lot lately. Her father dying was bad enough, but you and your friends only made it worse.'

'That's not fair, George,' I felt bound to say. 'If you think about it hard enough, you'll know it's not fair. Diana's having you on.'

For the first time, he looked straight at me and there was a trace of comprehension in his eyes. Then he blinked furiously and said, 'I'd better be getting back. I've promised to take her out to dinner.'

He strode out of the office, a knight on a white charger returning to his damsel in distress. I understood what had happened. His wife and children no longer needed him, his mother was dead, he was a man with no call on his emotions. Diana had got through to the part of him that longed for someone to cherish and protect.

When I sat down at my desk my legs were shaking, my mind a whirl. It was all so unreasonable, so unjust. I picked up the telephone, badly in need of someone sympathetic to talk to. Colin answered when I called Trudy and said she was out. 'She's taken Melanie and Jake to see *101 Dalmatians*. By the way, her bottle stall will be up and running on Sunday. She was going to call you.'

'I'll be there,' I promised.

Then I rang Mum. I couldn't explain what had happened, it would only upset her, but at least she would be a friendly voice. To my dismay, when the receiver at the other end was picked up my father reeled off the number. He always sounded mild, rather genial, on the telephone and it was hard to connect the pleasant voice with the man I knew. I didn't waste time with small talk. 'Is Mum there?'

'She's in bed with a touch of flu.'

'Oh!' I was temporarily flummoxed. 'Oh, well, give her my love and say I'll come and see her tomorrow after work. I'd come tonight, but I've promised to meet someone at Flo's.'

'All right, luv. How's things with you?'

'Fine,' I said brusquely. ''Bye.'

Bel would be only too willing to provide sympathy in buckets, though I wouldn't mention anything about kidnapping, or she was quite likely to burst a blood vessel.

3

'It's only me, Mum,' I called, as I ran upstairs. I found her propped up against a heap of pillows looking sleepy, but pleased with herself.

'Hello, Millicent.' She smiled when I went in and planted a kiss on her plump, pasty cheek. 'I'm all on me own. Your dad's gone to the pub and Declan's round at a mate's house.'

'How do you feel? I've been worried about you all day.' Halfway through the morning, I had wondered suddenly if flu was the real reason for her being in bed. Maybe my father had been up to his old tricks again.

'There's no need to worry, luv.' The contented smile was still there, enough to convince me that my suspicions were unwarranted. 'I'm really enjoying lying here and being waited on. Our Declan's been looking after me, and Trudy came this afternoon with some grapes. Now you've brought a lovely bunch of carnations, me favourite.' She buried her nose in them. 'They smell dead gorgeous. It's nice to know me children care about their mam. I even got a get-well card from Alison, though I don't suppose it was her idea to send it. I had to ring up on Sunday and say I couldn't go. The bug had already caught up with me by then, and I didn't feel up to the drive.'

'You should have rung, Mum. I would have come before.'

'I didn't want to bother you, Millicent. I know you're always busy.'

'Oh, Mum!' I stroked her brow, which felt rather hot. 'You've got a temperature,' I said, with a frown

'The doctor's given me some tablets. Look what the women in the shop sent.' She pointed to a little wicker basket of dried flowers on the bedside table next to Alison's card. She seemed far less bothered about being ill than that everybody had been so kind. 'Mrs Bradley from next door keeps bringing bowls of home-made soup. The potato's nice and tasty, but Declan ate the onion.' She giggled girlishly. 'I might be sick more often if this is the sort of treatment I can expect. Your dad's even brought a cup of tea up twice. I think he's a reformed character.'

'Don't bank on it, Mum.'

'I won't, luv. Look!' She patted her stomach. 'I've lost weight. This nightie would hardly go round me before but now it's dead loose. I used to be slim as a girl, just like you.'

'I know. Your wedding photo's downstairs.'

'That's right. I'd like to be slim again by the time I move to Oxford.' She giggled again. 'Start a new life with a new figure.'

I stared at her anxiously. Her expression was as innocent as a baby's. She'd lived under the iron hand of her husband for thirty years and had no idea how to cope with the world outside – how to deal with landlords other than the council, for instance, and the social security people could easily convince her she wasn't entitled to a penny. 'Are you still set on that idea, Mum?'

'Oh, yes, luv.' She smiled radiantly. 'I'm looking forward to it, not just seeing our Alison more often but living on me own. I thought I might go back to nursing. They say the National Health Service is understaffed.'

'Nursing!' I gasped. 'I never knew you'd been a nurse.'

'I was halfway through training to become state registered when I married your dad.' She sighed. 'I was sorry to give it up.'

'You should have finished your training, then got married,' I said indignantly.

'Life doesn't always go the way you want it, Millicent.'

'I suppose not.'

There was a noise downstairs. 'Jaysus!' she gasped, terrified. 'I hope that's not your dad back! I hope he hasn't heard.'

But it was only Scotty, bored with being left alone and looking for company. He came bouncing up the stairs and leaped on to the bed, settling himself comfortably between Mum's legs. He pushed his nose between her knees and looked at her adoringly.

'How's Flo's place coming along?'

'I'm nearly there,' I lied.

Mum laughed. 'Oh, come off it, luv. I don't know what you're up to but I've been to Flo's, remember? You can't kid me it takes six or seven weeks to sort out a one-bedroom flat.'

'Oh, Mum!' I slipped off my shoes and sat in my father's place on the bed. It was time I told her the truth. I took my mother's white hand, threaded with startling blue veins. 'I love it there, and I'm having a great time. I've met all sorts of interesting people. You already know Bel, then there's Charmian and Herbie upstairs, a young man next door who comes from Kirkby and was in my class at school, and . . . well, this other guy who knew Flo.'

'Bel used to be very glamorous.'

'She still is.'

'So you haven't done a thing,' Mum said, smiling.

'We've drunk all Flo's sherry and I've cleared out her bureau – well, almost. Otherwise, the place is no different from the first day I went.'

'Have you been paying the rent?'

'No, Mum.' I'd remembered to ask Charmian when the rent collector called. He came monthly, she said, and had been twice since Flo died but had never mentioned the basement flat. Next time he came Charmian had promised to ask about it. 'Flo must have paid several months in advance,' I told Mum. 'So far, I haven't come across a rent book.'

'I'd love to see the place again,' she said wistfully. 'See if it's changed much.'

'Come next week, Mum.' I couldn't keep the flat to myself for ever. 'Come one evening when I can show you round. The weekend would be even better. There's a takeaway round the corner. I'll buy more sherry and we can have a feast. Bel would love to meet you again, and you'll like Charmian.'

Mum squeezed my hand. 'I'll come as soon as I'm better. Now, I'm in a lovely hazy daze, all them tablets. I hope you won't mind if I go to sleep in front of you.'

'I'll make myself a cup of tea when you do.'

We talked in a desultory way about Declan: he'd had a form from a college, had filled it in and sent it off. Wasn't it smashing Trudy having her own stall? 'I hope I'm well enough to go by Sunday,' Mum said sleepily.

When her head began to droop I released her hand. I stayed where I was for a while, glancing round the dismal room. Years ago, Mum had painted all the furniture cream to make it look like a matching set, but she hadn't rubbed the varnish off underneath and the paint had started to peel.

Perhaps she'd like that lovely stuff in Flo's bedroom, which I coveted – except that she was moving to Oxford. Where on earth did she get the courage from even to think of changing the course of her life at fifty-five? I sighed, got off the bed, adjusted the pillows and drew the bedclothes up to her shoulders. There was no heating upstairs and the air smelt cold. Scotty, also asleep by now and snoring gently, gave a little grunt when the eiderdown beneath him was disturbed.

Downstairs, I put the kettle on and stood watching until it boiled. It felt strange being in this house, danger free, able to do anything I wanted. Yet I still felt on edge, scared I might break something or put something down in the wrong place. I poured the water into the pot, stirred it to make the tea strong, then took a cup into the lounge. The fire was dying, the hearth full of ash. I threw on a few more coals and watched them slowly catch alight. On the right-hand side of the fireplace an owl made out of string was hanging from a nail that protruded crookedly from the wall. Dad's best belt had hung there once, the one he wore on Sundays: black leather, two inches wide, the heavy brass buckle with a deadly sharp prong. I touched the owl gingerly: such an innocuous thing to put in its place.

The back door opened and my father came in. I was still fingering the owl. 'This is where you used to keep your belt,' I reminded him.

His face flushed a deep, ugly scarlet, but he didn't speak. How did he feel, I wondered, now that his children had grown up and we could see him for what he was? Was he ashamed? Uncomfortable? Embarrassed? Or perhaps he didn't give a damn.

I looked at him, properly for once, and tried to relate the handsome, shambling, probably drunken figure to the photo of the bright-eyed baby at Flo's, but it was inconceivable to think that they were the same person. My gaze returned to the owl. 'You nearly blinded our Trudy with that belt.'

He'd been lashing out at Trudy, the skirt of her gymslip scrunched in a ball in his hand. When she tried to get away, he dragged her back so violently by the collar of her school blouse, that she'd choked and lost consciousness. He probably hadn't meant the buckle to hit her forehead, narrowly missing her eye, but Trudy had been left with a permanent reminder of the incident every time she glanced in the mirror.

My father looked at me, bleary-eyed and bewildered. He still didn't speak.

'Mum's asleep,' I said. 'Tell her goodbye from me.'

He spoke at last. 'Did she seem all right to you? I've been worried. She's had a terrible temperature.' His voice was gruff and querulous.

'I think she'll live.' Could it be that he actually *loved* my mother? That he loved us all? I took my cup into the back kitchen and washed it, then left by the back door without saying another word.

Mrs Bradley was leaning on next door's gate talking to another woman.

'How's your mam, luv?' she asked. She was smartly dressed in a sequinned frock and the gigantic fur coat that she wore when she went ballroom dancing with Mr Bradley.

'She seems much better.'

'That's good,' Mrs Bradley said comfortably. 'I was just saying to Norma here how much better everywhere looks without that wreck of a car littering the place.'

Not only had the burnt out car gone, but the boarded up house was occupied. There were lace curtains in the windows and a television was on in the lounge.

'We got a petition up and sent it to the Council, didn't we, Norma?' Norma nodded agreement. 'What right have some folks got, spoiling the street for the rest of us? It's a respectable place, Kirkby. I remember us moving from Scotland Road in nineteen fifty-eight. It was like a palace after our little two-up, two-down. Will was tickled pink to have a garden.'

I went over to my car, unlocked the door and paused for a moment. Mrs Bradley and Norma were still talking. Mr Bradley came out, a thick car coat over his old-fashioned evening suit. He waved and I waved back.

Still I waited by the car, the door half-open. For the first time, I noticed the pretty gardens. Some of the original front doors had been replaced with more ornate designs, heavily panelled with lots of brassware. There were coachlamps outside several houses. It dawned on me that there was nothing wrong with Kirkby! It was all in my head, all to do with my childhood, my father, school. I'd centred my loathing on the place when it was my life that was wrong!

'What's up with George?' June demanded, for the umpteenth time. 'He's been like a bear with a sore head this week.'

Elliot swung his well-shod feet on to the desk. 'Perhaps he's going through the male menopause.'

'I reckon he's missing Diana.' Darren grinned.

Everyone except me hooted with derision, and Oliver said miserably, 'She'll be back on Monday, spreading her usual discord and as moody as hell.'

'Actually,' June hissed, 'I didn't say anything before in case I was hearing things, but Diana rang George this morning and when I put her through I could have sworn he called her darling.'

There was a gasp of disbelief.

'Never!'

'I don't believe it!'

'You must have been hearing things, June.'

It figures, I thought. She's managed to wrap him round her little finger. I was glad no one seemed to have noticed that it was me, more than anyone, on whom George vented his bad temper. One day, I'd tried to explain that I'd done nothing wrong, but he was only interested in Diana's version of the story.

What on earth would it be like when she returned? Awful, I decided. She'd be lording it over everyone, particularly me. I wondered if I should look for another job, but my only qualification was a single A level, along with the time spent working at Stock Masterton. Would another estate agent take me on with such a paltry record? I tried to tell myself that it didn't matter, but in my heart of hearts I knew it did. The time I spent at Flo's, the nights with Tom O'Mara, were bound to end sometime, and I'd have to live in the real world again, where my job mattered very much. I had a mortgage, I had to eat. And if I left this job, I'd have to return the car.

Taking advantage of George's absence, Darren and Elliot went home early, followed shortly by June. I suggested that Oliver make himself scarce and I would stay until six in case there were any phone calls: the office closed an hour earlier on Saturday. Oliver accepted the offer thankfully. 'We're in the middle of decorating. I'd like to get it done by Christmas.'

The door had hardly closed when it opened again. I looked up, thinking Oliver had forgotten something.

'I've been waiting across the road for everyone to go,' said James. 'I was praying you'd be the last.'

Over the past few weeks I had almost forgotten James's existence, and was surprised at how glad I was to see the tall, familiar figure; so glad that, for the moment, I put to the back of my mind what had happened the last time we met. He wore a new suit, grey flannel, and a pale blue shirt, and was leaning against the door regarding me shyly.

'Hi,' I said.

'Phew!' He put his hand on his chest in a gesture of relief. 'I was expecting to have something thrown at me – a computer, a telephone, a notebook, at least.' He came down the room and perched on the edge of Diana's desk. 'How's life?'

'Ninety per cent fine, ten per cent lousy.'

'Tell me about the lousy ten per cent.'

I'd always been able to talk to him about humdrum, day-to-day matters. We spent ages discussing the meaning of a film we'd just seen, what frock I should wear to a party, his job, mine. It would have been a waste of time trying to talk to Tom O'Mara about office politics or Mum being ill, Trudy having a bottle stall or Declan going to college. Perhaps that was why I was so pleased to see James – not as a lover but as a friend.

I told him all about the week's events, and about Diana's treachery. 'Now George is really cross with me and I think I've blown my job.'

'But that's totally unfair!' James expostulated angrily.

It was comforting to hear Diana being called a conniving bitch and that George was a fool to let himself be taken in. I felt better after listening to James's loudly expressed indignation and didn't demur when he offered to buy me dinner.

'Shall we go to the wine bar where we first met?'

'I'd prefer to try that new place by the Cavern.' I didn't want to go somewhere that evoked old memories in case he got the idea that everything was back to normal, which it wasn't. 'I'll just ring home, make sure my mother's all right.'

Declan answered and assured me that mum was fine.

'Say hello to Declan for me.' James mouthed.

'James says hello, Declan.'

'I thought mam said James was history?'

I laughed. 'Bye, love.' I took a mirror out of my handbag, powdered my nose, combed my hair, retouched my lipstick. When I looked up James was watching me with an expression on his rugged face that I remembered well. Our eyes met, he shook his head slightly, as if remonstrating with himself, then turned away. 'I'm sorry,' he said. 'I'm doing my best not to put a foot wrong. I promise not to say a word out of place until the time feels right.'

I began to regret accepting the dinner invitation because I knew I would never feel the same about James after what had happened, but I hadn't the heart to change my mind when he was being so nice.

The restaurant was filled with memorabilia of the Beatles' era. We ordered salad, baked potatoes and a bottle of wine. While we waited, I asked, 'How's the Socialist Workers' Party?'

He looked faintly embarrassed. 'I never went back – it's not really my scene. They were a decent crowd, but I only joined to please you.'

'To please me! I can't remember ever expressing left-wing opinions,' I exclaimed. 'I'm totally uninterested in politics.'

'So am I, though those dockers got a raw deal and I'm on their side. No, I joined because I got the impression you thought I was shallow. I was trying to prove I had some depth.' He glanced at me curiously. 'Did I succeed?'

'I don't know.' I shrugged. 'I never thought about it much.'

'I doubt if you ever thought about me much,' he said drily.

'You promised not to say things like that,' I admonished.

'I'm not criticising,' he assured me. 'I'm trying to be coolly matter-of-fact. I pressurised you too much. I fell in love with you, deeply, passionately, wholeheartedly, and expected you to love me back in exactly the same way at exactly the same time. I wasn't prepared to wait. I wouldn't let you breathe.' He made a face. 'I'm used to getting everything I want, you see.'

'Including girls throwing themselves at you since you were fifteen!' I reminded him.

'Aw, shit, Millie.' He cringed. 'I'd had too much to drink, and I'd been waiting all week for you to call. I couldn't believe it was over between us.'

I played with my food. 'You nearly hit me, James. You would have, if Tom hadn't appeared.'

His face flickered with pain. 'So that's his name.' He leaned across the table, put his hand on mine, then hastily removed it. 'I would never, never have hit you, darling.'

There, in such civilised surroundings, it was easy to believe that he was a decent, honourable man who'd been driven over the edge. If I could feel about him as he did about me, everything would be perfect. He began to eat, but only because the food was there. 'This Tom,' he said, in a strained voice, 'are you in love with him?'

'No.'

'Is he with you?'

'No.'

'Who is he? How did you meet?'

'He was a friend of Flo's.' I smiled. 'She had an affair with his grandfather.'

'So, history is repeating itself.'

'Something like that.' I sipped the wine, which seemed preferable to the food. 'Look, can we change the subject?' I felt uncomfortable discussing my current lover with my old one.

'Perhaps that wouldn't be a bad idea.' James sighed. 'I'm trying valiantly to be grown-up but I think I'm about to explode with jealousy.'

We left the restaurant, the meal hardly touched but the wine finished, and strolled down Water Street towards the Pier Head. After a while, I linked James's arm. 'I'd like us always to be friends,' I said.

'Only a woman would ask a man who was crazy about her to be her friend,' he said with a dry chuckle.

'What would a man do in the same situation?' I asked.

'Run a mile, change his phone number, move house if necessary. If some woman had been chasing me as vigilantly as I was chasing you, I would have done all three in order to get away. You were very patient, Millie.'

The nearer we got to the river, the colder and more sharply the November wind blew. With my free hand, I tried to turn up the collar of my coat. James stopped, released my arm, and did it for me. 'I was with you when you bought this coat. You couldn't make up your mind whether to buy this colour or black. I said I preferred black, so you bought the other.' Still holding the collar by its corners, he said softly, 'Is that really all that's left for us, Millie, to be friends?'

'James . . .'

He released my collar and tucked my arm back in his. 'Okay, friends it is. Am I allowed to ask if I can see you again within the relatively near future?'

'Perhaps one night next week?'

We dodged through the traffic towards the Pier Head, where we propped our arms on the rail and stared at the lights of Birkenhead, reflected, dazzling, misshapen blobs, in the choppy waters of the Mersey.

'You know,' James said softly, 'we see movies about great love affairs that make us conventional folk seem very run-of-the-mill. We never imagine ourselves having the same passionate feelings as the characters on the screen, yet over the last few weeks, no one could have felt more gutted than I have. I was convinced I'd rather die if I couldn't have you.'

I said nothing, but shuddered as the wind gusted up my skirt.

James stared intently at the lights, as if the words he wanted to say were written there, prompting him. 'I wished I were a philosopher, who could cope with things more...' he grinned, '... more philosophically. Or a spiritual person, who would look at it with an intellectual sort of fatalism. But I don't go to church, I'm not even sure if I believe in God.'

'Did you come to a conclusion?' I asked gently.

'Yes – that I didn't want to die after all. That life goes on, whatever horrendous things might happen.' He grinned again. 'And that I still love you as much as I ever did, but less frenetically. Even so,' he finished, on a mock-cheerful note, 'I could easily throttle this Tom character.'

It had started to rain, so we walked back quickly to where my car was parked. On the way, he asked what was wrong with my mother.

'Flu. She's almost better.'

'I was always kept well hidden from your family. I only met Declan by accident. Were you ashamed of me or something?'

'Of course not, silly. It's them I was –' I stopped. All of a sudden I didn't care if he knew every single thing there was to know about me. 'Actually, James, my sister's having a stall at a craft market tomorrow. Perhaps you'd like to come if you're free.'

I was back at Flo's, going through the remainder of her papers. For the first time, I felt the urge to hurry things along, to finish with the bureau, get started on the rest of the flat. I emptied out the contents of a large brown envelope. Guarantees, all of which had run out, for a variety of electrical goods. I stuffed them back into the envelope and threw it on the floor. The next item was a plastic folder containing bank statements. I leafed through them, hoping they would give a clue to how the rent was paid. If Flo had set up a standing order, it would explain why the collector hadn't called, and also why there'd been little in the post – no electricity or gas bills, no demand for council tax. I admonished myself for being so negligent. I should have done this long ago, got in touch with the bank, sorted out Flo's financial affairs.

To my surprise, the account was a business one, begun in 1976 according to the first statement. The current balance was – my eyes widened – *twenty-three thousand, seven hundred and fifty pounds, and elevenpence.*

'Flo Clancy!' I gasped. 'What the hell have you been up to?'

I grabbed the next envelope in the rapidly diminishing pile. It was long and narrow and bore the name of a solicitor in Castle Street, a few doors along from Stock Masterton. My hands were shaking as I pulled out the thick sheets of cream paper folded inside, the pages tied together with bright pink tape. It was a Deed of Property, dated March 1965, written in complicated legal jargon that was hard to understand. I had to read the first paragraph three times before it made sense.

Fritz Erik Hofmannsthal hereinafter referred to as the party of the first part of Number One William Square Liverpool hereby transfers the leasehold of the section of Number One William Square hitherto known as the basement to Miss Florence Clancy hereinafter referred to as the party of the second part currently resident in the section of the property which is to be transferred for a period of one hundred years . . .

No wonder no one had called to collect the rent! Flo owned the leasehold of the flat in which she'd spent most of her life. My brain worked overtime. Fritz Erik Hofmannsthal! It was Fritz's laundry where Flo had worked; Mr and Mrs Hofmannsthal had spent a weekend on the Isle of Man every month for over twenty years.

'Oh, Flo!' I whispered. I went over and picked up the snapshot taken outside the laundry nearly sixty years before; Flo, with her wondrous smile, Mr Fritz's arm around her slim waist.

I had no idea why I should want to cry, but I was finding it hard to hold back the tears. I felt as if I knew everything there was to know about Flo Clancy: the lover lost on the *Thetis*, the baby who had gone to another woman, the servicemen she'd made love to in this very flat. Now Mr Fritz . . .

Yet the more I knew, the more mysterious Flo became. I wanted to get under her skin, know how she felt about all the tragedies and romances in her life, but it was too late, far too late. Not even Bel knew the things that I did about her lifelong friend. I'm glad it was me who went through her papers, I thought. I'll never tell another soul about all this.

Of course, I'd have to tell someone about the money and the property. It dawned on me that, under the circumstances, Flo would almost certainly have made a will.

Curious, I was about to go back to the bureau, when the front door opened and Tom O'Mara came in, his face, as usual, sombre and unsmiling, and looking like a dark, sinister angel in a long black mac.

I caught my breath, and half lifted my arms towards him as he stood staring at me from just inside the door. 'I'm neglecting the club because of you,' he said accusingly, 'neglecting me family. You're on me mind every minute of every day.' He removed his coat and threw it on the settee. 'You're driving me fucking crazy.'

'I'll be finished here soon, then I'll be back in Blundellsands. You won't want to come all that way to see me.'

'I'd come the length of the country to be with you.'

I wanted him to stop talking, to take me in his arms so that we could make love. I forgot about James, about Flo, Stock Masterton. All I wanted, more than anything on earth, was for Tom O'Mara to bury himself inside me.

Tom shook himself, gracefully, like a cat. 'I think I'm in love with you, but I don't want to be.' He wiped his wet brow with his hand. 'I feel as if I'm under a spell. I want to keep away from you, but I can't.'

'I know,' I murmured. I didn't like him, I couldn't talk to him, he was hard, unsympathetic, a crook. But I felt drawn to him as I'd been drawn to no man before.

We made love in a frenzy, without tenderness, but with a passion that left us both speechless and exhausted. When I woke up next morning, Tom was still asleep, his arm around my waist. I wanted to slip away, escape, because I was frightened. Instead, I turned over and stroked his face. His green eyes opened and stared into mine and he began to touch me. We were locked into each other. There was no escape.

Flo

1

1962

Sally and Jock's son, Ian, died as he had lived; quietly and bravely and without a fuss. He was sixteen. The funeral took place on a suffocatingly hot day in July and the crematorium chapel was packed. The mourners stood and knelt when they were told, their movements slow and lethargic, a sheen of perspiration on their faces, their clothes damp. There were flowers everywhere, their scent sweet and sickly, overpowering.

Flo was at the back, fanning herself with a hymn book. She hated funerals, but who in their right mind didn't? The last one she'd been to was for Joanna and Jennifer Holbrook. Joanna had passed away peacefully in her sleep, and the following night her sister had joined her. But at least the twins had managed more than four score years on this earth, whereas Ian . . . She averted her eyes from the coffin with its crucifix of red and white roses. The coffin was tiny, because he'd grown no bigger than a ten-year-old and every time she looked at it she wanted to burst into tears.

She wished she'd asked Mr Fritz or Bel to come with her. She knew hardly anyone except Sally and Jock. Grace, their daughter, was a cold, aloof girl, who'd always resented the care and attention bestowed upon her invalid brother. She was in the front pew next to her dad, looking bored and not the least upset. She wasn't even wearing dark clothes, but a pink summer frock with a drawstring neck.

The woman on Grace's other side, who was kneeling, her head buried in her hands, must be melting in that black, long-sleeved woollen frock, she thought. Then the woman lifted her head and whispered something to the girl.

Martha.

Oh, Lord! She looked like an ould woman, her face all wizened and sour. She might well have achieved the coveted title of Mrs before her name and

566

a lovely daughter but, if her expression was anything to go by, it had done nothing to make her happy. Or the nice new flat in Kirkby that she'd moved into a few years ago when Elsa Cameron had stuck her head in the gas oven and ended her tragic life. Perhaps happiness was in the soul, part of you, and it didn't matter what events took place outside. Some people, Martha was one, were born to be miserable.

'I'm happy,' Flo told herself. 'At least on the surface. I make the best of things. I'm happy with Mr Fritz, and me and Bel still have a dead good time, even though we're both gone forty – but I don't half wish we were twenty years younger. I'd love to go to the Cavern, I really would, and see them Beatles lads in the flesh.'

She was vaguely aware of someone genuflecting at the end of the pew. Then the person knelt beside her and whispered, 'Hello, Flo.'

'Hugh!' She flushed with pleasure and patted his arm. He was twenty-three and, as far as Flo was concerned, the finest-looking young man on the planet: tall, slender, with a gentle face, gentle eyes and the sweetest smile she'd ever seen. His hair had grown darker and was now a dusky brown, only a shade lighter than his father's, though it wasn't curly like Tommy's. He was mad about music and haunted the Cavern; she always listened to the charts on the wireless so she could talk to him on equal terms.

'I thought you couldn't get off work?' she said softly. He'd served an apprenticeship as an electrician and worked for a small firm in Anfield.

'I told them it was a funeral. They couldn't very well refuse. Ian was me friend, he taught me to play chess. Anyroad, I promised Kate I'd come.' He nodded towards the front of the church, and a girl in the row behind Sally and Jock turned round as if she'd sensed someone was talking about her. She had the Clancys' green eyes and silvery hair, and Flo had the strangest feeling she was looking at her younger self in a mirror.

So, this was Kate Colquitt. She'd been at St Theresa's Junior and Infants' school when Flo last saw her, that hulking great lad, Norman Cameron, never far from her side. Sally was right to say she'd grown into a beautiful young woman. Kate twitched her lips at Hugh, almost, but not quite, in a smile, because this was, after all, a funeral. The man kneeling next to her must have noticed the movement. He twisted round and gave Hugh a look that made Flo's blood curdle, a look of hate, full of threats, as if he resented his companion even acknowledging another man's existence.

Norman Cameron, still watching over Kate like an evil guardian of the night.

Everyone stood to sing a hymn: 'Oh, Mary, we crown thee with blossoms today, Queen of the Angels and Queen of the May.' It wasn't May and wasn't appropriate, but it had been Ian's favourite.

Flo saw Norman Cameron find the page for Kate, as if she was incapable of finding it for herself. She felt concerned for the girl, although she hardly knew her. Sally said Norman wanted them to get married and Martha, anxious as ever to meddle in other people's lives, was all for it. Kate had managed so far to hold out. She was working at Walton hospital as an auxiliary and wanted to become a state registered nurse.

'Norman's had a terrible life,' Sally had said, only a few weeks ago. 'No one could have had a worse mam than Elsa, yet the poor lad was inconsolable when she topped herself. I feel dead sorry for him. But he makes me flesh creep, and he's so much in love with Kate it's unhealthy. You'd think he owned her or something.'

'She should find herself another boyfriend,' Flo said spiritedly. 'Try and break away.'

'I reckon Norman would kill any man who dared lay a finger on her.'

'Lord Almighty!' Flo gasped.

The hymn finished, the priest entered the pulpit and began to speak about Ian. He must have known him well because his words were full of feeling: a bright, happy lad who'd borne his illness with the patience of a saint and had almost made it to adulthood due to the selfless commitment of his parents. The world would be a sadder and emptier place without Ian Wilson. Heaven, though, would be enriched by the presence of such a pure, unsullied soul . . .

Flo switched off. Any minute now, he'd start telling Sally and Jock that they should feel privileged their child was dead and had gone to a better place, where he was, even now, safely in the arms of God.

The priest finished. Flo buried her head in her hands when it was time for them to pray. The soft whisper of the organ came from the grille in the wall, the sound gradually growing louder, but not enough to hide a slight whirring noise. Flo peeped through her fingers and saw the curtains behind the altar open slowly and the coffin slide out of sight. The curtains closed and there was an agonised gasp from Sally as her son disappeared for ever. Jock put an arm around her shoulders, and Flo imagined the little curling red and blue flames licking the coffin, spreading, meeting, then devouring it and its precious contents, until only the ashes remained.

'Don't cry, Flo.' Hugh offered her his hanky.

'I didn't realise I was.' She pushed the hanky away. 'You look as if you might need it yourself.'

The service over, they went outside, where the heat was almost as great as it had been in church. When everyone stood round the display of flowers, which were laid out on the parched grass, the blooms wilting rapidly in the hot sunshine, Flo kept to the back. She could see her own wreath, irises and white roses, and would have liked to look for the flowers that Bel and Mr Fritz had sent, but didn't want to come up against Martha, particularly not today.

Hugh was talking to the bereaved parents. He shook hands with Jock and kissed Sally's cheek, very grown-up, very gentlemanly. Nancy O'Mara had raised him well. If she'd been there, she would have felt as proud as Flo. He came over. 'I have to be getting back to work.'

'I'll be going meself in a minute, after I've had a word with our Sally.'

He looked surprised. 'I thought you'd be going back to the house.'

'You're not the only one who has to be at work.'

'In that case,' he said, trying to sound casual, 'I'll give you a lift part of the way.' He had a car, his pride and joy, a little blue Ford Popular.

'That'd be nice, luv. Ta.'

What was she supposed to say to Sally? 'I'm dead sorry, Sal. I feel terrible for you. He was a lovely lad. I don't know how you'll cope without him.' After a few stumbling phrases, she threw her arms around her sister. 'Oh, Lord, Sal, you know what I mean.'

'I know, girl.' Sally nodded bleakly, then grabbed Flo's arm. 'Sis, I want you to do something for me.'

'I'll do anything, Sal, you know that.'

'Make things up with our Martha.' She shook Flo's arm impatiently. 'There's enough misery in the world without adding to it when there's no need. Martha would be overjoyed if you two were friends again.'

Flo glanced at Martha, who was talking to her daughter, Norman Cameron a dark shadow by her side. They weren't exactly a happy family group, but the mother and daughter relationship was there for all to see. Then she looked at Hugh, waiting, hands in pockets, for his 'friend' Flo, and she felt a sense of loss as vivid and painful as the morning she'd woken up and discovered her son had been taken away. Martha hadn't just stolen her son, she'd stolen her life.

Very gently, she removed her sister's hand. 'Anything but that, Sal,' she said.

'I'll miss Ian,' Hugh said, when they were in the car. He smiled shyly. 'I'll miss Kate, too. She was often there when I went to see him. It was the only place she went without Norman Cameron in tow.'

'D'you fancy her, luv?' They would make a perfect couple, Flo thought excitedly. The Catholic Church forbade relationships between cousins, though marriage might be possible with a dispensation. But as neither Hugh nor Kate were aware that they were related, there would be no need for the Church to become involved.

His pale cheeks went pink. 'She's okay.' He'd had several girlfriends, all of whom Nancy had disliked on sight. 'You'd think I was royalty or something,' he'd grumbled to Flo. 'She doesn't think any girl I bring home is good enough for me.'

Flo was inclined to agree, though where Nancy was concerned she always kept her opinions to herself.

Hugh dropped her off in Lime Street. 'See you soon, Flo, perhaps tomorrer.'

It was too nice a day to sit on a bus and Flo decided to walk home. She was in no hurry. Although she'd told Hugh she should be at work, her shift didn't start until two. A few years ago, when launderettes had sprung up all over the place and White's Laundry saw their work trickle away to almost nothing, Mr Fritz had closed the place down. Then he had opened a chain of launderettes, six in all, and put Flo in charge of the biggest, an ex-chandler's shop in Smithdown Road, less than a mile from William Square.

'Hello, gorgeous!' A man, quite good-looking, was standing in front, blocking her way.

'Hello . . .' She stared at him, frowning, before realising that he was a stranger trying to pick her up. 'I thought I knew you,' she said, exasperated.

'You could, very easily. I'd certainly like to know you.'

'Get lost,' she said, but smiled as she dodged past. It was flattering to think that at forty-two she could still attract men. She caught a glimpse of her reflection in the windows as she walked up Mount Pleasant. She never wore black, apart from skirts, and Bel had loaned her a frock for the funeral; very fine cotton with short sleeves and a sunray-pleated skirt. The wide belt made her already slim waist look tiny. She hadn't put on an ounce of weight with age. When they went on their regular visits to the Isle of Man, Mr Fritz complained that she looked no more than thirty. People would think he was spending a dirty weekend with his secretary.

'We're not married, so it is a dirty weekend.' Flo giggled.

He looked horrified. 'Flo! Our weekends together have been the most beautiful times of my life. Nevertheless,' he grumbled, 'all the other guests probably think they're dirty.'

Flo offered to dye her hair grey and draw wrinkles on her face, but he said that wouldn't do either. 'I rather enjoy getting envious glances from other men.' There was no pleasing him, she said.

She passed the women's hospital where Nancy O'Mara had recently had a hysterectomy. Hugh, the dutiful son, had gone to see her after work every night. On the way home, he sometimes called in at the launderette. He usually popped in at least once a week.

'How's Mrs O'Mara?' she asked. It sounded silly, but she could never bring herself to refer to Nancy as his mam.

'Progressing normally, according to the doctor.'

During the time he'd been at secondary modern school, she'd thought she'd lost him. Until then, he'd got into the habit of sticking his head round the door of the laundry on his way home from St Theresa's, just to say hello. When he changed schools, she had the good sense not to wait for him outside when she went to the bank on Fridays, reckoning an eleven-going-on-twelve-year-old in long trousers wouldn't be seen dead playing ball in the Mystery with a woman almost twenty years his senior.

'Where's your little friend?' Mr Fritz asked, after Hugh hadn't shown his face in months.

'He's at a different school and comes home a different way,' Flo explained, doing her best not to appear as cut up as she felt about it.

'That's a shame. I'd grown quite fond of him.' He gave Flo a look full of sympathy and understanding, as if he'd guessed the truth a long time ago.

The months became years. She saw Hugh once when he was fourteen. He was on his way home with a crowd of lads who were kicking a tin can to each other on the other side of the road. She was glad his collar was undone, his tie crooked, that he looked an untidy mess. She was even glad about the tin can. Nancy might not like it, but he'd found his place, he'd made friends, he was one of the lads. She felt a tug at her heart as she melted into a shop doorway out of sight. If only he was coming home to me!

Although Flo had a great time in the launderette – the customers came in with so many funny stories that her sides still hurt with laughter when she went home – she could never get her son out of her mind. She heard through Sally that he'd left school and begun an apprenticeship as an electrician. It wasn't what she would have chosen for him: she would have liked him to become something grander, perhaps even go to university.

It wasn't until almost five years ago, Christmas 1957, that she had seen Hugh again. The launderette was festooned with decorations, drooping in the damp. All afternoon she'd been pressing home-made mince pies and sherry on her 'ladies', as she called them – a few had even returned with more washing they'd scraped together because they'd had such a good time. The bench was full of women waiting for the machines to finish, and Flo was slightly tipsy, having drunk too many people's health when she wished them merry Christmas. Mr Fritz usually toured his six establishments daily to ensure that the automatic machines were working properly and not in need of his expert attention, but always ended up at Flo's because it had the nicest atmosphere. His brown eyes twinkled as he accused her of being in charge of a launderette while under the influence of alcohol. Just then the door opened for the hundredth time that day and he said, 'Why, look who's here!'

Hugh! A shy, smiling Hugh, in an old army jacket with a small khaki haversack thrown over his shoulder.

My son has grown up! She wanted to weep for all the years she'd missed. She wanted to hug and kiss him, to ask why he'd deserted his mam for so long, but merely smiled back and said, 'Hello, luv.'

'You've grown some,' Mr Fritz said enviously. 'You must be six foot at least.'

'Six foot one,' Hugh said modestly.

He never explained why he hadn't come before, why he'd come now, and Flo never asked. She guessed it was something to do with age, that between eleven and seventeen, he hadn't felt it proper for her to be his friend, but as he'd grown older something had drawn him back. She didn't care what it was. It was enough that he'd come, and continued to come, to tell her about his job, his girlfriends, how he was saving up to buy a car. Once, a few months ago, he had said, 'I wish me mam was a bit more like you, Flo. She thinks I'm crackers to want a car, but you wouldn't mind, would you?'

'I should have caught the bus,' she muttered, halfway home, when the straps of her high-heeled sandals began to dig into her feet. It would be a relief to reach William Square, where she'd have a nice cool bath before she went to work.

Stella Fritz would have a fit if she could see the square now. There was scarcely a house left that hadn't been turned into flats or bedsits and they all looked run down, uncared-for. Even worse, one or two women – Flo refused to believe they were prostitutes – had begun to hang around at night, apparently waiting for men to pick them up. Twice, Flo had been propositioned on her way home in the dark, and Bel had threatened that if anyone else asked how much she charged, she'd thump them. There were frequent fights, which led to the police arriving. Mr Fritz moaned that the place was becoming dead rowdy, and Flo, who loved the square and never wanted to live anywhere else, had to concede that it had deteriorated.

She felt better after the bath and when she had changed into a pale blue cotton frock and canvas shoes. All afternoon, she couldn't get Sally out of her mind. On numerous occasions her ladies wanted to know what was wrong. 'You look as if you've swallowed a quid and shat a sixpence. What's up, Flo?'

If she told them about Ian, she knew what would happen: their great, generous hearts would overflow with sympathy, which would be expressed in flowery, dramatic language a poet would envy. She would only cry, she might possibly howl. She told them she was feeling out of sorts, that the heat was getting her down

Flo loved her ladies. They were coarse, often dirt poor, but they struggled through life with a cheerfulness of spirit that never ceased to amaze her. Through the door they would burst in their shabby clothes, which were usually too big or too small, too long or too short, carrying immense bags of washing. There were black ladies and white ladies, quite often grossly overweight because they existed on a diet of chip butties, but always with a smile on their careworn, prematurely old faces, making a great joke of their bunions and varicose veins, the swollen joints that plagued them, the mysterious lumps that had suddenly appeared on their bodies that they intended to ignore. 'I couldn't go in the ozzie and let them take it away, could I? Not with five kids to look after, and me ould feller propped up in the boozer all day long.'

It could be seven kids, ten kids, twelve. Most of the husbands were unemployed, and more than a few of Flo's ladies went out cleaning early in the morning or late at night. It was their money that paid the rent and put food on the table, but that didn't stop some husbands taking out their frustration with the government and society in general on their wives. Flo often found herself bathing bruises or bandaging cuts, cursing the perpetrators to high heaven.

But the women refused to listen to a word of criticism of their men – 'He couldn't help it, luv. He was stewed rotten. He wouldn't dream of hitting me when he's sober,' which Flo found an unsatisfactory explanation for her ladies' sometimes appalling injuries. She cosseted them, made them tea, laughed at their jokes, admired them. The only thing she refused was to let them do their washing on tick, which Mr Fritz had strictly forbidden. 'Before you can say Jack Robinson, they'll have run up a huge bill and we'll never get paid. No, Flo. They put their own coins in the machine and that's final. And if I find you've been loaning your own money, I'll be very cross indeed. They're a canny lot, and pretty soon you'll be subsidising washing for the whole of Toxteth.'

The thought of Mr Fritz being cross wouldn't have caused a tremor in a rabbit, but Flo was careful to take heed of his advice.

At seven o'clock on the day of Ian's funeral, it was a relief when she could turn the Open sign to Closed. Mr Fritz came and went, promising to have some iced tea ready for when she came home – he was obsessed with his new refrigerator. It would be another hour before all the machines were finished and she could tidy up and leave. The place felt like an oven. Perhaps that was why she had remained so slim: since she was thirteen, she'd spent a high proportion of her waking hours in the equivalent of a Turkish bath.

Bel had been promoted to manageress of ladies' outerwear in Owen Owens: long coats, short coats, raincoats, furs. She was frequently wined and dined by representatives of clothing firms who wanted her to stock their products. Occasionally, when Flo had nothing better to do, she would go to Owen Owens and listen while Bel dealt with a customer.

'Modom, that coat looks simply divine on you. Of course, Modom has a perfect figure, and red is definitely your colour.' The accent, Bel's idea of 'posh', and the voice, haughty yet obsequious, was stomach-churning.

When the customer wasn't looking, Bel would make a hideous face at Flo, and mouth, 'Sod off!'

On her way home from the launderette, Flo let herself into her friend's flat in Upper Parliament Street, where Bel was lying on her luridly patterned settee wearing black satin lounging pyjamas and reading *She*. She looked up and grinned widely, the deeply etched laughter lines around her eyes and mouth adding yet more character to her already animated face. 'You look as if you've just been for a turn in one of your machines,' she said.

'I feel as if I have.' Flo threw herself into an armchair with a sigh. Bel's flat wasn't relaxing, more like a fairground with its bright walls and ceilings, and curtains that could do serious damage to the eyes. Still, it was nice to sit in a comfortable chair at last. 'I want you to promise me something, Bel,' she said.

'What, luv?'

'If I die before you, make sure I'm buried, not cremated. I want a few bits of me left to rise to heaven when the Day of Judgement comes.'

'Rightio, Flo,' Bel said laconically. 'I don't give a stuff what they do with me. Once I'm dead, they can throw me in the Mersey for all I care, or feed me to the lions at Chester Zoo.'

'Another thing, Bel. I've taken out an insurance policy to cover the cost of me funeral. It's in the first-aid box in the cupboard by the fireplace, the right-hand side. I'd put it in the bureau with all me papers, but you'd never find it. I can never find anything meself.'

'That's because you keep every single bit of paper that drops through your letterbox,' Bel snorted.

'It's a legacy from Stella Fritz. I always kept me bills in case she accused me of not paying the 'leccy, or something. Now I can't get out of the habit. Anyroad, when I'm looking for something, it's nice reading through me old letters. I've still got the ones you sent during the war. You can have them back if you like.' She didn't say, because Bel would have been disgusted, that it was quite interesting to look at old bills, see how much prices had gone up.

Bel grimaced. 'Thanks, but no thanks.'

'One more thing. Under no circumstances must our Martha come to me funeral. I'm not having it, d'you hear?'

'I hear, Flo, but why all this morbid talk about death and funerals?'

'I took the policy out years ago. It was this morning at the crematorium that I decided I'd sooner be buried.'

'Flo!' Bel's face was a tragedy. 'I'd completely forgotten about Ian's funeral. Was it awful, luv? How's your Sally taking it? Did the dress fit all right?'

'The dress looked simply divine,' Flo said tiredly. The expression had become a joke between them. 'As for the other, it was awful, yes. Sally's taken it hard, and so's Jock.'

'Shall we do something exciting tomorrer night, Sat'day, like go somewhere dead extravagant for a meal? It might cheer you up.'

'Sorry, Bel, but I'm going on retreat in the morning.'

Bel groaned. 'You're a miserable bugger, Flo Clancy. What do you do on these retreats, anyroad?'

'Pray,' Flo said virtuously.

'They're a waste of time – a waste of life!'

'I don't see you doing anything earth-shattering.'

'I've got an important job.'

'So've I.'

'I get taken out to dinner.'

'Mr Fritz takes me out to dinner sometimes.'

'He takes us both, so that's not counted.' Bel sat on the edge of the settee and rested her chin in her hands. She said, thoughtfully, 'Actually, Flo, it's well past the time you and Fritz got something going together.'

Flo laughed. 'I'm happy as I am, thanks all the same. Anyroad, it's well past the time you found yourself another husband.'

Bel ignored this. 'These damn retreats, I can't think of anything more boring and miserable than praying non-stop for two whole days.'

'Oh, I dunno,' said Flo. 'The thing is, I always come back feeling spiritually uplifted and enriched.'

2

'I can't understand it,' Sally said distractedly. 'It's as if Ian was the glue that kept us together.' She ran her fingers through her short, greying hair. 'But when did me and Jock need anything to keep us together? I love him, and I know he loves me. Remember the day we met him and his mate, Flo, on the New Brighton ferry?'

'I'll never forget that day, luv.' It was the last time she had seen Tommy O'Mara.

Her sister's marriage was falling apart. Grace didn't help. She accused her mam and dad of always having cold-shouldered her, of making her feel second best. 'Then me and Jock have a go at each other,' Sally moaned. 'I tell him it's his fault Grace feels the way she does, and he says it's mine.'

The only good thing to come out of the whole sad business was that the two sisters had become close again. Sally frequently turned up at the launderette just as Flo was closing, and they would walk back to William

Square, arm in arm. Jock went to a social club in Kirkby almost every night – 'As if all he wants is to have a good time with his mates. I think I remind him too much of what we went through with Ian. He won't come with me to church.'

'I don't know what advice to give, Sal,' Flo said truthfully. She thought her sister spent far too much time in church, but preferred not to say so. 'Perhaps it's just a stage he's going through. He needs to let off steam. Jock's a good man at heart.'

'It's not advice I need,' Sally sniffed, 'just someone to talk to. Our Martha's come up with enough advice to write a book, from giving our Grace a good hiding to wiping the floor with Jock.'

'Both of which would do more harm than good.'

'That's what I said. Mind you, her Kate's been a great help. She often comes round to see me.' Suddenly Sally seemed to find a mole on the back of her hand enormously interesting. Without meeting her sister's eyes, she mumbled, 'I can't understand how our Martha ended up with such a lovely daughter, and we were landed with Grace. Oh!' she cried tearfully. 'Forget I said that. I love my girl, but I don't half wish she were different.'

'I wish all sorts of things were different, Sal.' Flo sighed. 'You must bring Kate round to see me sometime. I'd like to get to know her.'

She had never intended it to be this way, but it had all started the day she first saw Tommy O'Mara through a mist of steam in Fritz's laundry: Flo's life seemed to be divided into little boxes, each one carefully marked 'Secret'.

Martha and Sally knew this about her, Mr Fritz knew that. Hugh O'Mara thought he was her friend. No one knew about the servicemen during the war. There were her bogus 'retreats'. Bel, who thought she knew everything there was to know, knew virtually nothing, only that for a short time before the war she'd gone out with Tommy O'Mara.

Flo often worried that one day something might be said that would lift the lid off a box, give away one of her secrets, expose one of her lies.

It nearly happened the day Sally came to the flat, bringing Kate Colquitt with her. Bel was there, and they'd just watched *Roman Holiday* on television – Bel still went weak at the knees over Gregory Peck.

'This is Kate Colquitt, our Martha's girl,' Sally said.

Flo could have sworn that Bel's ears twitched. She still longed to know why Flo and Martha never spoke. 'Martha's girl, eh! Pleased to meet you, Kate. How's your mam keeping these days?'

'Very well, thank you.' The girl had a sweet, high-pitched voice.

'Why didn't you bring her with you?' Bel enquired cunningly. Flo threw her a murderous glance. Bel caught the look and winked.

Kate merely replied, 'Me mam doesn't know I've come.' She turned to Flo, green eyes shining in her lovely fresh face. 'I've always wanted to meet you, Auntie Flo. I saw you at Ian's funeral. I was going to introduce meself, but when I looked for you you'd gone.'

'Please call me Flo. "Auntie" makes me feel a bit peculiar.'

'Okay.' She followed her aunt into the kitchen when Flo went to make a pot of tea, chatting volubly. 'I like your flat, it's the gear. I'd love a place of me own, but me mam's dead set against it. She says I'm too young. How old were you when you came here, Flo?'

'Twenty.'

'There! Next month I'll be twenty-two. So I'm not too young, am I?' She looked at Flo, wide-eyed and artless.

'I was a very old twenty,' Flo muttered. An incredibly old twenty compared to this girl, who was too innocent for this world. She looked as vulnerable and defenceless as a flower by the wayside.

'There are times,' Kate sighed, 'when I'd love to be by meself. Y'know, read a book and stuff, watch the telly.'

Flo imagined her mother, Martha the Manipulator, never allowing her daughter a minute's peace. 'Why do you need a red bow in your hair when you're only going to see Josie Driver?' 'I'd sooner you didn't go out with a Protestant, Sal.' 'You've always got your head buried in a book, Flo Clancy.' And then there was Norman, which meant that Kate had two overbearing people to cope with, wanting her to do things their way. Sally said that he had moved to Kirkby and he was round at the house almost every night.

'Are you having a party on your birthday?' Flo asked brightly, as she arranged the cups and saucers on a tray.

'Just a few friends. You can come if you like.'

'Ta, luv, but I don't think that's such a good idea.' She picked up the tray. 'D'you mind bringing that plate of biscuits with you, save me coming back?'

'What happened between you and me mam, Flo?' Kate enquired earnestly. 'Auntie Sally says I'm not to mention I've been to see you. It must be something awful bad.'

Flo chuckled. 'That's something you need to ask your mam, luv.' One thing she knew for certain was that the girl wouldn't get a truthful answer.

They went into the living room. 'You took your time,' Bel said. 'I'm parched for a cuppa.'

'I remember you used to wait for Hugh O'Mara outside St Theresa's,' Kate went on, 'though I didn't know you were me auntie then.'

Bel's head jerked upwards and she looked at Flo, her face full of questions.

The very second Sally and Kate left, Bel burst out, 'Hugh O'Mara! Who's Hugh O'Mara? Is he related to Tommy? I didn't know he had a kid.'

'Why should you?'

'I thought you'd have said.'

Flo explained that Hugh had been born after Tommy died. It was hateful giving credit to Nancy for something she'd done herself, but too much time had passed for Bel to know the truth. Flo couldn't have stood the gasps of incredulity, the astounded comments. Bel *would* have crawled through the snow to get back her baby. Bel would have stood on the rooftops screaming to the world that her baby had been stolen, then demolished Nancy's front door with a battering ram once she had discovered where he was. The realisation that another woman wouldn't have taken it as meekly as she had made Flo feel uneasy. It was a bit late to regret what a coward she'd been, too easily influenced by the wishes of her family.

'That's all very well,' Bel hooted, when Flo finished her careful explanation, 'but what the hell were you doing waiting for the lad outside St Theresa's?'

I should have been a spy, Flo thought. I would have been brilliant at lying meself out of the most dangerous situations. She said that a woman at the laundry had had a son in the same class as Hugh. 'They were friends. I used to go by St Theresa's on Fridays on me way from the bank. Peggy asked me to make sure Jimmy was going straight home. That's how I met Hugh. He was a nice lad, quite different from his dad. I still see him,' she added casually. 'If he's passing the launderette, he might drop in.'

'Why didn't you tell me this before?' Bel said, outraged out of all proportion.

'I didn't think you'd be interested.'

'Why, Flo Clancy, you know I'm interested in *everything!*'

'Well, you know now, don't you?' Flo snapped.

It was a whole year before Jock tired of the social club and Sally stopped going quite so often to church. The old harmony was restored. It helped when Grace got engaged to a nice young man called Keith, who worked in a bank, and became absorbed in plans for her wedding eighteen months off at Easter 1966. 'Jock's pulling out all the stops. It's going to be a grand affair,' Sally announced. 'He thinks if we spend all our savings she'll realise we love her just as much as we did Ian.'

Sally continued coming to William Square, sometimes bringing Kate Colquitt with her. Flo and Kate got on like a house on fire. 'You should have had kids, Flo,' said Bel, who usually managed to be there when visitors came. 'You would have made a wonderful mother.'

It was a bitterly cold January afternoon, a month after her twenty-third birthday, when Kate turned up alone at the launderette. 'I hope you don't mind. I finish work at four.' She made a nervous face. 'Norman's off with a terrible cold and he's moved in with us for a while so me mam can look after him. I don't feel like going home just yet. I can't stand it when both of them get on to me.'

'I don't mind a bit, luv.' Flo sat the girl in her cubby-hole and made her some tea. Once she'd warmed up, she'd let her loose among her ladies, who'd soon make her forget her troubles. 'What do they get on to you about?' she asked.

Kate raised her shoulders and heaved a great sigh. 'Norman wants us to get married and me mam thinks it's a grand idea. He's so sweet. I can't remember a time when he hasn't been around, yet . . . oh, I dunno. It's worse now Grace is engaged – she's four years younger than me. Mam keeps saying I'll be left on the shelf, but I'm not sure if I care. I've started training to be a State Registered Nurse, and I'd like to finish before I settle down. In fact, sometimes I think I wouldn't mind staying single like you, Flo.'

She made herself useful, helping to untangle washing that had knotted together in the spin-driers, and getting on famously with the customers. She was still there when Flo was about to turn the Open sign to Closed, and Hugh O'Mara came in wearing the leather coat that had taken three months to save for, and which Nancy strongly disapproved of him wearing for work.

'Hugh!' Kate cried, her face lighting up with pleasure. 'I haven't seen you in ages.'

He appeared equally pleased to find her there. They sat on a bench, heads together, engrossed in conversation, and when the time came for Flo to lock up, the pair wandered off happily, arm in arm. A few days later, Kate turned up again, then Hugh arrived as if it had been prearranged. The same thing happened the next week and the next, until Flo got used to Tuesday and Friday being the days when Kate came to help untangle the washing, was joined by Hugh, and they would go off together into the night. She watched, entranced, as the looks they gave each other became more and more intimate. She realised they were falling in love, and couldn't have approved more. Her son would never find a prettier, nicer, more suitable wife than Kate Colquitt. She felt sure that even Nancy would be pleased when she was told. So far, everyone except Flo was being kept in the dark.

As the months crept by they were still in the dark. It was obvious to everyone in the launderette, including Mr Fritz, that the young couple were mad about each other, but Kate was too scared to tell her mam. 'She never liked Hugh much. She said there was something not quite right about his background.' She asked Flo how people got married in Gretna Green.

'I've no idea, luv,' Flo confessed, exasperated. She badly wanted to interfere, to tell them to get a move on, but held her tongue.

'Martha suspects Kate's got a secret boyfriend,' Sally remarked one day.

Apparently there were nights when Kate didn't get home till all hours and refused to say where she'd been. Poor Norman Cameron was doing his nut.

Flo wondered if Kate was more scared of Norman than of her mam. 'He'd kill any man who laid a finger on her,' Sally had said once. Perhaps she was scared for Hugh. Or maybe she was enjoying the clandestine nature of the affair, just as Flo had enjoyed her illicit meetings with Hugh's father all those years ago.

Secrecy must have run in both families, the O'Maras and the Clancys, because Kate and Hugh continued to see each other for over a year before everyone found out and all hell broke loose.

Flo had been out of bed barely five minutes when there was a pounding on the door. She opened it, still in her dressing-gown, and Sally came storming in, her normally placid face red with rage.

'Why aren't you at work?' Flo said, in surprise. Sally had been working full-time at Peterssen's the confectioner's to help with the wedding expenses, which were turning out to be horrendous. She wondered why her sister was so angry. Had Jock gone off the rails again? Grace was getting married on Saturday – perhaps she'd called it off or, even worse, perhaps Keith had.

Either Sally didn't hear the question or she ignored it. 'You knew, didn't you?' she said, loudly and accusingly.

'Knew what?' Flo stammered.

'About Kate and Hugh, soft girl. Nancy O'Mara passed the launderette on the bus last night and she saw them come out kissing and canoodling, so you must have known.'

'So what if I did?'

'You're a bloody idiot, Flo Clancy, you truly are. They're *cousins!*'

'I know darn well they're cousins. What's wrong with that?'

'They're *Catholic* cousins. The Church forbids that sort of thing between cousins.' Sally was staring at her sister belligerently, as if Flo had committed the worst possible crime. 'I hope they're not planning on getting married or anything daft like that.'

'They are, actually, once Kate plucks up the courage to tell her mam. It's not illegal. As they don't know they're related, under the circumstances it never entered me head that anyone would care.'

'Holy Mary, Mother of God.' Sally groaned. 'Not care! You never heard anything like the commotion that went on in our Martha's last night. 'Stead of going home, Nancy went straight to Kirkby, then Martha sent for me. We had to turn Norman Cameron away as we didn't want him listening to private family business. Me and Nancy had left before Kate came home. Christ knows what Martha said to the girl. And what's Nancy supposed to tell Hugh?' She groaned again. 'Why the hell didn't you do something to stop it, Flo?'

Flo gave a little sarcastic laugh. 'Such as?'

'I don't know, do I?'

'I suppose,' Flo said slowly, conscious of her own anger grating in her voice, 'I could have said "Sorry, Hugh, but you're not to have any romantic notions about Kate Colquitt, because the truth is, I'm your mam, not Nancy, which means you're cousins." That might have stopped it, and I'm sure everyone would have been dead pleased, particularly Martha and Nancy.'

Sally's rage subsided. 'I'm sorry, luv. Our Martha got me all worked up. I hardly slept a wink all night, but I shouldn't have blamed you.' She looked curiously at her sister. 'Did you ever think about telling him when he got older?'

Flo had thought about it a million times. 'Yes, but I decided it wouldn't be fair. It might do the poor lad's head in, knowing the truth after all this time. He'd feel betrayed. All the deceit, all the lies. He might never want to see either me or Nancy again, and he'd be the one who'd suffer most.'

Sally shivered suddenly. 'It's cold in here.'

'I'm used to it. I'll turn the fire on.'

'What are we going to do, Flo, about Kate and Hugh?'

'Leave them alone, do nothing. Let them get wed with everyone's blessing.'

'Come off it, Flo. You must be out of your mind,' Sally said resignedly.

'I've never felt saner.' Flo's voice was cold. 'You, Martha and Nancy are nothing but a bunch of hypocrites. You pride yourselves on being great Catholics, yet you're quite happy to let me son be lied to all his life. Martha and Nancy caused this mess and I don't see why Hugh and Kate should suffer. Anyroad, marriage isn't out of the question. Perhaps they can get a dispensation?' She couldn't understand the need some people had to interfere in other people's lives. The young couple had fallen in love in all innocence, and they were perfect for each other. She was desperate for them to be left alone, not be parted over some silly rule that couldn't even be explained to them. Kate was a nice girl, but she was weak. Once Martha got to work on her, Flo couldn't imagine her holding out.

'I suggested a dispensation,' Sally said tiredly, 'but Martha and Nancy nearly hit the roof. How would they explain the situation for one thing? It's not just the parish priest who gets involved, it can go up as far as the bishop. And it means Hugh and Kate would have to know the truth.'

'But, Sal,' Flo tried to convey her desperation to her sister, 'we're the only ones who know they're cousins. It's not against the law of the land. If all of us kept our traps shut, Hugh and Kate could get married tomorrer.'

To her relief, Sally looked more than half convinced. 'There might be something in what you say,' she conceded. 'I'll go straight to Kirkby and see our Martha.'

Over the next few days, Flo tried to ring Sally several times from the telephone in the launderette, but either there was no reply or Jock said she was out somewhere, busy with arrangements for Grace's wedding. There was no sign, either, of Hugh or Kate. She prayed that Hugh wouldn't be annoyed or get into trouble if she rang him at work, but when she did, she was told he hadn't been in all week. Desperation turned to frustration when she realised there was nothing she could do. She thought of going to Martha's, or to Clement Street to see Nancy, but she didn't trust herself not to blurt out the truth if there was a row.

She had bought a new outfit for Grace's wedding: a pale blue and pink check frock with a white Peter Pan collar, a white silk beret and gloves, and high-heeled linen shoes. On the day, she went through the motions, chatting to the guests, agreeing that the bride looked like a film star in her raw silk dress. She did her best to get Sally on one side and pump her for information, but found it impossible and came to the conclusion that her sister was avoiding her. She wanted to know why Martha wasn't there and what on earth had happened to Kate, who was supposed to be a bridesmaid.

The ceremony had been over for twenty-four hours, the newly wedded couple had already landed safely in Tenerife to start their fortnight's honeymoon when Sally came to William Square to tell Flo that, at the same time as Grace had been joined in holy matrimony to Keith, in another church in another part of Liverpool, Norman Cameron had taken Kate Colquitt to be his wife. It had been a hastily arranged ceremony, with an emergency licence, attended by only a few friends. The bride wore a borrowed dress. They were spending two days in Rhyl for their honeymoon

'Martha made me promise not to tell you,' Sally said. 'She thought you might turn up and make a fuss.'

'Since when did I ever make a fuss?' Flo asked bitterly. 'I let her tread all over me. I let her ruin me life, just as she's ruined Kate's.' She thought of Hugh, who must have felt betrayed when he heard the news.

'You're exaggerating, Flo. Norman has loved Kate all his life. Now his dreams have come true and they're married. He'll make the best husband in the world.'

Perhaps Norman's dreams had been nightmares, because the stories that reached Flo in the months and years that followed scarcely told of a man who loved his wife.

Kate Colquitt, now Cameron, had become pregnant straight away. Late the following November she gave birth to a daughter, Millicent. Flo hadn't set eyes on Kate since the girl had walked out of the launderette on Hugh's arm just before Easter. She felt hurt at first, until a dismayed Sally informed her that Norman hardly let his new wife out of doors. 'She can go to the local shops and to church, but no further. I can't think why, but he doesn't trust her. Perhaps he knows about Hugh O'Mara, but Kate was single then so what does it matter?'

On impulse, Flo decided to go and see her niece at the maternity hospital. Afternoon visiting was from two till three so she arranged for the woman who did the morning shift at the launderette to hang on until she got back. 'I'm off to see me niece in hospital,' she said proudly. 'She's just had a baby, a little girl.'

'Would you like to see the baby first?' the nurse enquired, when Flo asked where she could find Mrs Kathleen Cameron.

'That'd be nice.'

The hospital bustled with visitors, mainly women at this time of day. 'That's her, second row back, second cot from the end.' The nurse's voice dropped to a whisper: 'I wouldn't want anyone else to hear, but she's one of the prettiest babies we've ever had.'

Flo was left alone to stare through the nursery window at the rows of babies. Some were howling furiously, their little faces red and screwed up in rage. A few were awake but quiet, their small bodies squirming against the tightly wrapped blankets. The rest, Millicent Cameron among them, were fast asleep.

'Aah!' Flo breathed. She was perfect, with long lashes quivering on her waxen cheeks, and a little pink rosebud mouth. Hugh had probably looked like that. She wondered if he'd also had such a head of hair: masses of little curls, like delicate ribbons. I never even knew how much he weighed, she thought. She pressed her forehead against the glass in order to see better. 'I wish you all the luck in the world, Millie Cameron,' she whispered. 'And I tell you this much, luv, I don't half wish you were mine.'

She left the nursery and went to the ward, but when she looked through the glass panel in the door, Martha was sitting beside Kate's bed. Flo sighed and turned away. On the way out, she took another long look at her new great-niece. She felt tears running warmly down her cheeks, sighed, wiped them away with her sleeve and went home.

Almost two decades passed before she saw Kate Cameron and her daughter again.

The girl came into the launderette and looked challengingly at Flo. She had jet black wavy hair, wide brown eyes, and enough makeup on her coarse, attractive face to last most women a week. She seemed to be wearing only half a skirt, and a sweater several sizes too small so it strained against her large, bouncing breasts. A cigarette protruded from the corner of her red, greasy mouth, and she spoke out of the other corner like Humphrey

Bogart. 'Are you the one who's a friend of Hugh O'Mara?' she demanded in a deep, sultry voice.

Flo blinked. 'Yes.'

'He said I could leave a message with you. If he comes in, tell him I'll meet him outside Yates's Wine Lodge at half past eight.'

'Rightio. What name shall I say?'

'Carmel McNulty.' The girl turned, flicked ash on the floor, and strode out, hips swaying, long legs enticing in their black, fishnet tights.

Flo's ladies were all eyes and ears. 'Was that Carmel McNulty?' one enquired eagerly.

'Apparently so,' Flo conceded.

'I hope that nice Hugh chap isn't going out with her. She's no better than she ought to be, that girl.'

Everyone seemed to know or have heard of Carmel NcNulty.

'Didn't her last feller end up in Walton jail?'

'She was a hard-faced bitch even when she was a little 'un.'

'I'd give my lads the back of me hand if any of 'em dared to look twice at Carmel McNulty.'

Flo listened, appalled. In the year since Kate had got married, Hugh had never mentioned her name, or been seen with another girl. Surely he didn't have designs on Carmel McNulty. Maybe she had designs on him. Hugh was a catch – one of the best-looking men in all Liverpool, with his own car and a good, steady job. Perhaps she was prejudiced, but Flo couldn't understand why there wasn't a whole line of women queuing to snap him up.

Having demolished Carmel McNulty, Flo's ladies began to put her back together again. 'Mind you, Carmel's got her hands full with her mam. How many kids has Tossie got?'

'Twenty?' someone suggested.

'Twenty!' Flo squeaked.

'Nah, I think it was eighteen at the last count.'

'Carmel's the eldest and she's had a babby to look after ever since she wasn't much more than a babby herself.'

'She still looks after 'em. I saw her only the other Sunday pushing a pramload of kids down Brownlow Hill.'

'You can't blame her wanting a good time after all that. How old is she now?'

'Nineteen.'

Six weeks later Hugh O'Mara and Carmel McNulty were married. The bride held her bouquet over her already swelling stomach. Flo went to the church and watched through the railings. It was more like a school outing than a wedding, as hordes of large and small McNultys chased each other around the churchyard.

Nancy O'Mara hadn't changed much: she still wore her black hair in the same enormous bun and the same peculiar clothes, a long flowing red dress and a black velvet bolero. She looked as if at any minute she might produce castanets and start dancing, except that her face was set like yellow concrete in an expression of disgust. According to a rather sullen Hugh, she loathed Carmel and Carmel loathed her. Nancy had only come to the wedding because of what people would say if she didn't.'

'It serves you right,' Flo murmured. 'If it weren't for you and our Martha, Hugh would be married to Kate by now and everyone would be happy, apart from Norman Cameron.' Instead, Kate was stuck with a man who kept her a prisoner, and Hugh was marrying a woman he didn't love. There was nothing wrong with Carmel: once she'd got to know her, Flo liked the girl. She was big-hearted, generous to a fault, and as tough as old boots. But she wasn't Hugh's type. Flo clutched the railings with both hands. Her son was doing his best to look as if he was enjoying his wedding day, but his mam could tell he was as miserable as sin.

Flo went through the backyard of the terraced house in Mulliner Street and let herself into the untidy kitchen. She shouted, 'Is he ready for his walk yet, Carmel?'

Carmel appeared in slacks and one of Hugh's old shirts, a cigarette between her lips. She looked exhausted. 'The little bugger kept us awake half the night laughing! I'll be glad to be shut of him for a few hours, I really will.'

A small boy burst into the kitchen and flung his arms around Flo's legs. 'Can we go to the Mystery? Can we play ball? Can I have a lolly? Can I walk and not sit in me pushchair?'

Smiling, Flo loosened the arms around her legs and picked the child up. 'You're a weight, young man!'

Tom O'Mara was over-active and inordinately precocious for a three-year-old. Even as a baby, he had hardly slept. He didn't cry, but demanded attention with loud noises, which got louder and louder if he was ignored. As he grew older, he would rattle the bars of his cot and fling the bedding on the floor. Lately, he'd begun to sit up in bed in the early hours of the morning chanting nursery rhymes or singing, and now, apparently, laughing. He could already read a little, count up to a hundred and tell the time. Carmel said she'd never come across a child quite like him. 'I feel like knocking bloody hell out of the little bugger, but you can't very well hit a kid for being happy!'

When relations between Carmel and her mother-in-law broke down completely and Nancy was barred from Mulliner Street, Flo grasped the opportunity and offered to take her grandson out in the mornings.

'Would you, Flo?' Carmel said gratefully. 'Honest, I don't know where

Hugh found a friend like you. I wish you were me mother-in-law, I really do.'

It was June, not exactly hot, but quite warm. Flo played football with Tom until her limbs could no longer move. She lay on the grass and declared herself a goal post. 'You can kick the ball at me, but don't expect to have it kicked back. I'm worn out.'

Tom sat on her stomach. He was a handsome little chap with the same devil-may-care expression on his face as his grandad. 'Are you old?'

'Is fifty-one old? I'm not sure.'

'Dad's old.'

'No, he's not, luv. He's nineteen years younger than me.'

'Mam says he's old.'

Things were not well with the O'Maras. In the evenings, after being stuck in the house all day with a child who would crack the patience of a saint, Carmel was anxious for a break, a bit of excitement. Hugh, who worked hard and was rarely home before seven, preferred to stay in and watch television. Flo had offered to babysit and did occasionally at weekends, but in the main the couple stayed put, much to Carmel's chagrin. She declared loudly and aggressively that she was bored out of her skull and might as well be married to an old-age pensioner.

Flo couldn't help but sympathise. Hugh was growing old before his time. He already had a stoop, his hair was thinning, his gentle face was that of a man weighed down by the cares of the world. He was unhappy. Flo could see it in his dead, green eyes. He didn't seem to care when Carmel started going out alone. She was going clubbing, she announced. Hugh was welcome to come with her if he wanted, otherwise he would just have to like it or lump it.

After the launderette had closed, Flo often went to Mulliner Street to sit with her son. She had never thought she would have the freedom to be alone with Hugh, Nancy out of the picture. Even so, she would have preferred the circumstances to be different. They didn't talk much. He sat with his eyes fixed on the television, but she could tell he wasn't really watching.

'Do you see much of Kate nowadays?' he asked one night.

'No, luv. I haven't seen her in years.'

'I wonder how she is.'

She didn't dare repeat the things Sally told her – Hugh was miserable enough. 'She's had another baby, a little girl called Trudy,' was all she said.

Another night he said, 'Why did you wait for me outside St Theresa's that day, Flo? I've often wondered.'

'I wanted to meet you. I knew your dad, remember?'

'That's right. What was he like? Mam never talked about him much, except that he died on that submarine.'

'The *Thetis*. He was an ould divil, your dad. Full of himself, dead conceited. Women were after him like flies.' Perhaps she should have come up with a more positive, more flattering description, but at least she hadn't told him his dad had lied through his teeth.

Hugh allowed himself the glimmer of a smile. 'Not like me.'

'No, I'm pleased to say.' She didn't like the way he always talked about the past, as if he'd given up on the future. Usually, Tom could be heard upstairs, where he'd been put to bed hours ago, making aeroplane or car noises, but Hugh seemed unaware of his delightful son and his attractive wife – who might be as common as muck but was basically a good girl, anxious to be a good wife. Carmel was only twenty-three: she needed a husband who did more than just bring home a regular wage. If only Hugh would take her out now and then, she'd be happy, but he didn't seem to care.

In the Mystery, Tom bounced several times on her stomach. 'Strewth, luv,' Flo gasped. 'Are you out to kill me?'

'Can we go to your house for a cuppa tea?'

'There isn't time, Tom. It'd make me late for work.' Sometimes when it was raining she took him to William Square and read him books, which he adored. 'I'll get you an ice lolly, then take you back to your mam.'

He gave her stomach a final, painful bounce. 'Rightio, Flo.'

When she returned the kitchen was still in a state. It was unlike Carmel not to tidy up – she usually kept the house spotless. Flo went into the living room and could hear voices upstairs, one a man's. 'Carmel,' she shouted.

It was several minutes before Carmel came running down. She'd changed into a mini-skirted Crimplene frock. Her lipstick was smudged.

Flo frowned. 'Is Hugh home?'

The girl looked at her boldly. 'No.'

'I see.'

'I doubt if you do, Flo. If you were married to that drip Hugh O'Mara you might see then.'

'It's none of me business, is it, girl?' Flo considered herself the last person on earth entitled to criticise another woman's morals, but her heart ached for her unhappy, lacklustre son.

Tom had turned five and been at school only a matter of weeks when Carmel walked out for good. 'She's gone to live in Brighton with some chap she met in a club,' Hugh said wearily. 'She said she would have taken Tom but her new feller doesn't want to be landed with a kid. "Flo will look after him," she said.'

'I'll be happy to.' It would never have come to this if I'd been allowed to keep me baby, Flo thought sadly.

'There won't be any need,' Hugh said, in his expressionless voice. 'I'm moving back in with me mam. She'll take care of Tom. She's not seen much of him 'cept when I took him round.'

Flo turned away, her lips twisted bitterly. She supposed that that was the last she would see of her grandson, but on the day that the family moved to Clement Street to live with Nancy, Tom O'Mara burst into the launderette after school. He was everything his father had never been: untidy, uninhibited, full of beans. 'Hiya, Flo,' he sang.

'What are you doing here?' she gasped. He'd come half a mile out of his way to get there. She noticed he had a skull and crossbones drawn upside down on both knees. 'Mrs O'Mara will be worried stiff wondering where you've got to.'

'You mean me gran? Don't like her. Me mam always said she was an ould cow. Can I have a cuppa tea, Flo?' He settled on a bench and allowed himself to be made a fuss of by Flo's ladies.

'How on earth could Carmel McNulty bring herself to walk out on such a little angel?'

'He's the spitting image of Hugh.'

'He's the spitting image of Carmel.'

From then on, Tom never failed to turn up for a cup of tea after school. Nancy couldn't control him and Flo didn't even try.

3

Mr Fritz was seventy-five, the same age as the century, and becoming frail. His limbs were swollen and twisted with arthritis, and it was heartbreaking to see him struggle up and down the basement steps with his stick. Even worse, more important parts of his body had ceased to work. He and Flo went to the Isle of Man rarely nowadays, and then only to lie in each other's arms.

'I'm sorry, Flo,' he would say mournfully, 'I'm like one of my old washing-machines. I need reconditioning. A new motor wouldn't do me any harm.'

'Don't be silly, luv. I'm not exactly in tip-top condition meself,' Flo would answer. In fact, she was as fit as a fiddle and missed making love.

Increasingly his family came over from Ireland to see him. Flo found it difficult to recognise the hard-eyed middle-aged men and women as the children she'd once played with, taken for walks and to the pictures. Their attitude towards her was unfriendly and suspicious. She sensed that they were worried she might have undue influence over the man with whom she'd shared a house for so long, a house that was now worth many thousands of pounds, added to which there were the six launderettes. All of a sudden, the little Fritzes seemed to regard their father's welfare of great importance.

'Harry would like me to live with him in Dublin,' Mr Fritz said, the night after Ben and Harry had been to stay for the weekend. 'And I had a letter from Aileen the other day. She never married, you know, and she wants me to live with her!' He chuckled happily. 'It's nice to know my children want to look after me in my old age, don't you think, Flo?'

'Yes, luv,' Flo said warmly. She felt frightened, convinced that it was their inheritance his children were concerned with.

'I told Harry that, if I went, I'd want nothing to do with Stella.' Flo went cold. He was actually considering Harry's offer. 'He said they hardly see her nowadays. She's still on the same farm and the toilet facilities are barely civilised, which is why none of them go to visit.'

It turned out he just wanted to spend a long holiday in Dublin, to get to know his children properly again. 'I would never leave you, Flo,' he said. 'Not for good.'

While he was away, the launderettes could virtually run themselves, but for the second time in her life, Flo was left in charge of Mr Fritz's business. This time though, an agent would collect the money each day and bank it. Flo would be sent a cheque to pay the staff, with the power to hire and fire should the need arise. Herbie Smith, a reliable plumber, had promised to be on call in case any of the machines broke down.

Harry came over from Ireland to fetch his father, and Flo longed to remind this cold, unpleasant man that he'd once had a crush on her. Mr Fritz made his painful way down the steps towards the taxi that would take them to the Irish boat. He gave Flo a chaste kiss on the cheek. 'I'll be back in three months. Keep an eye on upstairs for me.'

'Of course, luv. I've done it before, haven't I?' Flo had no idea why she should want to cry, but cry she did.

'So you have, my dear Flo.' There were tears in his own rheumy eyes. 'The day I came home from the camp and found you here will always remain one of my fondest memories, though not as precious as our weekends together.' He grasped both her hands in his. 'You'll write, won't you? Has Harry given you the address in Dublin?'

'I'll write every week,' Flo vowed. Harry was looking at them darkly, as if all the family's suspicions had been confirmed. 'C'mon, Dad,' he said, making no attempt to keep the impatience out of his voice. Flo felt even more frightened for Mr Fritz, the man she had loved since she was thirteen, not romantically, not passionately, but as the dearest of friends. 'I'll miss you,' she sobbed. 'The place won't seem the same.'

'It's not for long, Flo. The three months will go by in a flash.'

He'd been gone less than a fortnight when Flo heard noises coming from upstairs as if furniture was being moved around. She ran outside. The front door was open and two men were struggling down the steps with the big pine dresser from the kitchen. A removal van was parked further along the square.

'What's happening?' she cried.

'We're taking the good stuff to auction and leaving the rubbish behind,' she was told brusquely.

Flo returned to the basement, knowing that her worst fears had been realised. Mr Fritz would never again live in William Square.

Soon afterwards, a gang of workmen descended on the house. Each floor was being converted into a separate flat, and Flo feared for herself. She'd always insisted on paying rent, but it was a nominal sum. What if the little Fritzes put up the rent so that it was beyond her means? What if they threw her out? She couldn't imagine living anywhere else, where she might have to share a kitchen and lavatory with other tenants. Flo had grown used to her subterranean existence, where she happily ignored the real world. The years were marked for her not by the election of various governments, Labour or Conservatives, the Cuban crisis or the assassination of an American president, but by films and music, *Gone with the Wind, Singing in the Rain, The Sound of Music.* Paul Newman, Marlon Brando, the Beatles . . .

'Mr Fritz would never throw you out!' Bel scoffed.

'I'm not sure if he's got much say in things any more,' said Flo.

'You can always live with me.'

'That's very kind of you, Bel, but I couldn't stand you bellowing down me ear all day long. And it's not just the flat I'm worried about, what about me job?' Each week, she sent her rent, along with a little report: a woman had left and she'd had to take on someone new, a machine had needed servicing and she enclosed Herbie Smith's bill. The address Harry had given her turned out to be a firm of accountants, and although she frequently enclosed a letter for Mr Fritz, there'd been no reply so far, and she wondered if her letters were being passed on.

Four families moved in upstairs, but Flo heard nothing about her own situation. 'Perhaps the little Fritzes are playing games with me,' she said to Bel. 'Lulling me into a sense of false security, like.' She might come home one day to find the locks changed and her furniture dumped on the pavement.

Bel made one of her famous faces. 'Don't talk daft. Y'know, what you need is to get away for a while, leave all your troubles behind. I've been thinking, why don't we go on holiday? A woman at work is going to Spain for two whole weeks on a charter flight, I think it's called. It's ever so cheap and she said there's still a few places left.'

'Spain! I've never been abroad.'

'Neither have I since I left the forces, but that's no reason not to go now. We might cop a couple of fellers out there.'

The small swimming pool shone like a dazzling sapphire in the light of the huge amber moon, and the navy sky was powdered lavishly with glittering stars. Less than fifty feet away, the waters of the Mediterranean shimmered and rustled softly and couples were clearly visible lying clasped in each other's arms on the narrow strip of Costa Brava sand. Somewhere a guitarist was strumming a vaguely familiar tune, and people were still in the pool, although it was past midnight. There was laughter, voices, the clink of glasses from the outside bar.

Flo, on the balcony of their room on the second floor of the hotel, refilled her glass from the jug of sangria and wondered if you could buy it in Liverpool. Wine was so cheap that she and Bel were convinced they would never be sober if they lived in Spain.

They'd been lucky to get a room with a view like this. The guests on the other side of the building could see only more and more of the hotels that cluttered the entire length of coast.

Someone opened a door by the pool and a blast of music filled the air: The Who, singing, 'I can See For Miles . . .' 'Miles and miles and miles,' Flo sang, until the door closed and all she could hear was the guitarist again. Every night at the Old Tyme Dance while she was being led sedately around the floor to the strains of 'When Irish Eyes Are Smiling', or 'Goodnight, Eileen', she thought enviously of the youngsters in the other ballroom leaping around madly to the sound of Dire Straits or ABBA.

Bel hadn't bothered to inform her that the group they were travelling with were old-age pensioners. Flo had been horrified when they got on the plane and she found herself surrounded by people with hearing aids and walking sticks and not a single head of hair in sight that wasn't grey.

To her further consternation, there were actually a few wolf-whistles – in this company, two women in their mid-fifties must seem like teenagers: Bel still managed to look incredibly glamorous, though her lovely red hair was in reality lovely grey hair that had required a tint for years.

There were still five more days of the holiday to go, and Flo supposed she'd had quite a good time. During the day, they wandered round Lloret del Mar, admiring the palm trees and the sparkling blue sea. They bought little trinkets in the gift shops. She got Bel a pretty mosaic bracelet, and Bel bought her a set of three little brass plaques that had taken Flo's fancy. Then they had found a bar that stocked every liqueur in existence and were sampling them one by one. Flo had sent cards to everyone she could think of, including Mr Fritz, though she had no faith that he would get it. Why had he never written as he'd promised? It was six months since he'd left William Square and she worried about him all the time. If she didn't hear soon, she resolved to go over to Ireland in search of him, even though she didn't have a proper address.

Evenings, they went dancing. Flo wrinkled her nose: she hated being taken in a pair of gnarled, sunburnt arms for the Gay Gordons or the Military Two-step or, somewhat daringly, a rumba, played to a slow, plodding beat in case it overtaxed a few dicky hearts. Mr Fritz was old, but in her eyes he had always remained the same lovely little man with brown fuzzy hair and twinkling eyes she'd first met in the laundry. The other night one sly old bugger in fancy shorts had had the nerve to get fresh during the last waltz.

'You're no spring chicken yourself,' Bel snorted, when Flo complained.

'I wouldn't mind dancing with fellers me own age,' Flo said haughtily. Bel had taken up with Eddie Eddison, a widower in his seventies, who came from Maynard Street, though it seemed daft to come all the way to Spain to click with a feller who lived only two streets away in Liverpool.

Most nights when Bel wasn't looking, Flo slipped away. She enjoyed sitting on the balcony, staring at the sky, listening to the sounds by the pool, drinking wine. When she got home, she might do something with her backyard, paint the walls a nice colour, buy some plants and a table and chairs, turn it into one of them patio things. It would be pleasant to sit outside in the good weather. The flat could get stuffy when it was hot.

That's if the flat remained hers. Oh, Lord, Bel would be cross if she knew she was worrying about the flat again. Flo rested her arms on the balcony and stared down at the pool. Even at this hour children were still up. Two little boys, one about Tom O'Mara's age, were splashing water at each other in the shallow end. If only she could have brought Tom with her. He would have had the time of his life. Instead of dancing with men old enough to be her father, or sitting alone on a balcony, she could have been down at the pool with Tom. It seemed a normal, everyday thing to do, to bring your grandson on holiday, but the things that normal, everyday people did seemed to have passed her by.

Flo sat back in her chair and sighed. Another few days and they could go home. She couldn't wait, though she wouldn't let Bel know she was homesick. She would laugh and smile, and look cheerful, pretend to be having a great time, make the best of things as she always had.

Out of the corner of her eye, she glimpsed a star shoot across the sky. It disappeared into the infinite darkness – or was it just her imagination that she could see the faintest, barely discernible burst of yellow, which meant that millions and millions of miles away there'd been an almighty explosion?

The idea made her shudder, and she remembered being told as a child that God had created the world in seven days. 'But did He create the universe as well, Dad? Did He create the sun and the moon and the stars at the same time?' She couldn't remember what his answer had been.

It was ages since she'd thought about Dad. Living in Burnett Street had been perfect when he was alive and Martha had yet to assume the role of Being In Charge. Flo had never planned on getting married, but had just known that one day she would and that she would have children, two at least. Then, as if the shooting star had struck its target, Flo felt as if every muscle in her body had instantly wasted, as if every bone had turned to jelly. All that was left was her heart, which pounded like a hammer in her cavernous chest.

She'd spent her entire adult life in the way she was spending this holiday! Making the best of things, pretending to enjoy herself. *Waiting for it to end!*

'Oh, Lord!' The awful feeling passed as quickly as it had come, but in the mad scramble of thoughts that followed she knew that she should have made the best of things in a more practical way, by marrying Gerard Davies, for instance, or almost any one of those other young servicemen. It was no use blaming Martha. It was Flo's own fault that she'd wasted her life.

The basement flat felt unusually chilly when she arrived home from Spain to find three letters waiting for her on the mat. She went through them on her way to the kitchen to put the kettle on, aching for a cup of tea made with ordinary leaves instead of those silly teabags. Two were bills, but she stopped in her tracks when she saw the name and address of a solicitor in Castle Street on the third. She'd never had a letter from a solicitor before, and her hands were trembling as she tore it open, convinced that the little Fritzes were demanding formally that she quit the flat.

The heading was enough to make her burst into tears. 'Re: Fritz Erik Hofmannsthal (deceased).'

He was dead! *Mr Fritz was dead* – and not one of his children had bothered to let her know. Flo forgot the tea and poured a glass of sherry instead. Her imagination ran riot as she thought of all the different ways he might have died, none of them pleasant. She'd like to bet he'd wanted to return to William Square and be with her, but his children hadn't let him. Lovely, long-cherished memories flicked through her brain: the laundry on Tuesdays when he'd brought cream cakes, the day Stella had taken the photograph of him and his girls outside – the family had just come back from Anglesey and seemed so happy. How strange and cruel life could be that it should all have turned so sour. She recalled their first weekend in the Isle of Man, two old friends comfortably together at last.

It was a long time before she could bring herself to read the letter, to learn that dear Mr Fritz had bequeathed her the leasehold of the basement flat, as well as the launderette in Smithdown Road. The letter finished, 'We would be obliged if you would telephone for an appointment so that arrangements can be made for various papers to be signed.'

'Mr Hofmannsthal's children are seeking to question the validity of his will,' the solicitor informed her. He was younger than expected, not the least bit pompous, and from his build and his broken nose, looked like a rugby player or a boxer. 'But as same was dictated in my presence ten years ago while my client was in full possession of his senses, there is no question of it not being valid.'

'I don't think the little Fritzes liked me very much,' Flo said, in a small voice. 'Least, not since they stopped being little.'

'They like you even less now, which isn't surprising. You're very much the fly in the ointment. They want the house in William Square put on the market, but it won't fetch anything like it would have done had the basement been included.' The solicitor smiled, as if this pleased him enormously.

'I'm sorry,' Flo said weakly.

'Good heavens, Miss Clancy!' he exploded. 'Sorry is the very last thing you should be. It's what my client, Fritz Hofmannsthal, wanted, and I'm sure he had the best reason in the world for doing so.'

Flo felt herself go pink, wondering what Mr Fritz might have told him. 'Do I still have to look after the other launderettes?' she enquired.

The solicitor was so outraged to discover that she'd been 'acting as manager', as he put it, for six whole months without even so much as a thank-you from the little Fritzes, that he suggested putting in a claim against the estate for 'services rendered'. 'We'll demand ten pounds a week for the period involved, and probably end up with five. Will that suit you?'

Flo was about to say she didn't want a penny, but changed her mind. Even if she gave away the money, it was better than the little Fritzes having it. 'Five pounds a week would be fine,' she said.

The whole thing went into another of Flo's invisible boxes marked 'Secret'. If people found out, they would wonder why Mr Fritz had remembered her so generously. She owned her own property. She owned her own business. But no one would ever know.

In his day Edward Eddison had been a professional magician and had appeared halfway down the bill in theatres all over the country. When he married Bel Szerb in a register office two months after their holiday in Spain, he produced two white doves from his sleeve, which fluttered around the room, much to the annoyance of the registrar who disapproved of confetti, let alone live birds.

Bel, gorgeous in lavender tulle and a feathered hat, screamed with laughter when a bird settled happily on her head.

Flo, still shaken by the strange, unsettling thoughts she'd had in Spain and the loss of Mr Fritz, felt depressed when the ceremony was over, and Bel and Eddie departed to Bournemouth on their honeymoon. The newly-weds intended to live in Eddie's house in Maynard Street, and Bel planned on doing the place up from top to bottom. Flo tried to cheer herself up by decorating her own flat. She painted the walls white and the big wooden beams across the middle of the room black. The plaques Bel had bought her in Spain went well against the glossy surface, and when she mentioned this to her ladies, they presented her with several more. She painted the little yard a pretty rose pink, bought garden furniture and plant-holders, but when it came to new furniture for inside, she couldn't bring herself to part with a thing. After all, Mr Fritz and Jimmy Cromer had struggled downstairs with the settee and chair out of Stella's sitting room, as well as the big sideboard, which was probably an antique – if the little Fritzes had known it would probably have gone for auction, along with the lovely oak wardrobe and chest-of-drawers in the bedroom. As for the brass bed, she'd no intention of changing it for one of those padded-base things like they'd had in Spain – it had been like sleeping on wooden planks. She even felt quite fond of the little rag rug in front of the fire, which had been there when she arrived. She made do with buying pictures for the walls and armfuls of silk flowers to arrange in vases, and a nest of round tables to put the vases on. The big table she folded against the wall because she rarely used it. Nowadays, she ate on the settee in front of the television. Last Christmas, Bel had bought her a coffee table for this very purpose, an ugly thing, Flo thought secretly, with legs like clumps of giant onions.

The only light that glimmered through this dark period was her grandson Tom, seven years old and a continual thorn in the side of Nancy O'Mara, just like his grandad. Tom came and went as he pleased, no matter what Nancy told him. Hugh, of whom Flo saw little these days, appeared to have given up on his son and took no interest. On Sundays, Flo would return from Mass to find Tom sitting on the steps outside her flat, ready to spend the day with her. She took him to matinée performances at the cinema. Once she got used to the idea that she was her own boss and could take time off whenever she pleased, she and Tom sometimes went to football matches to see Everton or Liverpool play.

Tom was at Flo's place too often to be kept hidden in one of her secret boxes, so Bel got used to finding him there, though she thought it most peculiar. 'You're obsessed with the O'Maras, Flo,' she hissed. 'Tommy, Hugh, now little Tom.'

Gradually the dark period passed. It was a relief when the unpleasant middle-aged couple on the ground floor moved out, and a beautiful black girl, still a teenager, with two small children, moved in. But Flo was shocked to the core when she discovered that Charmian was one of the women who took up position along the railings of the square each night. Even so, it was hard not to say, 'Good morning,' or 'Isn't it a lovely day?' or 'We could do with some rain, couldn't we?' when they came face to face. The two became rather wary friends, although Charmian continually felt the need to defend her doubtful and precarious lifestyle. 'Me husband walked out on me. No one'll give me a job with two kids under school age. How else am I supposed to feed 'em and pay the rent?' she demanded aggressively, the first time she came down to the basement flat.

'Don't go on at me, luv,' Flo said mildly. 'It's your life. I haven't uttered a word of criticism, have I?'

'I can see it in your eyes. You're disgusted.'

'No, I'm not, luv. The disgust is in your own eyes. I think you're ashamed, else you wouldn't go on about it so much.'

Charmian stormed out, but returned the following night to say, 'You're right, but I don't know another way to keep me head above water.'

Flo said nothing. As the months rolled by, she listened patiently while Charmian struggled loudly and vocally with her conscience. When the woman who worked the morning shift in the launderette gave in her notice, Flo casually mentioned it to her upstairs neighbour. 'There'll be a job going the Monday after next, eight till two. The pay isn't bad, enough for the rent and to keep two kids without too much of a struggle.'

Charmian glared at her. 'Is that a hint?'

'No, luv, it's an offer.' Flo shrugged. 'It's up to you if you take it.'

'What about the owner? He mightn't want an ex-pro working in his bloody launderette.'

The girl scowled, but she hated what she was doing and Flo could tell that she was tempted. 'The owner will go on my recommendation.'

'And you'd recommend me when you know . . .' Two large tears rolled down the satiny cheeks. 'Oh, Flo!'

4

Eddie Eddison didn't last long. He died a happy man in the arms of his glamorous wife only eighteen months after their wedding. Bel was left with a hefty weekly pension, a gold Cortina saloon, and immediately began to take driving lessons.

Charmian gave up her job when she married the emergency plumber, Herbie Smith, who moved into the ground-floor flat with his ready-made family. Unlike his dad, Tom O'Mara didn't desert his friend Flo when he started comprehensive school. He was a cocky little bugger, full of confidence and sure of his place in the world. It didn't bother him being seen going to the pictures on Sunday afternoons with a middle-aged woman, or two middle-aged women if Bel decided to come. Bel had transferred her affections from Gregory Peck to Sean Connery.

1983

When his dad died Tom was fifteen, and the cockiness, the confidence, turned out to be nothing but a sham.

The firm in Anfield swore that the accident had been caused by negligence on the part of their workman, Hugh O'Mara. The house he was rewiring was dripping with damp: he'd been a fool to try fitting a plug in a socket that was hanging off the wall, the existing wiring having been installed half a century before. Knowing O'Mara, he'd probably had only half his mind on the job. His heart hadn't been in it for years. He was usually in either a trance or a daydream, the boss was never sure. Anyroad, the stupid sod had been thrown across the room, killed instantly.

Flo didn't go to the funeral. She couldn't have stood it if Nancy, the Welsh witch, had behaved as she had outside the gates of Cammell Laird's, weeping and wailing and making an exhibition of herself. At least she'd had a claim on Tommy, but she'd none on Hugh.

It was as if Hugh had already been dead a long time, Flo thought, strangely unmoved, as if she had already mourned his loss. Tom, though, was distraught. He came into the launderette after the funeral, his face red and swollen as if he'd been crying for days. Flo took him into her cubicle out of the way of her ladies' curious eyes.

'No one wants me, Flo,' he wept. 'Me mam walked out, me dad went and died on me, and Gran doesn't like me.'

He was almost as tall as her. Flo's heart ached as she stroked his bleak, tearstained face. If only her own history could have been rewritten, how would things have turned out then? 'I like you, luv,' she whispered.

'Promise not to die, Flo. Promise not to go away like everybody else.' He buried his face in her shoulder.

'We've all got to die sometime, luv. But I won't go away, I promise that much. I'll always be here for you.'

Tom took a long time to recover from the loss of his dad. When he did, there was a callousness about him that saddened Flo, a chill in his green eyes that hadn't been there before. He left school before he could sit his O levels and moved out of his gran's house to doss down in the homes of various friends, sleeping occasionally on Flo's settee if he was desperate. He got a job helping out at St John's market. 'I'm going to start a stall meself one day,' he boasted. 'There's no way I'm working for someone else all me life, not like me dad.'

He brought her presents sometimes: a portable wireless for the kitchen, expensive perfume, a lovely leather handbag. She accepted them with a show of gratitude, although she was worried sick that they were stolen. He even offered to get her a colour telly at half the list price.

'No ta, luv.' She would have loved a colour telly, but felt it might encourage the criminal tendencies she was convinced he had.

Bel was doing her utmost to persuade her friend to retire in May, when she turned sixty-five. 'You've worked non-stop since you were thirteen, Flo,' she said coaxingly. 'That's fifty-two long years now. It's time to put your feet up, like me.'

Tact had never been one of Bel's stronger virtues: the reason behind her solicitude for Flo's welfare was obvious. 'You only want me to retire so you'll have company during the day.'

'True,' Bel conceded. 'But that doesn't mean it's not a good idea.'

The launderette provided a good, steady income, and Flo had no intention of giving up, not while she remained fit and well, though she got tired if she was on her feet for too long. Her ladies had changed over the years, but they were still the irrepressible, good-humoured Scousers she loved. Nowadays not all were poor: they went on holiday to places like Majorca and Torremolinos and brought brasses back for Flo's walls.

When the letter came from the property firm in London offering to buy her out for twenty-five thousand pounds, her first instinct was to refuse. The firm was acting for a client who wished to turn the entire block into a supermarket. But the offer had come as a boon to Flo's neighbours. Hardly anyone ordered coal at a coal office, these days, when they could phone from home. Who'd buy wallpaper and paint from a little shop that had to charge the full price when it could be got for much less from a big do-it-yourself store? The watch-repairer, the picture-framer, the cobbler all reported that business was at an all-time low. Flo couldn't bring herself to turn down the offer and spoil things for those who were desperate to take it.

There were thousands of pounds in the bank now and not much to spend it on. Flo went to see the solicitor in Castle Street and made a will. She'd never thought she'd have property and money to leave behind, but she knew who she wanted to have it. She put the copy at the bottom of the papers in the bureau – one of these days, she must clear everything out.

There was stuff in there she'd sooner people didn't know about when she died.

She bought the coveted colour television, a microwave oven, because they seemed useful, and a nice modern music centre, hoping that the man in Rushworth and Draper's didn't think a woman of her age foolish when she chose a dozen or so records: the Beatles, Neil Diamond, Tony Bennett. She didn't *feel* old, but later the same day, when she was wandering around Lewis's department store, she saw an elderly woman, who looked familiar with rather nice silver hair, coming towards her. As they got closer, she realised she was walking towards a mirror and that the woman was herself. She *was* old! What's more, she looked it.

When Bel was told she laughed. 'Of course you're old, girl. We all grow old if we don't die young. The thing is to get the best you can out of life till it's time to draw your last breath. Let's do something dead exciting this weekend, like drive to Blackpool. Or how about London for a change?' She was fearless in the car and would have driven as far as the moon if there'd been a road.

'Oh, Bel,' Flo said shakily, always grateful for her friend's unfailing cheerfulness and good humour. 'I'm ever so glad I went to Birkenhead that morning and met you.'

Bel squeezed her hand affectionately. 'Me too, girl. At least one good thing came out of that business with Tommy O'Mara, eh?'

'Where did we go wrong, Flo?' Sally cried. She asked Flo the same question every time they met.

Flo always gave the same reply. 'Don't ask me, luv.'

Ten years before, Grace, Keith and their two sons had upped roots and gone to live in Australia. Sally and Jock only occasionally received a letter from their daughter, and Grace ignored their pleas to come and visit. Jock was becoming surlier in his old age, Sally more and more unhappy. One of these days, she said bitterly, she was convinced she would die of a broken heart.

'I could easily have done the same when me little boy was taken,' Flo said. She thought of Bel with her three husbands and three lost babies. In her opinion, Sally was giving up far too easily. 'You and Jock have still got each other, as well as your health and strength. You should go out more, go on holiday. It's never too late to have a good time.'

'It is for some people. You're different, Flo. You're made of iron. You keep smiling no matter what.'

Flo couldn't remember when she'd last seen her sister smile. It was impossible to connect this listless, elderly woman with the happy, brown-haired girl from Burnett Street.

Sally went on, 'I remember when we were at school, everyone used to remark on me sister with the lovely smile.'

'Why don't you come to the pictures with me and Bel one night?' Flo urged. 'Or round to William Square one Sunday when Charmian usually pops down for a sherry and a natter.'

'What's the use?'

Grace didn't bother to cross the world to be with her father when her mother died. Sally's heart gave up one night when she was asleep in bed, but perhaps it really had broken.

Bel went with Flo to the funeral on a dreary day in March. It was windy, dry, sunless. Grey clouds chased each other across a paler grey sky. Jock held up remarkably well throughout the Requiem Mass. When Flo had gone to see him, he said that he intended moving to Aberdeen to live with his brother, and she could tell that he was looking forward to returning to the city of his birth. It was as if he and Sally had dragged each other down in their misery, frozen in their grief, unable to come to terms with the loss of Ian, and Grace's indifference. Flo had expected that Sally's death would be the last straw for Jock; instead, it seemed to have released him from a state of perpetual mourning.

It was obvious that Martha, stiff with self-importance, was relishing her role of Being in Charge. Jock, a bit put out, said that she'd taken over the funeral arrangements, had ordered the coffin, the flowers, seen the priest. In the cemetery, in the wind, beneath the racing clouds, Flo saw the gleam in her sister's eyes behind the thick-lensed glasses that she remembered well, as if this was a military operation and she'd like to tell everyone where to stand. When the coffin was lowered into the grave, Jock suddenly put up his hand to shield his eyes and Martha poked him sharply in the ribs. It wasn't done for a man to cry, not even at his wife's funeral. That gesture put paid to the vague thoughts Flo had had of exchanging a few polite words with her sister.

The Camerons were there, Norman handsome and scowling – but, oh, Kate had changed so much, her lovely hair chopped short, her once slim figure swollen and shapeless. There was a battered look on her anxious face, no bruises, bumps or scars, but the same look some of Flo's ladies had, which told of a hard life with many crosses to bear. Yet her eyes remained bright, as if she retained a hope that things would get better one day – or perhaps the light in her eyes was for her children, who would have made any mother proud. Millicent, whom Flo had last glimpsed in the hospital, only a few days' old, had grown into a graceful, slender young woman, with none of her mother's vulnerability apparent in her lovely, strong-willed face. She was with her husband, as was Trudy, whose wedding had been only a few weeks before. Trudy was pretty, but she lacked her sister's grace and air of determination. However, it was the son,

Declan, who took Flo's breath away. A slight, delicate lad of ten, it could have been her own little boy she was staring at across the open grave. The Clancys might well be pale-skinned, pale-haired and thin-boned, but they had powerful genes that thrust their way forcefully through each generation. There was no sign of Albert Colquitt in Kate, no indication that Norman Cameron was the father of these three fragile, will o'-the-wisp children. There was another girl, Flo knew, Alison, who had something wrong with her and was in a home in Skem.

'Aren't we going for refreshments?' Bel was disappointed when the mourners turned to leave and Flo made her way towards the gold Cortina.

'I'm not prepared to eat a bite that's been prepared by our Martha,' Flo snapped. 'And don't look at me like that, Bel Eddison, because there's not a chance in hell I'll tell you why. If you're hungry, we'll stop at a pub. I wouldn't mind a good stiff drink meself.'

Sally had gone, to become a memory like Mam and Dad, Mr Fritz and Hugh. Each time someone close to her died, it was as if a chapter in her life had come to an end. One day, Flo too would die and the book would close for ever. She sighed. She definitely needed that drink.

September, 1996

Flo pressed her fingers against her throbbing temples, but the pressure seemed only to emphasise the nagging pain. She knew she should have been to the doctor long ago with these awful headaches but, as she said to Bel, 'If there's summat seriously wrong, I'd sooner not know.' There were times when the pain became unbearable, and all she wanted to do was scream: it felt as if an iron band was being screwed tighter and tighter around her scalp. A glass of sherry made it worse, two glasses made it better, and with three she felt so light-headed that the pain disappeared. Getting drunk seemed preferable to having her head cut open and someone poking around inside, turning her into a vegetable. Peter, the nice young lad from next door who reminded her so much of Mr Fritz, got rid of the bottles for her because she felt too embarrassed to put them out for the binmen.

A concerned Bel had persuaded her to have her eyes tested, but the optician said she had excellent sight for a woman of her age, though he prescribed glasses for reading.

Mam, Flo remembered, had been terrified of letting a doctor near her with a knife. The girls used to get upset, worried that she'd die. But Mam had only been in her forties. Flo was seventy-six, nobody's wife, nobody's daughter, with no children to care if she lived or died. Bel would miss her terribly, Charmian less so, what with a husband, two kids and three grandchildren to look after since Minola had gone back to school. Tom O'Mara didn't need her so much now that he was married with a family, two lovely little girls, though he still came to William Square regularly, at least once a week, often bearing food from the Chinese takeaway around the corner and a bottle of wine. She never asked how he made the money he was so obviously flush with. After years spent living on his wits, involved in ventures that were barely this side of legal, he was now something to do with a club that he adamantly refused to talk about. Flo suspected she was probably the only person on earth who knew the real Tom O'Mara, the man who loved and fussed over her tenderly, and brought her little presents. Outside the four walls of her flat, she'd like to bet that Tom was an entirely different person – even his wife and children might not know how soft and gentle he could be. Bel, who couldn't stand him, had to concede it was decent of him to put Nancy in a posh nursing-home in Southport when her mind went haywire and she could remember nothing since the war.

Music filled the basement flat, reaching every nook and corner, wrapping around her like a magic blanket woven from the dearest of memories. And shadows from the lamp Tom had brought from abroad passed slowly over the walls, the figures lifesize. When Flo felt especially dizzy, the figures seemed real, alive. He had brought the record, too, not long ago. 'Close your eyes,' he said teasingly, when he came in. 'I've got you a prezzie, a surprise.'

So Flo had closed her eyes, and suddenly the strains of 'Dancing in the Dark' came from the speakers at each end of the room. Her eyes had snapped open and for several seconds she felt muddled. She'd told no one that this was the tune she and Tommy had danced to in the Mystery more than half a century ago. 'What made you buy that, luv?' she asked querulously.

'You've been humming it non-stop for months. I thought you'd like to hear it sung by an expert. That's Bing Crosby, that is, the one who sings "White Christmas."'

'I know who Bing Crosby is. It's lovely, Tom. Ta very much.'

At first she didn't play the record much, scared of raking up the painful past, but lately, as her head got worse and she couldn't read, not even with her new glasses, she played it more and more often. It was soothing, better than a book, to remember her own romantic affair, more passionate and tragic than anything she'd ever read. She saw herself dancing under the trees with her lost lover, making love, whispering what was to be their final goodbye.

Bel had told her she should exercise more, not sit like a lump in front of the telly getting sozzled every day. 'I ride for miles every morning on me bike in the bathroom,' she hooted loudly, through her ghastly new dentures, which were much too big and made her look like an elderly Esther Rantzen.

'I'm seventy-six, Bel,' Flo said indignantly. 'I'm entitled to be a sozzled lump at my age.' What would she have done without Bel? Without Charmian and Tom, Mr Fritz, Sally, even Hugh, her son, for a while? She'd been lucky to have so many people to love and love her back.

'What time is it?' She looked at the clock. Just gone six. But was that night or morning? What month was it? What year? It was frightening when she couldn't remember things, when she forgot to go to bed, forgot to eat, forgot to watch one of her favourite programmes on the telly. Once she'd nearly gone out in her nightie. One of these days she'd forget who she was. It wasn't that she was losing her mind like Nancy. She smiled. No, the trouble was, she was either in terrible pain or as drunk as a lord.

She went over to the window and lifted the curtain, but still couldn't tell if it was dawn or dusk. A thick mist hung in the air, suspended a few feet from the pavement. There were noises in the square, but there always were, no matter what the time; a car drove away, she could hear people talking, someone walked past and she could see less of them than usual because their knees were shrouded in mist. She heard the clink of milk bottles. It must be morning, which meant she'd been sitting up all night.

The record, which she'd played countless times, came to an end yet again. Oddly, the ensuing silence felt louder than the music. It was a buzz, as if she was surrounded by a million bees. As she listened to the silence, Flo's mind drained of everything and became completely blank. She sat on the chest in front of the window and wondered what was she doing in this strange room full of shadows. There was too much furniture, too many ornaments, too many flowers. She didn't like it. A memory returned, crawling like a worm into her head: she lived in Burnett Street with Mam and Dad.

'But what am I doing here?' she asked of the strange room and the shadowy figures passing overhead. There was no answer. Had she been visiting someone? Whose house was this?

'Is anyone there?' Still no answer. Flo pressed her hands together distractedly, trying to make up her mind what was the best thing to do. Get away from this place, obviously, go home. Even better, go into work early, get on with the pressing left over from yesterday. It would give Mr Fritz a nice surprise when he came in.

She saw a coat hanging behind the door that looked faintly familiar. She put it on and went outside. A man was running towards her dressed in a funny red outfit, just like Father Christmas. 'Mr Fritz!' She smiled.

The man reached her. 'It's Peter Maxwell, Flo, from next door. I've been for a run. But what are you doing out so early, luv? It's awful damp. You'll get a chill.'

'I've got to go somewhere,' she said vaguely.

'Would you like me to come with you?' The man was looking at her worriedly.

'No, ta,' she told him pleasantly.

She set off into the wet mist at a fast pace, along Upper Parliament Street and into Smithdown Road, passing closed shops and empty shops, new buildings and old, Clement Street and Mulliner Street, names that seemed familiar, though she couldn't remember why. She looked for the dress shop, which had that lovely lilac frock in the window – she'd seen it only yesterday and intended to buy it. Later, in the dinner hour, she might well come back and get it. But she couldn't see the shop anywhere. The fog didn't help – perhaps that was why no trams were running – she could scarcely see across the road. Worse, when she turned into Gainsborough Road, there was no sign of the laundry. A brick building stood in the place where the old wooden shed should be, a clinic, with notices in the window advertising a playgroup, ante-natal classes, a mother-and-toddler group.

'Oh, Lord!' Flo groaned. The fog seemed to have entered her head. It lifted briefly when she read the notices and wondered how she had got to Gainsborough Road. Why was her heart racing? Why did her legs feel so weak? She didn't realise she'd walked for miles with the energy of a young girl. The fog drifted in again, smothering the pain and everything that was real.

'I'll go and see Mam and Dad.' She made her way towards Burnett Street. The fog in her head cleared for a second when she stood outside the three terraced properties at the end of the street and remembered that they'd been built on the spot where the Clancys' and two neighbouring houses used to be. She stood for a moment, staring up at the tiled roofs, the small windows. The door of the middle house opened and a man in a donkey jacket and greasy overalls came out.

'Are you after something, missus?' he demanded irritably, when he found an elderly woman standing virtually on his doorstep.

'I used to live here,' said Flo.

'You couldn't have.' He scowled. 'Me and the missus were the first to move in when the place was built forty years ago.'

The fog had descended again, enveloping her brain. 'There used to be a bay window and steps up to the door.' She put a trembling hand to her forehead. 'Did it get bombed? Is that what happened?'

'Look, luv,' the man's gruff voice became kind, 'you seem a bit confused, like. Would you like to come inside and me missus'll make you a cup of tea, then take you home? You live round here, do you?'

'I thought I lived here.' Flo wanted to cry. She said fretfully, 'Is the Mystery still there?'

'Of course it is, luv, but this isn't a good time to go walking in the park.'

But Flo was already on her way, nineteen years old, with a red ribbon in her hair, about to meet Tommy O'Mara outside the gates for the first time. She felt as if she was walking towards her destiny, and that afterwards nothing would be the same again.

He wasn't there. He was probably inside waiting under one of the trees, which were shrouded in a veil of mist. The wet grass quickly soaked through her shoes as she made her way towards them. A whiff of reality returned when she noticed the road leading from gate to gate, and the sports arena glimmering palely through the haze, things that hadn't been there before.

It was 1996, not 1939. 'Flo Clancy,' she breathed, 'you're making a right fool of yourself this morning.' She'd better catch the bus home while she had the sense to do it. But she hadn't brought a handbag, she had no money. She wept aloud. 'I feel too weary to walk all that way back.'

She plodded back towards the gates. It wouldn't be a bad idea to take the red ribbon out of her hair. It must look dead stupid on an ould woman. She blinked when she found there was no ribbon there. Martha must have snatched it off before she left the house.

Poor Martha! Flo had never before had such a feeling of sympathy for the sister who'd never had much happiness in her life, if any. 'It's time to forgive and forget, luv.' Sally must have said that a hundred times over the years.

'I'll go and see her tomorrer,' Flo vowed. 'I'll take her a bunch of flowers.' At that moment, she couldn't precisely remember where Martha lived, but it would come. The fog inside her head kept lifting and falling, she kept drifting backwards and forwards in time, and the present was becoming confused with the past. She was leaving through the gates when she heard a shout. 'Flo!'

Flo turned. Her face melted into a smile, the dimples deepened in her wrinkled face, she could feel the brightness shining from her eyes as she watched Tommy O'Mara emerge from the white mist that swirled and floated in and around the Mystery and come towards her. She stood stock-still, waiting for him, waiting for him to take her in his arms.

She waved. Oh, he was a divil of a man, with his swaggering walk, a red hanky tied carelessly around his neck, an old tweed cap perched jauntily on the back of his brown curls. She had never stopped loving him. She never would.

'Flo, girl,' he called again.

'Tommy!' Flo held out her arms to welcome her handsome lover, who had never told a lie, had meant everything he'd said, who would have married her one day if he hadn't gone down with the *Thetis*. They would have lived happily ever after with their child. Then, from somewhere within the hazy clouds, she heard the orchestra of her dream a lifetime ago, playing 'Dancing in the Dark'. Her tired old body was swaying, this way and that, to the music that swelled and quivered in the smoky, dew-spangled morning.

She didn't hear the lorry backing slowly through the fog and the gates of the Mystery. It hit her full square, flinging her forward, and the phantom figure of Tommy O'Mara was the last thing Flo saw before she died.

The lorry drove away, the driver unaware that he'd hit anyone.

It was a young lad on his way home from his paper round who found the body. He stared at the old woman lying face down on the path. Was she dead, or had she just fainted?

He knelt down and gingerly turned the old girl over by the shoulder. She was dead all right, he could tell, but, Jaysus, never in all his life before had he seen such a brilliant smile.

Millie

1

The church hall was an Aladdin's cave of treasures; stalls with handmade jewellery, tie-dyed T-shirts, embroidered waistcoats, patchwork cushions, pottery, paintings, intricately moulded candles far too elegant to burn. But I'm sure I wasn't prejudiced in thinking our Trudy's stall was the most outstanding of all – and the cheapest.

Colin had added a shelf to the back of a pasting table so that the glassware could be exhibited on two levels. Nightlights flickered in painted wineglasses and tumblers that had been placed between the taller bottles so that the flames glittered through the jewel-coloured glass, the patterns outlined lavishly in gold or silver. The stall was alive with every imaginable hue – 'Like a rainbow on fire,' I said, and sighed with satisfaction when everything was done. I'd come early to help Trudy set up.

Trudy was shaking, as if she was about to take the starring role in her first play. 'What if I don't sell a single thing?'

'Don't be daft. I've got my eye on at least five bottles for Christmas presents.'

'I can't take money off me sister.'

'What nonsense! There's no room for sentiment now you're a businesswoman, Trude.'

'Oh, Mill!' Trudy glanced left and right at the other stallholders, most of whom had finished setting up and were waiting impatiently for the doors to open at eleven o'clock. 'I feel dead conspicuous.'

'You look perfectly okay to me. Would you like a cup of tea?'

'I'd love one. But don't stay away long, Sis,' she called nervously, as I went towards the room behind the stage where tea and coffee were being served. 'I can't do this on me own.'

It turned out to be a day when the Camerons came of age, I thought afterwards, when we appeared to be just like any other family. James came at exactly half past eleven, as promised. Declan was already there, deeply interested in the process of tie-dying. Mum arrived at midday, her face red and bothered. Beads of perspiration glistened on her brow, although the November day was cold. I went to meet her. 'Your dad turned dead nasty when he realised I was going out,' she panted. 'He insisted I made his dinner first. I've put it in a low oven for when he comes home from the pub, but I daren't think what it'll be like by then.' She dropped her handbag, bent to retrieve it, then dropped the car keys and her gloves. 'How's our Trudy getting on?'

'Her bottles are selling like hot cakes. Half have already gone. She's not asking nearly enough.' Trudy hadn't even noticed I was no longer there. Flushed with confidence, she was coping with her busy stall on her own. I clutched my mother's arm. 'Mum, could you come back to Flo's with me when this is over? There's something I want to show you.'

'What on earth can that be, luv?'

'You won't know till you've seen it, will you?'

She shook her head. 'I couldn't possibly, Millicent. Your dad was in a terrible mood. It'd be best if I went straight home.'

'In that case I'll come over tonight and fetch you,' I said firmly. 'There's something you've got to see.'

James had already been introduced to Trudy. It was time he met my mother. How could I ever have felt ashamed, I wondered, with a lump in my throat, of this warm-hearted, kind woman, whose face shone with pleasure as she said, 'I'm ever so pleased to meet you, James, luv. Does your mam call you Jim or Jimmy?'

When Colin arrived with Melanie and Jake after dinner, Trudy's stall was almost empty. Starry-eyed and triumphant, she'd taken over two hundred pounds. 'I can't believe people are actually willing to pay for me bottles. Just imagine, they'll be on window-sills all over Liverpool.' She promised to paint more for me over the next few days. Mum was in her element. She wandered around, saying, 'I see you've bought one of me daughter's bottles. Aren't they lovely?' If people were inclined to stop and chat, she'd tell them about her other daughter. 'That's her over there,' I heard her say more than once. 'That's our Millicent. She works for an estate agent in Liverpool town centre. And that's me son, the lad in the brown jersey. He's going to college next year.'

To everyone's astonishment, Gran turned up and bought the last of Trudy's bottles. 'I couldn't very well not come, could I?' she grunted sourly. 'Someone gave me a lift. I hope our Kate came in the car so she can take me home.'

I studied my grandmother carefully. This was the woman who'd given Flo's baby to Nancy O'Mara. Oh, how I'd love to find out exactly what had happened. But this wasn't the right time – would there ever be a right time to raise such an emotive subject?

We all went into the room behind the stage for a cup of tea. Trudy folded up her stall and joined us, which meant that there were three Camerons, four Daleys, Martha Colquitt and James – who were, inexplicably, having an animated conversation about football. The only person missing was my father, which probably accounted for the jubilant atmosphere.

'I never thought I'd witness this,' Colin whispered to me.

'Witness what?'

'Well, it's almost a case of Happy Families, isn't it? It's the way you'd expect any normal family to behave. Everyone's had a great day, including the kids.'

When it was time to leave, I arranged to pick up Mum at seven o'clock and take her to Flo's flat. My father would have gone out again by then.

'I wish you'd tell me what it's all about,' she said.

'What is it all about?' James asked later. We'd driven into town in our separate cars and met up in a restaurant for a meal. 'I'd hoped we'd spend the rest of the day together.'

I ignored the last comment. 'It's something truly amazing and wonderful,' I said happily. 'Auntie Flo's left her flat and all her money, nearly twenty-four thousand pounds, to Mum. I only found a copy of the will last night. I want her to be at Flo's when she reads it for herself.'

When I drew up outside, the house in Kirkby was in darkness. Surprised, I went round to the back. The kitchen door was unlocked, which meant that someone must be in. 'Mum?' I shouted. 'Declan? Is anybody home? It's me.'

A faint noise came from upstairs, a whimper. Alarmed, I switched on the light on the stairs and went up. 'Mum?' I called.

'In here, luv.' The voice, little more than a whisper, came from the front bedroom. I pushed open the door and reached for the light switch.

'Don't turn the light on, Millicent.'

I ignored her. In the dim glow of the low wattage bulb, I saw my mother half sitting, half lying in bed. Her right eye was swollen, her lip split and bleeding. She had bruises on both arms. She looked utterly wretched, but despite everything, there was still that indefatigable look in her eyes, as though she was the most resilient victim in the world, who would survive whatever came her way. I was convinced that if a tank rolled over her, she would pick herself up and carry on as if nothing had happened.

'Mum! Oh, Mum, what's he done to you?' Rage enveloped me like a cloak and I could scarcely speak. If my father had been there, I think I could easily have killed him.

'Close the curtains, luv. I don't want people seeing in.'

I drew them with an angry flourish, and sat on the bed. Mum winced.

'It's not as bad as it looks,' she said. 'I tried to ring you, stop you coming, but all I got was your machine.'

'I've been in town with James.' I forced myself to speak calmly.

'Mrs Bradley dabbed some TCP on it, and she bathed me eye an' all. I'm just a tiny bit tipsy too. She gave me this great big glass of brandy. She wanted to call the police, but I wouldn't let her.' Over the years, Mrs Bradley had frequently threatened to report Norman Cameron, but Mum had always stopped her. 'I told her this was the first time he'd hit me in years, which is the God's honest truth.'

'What brought it on, Mum?'

She shrugged, then winced again. 'His dinner was ruined. I knew it would be, stuck in the oven all that time.'

'You mean this . . .' I gestured towards the black eye, the split lip, the bruises – '. . . is solely due to a ruined dinner?'

'Only partly. I was out an awful long time, Millicent, nearly four hours. And, oh, it was a lovely afternoon.' Her eyes brightened when she thought about the day that had gone. 'I really enjoyed meself, what with our Trudy doing so well, Colin and the kids being there, your gran turning up, you and Declan. James is ever such a nice chap, I really liked him.' She managed a laugh. 'I even bought meself a pair of earrings to wear at your wedding – little red flowered ones to go with me best coat.'

'Oh, Mum!' I lightly touched her fading hair.

She sighed. 'He could never stand me being happy. I daren't ever come in with a smile on me face that I got from somewhere else, it always riled him. It makes him feel shut out, and he hates that. Today I just didn't think. I suppose I expected him to be pleased about Trudy and everything. 'Stead, he just lashed out at me. He'd been getting more and more worked up the longer I stayed out.'

'He's always been a miserable bugger,' I said acidly.

There was a long silence. Mum seemed to have drifted off into a world of her own. A motorbike growled to a halt outside. I got up and looked through the curtains. A girl from a house opposite came out, got on to the pillion, and the bike shot away. I stayed at the window, though there was no longer anything to see apart from the orange street lights, the still houses, the occasional car driving by. A group of boys wandered past, kicking a football to each other. Then my mother spoke in a soft, far-away voice: 'I remember once, I was only a titch, two or three. We'd been out for the day, your gran and me. It was late when we got back. Did I ever tell you we lived with Elsa Cameron for a long time? Anyroad, Elsa was out, and we heard noises coming from the cupboard under the stairs, terrible sobs. The poor little lad had been shut in there in the dark for hours. You never saw anything like his eyes, all feverish and bright, as if he'd have gone mad if he'd been left there much longer. He was only six.'

'Who are you talking about, Mum?' I asked perplexed.

'Why, your dad, luv. After that, your gran never left him alone with Elsa again. She had that illness, they call it purple depression or something now. She should never have been allowed to keep a child.'

I felt myself grow cold. I recalled the photo in Flo's flat of the grim-looking woman with the beautiful baby on her knee, the baby that had become my father. I tried to visualise the monster who had conducted a reign of terror throughout our childhood as a terrified little boy of six. It was hard. 'Why have you never told us this before, Mum?' I asked shakily.

'Your dad made me swear never to breathe a word to another soul. I suppose he felt ashamed. I'd be obliged if you didn't mention to him that I'd told you.'

'It might have helped us to understand.' It only might have.

'I suppose things would have been different if I hadn't let him down,' she said, half to herself.

'In what way, Mum?'

Her face went blank, as if she'd said too much. 'Oh, it doesn't matter, luv. It's a long time ago now. Do you fancy a cup of tea? I'm dying for one meself. I haven't had one since I came home.'

'I'll make one straight away. Where's Declan?'

'He's not back yet. He went off with the couple who made them funny-coloured T-shirts.'

While I made the tea my mind was in a whirl. I had no idea what to think. No matter what had happened to my father, it was impossible to excuse the things he'd done. It wasn't Mum's fault, or his children's, that his own mother had suffered from puerperal depression. Why take it out on us?

When I returned to the bedroom with the tea, Mum said, 'What's the big surprise for me at Flo's? Or are you still not prepared to tell me unless I'm actually there?'

'I'd forgotten all about it!' I took hold of both Mum's hands. 'Prepare yourself for a shock. Flo's left you her flat and all her worldly wealth. Twenty-three thousand, seven hundred and fifty-two pounds and eleven-pence to be precise.'

I didn't leave until my father came home. The back door opened, I kissed Mum goodbye, and went downstairs. He was coming through the kitchen, unsteady on his feet, eyes blurred.

'If you lay a finger on my mother again,' I said, in a grating voice that made my ears tingle, 'so help me, I'll kill you.' He looked at me vacantly, as if he wasn't sure where the strange voice had come from. 'Do you understand?' I persisted.

He nodded. I paused, my hand on the front door, feeling oddly perturbed by the look of naked misery on his face, which I probably wouldn't have noticed before. Then he said something that didn't make sense, but nevertheless made my stomach curl.

'It's all your fault.'

I was scratching through my mind, trying to think of a response, when I realised he was drunk, talking rubbish. I shook myself and left.

I'd tried to talk Mum into leaving there and then. Flo's flat was ready to move into. Wasn't it fortunate I hadn't touched a thing? The place was exactly as Flo had left it.

'There's no hurry, luv,' she said. 'Your poor dad'll be feeling dead sorry about things for a week or two. I'd sooner tell him, face to face, when I'm ready to go. I owe him that much, and I won't be scared, not now I've got money and somewhere to live. It makes me feel strong.' She still looked stunned, as if she couldn't get over the news of her good fortune. 'I remember saying to Flo how much I liked her flat when I first went there. I can't believe it's mine,' had been her initial reaction.

'Don't tell Dad about the money yet,' I warned. 'If he got his hands on it, every penny would go in no time on the lottery and the horses.'

'I may look a fool, Millicent, I've probably been a fool for most of me life, but I'm not that stupid.'

'Come and have a proper look round in the morning,' I said excitedly. 'I'll take the day off work. I've still got two days' holiday left, I was leaving them till Christmas.' My mind was working overtime, sorting out my mother's life. 'You need only stay at Flo's for a few months, then you can sell it and buy a similar place in Oxford.'

'Mmm, I suppose I could,' Mum said, in a dreamy, rather vague way that made me wonder if she could ever bring herself to leave Kirkby when it came right down to it.

'Do you still love him?' I demanded sharply.

'No, Millicent. I never loved him. The trouble is, you might find this hard to believe, but he loves me, he always has. I'm not sure how he'll manage with me not here.' She laughed girlishly when she saw me frown 'Don't worry, I'm going. I'd already planned to, hadn't I? It's thirty years last Easter since we were married, so I've done me stint. You and Trudy have got your own lives, Declan will be off soon. Now, Alison comes first.'

'And you? What about you?' I was doing my best to hide my impatience. 'Isn't it time you put yourself first?'

'I'll be doing that when there's just me and Alison.'

Later, when I parked the car in William Square, I thought sadly that this would be one of the last nights I would spend there. But the place was staying in the family, at least for a while. Even if that hadn't been the case, I could still come back to see Bel and Charmian. As I went down the steps to the basement room, I saw that the light was on and my heart lifted eagerly. I opened the door. Tom O'Mara was sitting on the settee watching television, his feet resting on the coffee table. Everything that had been good or bad about the day that would shortly end was forgotten.

'Hi,' he said. Our eyes met. 'You're late.'

'No, you're early.'

'Whatever.' He stood up and took me in his arms and we locked together in a long, lingering kiss. I couldn't wait for us to make love, I couldn't wait a minute longer. Neither could he. He picked me up and, still kissing, carried me into the bedroom.

Later, when it was over, Tom fell asleep, but I had never felt more wide awake, as if little electric currents were passing endlessly around my head. The affair had to end some time. He would never get divorced, and I didn't want him to. Perhaps, now that I was moving back to Blundellsands, it was time to call a halt. But could I bring myself to turn him away? Would he let me? Had I the will to resist if he flatly refused to be turned away?

My restless brain refused to stop working. Would Mum be safe in Toxteth, even if it wasn't going to be for ever? It hadn't crossed my mind till now. I thought of the few people I knew who already lived here: Charmian and Herbie and their children, Bel, Peter Maxwell, nice, respectable, honest people, like Flo. Anyway, Mum would be safer anywhere in the world, including Toxteth, than with her husband.

When I got up in the morning, I must clear the bureau of the things that gave away Flo's secrets. I'd keep the love letters, the photo of the little boy who looked so much like Declan, and the drawing he'd done of 'MY FREND FLO'. No wonder Tom had felt so drawn towards her. He was her grandson. I recalled how indifferent he'd been with Nancy.

'Don't worry, Flo,' I whispered. 'Everything's safe with me.'

At half past nine next morning, I asked Charmian if I could use her phone – I never remembered to bring my mobile to William Square – and called Stock Masterton to say I wasn't coming in. Oliver answered. 'Diana's back,' he hissed. 'She's ruling the roost already.'

I groaned. 'I'm not looking forward to tomorrow.'

Next, I called the solicitor in Castle Street who'd dealt with Flo's affairs and made an appointment for late that afternoon.

Downstairs again, the bureau looked pathetically empty, the papers I wanted to keep already stowed in the boot of the car, the rest thrown away. I dusted everywhere, swept the yard, pulled the last few dead leaves off the plants, had a word with the same black cat that had watched me before. Then I cleaned the kitchen and the bathroom, although they'd scarcely been used, but I wanted everywhere to look perfect for when Mum came.

The flat looked different today, not just cleaner but more impersonal. I didn't feel quite so much at home.

I'd barely finished when there was a knock on the door. It was too early for Mum. Perhaps it was Charmian inviting me upstairs for a coffee. I rather hoped so. Charmian had been thrilled to learn that my mother was moving in below. I was sure they'd get on well together.

'Gran!' I remarked in astonishment, when I opened the door. 'Come in.'

'Your mam phoned with the news this morning,' Martha Colquitt said grumpily, as she crunched into the living room in the crêpe-soled, fur-lined boots that were almost as old as I was. She wore a camel coat, and a jersey hat shaped like a turban with a pearl brooch in the middle. The room instantly began to reek of mothballs and liniment. 'I had an appointment at the women's hospital, so I thought I'd come and look the place over.'

'What's wrong? I mean, why did you have to go to hospital?' None of us Cameron children had much affection for our grandmother, but it was impossible to imagine life without her bad-tempered presence.

Gran was predictably bad-tempered with her reply. 'I dunno what's wrong, do I?' she barked. 'They took X-rays and did tests. I have to wait for the results till I know what's wrong.' Her voice softened. 'So this is where she lived, our Flo. I always wondered what it looked like.' She walked into the room. 'This is her all over. She liked things to be pretty.'

I watched her closely. I'd never seen her face so gentle, almost tender, as she surveyed her sister's room. 'Take your coat off, Gran,' I said. 'Would you like a coffee?'

'I never touch coffee, you should know that by now. I'll have tea. And I'll not take me coat off, thanks all the same. I'm not stopping long.'

'I'm afraid there's only powdered milk.'

Gran shrugged. 'I suppose that'll have to do, won't it?' Her head was cocked on one side, she was almost smiling as she watched Flo's lamp turn round. 'I'm dying for a ciggie and it tastes better with a cup of tea.'

When I came back, she was examining the drawing on the wall over the mantelpiece, which I'd meant to take down.

'What does this say?' She peered at it closely, her nose almost touching the wall. 'I can't see in these glasses, and I left me reading ones at home. I could never get along with them bi-focals.'

'It says, "MY FREND FLO". It was done by someone called Hugh O'Mara.'

Gran took a step back, but continued to stare at the drawing. I would have given anything to know what was going on inside her head. A faint hum came from upstairs, Charmian was vacuuming the carpets. One of Minola's children gave a little shriek. Gran was still looking at the drawing, as if she'd forgotten I was there. I licked my lips, which suddenly felt dry. I didn't want to upset her, but I *had* to know.

'He was Flo's son, wasn't he, Gran? She had him by a man called Tommy O'Mara who died on the *Thetis*. He probably never knew she was pregnant.' I licked my lips again before plunging on. 'You gave him away to Tommy's wife, Nancy.'

'What in God's name are you talking about, girl?' She spun round, wobbling slightly when her clumsy boots became tangled with each other. I felt myself shrivel before the angry eyes behind the thick lenses. 'What the hell do you know about it?'

'I know because Nancy told me.'

'Nancy!' The yellow lips split in a hoarse, unbelieving laugh. 'Don't talk rubbish, girl. Nancy's dead.'

'No, she isn't, Gran. I met her the other week. She's in a nursing-home in Southport. She said . . .' I screwed up my eyes and tried to remember word for word what Nancy had said. I visualised the old liver-spotted face, the hot dark eyes, the long fingers clawing at my arm. 'She said, "Your Martha gave him to me fair and square. You're not getting him back. I'll kill him first." Her's mind's gone,' I finished. 'She thought I was Flo.'

Gran's face crumpled and she started to cry, an alarming and uncomfortable sight. She stumbled back into a chair and lit a cigarette with shaking hands.

'Gran!' I put the tea down, ran across the room and knelt at her feet. 'I didn't mean to upset you.' I was angry with myself for being too curious, too uncaring, yet I knew I wouldn't have hesitated to do the same thing again.

'It's all right, Millicent. Where's that tea?' There was a loud sniff, a quick removal of spectacles to wipe her eyes, a conscious effort to pull herself together. She looked embarrassed, unused to revealing any emotion except anger. Her hands were still shaking as she took the tea, though she'd recovered enough to grimace disapprovingly at the mug. She said, 'I never regretted what I did. It's hard for you young 'uns to realise the disgrace it was in those days for a baby to be born on the wrong side of the blanket. The whole family would have suffered.' Her face was hard again, her tone fierce. This was the grandmother I had known all my life. 'Nancy kept her head down and Hugh well hidden for a good six months. We never dreamed Flo would recognise the baby after all that time.'

She wasn't sorry! Despite everything that had happened, losing her sister for a lifetime, she still wasn't sorry. Frowning, she jabbed the air with her cigarette. 'I can't understand this business with you and Nancy. Who told you about her? Who took you to see her in Southport?'

I sank back until I was sitting cross-legged on the floor, the heat from the gas-fire hot on my shoulders. 'Tom O'Mara did. He's Nancy's grandson – or Flo's grandson. I'm not sure how to describe him.'

'Tom O'Mara!' Gran's eyes narrowed. She stared, her gaze so penetrating, so intensely suspicious, that I knew straight away she'd guessed what was going on. I felt my cheeks burn.

At the same time, to my surprise, her face turned parchment white. Her bottom lip quivered. She looked a hundred years old. She put the half-full mug on the floor, the cigarette fell in, sizzled briefly and floated on the top, but she didn't seem to notice. She immediately lit another. 'I reckon there's a curse on the Clancys and the O'Maras,' she said. Her voice was dull, listless, almost funereal. It scared me.

'What do you mean?'

'Well, first there was Flo and Tommy.' She took a long, hard drag on the cigarette, and the end glowed bright red. 'Then our Kate and Hugh. Would you believe they actually wanted to get married?' She gave a little strained laugh, and nodded at me incredulously.

'Why couldn't they get married?' I ventured. *I'd nearly had Hugh O'Mara for a father!*

'Because they were cousins, of course,' Gran explained, as if to a child. 'It's not allowed – least, it wasn't then. Fortunately, Norman stepped in like the good lad he always was, even though he knew he was accepting soiled goods. Poor Norman ... Until then, he'd worshipped the ground your mam walked on. He would have made the best husband in the world if she hadn't spoiled things.'

'I don't know what you're talking about, Gran.'

'I'm talking about your mam being up the stick when she married Norman Cameron.' She still spoke in the same flat, dull voice, which seemed at odds with the rather coarse expression. 'We told her Hugh O'Mara had done a bunk once he knew she was pregnant, else we'd never have got her up the aisle.'

'Who's we?' I said weakly.

'Me and Nancy. As if we could have asked for a dispensation, like our Sally suggested. Imagine telling the Church authorities about our Flo's dirty little secret.' She almost choked on the last words.

Upstairs the vacuuming had stopped. I heard the front door open and Charmian come out with the children. I felt totally mixed up. My brain, which had been working so well the night before, could no longer take anything in. What was this leading up to?

'If Mum was pregnant when she married my father,' I said slowly, 'then what happened to the baby?'

'I'm looking at her.'

'Me?'

'Yes, Millicent, you.' Gran's eyes had shrunk, skull-like, deep into their sockets. She took another long puff on her cigarette, and blew the smoke out in an equally long sigh. 'You know what that means, don't you?'

I felt myself tingle all over. 'Hugh O'Mara was my father?'

'That's right. It means something else an' all. Jesus, Mary and Joseph!' She groaned. 'It was bad enough with our Kate! I bet the devil's laughing up his sleeve at the moment.' She leaned forward, her eyes boring into mine. 'Think, Millicent, think what it means.'

So I thought very hard and eventually came up with the answer. 'It means that Tom is my brother, my half-brother,' I breathed.

2

'Millie,' Diana said importantly, 'Will you come here a minute, please?'

'Yes, miss.' I abandoned the photocopier and stood in front of Diana's desk, my hands clasped meekly behind my back. June grinned and Elliot stifled a giggle.

Diana looked at me suspiciously, not sure if she was being made fun of. She flourished a sheet of paper. 'This property you went to see last week, the one in Banks. On the particulars you describe the upstairs as having a recess with a window. You quite clearly don't know that this is what's called an oriel window. Would you change it, please, before we run the details off?'

The first thing I'd done when I was promoted was buy a book on architecture so that I could accurately describe any unusual aspects of a building. 'I'm afraid you've got it wrong, Diana,' I said sweetly. 'An oriel is a recess in the projection of a building. There's no projection on the house in Banks, just a recess.'

Diana waved the paper again. 'I beg to differ. I think I know what an oriel window is by now.'

'Millie's right,' Oliver said, from across the room. 'I doubt if I could have described it better myself.' The man sitting next to him at the same desk, nodded. Barry Green had only started the day before. He was taking over as assistant manager when Oliver transferred to Woolton on 1 January. 'I second that,' Barry said, with a charming smile.

'Even I knew that,' June chortled.

'Oh!' Diana got up and flounced into George's office. She slammed the door, and everyone glanced at each other in patient resignation when we heard the sound of her raised, complaining voice.

'Actually,' June said, 'I've never heard of an oriel window. I just wanted to get up Madam's nose.'

'I must say,' Barry Green remarked, 'that I'm glad the horrendous Miss Riddick won't be here much longer. I don't know what's got into George but he's well and truly smitten.' Barry Green had given George his first job thirty years ago, and they had remained friends ever since. His vast experience as an estate agent hadn't prevented him from being made redundant when the chain he worked for had been taken over by a building society. He reminded me of actors in the old black-and-white British films I sometimes watched on television. In his sixties, with bountiful silver hair, perfectly coiffured, he wore a light grey suit with a slight sheen, and an eggshell blue bow-tie. His diction, like his hair, was perfect, as was his moustache, two neat, silvery fish. He looked the embodiment of a 1930s ladies' man, but appearances were deceptive. Barry had a wife, Tess, four children and eight grandchildren, whose various achievements he let slip into the conversation whenever he found the opportunity. One son was an architect, his two daughters had given up dazzling careers when they started their families, several grandchildren were already at university, including the one who could walk at eight months and play the piano when she was three. He rarely mentioned his youngest son, who was abroad, but no one asked what he was up to in case Barry launched into another long, adulatory explanation.

There was nothing subtle about the change of atmosphere in Stock Masterton since Diana had returned yesterday. I wondered if it was just my imagination that I was being picked on more than the others. If I hadn't been so preoccupied with my own life, it might have mattered more. Diana wasn't rude, merely loudly and forcefully officious. She kept telling people what to do when they already knew, offering advice when it wasn't needed. She was having an affair with the boss and wanted everyone to know how much her stock had risen.

'What did you mean,' I said to Barry, 'about Diana not being here much longer?' Maybe she was leaving to marry George.

'Because she's coming to Woolton with me.' Oliver sighed. 'George only told me yesterday. She's got a title, assistant manager. I'm not sure if I can stand it.'

'Your bad luck is our good fortune,' I said cheerfully. With Diana out of the way, perhaps I could get back on good terms with George.

This seemed unlikely when Diana appeared, saying, 'George would like a word with you, Millie.'

'I'd be obliged,' George said coldly, when I went in, 'if in future you'd refrain from upsetting Diana in front of the entire office. Everyone makes mistakes from time to time. It doesn't help to have them exposed in public.'

I made one of the faces I'd caught off Bel. 'Isn't this all a bit juvenile, George, like telling tales at school?'

'It's not long since the poor girl's father died. She's feeling very vulnerable at the moment.'

'So am I,' I said curtly. I'd scarcely slept for two nights in a row and was already sick to death of the situation at work. I knew I was only sinking to Diana's level when I said, 'It was Diana who pointed out my mistake first – what she thought was a mistake. I put her right, that's all. As she did it in front of the entire office, Oliver and Barry merely backed me up.'

'Oh, is that what really happened?' George looked nonplussed.

'Yes, George, it is.'

'I'm sorry, I must have got the wrong end of the stick.' He became quite friendly and asked how I was getting on with the flat in William Square.

'It's a long story, George. Perhaps I could tell it to you one day over lunch?' I'd only tell him the least important bits.

'Great idea, Millie. We'll do that, eh?'

Diana was scowling at me through the glass partition. I resisted the urge to stick out my tongue, and reckoned there was no chance of having lunch with George once she got back to work on him. She seemed to be pursuing a private vendetta against me.

When I came out, June shouted, 'There's just been a phone call, Millie. Some woman particularly asked for you. She says her boss, a Mr Thomas, has a property to sell as soon as poss in Clement Street off Smithdown Road, number eighteen. It belonged to a relative. He wants a valuation. I looked in the diary and told her you'd be there at two o'clock.'

'I think I'll go,' Diana stretched her arms. 'I feel like some fresh air.'

'They asked for Millie,' June said pointedly.

'This is an estate agent's, not a hairdresser's,' Diana snapped. 'It doesn't matter who goes.'

Oliver said sweetly, 'Yes, it does, Diana. It might be a former client who would prefer Millie rather than another member of staff.' He winked at me. 'Will you be all right on your own? Take Darren, if you'd feel safer.'

'I doubt if I'll come to any harm in Clement Street, it's too built-up.' Female staff weren't usually sent to deal with properties if a man on his own was involved.

It felt odd to drive past William Square and think of Flo's flat, as familiar now as the back of my hand, waiting for my mother to move in on Friday. Yesterday, she'd astounded me by announcing that when the time came for Alison to leave Skelmersdale, she'd have her in William Square instead of going to Oxford.

'Is that wise, Mum?' I said worriedly. 'You realise it's a red-light area. That girl outside is a prostitute. And it can be very violent.'

'I don't know what's wise or not, luv. Our Alison's always had plenty of care and attention, but she's never had much love. The change is bound to upset her, whether she goes to Oxford or comes to me, so I'd like to give it a chance.' Kate's eyes glistened. 'We'll sleep together in the same bed and I'll hold her in me arms if she'll let me. As to the prostitutes, they're only working girls who've fallen on hard times. They won't harm our Alison. The violence I'll just have to take a chance on. After all, I can always move, can't I?'

I regarded her doubtfully. 'I hope you're not making a terrible mistake. What will you live on?'

'I'll eke out the money Flo left so it lasts as long as possible. In a few years, I'll be due for me pension. I might get a carer's allowance for looking after Alison. Don't worry, luv,' she said serenely, 'I'll be all right. I haven't felt so happy in ages.'

Perhaps the last time she'd been happy was with Hugh O'Mara. Even now, the next day, I found it difficult to grasp what Gran had told me.

I turned into Clement Street, found a place to park, took a photograph of number eighteen, then knocked at the door. The street was comprised of small terraced properties, the front doors opening on to the pavement. The house in question had been relatively well maintained, though the downstairs window-sill could have done with a fresh coat of paint. I noticed the step hadn't been cleaned in a while.

The door opened, 'Hello, Millie,' said Tom O'Mara.

Yesterday, I'd written to him, then fled back to Blundellsands when I came out of the solicitor's with my mother, so there would have been no one in when he turned up at Flo's last night. I'd thought long and hard about what to write. In the end, I'd merely stated the facts baldly, without embellishment or comment. I didn't put 'Dear Tom', or who the letter was from, just a few necessary words that explained everything. He would know who'd sent it. I'd posted it to the club because I didn't know his address.

Tom turned and went down the narrow hallway into a room at the rear of the house. He was dressed in all black: leather jacket, jeans, T-shirt. I took a deep breath and followed, closing the door behind me. The room was furnished sixties style, with a lime green carpet, orange curtains, a melamine table, two grey plastic easy chairs, one each side of the elaborate tiled fireplace, which had little insets for knick-knacks. Everything was shabby and well used, and there were no ornaments, or other signs that the place was inhabited.

'This is where me gran used to live,' Tom said. His jacket creaked silkily as he sat in one of the chairs and stretched out his long legs. He wore expensive boots with a zip in the side, and looked out of place in the small dark room with its cheap furniture. I sat in the other chair. 'I bought it years ago as an investment. I got tenants in when Nancy went to Southport. Now they've moved I thought I'd sell. They say the price of property has started to go up.'

'When did you decide to sell?'

'This morning, when I heard from you. It made a good excuse. I got a woman from the club to ring the place you work. I had to see you again.'

'Why?'

'I dunno.' He shrugged elegantly. 'To see what it felt like, maybe, knowing you were me sister, knowing it was over.' He looked at me curiously. 'Didn't you want to see me?'

'Oh, I don't know, Tom. I've no idea what to think.' I felt slightly uncomfortable, but not embarrassed or ashamed. I'd pooh-poohed Gran's gruesome claim that the family was cursed, that the devil was involved, and the world was about to end because a half-sister and brother who'd known nothing about their relationship had slept with each other. 'We didn't know, Gran. It wasn't our fault. If it hadn't been for all the secrets . . .' It was irritating to know that I was now accumulating secrets of my own, things I couldn't tell my mother or Trudy or Declan. 'Don't repeat a word of this to your mam,' Gran pleaded. 'I'd be obliged if you wouldn't mention to your dad that I told you,' Mum had said the other night, about something or other I couldn't remember right now.

'You can go back to that boyfriend of yours,' Tom remarked drily. 'What's his name?'

'James.'

He looked amused. 'James and Millie. They go well together. What's Millie short for, anyroad? I always meant to ask.'

'Millicent.'

There was silence. Then Tom said something that made my stomach lurch. 'Will you come upstairs with me?' He nodded at the door. 'There's a bed.'

'No!' Despite my vehemently expressed horror, somewhere within the furthest reaches of my mind, I remembered what we'd been to each other and did my best not to imagine what it would be like now.

'I just wondered,' Tom said lightly. 'It's not that I want to, bloody hell, no. The whole idea makes me feel dead peculiar. I'm just trying to get things sorted in me head.'

'It's all over, Tom.' I could hardly speak.

'Christ, Millie, I know that. I'm not suggesting otherwise.' He smiled. Over the short time I'd known him, he'd rarely smiled. Whenever he did, I'd always thought him even more extraordinarily attractive than he already was, more desirable. I had that same feeling again, and it made me slightly nauseous. He went on, 'I wish we'd found out we were related before we . . .' he stopped, unwilling to say the words. 'It would have been great, knowing I had a sister.'

'And knowing Flo was your gran.' And my gran, I realised with a shock.

'Aye.' He nodded. 'That would have been great an' all.'

I refused to meet his eyes, worried about what I might see there. It seemed sensible to get away as quickly as possible. I took my notebook out of my bag and said briskly, 'Is it really your intention to put the house on the market?'

'I'd like to get rid of it, yes.'

'Then I'd better take some details.' I stood, smoothed my skirt, conscious of Tom watching my every move. I didn't look at him. 'I'll start upstairs.'

Quickly, I measured the rooms, made a note of the cupboards, the state of decoration, the small modern bathroom at the rear. Downstairs again, I took a quick look in the lounge, which was the same size as the front bedroom and had a black iron fireplace with a flower-painted tile surround, which could be sold for a bomb if it was taken out. There was an ugly brocade three-piece with brass pillars supporting the arms – I must tell Tom to get rid of the furniture.

In the hall, I paused for a moment. Tommy O'Mara had lived here, walked in and out of the same rooms, up and down the same stairs, sat in the same spot where I'd sat only a few minutes ago when I talked to his grandson. One day, a long time ago, Martha Colquitt, my other gran, had probably come to this house bringing Flo's baby with her, the baby who'd turned out to be my father. I stood very still, and in my mind's eye, I could actually see the things happening like in an old, faded film, as if they were genuine memories, as if I'd lived through them, taken part. It was an eerie feeling, but not unpleasant.

When I went into the living room, Tom O'Mara had gone. He'd left the key to Flo's flat on top of my handbag. He must have slipped out of the back when I was upstairs, and I was glad that my main emotion was relief, mixed with all sorts of other feelings that I preferred not to delve into. A car started up some way down the street and I didn't even consider looking through the net curtains to see if it was him. In one sense, I felt numb. In another, I felt entirely the opposite. I knew I would never make love with another man the way I had with Tommy O'Mara – Tom! The thing that had drawn us together was a crime, yet it would be impossible to forget.

When I returned to the office, Diana was cock-a-hoop. She'd just shown the Naughtons round a property in Childwall, and they were anxious to buy.

'How many places did you show them, Millie – ten, a dozen? I only took them once and they fell in love with it straight away,' she crowed.

'I'm sure they were more influenced by the house than the agent,' I said mildly. Right now, I couldn't give a damn about the Naughtons, or Diana.

After my parents' thirty brutal, wretched years of marriage, I expected there would be something equally brutal about its end: a fight, a huge scene, lots of screaming and yelling. I even visualised my father physically refusing to let Mum go. In other words, I was dreading Friday. Several times during the week, I asked Mum, 'What time are you leaving?'

'For goodness sake, Millicent, I don't know. It's not high noon or anything. I'll pack me suitcase during the day, and once I've had me tea I'll tell him I'm off before he has time to brood over it.'

'It can't possibly be that simple, Mum.'

'He can't stop me, can he? He can't guard over me for ever.' She bit her lip thoughtfully. 'I'll leave him a casserole in the fridge for the weekend.' She smiled at me radiantly. Over the last few days, the anxious lines around her eyes and mouth had smoothed away. I had never known her look so happy.

'I'll come straight from work and give you a lift,' I offered.

'There's no need, Millicent. I'll catch the bus. I won't have much to carry – a suitcase, that's all.'

I didn't argue, but on Friday, as soon as I finished work, I drove straight to Kirkby. Trudy had obviously had the same idea. When I drew up the Cortina was parked outside the house.

My mother was kneeling on the kitchen floor playing with Scotty, who was lying on his back, wriggling in ecstasy as his tummy was tickled. 'I'll really miss this little chap,' she said tearfully, when I went in. 'I'd take him with me if there was a garden. But never mind, he'll be company for your dad.'

'Where is he?' I asked.

'In the front room.'

'Does he know?'

'Yes. He's taken it hard, I knew he would. He pleaded with me to stay. He promised to turn over a new leaf.'

'Really!' I said sarcastically.

Mum laughed. 'Yes, really.'

'Do you believe him?'

'Not for a minute, luv. I don't think he could, no matter how much he might want to.'

Trudy came into the room with a plastic bag. 'You'd forgotten your toothbrush, Mum.' She grinned at me. 'Hi, Sis. She's hardly taking a thing, just a few clothes, that's all.'

'I don't want to leave your dad with the house all bare. It'll be nice to start afresh with Flo's stuff. I must say,' Mum nodded at the ancient stove, 'I'll be glad to see the back of that ould thing.'

'Flo's is even older,' I said.

'Yes, but she's got a microwave, hasn't she? I've always wanted a microwave. Now, Trudy,' she turned to my sister, 'I want you to promise that you'll bring Melanie and Jake to see their grandad from time to time. He loves them kids, and it would be cruel to deprive him of their company.'

Trudy rubbed the scar on her left eyebrow and muttered, 'I'm not promising anything, Mum. We'll just have to see.'

'Well,' Mum said cheerfully, 'it's time I was off.'

The moment had come. Trudy and I looked at each other, and I saw my own incredulous excitement reflected in her green eyes as we followed Mum into the hall, where she paused at the door of the lounge. The television was on, a travel programme showing an exotic location with palm trees, sun and sand. To my surprise, Declan was sitting on the settee reading a newspaper. My father – the man I'd always thought was my father – was smoking, apparently quite calm, but there was something tight about his shoulders, and he seemed to hold the smoke in for too long before he blew it out again.

'I'm going now, Norman,' Mum said. She spoke as casually as if she were going to the shops. I sensed a subtle shifting of power.

Her husband shrugged. 'Please yerself,' he said.

'Your clean shirts are in the airing cupboard, and there's a meat casserole in the fridge. It should last at least two days.'

Declan got up. 'I'll come out and say tara, Mam.'

'Heavens, lad! I'll be seeing you tomorrer. You promised to come to dinner, didn't you? There's no need for taras.'

'Yes, there is, Mam. Today's special.'

Trudy picked up the suitcase and we trooped outside. Dry-eyed and slightly breathless, Mum paused under the orange street lights, looking back, her brow furrowed in bewilderment, at the house of silent screams and hidden tears, as if either that, or the future she was about to embark on, was nothing but a dream. Trudy put the case into the boot of the Cortina, Mum gave a queenly wave, and the car drove away.

It was as easy as that.

Declan and I were left standing at the gate, with me feeling inordinately deflated by this turn of events. I'd expected to take my mother to William Square, help her settle in, show her where everything was, gradually hand the place over. But now I felt excluded, unnecessary. All of a sudden it hurt badly, imagining other people going through Flo's things, sitting in Flo's place, watching her lamp swirl round, playing her favourite record.

Scotty came out and licked my shoe. I picked him up and buried my face in his rough, curly coat to hide the tears that trickled down my cheeks. I'd never felt so much at home anywhere as I'd done at Flo's. From the very first time I'd gone there, the flat had seemed mine. I knew I was being stupid, but it was almost as if I'd entered my aunt's body, become Flo, experienced the various highs and lows of her life. I'd discovered something about myself during the short time I'd spent there, though I wasn't sure what it was. I only knew I felt differently about things, as if Flo had somehow got through to me that I would survive. Never once, in all the nights I'd slept there, had I dreamed the old dream, heard the slithering footsteps on the stairs, wished I were invisible.

I sighed. I could follow the Cortina, still help Mum settle in, but I knew I was being daft, feeling so possessive about a basement flat that had belonged to a woman I'd never even spoken to.

'What's the matter, Sis?' Declan said softly.

'I feel a bit sad, that's all.'

Declan misunderstood. 'Mam will be all right, you'll see.'

'I know she will, Dec.' I put Scotty down and gave his beard a final rub, wondering if I would ever see the little dog again. 'Will he be all right?'

'Scotty's the only member of the family Dad's never laid a finger on.' Declan grinned.

'And what about you? You can always sleep on the sofa in my place until you find somewhere of your own.' I'd welcome his company at the moment. The thought of returning, alone, to Blundellsands and the flat I'd been so proud of was infinitely depressing.

'Thanks, Millie, but I think I'll stay with me dad.'

I stared at him, open-mouthed. 'But I thought you couldn't wait to get away?'

'Yes, but he needs me, least he needs someone, and I suppose I'll do.'

'Oh, Dec!' I touched his thin face. My heart felt troubled at the idea of my gentle brother staying in Kirkby with Norman Cameron.

'He can't be all bad,' Declan said, with such kind reasonableness, considering all that had happened, that I felt even worse. 'I know he loves us. Something must have happened to make him the way he is.'

I thought of the little boy locked in a cupboard. 'Perhaps something did.' I watched Scotty sniffing the rose bushes in the front garden. One day, I might come back. Perhaps we could talk. Perhaps.

A taxi drew up outside the house next door and hooted its horn. The Bradleys came out, dressed in their ballroom-dancing gear.

'Has your mam gone?' Mrs Bradley shouted.

'A few minutes ago,' I replied.

'About time, too. I'm going to see her next week.' Mr Bradley helped to scoop the layers of net skirt into the taxi. As it drove away, I said, 'I suppose I'd better go, it's cold out here.' I kissed Declan's cheek. 'Take care, Dec. I won't stop worrying about you, I know I won't.'

'There's no need to worry, Mill. Nowadays, me and Dad understand each other in our own peculiar way. He accepts me for what I am.'

I paused in the act of unlocking the car. 'And what's that, Dec?'

Beneath the glare of the street lights, Declan flushed. 'I reckon you already know, Sis.' He closed the gate. 'Do you mind?'

'Christ Almighty, Dec!' I exploded. 'Of course I don't mind. It would only make me love you more, except I love you to death already.'

'Ta, Sis.' He picked Scotty up and waved a shaggy paw. 'See you, Mill.'

I started up the car and watched through the mirror as my brother, still hugging Scotty, went back into the house. A door had opened for my mother, at the same time as one had closed for Declan.

3

Every morning, I woke up with the feeling that I'd lost something infinitely precious. I had no idea what it was that I'd lost, only that it had left a chasm in my life that would never be refilled. There was an ache in my heart, and the sense of loss remained with me for hours.

My flat, my home, seemed unfamiliar, like that of a stranger. I stared, mystified, at various objects: the shell-shaped soap dish in the bathroom, a gaudy tea-towel, the yellow filing basket on the desk, and had no idea where they'd come from. Were they mine? I couldn't remember buying them. Nor could I remember where particular things were kept. It was as if I'd been away for years, having to open cupboards and drawers to search for the bread knife or a duster. There was food in the fridge that was weeks old: wilted lettuce, soggy apples, a carton of potato salad that I was scared to take the lid off. The cheese was covered in mould.

The only place where I felt comfortable and at ease was the balcony. Most nights I sat outside wearing my warmest coat, watching the branches of the bare trees as they waved, like the long nails of a witch, against the dark sky. I listened to the creatures of the night rustling in and out of the bushes below. There were hedgehogs, two, never seen during the day. The light from the living room was cast sharply across the untidy grass and straggly plants – no one tended the garden in winter – and under the light I read the book that Tom O'Mara had given me about the *Thetis*. I read about the bungling and ineptitude of those at the top, the heroism and desperation of the ordinary seamen as they tried to rescue the men who were trapped, so near and yet so far.

How would it have been, I wondered, if Tommy O'Mara hadn't died? How differently would things have turned out for Flo?

I felt very old, like someone who knew that the best years of their life were over and was patiently sitting out the rest. Having a birthday didn't help. I turned thirty, and became obsessed with wondering how the next ten years would turn out. What would I be doing when I was forty? Would I be married, have children? Where would I be living? Where would I be working? Would Mum still be living in William Square with Alison?

Which was stupid. I told myself how stupid I was being a hundred times a day, and made sure no one guessed how dispirited I felt. When I went with James to the theatre one night, I sat in the bar in the interval while he went to fetch the drinks. He came back, saying, 'Are you all right, darling? I looked across and your face was terribly sad.'

'I'm fine,' I said confidently.

'Are you sure? Is it over between you and that Tom chap? I've kept longing to ask. Is that why you're sad?'

'I said I wasn't sad, James, though it is over between me and Tom.'

He looked relieved. 'I'm glad there's no one else.'

'I never said that!' His face collapsed in hurt. I knew I was being horrid, but the last thing I wanted was to offer him encouragement. The strangest thing had happened with James, and I didn't know how to deal with it.

He'd promised not to pressurise me and he hadn't, but in the few times I'd seen him since we'd broken up, then come together again, he wanted to know every little thing about me, every detail. It was as if now that he could no longer have my body he was determined to possess my mind. Perhaps some people were willing to divulge their every thought, their every wish, but I wasn't one of them.

It was hard to escape from such overpowering, almost suffocating love, his tremendous need, which some women might have envied. It was also hard to reject, as if I was giving away something uniquely precious by refusing him. Such love might never come my way again. He appeared to worship the ground I walked on.

Where had I heard those words said before only recently? The bell rang once to indicate that the interval was nearly over and I finished off my drink. Back in the theatre I remembered. They were the words Gran had used to describe how Norman Cameron had felt about my mother . . .

The curtain rose, but as far as I was concerned the actors' efforts were wasted. I had no idea what had happened in the first act. Perhaps you could love someone too much, so much that you resented all the things they did without you, resented them even being happy if you weren't the reason why they smiled.

It wasn't strictly true to hint that there was someone else, but tomorrow night I was meeting Peter Maxwell. He was going to show me where the tall, wild forests had once been in Toxteth, which King John had turned into a royal park and where he had hunted deer and wild boar.

'It's incredible!' I breathed, the following evening, as we strolled through the icy drizzle along Upper Parliament Street and into Smithdown Road. I closed my eyes and tried to imagine I was stepping through a thick forest and the drizzle was the dew dripping from the trees at dawn.

'The area's mentioned in the Domesday Book,' he said proudly.

I forgot how cold the night was as he explained, with mounting enthusiasm, that Lodge Lane was called after one of the King's hunting lodges, that the ancient manor of Smethedon was where the name Smithdown came from. The descriptions, the words he used seemed incongruous, as we passed the narrow built-up streets and endless shops. Traffic fizzed by in the wet; cars, buses, lorries, headlights fixed on the noxious fumes spewing out from the vehicles in front, and reflected in the watery surface. We seemed to be walking through a toxic yellow fog, as Peter talked about Dingle Dell, Knot's Hole, sandstone-cliff creeks, glens, farms, a game reserve. He even quoted a poem – 'The Nymph of the Dingle'.

'It's fascinating, Peter,' I said, when he paused for breath. His black bushy hair and beard glistened in the damp, as if they'd been touched with frost.

'I've not nearly finished, but this isn't a good night. Perhaps we could come one Sunday. I can show you other places. Did you know that less than two centuries ago Bootle was a spa? There used to be watermills, springs, sandhills and fields of flowers?'

I confessed I'd had no idea. He asked if I'd like a drink, and when I said yes he steered me into the nearest pub. 'Will it be safe in here?' I asked nervously.

'I doubt it,' he said soberly, though I noticed his eyes were twinkling. 'We're probably taking our lives in our hands.'

The pub was old-fashioned, Victorian, with sparkling brasses and a gold-tinted mirror behind the bar. The few customers looked very ordinary and not in the least threatening.

'Well, we seemed to have survived so far,' Peter said, apparently amazed. 'What would you like to drink?'

I poked him in the ribs with my elbow. 'Stop making fun of me. I'd like half a cider, please.'

A few minutes later he returned with the drinks. 'Sorry I was so long, but the barman offered me five thousand quid to carry out a contract-killing. See those old girls over there?' He pointed to two elderly women sitting in a corner. 'One's a Mafia godfather in disguise, the other is the chief importer of heroin in the northwest. The cops have been after her for years. She's the one he wanted me to kill.' He took his donkey jacket off and threw it on a vacant chair. Underneath, he wore a polo-necked jersey, which had several loose threads. He regarded me solemnly. 'I refused, of course, so I doubt if we'll get out of here alive.'

By now, I was doubled up with laughter. 'I'm sorry, but I always feel a bit fearful around here.'

'It sounds priggish, but the worst thing to fear is fear itself. Taking the worst possible scenario, no one's safe anywhere.'

'I like being with you, it's rather soothing.' I smiled, feeling unusually contented.

He stroked his beard and looked thoughtful. 'To be "soothing" is not my ultimate aim when I'm with a beautiful young woman, but it'll do.'

I welcomed the fact that he was so easy to be with, relaxing, particularly after the intensity of James, and the total preoccupation Tom O'Mara and I had had with each other. There was a hint of flirtatiousness between us, which meant nothing. He reminded me about the Christmas concert at his school next week. 'You promised you'd come.'

'I hadn't forgotten.' It would soon be Christmas and I hadn't bought a single present. I must remind Trudy about the bottles she'd promised to paint, and remembered that one had been for Diana. After the way things had gone, I wasn't sure whether to give it to her or not.

For the next half-hour, we chatted about nothing in particular. We'd been in the same year at school, which meant that Peter had also recently had his thirtieth birthday, and we discussed how incredibly old we felt. 'It's quite different from turning twenty. Twenty's exciting, like the start of a big adventure. Come thirty, the excitement's over,' he remarked, with a grin.

'Don't say that. You make thirty sound very dull.'

'I didn't mean it to sound dull, just less exciting. By thirty you more or less know where you are. Would you like another drink?'

'No thanks. I thought I'd pop in and see my mother. I left my car in William Square.'

'I've already met your mum. She seems exceptionally nice.' He reached for his jacket. 'Come on. If we make a sudden rush for the exit, we might get out of here all in one piece.'

It was only natural that Mum should have the keys to Flo's flat. Even so, I felt slightly miffed at having to knock to be let in. Fiona, who was draped outside in her usual spot, condescended to give me a curt nod.

'Hello, luv!' Mum's face split into a delighted smile when she opened the door. 'You're out late. It's gone ten.'

Peter Maxwell leaned over the railings. 'Hi, there, Kate. 'Night, Millie. See you next week.'

'Goodnight, Peter.'

'Have you been out with him?' Mum sounded slightly shocked as she closed the door.

'He's very nice.'

'Oh, he's a lovely young feller. I knew his mam in Kirkby. She's a horrible woman, not a bit like Peter. No, I just thought you and James were back together for good, like.'

'We're back together. I doubt very much if it's for good.'

Mum shook her head in despair. 'I can't keep up with you, Millicent.' Then, eyes shining, she demanded, 'What do you think of me new carpet?'

In the two weeks since I had left and my mother had taken over, much in the flat had changed. Too much, I thought darkly, but kept my opinion to myself. It was none of my business, but as far as I was concerned Flo's flat had been perfect. I wouldn't have altered it one iota. But now the silk flowers had gone because they gathered dust, as well as the little round tables and the brasses on the beams. Colin had fitted deadlocks on the windows, a heater on the bathroom ceiling and, with Declan's help, was going to wallpaper the place throughout. 'Something fitting,' Mum announced excitedly, 'little rosebuds, violets, sprigs of flowers.' She would have liked a new three-piece, but needed to conserve the money and was buying stretch covers instead. 'I don't like that dark velour stuff. It's dead miserable.' Next week, British Telecom were coming to install a phone.

I regarded the maroon fitted carpet. 'It looks smart.' I far preferred the faded old linoleum. 'What's happened to the rag rug?'

'I chucked it, luv. It was only a homemade thing.'

Trudy came out of the bedroom, struggling with a cardboard box full of clothes. 'Hello, Sis. I didn't know you were here. I'm just sorting out the wardrobe. Phew!' She plonked the box down and wiped her forehead with the back of her hand. 'I'll take this lot to Oxfam tomorrow, Mum. Hey, Mill, what do you think of this? I thought I'd keep it. It's not at all old-fashioned.' She held up the pink and blue check frock with a Peter Pan collar. 'I'm sure it'll fit.'

'It's lovely, Trude.' It had fitted me perfectly. George had said it made me look sweet and demure.

'Help yourself to anything that takes your fancy, Millicent,' Mum said generously.

'There's nothing I want, Mum.' I felt all choked up. It was horrible to see Flo's things being thrown away, given to Oxfam. I didn't even want Trudy to have the check frock. Then I thought of something I did want – wanted desperately. 'Actually, Mum, I'd like that lamp, the swirly one.' I looked at the television, but the lamp wasn't there, and I felt a thrust of pure, cold anger. If it had been chucked away I'd track it down, buy it back from Oxfam . . .

'I'm afraid your gran's already nabbed it,' Mum said apologetically. 'I wish I'd known, luv. You should have said before.'

If I'd known she was going to tear the place apart, I would have. I knew I was being unreasonable, and felt even more unreasonable when I refused a cup of tea. 'I only came for a minute to say hello. I think I'll have an early night.'

I'd never felt less like an early night. Outside, I thought about calling on Charmian, but the ground-floor flat was in darkness – Herbie had to get up at the crack of dawn for work. Peter Maxwell's light was on, but did I know him well enough to call at this hour? He might think I was being presumptuous, a bit pushy.

Fiona, in a short fur coat, thigh-length boots, and no other visible sign of clothing, was staring at me suspiciously, as if I'd set myself up in competition. I got into the car and drove round to Maynard Street. It was weeks since I'd seen Bel, though she'd been to William Square to renew her acquaintance with Mum.

'She'll probably think me an idiot.' I didn't even switch the engine off when I parked as near as I could to Bel's house, but drove off immediately. On my way to Blundellsands, I slipped a tape into the deck and turned up Freddie Mercury's powerful voice as loud as it would go to drown my brain and stop me from thinking how much I would have liked someone to talk to. It didn't work, so I turned it down and talked to myself instead. 'I must pull myself together, keep telling myself there is Life After Flo. Tomorrow I'll take a proper lunch break, buy some Christmas presents. I'll get jewellery for Mum, gold earrings or a chain.' By the time I got home I was still musing on what to get Declan, feeling more cheerful. My flat was slowly beginning to feel my own again, though it still seemed oddly empty when I went in.

Mum's decorating splurge was catching. I didn't want to change the colour of my own living-room walls, but a wide frieze would look nice, or stencilled flowers. I decided I'd take a look at patterns at the weekend.

Next day after lunch, I was showing June the gold chain with a K for Kate that I'd bought for Mum, and the red-velvet knee-length dress with short sleeves I'd got as a Christmas present for myself, when George called, 'Can I have a word with you, Millie?'

'Sit down,' he said shortly, when I entered his office. This was always a bad sign, and I wondered what I'd done wrong now. He cleared his throat. 'I've been having a long talk with ... with someone about your position in the firm. It was pointed out that you have no qualifications for the job you do. Darren and Elliot both have degrees, and even June has three A levels.' He regarded me sternly, as if all this was new to him and he'd been misled.

'You knew that when you took me on, George. You knew it when you promoted me.' I tried to keep my voice steady. 'I've always carried out my work satisfactorily. No one has ever complained.'

George acknowledged this with a cursory nod. 'That's true, Millie, but it was also pointed out that there are a lot of people around, highly qualified people, who might do the work even better. Yet by employing you, I am, in effect, denying one of these people a position with Stock Masterton.' He leaned forward, frowning earnestly. 'Look at that business with the Naughtons, for example. You must have shown them around a dozen properties, but Diana had only to take them once and a deal was clinched on the spot.'

I clenched my fists, feeling the nails digging painfully into my palms. My heart thumped crazily. 'Are you giving me the sack, George?' I'd never find another equivalent job if I was sacked.

He looked slightly uncomfortable. 'No, no, of course not. We, that is, I, thought it would be a good idea if you went to Woolton with Oliver and Diana.'

'I don't understand,' I stammered. 'If I'm useless here, I'll be just as useless in Woolton.'

'No one's said you're useless, Millie. Oh dear!' He put his hand to his chest. 'I feel a panic attack coming. Lately, I've been having them quite frequently. No, we ... I think you should be our receptionist. After all, that's what you were originally taken on as.'

It was so unfair. I'd never asked to be promoted, it had been all his idea. I blinked back hot tears of anger. No way would I let him see me cry. I knew I'd be burning my boats, but didn't care. I said, 'I'm afraid that isn't acceptable, George. I'd sooner leave. I'll finish at the end of the month.'

It hadn't gone quite the way he wanted – the way he knew Diana wanted. He rubbed his chest, frowning. 'Then you'd be breaking your contract. One month's notice is required, dated the first of the month.'

'In that case,' I said coolly, though I felt anything but cool, 'I'll leave at the end of January.' I got up and went to the door. 'I'll let you have my resignation in writing this afternoon.'

It was worse, far more shocking, than having discovered all those closely kept family secrets. I'd been dumbfounded to learn that my father wasn't who I'd thought he was. But I'd rejected Norman Cameron a long time ago, and the news didn't matter now – in fact, it was welcome. As for Tom O'Mara, I had thought I would never forget, but already it was hard to remember the way we'd felt about each other. There was just relief that it was all over, though I knew I would worry about him, watch for his name and any mention of Minerva's in the paper, hope that he wouldn't come to harm in the vicious world he lived in. After all, he was my brother.

But the business with my job – trivial in comparison to the rest – was different, directed against me personally. I felt as if someone had just delivered a mammoth blow, knocking all the stuffing out of me. I realised that my job had given me a sense of identity, a feeling of achievement, and without it I was nothing. I hadn't, after all, done better than the other girls in my class, the ones who'd seemed so much smarter than me. I was the backward child again, the girl who could hardly read, so hopeless that I hadn't been entered for a single O level.

Later, when I tried to type a letter of resignation, my fingers no longer seemed capable of accepting messages from my brain. I'd thought George was my friend. I'd tried to help Diana. Why had they turned against me? I felt betrayed.

In the window, through the glass around the boards showing the houses Stock Masterton had for sale, I watched the people passing, their bodies crouched protectively as they fought their way through the gale that howled up Castle Street from the Mersey. I longed to go down to the Pier Head, hold on to the railings, let the wind blow me any way it wanted.

There was a photo of Nancy's house on one of the boards in the window, between the house in Banks which didn't have an oriel window, and a manor house with ten acres of grounds priced at half a million, which George dealt with exclusively. I'd asked Oliver if he would please send someone else to Clement Street if a prospective purchaser wanted to view. 'I know the chap who's selling it slightly. I'd sooner not go,' I said. I still felt the same when the keys for the property arrived through the post, which meant that no one would be there. Unlike Flo's flat, Nancy's house, the place where she'd lived with Tommy O'Mara, where the father I'd never known had been raised, would go to strangers, who would know nothing about the drama that had taken place. People rarely thought about previous owners when they bought a house, no matter how old it was. As far as they were concerned, its history began when they themselves moved in.

Across the office, Darren and Elliot were having a deskbound lunch, eating sandwiches and giggling over something in *Viz*. I felt envious of their gloriously trouble-free lives. June was on the telephone, Barry's carefully combed silver head was bent over a heap of files. Oliver was out with a client. In his office, George, who usually made his presence loudly felt, was strangely quiet. At the next desk, Diana was singing a little tune as she typed into her computer. Was there a note of triumph in her voice? She must know why George had called me in, be aware of my humiliation. Was it worth making a fuss, I wondered, causing a row, telling Diana exactly what I thought in front of everyone? No, it wasn't, I decided. George seemed slightly ashamed of what he'd done. If I left quietly, at least I'd get a good reference, possibly a glowing one if he felt contrite enough.

Oliver returned, his face flushed by the wind. He hung up the keys. 'Whew!' he exclaimed. 'That was a proper shambles. Mum and Dad insisted on viewing the loft, so I went up with them, then one of the kids pushed the ladder up and the damn thing got stuck halfway. I thought I'd be there all afternoon. I managed to do a Tarzan and swing myself down.'

Diana said, 'I was beginning to wonder why you were taking so long.'

'Were you now! I didn't realise you kept an eye on my movements.' Oliver took his coat off, then put it on again. 'I think a beer and a snack in the Wig and Pen is called for after that misadventure. Come on, Millie, I'll treat you.'

I looked up, surprised. Oliver had never made such an offer before. 'I've already been to lunch.'

At the same time, Diana said quickly, 'She's already had lunch, Oliver.'

Oliver poked his head inside George's office. 'I'm off for a quick bevy, George, and taking Millie with me. Okay?'

George didn't look up. 'Okay,' he mumbled.

'Okay, Diana?' Oliver raised his eyebrows questioningly.

'It's none of my business, is it?'

'Too right it isn't.'

'What was all that about?' I asked, when we were outside. The wind gripped me immediately, powerfully, blowing my hair up into a fan around my head. The air was sharp and clean and refreshingly salty. I twisted my face to and fro, trying to breathe in as much as I could, until I felt almost light-headed.

Oliver's usually good-natured face twisted into a scowl. 'I loathe that bloody woman. I can't abide the thought of working with her. I want her to know that when we move I'm the one in charge. She thinks I'm a wimp who can't take decisions, but she doesn't realise how much George regards Stock Masterton as his baby. Take a major decision over his head and he goes ballistic. She'll find that out for herself soon enough if she starts throwing her weight around.'

When we turned into Dale Street the wind lessened fractionally. Oliver's scowl disappeared and he said kindly, 'Enough of my hang-ups. It's you I'm worried about. You look as if you've been crying, which is why I asked you out.'

I clapped my hands to my cheeks, which felt both hot and cold. 'I haven't been crying, but I'm dead upset. Is it so obvious?'

'Yes. I don't want to pry. Don't tell me if it's something private.'

We arrived at the Wig and Pen, where the midday rush was over and only a few tables were occupied. Oliver brought me a whisky and a chicken sandwich, and I told him what had happened. 'I feel gutted,' I finished. I could have said more, much more, but kept myself to a few short words.

Oliver shook his head unbelievingly. 'Darren and Elliot may well have degrees, but neither has an ounce of charm. As for Diana, she positively alienates the clients. She's in completely the wrong profession, which George knows only too well. He's talked about letting her go more than once.' He shook his head again. 'I don't understand the sudden turnaround. Mind you, the poor man has been an emotional wreck since his wife walked out with the children. He's easy prey for any woman who sets her cap at him.'

'But why does Diana hate me so much?' I wailed.

'That's easy to explain.' Oliver smiled and patted my hand. 'George was smitten with you right from the start. I think I can safely say that your promotion had more to do with your legs than your capabilities, not that you didn't make a good fist of the job once you had it,' he added hastily, when he saw my dismayed expression. 'I wasn't the only one to notice, Diana did, too. She's jealous of you, Millie. She wants you out of George's way.'

'I knew George liked me, that's all,' I muttered. 'You see an awful lot, Oliver.' I felt a bit better. I'd been demoted because of another person's weakness, not my own, though it didn't change the fact I was about to give up my job.

On the way back to the office, Oliver said, 'By the way, you mentioned the Naughtons. Mr Naughton rang this morning to say they've withdrawn from the house in Childwall. They parked outside for several nights. Apparently, there's several teenagers next door, belting music out till all hours, which they find totally unacceptable – it would seem the neighbours they have now are darn near perfect.'

Despite everything, I couldn't help laughing. The talk with Oliver had done me good. I even felt a tiny bit flattered. Diana might well have had the upper hand at the moment but, incredibly, it was me who had the power. If I wanted I could ruin everything. I was no good at flirting, but I knew how it was done, I could learn. I didn't know I'd ever had George, but I could easily get him back. It was a challenge I might once have welcomed but, thinking about it now, it seemed rather demeaning.

'About the Naughtons,' I remarked, 'it's time someone suggested they stay put. They're already in their ideal house, and they'll never find another like it.'

'Someone already has – me. Mr Naughton said he'd never wanted to move, it was all his wife's idea. He's going to try to talk her out of it. If he's successful, every estate agent on Merseyside will breathe a big sigh of relief.'

4

There was no tortuous Christmas dinner in Kirkby this year to bring back memories of the bleak dinners that had gone before. Norman Cameron had always nursed a decidedly unfestive spirit throughout the holiday, grim and bitter, his dark eyes searching for any signs of unwelcome gaiety from his children, rationing our time spent in front of the television or with our presents. For the first time, with a glimmer of understanding, I wondered if his own childhood Christmases had been so dark that he could see no other way, though I wasn't convinced I would ever have the Christian charity to forgive.

This year, we had dinner at Flo's without Norman. The dining table was pulled out as far as it would go, so big that only a sheet would cover it. It was set for eight, and there was already a trifle laid out, mince pies, an iced cake from Charmian, the plates intertwined with tinsel. Night-lights in delicately painted wine glasses were waiting to be lit when the meal began. Mum asked Trudy if she would bring her cutlery because there wasn't enough, so Trudy bought her a set for Christmas. It wasn't an expensive set, the handles were bright red plastic, but they looked perfect on the table with the red paper napkins.

There was a real tree in the window, the coloured lights shaped like pears, and new decorations strung from wall to wall. The flat – no longer Flo's with its carpet, new curtains and pink-and-white-flowered wallpaper – was warm with the smell of roasting turkey and Christmas pudding. Melanie and Jake were persuaded that it was too cold to eat on the wooden table in the yard. 'You can have a drink out there afterwards,' Trudy told them, 'as long as you get well wrapped up first.'

Bel was there. She'd always had dinner with Flo on Christmas Day, ever since she'd come out of the forces, she'd hinted, and she wasn't looking forward to eating alone for the first time in her life. 'Mr Fritz always came. Later I used to bring Edward, and Charmian would come down with her little ones. When she married Herbie, me and Flo used to have our dinner upstairs.' She turned up on the day in her leopardskin fur coat, a silver lamé suit and high-heeled silver boots, her hair a magnificent halo of russet waves and curls, and her lovely old face as shrivelled as one of the nuts in the bowl on the sideboard. The first thing she did was grab my hand. 'I've not seen much of you lately, girl. I thought we were friends.'

'I nearly called one night, but it was awfully late,' I explained. 'I wanted someone to talk to, but I was worried you'd think I was stupid.'

'Jaysus, Millie. You're talking to the stupidest woman in the world. I always welcome company, no matter what the hour. What was it you wanted to talk about?'

'I can't remember now. I think I was missing Flo.'

'You never met her, but you miss her. Now, that really is stupid.' Bel's beautiful eyes were wise. 'Mind you, luv, I understand, I'll never stop missing Flo.' The violet eyes searched the room. 'Where's your gran, by the way? There's something I've always wanted to ask Martha Colquitt.'

'She's at an old-age pensioners' do in Kirkby.' Gran needed an operation, only minor, but her own prognosis was gloomy – she was convinced she'd die: 'Me mam swore she'd never let a surgeon near her with a knife,' she'd said. 'I don't trust them doctors.'

I gave Bel her present, an unusual oval-shaped bottle that Trudy had painted various shades of blue and green. Bel gave me an intricately patterned mosaic bracelet. 'It's not new, Flo bought it me in Spain. I thought you'd like it as a memento.'

'Oh, thank you,' I breathed. I fastened the bracelet on to my wrist. 'I'll treasure it all my life.'

Mum presided over the table. I could scarcely take my eyes off my new mother, and every now and then noticed the others glancing at her curiously, as if they, too, found it hard to believe that this Kate Cameron had been lurking behind the old one for so many years. She already looked thinner. Charmian had trimmed and silver-tinted her hair the day before, and the thick, straight fringe and feathery cut took years off her. For the first time in ages, she was wearing makeup, and had bought a new dress – the last new one had been for Trudy's wedding ten years ago. It was plain dark green, emphasising the colour of her sparkling eyes. She already had my present, the gold chain with K for Kate, around her neck. Mum was reborn, confident, relaxed, with her children all around her, except for Alison who was coming to tea that afternoon. 'As an experiment, like, to see how she gets on. See if she takes to the place.' It would be best if not too many people were around in case it frightened her. I was going to Southport to have tea with James's family, the Daleys to Colin's parents in Norris Green. Bel had been invited upstairs. Only Declan would be there to see if his sister felt at home in William Square.

Declan seemed perfectly content living in Kirkby with his father. They saw little of each other, Norman either at work or in the pub, and Declan deeply involved with helping the couple he'd met at the craft fair with their tie-dyed T-shirts. His own first attempts had been highly professional, and Melanie and Jake had been given one each as a present. Next September, he was starting a course in fabric design.

'What about that young feller from next door?' Bel said suddenly. 'Flo always had him in for a drink on Christmas Day.'

I offered to fetch Peter Maxwell. It was a still, windless day, without a patch of blue in the sombre grey sky. The leathery leaves on the trees in the central garden shone dully, still wet with dew. Cars lined the square, but otherwise it was empty, no sign of Fiona or the other girls, who must be having a rare day off. Gran had once mentioned that Flo had spent her first Christmas in the flat entirely alone: Mrs Fritz had gone to Ireland. I wondered what it had looked like then, with only a few cars and a single family living in each house.

Peter was getting ready to have Christmas dinner with a colleague from school. There was just time for a drink with the Camerons.

'Did you enjoy the play?' he asked, as he walked around the plain room with its clean-cut furniture, so different from next door, turning off lights and testing locks.

'It was very cleverly written and well acted,' I said tactfully. It had been awful and I hoped he hadn't any ambition to become a playwright. 'I found it hard to talk to the other teachers, though. I kept expecting to get marks out of ten whenever I answered a question.'

'They liked you. Quite a few said next day what a cracking girl you were.' He took his coat off the rack, and dark eyes glinted at me mischievously. 'They wanted to know when we were getting married.'

'What did you say?'

'What do you think I said?'

I stuck my finger under my chin and thought hard. 'Never?'

Peter laughed. 'Precisely! There's no spark, is there, Millie? I wish there were because I like you very much. We know things about each other that would be hard to tell other people.' He looked at me quizzically. 'Could you pretend I'm a woman so we could be best friends?'

'Oh, Peter!' He was right, there was no spark. If we went out together for long enough we might get married because it seemed the comfortable thing to do, but it wasn't what I wanted – and neither did he. 'You'd need to do something about your beard before I could remotely regard you as a woman, but there's nothing wrong with having a man for a best friend.'

He kissed my forehead, as if to seal our friendship. 'Friends it is, then. Now, where's that drink? Has your mum got beer? I'm not a wine person.'

I was convinced that nowhere on earth could a family have enjoyed their Christmas dinner more than the Camerons. It was nothing to do with the food, though for the first time in months I ate a proper, three-course meal, and the skirt of my red-velvet dress felt tight when I'd finished. It was to do with a shared sense that the nightmare had ended. It had already faded, a little, for Trudy and me, but now it was well and truly over for Mum. As for Declan, he was coping. The only awkward moment came when Melanie, pulling a cracker with her father, said in surprise, 'Where's Grandad?'

'He couldn't come, luv,' Mum said firmly. She looked anxiously at Declan 'He's all right, isn't he?'

'Fine, Mam. He'll have found a pub that's open all day. That's where he'd have been, anyroad.'

'I suppose so.' A shadow almost cast itself over Mum's face, but she blinked it away. 'I'll go round in a day or so, give the house a bit of a clean, like, take him some rations.'

Later, when Trudy and I were washing the dishes, Trudy said, a touch bitterly, 'What a pity she couldn't have brought herself to do this years ago. Think of all the misery it would have saved.'

'It was the money and the flat that gave her the courage, Trude.'

'I'd never have stood it for a minute. I'd have been off the first time he laid a finger on me, and once he'd touched me kids . . .' Trudy shook her head. It was beyond her comprehension.

I reached for a fresh tea-towel – the one I was using was sopping wet. 'We're a different generation, but there's an even newer generation of kids roaming the streets of London and other cities who've run away from violent homes. Why didn't we run away, Trude? He nearly killed you once, but you still stayed. You waited for Colin to rescue you, like I waited for Gary.'

Trudy stared at me blankly. 'I think I felt paralysed,' she whispered.

'Maybe Mum did, too.' One day soon, despite my promise, I resolved to tell Trudy and Declan about the little boy locked in the cupboard. They had a right to know, and could be left to make their own judgement.

Melanie and Jake were aching to sit in the yard. Colin put their coats on, Kate supplied a glass of lemonade and a plate of mince pies and, giggling, they perched themselves on the bench in front of the wooden table. I watched through the window, bemused. It seemed such an uncomfortable thing to do on a cold day in December, and I marvelled at the children's ability to turn it into a great adventure. Colin and Trudy came indoors, shivering. 'Perhaps we could get some garden furniture?' Trudy suggested. They began to discuss the best sort to buy, wood or plastic. They would have preferred wrought-iron, but it was too expensive.

It was just such mundane, ordinary decisions that made the world go round, I thought wryly. Freed from the tensions and the dreary atmosphere of our old house, I became aware of the easy-going intimacy between Colin and my sister, the way they smiled at each other for no reason in particular, as if they were passing on an unspoken message or reading one another's thoughts. I noticed the way they seemed to form a unit with their children, a little world of their own. I thought how satisfying it must be to have little human beings completely dependent upon you, loving you without question, the most important person in their lives. To my surprise, I felt envious of my sister.

Though I could have what she had, I thought later at the Athertons', I could have it easily, straight away. I could be a wife, possibly a mother, by next Christmas. All I had to do was say yes to James. I'd no longer have to worry about my job. I could share in some of this . . .

The difference between my mother's Christmas table and the Athertons' couldn't have been greater. Cut-glass decanters, crystal glasses, heavy silver cutlery with embossed handles, beautifully laundered napkins in silver rings were laid with geometrical precision on a vast expanse of rich,

639

gleaming mahogany, with a rather formal display of upright chrysanthemums in the centre. The dining room was about half as big again as Flo's entire flat, with only a fraction of the furniture. The curtains were ivory satin, drawn carefully to hang in smooth, symmetrical folds.

Mrs Atherton had kissed me coolly on the cheek. 'It's ages since we've seen you, dear. What have you been doing to my son?'

'Nothing that I know of,' I replied, startled. Had James told her about our problems? Or Mrs Atherton might have guessed. After all, she was his mother.

Anna, James's sister, was up from London with her husband and two children. I'd never met her before and found it hard to believe that she'd been an anarchist at university. Her husband, Jonathan, was a dealer in the City, a hearty, fresh-faced man with neat brown hair and designer spectacles. The children, boys, were equally neat, in white shirts, grey pullovers and shorts. They were well behaved and said little, even when their parents encouraged them to talk. I found myself yearning for Melanie and Jake's bright faces, their inability to keep quiet no matter how many times they were told. I longed to discuss garden furniture and tie-dyed T-shirts. Instead, I was forced to listen to Jonathan's talk of bull markets and bear markets, shorts, longs and mediums, stocks and shares. He'd recently netted a cool hundred thou profit on a highly risky venture in Indonesia that everyone else had been too afraid to touch. Anna, blonde hair swinging, pretty face glowing with admiration, leaned over and stroked his chin. 'You're so clever, darling!' she cooed.

Throughout the meal, James kept his eyes glued on me so firmly that I felt uncomfortable. Afterwards we went into the vast, chintzy living room, where he sat on the arm of my chair, towering over me. I felt as if I'd been stamped with his personal seal of ownership.

Jonathan gave his rather unfortunate high-pitched giggle and said to James, 'Understand you've given up flirting with left-wing politics, brother-in-law. Are you still marching with those wretched dockers?'

'I haven't for some time,' James admitted.

So far, Mr Atherton hadn't opened his mouth except to eat; his eyes were always far away, thinking of other things, probably business. He spoke now, with contempt in his voice: 'Lazy buggers, don't know which side their bread's buttered. It's about time they got back to work.'

I had no idea if I was pro-establishment or anti, or if my politics were left or right, I only knew it made my blood boil to hear the dockers being called 'lazy buggers' by a man smoking a fat cigar who owned three garages. I wished I knew some hard facts and figures that I could quote in the dockers' defence, but I knew nothing about the dispute other than it was happening. I jumped up. 'Excuse me.'

In the eau-de-nil tiled bathroom with its matching carpet and fittings, I stared unseeingly at my reflection in the mirror and realised, with a sense of overwhelming relief, that I was wasting James's time. I felt alien from his family. If I loved him, I would have taken them on and done my best, but I didn't love him and never would. 'I'm glad I came,' I whispered. 'It's helped me make up my mind once and for all.'

When I came out, James was hovering on the landing, and I felt a stab of anger. I wanted to say something coarse and brutal: 'Would you like to have come in to watch me pee?'

He stared at me and I felt repelled by the abject adoration in his eyes. 'You look lovely in that dress,' he said huskily. 'You suit red.' He tried to take me in his arms, nuzzle my hair, but I pushed him away. He patted his pocket, 'I've a present for you, a ring.'

'I don't want it!'

'But, Millie . . .' His lips twisted in an arc of misery. 'Is it this other chap you've been seeing?'

'I haven't been seeing another chap – least I have, but he's just a friend. There's no one, James. No one!' I emphasised the last word, my voice unnaturally shrill, to impress upon him that I was announcing I was free – and he was free to forget me and find someone else.

We began to argue. He refused to believe I meant what I said. Anna must have heard the raised voices. She came out into the hall downstairs. 'Are you two all right?' Her laugh tinkled up the stairs. 'Oh, you're just having a little domestic.' She made a show of pretending to creep back into the room.

James's eyes were glassy, his face was swollen, red. I didn't know this man. Falling in love with me had changed him for the worse. 'It can't be over,' he insisted doggedly.

'It is, James.' I was worried that he was about to hit me. His fists were clenching and unclenching, as if he was itching to use them and it could only be on me. Then I did something that surprised me later when I thought about it. I flung my arms around his neck and hugged him tightly. 'James, I'm bad for you,' I whispered urgently. 'Can't you see? There's something not quite right about the way you love me.' I stroked his neck. 'One of these days, you'll meet someone else who you'll love in a quite different way, and everything will be wonderful for you both.' I pulled away. 'Goodbye, darling,' I said softly.

He remained silent, his eyes no longer glassy, but full of misery and shock. I thought, I wasn't sure, that there was also a trace of comprehension that I could be right.

I flew down the stairs, opened the door of the living room, and said breathlessly, 'I'm awfully sorry, I have to go. Thank you so much for the meal. It was lovely. No, no, please don't get up,' I implored, when Mrs Atherton began to get to her feet. 'I'll see myself out.'

It was past nine when I got back to Blundellsands. The first thing I did was ring my mother. Alison had been very quiet but not too disturbed by the strange surroundings. 'She didn't flick her fingers, the way she does when she's upset,' Mum said gratefully.

Relieved, I hung up my red dress carefully and ran a bath. Afterwards I watched a Woody Allen film on television, then went to bed with a book and a glass of warm milk, feeling contented and relaxed.

Just after midnight the telephone rang. I prayed it wouldn't be James, pleading for a second chance or a third, or whatever it would be by now, but when I picked up the extension by the bed, Peter Maxwell said cheerfully, 'Hi! I've just got in and thought I'd give you a ring. Did you have a nice day?'

'Nice and not so nice. I finished with a boyfriend. It wasn't very pleasant.'

'The hunk from the party?'

'That's right.'

'I didn't realise you were still seeing him. He's definitely not your type.'

'Are you going to be the arbiter of who's my type from now on?' I smiled at the receiver.

'It's what friends are for. I shall always ask for your opinion on any future girlfriends.'

'It shall be given with pleasure,' I said graciously. We chatted idly, and he was about to ring off when I remembered something. 'By the way, knowing it won't be taken the wrong way and you'll think I'm after your body or your money, would you like to come to a drinks party tomorrow afternoon?'

'Sorry, but I'm taking a group of first-years to a pantomime. Will you be at Charmian's on New Year's Eve?'

I said I would, and we promised each other the first dance.

The drinks party was being held at Barry Green's. He had casually offered an invitation to the whole office. 'We've been having one on Boxing Day for more than thirty years. The world and his wife usually come. Any time between noon and four, you're all welcome.'

Elliot and Darren had wrinkled their noses: a drinks party sounded much too tame. June would be away. Oliver welcomed the idea of escaping from his kids for a few hours. 'I love them, but it's usually hell on earth at home over Christmas.' George, who always went anyway, would be there with Diana, bringing his children who were over from France. I had intended taking James, but now I would have to go alone.

The Greens' house in Waterloo, only a mile from my flat, was semi-detached and spacious, the furniture and carpets shabby and worn. The Christmas decorations looked well used, as if the same things were hung in the same place year after year. Everywhere had a comfortable, lived-in look, very different from the Athertons' Ideal Home. By the time I got there it was already crowded. Barry's wife, Tess, let me in. She was a pretty woman with a tumble of grey curls and a wide, smiling mouth, wearing an emerald-green jumpsuit. She took my coat and ordered me to mingle. 'I'll do the hostess bit later and we'll have a proper talk. Right now, I'm busy with the food.'

I found Oliver and his alarmingly aggressive wife, Jennifer, waved to George, who was standing in a corner with two rather sullen teenagers, clutching his chest as if in the throes of a panic attack. There was no sign of Diana. Barry came up with a tray of drinks. 'Food's in the kitchen, help yourselves, won't you?' He'd abandoned the usual bow-tie for a Paisley cravat under a canary-yellow pullover.

Over the holiday, Jennifer had been pressing Oliver remorselessly to start his own estate agency. 'Then he won't get pissed around rotten by whoever George happens to be screwing at the moment. I told him, "Millie will go in with you."' She gave me a painful but encouraging dig. 'You would, wouldn't you, Millie? You could be his assistant.'

'Willingly,' I said, with a smile. Oliver groaned.

Over the next few hours, I well and truly mingled. Several guests were estate agents, and we gravely discussed the state of the market. Was it up or down? One man gave me his card. 'If you should ever think of changing your job . . .' Barry introduced me to his children: Roger, the architect, an earnest man in jeans and an Arran sweater, Emma and Sadie, who would take the world by storm for a second time as soon as their children were old enough and they could resume their careers.

'Where's your other son?' I asked. 'Is he still abroad?'

Barry's perfectly groomed moustache quivered slightly. 'According to his mother, Sam won't be gracing us with his presence until New Year's Eve.'

Later, I forced myself to approach George. He eyed me appreciatively in my red dress before introducing me to his children, Annabel and Bill. 'Have you had a nice holiday?' I asked them.

They both shrugged. 'Okay.'

'I haven't a clue what teenagers get up to nowadays.' George sighed and looked harassed. 'I think they've been rather bored.' Bill rolled his eyes to confirm that this was definitely the case.

'Why don't you take them to the Cavern?' I suggested.

'Oh, Dad, would you?' Annabel pleaded. 'The girls at school will turn green if I tell them I've been to the Cavern.'

'Aren't I a bit old?' George said plaintively.

'You can just hover in the background,' I said. 'By the way, where's Diana? I thought she'd be here.'

George shrugged vaguely. 'She spent Christmas at her place. I haven't seen her in a few days.'

'Diana's horrible!' Bill burst out. 'You'll never guess what she did. She actually drew up a timetable of things for us to do – the pantomime, McDonald's, card games, charades, and idiotic films to watch on telly. She seemed to think we were children!'

Tactfully I wandered off. People had begun to leave. For the first time, I was aware of being the only youngish woman without a partner, and felt conspicuous as the crowd thinned, though I told myself I shouldn't care. I went upstairs to look for my coat. It was with a pile of others in what appeared to be Barry and Tess's untidy bedroom. I was putting it on when Tess came in, wearing her rather impish smile. 'Ah, there you are, Millie! I've been so rude. I always like to have a little chat with guests who've come for the first time, get to know them, as it were.' She sat on the bed and patted the space next to her. 'Sit down a minute.'

Under Tess's friendly questioning, I revealed all sorts of things about myself I wouldn't normally: about Diana, being demoted, James, and the awful tea at the Athertons' the day before.

'Never mind, love,' Tess said comfortingly. 'Things always turn out for the best in the long run, or so I've always found. Oh, well,' she levered herself off the bed, 'I'd better go downstairs and be the good hostess. I always feel a sense of relief when it's over, but sad too that it will be another year before I see some of our friends again. The children always found them a bit of a giggle, but they wouldn't miss their mum and dad's Boxing Day party.'

'Except Sam,' I reminded her.

'Ah, yes, Sam. He's in Mexico.' I was surprised when Tess looked at me rather speculatively, then said, 'Let me show you our Sam.' She opened the drawer in a bedside cupboard and took out a sheaf of newspaper cuttings. 'Barry doesn't know I've kept these. He's rather ashamed of Sam.' She handed me a cutting. 'That's him, in the *Daily Express*.'

A wiry young man with crew-cut hair was standing on a wall, baring his chest defiantly to the world. He held a banner aloft proclaiming, AXE THE TAX. Several policemen were reaching up in a vain attempt to grab his feet. 'He was sentenced to three months in prison or a thousand-pound fine for that,' Tess said proudly. 'Barry paid the fine and he was released, much to Sam's disgust. They rub one another up the wrong way, yet secretly they think the world of each other.'

There was a photo of Sam at the gates of Greenham Common with his then girlfriend, several of him protesting during the miners' strike. 'He hasn't been in court for years,' Tess said, slightly disappointed. 'Our three elder children are very conformist, but Sam takes after me. I used to go on CND marches when I was a girl – Barry disapproved of that, too.'

'What's he doing in Mexico? Has he gone to start a war?' I wasn't sure if I approved of Sam or not, but I admired his independent spirit.

'Oh, no. He's a record producer. He spends three or four months of the year travelling the world, taping folk songs, tribal music, that sort of thing. Then he comes home and turns them into proper recordings. He's got a studio in the attic. Much to his dad's amazement he's doing very well.' Suddenly she changed the subject, rather drastically, I thought. 'I expect your mum worries about you, still single at your age?'

'She does, yes.'

Tess hadn't changed the subject, after all. 'I worry terribly about Sam. He's thirty-three and I wish he'd establish some roots, start a family, have something more worthwhile to come home to than boring old Mum and Dad.'

A woman came in to collect her coat and Tess put the cuttings away. I thanked her for a lovely time and went home.

Over the final days of the year, I felt like two different people. There was only a skeleton staff at work and I had several half-days off, during which time I stencilled flowers on the corners of the living room and cleaned the flat from top to bottom, whistling tunelessly, happy. But when I stopped for a break, my mood would darken and I would feel restless, haunted by a sense of failure and hopelessness. There'd been a time, not long ago, when I'd considered myself the only Cameron with an aim in life and any hope of a bright, successful future, but now I was the one with nothing to look forward to. Empty years loomed ahead, a vast, yawning abyss.

Mum had got a job in an office and would start the following week. 'Only making the tea, running a few errands.' She'd giggled merrily. 'I'll be the office junior. It's just temporary, till Alison comes.'

Trudy was gearing up for when Melanie started school in January or painting bottles for the stall she intended having every week. Should I get a hobby? I wondered. I rang Declan several times, worried that Norman would answer and whether I should engage him in conversation if he did, but there was never any reply. I badly missed Flo's flat, where I'd been quite happy to do nothing but watch the swirling lamp and listen to music. For want of something to do, on Sunday morning, I went to Mass at the Cathedral with my mother. I felt no spiritual reawakening or miraculous re-conversion in the remarkable circular building with its brilliant blue stained-glass windows, but on the way back to Flo's, I thought I might go again. Then something happened that I'd always dreaded.

Two boys were coming towards us. I hardly took them in, aware only that they were about fourteen and relatively well dressed. As they passed, one leaped at Mum and snatched the chain with K for Kate from around her neck.

Mum screamed, the boys ran only a short distance, then turned. The one who'd snatched the chain dangled it at us tauntingly, before they skipped away, laughing, almost dancing in their triumph.

'It could have happened anywhere,' Mum said later, when we were back at Flo's and she'd calmed down after I'd made us tea. 'It's not just Liverpool. It could have happened anywhere in the world.'

Something funny was going on between George and Diana – or perhaps there was nothing going on at all. Everyone managed to glean little pieces of information and put them together to make a whole. It appeared that George had suggested Diana return home when it became obvious that she and the children weren't getting on, but had made no suggestion that she come back now that the children had gone. She'd spent Christmas alone in the house where she'd lived with her father. Even Oliver had to concede he felt sorry for the haggard little woman who stumbled round the office as if she were drunk, ignored by George. It wasn't that George was being deliberately cruel, he was taken up with the new office, which was opening in a few days' time. He appeared to have forgotten that Diana existed.

Like Oliver, I was sorry for Diana. If I'd been gutted by my demotion, she must have been feeling as if the bottom had dropped out of her world. But I was terrified that I was seeing myself in another five or ten years' time. Might I one day find myself waiting for a kind word from a man I'd been hoping would rescue me from a life of loneliness?

'Is this the girl who's just dumped a guy who runs an Aston Martin speaking?' Peter Maxwell chuckled when I phoned him. 'Men are terrified of loneliness, not just women. Sit back, have a good time, and see what happens. Don't wait for things, don't expect them, they won't come any sooner. It's like that song Flo used to play all the time. We're all dancing in the dark.'

'You're very clever,' I said admiringly. We rang off, deciding that if we were still single at forty we would live next door to each other.

I thought of James, who was going through the same experience as Diana, and wondered if I'd been too cruel, too abrupt. If he hadn't followed me to the bathroom, I would have told him tactfully in a more appropriate place. I recalled the way he'd been outside the nightclub – it seemed like years ago, but it was only a few months – when he'd said he was sick of selling cars to idiots like himself. He wanted to do something more worthwhile with his life. And the time by the Pier Head when he told me how much he loved me. He'd joined the Socialist Workers' Party to prove he wasn't shallow. We'd got on well until he decided he was in love with me; from then on, he began to fall apart. I felt sure that one day James would marry someone who didn't play such havoc with his emotions. They would have several children, and he would be back in the Conservative

Party, still running his father's garage – perhaps all three – having forgotten he'd ever wanted to do anything else.

On New Year's Eve, I woke up with that aching feeling of loss again, a haunting sensation that something was missing from my life. I'd never been able to identify what it was, but in the darkness of my bedroom on the final day of the year, the knowledge came washing over me so forcefully that my body froze.

I was mourning the father I'd never known!

After a while, I made myself get up, convinced I might freeze altogether, die, if I stayed in bed any longer. I felt heavy and lethargic as I made myself a cup of tea. After I'd drunk it, I fetched the photo of my father, the one I'd found at Flo's, and stared at the sober little five-year-old, the only child not smiling. How would it have been if he'd married Mum? Would there have been a Trudy, a Declan, an Alison? If so, they would be different from the ones I knew now, and Tom O'Mara would never have existed. I remembered reading that if a time traveller went back to the beginning of time and destroyed a blade of grass, it could change the entire course of history.

It was all becoming too deep for me. Anyway, if I thought about it long enough it would be easy to cry and never stop. I took a long shower, made myself a decent breakfast for a change, then went to work, feeling only slightly better.

Stock Masterton was in turmoil. The Woolton office had been decorated and furnished; it was ready to move into the following day. To celebrate the opening, clients would be offered refreshments and a glass of wine. There were adverts in the local press, though no mention of the food and drink, otherwise there would be a deluge of people who had no intention of buying or selling a house.

Every file had been copied, duplicates made of the wall charts. The contents of Oliver and Diana's desks were transferred. People kept rushing in, collecting papers and rushing out again. I sat behind my desk, feeling dazed. I hadn't the faintest idea what was happening to me. Should I transfer my things to Woolton or not? George seemed to have forgotten that I was to have been the receptionist, just as he'd forgotten that Diana lived and breathed. I'd typed out my notice weeks ago and put it on his desk, but it had never been acknowledged. Yesterday he'd asked me to make an appointment early in January with a firm who were erecting a small estate in Seaforth and wanted Stock Masterton to handle the sales side.

'An appointment for you?' I enquired.

'No, for yourself, of course,' George replied testily. There was mention of someone called Sandra in the new office, but no one seemed sure what job she was to do.

Oliver was no help. He complained that he was being kept in the dark and was at loggerheads with George, though George hadn't noticed, and Jennifer, Oliver's wife, was touring commercial property agents, presenting him with sheafs of offices to rent when he got home. 'She's approached her father for a loan,' he said soon after I arrived. 'I told her that Diana's like a pricked balloon, but she said, "You never know, the whole thing might start up again." Would you come in with me, Millie?' he said plaintively. 'I don't think I could do it on my own.'

'I'd be glad to,' I told him, for the umpteenth time. Even if my job turned out to be safe, after all, I didn't think I could bring myself to trust George again.

To add further to my confusion Barry Green came up later in the morning and looked at me searchingly, as if he'd never seen me before, then gave a little 'Humph' of what sounded like approval. 'Tess has suggested I invite you round to dinner one night next week,' he said jovially. 'She said to please give her a ring if you'd like to come.'

I said I would, and meant it. I'd liked Tess enormously, and everything else about the Green household. I was thrilled to be asked to dinner.

Oliver took off again for Woolton. George was in his office, noisily slamming drawers and talking to himself. Everyone else was either at lunch or in Woolton, except for Darren, who had taken a client to view Nancy O'Mara's old house in Clement Street. I'd seriously thought of buying the place myself, cutting my mortgage by a third. After about half a minute, I realised it would be wrong, like going back instead of forward.

I leaned on my desk and thought about Flo, who would always remain a mystery, even though I knew so much about her. Had she been happy in the flat in William Square with her memories of Tommy O'Mara? Flo, with her secret lover, her secret child, the weekends spent with Mr Fritz on the Isle of Man.

George appeared, clutching his forehead dramatically, and announced that he was off to the Wig and Pen to have a pint and a panic attack. June had already left for lunch.

There'd been numerous times in the past when I'd been in the office alone, but when George slammed the door, it was like being shut in a place I'd never been before. I looked around uneasily, as if adjusting to strange new surroundings. There were decorations, very tasteful: a silver tree with 'presents' – a dozen empty boxes wrapped in red and green foil – and silver bells pinned to the walls. The fluorescent lights seemed to be humming much too loudly. Outside, people hurried past, loaded with carrier bags, and I remembered that the sales were on. The sound of the endless traffic was oddly muted, and I had a sensation of being in a different dimension, and while I could see the people, they couldn't see me. The light, bouncing off one of the silver bells on the wall behind, was reflected in turn on to the screen of the computer, and all I could see was the dark shadow of my head surrounded by a bright, blurred halo. I stared at the screen, hypnotised, and the shadows seemed to shift and change until I thought I could see a face, but it wasn't mine. The eyes were very old, set in deep, black hollows, the mouth was . . .

The phone on my desk rang stridently. I jumped and grabbed the receiver, glad to escape from the face on the screen. It was Declan.

'Could you come to Mam's early tonight?' he said eagerly. The Camerons and the Daleys had been invited to Charmian and Herbie's New Year's Eve party.

'Why?'

'You'll never guess what our Trudy's bought!' Declan paused for effect. 'Champagne! I've never had champagne before. We're going to drink to the future, before we go upstairs. Oh, and there'll be a special guest – Scotty!'

I laughed, delighted, and promised to be there by eight. When I rang off, there was no longer a face on the computer, merely the dazzling reflection of a silver bell, and the office appeared quite normal. A man tapped on the window and made the thumbs-up sign. He could see me, I was real. I smiled at him and he opened the door.

'You should bottle that smile and sell it, luv,' he said. 'You'd make a fortune.'

I knew then that I'd come through. My mind cleared, and I was myself again, but better than the self I'd been before. The future no longer seemed bleak and hopeless, but bright and full of promise. Never again would I dream about slithering footsteps on the stairs or wake up with a feeling that something was missing from my life. I stretched my arms as wide as they would go, scarcely able to contain the sensation of total happiness.

There was wine on Elliot's desk. I went over and poured myself a glass just as the door opened and a boy came in, not very tall, with an engaging face burned dark brown by the sun. He looked so ridiculous I had to smile. A long mac swirled around his muddy, wrinkled boots, but the comical thing about him was his hat: a brown felt beehive with a wide turned-up brim and a brightly patterned band.

'Hi!' He grinned, and lines of merriment crinkled beneath his eyes and around his mouth. I realised that this wasn't a boy but a man. I recognised the young rebel in the photographs Tess Green had showed me on Boxing Day, as well as her impish smile.

I returned to my desk. 'If you're looking for your father, I'm afraid he's out, I'm not sure where.'

'Shit,' he said amiably. 'Will he be long?'

'I'm not sure about that, either.'

'How come you know who I am?'

'Your mum showed me your photograph.'

He grinned again. 'Did she now?'

The atmosphere in the office had changed yet again. There was a tingling in the air, a crackle of excitement.

'So, you're just back from Mexico,' I said.

'That's right, early this morning. Dad had left for work by then, and Mum suggested I come and make my peace. I'd promised to be home for Christmas, you see, but got delayed. Dad gets worked up about these things, not like Mum. I had to borrow his matinée-idol mac. I mislaid my coat somewhere on the journey.' He gestured vaguely. 'He'll be annoyed.'

I could feel my lips twitching and longed to laugh. 'It's a pity you didn't mislay your hat instead.'

He removed the beehive and regarded it dispassionately. His hair was yellow, like wild straw. 'All the men wear them in Mexico.'

'This is Liverpool,' I reminded him.

'So it is.' He threw the hat to me like a frisbee. I caught it and put it on. 'It suits you. Keep it, not to wear, to hang on the wall.'

'Thanks. Help yourself to a drink while you're waiting.'

He poured a glass of wine and perched on the edge of his father's desk. I noticed his eyes were very blue, his face neither ugly nor handsome. It was an interesting face, open and expressive, and I could tell he had a great sense of humour. 'You obviously know loads about me,' he said, 'but I bet you'll be astounded to learn I also know a lot about you. You're Millie Cameron, you live in Blundellsands, have just dumped a boyfriend called James, and are in a bit of a tizzy over your job.'

'What on earth possessed your mum to tell you that?' I wasn't sure whether to be annoyed or not.

'Because – you'll be horrified to hear this – she really fancies you for a daughter-in-law. She started pinning my ear back about it the minute I arrived home. That's the real reason she asked me to come, not to see Dad but to see you.'

I released the laughter I'd been trying to contain ever since he came in. 'That's a mad idea.'

'I just thought I'd warn you, because I understand you've been invited to dinner next week, when Mum will really get to work on you.'

'Will you be there?'

'She'll handcuff me to the chair if I refuse. What about you? Will you come?'

'Under the circumstances,' I said gravely, 'I'll have to give the matter some thought.'

I removed the Mexican hat, which suddenly felt too heavy, and laid it carefully on the desk. The door opened and Oliver came in, followed by a sullen Diana.

'Do you fancy lunch?' Sam Green said. 'We can laugh ourselves silly over my mother.' Our eyes met fleetingly and I felt something pass between us. I had no idea if it meant something or not.

I reached for my bag. 'Why not?'

And why not go to dinner at the Greens next week. If the truth be known, I quite liked Sam Green, and fancied Tess for a mother-in-law. Nothing might come of it, but so what? As Peter Maxwell said, we were all dancing in the dark.

Some Kind of Hero

To Ken and Harriet with love, as always

1

Tess woke slowly, opening her eyes to the morning sunshine which streamed through the open window. She stretched, luxuriating in the feel of silk sheets against her bare skin.

And then she saw him, standing at the foot of the bed, his dark hair ruffled by the soft breeze. It was Colin Firth. In one hand he held a bottle of champagne, in the other a carton of Häagen-Dazs.

As their eyes met, he smiled enigmatically and said, 'Miss Doyle, the video's finished.'

Tess dragged her attention away from the rain drizzling down the window pane and back to the thirty expectant faces in front of her. She reached for the remote control. Damn, she'd been so busy daydreaming she'd missed the bit where Colin – sorry, Mr Darcy – emerged from the lake, all lean thighs and dripping masculinity. Her finger hovered longingly over the rewind button, then she stopped herself.

'Right, so what does that tell us?'

'That Mr Darcy's really sexy?' Becky Whiting sighed.

'Leave it out, he's ancient!' Jason Fothergill looked affronted. He was supposed to be Becky's boyfriend, but at fourteen years old, with terminal acne and an ink-stained shirt, there was really no comparison.

'I'd rather have him than you.'

Wouldn't we all? Tess thought. At least Becky Whiting *had* a boyfriend. Drooling over Darcy was the closest thing Tess had to a love life these days. 'I was thinking more of his relationship with Elizabeth Bennett. What does it tell us about that?'

'They haven't got one,' Jason muttered, fiddling with his biro. 'She's a right snotty cow. I wouldn't go out with her.'

'Nice tits, though.' A paper missile sailed from the other side of the classroom and caught him on the side of the head. Jason snatched up his exercise book and flung it, as the rest of the class, sensing a fight, began to jeer.

Tess took off her glasses and rubbed her eyes. Two weeks into the new school year and she was already counting the days until half-term. She had a headache throbbing in her temples, thanks to covering Marjorie Wheeler's double lesson with 9C earlier on. Most of them didn't know a simile from a smack in the face and didn't want to, either. Tess had spent half the lesson explaining Thomas Hardy's view of fatalism, and the other half trying to stop them shutting each other's heads in the desks.

'That's enough.' Her voice rose above the din. They all turned back reluctantly to face her. 'Can anyone say what this tells us about Darcy's feelings for Elizabeth?'

Thirty blank faces stared back at her. They couldn't have looked less comprehending if she'd asked the question in Swahili. 'No one got any ideas?' No reason why they should have. She'd only been telling them every day for the past fortnight.

She glanced at Paris Malone, who ducked her head and pretended to search for her pencil sharpener. Poor Paris. She'd learned the hard way that it didn't pay to be too clever at Haxsall Park Comp.

Just as Tess was wondering if she should take up a more rewarding career, like septic-tank cleaning, a voice piped up from the back of the classroom. It was the new girl, Emily Tyler. 'He's in love with her, but he doesn't know how to say it.'

Tess looked at her with surprise and gratitude. Everyone else just stared.

'Exactly. That's exactly what he feels.' Tess smiled encouragingly.

Emily went red and retreated behind her book.

'Then why doesn't he just come out and say it?' Mark Nicholls asked. He was the class stud – dark, brooding and brainier than he let on. Unfortunately, he preferred to direct his intelligence into making life hell for his teachers. 'Why doesn't he just say, "Fancy a shag?"'

Tess faced him. 'Because it would be a very short book.'

'Good.' Everyone smirked appreciatively at his joke, especially the girls. Tess ignored him.

'So how do we know he feels like that? Can you find any examples in the text?' she pressed on. But Mark had the class' attention now and was making the most of it.

'No offence, Miss, but why are we bothering to learn this old stuff? I mean, it's not exactly relevant to us, is it?'

Here we go. Tess suppressed a sigh. The kids always tried this argument when they wanted to distract her. If they were lucky, they could sometimes spin it out until the end of the lesson.

But not today. She met his eye unflinchingly. 'I'm sure it would be nice to study something relevant to you, Mark. But sadly *Loaded* magazine has yet to make it on to the GCSE syllabus.'

Everyone sniggered. A dull red flush crept up his neck. Normally Tess would never have set out to embarrass one of her pupils, but Mark Nicholls was too cocky for his own good.

She turned back to the class. 'Maybe Mark's got a point,' she said. 'How do you think Elizabeth and Darcy's relationship would go if Jane Austen was writing it today?'

That started a lively discussion. It might not have been quite what was in her lesson plan, but at least it kept them interested and stopped them throwing chairs out of the window.

The only one who didn't join in was Emily. She sat at the back, listening to Leanne Hooper and Jordan Nuttall gossiping on either side of her. Tess watched them consideringly. It was odd that she'd made friends with those two. They didn't seem to have anything in common. Leanne and Jordan had streaked hair, lipgloss and lovebites; Emily wore not a scrap of make-up and her dark hair was pulled back in a messy ponytail. Tess hoped she wouldn't start following their example too closely. She seemed such a nice girl.

Her father had seemed nice too, when he came to meet Tess before the start of term. The family had only recently moved to York from Leeds, and he was worried how Emily would settle in.

'We've had a few family problems recently,' he'd explained. Tess guessed that meant there'd been a divorce. If so, Emily certainly wouldn't be alone; she couldn't think of more than half a dozen kids in the class who had both parents still living at home. Some lived with their mothers, some with stepfamilies, others were being brought up by their grandparents. One lad was with foster parents after a long stint in a children's home.

It was the way things were in Haxsall. To the outside world, it seemed like a tough place to live, a 'problem area'. The local paper was always carrying stories of bored teenagers roaming the streets, vandalising shops and torching cars on the recreation ground. The bus company had refused to take passengers there after dark for a while after a gang threw stones at one of the buses. They made it sound like Beirut. There was even a joke about it in York: What do you call someone from Haxsall in a suit? The accused.

But Tess had lived there all her life and she knew there was a different side to the area. The papers only reported the bad news about a troublesome few. They didn't want to know about the close-knit community, where everyone knew and looked out for everyone else. They never printed stories about the good things that happened, the local shopkeepers who went round to the elderly checking if they needed anything, or the pubs that organised fund-raising events for local youngsters. Tess had more reason than most to appreciate the big-hearted people of Haxsall.

And it wasn't all rundown, either. Apart from the sprawling council estate in the centre, there were the tidy redbrick semis of the old town, built by Joseph Rowntree so his factory workers could escape the slum dwellings of the old inner city. Then there were the big houses on the fringes of Haxsall, the solid Victorian villas on Fox Lane and the smart new executive development on Hollywell Park overlooking the common.

She was fairly certain this must be where Emily and her family lived. No one from the council estate wore an expensive designer suit like Mr Tyler's. Not even the accused.

Ten minutes later the bell went for the end of the lesson. As they all made a dash for the door, Tess called Emily over. She came reluctantly, dragging her feet.

'I haven't had much chance to chat since you started here. I just wanted to make sure you're all right?'

'Fine, thanks.' Emily shrugged. She was as thin and leggy as a baby giraffe, and painfully conscious of it too, from the way she stooped, her arms folded defensively across her body. Tess felt like telling her how lucky she was; at barely five feet four, she envied any woman with supermodel height.

'So you're settling in all right? No problems?' Emily shook her head. 'I notice you've made friends with Jordan and Leanne?'

'They're all right.' She fiddled with a tendril of hair escaping from her ponytail. Her nails were bitten right down, Tess noticed.

'What about at home? Your dad mentioned you'd been through a bad time recently—'

'Everything's fine,' Emily cut her off. She glanced longingly at the door. Tess decided to put her out of her misery.

'Okay then, you can go. But don't forget, if you ever need anyone to—' But the door was already slamming behind her. Through the glass panel, Tess could see Leanne and Jordan waiting outside. When Emily emerged, they prised themselves off the wall and joined her. They talked for a moment and Emily jerked her head back towards the door. Then they all laughed and headed off down the corridor together.

Tess shook her head regretfully. Maybe she should have kept a closer eye on her, made sure she didn't get too well in with those troublemakers. She'd meant to, but like the aerobics classes she'd signed up for and the big pile of ironing in her airing cupboard, she hadn't got round to it.

This was her first term as Head of English, and since her promotion she'd been rushed off her feet, writing reports, planning lessons, dealing with staffing crises and making ends meet on her pathetically limited budget. Actually teaching the kids had become the easy bit, and the only part of her day Tess looked forward to.

She pressed the eject button on the video. Bringing in her precious tape of *Pride and Prejudice* had been a last desperate attempt to bring the text alive for her bored Year 10 class. But she had to admit, for all his attitude, Mark Nicholls had a point. How did she expect a bunch of stroppy fourteen-year-old boys to take an interest in Regency romance? It might be easier if they had the chance to read something modern too. But judging from the state of the stock cupboard, no one had bought any new books since Dickens produced his last masterpiece.

But all that would change once she got the extra money she'd asked for in her budget. Tess had already made a list of all the new novels she would buy. There would be some play texts too, and poetry. And she'd get rid of all the old grammar books, the ones that went on about syntactic structures and prepositional phrases and said nothing about how to write a really great story. She couldn't wait.

Then we'll see who's not relevant. She gathered up the homework books that had been dumped on her desk and put them in her oversized satchel bag, then made her way to the staffroom to grab a quick coffee before she went home.

Back in the 1960s, Haxsall Park had been a shining beacon in the new comprehensive system, a sprawling modern building of glass and concrete. But like the textbooks, it was beginning to look old and tatty around the edges. The beige paintwork in the corridors was peeling, and rain filled the potholes in the playground as Tess splashed through them towards the Portakabin that housed the staffroom.

It was always busy at the end of the day, as teachers gathered their coats and belongings before heading home. Some huddled around the windows, contemplating the dash through the rain to the car park. Others had retreated around the kettle. A few keen ones were catching up on their homework, hacking through essays with their red biros.

Helen Wesley held up a mug. 'Coffee?'

'Please.' Tess swept a pile of QCA reports off one of the armchairs and flopped into it.

'Bad day?'

'Not bad. Just exhausting.'

'Aren't they all?' muttered Jeff Kramer, Head of Science. He was busy circling jobs in *The Times Ed.* 'Never mind. Another ten weeks and it'll be Christmas.'

'It sounds like a lifetime.' Tess rested her head back against the cushions and stared at the cracks in the ceiling. 'Remind me again why I wanted to be a Head of Department?'

'The power? The glamour?' Helen handed her her coffee. She was Head of PE and Tess' closest friend at the school. In her late twenties, blonde, bouncy and like Melinda Messenger in a tracksuit, she was the reason no Haxsall Park boy ever missed games.

'Do I look glamorous to you? On second thoughts, don't answer that.' Tess shook the rain off her short dark hair. It was badly in need of a wash, but she had a feeling it wouldn't get done tonight, with the mountain of marking she had to do.

'Ah, so it's got to you already, has it?' Jeff lit up a cigarette and grinned at her through the curling smoke. He was a big, untidy-looking man in a shapeless sweater. 'Blimey, I thought you were supposed to be the enthusiastic one? What happened to the woman who was full of ideas? The one who was going to show us cynical old sods how it's meant to be done?'

'You try being enthusiastic when you've got that old cow Frobisher breathing down your neck.'

Helen smiled sympathetically. 'Still giving you a hard time, is she?'

'Like you wouldn't believe.' Cynthia Frobisher had been Head of English before being promoted to Deputy Head last term. And she never let Tess forget it. 'Honestly, she treats me like an incompetent teenager.'

'I wouldn't worry about it,' Jeff said. 'She treats us all like that.'

'I get it worse than you lot. She doesn't think anyone can run the English department the way she did. Except Marjorie Wheeler, of course, which is why she's so sick she didn't get the job.'

'Tess,' Helen interrupted her.

'I get fed up hearing how she used to do things,' Tess went on. 'Every time I come up with a new idea, she just looks down her nose at me and says—'

'Tess!' Helen shot a wary glance at the door. Tess didn't need to turn round to know Cynthia Frobisher was behind her. The hairs on the back of her neck were already standing on end.

Cynthia might only have been the Deputy Head but she was infinitely scarier than Eric Gant, the Headteacher. He was a kindly, white-haired old chap, who looked like he'd be more at home running the local bowls club than a big comprehensive. Mrs Frobisher, by contrast, looked as if she'd be happier running the Third Reich. She was in her fifties, hard-eyed and businesslike in a mannish trouser suit and flat shoes. Even her hairstyle was severe, falling in an uncompromising brown bob around her square face. She wore no make-up apart from a gash of alarmingly red matt lipstick that emphasised her mean mouth. She wasn't known as The Enforcer for nothing.

If she'd heard Tess' bitching, she gave no sign of it, as she swept in and dumped her armful of files on the coffee table. Tess eyed her nervously.

'Was there something you wanted, Cynthia?' The formidable Mrs Frobisher rarely ventured into the staffroom, preferring to keep to her office. But she still had an uncanny knack of knowing what they were all saying about her – thanks, no doubt, to her gossipy sidekick Marjorie Wheeler.

'Staff meeting.' She picked up the top file and flicked through it. 'Mr

Gant has asked me to deal with this, as he's tied up with the Chair of Governors.'

'Kinky,' Jeff said.

'Hang on a minute.' Tess frowned. 'I didn't know anything about a staff meeting?'

'Didn't you? I sent all the Heads of Department an email about it this morning.' Mrs Frobisher's eyes glinted. 'Perhaps you accidentally deleted it? I know IT isn't your strong point.'

Cynthia accidentally hadn't sent it more like, Tess thought. She'd checked her mailbox at lunchtime and there was no sign of it then. 'I'm sure even I can spot an email, Cynthia. Why didn't you mention it when I saw you earlier?'

'Really, I don't have the time to go running around the school checking up on people! I'm overstretched as it is. But if you're too busy, I'm sure we can struggle along without you?'

I bet, thought Tess. She could make all kinds of decisions behind her back, then run off to Eric Gant and tell him Tess wasn't doing her job properly. Wouldn't she just love that?

She smiled sweetly. 'I wouldn't dream of it, Cynthia. Just let me make a quick call.'

She slipped outside and phoned Dan from her mobile, asking him to put the casserole in the oven. He assured her he was doing his homework, but from the So Solid Crew track blaring in the background, she was sure he couldn't have been doing it very well.

When she got back, everyone was waiting for her. 'Phoning home, were you?' Cynthia asked, as if she hadn't been listening to every word. 'Family commitments can be such a worry, can't they? Especially in your situation. It must be hard for you to keep your mind on the job sometimes.'

Her voice dripped sympathy, but her eyes fooled no one, least of all Tess. She knew Cynthia didn't think she was up to the job and was just waiting for her to make a mistake. Which only made her more determined not to. 'Everything's fine, thank you,' she said tautly. 'Shall we get on with the meeting?'

Cynthia shuffled her papers. 'Mr Gant and the governors have been setting budgets for the coming year. They've looked at the resources available and at the areas with the greatest need, and they've come up with the following allocations for each department.' She handed round sheets of paper. Everyone grabbed theirs and scanned it eagerly.

'Great.' Jeff looked pleased. 'I can get that new equipment I wanted. The other stuff's falling to bits.'

All around there were sighs of relief or groans of dismay as the staff saw how much they had to spend. Tess said nothing. She couldn't bring herself to speak.

Finally she found her voice. 'There must be some mistake. My budget's been cut by twenty per cent.'

'That's right. Is there a problem?' Cynthia Frobisher looked innocent.

'But I asked for more money.'

'I don't see why. When I was running the English department I managed perfectly well on the amount you've been given. Less, in fact.'

Yes, and you only had to look in the stock cupboard to see why. 'But I need the money for new resources. I wanted to update the library, and buy some new texts—'

'What's wrong with the ones you have?' Mrs Frobisher looked frosty.

'They're a bit old-fashioned.' Everyone drew in their breath, sensing confrontation. Cynthia Frobisher had run the English department with ruthless efficiency for ten years. She wouldn't tolerate criticism, especially not from an upstart like Tess Doyle.

But Tess wasn't about to be put off. She'd stood up to bullies like Cynthia before. 'I just think the pupils should be aware that there have been books written in the last hundred years.'

'*Modern* texts, you mean?' Cynthia Frobisher's lip curled as if she'd just suggested they study *The Beano* for A Level. 'I'd call that dumbing down.'

'I'd hardly call Seamus Heaney and J.D. Salinger dumbing down, would you?'

Everyone looked at Cynthia. Tess suspected part of the reason she'd never updated the English resources was because she was out of her depth with anything other than the classics she'd studied at college. She was deeply suspicious of Tess' ideas because she was afraid of them. But Tess didn't want to make her feel threatened. She just wanted to do her job properly. Unfortunately, Cynthia's tight hold on the purse strings made that very difficult.

'Well, I'm afraid you'll just have to make do with mere Shakespeare,' she said. 'There's no money available.'

'There's money available for a new food tech room. And Jeff's equipment.'

Jeff bridled. 'You leave my equipment out of this!'

'That's necessary expenditure.'

'And learning about their own language isn't necessary?'

'As long as they can sign their name on a dole cheque they'll probably be able to cope,' Jeff sneered.

Tess shot him a furious look. 'I thought we were supposed to be raising standards?' she said.

'Raising standards yes. But not performing miracles,' he said. 'Let's face it, these kids will never achieve much.'

'They won't if they've got people like you teaching them.'

'You think it's all our fault? Look at the kind of homes they come from.

Half their parents are in jail, the other half don't care what their kids get up to, as long as they're out of the house. Most of them are single parents living off the state—' He saw Tess' face and shut up. 'No offence,' he muttered.

'None taken,' Tess said. 'You can't help being a bigot.'

'There's nothing wrong with our GCSE English results,' Cynthia interrupted, silencing them both. 'They're perfectly competent.'

'There's more to life than GCSE results.' There was another indrawn breath from around the room. Not as far as Mrs Frobisher was concerned, there wasn't. She ruled her life by the school league tables. 'You do realise that once they've passed their exam most of these kids are never going to pick up a book again because we've put them off for life?'

'That's hardly our problem.' Mrs Frobisher closed her file with a snap. 'Anyway, as I've already said, there are no more resources available. So you'll just have to do the best with what you've got, won't you?' She smiled, seeing Tess' frustrated expression. 'You really mustn't take it so personally, Tess,' she said. 'You're still very inexperienced. You'll soon learn there are certain limitations to this job.'

Don't I know it, Tess thought. She sat in silence through the rest of the meeting, her eyes fixed on the wall calendar. Someone in IT had scanned Mrs Frobisher's head on to the busty body of a Page Three girl. For once it didn't make her laugh, not even when Cynthia tried to pretend she hadn't noticed it.

'Patronising cow,' she muttered, as they pulled on their coats to leave half an hour later.

'Try not to get too upset about it,' Helen said. 'All her meetings are like that.'

'I wish someone had told me that before I took this job,' Tess sighed. 'You'd think Cynthia would be encouraging the English department to do well, but I just get the feeling she wants me to fall flat on my face.'

'Of course she does. She wouldn't want you to make a better job of it than she did, would she?' Helen stared at her as if she was stupid. 'Besides, we all know she wanted her little pet Marjorie to get the job.'

'She would have been a disaster.'

'We all know that too. But at least Cynthia could have stayed in control. Marjorie would never have stood up to her the way you do.'

Tess took another pile of marking from her pigeonhole and stuffed it into her already bulging satchel. 'And there's me thinking I could make a difference.'

'At Haxsall Park?' Helen smiled. 'You've got more chance of having Mr Gant's love child.'

Tess zipped up her bag and hitched it over her shoulder. 'If I thought it might get me a few new textbooks, I might try it,' she said.

2

It felt strange, walking into the new house. Everything looked familiar, but it still wasn't home. Even the furniture didn't seem right against the freshly painted magnolia walls.

Jack looked around. Maybe it would seem more homely when there were books back on the shelves, pictures on the walls and felt-tip stains on the pristine carpet.

Sophie was on one of the sofas with her three small cousins, glued to Sky One. Emily was stretched out on the other, her legs dangling over the arm, composing a text message on her mobile phone. Neither of them looked up when he walked in.

'Feet off the furniture, please.' He tapped Emily's trainers. She grudgingly slid them on to the floor. 'Where's Auntie Ros?'

Sophie turned her eyes from *The Simpsons* for a second. 'In the kitchen, unpacking.'

Jack listened. From beyond the door came the crash of pots, with an undercurrent of muted swearing. 'You two could have given her a hand.'

'I've been busy,' Emily said.

'On that thing, I suppose? Don't tell me you've been on it since you came home?'

'I've got a lot to say, haven't I? I mean, it's not like I see Katy at school any more. Not since we moved to this boring dump.'

'Hardly a dump, Em.' Jack looked out of the window at the crescent of brand-new executive homes, surrounded by neat lawns and flower beds. Each had a gleaming Audi or BMW in the drive. He'd found out on their first weekend he was the only one who didn't turn out to wash his every Sunday morning.

'Still boring, though.'

Jack glanced at her. Her dark hair fell across her face as she bent over her phone. Somewhere under those baggy combats and stroppy manner she was turning into a real beauty. Soon she'd be fighting the boys off.

Another hurdle for him to look forward to. He felt as if he'd dealt with them all over the past nine months, from Emily's raging PMS to Sophie's embarrassing questions about exactly where babies came from.

He braced himself. 'Did you have a good day at school?'

'Okay,' Sophie said, turning her attention back to the TV. At seven years old, she was a lot easier to handle than her big sister. She couldn't have been more different to Emily. She was placid and sweet-faced, with a penchant for girly dresses and glitter. While Emily dressed like an off-duty commando, Sophie looked like she'd borrowed her wardrobe from backstage at a Shirley Bassey concert. But he knew it was only a matter of time before the hormone time bomb exploded. She'd already started eyeing up the bras in Tammy Girl.

'Boring,' Emily grumbled.

'Made any new friends yet?'

Emily sent him a scathing look. 'I don't want new friends. I liked my old ones.'

'Me too,' Sophie chimed in.

'You can still see them. Maybe you could invite them round, once we're more settled in?'

It was meant as a throwaway remark, but he might have known Emily would pick up on it. 'You mean like a party? Cool.'

'Hang on, I didn't mean—'

'Yeah, a party!' Sophie joined in excitedly. 'When can we have it? Can I have a new dress?'

Panic swept over him. 'We'll see.'

'You mean forget it.' Emily's shoulders slumped.

'I mean we'll see.' He hurried off to find Ros before Emily had a chance to nag him into doing something he might regret.

Ros was cross-legged on the floor, surrounded by kitchen paraphernalia. She was dressed for action in jeans and a T-shirt, her dark hair caught up in a bandanna.

'I can't believe you've been in this house three weeks and you still haven't got round to unpacking all this,' she said. 'Why did you have to bring all this stuff anyway? The only thing I've ever seen you use is the microwave. I mean, do you honestly know what to do with this?' She held up a complicated-looking piece of equipment.

'No idea. Miranda bought it.'

Ros put down the whatever-it-was. 'I'm sorry, Jack. I didn't think.'

'Silly, isn't it?' He looked around at the piles of boxes, each one clearly labelled 'Kitchen'. 'I move house to get away from the memories and end up bringing them all with me.'

'You'll always have them with you. Besides, you wouldn't want to forget her, would you?'

'No, but sometimes it hurts to remember.'

Ros got to her feet and came over to give him a hug. She might have been his big sister, but she barely came up to his shoulder.

'It'll get easier, bro,' she promised. 'It hasn't been that long, has it?'

'Nine months, three weeks and four days. Not that I'm counting.' He looked at the heap of pots and pans littering the worktops. 'You're right though. I don't need half this stuff. There's no room for it anyway.'

He hadn't realised how small this kitchen was compared to their old one. There was no room for the big pine table where they used to eat surrounded by the kids' school books, Miranda's paperwork and the Sunday supplements they never got round to reading. The work surface was spotless, unlike the old one, which bore the scars of when Jack had let a hot pan scorch it, and there was no greasy stain on the wall where Sophie had thrown her food from her high chair. She was a great aim, he recalled.

'I think the word you're looking for is compact.'

'And does that go for the garden, too?' Jack looked out of the window over the neat oblong of lawn.

'It's manageable.' Ros followed his gaze. 'Just right for you. You hate gardening, remember?'

'True. Miranda is – was – the green-fingered one.' He stared out at the featureless garden, veiled by rain. The old one would have been changing now, the leaves turning gold, the pyracanthus on fire with glowing amber and red berries. If he closed his eyes, he could almost hear Miranda making a fuss about raking up the endless piles of leaves while Sophie skipped in and out of them, spreading them around again.

'Have I done the right thing, coming here?' he said.

'You had your reasons.'

'Purely selfish ones.'

He'd tried to get over it; God knows, he'd spent the best part of a year trying. But he still couldn't bring himself to go on living in the house where they'd once been so happy. He couldn't face waking up in that same bed, that same room, without her every morning. Sitting down to eat in the kitchen, which had once been so full of life. Dozing off in front of *Newsnight* without her to tease him about getting old.

He'd only been back to the house a few times since Miranda died. The first was on the day of the funeral. It was a couple of days before Christmas and it had crucified him to see the brightly decorated Christmas tree, with everyone's presents wrapped and piled up underneath, as if she'd just nipped out to the shops.

He couldn't face going back after that. So when his mother had asked them to stay – 'just until you get back on your feet' – he'd accepted with gratitude. His mother had stepped in to Miranda's role, looking after the girls and taking care of the practical things while he nursed his grief. He could pretend he was a kid himself again, waking up in his old room every morning, listening to his dad grumbling at how there was never anything decent on telly every evening, and burying himself in his work to blot out the hours in between. But he knew it couldn't last.

In the end his mother had hinted that perhaps the time had come for him to start looking after himself and his family.

'Of course, your father and I love having you and the girls here, but I don't think it would be good for you to stay,' she'd said.

He could have remained there for ever, just functioning, never having to think again. But he had to accept she was right. He needed to start looking after the girls, taking responsibility.

And the first thing he did was put the house on the market and look for somewhere new.

He convinced himself he was doing it for the girls' sake. They'd be happier getting away from Leeds and making a fresh start. And the suburb of Haxsall, four miles out of York, seemed a good enough place. But he knew he wasn't fooling anyone. Least of all them.

'I've uprooted them from their school, their friends,' he said to Ros. 'Just because I'm too much of a coward to go back. It's probably the last thing they need. Especially Emily.'

'She'll survive. She's tough.'

'Is she?' He looked through the half-open door at the dark head, still bent over her phone. 'I'm worried about her.'

'It's you I'm worried about.' Ros was ever practical. 'Have you thought how you're going to manage? It's not as if you're just round the corner any more. Mum and I can't drop everything and turn up in five minutes whenever you need a babysitter.'

'Emily can babysit. She's old enough now.'

'But what about a childminder for Sophie? You need somewhere for her before and after school. Especially with you having such a long commute now.'

'I've got someone.' At least that was something in his chaotic personal life he'd managed to organise. 'She's just around the corner so I can drop Sophie off on the way to work.'

'And what about if you have to work late one night? Or if one of the girls is sick? What will you do then?'

'I don't know, do I? I'll cope somehow. I'm not the only person with kids in the world, you know. You've got three.'

'I know, but that's different. I'm used to it.'

'Are you saying I'm not?'

She sent him a sceptical look. 'Don't get me wrong, I think you're a great dad. But let's face it, Miranda did most of the childcare stuff.'

'I did my share.'

'I know you did. So does Greg, but he still has a panic attack if I threaten to leave him on his own with ours.'

'That's because they're all so tiny. I expect he's worried he'll lose them down the back of the sofa or something. Anyway, other people manage and so will I. I'll just have to be more organised. And if it all gets too much, I'll hire a housekeeper.'

'Ooh, get you, Mr Moneybags!' Ros rolled her eyes. 'Seriously, you might have to think about cutting back on your hours at work. You can't keep putting in twelve-hour days, housekeeper or no housekeeper.'

'I can see Humphrey Crawshaw going for that, can't you? Especially with the Westpoint project going on.'

'Not Westpoint again!' Ros groaned. 'It's all Greg goes on about at the moment.'

'I'm not surprised. If the Westpoint shopping mall gets planning permission, it will be worth a hell of a lot of money to Crawshaw and Finch.'

'I bet it won't do your partnership chances any harm either?'

'I take it Greg's been gossiping again?' Sometimes having a brother-in-law working for the same company had its drawbacks.

Ros looked innocent. 'He might have mentioned something. He says everyone's very impressed with your design.'

'Maybe.' Jack delved into the nearest box and pulled out a wooden spoon. 'Where shall I put this?'

Ros grinned. 'Don't tempt me!'

They unpacked for a while, filling drawers and cupboards with things Jack had no idea how to use, and probably never would. Then Ros said, 'You know what you really need?'

Jack blew the dust off a chipmunk-shaped biscuit barrel. 'A skip?'

'A woman.'

'Bloody hell, Ros, not again! I thought you were supposed to be a feminist.'

'I don't just mean to cook and clean. I mean for you. You need someone.'

'No, I don't. I've told you before, I'm a one-woman man. Anyway,' he went on briskly, 'I can just imagine what the girls would have to say about that!'

'They'd get used to the idea. You shouldn't be alone, Jack. It's not right. And Miranda wouldn't have wanted it.'

'Maybe not.' But that didn't mean he wanted it either. He tried to visualise another woman in the house, cooking in the kitchen with Miranda's pots and pans, curling up beside him on the sofa, sharing his bed . . .

His mind shrank away from the picture. No, he couldn't do it. No matter how much he told himself to look to the future, he knew another woman would never be part of it.

'I'm fine the way I am,' he said. 'Anyway, you don't have to worry about me, Ros. The girls and I will be okay.'

'Are you sure about that?'

'Of course. You'll see, in six months' time I'll have it all under control. The girls will be settled, I'll be a partner and – I'll have mastered every gadget in this kitchen.'

'Yeah, right!'

'I'm serious.' He looked around. 'I could be the next Jamie Oliver if I put my mind to it.'

Ros folded her arms and confronted him across the kitchen. 'Okay, Jamie, what are you cooking us all for supper then?'

'I don't know about you, but I really fancy fish and chips . . .'

3

'I'm home!' Tess dumped her bag and umbrella in the hall. 'Dan?'

There was no sign of him. She sniffed the air. No sign of that casserole either.

She went into the kitchen and touched the oven door. It was stone cold. And there was the casserole dish, sitting on the worktop where she'd left it that morning.

'Daniel Doyle!'

He was in his room, hunched over his computer with his back to her, a pair of headphones clamped to his dark-blond head. Tess crept up and clapped her hand on his shoulder. He yelped with shock.

'Jesus! Mum!' He hit a key, blacking out the screen. 'Oh no, the casserole!'

'Don't bother,' said Tess as he made a move. 'We'll be eating at midnight if you put it in now. Honestly, Dan, couldn't you just do one simple thing?'

'Sorry, Mum. I was going to do it but I sort of got carried away.' He glanced back at the computer screen.

'So I see. I hope it was homework?'

'I finished that ages ago. This was – um – research.' He looked shifty enough for Tess to be suspicious.

'Dan, I hope you weren't hacking into the college files and changing your grades again? You know what they said last time—'

'Calm down, of course I wasn't. I'm not that stupid.'

No, you're not, Tess thought. That was what worried her. When it came to computers Dan was frighteningly bright. She, on the other hand, could barely set the video. It troubled her to think what he could be up to and she wouldn't have a clue.

Fortunately for her, he was pretty sensible about it, although he did get carried away at times. What worried her more was the amount of time he spent glued to the screen. He had the excuse that he was studying computer science at sixth form college, but it was still an obsession with him.

She sighed. 'I suppose it's a takeaway again, is it?'

'I'll fetch it.'

'No thanks. I know what you're like. If you get on those arcade games at the chippie, I'll never get my supper.' She headed for the kitchen to pick up her car keys. Dan followed. He was using his wheelchair tonight. He preferred his sticks to get around college because they made him feel less conspicuous, but they tired him out after a few hours.

'Anything you want me to do?'

'You could put the kettle on. I'll have a cup of tea before I go out again.'

She stood aside as he wheeled past her to pick up the kettle, then headed for the sink. Tess automatically leaned over and turned the tap on for him. 'Mum!' Dan batted her out of the way. 'For heaven's sake, I can fill a kettle you know!'

'Sorry.' Tess watched, humbled, as he flicked the switch. 'Did you have a good day?'

'Not bad. Mostly revision. We've got a test on Friday.' He reached across to unhook the mugs from the mug tree. Tess forced herself not to do it for him, knowing how much he hated to be fussed over. Typical Dan, fiercely independent as always. He might have inherited his father's fair-haired looks, but he had her fighting spirit.

And God knows they'd both needed it. She'd been barely more than a child herself when Dan was first diagnosed with Spinal Muscular Atrophy. Luckily it was the mildest form and not life-threatening, but it still felt like the end of the world, knowing her precious baby would never walk or run or play football like the other boys, that his muscles would gradually give up, waste away, become useless.

At first she'd cried her heart out, but then she'd realised her tears were out of self-pity, and that she was doing Dan no favours by feeling sorry for herself. In spite of her own terror of what lay ahead, she owed it to him to give him the most normal life she could. But it turned out to be a hard struggle. Tess had never considered herself a loud or difficult person, but she soon found making a nuisance of herself was the only way to get things done. That, and refusing to take no for an answer. Before she even knew what was wrong, she'd practically camped outside her GP's surgery until he stopped dismissing her as a neurotic mother and finally referred Dan to hospital. Later, when he was older, she'd had a similar battle with the education authorities when they said the local school wasn't equipped to cope with her son's special needs. She'd written letters to councillors, organised petitions and finally even helped raise the money herself to put in the necessary ramps and disabled toilets.

She'd also encouraged Dan to join in with the other kids where he could. He'd gone to parties, sleepovers, on school outings. And when occasionally some mindless idiot teased or bullied him, Tess had been right in there too, sleeves rolled up, fighting back.

Sometimes she felt as if she'd spent most of her life fighting. She could cope with that, but it was other people's prejudice, their ignorance and stupidity she found hardest to deal with. Those who assumed that because Dan was in a wheelchair he was somehow mentally subnormal. Others who spoke to her as if he couldn't answer for himself, or didn't look at him at all because they were too embarrassed. That was what made her mad these days. Why couldn't they see beyond the chair and realise what a confident, intelligent young man he was? If a little forgetful at times.

'There you go.' He put the mug down in front of her. 'What are you staring at?'

'You. I was just thinking how brilliant you are.'

'Mum!' The tips of his ears glowed fiery red with embarrassment. 'Just for making a cup of tea? Blimey, I'd hate to see you when I'm Head of Microsoft!'

It being Friday night, there was a queue at the chippie. The rain dripped off her short dark hair as she huddled inside her fleece, breathing in the glorious aroma of frying chips and vinegar and trying not to think about how starving she was.

There was the usual gang hanging around the arcade games. Tess recognised a few faces from Haxsall Park Comp, looking intimidating in their tracksuits and baseball caps. Not that she felt remotely threatened by them. They sent her uneasy looks, silently pleading with her not to acknowledge them in front of the older kids. It made her smile to think a word or a wave from her could destroy their street cred for ever.

Then she spotted Emily Tyler, hanging around the doorway. She looked different too, but just as awkward and leggy in baggy combat trousers and an oversized sweatshirt. For a moment Tess thought she might be with Leanne and Jordan, but then she noticed her father in the queue behind her. Now what was his name? John? James?

Jack. His name popped into her head a second before he saw her and smiled.

'It's Miss Doyle, isn't it?'

'Mr Tyler.' She slipped back in the queue to talk to him. 'How's the new house?'

'Chaos, I'm afraid. My sister's unearthing pots and pans as we speak. Hence the takeaway.'

'I don't have such a good excuse. My son just forgot to put the supper in the oven.'

'Your son?' His eyes flicked to her ringless left hand.

Tess changed the subject. 'How's Emily finding life at Haxsall Park?'

'I was just about to ask you the same question. Actually, I've been meaning to come in and see you, but what with the house move and work being so hectic I haven't had time.' He lowered his voice. 'I wondered if there were any problems I should know about?'

'Not that I'm aware of. I spoke to her today and she seemed okay. Why? Has she said anything to you?'

He shook his head. 'That's just it. She never tells me anything.'

'Typical fourteen-year-old. About as communicative as the Dead Sea Scrolls.' Tess grinned. 'Still, I don't think there's anything to worry about. She seems fine.' She didn't tell him about Leanne and Jordan. Hopefully that friendship would soon blow over once Emily found her feet.

'I'm glad to hear it.' He looked relieved. 'It's such a worry looking after Emily and her sister by myself.'

'Don't they have any contact with their mother?'

His smile disappeared. 'She died just before Christmas.'

'Oh, I'm sorry. I had no idea.' What an idiot, assuming he was a divorcee. Just because he didn't look old enough to be a widower. She should have known better, especially as she hated anyone jumping to conclusions about her and Dan.

Jack carried on. 'It's affected both of them badly, as you can imagine. Especially Emily. And then with the house move – it's been a lot for her to take in recently.'

'Of course.' And it wasn't just Emily and her sister who'd been affected by the last few months, she guessed. There were lines of strain around Jack Tyler's dark grey eyes that she was willing to bet hadn't been there a year ago.

Tess reached the front of the queue and gave her order. As the woman behind the counter wrapped up her fish and chips, she turned to Jack. 'Try not to worry too much,' she said. 'Children are more adaptable than we give them credit for. I'm sure Emily will bounce back.'

He didn't return her smile. 'I wish I had your confidence,' he said.

Dan had warmed the plates and poured her a glass of wine when she got home. Tess put it down to him still feeling guilty about not putting the casserole in the oven.

Until they were sitting in front of *EastEnders*, their plates perched on their knees, when he suddenly said, 'Do you ever think about my dad?'

Tess took a hasty slug of wine to drown the chunk of haddock she'd just swallowed whole. 'Not often. Do you?'

'Sometimes.' He stared at the screen. Phil Mitchell was flinging a punter out of the Queen Vic. 'Don't suppose he ever thinks about me, though,' he said wistfully.

No, I don't suppose he does. Tess remembered the letters and photos that went unanswered until she gave up sending them. Phil had shown no interest in Dan before or after he was born, and probably hadn't given either of them a second thought since. 'What's brought all this on?'

'Nothing. I just wondered, that's all.' Dan kept his eyes fixed on the screen where Ian was having a row with Auntie Pauline. 'So you've no idea where he might be now?'

'The last I heard he went to university in London. Why? Are you going to look him up?'

She was joking when she said it. But a quick look at Dan's face told her he wasn't. 'I was thinking about it.'

She reached for the remote control and hit the mute button. Suddenly the goings-on in Albert Square seemed unimportant. 'You've never mentioned it before.'

'I'm mentioning it now.' He looked defensive. 'I'm just curious, that's all. I've never met the man who was responsible for me being here.'

Responsible is hardly the word I'd use, Tess felt like saying. But she forced herself to stay quiet.

Dan glanced at her worriedly. 'You wouldn't mind, would you? I mean, you've always said if I wanted to find him you'd be okay about it.'

'Of course.' She toyed with her chips, which had suddenly lost their appeal. Talk about a shock! She'd always tried to be as open as possible with Dan about his father and the circumstances surrounding his birth. She'd also told him that if he ever wanted to trace him she wouldn't stand in his way. But saying something and meaning it were very different. And now it came down to it she realised she did mind. Very much.

'I shouldn't think he'd be that easy to track down,' she said. 'I know his parents moved away from here years ago. I don't have any other contacts for him.'

'There are loads of places I could look on the internet. It wouldn't be too difficult to find him.'

Of course. She might have known that wretched computer would come up with the answer. She stood up, gathering up their plates. 'Have you finished? I'd better get on with the washing up.'

Out in the kitchen, she plunged her hands into the hot soapy water and tried to get her thoughts together. She knew she was wrong to feel so angry, but she couldn't help it. Of course Dan had a right to know his father; it was naïve of her to imagine he wouldn't want to.

But at the same time, she couldn't help feeling it was deeply unfair. She was the one who'd taken care of Dan for seventeen extremely tough years. She was the one who'd struggled, made all the sacrifices. And now, out of nowhere, Dan had suddenly decided he wanted his dad.

Not that Phil had any right to claim that title. Not after the way he'd treated them.

He was her first serious boyfriend and she'd got pregnant the first time she slept with him. Looking back on it, she couldn't believe she'd been so stupid. If any of the girls in her Year 11 class had done that she would have been horrified. Although the girls in Year 11 were a lot more sophisticated than she was in those days.

But she'd had to grow up very quickly when the pregnancy test came back positive. After a sleepless night trying to get over the shock, the first person she'd told was Phil. His response wasn't exactly encouraging. While Tess was desperately anxious about her future, he was more worried about what his parents would say.

Even worse was telling her own mother. She didn't think she'd ever forget the disappointment on Margaret Doyle's face when she tearfully broke the news. Tess wished she would scream and shout, or even hit her. It would have hurt less.

Her mother was a strong, no-nonsense woman who'd brought up her two daughters on her own after their father died. She'd struggled to do her best for her girls, working long hours to provide for them. Her only wish was that they would grow up and make her proud.

She certainly wasn't proud of what Tess had done.

'And what does he have to say about it?' she'd asked.

'He said he'll marry me.' Tess sniffed back the tears, hoping it was the right thing to say.

'Very big of him, I'm sure.' She looked hard at Tess. 'Do you want to keep this baby?'

'I don't know.'

Margaret considered this. 'Right,' she said briskly. 'I think we should get this sorted out, don't you?'

She'd summoned a cowering Phil and his furious parents for a conference. One look at Daphne Purcell, hatchet-faced in a Country Casuals two-piece, and Tess had realised why he was so terrified of telling her. She was obviously the dominant one in the family and looked like she'd decided to dominate Tess and her mother too.

'You can forget about this ridiculous marriage idea for a start,' she'd said. 'You're both far too young.'

'If they're old enough to get themselves into trouble, they're old enough to take responsibility for it,' Margaret said.

Daphne looked her up and down, taking in the lined, unmade-up face, the threads of grey in her messy brown curls, the workworn hands that had never seen the inside of a manicurist's salon. In her eyes there was no doubt who was in control. 'That depends on what you mean by taking responsibility, doesn't it? Of course we're prepared to help. But I don't see why my son's life should be ruined over one mistake.'

'And what about my daughter's life? She's the one carrying this baby.'

'My Philip has a promising future ahead of him,' Daphne continued, ignoring her. 'He has a place at university and I'm not letting him throw all that away. He's very bright.'

'Not bright enough to take precautions, is he?'

'Neither is your daughter, apparently. Although it would hardly surprise me if she did this deliberately,' she muttered.

Margaret Doyle's face was expressionless. 'What's that supposed to mean?'

'Daphne, I really don't think—' Phil's father tried to interrupt, but his wife swatted him away like a troublesome fly.

'It stands to reason, doesn't it? My Philip would be a good catch for someone like your daughter.' Daphne looked around at the small but tidy council flat, her nose wrinkling. It hardly measured up to the Purcells' rambling Victorian pile on Fox Lane.

Tess saw her mother shift in her seat and for a terrible moment she thought she was going to knock Daphne out cold. Daphne must have seen the fighting glint in her eye too because she quickly said, 'But blaming each other isn't getting us anywhere. We need to decide what we're going to do about this mess. As I said, we're prepared to shoulder some responsibility. Meet some of the costs and so on.'

Margaret settled back in her chair. 'I'm glad to hear it.' But something in Mrs Purcell's face told Tess she wasn't talking about buying a pram.

'Now I'm sure you're as keen as we are to get this thing over and done with, so I've been making a few enquiries about clinics. Private, of course. We don't want to have to rely on the dreadful NHS for something as delicate as this—'

Tess watched her mother's expression change. 'You mean you want her to have an abortion?' she said slowly.

'Of course. Surely that's the only sensible option?' Daphne Purcell blinked.

'Sensible for you, you mean.'

'For everyone. You've said yourself we don't want our children's lives blighted by one mistake.'

Tess sat helplessly in the middle, watching them square up to each other. She looked at Phil, silently pleading with him to say something, but he wouldn't even meet her eye. He just stared at the floor like a ten-year-old who'd been caught with his hand in the biscuit tin.

Phil's father made another stab at joining in. 'Please, if we could just—'

'Shut up, Norman!' Daphne turned back to Margaret. 'You're not suggesting she should bring this unwanted child into the world?'

'Your son's child. And if he was half the man he pretends to be, he'd be taking care of my daughter instead of letting his mother fight his battles—'

'Will you both just shut up!' Margaret and Daphne turned to stare at Tess, who was on her feet between them. Phil was bug-eyed with terror.

She looked around, surprised at the silence. 'This is me we're talking about. When do I get a say in all this?' She took a steadying breath. 'Right. First of all, I've got no intention of marrying Phil. Not because I don't want to ruin his future, but because I don't want to ruin my own.'

Daphne looked pleased. 'Very sensible. Now, what I thought was—'

'But I'm going to keep the baby,' Tess went on in a rush. 'It's my baby. And I want it.' She hadn't realised how much until she'd heard them talking about getting rid of it.

She glanced at Phil. He looked as if he was about to throw up with fear.

'I see. Well, in that case—' When Daphne reached into her bag Tess thought she was going to pull out a tissue and start crying, but instead she took out a leatherbound cheque book and gold pen. They all watched in fascinated silence as she scribbled a signature on the cheque, tore it out and handed it to Tess.

'What's this?'

'What does it look like? It's a cheque, for you and the – child.' Her face was pinched with disapproval. 'It should be enough to safeguard your future. On the strict understanding that Philip doesn't have to be involved. There will be no further communication, no more demands on my son. Is that understood?'

Tess didn't reply. She stared down at the cheque, her mind boggling at all the noughts in front of her. She'd never seen such a large amount.

She turned to Phil. 'Is that what you want?' He didn't answer, just gazed out of the window, a faraway look in his eyes, as if he just wanted to jump through it and run away.

'Of course it's what he wants,' his mother snapped.

'Fine.' Tess looked at the cheque for another moment, enjoying the brief feeling of having that much money in her hands. Then slowly, deliberately, she tore it up. 'If that's the way you feel, I don't need you or your money. Don't look so worried, I'm not going to be pestering your precious son. I don't want my baby growing up with a pathetic wimp for a father anyway!'

That had made Phil look at her. But by then it was too late. This time it was Tess who turned her back on him.

Her mother didn't say a word after they'd gone. She picked up the empty cups and carried them through to the kitchen in silence. Tess followed her, hardly daring to speak. Finally she steeled herself and said, 'Say something, for heaven's sake. Even if it's only, "Never darken my door again."'

'Doesn't seem like there's much to say, does it? You've already made your mind up.' She pursed her lips. 'That was a lot of money you threw away in there.'

Tess stared down at her hands miserably. 'I know.'

'It's no fun you know, bringing a child up on your own. Especially with nothing coming in.'

'I could get a job—'

'At sixteen? What kind of job do you think you'd get? You'd end up like me, no qualifications and having to take anything that's going just to make ends meet.'

Tess stared at the cracked lino on the kitchen floor. Her mother was right. She'd ruined her life and condemned herself and her baby to a lifetime of poverty, all because of one stupid, defiant act of pride.

There was a long silence. Her mother washed the cups, set them on the draining board, and reached for the towel to dry her hands. 'You did the right thing,' she said at last.

Tess felt hot, stupid tears of gratitude welling up in her eyes. 'But the money—'

'We don't need them, or their money. We'll get by. Heaven knows, I managed with you and your sister after your dad died.' She wagged her finger at Tess. 'But I meant what I said, you're not getting any dead-end job. You're going back to school to get yourself some proper qualifications. Baby or no baby, I want you to make something of yourself.' She smiled grimly. 'You were right about that lad being a spineless wimp. A man who can't stand up to his own mother is no use to you.' She gave Tess' hand a brief, reassuring pat. 'We'll manage, lass. Don't you worry.'

And they did. After Dan was born, her mother gave up her job in the local newsagents' to look after him while Tess went back to school. She took on a couple of evening cleaning jobs to bring in some money, while Tess found a Saturday job stacking shelves in the supermarket. Her older sister Frances chipped in too, once she'd left college and found a job as a secretary. Between them they took turns to work and look after the baby.

It was hard, and the months seemed to pass in a blur of exhaustion, but they got by. Tess never regretted her decision, or asked for sympathy, even when she was weeping over her A Level revision and having to cope with a screaming, teething baby who'd forgotten how to sleep.

She made herself promise not to contact Phil. But at the hospital, after Dan was born, she wrote to him in a weepy fit after seeing all the other new dads proudly holding their babies. She told herself he had a right to know he had a son, but deep down all she really wanted was to be like the other new mums, being fussed over by their partners. She'd never felt so lonely in her life.

She sent the letter to his parents as she didn't know where Phil was living in London. It went unanswered. She convinced herself they hadn't passed it on. Anything rather than admit the truth – that he didn't care.

She wrote again when Dan was two years old, after he was diagnosed with SMA. She kept it very businesslike, saying Phil had to know he was a carrier of the gene, just in case he ever wanted more children. His wife or girlfriend would have to be tested too, to make sure she wasn't a carrier, otherwise there was a good chance their baby could be born with it. What she didn't say was that she felt alone and frightened. She was only nineteen, she'd just started at teacher training college and finding she had a sick son who would need care for the rest of his life was all too much for her to cope with alone.

But still there was no reply. That was when it finally dawned on her that Phil really didn't care.

And now this. No matter how many times she told herself Dan had a right to know his own father, it still hurt. It wasn't as if he'd ever shown any curiosity before. They hardly ever talked about Phil, for heaven's sake. So why now, out of the blue?

Dan came in as she was finishing the washing up. She sensed him watching her from the doorway. 'Are you okay, Mum?'

'Of course.' She dredged up a smile. 'Why shouldn't I be?'

'It's just you've been washing that mug for five minutes. You'll scrub the pattern off if you're not careful.' He hesitated. 'I don't have to get in touch with him, you know. Not if it's going to upset you.'

Tess looked over her shoulder at him. It dawned on her how much he was beginning to look like Phil, with his unruly dark-blond hair and grey-green eyes. But she was the only one who knew that. Dan had never even seen a photo of his father. It wasn't fair to deprive him of such a large part of his past.

'I'm just being silly. Of course you've got a right to find him. I just didn't realise it was important to you, that's all.'

'I've been thinking about him quite a bit lately. He was about my age when you last saw him, wasn't he?'

Tess froze. She'd never thought about it before but Dan was exactly the same age Phil was when she got pregnant. She hadn't realised quite how young they were. No wonder his mother had been so protective of him.

And now it was her turn to be protective. Dan might be seventeen years old, but he was still her baby. She only hoped his search for his father wouldn't end up hurting him.

4

Emily held the cigarette between shaking fingers and inhaled deeply. At first nothing happened, then suddenly a whoosh of hot, acrid smoke filled her mouth, her throat, her lungs. She felt as if she was drowning in burning tar. Gasping, she dropped the cigarette and fell back against the wall, coughing and choking, her eyes streaming.

'Muppet!' Leanne picked up the cigarette as it rolled towards the gutter. 'You've never tried it before, have you?'

'Bet that's not the only thing she hasn't tried!' one of the boys leered. Through a blur of watering eyes Emily caught their jeering expressions as they surrounded her.

She forced herself to laugh with them. These were supposed to be her friends, she reminded herself.

Luckily the boys lost interest and started kicking an empty can around the pot-holed playground. Leanne and Jordan sat on the wall, sharing a Silk Cut and pretending not to watch them. Emily sat and listened to them discussing last night's *Hollyoaks*, her mind elsewhere.

God, she was bored. All they ever talked about was who fancied who and who'd just been dumped by whom. If it wasn't boys, it was clothes and make-up. Emily reckoned Leanne and Jordan must know the entire contents of Miss Selfridge by heart. They'd seemed cool at first, and she was flattered when they singled her out on her first day to be their friend, but now she was beginning to wonder if they had a single brain cell between them.

She thought about her best friend Katy and the others and what they'd be doing back at her old school in Leeds, and felt sick with longing. She really missed them all, especially Katy. They texted each other all the time, but it wasn't the same. Her old school was beginning to feel like a distant memory. Just like her old life.

The bell rang and they made their way slowly across the playground. Autumn had come rushing in with a vengeance after a few mild days. The cold wind stripped the leaves off the solitary beech tree in the playground and whipped at her new blazer. She hated her pristine uniform. It screamed 'new girl'.

She hated the new house, too. Sophie had felt the same at first but now she seemed to be getting used to it. She'd made friends at her school, and her new bedroom was bigger than the boxroom she used to have at the old house, with plenty of space for all her rubbish. She had an adoring childminder after school who bought her sweets and allowed her to watch endless TV. They even had a woman who did the cleaning so her dad wasn't so stressed all the time. Everyone seemed happier, more settled. Except her. She felt like the odd one out all round.

It was Chemistry first lesson. Emily would have liked to get straight to class, but she made herself loiter with Leanne and Jordan in the cloakroom while they faffed around putting on lipgloss. Everyone else had gone apart from Paris Malone.

She was a strange girl. Always on her own, never speaking to anyone. She didn't even make the effort to look like the other girls. Her sweatshirt had faded from red to deep pink with too much washing, and her skirt was too short. So was everyone else's, but from the way Paris kept pulling hers down over her knees Emily was sure it wasn't deliberate. Her fair hair was held back in a straggly ponytail, and her glasses slipped down her nose as she packed her books into her shabby holdall.

The door to her locker was open and Emily glimpsed a flyer for an animal rights rally in Leeds pasted inside. She'd longed to go but her dad had insisted she was too young. She tried to catch Paris' eye to ask her about it but Leanne called her over to ask if she could borrow her hairbrush.

'You don't want to have anything to do with her,' she said loudly, running the brush through her streaked blonde hair. 'Everyone knows her mum's a right slag.'

Emily saw Paris' shoulders stiffen and waited for her to retaliate but she didn't. She went on sorting out her books, not looking up.

As Emily put the brush back into her bag, Mr Bunny stuck his balding head out of the side pocket. She made a grab for him but Jordan got there first.

'What's this?' She held it up by its tatty ear. 'See this, Lee? Emily's brought her ickle toy to school!'

'Give me that!' Emily snatched it out of her hand.

'Ooh, get her!' Leanne rolled her eyes. 'Wassamatter, worried we're going to pinch your ickle bunny wunny then?'

'Are you girls going to spend all day in here or what?' Fortunately Miss Doyle appeared in the doorway of the cloakroom, arms folded. She wasn't very tall but she was quite fierce when she wanted to be. 'Get a move on, you lot!'

Emily stuffed Mr Bunny into her bag and closed the zip. She felt silly, bringing him with her. Her mother had bought him when she was a baby. For years he'd gathered dust under her bed with all her other cuddly toys. But over the past few months he'd crept back on to her pillow. Emily didn't know why but she liked having him with her.

In Chemistry, Mr Kramer set them to doing an experiment to filter copper sulphate from sand. Emily had already done it in her old school, so she let Leanne and Jordan take charge and set up the experiment while she took notes. But her eyes kept straying to the far side of the classroom, where Paris was working on her own. Emily felt sorry for her, but sort of envied her too. At least she didn't have to listen to Leanne's non-stop commentary on the make-up habits of the rich and famous.

'. . . So I just thought it was a really good lipgloss, but my mum reckons no lipgloss is that bloody good and of course she's had the fat sucked out of her bum and put in her lips. Which is a bit gross, but if it makes you look as good as Liz Hurley – oh shit, when was I supposed to put the water in?'

But Emily wasn't listening. She was too transfixed by what was going on on the other side of the lab.

Jordan was heading across the room. It looked as if she was on her way to put something in the bin, but Emily could see her veering towards the bench where Paris was working. Paris was too busy writing up her notes to notice Jordan's silent approach, but as Emily watched in horror, she casually but deliberately nudged the test tube. It smashed to the floor, splashing its contents everywhere.

Paris swung round and Emily held her breath, just as Mr Kramer descended on them, his white coat flapping. 'What's going on?' he demanded.

Tell him, Emily willed silently. 'Don't know, Sir,' Paris muttered. 'Must have been an accident.'

'Clumsy girl! Don't just stand there. Get it cleaned up.'

'Yes, Sir.' As she trudged off to fetch a cloth, Emily saw Leanne and Jordan exchange knowing smiles.

'Serves her right for being such a swot!' Leanne sneered.

Outrage burned inside Emily until she felt as if the roots of her hair were going to burst into flames. She wanted to lash out at Leanne and wipe the grin off her smug little face. Before she knew what she was doing, she was out of her seat and heading across the room to where Paris was on her hands and knees.

Paris looked up, and Emily caught a flash of apprehension in her eyes, quickly masked by defiance. Emily got down on her knees beside her and began picking up the shards of glass.

Neither of them spoke. Paris wrapped up the pieces of glass and put them in the bin, while Emily fetched a cloth and mopped up the spilled water. She felt ashamed, even though it wasn't her fault. She wanted to say something but Paris didn't meet her eye. She didn't even thank her for her help, just gathered up her books at the end of the lesson and hurried off.

'See?' Leanne whispered, as they left the lab. 'Pig ignorant.'

But Emily was determined, and in the cafeteria at lunchtime she deliberately avoided the place at the table Leanne and Jordan had saved for her, and headed over to the corner where Paris sat alone, her nose buried in a book.

'Is this seat free?' She put her tray down without waiting for an answer.

Paris glanced up. 'I wouldn't sit there if I were you. Your mates won't like it.'

'I don't care.' Emily shot a defiant look over her shoulder. Leanne and Jordan were watching her. 'I can do what I like, can't I?'

'Please yourself.' Paris went back to her book. 'But don't blame me.'

A few minutes later, Emily began to wonder if she'd made the right decision. She'd expected Paris to be grateful, not ignore her.

'What are you reading?'

'*Of Mice and Men.*'

'Um – good, is it?'

'S'okay. Not his best.'

Meanwhile, Jordan and Leanne were sending her black looks from the other side of the cafeteria.

In the end she put down her knife and fork and said, 'Look, if you'd rather I sat somewhere else, you only have to say.'

'I'm doing it for your own good. Believe me, you really don't want those two giving you a hard time.'

'I told you, I don't care. I can look after myself.'

'Ooh, hard case.' Emily noticed the glimmer of a smile.

Encouraged, she said, 'So why don't they like you?'

Paris put down her book and pretended to consider the question. 'It could be that they feel threatened by my intellectual superiority. But I think it's probably because my mum is a slapper and we live on the council estate. I expect that lot have filled you in on all the gory details already? Thought so,' she said, as Emily blushed. 'They never miss a chance.'

'They're hateful.'

'That's no way to talk about your best friends.'

'They're not my friends.'

'You seem pally enough. Anyway, you should consider yourself lucky. You've seen what they're like if they don't like someone.'

'Why don't you fight back?'

'What's the point? It's not going to change anything. Better to just ignore them and hope they get bored.' Close up she was very pretty, prettier than Leanne and Jordan, although she looked as if she was doing her best to hide it, with her shapeless clothes and hair drawn back off her face.

Emily looked around her. 'I hate this place.'

'Join the club.' Paris looked at her over the edge of her book. 'What was your last school like?'

'Better than this dump. If I'd had my way, I would have stayed there.'

'But your parents wanted to move, right?'

'My dad did. My mum's dead.'

'Oh.' Paris was silent for a moment. 'When did that happen?'

'Last year.'

'She wasn't very old, then?'

'Thirty-six.' Emily squirmed in her seat, hoping Paris wouldn't ask any more. She couldn't trust herself to talk about it.

Luckily, she changed the subject. 'It's tough, changing schools. I should know. This is my third since I was eleven.'

'Are you serious?' Emily stared at her. 'Why?'

Paris shrugged. 'We move around a lot. My mum has trouble settling down. Actually, what she really has trouble with is paying the rent. That's why we keep being evicted.' She smiled. She had a nice smile.

'And your dad doesn't live with you?'

'Hardly! I don't even know who he is. I don't think my mum does, either. She says she was drunk at the time.'

Emily stared at her. 'You're not serious?'

'Would I joke about something like that? She says I was called Paris because that's where I was conceived, but since she's never had a passport I don't think that's true somehow. Still, I suppose it's better than being christened Rowntree Park, isn't it?'

Emily giggled. 'You're lucky it didn't happen in a pub, or you might have been called Queen Victoria!'

They were still laughing when Leanne whisked past their table and knocked Paris' drink all over her lunch.

'Oops, silly me,' she trilled. 'I am clumsy, aren't I?'

Emily shot to her feet, but Paris held on to her. 'Leave her. She's not worth it.'

'You're not going to let her get away with it, are you?' Emily seethed, as Leanne sauntered back to her table.

'Like I said, it's better just to stay out of their way.'

'We'll see about that.' Before Paris could stop her, Emily made her way over to the table where Leanne and Jordan were sitting. As she brushed past the table, she nudged a bowl of chocolate ice cream into Leanne's lap.

'Oops, silly me,' she smiled sweetly. 'I am clumsy, aren't I?'

'You shouldn't have done that,' Paris whispered, as Leanne stalked off to the loos, followed by Jordan.

'Why not? She deserved it.'

'I know.' Paris glanced apprehensively over her shoulder. 'But I think you've just started World War Three.'

5

'What do you mean, you've found him?'

It was just before eight in the morning and Tess was on her hands and knees searching through the cupboard for her shoes when Dan broke the news. She emerged, shoe in one hand, half a slice of toast in the other. 'How could you have found him already? You've only been looking a week!'

Dan looked sheepish. 'Actually, I'd sort of been looking for a while before I said anything to you.'

'I see.' So that explained all those late-night computer sessions. And she thought he'd been doing something innocent, like downloading porn. 'Why didn't you tell me?'

'I didn't want you to go mad.'

'Why should I go mad?'

'I don't know, but you're going a bit mad now.'

'I am not!'

'So why are you wearing odd shoes?' Tess looked down. In her agitation, she'd put on one black slingback and one brown one.

'The light's bad. We really need a new bulb in there.' She took off the brown shoe and threw it to the back of the cupboard.

'Anyway, I didn't think I'd find him so quickly,' Dan went on. 'But it turns out he wasn't that difficult to track down.'

Tess found the missing black shoe, stuffed the rest of her toast in her mouth and pulled it on while she took it all in. She was still in a state of shock. She thought she'd have time to get used to the idea of Dan tracing Phil. She actually hoped maybe he wouldn't be able to find him. But she'd reckoned without her son's determination and detective powers.

'How do you know you've got the right person? There must be hundreds of Philip Purcells in the country. Thousands, even—'

'Maybe. But the date and place of birth are the same. That would be too much of a coincidence, wouldn't it?' He paused, watching her. 'Don't you want to know where he is?'

Not really, Tess thought. She'd lived without knowing for seventeen

686

years, her curiosity was unlikely to get the better of her now. But then she saw Dan's eager face. 'Go on, then. Where is he?' Too much to hope he was in jail.

'Down south. Near Basingstoke.'

Thank God for that. She was worried he'd turn out to be living in the next street. Although she hated herself for it, she couldn't help asking, 'Is he – um – married or anything?'

'Dunno. I've just got a name and address.'

Tess thought about it for a moment. 'So what happens now?' she asked.

'I'd really like to get in touch – if that's all right with you?'

She dodged the question. 'You're just going to ring him up? Out of the blue?'

'I thought about writing to him. It might be less of a shock that way.'

She nodded. Of course. Trust Dan to think of the careful, considered approach. If it was left to her, she would have jumped straight in there with both feet and probably ruined everything.

A thought occurred to her. 'Do you – er – want me to do it?'

'Do you want to?'

Absolutely not. As far as she was concerned, the swine didn't even deserve a Christmas card. But this wasn't about her, it was about Dan. 'If you think it will help.'

He must have seen the reluctance on her face. 'It's okay, Mum. I'd prefer to do it, if you don't mind?'

She nodded. Whoever wrote that letter, it would still be a hell of a thunderbolt for Phil. She wouldn't have minded being a fly on the wall when he opened it.

But what if he didn't open it? What if he ignored it, just like he had the letters she'd sent him all those years ago? After seventeen years of pretending his son didn't exist, she couldn't imagine him suddenly rushing forward to claim him. He'd probably got married, had a family of his own. Maybe he hadn't even told them about Dan? If that was the case, he wouldn't thank him for turning up out of nowhere.

She thought about it as she rushed around the house, gathering up her bags and coat and searching for her keys. She was so preoccupied she didn't even bother to protest when Dan retuned the car radio to Viking FM. By the time she pulled up outside his sixth form college she knew she had to say something.

'About your father. You won't expect too much, will you?'

He grinned. 'You mean he might turn out to be a sad old git who likes Pink Floyd?'

Tess smiled. 'That wasn't quite what I had in mind. He may have moved on with his life.' She chose her words carefully.

'And he might not want me to be part of it? It's okay, I've thought of that. I won't mind if he doesn't want to know. I just want to meet him, that's all. I don't want to mess up his life or anything.' Dan smiled, but his eyes were sad. He was already steeling himself for rejection, she could tell.

'How could you mess up anyone's life? You're my little angel!' She enveloped him in a jokey hug, knowing it would drive him mad.

Dan pushed her away, blushing. 'Gerroff! People are looking.'

Tess grinned and waved as he headed towards the college building, making slow progress on his sticks. Her manic smile lasted until he'd turned the corner and disappeared out of sight. Then it was replaced by a scowl.

Bloody Phil. Wherever he was, whatever he was doing, she hoped he'd show his son more consideration than he'd ever shown her.

It was still on her mind at lunchtime, when she and Helen gathered with the others in the staffroom. Tess was standing at the copying machine, printing out some worksheets.

'I'm just worried Phil won't want to know him,' she said. 'It'll be like he's rejecting him all over again. Dan's been through a tough enough time, he doesn't need that.'

'He knows what he's doing.' Helen was her usual soothing self. 'Honestly, Tess, he's practically an adult. Old enough to look after himself.'

'Old habits die hard – oh, bugger!' Tess turned back to the photocopier, which had stopped chugging away and was now making an ominous whirring noise. 'What's wrong with this bloody thing now?'

'Try wiggling the tray. That usually works for me.'

Tess lifted the cover and peered inside. She punched a few buttons experimentally. Nothing happened.

'Must be a paper jam,' Helen said. 'It's always doing that.'

'Wretched machine. I'd be quicker doing this on a John Bull printing kit.' Tess crouched down and peered at the murky underside of the printer.

'Anyway, how do you know Phil will reject him?' Helen said. 'Maybe he's longing for the chance to get to know his son.'

'And maybe he's forgotten all about him.' Tess reached in and pulled out a handful of mangled paper. 'Let's face it, if he'd really wanted to come back and find us, it wouldn't have been that difficult, would it? I mean, it's not as if we've moved to the other side of the world and taken on a new identity. No, I expect he's got a family of his own by now. He's probably forgotten Dan even exists. That's what I'm really afraid of.'

'Are you sure about that?' Helen looked shrewdly at her.

'What do you mean?'

'If you ask me, you're more worried about what will happen if Phil doesn't reject him. Maybe you're feeling a teeny bit threatened? A bit possessive, maybe?'

'Rubbish!' Tess stood up and brushed the dust off her skirt. 'I've always said Dan has a right to find his father, if that's what he wants.'

'But admit it. You're secretly hoping he'll turn out to be a loser.'

Tess said nothing as she refilled the paper tray and pressed the Start button for the third time. 'Okay, so maybe I am. A bit,' she said reluctantly. 'But how would you feel if you'd brought a child up single-handed for seventeen years and then he suddenly turned round and announced he wanted his father? The father who'd abandoned him before he was even born?'

'I'd feel proud I'd brought up such a mature, sensible young man.'

'Cobblers. You'd be miffed as hell, and so am I. However you try to dress it up, it still feels like a kick in the teeth.'

'You know Dan doesn't see it like that. He loves you. He's just curious about his dad, that's all. This isn't a popularity contest, Tess.'

'Isn't it? That's what it feels like.' And Helen was right. Deep down she was secretly hoping Phil would turn out to be a god-awful nerd with appalling taste in clothes and music. Preferably a Lada driver too. 'Damn!' She jabbed at the buttons as the photocopier ground to a noisy halt again. 'This thing is beyond a joke.'

'Try wiggling the tray again. What are you doing, anyway?'

'Copying some worksheets for my Year 8 class. I can't face those wretched grammar books again.'

'Worksheets?' Helen recoiled in mock horror. 'We know what Mrs Frobisher will have to say about that, don't we?'

'Mrs Frobisher can go and – oh no! Now look what's happened.' She pulled her arm out of the copier, her pristine white sleeves stained with dark smudges.

'It's a miracle,' Helen marvelled. 'That's the first time I've seen it print on anything. Shame it's your shirt, though.'

'What exactly are these?' Marjorie Wheeler looked down at the bundle of papers Tess had just given her with the same distaste as if she'd just slapped a decomposing mackerel in her hand.

'They're worksheets, Marjorie.'

'I can see that. What are we supposed to do with them?'

Tess bit back the suggestion that sprang immediately to mind. She could feel her enthusiasm beginning to crumble in the face of Marjorie's implacable resistance. Marjorie Wheeler was ten years older than Tess and had been her rival for the Department Head's job. As far as she was concerned, it was rightfully hers. Mrs Frobisher had spent five years grooming her as her successor until Tess whipped in and stole it. Now she saw it as her duty to uphold Mrs Frobisher's standards in the face of Tess' arrant sloppiness.

Tess understood her resentment and tried to make allowances. But sometimes it could be very wearing. 'I thought we could use them in class sometime. Maybe in conjunction with some free writing?'

'Free writing?' Marjorie looked so appalled Tess wondered if she'd misheard and thought she'd asked her to try some free love.

'Yes, you know – allow them to stretch their imagination?'

Still the same blank but horrified expression. How could she expect Marjorie to teach the kids anything about imagination, when her own was so shrivelled it would fit in a matchbox? In fact, everything about her seemed small and mean, from her tightly buttoned twinset to her permanently pursed mouth.

'Sounds like a good idea.' Tess could have hugged Stephen Kwarme, the newly qualified teacher, and not just because he was tall, muscular and looked like a younger and even more gorgeous Denzel Washington. 'It'll make a change from those grammar books, anyway.'

'There's nothing wrong with grammar,' Marjorie hissed. 'Grammar is one of the essential building blocks of the English language. Without grammar, there would be nothing but disorder, and chaos, and—'

'I agree,' Tess said hastily. 'But there's nothing wrong with trying something new, is there?'

Marjorie looked down at the paper in her hand. 'It seems rather unnecessary to me. Mrs Frobisher always said—'

'Yes, well, Mrs Frobisher isn't Head of Department any more, is she? I am.'

'More's the pity,' Marjorie muttered. Tess fought the urge to say something cutting. She was supposed to be motivating the staff, getting them on her side. Although nothing short of a white flag and total surrender would get Marjorie Wheeler to lower her guard. Which was a shame, because with the right amount of coaxing, Tess was sure she could be a good teacher.

'Look, it was just an idea. If you'd rather plan your own lessons—' She went to take the worksheets back but Marjorie clasped them to her chest.

'No,' she said. 'I'll – er – take these away and look at them.'

As they watched her scuttle out of the staffroom, Stephen said, 'You know where she's going, don't you?'

Tess nodded. 'Straight to show them to Mrs Frobisher. I expect they'll be working themselves into a lather of indignation and plotting my downfall over a plate of chocolate digestives within half an hour.'

'Doesn't it bother you?'

'I try not to let it. Hopefully I'll win her round one day.'

'I wouldn't bet on it. She seems very set in her ways.'

'And I'm very determined.' She looked at the box Stephen had just hauled into the staffroom. 'What's this lot?'

'Just some junk from my last teaching prac. I keep meaning to go through it, see if there's anything I want to keep that might be useful.'

Tess reached in and took out a photo. It was a team photo of some rather gorgeous-looking men in football kit. Stephen was at the front, nursing a trophy between his muscular thighs. 'I didn't know you played?'

He nodded. 'Our college won the championship last year.'

'You won't see many of them here. The last time Haxsall Park won a trophy for anything Abba had just won the Eurovision Song Contest. Come to think of it, that was about the same time Mrs Frobisher last bought a textbook.'

Stephen smiled. 'I know what you mean. Some of the books we've got were around when Noah took his GCSEs. And the library's even worse. Do you know, that woman only allows the kids to take out one book every month?'

'I know.' Tess had been having run-ins with Mrs Tate the librarian for ages. She ran the library with the same ruthless efficiency and lack of flair that Mrs Frobisher had used on the English department. Her idea of avant-garde modern literature were the Biggles books. But the real problem was she treated every book on the shelves as if it was her own. The last thing she wanted to do was let any of them fall into the clutches of some grubby teenager. 'I just wish I could do something to wake everyone up. Something that would grab the kids' attention, really get them interested. I don't suppose you've got any ideas?'

Stephen thought for a moment. 'Nude poetry readings?'

'Might be a bit chilly.' Tess looked back down at the photo in her hands. Although she wouldn't mind getting a better look at Stephen's fabulous physique . . .

She stuffed the photo back into the box before she broke into a sweat thinking about it, and quickly pulled out another. This was of a group of teenagers in old-fashioned costume, gathered on a stage. Stephen was standing next to a gawky-looking boy in a dress. 'So what's this? The college cross-dressing team?'

Stephen grinned. '*Charley's Aunt*,' he said. 'We had a very enthusiastic drama group in my old school.'

'It must have been enthusiastic to get a fifteen-year-old boy to wear a frock!' Tess tried to imagine persuading Jason Fothergill or Mark Nicholls that it would be a good idea to parade around in front of their peers in a shawl and bonnet.

And then it came to her.

'That's it,' she said. 'Stephen, you're a genius!'

'Why? What have I said?'

'I'll tell you later. After I've had a word with Cynthia.'

6

That afternoon, Leanne and Jordan caught up with Emily on the way to PE. She was immediately on her guard, but they were surprisingly friendly.

'We don't want to fall out with you,' Leanne said. 'It's just *her* we can't stand.' She nodded to where Paris lingered behind them, watching and waiting.

'She's all right.'

'You don't know anything about her. Her mum's a slag. And she's been inside. Bet she didn't tell you that, did she?' Leanne smirked. 'Your mate Paris had to go into care. She's even got a social worker.'

Emily stuck out her chin. 'So?'

'And she's got loads of brothers and sisters, all by different dads. Sometimes her mum makes her stay off school to look after them, if she's too hungover or wants to go out nicking.'

Emily glanced over her shoulder. Paris had gone. 'At least she's not brain-dead,' she said. 'At least she can talk about something else but whether Posh Spice has had a sodding boob job!'

'Fine, if that's the way you feel.' Leanne shrugged. 'You stick with her. But don't say we didn't warn you.'

'Ooh, I'm scared.'

'You should be,' Leanne called back over her shoulder as she and Jordan headed off to the playing field.

She and Paris were the last to be picked for the team. As they stood shivering together on the touchline Paris said, 'Just so you know, I've only got two brothers.'

'What about the rest of it?'

'Mostly true.' Her face flashed defiance.

Emily looked up at the greying sky. 'I really hate hockey,' she said.

'At least we've got something in common.'

She ended up marking Jordan in defence. Luckily she was a bit of a wimp without Leanne to back her up, and apart from a couple of whacks in the shins when the teacher wasn't looking, Emily managed to escape unscathed.

They were getting changed after showers when she realised Mr Bunny was missing. Heart racing, she upended her bag, spilling books out on to the wet floor. But he was gone.

'Lost something?' Leanne asked innocently.

'What have you done with it?'

'I don't know what you're talking about.'

'No need to snap her head off, she was only asking if you'd lost anything,' Jordan said.

Emily held out her hand. 'Give it back.'

'Give what back, Em?'

'You know.' She felt the blush rising as silence fell around the changing room.

'You mean your bunny wunny? Thought you'd be a bit old for toys by now.'

'What's going on?' Paris stood behind her, drying her hair.

'And you can stay out of it, council kid.' Leanne thrust her face close to hers, so close she could almost count the freckles crowding her pudgy cheeks. 'Look, she's crying. Has Mummy's ickle baby lost her ickle toy, then?'

'Leave her alone,' Paris said. 'Her mum's dead.'

There was something about those piggy eyes and that screwed-up mouth so close to her face that made Emily snap. Before she knew what she was doing, she'd reached out and yanked a handful of frizzy blonde hair. Leanne screamed and twisted free, then flew at Emily, punching and clawing. A second later, they were circled by girls in various states of undress, all yelling. Their screams filled Emily's head as she went down, Leanne on top of her, pinning her to the hard wet floor. She hit out wildly, then felt a crunching pain as a fist made contact with her lip. Somewhere beyond the screams, she heard Paris' voice, pleading with them to stop. And then, 'What's going on?' The circle parted for Miss Wesley to come through.

Leanne immediately burst into tears. 'It was them, Miss,' she sobbed. 'They attacked me, the two of them.'

'That's right, Miss,' Jordan joined in. 'They just went for her.'

Miss Wesley turned to Emily. 'Is this true?'

Emily staggered to her feet, blood trickling from her lip. 'She started it.'

'And what exactly did she do to you?'

'She – she –' Her face flamed. She couldn't say it.

She looked around, waiting for someone to defend her. Blank faces stared back. They were all too scared of Leanne and Jordan to say anything.

'I see.' Miss Wesley folded her arms. 'Maybe you'd prefer to tell Mrs Frobisher? Go along to her office, the pair of you.'

'A school play?'

Tess and Cynthia Frobisher faced each other in the Deputy Head's office. Cynthia sat dominantly behind the desk, leaving Tess the low chair on the other side. It was impossible to assert oneself while sinking into its leathery depths.

'You want to put on a school play?' She made it sound as if Tess had suggested a nude revival of *Oh! Calcutta!*.

'Why not? It'll be fun.'

'It'll be a disaster.'

'How can you say that?'

'Because we've done it before and it's always been a nightmare. The students simply aren't up to it. Let's face it, most of them have trouble remembering their own names, let alone lines. They're not interested.'

Tess held on to her temper with effort. Like it or not, she needed Cynthia's cooperation. She wasn't going to get anywhere without it. 'You're not giving them a chance.'

'Only because I know what they're capable of! And where would the money come from? We can barely cover lessons, let alone finance some lavish production.'

'It doesn't have to be lavish. We're talking about a school play here, not a remake of *Ben Hur*! Anyway, it would pay for itself once we start selling tickets.'

'Sell tickets?' Cynthia sat back, nostrils aquiver. 'You're not seriously expecting people to *pay* to see this debacle, are you?'

'Why not? Hopefully we'll even make a profit. We could buy some new books for the school library—'

'But that's tantamount to begging!'

'I wouldn't have to beg if you'd let me have more money.'

There was a tense pause while Cynthia weighed up the situation. Then she gave Tess her most patronising smile. 'Look, I know you mean well, but you simply don't have the experience to know when to use your judgement in these things. I'm sure in a few years you'll come to realise I'm right.'

That's if I haven't buried a hatchet in your head before then, Tess thought. She struggled to get out of her seat. 'Fine,' she said. 'I'll just go and tell Mr Gant you're not keen on the idea, shall I? Only he seemed to think it might work. But what does he know? I mean, he's only the Headteacher. He doesn't have your years of experience, does he?'

Cynthia paled. 'You've spoken to Eric?'

'Of course. I had to get his say-so before I approached you, didn't I?' Tess glanced at the phone, praying she wouldn't pick it up and call him. It would be too humiliating to be caught out telling such an outrageous lie.

Cynthia straightened the papers on her spotless desk, a sure sign she was annoyed. 'You should have come to me first, instead of bothering the Head. We're supposed to be working together.'

Funny how she never thought of that when she 'forgot' to send important emails and called staff meetings behind her back. Tess smiled beatifically. 'Of course we are, Cynthia. And I'm sure if we put our heads together, we can make this a huge success.'

But from the tight-lipped look on Cynthia's face, it was clear this play would take place over her dead body.

'It's so bloody unfair!' Emily complained, as they made their way up the stairs to Mrs Frobisher's office. 'Leanne's a lying cow!'

'She'll get away with it,' Paris shrugged. 'She always does.'

They headed off the main staircase and through the double doors. As they neared the door marked 'Deputy Head', Paris whispered, 'Try not to meet her eye. And whatever you do, don't answer back. She hates that.'

Miss Doyle was in Mrs Frobisher's office. 'Emily?' She looked up in surprise as the secretary showed them into the room. 'What are you doing here? What have you done to your face?'

'They were fighting in the girls' changing rooms,' the secretary announced behind them. 'Miss Wesley just called. Apparently they both set about Leanne Hooper.'

'Surely not?' Miss Doyle looked in bewilderment from one to the other. 'Paris, I can't believe you'd do something like that?'

Before Paris could answer, Mrs Frobisher said, 'I think I'd better talk to these two, Miss Doyle. We'll finish our little chat later, shall we?'

Miss Doyle didn't move. 'If you don't mind, Mrs Frobisher, these girls are in my form. I'm sure I can sort this out.'

Mrs Frobisher's smile became steely. 'Miss Wesley sent them to me.'

'But I know them.'

'Exactly. So your judgement is bound to be clouded, isn't it?'

For a second Emily thought Miss Doyle was going to lunge across the desk and grab a handful of hair just like she had Leanne's. But instead she got up and said, 'Fine. But I shall be talking to them myself later.'

'That's entirely up to you.'

Miss Doyle turned to Emily. 'I'd go to the medical room as soon as you're finished in here. That lip looks nasty.'

Emily's heart sank a little lower as the door closed behind her. She felt as if they'd just lost their only ally.

She turned to face Mrs Frobisher. She was ancient with a slash of vivid red lipstick on her thin mouth, a helmet of brown hair and eyes that lacked any sympathy.

Unnerved, she blurted out, 'It wasn't Paris. She had nothing to do with it.'

'I beg your pardon? I wasn't aware I'd invited you to speak?'

'I know, but I just wanted to tell you—'

'When I want you to say something I'll ask you. Now, just for that outburst we will all sit in silence for five minutes to give you time to reflect on your behaviour.'

The minutes stretched by. Emily tried to compose herself, anxious to get her story straight. But she was thrown off her guard when, as soon as five minutes had passed, Mrs Frobisher turned to her and said, 'Now, perhaps you could tell me what you think gives you the right to go around attacking other girls?'

'I didn't attack her!'

'Apparently there are witnesses who say you did.'

'Yes, but they're liars.'

'So everyone is lying except you?'

'Well – yes.' She heard Paris groan beside her.

'And you're saying you didn't lunge at her and pull her hair?'

'I did, but—'

'I'd call that attacking someone, wouldn't you?'

She was like a barrister on the telly, the way she twisted everything around. It was worse than being grilled by Anne Robinson. Emily was determined not to lose her cool. 'I'd call it retaliation,' she said.

Mrs Frobisher's eyes narrowed. 'Oh, you would, would you? And what exactly were you *retaliating* against?'

'She'd stolen something from me.'

'I see. And what had she stolen?'

Emily stared down at her hands. 'A toy rabbit,' she mumbled.

'Speak up, I can't hear you.'

'I said a toy rabbit.'

Mrs Frobisher's crimson lips stretched into a sneer. 'A toy rabbit? You beat a girl up because she stole your *toy*?'

'I didn't beat her up,' Emily said. 'She attacked me.'

'I don't blame her. If you go around pulling hair, what do you expect?' Mrs Frobisher turned to Paris, who'd been staring into space since they'd sat down. 'And you. What was your part in all this?'

'I told you, she didn't do—' Emily saw Mrs Frobisher's face and shut up.

'I wasn't asking you. Besides, knowing her background, I find that very hard to believe.'

Outrage flowed like heat through her veins. 'That's not fair!'

'I beg your pardon?'

'Don't,' Paris whispered, but Emily was too angry at the injustice to care. 'I said it's not fair. Why do you believe a cow like Leanne and not her?'

Mrs Frobisher looked about ready to explode. 'I realise you're new to this school and so your standards may be a little lower than we're used to.'

Her eyes were like chips of granite. 'But I have to tell you that kind of behaviour simply won't be tolerated at Haxsall Park. You do not go around attacking other students, and you certainly don't speak to a senior member of staff the way you have just spoken to me.' She drew back in her seat and looked down at them. 'I was thinking of giving you the benefit of the doubt as it's your first term and you've obviously fallen under a bad influence . . .' Her eyes shot towards Paris. 'But after listening to your outburst I have to say I've changed my mind. You will both have an hour's detention tomorrow night.'

'But—' Emily began to protest, but Paris seized her arm and dragged her out of the office. 'That's so unfair!' she shouted, when they were safely out of earshot.

'Told you, didn't I?'

'But you didn't deserve it! If anyone does detention, it should be that lying bitch Leanne Hooper.'

'Let it go,' Paris said. 'Come on, we'll be late for French.'

'You go on, I'll catch you up. I've got to go to the medical room.'

'Do you want me to come with you?'

'No, it's okay. I'll catch you up.'

Paris looked wary. 'You're not going to do anything stupid, are you?'

'Like what?'

'I dunno. Do a runner, or something.'

'Don't you think I'm in enough trouble? Now, go on, you'll be late.' She gave her a push. Paris hesitated, then headed off, leaving Emily alone.

Don't cry, she warned herself, but she couldn't help it. She'd wept a lot over the past year, but this time they were tears of rage and frustration.

She fled outside before anyone could see her. It was late afternoon and the sky was full of bruised purple clouds. The threat of rain hung in the air.

Emily hugged her arms around her, but she couldn't bring herself to go back inside. She never wanted to go back there. If she had to face Leanne Hooper, she'd do a lot worse than pull her hair.

The school gates lay ahead of her. Emily licked her swollen lip, tasting blood. Then she started walking. With every step she expected someone to call her back, but no one did. She was through the gates and out in the street before she even knew what she was doing.

7

It was nearly two when Jack rushed into the glass and steel offices of Crawshaw and Finch, a Starbucks' Americano in one hand, Next carrier bag in the other.

His PA, Vicky, looked up from her keyboard. 'Not trouble with the washing machine again?'

'It's a nightmare. Thanks to Sophie's PE kit, all my shirts now have an interesting tie-dye effect.'

Vicky followed him into his office. 'You do know you're not supposed to put whites in with coloureds, don't you?'

'I do now.'

'Maybe you should try reading the instructions next time?'

'Have you ever tried reading an instruction manual written by a team of Japanese dyslexics?' He ripped the wrapping off his shirt. Vicky watched him with amusement.

'Anyway, I thought your cleaner did your washing and ironing these days?'

'So did I. Apparently that was something else I got wrong.'

Somehow, he'd ended up with the Jennifer Lopez of the cleaning world, a domestic diva who was prone to downing tools and going home if he accidentally bought the wrong brand of bathroom mousse.

He and Pauline differed wildly on what her domestic duties should be. He thought she should clean the house, stack and empty the dishwasher and do the occasional load of washing and ironing if he left it out for her. She thought she should drink coffee, watch *Trisha*, phone her friends and squirt some Pledge into the air five minutes before he walked in the door. He sometimes toyed with the fantasy of firing her, but they both knew he'd never have the nerve.

As he pulled the cardboard dressing from under the collar, a plastic clip pinged out from nowhere and narrowly missed his eye. 'Bugger! Why do these bloody things have so many pins and clips and bits of plastic?'

Vicky rolled her eyes. 'I'll leave you to it. Let me know if you can't manage the buttons on your own.'

He pulled off his shirt and tie and was just removing yet another pin he'd overlooked, when the door opened again. Without turning round, he said, 'It's all right, I am capable of dressing myself. I'm a big boy now.'

'So I see.'

He swung round. Charlotte Ferguson stood in the doorway. Like him, she was one of the senior planning consultants, thirty years old, tall and willowy with sleek auburn hair and challenging hazel eyes that could shrivel a man's gonads at fifty paces.

Those same eyes were now fixed appraisingly on his bare chest. Jack clutched his shirt protectively against him. 'Charlie! Can I help you?'

'I've brought that revised junction layout for you to look at.'

'Thanks. You can just leave it, if you like?'

'It's okay, I'm in no hurry.' She sat down, smiling mischievously. 'Besides, I'm enjoying the show.'

He turned away from her to button up his shirt, but he could still feel her eyes giving his rear the once-over. 'You realise I could probably do you for sexual harrassment?'

'I'm not the one parading around the office topless.'

For an instant as he turned his eyes dropped to her cleavage and then shot back up to meet her eyes. 'Right. Erm. Now, about that layout?'

'This is what I've come up with so far.' She came round to his side of the desk and spread the plans in front of him. 'You see the problem? I thought if we could just move this junction over to here –' As she leaned across, Jack caught a whiff of her sharp, sexy scent. He also realised she wasn't wearing anything under her black tailored Nicole Farhi jacket. 'That would ease the traffic build-up and take away some of the council's objections. What do you think? Jack?'

'What? Oh yes, right.' He averted his eyes from her plunging neckline. For heaven's sake, what was he thinking of? Charlie was a friend, a colleague. She was also not the kind of woman you treated lightly. Not if you valued your manhood, anyway. 'You're the traffic engineer. I'm just a humble architect, remember?'

'Not so humble from what I've heard.' Charlie rolled up the plans. 'Word is you're in line for the top job.'

'Me and everyone else.' It was no secret that Alec Finch was due to retire at the end of the year. For the past few months speculation had been raging over who would be offered his place in the partnership.

'Yes, but you're bound to get it. The others are all butt-kissing toads. They can't have a pee without emailing the boss about it.'

'What about you? You could be in the running.'

Charlie shook her head. 'I haven't been here long enough. But if Alec had decided to retire next year instead of this, I might have given you a run for your money.'

'I don't doubt it.' Charlie might be one of his nicer colleagues, but she was also one of the most ambitious. And she wasn't above using her sex appeal to get her way.

'Anyway, if I can't have the job myself I'd rather you did,' she said.

'Thanks. You're great at massaging egos.'

'I'm great at massaging all kinds of things.'

He was still wondering how to answer that when the door flew open and a man stormed in, followed by a breathless Vicky.

'Are you Mr Tyler?' he demanded. He was about sixty, stocky with thinning sandy hair.

'I tried to stop him,' Vicky said to Jack. 'I told him he needed an appointment—'

'It's okay, Vicky.' Jack stood up. He towered over the other man, although from the look of his flattened boxer's nose he still wouldn't have fancied taking him on. 'I'm Jack Tyler. And you are?'

'Sam Dobbs.' He ignored the hand Jack offered. 'I want to talk to you about this Westpoint thing.'

'I'll call security.' Charlie reached for the phone, but Jack stopped her.

'There's no need for that. What did you want to say, Mr Dobbs?'

Sam Dobbs looked taken aback. He'd obviously been expecting a fight. 'You can't let it go ahead. It would devastate the local community.'

'For heaven's sake!' Charlie snorted. 'We're building a shopping centre, not dropping an atom bomb!'

'You might as well be.' He turned to Jack. 'These shops are nothing to do with us. We don't even want them. It'll just mean more traffic clogging up the streets and less green space for the kids to play, not to mention all the local shops being put out of business.'

'As far as traffic goes, I think you'll find—' Charlie began to say, but Sam held up his hand.

'No offence, love, but I'm talking to the boss here.' He looked at Jack. 'You've got to stop this thing.'

Jack, who'd been trying not to smile at Charlie's outraged expression, pulled himself together. 'I'm sorry, Mr Dobbs, but you're talking to the wrong man.'

'You designed the thing, didn't you?'

'Yes, but we're only acting as consultants. If you want to object, you need to talk to the council. They give the final yes or no to the scheme.'

'Aye, and we all know what they're going to say, don't we? You lot are all in this together.'

Jack suppressed a sigh. Why did everyone always assume there was a big conspiracy going on? 'Actually, that's not quite true. There's going to be a public inquiry on Westpoint.'

The old man looked suspicious. 'Oh aye? And what's that when it's at home?'

'It's an independent inquiry, Mr Dobbs. A government-appointed planning inspector listens to all the arguments, then decides whether the project should go ahead. Like a court case.'

'I know all about court cases. The ones with the fanciest barristers always win.' He leaned forward across the desk, thrusting his face so close Jack could see the thread veins in his weatherbeaten cheeks. 'What chance do us ordinary people have against you lot, with all your money? I wouldn't be surprised if you were all in it together. You'll probably just give this inspector bloke one of your funny handshakes and the deal will be as good as done.'

'I wish it were that simple,' Jack muttered. 'Look, if you feel that strongly about it, why don't you try and muster some local support? Form an action group or something?'

'What's the point? No one wants to listen to us. No one cares what we think.'

'Perhaps they might, if you had a coherent argument to put across?'

Sam Dobbs' calloused hands balled into fists at his sides. Then the fight seemed to go out of him. 'I knew it was a waste of time coming here.' He looked from Jack to Charlie and back again. 'You're all the same, in your expensive suits and smart offices. It's all about profit with you lot. You don't care what's happening out there in the real world as long as you can drive around in your bloody Porsches!'

He was still mumbling to himself as Jack eased him out of his office and closed the door.

'What a rude little man,' Charlie said. 'You should have let me call security.'

'And give him the chance to go bleating to the local press? Westpoint is unpopular enough without attracting even more bad publicity.'

'I didn't realise it was that bad?'

'Bad?' He sat down and rubbed his eyes wearily. 'Sometimes I think it would be easier to build a bacon factory in Tel Aviv.'

He'd always known Westpoint was going to be a problem. A consortium of property developers had got together to build a major new retail park on an old airfield just outside the city. As planning consultants, it was Crawshaw and Finch's job to make sure the whole project went smoothly, from designing the buildings to making sure they obtained planning permission. But not surprisingly, the local residents weren't thrilled by the idea of several big department stores at the bottom of their gardens, and had kicked up so much fuss the whole thing had been referred to a public inquiry.

And contrary to what Sam Dobbs believed, it wasn't just a matter of

701

'funny handshakes'. If the inspector decided the locals had a case, he might recommend refusal. Which meant months of hard work down the drain, not to mention Jack's chances of securing the partnership.

Thanks to Mr Dobbs' unscheduled appearance, Jack was late for the Westpoint consortium meeting. As Westpoint were their most important clients, Crawshaw and Finch had wheeled out their biggest guns. Humphrey Crawshaw himself was chairing the meeting, surrounded by the heads of the legal, finance and environment departments. Jack's brother-in-law Greg, who was coordinating the project, sat beside him.

On the other side of the table were the suits from Westpoint, headed by Peter Jameson, a small man with sleek silver hair.

Jack nodded a greeting at everyone and took his seat at the far end of the table, next to Bernard Sweeting the environment expert, who was doodling trees on his A4 jotter.

Humphrey opened the meeting and passed it over to Greg, who consulted his notes for a moment.

'As you know, the council has given planning permission in principle for the Westpoint Centre to go ahead,' he began. 'But our plans have met with some local opposition. The residents aren't happy with the amount of disruption and extra traffic that may be generated by the scheme, and the city-centre retailers fear the centre will attract customers away from the city. Between them, they've managed to make enough noise for the local press to take an interest and have recently started a campaign to stop Westpoint going ahead.'

'We know that.' Peter Jameson looked irritable. 'We're all well aware of the problems. We hired you to get rid of them, not tell us what they are!'

'I'm coming to that.' There was a sheen of perspiration on Greg's upper lip as he flicked through his file. Not for the first time, Jack felt relieved he wasn't the one coordinating this project. Humphrey had approached him to do it, but he'd turned it down because Miranda had just died and he didn't feel he could handle it.

But he felt guilty as he watched Greg stumbling through his presentation. Jack had suggested him for the job but Ros had admitted he'd been having sleepless nights over it.

'We felt the best way forward was to launch a PR counter-offensive, to try and get public opinion on our side.' Greg found his place and carried on. 'We're about to produce a mailshot of our own, highlighting the positive benefits for the community. Greater retail opportunities, creation of local jobs, environmental benefits—'

'Environmental benefits?' Peter Jameson looked blank. 'Are there any?'

They all turned to Bernard Sweeting, who dropped his pen in panic. 'Well – um – we'll be planting fifty trees as part of the scheme.'

'Are we? That sounds good.' Peter nodded his approval.

'Unfortunately we're pulling down a hundred to build it.'

'Although obviously we won't be telling anyone that,' Greg put in. Jack noticed Peter Jameson's expression and cringed inwardly.

'Yes, but it doesn't take a genius to find out that kind of information, does it? The press will be on to us in five minutes.' He pinned Greg with a glacial stare. 'Frankly it seems a ridiculous idea to highlight the environmental benefits when any fool can see that at the end of the day there will be a few less acres of green space and a few extra roads.'

'Yes, but—'

'I'm afraid you're going to have to do better than that if you're going to stay in charge of this project.'

Greg looked crushed. He was a big, solid man with fair hair, merry blue eyes and the look of an overgrown, naughty schoolboy. In this case, a schoolboy who had been cornered by the playground bully.

'I think what Greg's trying to say is that we need to get the local authority on our side,' Jack stepped in quickly. Everyone turned to look at him. 'If they decide to take on board what the residents are saying, they could change their mind about granting us planning permission. Then we'd be in real trouble. We've got to give them a reason to get behind the Westpoint scheme. Show them they stand to gain by it going ahead. That's what you were coming to, wasn't it, Greg?'

Greg, who was still gathering his thoughts, stared at him blankly. 'What? Oh – er – yes.'

'You mean like a bribe?' Peter's eyes glittered.

'More like an . . . incentive. We thought we might offer them something they really need – like a new bus terminal. We could design it, give them the land and a bit towards the cost. And it would get around the problem of the increased traffic being generated by showing we're encouraging the use of public transport.'

There was a silence. Then Peter Jameson said. 'That seems like the most sensible suggestion anyone's come up with so far.'

'It's something we've been working on as a team for a while,' Jack said. 'Greg asked me to put something on paper a few days ago.' He looked down the table at his brother-in-law. 'I'm sorry I haven't managed to get back to you until now.'

'Er – no problem.' Greg shuffled his papers in front of him.

As the meeting closed, Humphrey Crawshaw cornered him. 'Excellent contribution as ever, Jack.'

'It was a team effort,' he insisted.

'Perhaps.' Humphrey sent him a shrewd look. 'It's just a pity you're not at the head of the team. I'm sure Jameson agrees.'

703

As he walked away, Jack noticed Greg standing there. From the look on his face, it was clear he'd heard every word.

'He's right,' he said. 'You should be the one in charge, not me.'

'Take no notice of them. You're doing a great job.'

'Yeah, right. That's why Jameson made such a fool of me in there. Face it, Jack, the man hates me.'

Jack wished there was something he could say. He hadn't realised Greg had taken it so much to heart. Usually he was always laughing, treating everything as a huge joke, including work. 'I work to live, not the other way round,' he always said, whenever Jack was burning the midnight oil over a drawing. 'Besides, there's only room for one rising star in this family.'

'Take no notice of Jameson, he's just a bully,' he said. 'You were always pretty good with bullies at school, as I recall?'

They'd been friends ever since they met at secondary school in Leeds. Back in those days, Greg had been his unofficial minder. Nobody messed with Jack Tyler when scrum half Greg Randall was around. 'Remember that time some kid stole my lunch money and you flushed his head down the toilet? What was his name?'

'Tony Jefferson.' Greg smiled reluctantly. 'Much as I'd like to, I think I'm a bit old to be stuffing Peter Jameson's head down the bog!'

'Nice thought though, isn't it?' Jack grinned.

They were still laughing at the idea when Vicky stuck her head round the door. 'Jack, I've got Emily's school on the phone.'

He sighed. 'Oh God, what's she done now?'

'That's just it, they don't know. They think she's run away!'

8

Emily's bravado deserted her once she was outside the school gates. She stood shivering in the street, with no idea what to do next. She'd always fancied the idea of bunking off, but now she didn't feel clever at all. She felt like crying. Her school bag was still in the cloakroom, as was her coat. All she had were a few coins left over from her dinner money. It was too cold to wander the streets and she couldn't go home because she'd left her key in her bag.

She sat in the bus shelter, jingling the coins in her pocket. If she managed to con the driver into thinking she was a half fare, she could make it into the city centre. After that she wasn't sure what she would do.

A shadow fell over her. She looked up. There was Miss Doyle, holding Emily's coat and school bag.

'I thought you might be needing these.'

'Thanks.' Emily took them gingerly. 'How did you know where I'd be?'

'The bright ones always try to catch the first bus out of here. The others just go to the chippie and play on the arcade games. Although I have to say it wasn't exactly bright to walk out of school in the first place. Mind if I sit down?'

Emily shuffled along to make room for her. Miss Doyle sat down and they both stared up the empty road for a moment, looking for the bus that had so far failed to appear.

'Well,' Miss Doyle said. 'It's been quite a day for you, hasn't it?' Emily shrugged. 'So why did you run away? Was it because of Leanne and Jordan?'

'No! They don't scare me.'

'What, then?'

'I was just angry.' She explained what had happened in Mrs Frobisher's office. 'It wasn't fair,' she said. 'She shouldn't have taken it out on Paris. It was my fault, not hers.'

'If anyone was at fault, it was Leanne.'

'Yes, but they're not going to punish her, are they?'

'Probably not,' Miss Doyle agreed. 'But I'm a great believer in what goes

705

around, comes around. And if it's any consolation, I bet one day Leanne and Jordan will get their come-uppance.'

'I'd like to be the one to give it to them.'

Miss Doyle smiled. 'I'll pretend I didn't hear that.' She stood up. 'We can't sit around here all day. I think it's going to rain any minute.'

Emily's defiance returned. 'I'm not going back to school.'

'I don't think there's much point, do you?' Miss Doyle looked at her watch. 'It's practically home time anyway. Why don't I give you a lift home? I've finished lessons for the day. Unless there's somewhere else you were planning to go?'

'Nowhere special.' Although there was somewhere. She'd been wanting to go for months.

Miss Doyle must have read her face, because she said, 'Look, if you need a lift anywhere, I'm happy to take you.'

Emily bit her lip. 'It's a long way.'

'I'm in no hurry. Like I said, I'm free for the rest of the day.'

She stared at her shoes, wondering whether to risk telling her. 'I'd like to go to the cemetery in Leeds. To see my mum.'

'Do you want me to take you there now?'

She looked up. 'Would you?'

'If that's what you want.'

Emily gazed down the road. There was no sign of the bus.

'Unless you'd prefer your dad to take you?'

'No chance! He won't go. He never goes to see Mum. I've asked him loads of times if he'd take us, but he always says no.'

'Maybe he's afraid it will upset you?'

'I'm not a kid!' Emily snapped. 'It's him who doesn't like being there, not me. He only thinks of himself. Just like when he moved here.'

Miss Doyle was silent for a moment. Then she said, 'In that case, I think we should go. We could buy some flowers on the way, if you like?'

'Are you sure?'

'Why not? I think school can manage without both of us, just this once. As long as we don't make a habit of it. But we'll have to let your dad know.'

'No!' Emily sat back down.

'Emily! The school will have contacted him by now. He'll probably be on his way home, worried sick. I've got to tell him.'

'I don't want him to know.'

'Fine. Then we're not going anywhere.' Emily stared at Miss Doyle, surprised. Adults had tiptoed around her so much since her mum died, it came as a shock to find someone who stood up to her.

'Okay,' she agreed reluctantly. 'But do you have to tell him exactly where we're going? He'll only be angry or try to stop me.'

'I can't believe that. Why should he try to stop you?'

'I told you, he doesn't want us to visit Mum. He wants us to forget all about her. You don't know him.'

Miss Doyle looked as if she might argue, then changed her mind. She pushed her glasses up her nose and thought for a moment. 'Tell you what, why don't I leave a message on your answer machine at home? I'll just tell him we've gone to Leeds but not exactly where we're going. How about that?'

Emily smiled. 'Deal.'

Miss Doyle's car was a wreck, but cool with it. It didn't look like a grown-up's car, not like her dad's boring BMW, or the Peugeot her mum used to drive. It didn't have a CD player or air conditioning. All it had was a radio cassette player, tied in place with a tatty bit of string. But she had some decent tapes, really good music like The Chemical Brothers instead of that sad old Phil Collins stuff her dad always played. And the glove compartment was stuffed with chocolate wrappers.

'It's my ecosystem,' Miss Doyle explained as she squeezed herself in behind the wheel. 'I've got everything I need to survive in here. Music, food – there's even some homework on the back seat, if I ever get bored in a traffic jam. Sorry, I've eaten all the chocolate, but I think there are still some jelly babies in the seat pocket next to you. I have put them out of reach otherwise I'd be hyperactive by the time I got to school.' She did an impression of a maniac, planted her foot on the accelerator and shot forward into the incoming traffic.

Emily giggled. She'd never seen a teacher out of school before, and she was shocked at how nice Miss Doyle was. She couldn't imagine any adult, let alone a teacher, listening to hardcore dance music and stuffing their face with jelly babies.

They passed the time on the way to Leeds with a discussion on the best way to eat them. Emily was all for nibbling the arms and legs off first, but Miss Doyle came down firmly on the side of decapitation. 'I don't know, it just seems kinder if they can't see what's happening to them,' she reasoned.

On the way, they stopped off and bought some flowers. Heavily scented cream roses tinged with pink, her mum's favourites. Miss Doyle paid for them. 'Pay me back some other time,' she said when Emily took out her meagre handful of coins.

It felt weird being back at the cemetery again after all this time. She'd thought she could handle it, but going through those wrought-iron gates brought it all flooding back. Coming through them in the back of the slow-moving black car, seeing everyone gathered by the grave. Then, as the car in front wheeled slowly round, getting her first glimpse of her mother's coffin in the back. It looked so small. Emily had tried to pretend it was nothing, just an empty box. She'd almost managed it too, until she saw the flowers. White carnations spelling out the word 'Mum'.

It was the same feeling she got now, looking at her mother's gravestone.

The pale marble gleamed in the gathering dusk, the name picked out in black letters, 'Miranda Rachel Tyler'. Emily gulped in the cold air.

'I'm just going to have a look round,' Miss Doyle said. 'Come and get me when you want to leave.' Then she walked away, threading her way between the gravestones, leaving Emily to cry on her own.

Tess trudged up the path to the far end of the cemetery, her collar turned up against the cold spitting rain. The air smelt of freshly cut grass and rotting leaves. She sat on a bench under the dark canopy of a yew tree and watched Emily arranging the flowers on her mother's grave. Poor kid, she looked so young in her school uniform. Too young to have to cope with something so tragic.

She wished she could have made her first couple of weeks easier for her. She'd been furious when she found out Mrs Frobisher had given her and Paris detention.

'The girl's got to learn,' she'd said, when Tess argued with her about it. As if she hadn't had enough hard lessons in life already.

It was getting dark when Emily finished arranging the flowers and came to find her.

Tess smiled. 'Ready?'

Emily nodded. Her eyes were red-rimmed. 'Thanks.'

They walked back to the car in silence. Tess could tell there was something on Emily's mind, but she waited for her to speak.

Finally she said, 'Have you ever known anyone who died?'

'My dad. But it was a long time ago now. I was about your age.'

'And do you still miss him?'

Tess thought back to her father, Martin Doyle. A big man, always laughing. Even when he was angry there was always a twinkle in his eye. 'Very much,' she said. 'Although the pain does fade away a bit as time goes on, so you end up with just the good memories.'

Emily kicked at a pile of leaves. 'I don't think I'll ever have any good memories.'

'You might think that now, but wait and see.'

'You don't understand! I can't have good memories because—' she broke off.

'Because of what, Emily?'

'It doesn't matter.' She didn't say any more until they reached the car. Then, as Tess searched for her key, she blurted out, 'I was with her. When she died.'

'I didn't realise. How awful for you.'

'It was.' Her face was haunted. 'No one knows what it was like. No one knows what happened.'

'Do you want to tell me about it?'

She said nothing. They got into the car and Tess started it up, then joined the slow crawl of traffic heading out of Leeds.

'Why do they call it the rush hour, when no one's going anywhere?' she wondered aloud.

She was just reaching for the jelly babies when Emily suddenly said, 'We were out late-night Christmas shopping. She kept saying she had a headache, but I took no notice.'

Tess glanced sideways at her.

'I needed her to see the trainers I wanted for Christmas, to make sure she knew the right ones to get.' She stared straight ahead of her at the red tail lights of the car in front. 'We had a row about it, because she wouldn't go back to the shop. She just wanted to get home. I started getting angry, I told her I hated her, then she sort of – collapsed.' Like a dam breaking, her words came out in a rush, tumbling over each other. 'I didn't know, did I? I didn't know she was going to die.'

'Of course you didn't.'

'I would never have said it if I'd known. I didn't hate her, I didn't. But I never got the chance to tell her I didn't mean it.'

Tess swallowed the lump in her throat. 'Have you told your dad about this?'

'No! And I don't want you to tell him either.'

'Of course I won't, not if you don't want me to. But I think you should talk to him. He's worried about you.'

'How can I tell him I killed Mum? He'd hate me.'

'Emily, you didn't kill your mum.'

'How do you know? You weren't there. No one was. Except me.'

'I'm sure she could have collapsed at any time.'

Emily looked down at her bitten nails. 'That's what the doctors said at the hospital.'

'You see? So how could it have been your fault? Your dad could have been with her, or your sister. Or she might have been on her own.'

'No, it was me. If I hadn't shouted at her about those stupid trainers . . .' She fumbled in her pocket for a tissue. 'I wish I hadn't said those things. I wish I hadn't told her I hated her.'

'We all say things we don't mean,' Tess said. 'Your mum would have known that. She would have known how much you loved her.'

'Do you think so?' Emily sniffed back the tears.

'Of course. My son tells me he hates me every time I say he can't do something, but I know he doesn't mean it. Mothers know these things.'

They talked as they drove home, about music, school, Emily's friends back in Leeds. Tess wondered if Jack Tyler understood how much his daughter missed them.

As they turned off the A64 into the leafy suburbs of York, Emily said, 'I didn't know you had a son.'

'Where do you think the tapes come from?' Tess held up a cassette. 'Dan's studying for his A Levels at sixth form college.' She smiled at Emily's surprised expression. 'Go on, say it. You didn't think I was that old.'

'I didn't. You seem really young.'

'Everyone's parents are old, Emily. And old-fashioned. And not one of them knows what they're talking about.' That coaxed a smile out of her. 'Why don't you talk to your dad about what you've told me?'

'No!' Emily sank down in her seat and looked sullen. 'He wouldn't understand.'

'He might, if you gave him the chance. I'm sure he knows there's something on your mind.'

'He doesn't. He's too worried about himself to care how we feel. That's why he works all the time.'

'I expect he has a very demanding job.'

'It's not that. He just doesn't want to be with us.'

'Why ever not?'

'Because we remind him too much.' She looked at Tess, her eyes huge and desolate in her pale face. 'He wants to forget about everything. That's why we moved house. And that's why he never goes to the cemetery. He doesn't want anything to remind him of her.' A tear escaped down her cheek and she brushed it away. 'I think he'd move away from us if he could.'

'Oh, Emily! I'm sure that's not true. Your dad really loves you. He wants what's best for you. Maybe he just doesn't know what that is yet.'

'Or he doesn't care,' Emily mumbled.

Following Emily's directions, Tess skirted the estate, past the parade of shops and headed out to the common. She was right, the Tylers did live in Hollywell Park. She'd seen the army of builders at work during the spring, but this was the first time she'd seen the 'executive development', as it called itself, in all its glory. It was certainly impressive, the gleaming new detached houses with their double garages and spreading lawns spaced out along wide, sweeping arcs of road. Not a burnt-out car or abandoned shopping trolley in sight. A bit different to her own modest two-bedroom bungalow just beyond the council estate.

As they neared the house, Emily chewed on her lower lip and said, 'Do we have to tell him where we've been?'

'I think he's going to want to know, don't you?'

'Couldn't we just say I had to come with you on an errand or something? He'll only get in a stress if I tell him the truth.'

Tess nodded ahead of her, where she'd spotted the silver BMW in the drive. 'I think it's a bit late for that, don't you?'

9

He came rushing out of the house as Tess pulled up, still in his office clothes, his face as white as his shirt.

'Hello, Dad.' Emily looked sheepish.

'Emily.' He threw open the car door for her to get out. 'Where the hell have you been?'

'Didn't you get my message on your machine?' Tess asked, getting out of the car.

He swung round to face her. 'I did, thank you. It was waiting for me when I got home. After I'd spent an hour driving round the streets, looking for my daughter and going out of my mind.' His voice was icy with sarcasm. 'Do you mind telling me what you were thinking of, taking my daughter to Leeds without my permission?'

'She didn't take me, I wanted to go,' Emily protested, but he ignored her.

'Well?' he said. 'I'm waiting.'

Tess faced him unflinchingly. 'What was I supposed to do, let her roam the streets?'

'As a teacher, I would have thought it might have occurred to you to take her back to school.'

'She didn't want to go.'

'Oh, and that's all right with you, is it? A child doesn't want to go to school, so you don't make them? Is that how you treat truants, Miss Doyle? Take them for coffee at Harvey Nics?'

'Actually, we went to visit her mother's grave.'

She hadn't meant it to come out like that. Seeing his face now, she wished she'd kept her mouth shut.

'You did what?'

'I was going to tell you—' Emily tried to interrupt, but Jack turned his back on her. All his rage was directed at Tess.

'She wanted to go and see her mother,' Tess repeated.

'I see. And if she'd wanted to visit a methadone clinic, or the local cancer ward, I suppose you would have taken her there too?'

'Dad—'

'It's hardly the same thing,' Tess defended herself.

'Dad, please!'

'EMILY, GO TO YOUR ROOM!'

For a moment she stood her ground, fists tightening at her sides. Then, with a choked sob, she dashed off, leaving the front door quivering in its frame behind her.

Jack turned back to Tess. 'Now look what you've done.'

'Me?'

'I can't believe a teacher of all people would behave so irresponsibly. I suppose this is some kind of trendy educational theory, is it? To make children confront the harsh realities of life and death?'

'Now you're being ridiculous.'

'Ridiculous?' A muscle pounded in his cheek. 'Miss Doyle, I have spent the past nine months trying to help my daughters get over the trauma of their mother's death. Why do you think we've moved here, if not to get away from it? And now you go and stir it all up with your well-meaning, do-gooding—'

'Perhaps that's the problem?' Tess said.

'What?'

'I realise you're angry, and I'm not saying what I did was right. But what you're doing isn't right, either. You say you're helping them get over the trauma but you're not. All you're doing is burying it, trying to pretend it never happened.'

'Now just a minute—'

'Do you really think moving house will help Emily get over what happened? Do you seriously imagine she can forget something like that just by changing addresses? The pain hasn't gone away, Mr Tyler. And you won't make it go away by pretending it doesn't exist.'

'I'm not.'

'I'm sorry, but that's exactly what you're doing. Emily desperately wants to talk about her mother's death. She needs to talk about it. But she can't, because she knows you want to block it out.'

He looked rattled. 'That's nonsense. No one's trying to block anything out.'

'So why can't she tell you she wants to visit her mother's grave? Why does she feel she has to do it in secret? And why—' She stopped herself.

'Go on,' he said quietly.

'I can't. I promised Emily.'

The fact that he was trying to contain his anger only made him seem more threatening. 'So you're telling me my daughter can confide in you, a total stranger, but she can't talk to me, is that it?'

'Look, I'm not saying it's your fault—'

'Don't patronise me, Miss Doyle.'

'I'm not. I'm just trying to make you see that Emily needs to talk about what happened to her mother.'

'Don't you think she's been hurt enough, without me dragging it up every five minutes? You may not realise this, but Emily was with her mother when she died—'

'I know. She told me.'

He stopped. 'She told you? When?'

'When we were at the cemetery.'

'What exactly did she tell you?'

He looked so upset, she wished she could tell him. But she'd promised Emily and she couldn't break her word. 'I think you should ask her that. Unless you're the one who can't talk about it?'

'Don't try to psychoanalyse me, Miss Doyle. A five-minute conversation with my daughter hardly gives you an insight into me and my family.'

'I'm sorry, I didn't mean—'

'Emily's my daughter and I'll deal with this in my own way.' His voice was clipped with anger.

Tess stared at him in frustration. 'You know what? Emily was right about you. You don't want to listen, do you? No wonder she doesn't feel she can talk to you.' She headed to her car, then stopped and turned back. 'But shall I tell you something, Mr Tyler? Your daughter is a frightened, lonely little girl. So I suggest you deal with it very soon.'

She got into her car. Jack watched her, his mouth opening and closing in mute rage.

'I hope you don't think this is the end of the matter?' He finally found his voice as she started up the engine. 'What you did today was gross misconduct. I'll be speaking to your Headteacher about it!'

Emily pulled the pillow over her head to shut out the shouting. She heard the front door bang, followed by the sound of Miss Doyle's car backfiring down the road. Then footsteps came up the stairs, stopping outside her bedroom door.

'Em?'

'Go away.'

'Emily, we need to talk.'

'I said go away!'

She could sense him hesitating, then the door opened. 'Emily—'

'What did you have to shout at her like that for? She didn't do anything wrong!'

'Oh, I think she did.'

'No, she didn't. I was upset and I wanted to go and see Mum, so she

713

took me. She was the only one who was nice to me in that whole stinking school, and now you've gone and ruined it all!'

The bed creaked under his weight as he sat down. 'Why didn't you tell me you wanted to see Mum's grave?' he said at last.

'I did, loads of times. You always said no.'

'I would have taken you, if you'd really wanted to go.'

'I did! Anyway, I don't need your permission!'

'You're right. You don't.' His breathing filled the silence. 'Look, Emily, if there's ever anything you want to talk about, you know I'll listen.'

'Yeah right. Just like you listened when we told you we didn't want to move here.'

'That was different. The thing is, I'm your father. If you've got anything on your mind, you should talk to me.' He hesitated. 'You've never really said what happened when Mum—'

'Stop it!' Emily pulled the pillow tighter over her head to block him out. 'I don't want to talk about it.'

'You talked to Miss Doyle.'

'So? She listened.'

'I'd listen, if you wanted me to. Em?'

Silence. She lay rigid, hardly breathing, waiting for him to give up. In the end he did.

'I'm sorry, I'm not very good at all this heart-to-heart stuff, am I? That was your mum's department. All I seem to do is cock it up.' He stood up. 'I'll go and get tea ready then, shall I? Microwave pizza okay for you?'

As he headed for the door, she thought about what Miss Doyle had said, about giving him a chance. 'Dad?' She rolled over, still hugging the pillow.

'Hmm?' The sadness in his face made her feel wretched. She desperately wanted to talk to him, but how could she? How could she drag up the memories he was doing his best to forget?

'Microwave pizza's fine,' she said.

To Emily's relief, Miss Doyle greeted her as if nothing had happened the following morning. Jordan and Leanne scowled as she took her seat at the back of the classroom. Leanne was sporting a bruised, puffy eye, inexpertly hidden under thick make-up. Emily wondered if she'd done it during their fight. She couldn't remember lashing out with her fists but she was pleased if she had.

She slid into the seat next to Paris. As usual, she had her nose in a book.

'I thought you might have gone on the run?' she said, not looking up.

'I nearly did.'

'Everyone was talking about it yesterday. You're a bit of a hero. It's not everyone who starts a fight and plays truant on the same day.'

Emily grinned. At least it was nice to be known as something other than the nerdy new girl.

'By the way, I've got something for you.' Paris put down her book and reached into her bag. 'He's a bit muddy, I'm afraid.'

In her hands was Mr Bunny. Emily gasped, 'Where did you get him?'

'Best you don't ask. As my mum always says, if you don't know nothing, the police can't do you for being an accessory.'

'What?'

Miss Doyle looked up. 'Can you keep it down at the back, I'm trying to do the register.' She pushed her glasses back up her nose. 'Leanne Hooper?'

'Here, Miss.' Leanne shot a look of loathing at Paris from her one good eye. Emily looked from one to the other and suddenly it dawned on her. 'You didn't?'

Paris gave one of her rare smiles. 'Like I said, best you don't ask,' she said, and went back to reading her book.

'Bloody hell, Tess, you took his daughter to a graveyard. What did you expect, a pat on the back?'

'I was only trying to help.'

'But you broke every rule in the book. Including aiding and abetting a truant. What were you thinking of?'

'I don't know, do I? It just seemed like the right thing to do at the time.' Tess spooned coffee into the mugs. The lesson before lunch break was her free period and she was supposed to be catching up on her marking for the afternoon. But with everything that had happened that morning she couldn't concentrate.

And of course Helen had followed her into the staffroom to catch up on the gossip. It wasn't just Emily's bunking off that was the talk of the school.

She hitched herself on to the desk, showing off a lot of smooth, tanned thigh under her netball skirt. 'So what else did Eric say to you?'

'What didn't he say?' Now she knew how the kids felt, being dragged up in front of the Headteacher. 'The way he went on about it you'd think I'd taken her to see a live sex show. He thinks Mr Tyler might remove Emily from the school.'

'Blimey, that's a bit of an overreaction, isn't it?'

'I don't know. I suppose I can't blame him. He's right, I should have talked to him first. For all I know, I could have scarred his daughter for life.'

They both turned as Jeff Kramer came into the staffroom, a pile of marking under his arm. He took one look at Tess and headed for the furthest corner of the room.

Tess sighed. 'There's someone who wouldn't be sorry to see me get sacked.'

'Take no notice of him. He's only sulking because Cynthia's told him he can't have his new equipment.'

'Yes, and whose fault is that?' She couldn't believe it when she got to work that morning and found out Cynthia Frobisher had called another staff meeting while she was in Leeds and announced she was cutting everyone's budgets to cover the cost of the school play. It wasn't until she was snubbed in the staffroom that she realised they all blamed her, which was probably just what Cynthia intended.

'Don't let it get to you,' Helen advised. 'They'll get over it.'

'This isn't about the money. It's about Cynthia being vindictive. She didn't have to cut those budgets, she just did it so everyone would hate me.' Tess helped herself to a custard cream from the tin, even though lunchtime was only ten minutes away. 'Thank God she's not in this morning. If she found out about Emily Tyler, she'd be howling for my blood.' She crunched thoughtfully. 'It's at times like this I wonder if I'm really cut out to be a teacher.'

'Don't say that. You're brilliant.'

'The rest of the staff don't seem to think so. Besides, I let myself get too involved.'

'Okay, so you get a bit carried away sometimes. But that's only because you care.'

'Didn't care about my equipment though, did she?' Jeff Kramer grunted from the other side of the room. 'And I hope those biscuits are coming out of *your* budget,' he added, nodding at the ginger nut Tess had just taken from the tin.

She was just about to give him a suitably cutting reply when they were interrupted by Pam, the school secretary. 'Sorry to butt in, but Mr Tyler's here to see you, Tess.'

She looked at Helen. 'Oh God, what does he want?'

Helen grimaced. 'Your head on a plate, probably.'

He was waiting in reception, pretending to admire a photo of Eric Gant and not to notice the admin staff were all ogling him. Tess squared her shoulders and greeted him with her most professional smile. 'Mr Tyler. What can I do for you?'

'I think we need to talk, Miss Doyle.'

Tess glanced at the admin girls, all tapping at their keyboards while their ears strained to catch the gossip. 'Perhaps you'd like to come to my classroom?'

'Thank you.'

Tess wasn't sure which of them was feeling the effort of being polite the most. Him, probably. Had he come to tell her he'd decided to take Emily away? She couldn't bear to think the poor girl's life might be disrupted again because of her.

By the time they'd reached her classroom she knew she had to say something.

'Miss Doyle—'

'Look, Mr Tyler, I know you're angry and you have a right to be. I was in the wrong. I apologise.'

'Can I just—'

'Please. You had your say yesterday, and now it's time for mine. Like I said, I know I was in the wrong. But I don't think taking Emily away is the answer.'

'I don't think you understand—'

'I understand perfectly. You're upset and you're angry, but if you could just take a moment to reconsider—'

'Miss Doyle, I have no intention of removing Emily from this school.'

'Oh!' Tess stopped short. 'But Mr Gant said—'

'When I spoke to him last night I was angry. I wasn't thinking straight. I realise taking Emily away would be a bad idea.'

'I see. So what have you come to see me for?'

'I came to apologise. Or rather, I've been sent.' He didn't meet her eye. 'My daughter seems to think I overreacted.'

'Oh.' Was this the same man who'd phoned the Headteacher the previous evening demanding she be sacked?

The bell rang, followed a second later by the stampede of feet thundering past. 'Lunch,' Tess explained, seeing Jack's startled expression. She hesitated, then said, 'Look, I don't suppose you fancy joining me for something to eat? After the morning I've had I could really do with a break, and I don't think I can face the canteen.' She saw his quick frown. 'On second thoughts, forget I asked. It was a silly idea anyway—'

'I'd love to,' Jack said.

The Three Legged Mare, or the Wonky Donkey, as it was better known among the locals, was quiet at lunchtime. Over in one corner a couple of businessmen – sales reps, by the look of them – were grabbing a pint and a sandwich before heading back on the road. In the other were a group of Haxsall Park teachers, heads together around a table. Marjorie Wheeler was among them, Tess noticed. She didn't usually socialise with the rest of the staff. It was amazing what a bonding experience a good bitching session could be. She turned away quickly.

'What are you having?' Jack asked.

'Just an orange juice, please. I've got George Orwell with my GCSE lot this afternoon.'

'I think I'll risk a pint. I'm only designing a block of flats.' He looked over the top of her head. 'Why are those people staring at us?'

717

'They're from my school.' Tess waved in greeting. They all turned their backs on her and carried on talking.

'They don't seem very friendly.'

'No, well, I'm not exactly popular at the moment.'

'Why not?'

'I want to put on a school play.'

Jack's eyebrows rose. 'And is that such a crime?'

'It is if they're paying for it.' She explained briefly about Cynthia's *coup de grâce*.

'And this is the woman who gave Emily detention? She sounds a nightmare.'

'She is.' Tess glanced back at the group clustered around the table. 'Do you mind if we sit over there? I can't stand them watching us, waiting for me to choke on my baguette.'

They ordered their food and took their drinks to a window table overlooking the village green, as it was called. It was a picturesque name for little more than a grassy triangle with a clump of beech trees and a couple of swings, bordered on one side by the pub, and on the others by the Blockbuster video shop and the Haxsall Tandoori.

As their food arrived, Jack said, 'Emily tells me you've been very good to her.'

'I try. It can't have been easy for her, making a new start.'

'No.' He stared down at his pint. 'I hope I haven't made things even more difficult for her, losing my temper last night.'

'Of course not. Why would you?'

'She's worried you might hate her because of me.'

'Emily's a great kid. Nothing can change that.' She picked the lettuce out of her sandwich. 'Anyway, you had every right to be furious. What I did was stupid.'

He didn't argue with that, she noticed. 'It wasn't just that. I was jealous too.'

'Jealous?'

'I couldn't believe you'd managed to get through to Emily when I'd been trying for so long.' His voice was quiet. 'She's never told me what happened the day her mother died. Don't worry, I'm not asking you to tell me,' he said quickly. 'I'm just surprised, that's all.'

And hurt. Tess could see the unhappiness in his face. Poor man, he must have felt as if he'd failed. 'She probably just found it easier to talk to a stranger.'

'No, it's more than that. I arranged for her to see a grief counsellor after Miranda died. She wouldn't talk to her.'

'Maybe it was too soon?'

'Or maybe it was the wrong person.' His eyes were serious. 'You're right,

I'm the one who should be talking to her. I should have tried harder to get through to her.'

'Get through to a fourteen-year-old girl? You'd stand more chance of communicating with aliens on another planet!'

'You managed it.'

'I've had a lot of practice.'

He pushed his salad around his plate, then gave up and put his fork down. 'I still should have tried harder. But I've been so wrapped up in my own feelings lately, I haven't given much thought to hers.'

'That's not surprising.'

'But I shouldn't be, should I? I'm all they've got. I should be there for them.'

'You're also human. You're bound to make mistakes.'

'Miranda didn't,' Jack said quietly. 'She had everything brilliantly organised. And she was great with the girls. She always seemed to know the right thing to do or say. I just keep putting my foot in it.' He looked rueful. 'Those children are a complete mystery, like the washing machine. They're noisy, unpredictable, and I never know when they're going to blow up.'

'Except unlike the washing machine they don't come with an instruction manual.'

'Even if they did, I probably wouldn't be able to understand it.' Jack sank his chin into his hands. 'That's what's so frustrating. In my job I know what I'm doing. I solve problems every day, and I'm good at it. But at home I'm faced with all these things I just don't know how to deal with. It's a scary feeling.' He turned his glass round in front of him. 'I think that's why I've been spending so long at the office. I keep saying it's pressure of work, but it isn't. It's just the only place I feel in control.'

'You're not the only one who gets scared, you know.'

'No?'

'Of course not. Most of us just muddle through, making it up as we go along.'

'Is that what you do?'

'Most of the time.'

'I bet you don't. I bet you're a brilliant mother.'

'I think Dan might disagree with you there!' she laughed.

'That's your son, is it? How old is he?'

'Seventeen.'

'Really?' He tried to hide it, but she could tell he was shocked. 'You must have been very young when he was born?'

'If you're asking was he an accident, then yes, he definitely was. I got pregnant on my sixteenth birthday. Some present!'

'So you weren't much older than Emily. I can't imagine her having a baby.'

'Neither could my mum, believe me.'

'Was she furious?'

'More upset than angry, I think. I was the brains of the family, you see. The one who was meant to do so well for herself.' She gazed into the depths of her glass.

'I'd say you've done pretty well for yourself.'

'Only because Mum stood by me. She was brilliant. I couldn't have coped without her.'

'What about Dan's father?'

'Not quite so supportive, I'm afraid.' Tess pushed her plate away from her. 'I thought we were serious about each other, but me getting pregnant was a bit too serious for him.'

'You mean he walked out on you?'

'I think ran is a better word. As fast as his legs could carry him.'

Jack smiled. 'I take it you don't see him any more?'

'It's funny you should ask that.' She told him about Dan tracking Phil down. 'I don't know if he's written to him yet, but I know he will. Dan can be very determined when he wants something.'

'Sounds like his mother.'

'No, I'm just pig-headed.'

They sat in silence for a while. Then Jack said, 'So how do you feel about seeing your ex again?'

'I try not to think about it. I don't even know if I will see him. Maybe he'll only want to see Dan. Or maybe—'

'Maybe he won't want anything to do with either of you?'

She nodded. 'Although I don't know which scares me more, him getting in touch or not getting in touch.' She took a sip of her orange juice. 'But you don't want to hear me droning on about my problems.'

'Why not? It makes a change from having to think about mine.'

They chatted for a while longer, until Tess noticed the rest of the staff heading for the door. 'Oops, I think that's my cue to leave.'

Jack glanced at his watch. 'I'd better make a move too. I've got a meeting in Leeds at two thirty.'

As they walked out to his car, he said, 'I don't suppose you'd like to come to a party, would you? As part of my penance for losing my temper, I've had to agree to Emily having a house-warming. She spent most of last night on the phone, fixing up for her friends from Leeds to come over.'

'In that case, I'd better not. I don't think Emily would appreciate her form teacher being there.'

'Probably not, but I could use the moral support. Please?'

'I'll check my diary.' She'd already made up her mind not to be there. She could just imagine Emily's face if she turned up. 'When is it?'

'The end of October. I'm putting it off for as long as possible.' They reached his car. 'Can I give you a lift back to school?' he asked.

Tess shook her head. 'I need the exercise. Well, thanks very much for lunch, Mr Tyler.'

He smiled. 'I think since I've invited you to a party you could get away with calling me Jack, don't you?'

10

'Come on, Em, you'll be late!'

And she wouldn't be the only one. Jack glanced at his watch. It was almost eight. He had a site meeting with the council planners to discuss the Westpoint development at nine, and he hadn't even had a chance to look at their comments on his last set of revised drawings yet. He'd brought them home to work on but Emily had been having trouble with her maths homework and he'd spent the evening explaining the intricacies of trigonometry instead. By the time he'd made supper and stacked the dishwasher, then restacked it because it made funny noises, there wasn't much time for doing anything but dozing off in front of *Sex and the City*.

And then he'd been up in the night because Sophie felt ill. There was still a greenish tinge to her face as she stared into her bowl of Frosties.

'Get a move on, Sophie!'

She looked up at him. 'I don't feel well.'

He'd never dreaded that sentence before, but he was just beginning to realise what it meant. Those four words could plunge his well-ordered world into chaos.

'Are you sure?' He felt her forehead. Over the past month or so, he'd begun to realise there was a difference between a real 'I don't feel well' and a 'We've got double maths I don't feel well.'

'My throat hurts and I feel sick.'

'Maybe you shouldn't go to school today. I'll call the childminder.'

Emily came downstairs just as he was leafing through his address book. 'What are you looking for?'

'The childminder's number. Sophie's not going to school today.'

'Lucky pig.' Emily helped herself to cornflakes.

'Can anyone remember what the childminder's surname is?'

'You mean you can't?' Emily looked appalled. 'Well, that's great, isn't it? You leave us in the care of some stranger and you can't even remember her name. What if she abducted us? How would you know where to start looking?'

'If she abducted you two, I'd probably start looking in the local asylums

– ah, here it is. Smith. No wonder I couldn't remember it.' He reached for the phone on the worktop and dialled the number. 'Try to eat something, Soph. It might make you feel better.'

The childminder made all the right soothing noises when she heard Sophie was feeling poorly, but her sympathy vanished when she realised Jack wanted to bring her round.

'What, all day?' she said. 'But my hours are before and after school during term-time. Those are the arrangements.'

'Well, yes – usually. But this is an exception, isn't it? I'll pay you, of course,' Jack offered quickly, but the childminder was having none of it.

'Sorry, I can't do it.' She raised her voice over the sound of the *Tweenies* in the background. 'I'm up to my ears in under-fives all day. Besides, what if she's got a bug? I don't want her spreading it round everyone else, do I? No, I reckon the best place for her is tucked up at home.'

I know how she feels, Jack thought as he put the phone down. Emily looked up from her cornflakes. 'I could stay off school and look after her, if you like?'

That was when Sophie dropped her spoon and threw up dramatically. Emily shot out of her seat in a second.

'Ugh, gross! On second thoughts, forget I said that. I'm out of here.' She scooted into the hallway and a second later the door banged shut, leaving Jack and a forlorn-looking Sophie sitting at the kitchen table.

He mopped up the mess, got Sophie out of her school uniform and changed his own clothes, still wondering what the hell he could do.

Meanwhile the clock ticked on. Eight twenty-three. Even if he left now, he'd never make it to Leeds in time for that meeting.

He didn't realise he'd been muttering under his breath until Sophie emerged from her room in her *Simpsons* pyjamas. 'Sorry, Daddy,' she mumbled.

'That's okay, sweetheart, you can't help it.' Jack dredged a smile from somewhere. 'We'd better find someone to look after you.'

The first thing he heard when Ros picked up the phone was a blast of the *Tweenies*. Was that all anyone ever watched?

She sounded breathless. 'Jack, hi. How's it going?'

'Not very well, actually—' he started to tell her, but she cut him off.

'Look, can I call you back in a couple of hours? You just caught me. My next-door neighbour's come round to look after the kids and I'm sneaking out while they're distracted.'

'Oh.'

'Why? Is there anything wrong?'

'No – well, yes, as a matter of fact. Sophie's ill and—'

'What's wrong with her? Nothing serious?'

'I don't think so. She's just been sick. But the thing is—'

'Have you taken her to a doctor?'

'Well, no. She was only sick about ten minutes ago. But I just wanted—'

'Does she have any other symptoms? Headache? Stiff neck? Have you tried shining a light in her eyes?'

'Who do you think I am, the bloody Gestapo?' Jack was exasperated. 'She's fine, honestly. Just a tummy upset, that's all. But the thing is, I've got a really important meeting this morning and the childminder won't take her, so I wondered if I could drop her off at yours? Just until I get through with this meeting. It won't take long and I'd be really grateful,' he went on in a rush. 'I wouldn't ask you at such short notice but I'm desperate.'

Ros sighed. 'I'd love to help, Jack, but the thing is I've got a job interview at nine.'

'A job? You?' He forgot his own panic.

'Don't sound so surprised. I may have spent the last six years up to my elbows in Play-Doh and dirty nappies, but I do still have a few brain cells to rub together, you know. And now Ben's at school full-time I thought I should start using them again. I've got an interview at the library.'

'Good for you,' Jack said.

'But not for you. What about Mum? Can't she help?'

'I tried her. She'd already left for her yoga class.'

'Of course, it's Tuesday, isn't it? Isn't there anyone else? What about your cleaner? Or one of the mums from school?'

'It's Pauline's day off and I don't really know any mums. I'm afraid I'm a bit stuck.' He fought and failed to keep the self-pitying note from creeping into his voice.

He could hear Ros chewing her lip on the other end of the line. 'Look, why don't I just put off this interview? I'm sure if I rang the library—'

'Absolutely not. I won't hear of it. You go and get that job.'

'Well, I don't know about that!' Ros laughed shakily. 'I'm probably wasting my time anyway.'

'Rubbish. That library needs you.'

'Look, I'll call you when I get out, okay? Maybe I could come round to your office and pick Sophie up?'

'Fine. And good luck, Ros.'

'Thanks.' He put the phone down, and glanced at the clock. There was nothing else for it. 'Get dressed, Sophie,' he called up the stairs. 'Daddy's taking you to work.'

There were raised eyebrows all round when he turned up at the airfield half an hour late and with Sophie in tow. Fortunately neither Peter Jameson nor Humphrey Crawshaw were there, though Greg and two men from the council's planning department were.

Greg left the two men and plodded across the field to greet him at the gate.

'Hello, Princess.' He bent down and scooped Sophie into his arms. 'What are you doing here?'

'She's not well enough for school. And I wouldn't do that if I were you. She threw up in the car,' he added, as Greg swung Sophie high in the air.

'Oops!' He put her down quickly. 'Don't you think she'd be better off at home if she's ill?'

'I didn't have much choice. It was either bring her or let everyone down. Anyway, she seems a lot better now.' He looked down at her. She'd lost her green colour and perked up tremendously since she'd been sick all over his upholstery.

'Poor sod, it must be a nightmare for you.' Greg looked sympathetic. 'Tell you what, why don't I keep her busy for a few minutes while you talk to the planning guys?'

'What about you? Shouldn't you be talking to them?'

'I've already had my grilling, thanks very much. It's you they want to talk to now.' Greg put his arm around Sophie. 'I'll show this young lady round the site and join you later, okay?'

In spite of Greg's help, the meeting didn't go well. Unfortunately the council planners had been over his drawings in the tiniest detail and asked all kinds of searching questions. Jack tried to bluff his way through and wished he'd spent more time preparing the night before, instead of doing Emily's homework. He could tell the planners weren't impressed.

By the time Greg joined them, he was floundering. Fortunately his brother-in-law had done his research this time and was able to fill in when Jack's mind went blank.

Finally the planners went away, apparently satisfied. Jack turned to Greg. 'Thanks for rescuing me. And for looking after Sophie.' He looked around the empty field. 'Where is she, by the way?'

'She got bored. Said she was going for a walk.' Greg scanned the horizon. 'Funny, I thought she'd be back by now.'

'Greg! You were meant to be keeping an eye on her.' Jack sprinted across the field. How could he lose both his children in the space of a week?

After five minutes of panic-stricken searching, he found her at the far end of the site. She was digging a hole with a stick, unconcerned that she'd nearly brought on a heart attack in her father.

'Sophie!' He doubled over, panting for breath. 'Why did you go wandering off like that?'

'Sorry. I was digging for treasure. Look what I've found.' She held her grubby fist out to him.

As the site was a former airfield, he was expecting a bit of old propeller, maybe a fragment of nose cone left over from a Second World War

Lancaster. He wasn't expecting the earth-clotted lump Sophie dropped into his hand.

'What is it, Daddy?' she asked.

'I'm not sure.' He picked the earth off it. Underneath, it was long and smooth and jagged at the ends, as if it had shattered off a larger piece. 'It looks like a bit of bone to me.'

'Bone!' Sophie stared up at him, wide-eyed. 'Do you think there's a dead body down there?'

'More likely a dog's buried it.' Jack examined the chunk of bone for a moment, then slipped it into his pocket. 'Come on, let's get back to the office.'

He'd left the car in a disused yard behind the airfield. As he rounded the corner, he spotted a youth in a baseball cap, squatting down beside one of the wheels.

Sophie saw him too. 'What's that boy doing?'

'Letting down my tyres. Oi, you!'

The young man looked up, saw him and sprinted off. Jack ran after him. He had a head start, but as he reached the rundown buildings on the far side of the field he caught his foot and went sprawling. Jack landed on top of him, knocking the wind out of them both.

'Let me go! You're breaking my arm!'

'I'll break your neck, you little—'

'You heard him. Let him go.'

Jack looked up as a shadow fell across them. Standing over him were three similar-looking youths in baseball caps and tracksuits, all armed with lethal-looking spanners.

And with them, looking even more menacing, was Sam Dobbs.

11

'Let him go,' he said again. His voice was low and threatening.

Jack tightened his grip on the boy's collar. 'He was vandalising my car!'

'That's no reason to break his neck, is it?'

Jack looked around at the scowling faces. 'Call them off first.'

Sam turned to the youths. 'All right, lads. Show's over. Get back to work.'

'But Darren—'

'I said back to work!' Grumbling, they lumbered off back towards the rundown sheds. Sam looked at Jack. 'They didn't mean any harm.'

'So why were they carrying those spanners?'

'They're mechanics, you daft sod. They heard the shouting and came to find out what all the fuss was about, like me.' He nodded at the boy. 'Do you think you could get off our Darren? He seems to be going a funny colour.'

Jack got up and brushed off his trousers. Sam pulled Darren out of the mud and gave him a clip round the ear.

'You're here to fix cars, you silly bugger, not wreck 'em! Now go and get yourself cleaned up. Sorry about that,' he said, as Darren went off in the same direction as the others. 'Bit over-enthusiastic.'

'Is that what you call it?' Jack pulled out his phone. 'We'll see if the police agree with you, shall we?'

'You don't want to phone them.' Sam's smile disappeared.

'Why not?'

'Because the lad's in enough trouble with them as it is. Why do you think he's here?'

Before Jack could answer, Sophie came puffing across the field towards them.

'Daddyyyy! I need the toilet!'

'You can use ours,' Sam offered. 'Round the back, second door on the left. It's all right, she'll be quite safe,' he added, seeing Jack's frown.

Jack looked around. 'What exactly is this place?'

727

'You mean you don't know? I thought you were meant to be the architect?'

'They're just marked down as empty buildings on the plan.'

'They were empty, until we started renting them a couple of years back.' Sam extended his arms to sweep the yard. 'Welcome to Second Chance. I'll show you around, if you like.'

He led the way to a Portakabin office where a girl not much older than Emily was labouring over a computer keyboard. 'We've got visitors, Melanie,' Sam said. 'See if you can get us a couple of cups of tea out of that kettle, will you? Oh, and look after Mr Tyler's little girl when she comes out of the loo. I'm just going to give him the grand tour.'

Jack followed him into the yard. It was littered with rusting car parts, bits of broken toilet cistern and piles of wood. Surrounding it were a number of sheds and outbuildings, all in various states of disrepair. But Sam looked proudly around as if it were Blenheim Palace.

'Great, isn't it?' he said. 'That's the garage over there. You've already met the lads. And over there's the plumbing workshop and the carpentry shop. Oh, and that's the sparks department.' From the far end came the muted throb of a dance track. 'Music while you work,' Sam grinned. 'Upstairs is the kitchen. I expect they'll be serving up lunch soon, if you'd like to join us?'

'That's very kind of you.' Jack watched a pair of young men in hooded sweatshirts carrying a TV set across the yard. 'But what exactly is this place? Who are all these people?' And why do I feel as if I'm watching CCTV crime footage? he wondered.

'They're just kids,' Sam shrugged. 'Kids trying to straighten their lives out after being inside.'

'Inside? As in prison?'

'Young offenders' institutions, mostly. We aim to keep them out of prison. That's why we're here.'

'I didn't realise there was a difference,' Jack said, and wished he hadn't as Sam sent him a disdainful look.

'No, you wouldn't. I bet you've never even had a parking ticket, have you? Prison is for grown-ups, it's the hard-core stuff. Teenagers are mostly sent to young offenders' institutions. But that's not to say they won't end up in prison if they're not careful.' He picked up a plank of wood that had fallen down and stacked it against the wall with the rest. 'Some youngsters don't get a break once they've done time. They can't get a job because they've got a record, so they can't make a new start. Sometimes the only way they can get by is to start robbing again.' He raised his hand in greeting as the two lads came loping back across the yard. 'We try to help. We teach them some skills, give them a real job. We give them the chance to wipe the slate clean and get back some self-respect. Hence the name – Second Chance.'

He led the way to the garage. Inside it was hot and dark, and the air was tangy with oil fumes. The three boys working on a Vauxhall Vectra gave him dirty looks from under the bonnet.

'So how do you pay for all this?' Jack asked.

'We earn it, of course. Part of the money comes from fundraising, but the rest we make ourselves, repairing cars and electrical equipment, doing joinery and plumbing jobs, that kind of thing. We're practically self-supporting.'

Jack suppressed a shudder. He wouldn't like the idea of a couple of young thugs in his house, second chance or no second chance. God knows what they'd stuff in their pockets.

His distaste must have shown on his face because Sam said, 'Thank God some people are a bit more trusting than you.'

'You've got to admit, it is a bit risky.'

'So when you get a builder round to fix your guttering or you send that posh car of yours for a service, how do you know the person doing it hasn't been inside?'

'Well—'

'Exactly. You don't. At least we're honest about it.'

'Honest?' Jack laughed. 'That's hardly the word I'd choose.' He looked around. 'I appreciate what you're doing and all that, but do you really think these kids are going to change?'

'Why not? I did.'

Jack stared at him. 'You were in prison?'

'No, but I would have been if the police had caught me one more time. It was breaking and entering mostly. Oh, and I stole a couple of cars like yours, just for a laugh. I was a kid, I didn't know what I was doing. Just like this lot. There but for the grace of God and all that.'

'You really believe that?'

'I have to.' Sam pulled off his scarf and for the first time Jack noticed the dog collar peeping out from the fraying neck of his jumper. 'It goes with the job, you might say. Ah, it looks like Melanie's got the kettle working. Shall we go inside?'

The Portakabin was cosy after the October chill. Sophie was happily helping Melanie with some filing. Jack and Sam pulled their chairs up to the electric heater and drank their tea.

'So, what do you think?' Sam helped himself to a biscuit out of the tin.

'It's very admirable. And you say you're renting these buildings?'

'We were, until the Westpoint lot took away our lease. You know they own this bit of land?'

Of course he did. He'd put several thousand square metres of prime retail space right where they were sitting.

'We offered to buy it from them but they wouldn't hear of it,' Sam went on. 'Although to be honest I don't think we could afford the kind of money they're asking. So that's it for us. Unless you could have a word with them?' He looked hopeful.

'It's not my decision to make,' Jack said. 'I'm just the planning consultant. But I don't think Westpoint would want to give all this away, not when they can develop it and make a profit.'

'That's what it's all about, isn't it? Profit.' Sam crunched on his biscuit and stared out of the window.

'Couldn't you find new premises? There must be somewhere suitable?'

'Oh, there is. Lots of places. Trouble is, every time the locals get wind we're moving in, they get up a petition against us. Then the council refuses us planning permission, and we're back to square one.'

'I suppose you can understand that. I wouldn't want a load of ex young offenders on my doorstep.'

'And I don't want a bloody great shopping centre on mine, but it looks like I'm going to get one.'

'I'm sorry I can't help.'

'Are you?'

Jack put down his cup. He sensed he'd outstayed his welcome. 'Come on, Sophie, get your coat on. I'd better get back to the office before they wonder where I am.'

'Don't let me keep you. I expect you've got lots more lives to ruin before you go home for your tea.'

'Reverend Dobbs—' he began, then gave up. There was nothing he could say that Sam Dobbs wanted to hear. 'I'll see you at the public inquiry,' he muttered.

'I liked it there,' Sophie announced, as they headed back to the car.

'Me too.' He took a last look back at the place.

'Daddy, what's a bastard?' Sophie asked.

'What?'

'B-A-S-T-A-R-D. It's on the front of your car, look.'

Jack stared in disbelief at the spray-painted bonnet. Then he looked back at the Second Chance building. Three faces at the workshop window ducked out of sight.

On second thoughts, fuck them, he thought. The sooner this place is demolished, the better.

Vicky was waiting when he got back to the office. 'You took your time. I thought you'd be back ages ago.'

'So did I.' He slumped at his desk and stared at the pile of unanswered mail that had somehow sprouted. 'Anything interesting happen while I was out?'

'Depends whether you think Humphrey Crawshaw baying for your blood is interesting or not.' Vicky smiled at Sophie, who was perched on her father's knee. 'He's asked to see you in his office as soon as you get in.'

'Great. Just great.' Jack ran a distracted hand through his hair. 'I'd better go in and see him.' He looked up at Vicky. 'Could you keep an eye on Sophie for me?'

'Sure. We can raid the office biscuit tin.' Vicky winked at her.

Greg was already in Humphrey Crawshaw's office, looking tense and unhappy. He shot Jack a warning glance as he walked in.

'Come in, Jack.' Humphrey's smile didn't reach his eyes. 'Take a seat. Herbal tea?'

Jack eyed the murky khaki brew. 'It's a bit early for me, thanks.'

'Now, Jack, I thought we should have a chat.' Humphrey's friendly manner didn't fool Jack for a second. He leaned back against his desk, a tall, distinguished-looking man in his early sixties, with not a spare ounce of flesh on him, thanks to a combination of marathon running, rigorous gym workouts and a highly disciplined diet. Just looking at him made Jack feel like a slob. 'I hear the meeting with the planners didn't go too well this morning. I'm a little concerned as to why.'

'I expect you already know.'

'I wanted to hear it from you.'

'Okay, then. My daughter was ill and couldn't go to school, so I had to bring her along.'

'It was a one-off,' Greg, ever the peacemaker, put in.

Humphrey ignored him. 'The workplace is no place for a child, Jack.'

'I realise that. But I didn't exactly have a choice. The childminder couldn't take her, and—'

Humphrey held up a silencing hand. 'With respect, that's your problem, not ours. What I expect from you is one hundred and ten per cent commitment. And I have to say, I'm not getting it at the moment.'

'I thought the meeting went very well, under the circumstances,' Greg said quickly.

Jack met Humphrey's eye unflinchingly. 'In what way?'

'Sorry?'

'In what way aren't you getting commitment from me? I'm still meeting my deadlines, aren't I?'

'Well, yes—'

'And my work is of sufficient standard?'

'More than sufficient, you know that. But I'm just not seeing the effort any more. You're not putting in the hours you used to.'

'That's because I have two daughters at home who need me.' Suppressed anger throbbed in his temple. 'I take my work home with me and if necessary I always make up any time I've lost. But I refuse to neglect my children because of some macho culture that says you have to be seen at your desk twelve hours a day just so you can earn brownie points from the boss.'

'Jack, please. I didn't mean to imply you weren't doing your job properly.' Humphrey backtracked wildly.

'I thought that's exactly what you were saying.'

'No one expects you to neglect your children. God knows, I've had kids myself, I know what it's like.' You also had a wife and a brace of nannies to look after them, Jack thought sourly. 'But we're a team and I see you as our top player. Our star striker, our David Beckham, if you like.'

'He's a midfielder,' Greg muttered.

'I rely on you,' Humphrey went on. 'I'm depending on you to bring this Westpoint project home. Don't let me down, will you?'

'My kids rely on me too,' Jack said, but Humphrey still wasn't listening.

'Now, I've organised a little get-together next week, just to oil the wheels with the Westpoint people. Stick it in your diary, will you? Kirsty can give you the details.'

'I'll see what I can do—' Jack began, then saw Humphrey's expression. 'I'll be there,' he said.

Greg followed him out of Humphrey's office. 'I'm really sorry about that,' he said. 'He was in a rage when I got back. God knows who told him.'

'I expect the planners called him to complain. I can't blame them, it was pretty unprofessional.'

'It was hardly your fault though, was it? You can't help Sophie being ill. Like you said, the girls have to come first.'

'Even if it costs me my job?' Jack's mouth twisted. 'I'm not much good if I can't provide for them, am I?'

'Come on, Jack. It won't come to that. You heard what Humphrey said. You're his top man. Okay, so he might whinge a bit sometimes, but he can't do without you.' He grinned. 'You're his star striker!'

Jack smiled reluctantly. 'Let's hope I don't end up on the subs' bench.'

Sophie was waiting for them when they got back to his office. She was sitting on the edge of Vicky's desk, chomping happily on a ham and tomato roll.

'A man with a big basket of sandwiches came round,' she said, wide-eyed. 'Vicky said I could have whatever I liked.' She looked at Greg. 'Someone wrote bastard on Daddy's car.'

'Did they now?' Greg turned to Jack, eyebrows raised. 'Wasn't Humphrey Crawshaw by any chance, was it?'

'Very funny,' said Jack.

'I went digging up at the field,' Sophie went on. 'And I found treasure, didn't I, Daddy? Show Uncle Greg what I found.'

'If it's a winning lottery ticket, I want half,' Greg said, as Jack dug in his pocket and pulled out the piece of bone.

'Nothing so exciting, I'm afraid.'

'So I see. What the hell is it?'

'Daddy says it's a bit of bone. It could be a dinosaur, don't you think?'

'Could be, sweetheart.' Greg turned it over in his hand. 'Tell you what, why don't I send it to our special archaeology department to find out?'

'You don't have to do that,' Jack protested, but Sophie was already wildly excited at the prospect.

'Really? Do you think it's old?'

'Maybe. You never know, it might even be as old as Daddy.'

12

A week later, Tess went to visit her mother. Margaret Doyle still lived in the same flat on the council estate where Tess and her sister had grown up. Apart from a smattering of new graffiti on the walls, the place hadn't changed much in thirty years. Children still chased each other on the grassy area at the front of the block, their bikes and skateboards abandoned around them. Washing fluttered like colourful bunting on makeshift lines stretched across the outside walkways that led to each front door.

Three women gossiping on the stairwell greeted Tess with nods and smiles as she puffed her way up to the third floor. Everyone knew Margaret Doyle and her daughters.

Her mother was waiting for her outside the flat. She hadn't changed much over the years either. There were a few more lines around her shrewd brown eyes and her dark hair was threaded with more grey than there used to be, but the brown skirt, beige cardigan and faded flowery slippers were just the same as when Tess had come home from school, dragging her bag behind her.

And she was still coming home from school now. Only this time it was someone else's homework she dragged with her.

Margaret greeted her with a nod, her arms folded. She wasn't the kind of mother who went in for big hugs and lots of kisses. Tess couldn't think of a time when she'd done either in the last ten years. But somehow that didn't matter. Other people might find her manner dour, but those close to her knew she would put herself out to help anyone in trouble. Although she'd probably give them a good talking-to and tell them to pull themselves together afterwards.

'This is a surprise,' she said. 'What's wrong?'

'Mum! Why does there have to be anything wrong? I just thought I'd pop round, that's all.'

She forced herself to meet her mother's eye, certain she must have guilt written all over her face. She never found it easy to lie to her. Margaret seemed to have an inbuilt truth radar.

Fortunately it wasn't working too well today. She sent her a suspicious look. 'You'd better come in, then. But watch yourself in the kitchen. I've got a man looking at my plumbing.'

The man in question was in his mid-sixties, tall with snowy hair and piercing blue eyes. He emerged from under the sink to give Tess a friendly smile.

'How do?' he said. 'You must be Teresa. I'm Ronnie. Your mum's told me all about you.'

'Really?' Tess turned questioning eyes to her mother.

'Ronnie's from the Over Sixties club. He's kindly offered to sort out my U-bend.' Was it her imagination, or did her mother look slightly flustered? 'I've been on to the council to do it but they take a year and a day to get round to anything.'

Ronnie came back out from under the sink, a wrench in his hand. 'That should do it.' He put down the wrench and wiped his hands on his overall. 'Try it now, Maggie.'

Maggie? Tess waited for her mother to point out that her name was Margaret, as she usually did, but she just leaned across and turned on the tap.

'Lovely.' She beamed as the water gurgled down the plughole. 'Thank you, Ronnie. How much do I owe you?'

'You know I'd never charge you anything. But a cup of tea might be nice?' Ronnie's blue eyes gleamed hopefully.

'It'll have to be some other time. Teresa's here now and we need to talk.'

'Oh, but I don't mind—' Tess began, but her mother was already hustling Ronnie towards the front door, barely giving him time to gather up his tools.

'Shall I see you on Friday? It's cribbage night,' he was saying as she closed the door in his face.

'He's a nice man, but he doesn't know when he's outstayed his welcome,' she said briskly. She turned the tap on again, allowing herself a small smile of satisfaction. 'But he's not a bad plumber, I'll say that for him.'

'He seems very nice,' Tess said.

'He's all right. Better than a lot of those old fools up there, always moaning about their aches and pains.'

Tess leaned back against the worktop and smiled teasingly. 'I didn't know you had a new man in your life.'

'I have no such thing!' Margaret looked outraged. 'There's nothing like that going on. Ronnie just offered to help me out with a few odd jobs, that's all.'

'He seemed very keen on you.'

'More fool him, then.' She flicked the switch on the kettle as it came up to boil. 'There'll never be anyone for me but your father.'

'Dad's been dead for twenty years.'

'What difference does that make?'

What indeed? Tess thought. The way her mother talked about him, anyone would think he'd died last week. Margaret was only forty when it happened, not much older than Tess was now. But since then she'd never known her mother even look at another man. She'd soon come to realise that it wasn't grief or guilt that stopped her, just the certain knowledge that she would never, ever find anyone she loved as much as Martin Doyle.

Tess envied her in a way. It must be wonderful to find one's soulmate like that. But so incredibly lonely to lose them.

She thought about Jack Tyler. Was that how he felt about his wife? Or would he eventually be able to move on, find happiness again? And if he did, would his children let him? Much as she welcomed the idea of her mother finding someone to keep her company now, she wasn't sure how she would have felt about it as a teenager.

Tess watched as Margaret poured a splash of boiling water into the pot, swished it around then tipped it out into the sink. 'You don't have to go to all that trouble,' she said. 'A teabag in a mug would do for me.'

'Aye, I daresay. But not for me. If you're going to do something, you might as well do it properly.'

That went for the rest of the flat too. It might be small and old-fashioned, but it was immaculately kept. The paintwork gleamed, the rugs were beaten to within an inch of their lives, and the air was scented with pine disinfectant and furniture polish. Tess knew without looking that there would be no dustballs or lost biros under the sofa, no crumbs lurking behind the microwave.

Not like her place. Tess also knew her slapdash attitude to domestic matters was a constant trial to her mother. She comforted herself that she was a working woman and therefore too busy to waste time worrying about limescale. But then she remembered Margaret had brought up two daughters single-handed, held down a job, looked after her grandson and still found time to buff up her bath taps.

But no matter how houseproud she was, Margaret still insisted they drink their tea around the kitchen table, the way they'd always done. The sitting room was for evenings and 'real' visitors, not for daughters dropping by.

So, apparently, were the custard creams. Tess looked around hopefully. 'No biscuits?'

'You'll spoil your tea.' Margaret pushed her cup across the table towards her. 'Well? Spit it out.'

Tess looked startled. 'What?'

'Whatever it is you've come to tell me.'

'I told you, I've just popped round for a visit.'

736

'And I'm Cilla Black! You don't just drop round out of the blue unless you've got something you want to say. So let's hear it. And stop playing with that spoon. You're stirring your tea, not calling the faithful to prayer.' She put her cup down. 'You're not pregnant again, are you?'

'Mum!'

'What? The last time you had that look on your face that's what you told me.' She picked up her cup again. 'Whatever it is, it can't be as bad as that.'

Want to bet? Tess picked up her spoon then, seeing her mother's disapproving expression, quickly put it down again. 'Dan's been in touch with Phil.' She braced herself. Her mother said nothing. 'He found his address on the internet,' she hurried on. 'I wasn't sure if he'd write back, but he did.'

'I'm surprised he had the nerve,' Margaret said stonily. She looked at Tess. 'And you let Dan do it?'

'I couldn't very well stop him, could I?'

'You could have done something. You could have taken that computer away for a start.'

'He'd only use another one. He's seventeen, Mum, not seven. Besides, he has a right to know who his father is.'

'Father! Some father he's been all these years! Where was he when Dan was teething and you were up all night in the middle of your exams? Where was he when you were working all hours to make ends meet? Where was he when he should have been paying maintenance?' She stabbed her finger on the plastic tablecloth to make her point. She'd painted her nails a pale frosted pink, Tess noticed. She couldn't remember her ever doing that before. 'I don't suppose he thought much about his son then.'

'No, I don't suppose he did,' Tess said wearily. 'But that's all water under the bridge now, isn't it? The important thing is, Dan wanted to get in touch with him, and Phil seems keen. We should be pleased for him.'

It was the wrong thing to say. Margaret put her cup down with a clatter. 'Pleased? Pleased that he's deigned to talk to his own son after seventeen years? Anyway, I'm not surprised,' she sniffed. 'The hard work's all done now, isn't it? Dan's nearly an adult. Why shouldn't he just sweep in and take all the glory?'

They drank their tea in silence. She could feel the weight of her mother's disapproval. She knew what Margaret would have done under the circumstances; shouted, stomped around, and generally frightened Dan out of the very idea of looking for his father. It might have been an effective way of solving the problem, but Tess couldn't bring herself to do it.

Finally, Margaret said, 'Where is he now, anyway?'

'Somewhere down south, apparently. He works with computers.'

'Earns a fair bit, I suppose?'

'I expect so.' Tess narrowed her eyes. 'I'm not going to ask him for money, if that's what you're getting at.'

'Why not? Dan will be at university in a year. That's going to cost a bit.'

'I'll manage.'

'I daresay you will. But it'd be a lot easier if that useless article helped out.'

'Mum, I don't want anything from him! I've coped without his money for seventeen years and I'll cope now.'

'You're stubborn, do you know that?'

'And we all know where I get it from, don't we?'

Margaret got up and busied herself refilling the teapot, but not before Tess caught a rare smile. 'Happen you're right,' her mother said. 'You don't want to give him any excuse to come interfering in yours or Dan's life.'

Tess bit her lip. 'Actually—'

'I mean, living all that way away, he's not likely to hop on a bus and visit, is he?'

'Well—'

'Mind you, it's a pity he's not in Australia.'

'He's coming to dinner next Thursday.' Tess closed her eyes as she said it, then opened them again to see Margaret staring at her, teapot suspended in mid-pour.

'Teresa, you're joking. Tell me you're joking?'

'Dan asked him,' Tess said helplessly. 'I didn't actually think he'd come, did I?'

'After what that man did to you, you're actually inviting him round?'

'Don't look at me like that. I'm not exactly happy about it either, you know.'

'Then tell him he can't come.'

'How can I? Dan's so excited about it, I don't want to disappoint him.'

'I know what I'd do.' Margaret shook her head. 'Honestly, Teresa, if you let that man over your doorstep, you're even dafter than I thought you were.'

'There's someone to see you, Jack.' Vicky looked uneasy, and Jack understood why when Sam Dobbs walked into his office, followed by one of the surly youths, who had a baseball cap and a pierced eyebrow.

'Hello, Mr Tyler.' Reverend Dobbs was dressed in his usual duffel coat and scarf, looking more like a *Big Issue* seller than a man of the cloth.

'You've got a bloody nerve, showing your face in here.'

'Now, before you start, just hear us out. Clint's got something he wants to say, haven't you, lad?' He snatched the baseball cap off the boy's head and shoved it into his hands. 'Well, come on. Let's have it.'

The boy lowered his shaven head. 'Sorry,' he mumbled. 'About your car.'

'It was you, was it?' Jack leaned back in his seat. 'Do you have any idea the kind of trouble you caused me? I didn't have a car for nearly a week. Not to mention all the insurance claims. I've got better things to do than fill out paperwork!'

'I said I'm sorry.' Clint stuck out his chin. A stud glinted on the end of it.

'I'm afraid that's not good enough. I should call the police.'

'You're not going to though, are you?' Sam stepped in. 'Look, the lad knows he did wrong and he's sorry for it.'

'Oh, really? And I don't suppose you had to drag him in here to apologise?'

'Of course I did. He's a kid, not bloody George Washington! But he's doing his best to make amends. It won't happen again.'

'Too right it won't. Next time I visit that site I'm coming by bus!'

'He just got a bit carried away, that's all. He was angry.'

'*He* was angry? How do you think I felt?'

'It was just a car, Mr Tyler. This is Clint's future you're taking away here. Without us, lads like him have got no chance of staying away from crime.'

'You mean like vandalising cars?'

Sam smiled. '*Touché*, Mr Tyler. But like I say, things are bad enough for these kids without you calling in the police. He'll pay for the damage, won't you, Clint?'

'It doesn't matter,' Jack said, as Clint's low brows sank even further. 'The company will pay for it.'

'Company car, eh? Nice.' Sam was impressed. 'All I get is a company bike. And even then I have to buy my own puncture repair kit!'

Jack laughed. He had to admit he liked Reverend Dobbs, in spite of his brusque manner and habit of hanging around with criminals.

'Tea?' he offered.

'No thanks, I'd better be getting back.' He looked at the drawings spread across the desk. 'No prizes for guessing what this is. Mind if I have a look?'

'Help yourself.' Jack pushed the papers across the desk at him. 'These are the elevated plans of what the finished buildings will look like.'

'Very nice. You've done a great job, Mr Tyler.'

'Thanks.'

'No offence to your designs, but I'd still rather not see them happen.'

Before Jack had a chance to reply, Charlie walked in. She took one look at Sam and his thuggish-looking companion and said, 'Right, this time I'm definitely calling security.'

'It's all right, love, I'll save you the bother.' Sam pulled his hat further down over his ears. 'I'll see you, Mr Tyler. Hope you don't have any more car problems.'

'What did he mean by that?' Charlie demanded as soon as the door closed behind them. 'He wasn't threatening you, was he?'

'He's not that bad once you get to know him.'

'That's not what you said when they trashed your car.' Charlie folded her arms and looked at him shrewdly. 'You're not going soft, are you, Jack?'

'No, but I can understand why they did it.'

'Well, I still think the lot of them should be locked up for life,' Charlie said.

'For trashing a car? Blimey, I'd hate to have you on my jury!' Jack pulled the drawing towards him and studied it. 'I wonder if there is any way I can incorporate Second Chance into this scheme?'

'Don't even think about it,' Charlie warned. 'Peter Jameson would go mad.' She dumped a fat ringbound file on his desk. 'Here, this will take your mind off it. It's that traffic study you wanted.'

Jack lifted the file with both hands. 'Looks like light bedtime reading.'

'It'll certainly send you to sleep.' She paused. 'Talking of cures for insomnia, what time are you getting to Humphrey's party tomorrow night?'

'Oh God, is it tomorrow?' Jack groaned. He hadn't fixed up a babysitter or anything. In fact he'd forgotten all about it. 'I think I might give it a miss.'

'But you can't!' Charlie sounded so dismayed Jack did a double-take. 'I mean – it's terribly important for your career. You know what Humphrey's like about people not coming to his soirées.'

'Maybe you're right.' He looked at the vast pile of work on his desk. 'I'll try to make it.'

She smiled. 'You'd better.'

'What do you think of this one?'

Charlie swished in front of the mirror, holding up a slip of black satin in front of her. Tom, her flatmate, barely glanced up from his copy of *What Car?*

'Are you sure you didn't try that one on ten minutes ago?'

'That one was long with thin straps. Pay attention, will you?' She turned back to the mirror. 'Do you think it's too tarty?'

'It's fine. If you're auditioning for *The Rocky Horror Show.*'

'Thanks. Your help is invaluable.' Charlie flung it down on the bed, where it joined Tom, Clive the cat, and a heap of other rejected outfits. Clive lifted his head and regarded her with sleepy yellow eyes. 'I don't even know why I'm asking you, anyway. You're hardly at the cutting edge of fashion yourself.' She looked disdainfully at his tatty trainers, ripped jeans and faded Spice Girls T-shirt.

'No, but I'm a man. And that's who you're trying to impress, isn't it?'

'Not at all. I'm just trying to decide what would look most professional for Humphrey Crawshaw's drinks party, that's all.'

'Fine. Then wear a nice, sensible suit. You can't get more professional than that, can you?' He flipped the page of his magazine. 'I take it Mr Perfect is going to be there?'

'I don't know who you mean.' She pulled an olive silk shift dress from the wardrobe and held it up against herself. Not bad. The colour brought out the green in her eyes, but it also added fire to her red hair, and she certainly didn't need that. She regarded it as her worst feature, especially having been teased over it for most of her life. Even though she was more drenched fox than belisha beacon, that didn't stop the kids at school calling her 'Ginge' and 'Carrot Top'.

At least the name-calling had stopped, but she still got tired of men sidling up and asking her if she was as fiery and passionate as her hair colour suggested. They usually found out when she gave them a stinging reply.

'You know. Him. Tom Cruise meets Christopher Wren.'

'You mean Jack Tyler? Yes, I think he might be there.' Who was she kidding? If he wasn't going, she wouldn't be going through these agonies. She would have worn her basic boring black and had done with it. And she certainly wouldn't have spent the best part of an hour blow-drying out the kinks in her stubbornly curly hair.

'What makes you think he's interested?' Tom asked from behind his magazine.

'What makes you think I am?'

'Hmm, let me think.' Tom pretended to consider. 'Could it be the way you mention his name every five minutes?'

'I do not!'

'No, you're right. It's more like every three. Or could it be the amount of time you spend getting ready for work every morning?'

'I have to look smart. We're not all scruffy computer geeks like you.'

'Just as well I am. There'd be no room in the bathroom for both of us in the morning.'

'You can always move out if you don't like it.'

'You don't mean that. You need me to help pay the mortgage, remember? Besides, what would you do without me to keep your feet on the ground? If I wasn't here, you'd work even more ridiculously long hours and forget to have a life.'

'There speaks a man who spends his life in front of a computer and doesn't remember to eat unless I put a sandwich in front of him.'

Charlie smiled affectionately. Tom was right; they needed each other. They'd been soulmates ever since they'd met at university. Since Tom was the most gorgeous man on campus and she was considered to be the best-looking girl, everyone had assumed it would only be a matter of time before they got together. But apart from a little light-hearted flirting, they'd confounded them all by staying just good friends.

'I can always find someone to sleep with, but I can't always find a good mate,' Tom had said, and Charlie agreed. Which was why, when she decided to buy her horrendously expensive canal-side flat in Leeds, Tom was the one she chose to share it with.

The arrangement had worked well for the past two years, mainly because they understood each other so perfectly. They were both ambitious, both workaholics – despite the laidback, studenty image he cultivated, Tom ran his own very successful website design business – and most importantly, neither of them was remotely interested in the other romantically. Tom had a string of beautiful, supermodel-like girlfriends and Charlie had Jack Tyler.

Or she would, if she got her way.

'So go on. What makes you think he's interested?' Tom asked again.

'Thanks for the vote of confidence!'

'I mean it. How long have you known him? Eighteen months? And he's never made a move on you, has he?'

'His wife died, remember? He's hardly likely to jump on me after that.'

She'd had a crush on Jack Tyler ever since she'd started at Crawshaw and Finch. He was the nicest and most approachable of her colleagues, as well as the best-looking. All the women in the office fancied him like mad. But Charlie had a strict hands-off policy when it came to married men – she'd been there before and it hadn't been a good experience. Certainly not one she'd like to repeat.

Not that she would have had the chance with Jack. As well as being one of the nicest men she knew, he was also the most faithful.

Charlie had met Miranda Tyler just once, at an office party shortly after she'd joined the company. She and Jack had made a striking couple, both tall, dark-haired and sophisticated. Charlie remembered watching her, so elegant and slender even after two children, and thinking how lucky she was to be married to someone like Jack.

A few months later, Miranda was dead. Overnight, Jack changed. He was like a zombie, in a total state of shock. Charlie felt deeply for him and longed to help, but it was as if he'd built up a wall around himself and hung a big 'Keep Out' sign on it. Despite being offered compassionate leave by Humphrey, he'd stunned them all by turning up at the office each day and working long, punishing hours. It was only the way he hid behind his office door and went for days without remembering to speak to anyone that gave away how he was really feeling.

He still worked long hours these days, but at least he talked more, although rarely about his wife or his family. Even though most of their conversations were frustratingly work-related, Charlie was sure she could be the one to help him through his heartache.

The only problem was she didn't know how Jack felt about her. She'd tried flirting a little, which hadn't had much effect, apart from making him slightly flustered. But was that embarrassed flustered or interested flustered? It was so difficult to tell with him. Sometimes she wondered if he'd even noticed.

But tonight would be the perfect opportunity to find out.

13

'Where is it you're going?'

Jack looked up from struggling with his cufflink and caught Emily's eye in the mirror. She was lying on her stomach on his bed, chewing her pencil as she composed her party guest list. It was beginning to look frighteningly long.

'I told you, my boss is having drinks at his house.'

'Sounds boring.'

'Believe me, it will be.'

'So why are you going?'

'I have to. It's work.'

'But you're always working,' she complained.

'True.' It certainly felt like it, anyway.

'Who'll be there?'

'I don't know. A lot of clients, probably. People from work. Your Uncle Greg.'

She picked moodily at the corner of the duvet cover where the stitching was coming undone. 'Will there be any women there?'

'Possibly. Does Auntie Ros count?' he joked, but she didn't laugh. Jack turned to face her. 'Look, Emily, I don't want to go to this thing, believe me. I can think of better things to do.'

'Why are you going, then?'

'Because your Auntie Ros won't give me a minute's peace if I don't – oh, sod it!' He gave up with his cufflink and threw it down on the dressing table. 'I never could manage these things.'

'Let me do it.' Emily uncurled herself off the bed and picked up the cufflink. Jack looked at her dark head bent over his sleeve as she fixed it in place. She'd grown much taller over the past months. She was almost up to his shoulder now and she looked so much like Miranda it hurt.

Christ, he missed her at times like this. He hated going to parties without her. If he closed his eyes, he could almost smell her perfume as she flitted from the bedroom to the bathroom, emptying her wardrobe, pulling out outfits and rejecting them before declaring she had nothing remotely decent to wear. But within half an hour she would look stunning, her hair dark and glossy, make-up perfect, dressed in something gorgeous. He would look at her and feel like the proudest man in the world.

Missing her was like an ache deep inside him. I can't do it, he thought suddenly. I can't go.

'Dad?' Emily had finished fastening his cufflink and was looking at him curiously. 'Dad, are you all right?'

He pulled himself together. Mustn't lose it in front of the girls. 'Course I am. Come on, we'd better get to Gran's before Uncle Greg goes without me.'

By the time they got to Leeds, Ros and Greg were already there, their kids tucked away safely in his mother's spare bedroom. The girls were having Jack's old room, and Jack was sleeping on the sofa that night.

'There you are!' Ros said. 'We thought you'd bottled out.'

'I nearly did.'

'Why? Humphrey's parties aren't that bad,' Greg grinned. 'At least there's always plenty of booze.'

'There could be wall-to-wall lapdancers and I still wouldn't fancy it.'

'And you're not drinking, remember?' Ros tapped her husband on the chest. 'I refuse to drive again just so you can get drunk and make a fool of yourself.'

'Yes, my love. Anything you say.' Greg rolled his eyes at Jack above his wife's head. Jack smiled back in sympathy. He'd lived with his big sister long enough to know what a bully she could be.

Sophie came into the room and wrapped herself around Greg's waist. 'Uncle Greg, did you find out anything about my treasure?'

Greg looked down at her. 'What treasure's that, sweetheart?'

'Her bone. You said you were going to send it to the laboratory,' Jack reminded him. 'She's been on about it for days.'

'Is it prehistoric?' Sophie asked hopefully.

'Oh, *that* treasure. No, sorry, Soph, I'm afraid your dad was right. It was just the remains of someone's Sunday lunch. A dog must have buried it there.'

Sophie looked disappointed. 'Can I have it back, then?'

'Sorry, love, I chucked it away. I didn't think you'd want it back.'

'Of course she doesn't,' Jack said quickly, as her lip jutted. 'What do you want with a manky old bone, Soph?'

'It might have been prehistoric,' Sophie muttered as she headed back to the kitchen. Greg watched her go.

'Oops, I think I've just lost my number one fan.'

'She'll get over it.' Jack turned to him. 'You didn't really send it to the lab, did you?'

'And make myself a laughing stock? What do you think?' Greg pulled a face. 'Peter Jameson thinks I'm a big enough idiot as it is.'

As they left, his mother and the girls were tucked up together on the sofa in front of a video, sharing a box of Maltesers. Jack wished he could stay in and watch it with them. He couldn't remember the last time he and the girls had enjoyed a night in.

'What are you watching?'

'Something with Julia Roberts.' No one lifted their eyes from the screen.

'Any good?'

'Don't know yet, we're still watching the trailers.'

Jack hesitated for a moment. Ros guessed what he was thinking and stepped in quickly.

'Oh no you don't. You're coming to this party. You never know, you might even enjoy yourself.'

He didn't enjoy himself. He stood with a drink in his hand, smiling and nodding while Peter Jameson cornered him about the new health club he'd just joined.

'The facilities are marvellous,' he droned on, as Jack stared into his empty glass with a glazed expression. 'Do you work out at all, Jack?'

'What? Oh no. No time these days.' He used to be a regular at the local gym. Now the only six packs he ever encountered were Sophie's favourite yoghurts.

'You should. The waiting list for mine is pretty long, but I'm sure I could pull a few strings and get you in.'

'Thanks. I'll – er – bear that in mind.' Once upon a time he would have jumped at the chance to earn some brownie points with an important client. Now he couldn't stop thinking about whether he'd forgotten to pack Sophie's teddy in her overnight bag. She couldn't go to sleep without it.

Just then Greg joined them and Jack allowed his jaw muscles to relax into his first genuine smile all evening.

'I'm sure my colleague here would be delighted to join your club, Peter.' He clapped his hand on Greg's bulky shoulder. 'He's gone to seed since he gave up playing rugby.'

'What are you talking about? I keep myself fit. I'll have you know I'm a keen follower of the Geri Halliwell workout video.'

'Yeah – from the sofa with a large whisky in your hand!'

'Why not? It's amazing how many calories leching burns off.'

Peter smiled thinly. 'I'm sure Graham wouldn't be interested in joining my club.'

There was an awkward moment where they both stared at their feet. Then Greg mumbled, 'The name's Greg.'

'What? Oh yes, of course. How could I forget?'

How indeed? It seemed unthinkable to Jack that the head of the Westpoint consortium could have forgotten the name of the man who was supposed to be coordinating the project. Either he had done it to be rude, or to underline how unimportant Greg was.

Whatever the reason, it must have hurt. Jack felt his brother-in-law's burning mortification as if it was his own.

He looked away, stared into the middle distance and longed for Miranda. At times like this, when things got really tedious, he could look across the room and see her there, charming someone, laughing at their jokes. She would catch his eye and smile, making it clear that even though she was with someone else, it was him she wanted. They would circle each other, silently flirting, until he was nearly mad with desire. Sometimes they'd barely get back to the car.

Suddenly there she was, smiling at him from the other side of the room. He blinked, then looked again, and realised with a shock that it wasn't Miranda. It was Charlie Ferguson.

A moment later she was by his side, looking stunning in bronze-coloured silk that clung to her well-toned curves and showed off her glorious autumnal colouring. Her hair was swept up in a loose, sexy style. The kind that only needed one tug of a pin to bring the whole lot tumbling down over her shoulders.

'Charlie!' Jack greeted her with relief. 'Do you know Peter Jameson?'

'We've met.' Charlie regarded him coolly, then said, 'You don't mind if I borrow Jack for a moment?'

'Of course.' Peter didn't meet her eye.

'Thanks,' Jack said, as they made their way swiftly through the crowd. 'Another five minutes of that and I would have run away screaming, partnership or no partnership.'

'You looked as if you needed rescuing.'

'I think poor Greg's the one who needs rescuing.' He glanced back to where Greg was desperately trying to talk to a disinterested Peter Jameson.

'He's a creepy little bastard.'

'Greg?'

'Jameson.' Charlie said it with such feeling that Jack turned to look at her in surprise. She was usually a fairly cool customer, good at hiding her emotions. But the look she gave Peter across the room was one of pure loathing.

'You sound as if you speak from experience?'

'Let's just say our paths have crossed before.'

Jack smiled. 'Now I'm intrigued.'

'Don't be. He doesn't deserve it.' She shrugged. 'It was just a boring case of sexual harrassment.'

'What?'

'Not me, you idiot. Christ, can you imagine me ever letting a little toad like that get the better of me?' Charlie laughed. 'No, it was a consultant at the planners where I used to work. We were doing some work on an apartment block he was developing and he seemed to think she was part of the package. She turned him down, so he got her thrown off the project.'

'Didn't she report him?'

'She tried, but the company hushed it all up. Didn't want to lose his valuable custom.' Charlie's mouth thinned with contempt. 'In the end, they gave her a nice fat pay cheque and sent her away. That was their idea of justice. Which is why I left.'

'You wouldn't have done the same?'

'Oh, I can understand why she did it. She knew she wasn't going to win, so she thought it was better to go with a pay-off and a decent reference than with nothing at all. But I would have stayed and fought, even if it cost me my job. There's no way I would have let him get away with it.'

'I can believe that.' Jack regarded her admiringly. He'd never had her down as the defenceless type. Charlie Ferguson might look fragile and feminine, but she was more than capable of taking care of herself.

Not like Greg. He glanced across the room to where his brother-in-law was still talking to Peter Jameson. At least he had his attention now. In fact, they looked to be quite deep in conversation.

He turned back to Charlie. 'Would you like a drink?'

'Please. Just a white wine spritzer. I'm driving.' She looked down at the empty glass in his hand. 'I take it you're not?'

He shook his head. 'I'm staying with my parents. They're looking after my daughters tonight.'

'How are they settling in to their new home?'

'Slowly, I think. Emily misses her social circle a bit more than Sophie, but at least she seems to be settling in at her new school. She's just auditioned for the school play.'

'Really?'

'And Sophie's made lots of friends at her new school. She's forever going round to other kids' houses for tea. I'm not quite sure of the etiquette, but I think I'm supposed to ask them back sometime.' He saw Charlie's glazed expression and stopped himself. 'I'm sorry, you should shut me up if I start droning on. I could bore for Britain on the subject of my daughters.'

'Not at all, it's fascinating.' She smiled brightly, a sure sign she hadn't listened to a word he'd said.

'Thanks, but I know there's nothing more tedious than listening to other people talk about their kids. Especially when you don't have any yourself.'

'Far from it.' She laid her hand across his wrist. 'You could never be tedious, Jack.'

Something about the husky way she said it confused him. She seemed to be standing a lot closer now, so close he could see the bronze flecks in her tawny eyes.

He gently extricated himself from her grasp. 'I'll – er – go and get those drinks.'

He was at the bar when Ros came up behind him.

'Who was that woman you were talking to?'

'Charlie Ferguson. She's one of our consultants.'

'So that's the famous Charlie, is it? Greg told me about her.' She glanced over her shoulder. 'He said she had the hots for you, but I didn't realise it was so obvious. Still, I suppose it would have to be, for Greg to notice.'

'What?' Jack laughed. 'Charlie? You've got to be joking.'

'Oh, come on, Jack. Even you can't be that thick. Anyone can see she was coming on to you. She homed in on you like a heat-seeking missile!'

'I think you've got the wrong idea. We're just friends, that's all. Not even that. More like work colleagues.'

'Then why was she flirting with you?'

'I hadn't noticed.'

'No, you wouldn't, would you? That's because you're a man. Trust me, she fancies you.'

Jack glanced across the room and caught Charlie's eye. She smiled and he looked away again sharply.

'You're blushing!' Ros laughed. 'Honestly, there's no need to be embarrassed about it, Jack. She's gorgeous. Isn't she, Greg?' She turned to her husband, who had just muscled his way through the crowd towards them, clutching a pint.

'What's that, my little Venus flytrap?'

'I was just saying how attractive Charlie is.'

'Oh God, yes. Absolutely stunning. Far too good for you, you lucky bastard.' He grinned at Jack. 'Not that I'm in any way envious,' he added, with a wary sidelong glance at his wife.

'What is this?' Jack looked from one to the other. 'I told you, there's nothing going on between me and Charlie.'

'That's all down to you, isn't it?' Greg said. 'Come on, Jack, everyone in the office knows she's after you. The only one who can't see it is you, apparently.'

'That's probably what she finds so attractive.' Ros nodded wisely. 'Women love a challenge.'

Jack looked from one to the other. It was as if they'd both started speaking Portuguese. 'Look, I don't know where you've got this idea from, but you're wrong. Charlie is no more interested in me than I am in Greg.'

'There you are.' Charlie edged her way in between them. 'I was wondering where you'd got to.'

Greg raised his eyebrows. 'You were saying?'

For the next twenty minutes Jack had to endure Ros' less than subtle interrogation of Charlie Ferguson. Why the poor woman didn't just walk away he had no idea. He felt like it, but sheer embarrassment kept him rooted to the spot as Ros probed into everything from Charlie's marital history – 'Not even a serious boyfriend? And you're how old?' – to her wardrobe – 'Manolo Blahniks, you say? They must have set you back a bit.' Charlie kept a fixed smile on her face but Jack could tell she was desperate to escape.

Finally, Greg rescued them both by fetching another round of drinks. 'So,' he said as he handed them out, 'how are the party preparations going, Jacko?'

'What party?' Charlie turned to him. 'You didn't tell me you were having a party.'

'It's not really my party. Emily – my daughter – is the one organising it.'

'Yes, but adults are invited too, aren't they?' Ros leapt in. 'We're going. You should come, Charlie. She could come, couldn't she, Jack? It's a week on Friday.'

Oh great. He could just imagine her bopping away to hard house garage funk or whatever they called it with Emily's disreputable mates. 'I don't really think it's Charlie's thing—'

'I'd love to,' she interrupted him.

'But they'll all be teenagers. Teenagers with acne and bad attitudes, smuggling in cider and sneaking upstairs to snog under the coats.'

'It sounds like fun.'

'I doubt it.'

'Don't be such an old fogey, Jack,' Ros scolded him. 'Charlie's not that old herself. She'd probably love it, wouldn't you, Charlie?'

'It's okay. Jack's right, it doesn't really sound like my sort of thing.' Charlie's smile was even more fixed as she took her spritzer from Greg. 'If you'll excuse me, I really should circulate.'

'You utter cretin,' Ros snapped as Charlie pushed her way through the crowd. 'Now look what you've done. You've scared her off.'

'*I've* scared her off? What about you? "Have you got a serious boyfriend, Charlie? Do like you children, Charlie?" You'd make the Gestapo sound laid back.'

'Why did you have to put her off like that? You could tell she wanted to come to that party,' Ros went on, ignoring him. 'It would have been your chance to get off with her.'

'*Get off* with her? I'm thirty-six, not sixteen. I don't want to get off with anyone.'

'Yes, but—'

'Ros, listen to me. For the last time, I DO NOT WANT TO GET OFF WITH CHARLIE FERGUSON!'

Of course, at that moment everyone seemed to stop talking and an unnatural hush fell, so that the only sound filling the room was his voice. Jack looked around quickly. Charlie was at the far side of the room, talking to a small balding man. From the look she gave him it was obvious she'd heard every word.

As had everyone else in the room, and most of the kitchen staff.

'Idiot,' Ros hissed.

He went home shortly afterwards. The evening had been more than long enough for him, but since Ros and Greg were still enjoying themselves, he left them to it and decided to take a taxi back to his parents' house.

Humphrey lived on the smart outskirts of the city, hardly the place where cabs cruised, especially not when it was lashing with rain. Jack tried to call one from his mobile, only to find he'd forgotten to recharge it. He thought about going back to Humphrey's, but the thought of walking back into that crowded room filled him with dread. Deciding he might have better luck finding a taxi in the city centre, he began to trudge up the dark, deserted, tree-lined avenue, dodging spray from the passing cars. Cold rain dripped off his hair and down inside his collar.

He'd only been walking five minutes when a sporty Audi slowed up and pulled over to the kerb ahead of him. Jack recognised it instantly, his heart sinking.

Sure enough, as he drew level, the electric window purred down and Charlie stuck her head out.

'Need a lift?'

Jack looked up the empty, rain-washed street. 'I was planning to find a taxi.'

'At this time of night? You'll catch pneumonia before you catch a cab round here.' She reached over and opened the door. 'Come on, I'll give you a lift. Don't worry, I promise I won't force myself on you!' She smiled impishly.

Jack groaned. 'Look, I'm really sorry about that.'

'It's okay. Although I must say I've never been rejected quite so publicly before.' She looked up at him. 'Are you getting in or not?'

Inside the car was warm, dark and luxurious. The smell of rich leather mingled with Charlie's lingering perfume. Jack sank back into the deep seat and let the soulful sound of Beverley Knight wash over him. It was the kind of car he and Miranda used to dream of owning, before real life took over and they had to swap looks and luxury for the practicality of washable upholstery and somewhere to stash comics and juice bottles.

'Can you tell me where I'm supposed to be going?' Charlie startled him out of his reverie.

'What? Oh, sorry.' He gave her directions to his parents' house. 'I was just indulging in a bit of car envy.'

Charlie smiled. 'I wondered why you had that big grin on your face. It is nice, isn't it? One of my many indulgences.'

'Lucky you, being able to indulge yourself.'

'Don't you?'

'Not these days.' He thought back wistfully to when he had time to himself. Spare hours to go to the gym, to lose himself in work, to go to a football match or watch the Grand Prix on TV. Now, if he was in front of the TV, he usually had the ironing board out.

Charlie smiled. 'Everyone needs to indulge themselves once in a while, Jack.'

They drove in silence. Charlie seemed fine, humming along to the CD as she manoeuvred the powerful car through the dark streets, but Jack still felt awkward about what had happened that evening. Finally, he said, 'Look, I am really sorry about what I said. I only said it to shut my sister up.'

Charlie smiled, not taking her eyes off the road. 'She is rather full-on, isn't she?'

'You'd noticed? She means well, but she's got this obsession with fixing me up with every single woman who comes along.' He glanced across at her. 'I'm sorry if she embarrassed you.'

'Sounds like you were the one who was embarrassed, not me.' She paused while she negotiated a roundabout. 'I take it you're not interested in being fixed up?'

'Not by my sister.'

'But in principle?'

'I don't know. I can't really imagine it somehow.' He watched the rain running down the window. 'I know it's been nearly a year, but I can't help feeling if I was with anyone else it would seem like I was being unfaithful somehow. And I don't know if I could start again after being off the market for so many years. I wouldn't have a clue what to do.'

Charlie smiled. 'I don't think it's changed much.'

'No, but I have.'

They fell into silence again. Charlie said, 'I don't think I've ever taken a man back to his mum's before.'

'I know. Pathetic, isn't it?'

'I think it's quite sweet.'

Five minutes later they pulled up outside his parents' house. As he got out, Jack said, 'Look, about the party—'

'It's okay, I understand. You don't have to invite me if you don't want to.'

'I do want to. I'd like you to come. That is, if you don't mind being knee-deep in over-excited teenage boys?'

'It can't be any worse than being knee-deep in Humphrey Crawshaw's cronies!' She smiled. 'Remind me again on Monday and I'll check my diary.'

They said goodnight and she drove off. Jack watched her go, relieved there had been no awkward moment over a goodnight kiss. He'd been wondering whether he should give her a peck on the cheek or something, but while he was still psyching himself up for it she'd bid him a brisk goodnight and then gone.

Ros and Greg must surely have got it wrong, he decided. He and Charlie Ferguson were just good friends.

Charlie arrived home to find the flat in darkness. Funny, Tom hadn't said anything about going out. Maybe he'd got a last-minute invitation from one of his many female admirers.

She crashed around in the dark for a while, swearing and banging her shins on the furniture until she found the light. Clive the cat emerged sleepily from Tom's bedroom, outraged at being woken. He never slept on Tom's bed unless Tom was in it. Alone.

'Tom?' Charlie stood in the bedroom doorway, peering into the darkness. 'Tom, are you awake?'

'I am now.' He emerged grumpily from under the duvet. 'What time is it?'

'Nearly eleven.' She flicked on the light. Tom screwed up his face against the sudden brightness. His dark hair was spiked up on end. 'Why are you in bed? Are you sick or something?'

'I just fancied an early night. Not a crime, is it?' He struggled to sit up, pulling the duvet up around his bare chest. 'You're back early. Don't tell me Mr Perfect didn't show up?'

'As a matter of fact he did. I've just given him a lift home.'

'Oh dear, you must be slipping. I expected you two to fall in through the door, tearing each other's clothes off.'

'He had to get back to see to his kids.' She sat down on the bed, narrowly missing Tom's feet. 'He's kind of obsessed with them.'

'Don't sound so surprised. He's their father, isn't he?'

'I know. I just didn't expect him to be so – devoted.' His face had lit up when he talked about them, the way it used to light up when they were discussing a challenging new project.

'If he's that devoted, you're going to have to get to know them. You'd love that, wouldn't you?' Tom smirked.

'Actually, I'm going to. He's invited me to his daughter's party.'

'You? At some kid's party?' Tom laughed. 'I can just imagine you with jelly and ice cream all over your Armani, getting in a strop because you can't win Pass the Parcel!'

'Not that kind of party, dummy. It's the other daughter. The older one. I think she's fourteen. Or maybe fifteen.' She was sure Jack must have told her, but she'd tuned out somewhere in the middle of the conversation.

'Oh God. You at a teenage rave? Do you know what you're getting into here?'

'Don't be such an old git. I can be very cool when I want to be.'

'Charlie, no one over twenty-one is cool to a fifteen-year-old.'

'Thanks, but I do remember what it's like to be a teenage girl. Probably a lot better than you, come to think of it.'

Tom shook his head. 'I still think you're on dodgy ground here. You know nothing about children.'

'So? It can't be that difficult to learn, can it?' She smiled confidently. 'I'll wrap those daughters of his round my little finger. They'll love me.'

And so would Jack. She'd already made her mind up about that.

14

Dan watched from the doorway as Tess rushed around the kitchen, still in her work clothes, clattering pots and pans.

'Shouldn't you be getting changed by now? He'll be here in twenty minutes.'

She stopped and looked down at herself. 'What's wrong with what I'm wearing?'

'Nothing. I just thought you might want to dress up a bit, that's all.'

'Dan, this is your father we're expecting, not a member of the royal family!' She lifted the lid on the nearest pan and gave the contents an exploratory poke. 'Anyway, it's you he's coming to see, not me.'

'All the same, you could put a bit of make-up on—'

'Excuse me?' Tess let the lid drop with a crash. 'Which is more important, me being dressed to the nines or me getting this dinner on time? Have you finished laying that table yet?'

Dan headed for the dining room, grumbling. Tess looked back down at her serviceable navy trousers and white blouse, now spattered with tiny dots of pasta sauce as well as smudges of ink where the photocopier had played up again. Maybe she should put on something a bit smarter. She didn't want to look as if she'd gone to any great effort just for Phil. But on the other hand, she didn't want to look as if she'd let herself go, either. There was a fine line between looking her best and looking as though she'd tried too hard, and she was afraid of crossing it. God forbid Phil should actually think she cared.

It was just one in a long line of fears and doubts that had plagued her ever since Dan announced his father was coming to dinner. With each day that passed she found it harder and harder to think of anything else. And now the big day was finally here. She'd felt sick with anxiety for hours, her emotions rebounding faster than a squash ball.

What if he'd changed beyond all recognition? What if he hadn't changed at all? What if he was married? What if he brought his wife and family with him? Tess wondered if the lasagne would stretch that far. Then fresh panic struck her. What if he was vegetarian? What if he, his wife and his ten

755

children were all strict vegans who lived on nothing but wheatgrass and macrobiotic mung beans?

She took another gulp from the large glass of red wine she'd poured herself the moment she got home. Frankly, that was the least of her worries. What she was really scared about was seeing him again after all these years.

Dan had offered to let her read the letter Phil had sent, but she couldn't bring herself to do it. She told herself it was Dan's business and nothing to do with her, but now she began to wish she had read it. At least then she might have been prepared. As it was, she had no idea what kind of man would be standing there when she opened the door.

She could tell Dan was going through the same kind of apprehension, even though he did his best to hide it. He'd skipped a couple of lectures at college to come home early. Tess had come back from work to find him dressed in a relatively clean version of his usual uniform of oversized sweatshirt and jeans, his untidy fair hair combed. Even his bedroom was unusually tidy, with his CDs back in their rack and his computer paraphernalia put away instead of strewn everywhere. Part of her was touched that he'd gone to so much effort for his father. The other part was miffed that he never did it for her.

Dan came back in as she was tossing the salad. 'All done.'

'Thanks.' She slapped his hand as it strayed towards the lemon meringue pie defrosting on the worktop. Then she noticed he was on his sticks. She'd been in such a rush when she came in, it hadn't registered. 'Aren't you using your chair today?'

He looked defensive. 'I don't need it all the time.'

'I know that. It's just you usually prefer it when you come home from college.'

'Well, I don't want it today. Okay?'

'Okay. No need to bite my head off.' She paused. 'Your father does know you're disabled, you know.'

He looked up sharply. 'How?'

'I wrote to him. When you were first diagnosed.'

'And he never wrote back?' Dan's expression was grim. 'Says a lot, doesn't it?' He gazed down at his sticks. 'That's probably why I haven't seen him since.'

'You know that's not true.'

'Do I?' She'd always taught him to ignore his disability, not to see it as an obstacle to anything he wanted to do. It shocked her to see him look so defeated.

Before she could answer there was a knock on the door. Tess and Dan stared at each other.

'That's him,' Dan said.

Tess glanced at the clock. 'It can't be, he's too early.' She took another gulp of wine. Suddenly she had the overwhelming urge to go to the loo.

Dan was already at the door before she'd made it out of the kitchen. Tess steeled herself as he opened the door. She came to the doorway, her smile fixed in place – and came face to face with her mother.

'Mum! What are you doing here?'

'That's a nice greeting, isn't it?' Margaret Doyle took off her headscarf, folded it carefully and put it in the pocket of her raincoat. 'And after I've waited nearly a quarter of an hour for the bus.'

'You do know Phil's coming round at any minute?'

'Oh, is it today? I had no idea.'

Tess gritted her teeth. 'I told you last week.'

'How am I supposed to remember everything you tell me?' Margaret pushed past her into the kitchen and dumped her handbag on the worktop. 'Shall I put the kettle on? Ooh, something smells nice. Is it foreign?'

Tess looked at Dan, who was making frantic eyebrow signals. But what could she do? Margaret Doyle was an unstoppable force when she wanted to be.

She hurried into the kitchen after her mother. 'Mum, I don't think you understand. Phil is coming round for dinner any minute now.'

'In that case, shouldn't you be getting ready?' She looked Tess up and down with a critical eye.

'But—'

'I'll keep an eye on the dinner, don't you worry. And you don't have to look at me like that. I'm not going to poison the man. No matter how much he deserves it,' she added.

'Mum!'

Margaret Doyle turned on her, hands on hips. 'Look, I'm just here to make sure he behaves himself, all right? I'm not going to make a scene or anything. I'm not even going to talk to him if I can help it.'

'Great. Just great.' As if this whole fiasco wasn't going to be awkward enough, she now had her mother's pointed silences to contend with.

She picked up the wine bottle to refill her glass. Margaret frowned. 'I hope you're not going to be half cut when he turns up? You're going to need your wits about you to deal with him, my girl.'

Strange, Tess thought. And there was me thinking the best way was to get so drunk I don't remember anything about it tomorrow morning. She left her mother poking at the lasagne as if it were some fascinating new breed of pond life she'd discovered, and went off to change.

Dan waylaid her on her way to her bedroom. 'What's Gran doing here? She's not going to frighten him off or anything?'

'Of course not.' Tess hoped she sounded more reassuring than she felt.

She had half an idea that Margaret might have bought herself a gun from one of the many dodgy characters on the estate and concealed it in that capacious handbag of hers. Nothing would surprise her about her mother.

She dithered for a long time over what to wear. She didn't want anything too sexy – although in a wardrobe full of jeans and sensible M&S suits, that wasn't very likely. She wanted something that said strong, independent, successful woman. Unfortunately, all that her wardrobe said was dowdy person who really should get out more. In the end she gave up and swapped her navy trousers for black and her shirt for a black top. She took off her pink fluffy slippers and put on a pair of heels, and was just touching up her lipstick when there was another knock on the door.

Oh Lord, this had to be him. She listened to the scuffle outside as Dan beat her mother to the front door. Then, with a last quick look in the mirror, she stood up and went to greet the man who'd changed her life and then walked out of it so many years ago.

Phil stood in the hall, half hidden behind an enormous bunch of chrysanthemums. He was flanked on one side by an excited-looking Dan, and on the other by a boot-faced Margaret.

As Tess emerged from her room, he turned to face her. Her first thought was that he looked the same. His face was a little older and craggier, and the fair hair was slightly receding, but those thickly lashed grey-green eyes hadn't changed. Or perhaps she only thought she recognised him because he looked so much like Dan.

'Tess.' And he still had the smile that had made her heart flip at sixteen years old. Except, she was pleased to note, it no longer flipped at thirty-four. Although she couldn't deny he'd grown from a good-looking boy into a handsome man, all she could think was thank goodness he hadn't dressed up too much. His casual but smart chinos and Aran sweater were a lot less intimidating than the suit she'd been half expecting.

She was suddenly, uncomfortably aware that everyone had stopped speaking. Her mother was tight-lipped and frosty, and Dan was too busy staring at the father who had suddenly materialised in front of him. His sticks, Tess noticed, were pushed as far back as he could get them without falling down.

Everyone seemed to be expecting her to say something, so she looked at the flowers. 'Are those for me?'

'Oh, sorry. Yes.' He dumped them in her arms. 'I didn't know what else to bring you. Nothing seemed appropriate somehow.'

'Seventeen years' back maintenance money would have been a start,' her mother muttered.

Tess shot her a silencing look. 'They're lovely. I'll put them in some water.' She headed for the kitchen. 'Would you like a drink?'

'I'll get it,' Dan offered. 'What would you like?'

'Whisky, please. If you've got it.'

'Did you have a good journey?' Tess asked.

'Fine, thanks.' Phil edged past Margaret, who was barring his way into the kitchen. 'It feels weird, seeing you again.'

'Doesn't it? You haven't changed much.'

'Neither have you.'

'I'm sure that's not true.' Tess patted her hair. 'I must have aged about a hundred years.'

'Absolutely not. You still look just the same as you used to.' Margaret tutted loudly. Phil turned to her. 'You haven't changed either, Mrs Doyle. You're as lovely as ever.'

Tess cringed and quickly checked there were no sharp instruments within her mother's reach.

Phil looked confident enough, but she could tell by his drumming fingers that underneath he was as nervous as hell. She couldn't blame him. It must have taken a hell of a lot of courage to come here tonight.

'So – um – what have you been up to since I last saw you?' he joked feebly.

Tess smiled back, ignoring her mother's snort of disgust. 'Oh, you know, this and that.'

'Bringing up a child virtually single-handed,' Margaret put in.

Phil glanced uneasily at her, then turned back to Tess. 'Dan tells me you're a teacher now? Funny, I didn't have you down as that type.'

'I know. I surprised myself.' She put the flowers in the sink and began searching in the cupboards for a vase. 'Actually, I quite enjoy it. Most of the time.' She found a vase and blew the dust off. 'I hear you've done pretty well for yourself?'

'Oh, I wouldn't say that. I'm a fairly small fish really. But I do run my own software company.'

'It still sounds impressive, but then I don't know a CD-Rom from a sardine, I'm afraid. But Dan assures me it's all very high-powered and he really does know what he's talking about. He's obsessed with computers.'

'Must be genetic,' Phil said, which earned him a scowl from Margaret.

Tess could see she was brewing up to make another cutting comment, so she quickly said, 'Why don't you go in and talk to Dan? He must be dying to quiz you about gigabytes and hard drives and things.'

As soon as Phil had gone, she turned on her mother. 'Mum, what are you playing at?'

'What am I playing at? You're the one who's giggling and falling all over him.'

'I'm just being nice to him.'

'Yes, well, as long as you don't expect me to do the same.'

'I don't expect you to do anything. I didn't even expect you to be here, if you remember. Come to think of it, why did you come round? You still haven't said.'

Her mother gave her an old-fashioned look. 'Someone's got to keep an eye on you. Don't forget what happened the last time you two were alone together.'

'I was sixteen years old! I've grown up a bit since then.'

'So you say,' Margaret said darkly.

'Besides, you don't seriously expect him to ravish me over the microwave – oh, hello again.' She looked up as Phil appeared in the doorway, a glass in his hand.

'Sorry to interrupt. I've just come to get some ice.'

'Oh. Right. Help yourself.' Tess opened the fridge door and stepped aside. She felt her face flaming. 'Dinner will be ready in about ten minutes.'

'Great.' With a quick smile, he slipped out of the room. No sooner had the door closed than Margaret said, 'Hmm, I can see how much you've grown up. Every time he looks at you, you start blushing like a schoolgirl!'

'The only reason I'm blushing is because I'm embarrassed at you for being so vile to him!' Tess hissed back. 'Look, no one's asking you to welcome him into the family. Just try to put up with him for Dan's sake. This is what he wants, remember? The least we can do is go along with it.'

'I suppose so,' Margaret agreed grudgingly. Then, just as Tess was breathing an inward sigh of relief, she added, 'Just don't expect me to talk to the smarmy little so-and-so.'

In spite of everything, dinner turned out to be a far more relaxed affair than Tess had hoped for. Her mother may have sat at the end of the table with a face like a sucked lemon, but at least Dan and Phil chatted away like they'd known each other for years. They talked about computers, college, Dan's A Levels and his career plans. It was astonishing how much they had in common, right down to a lifelong and sometimes over-optimistic support of Leeds United.

If Phil was at all fazed by Dan's disability, he didn't show it. Tess was grateful for that. Far from being resentful that the two of them were getting on so well, she found she was pleased for her son. Helen was right, it wasn't a popularity contest. Just because Dan got on well with his father didn't mean he loved her any less.

Half a bottle of Rioja helped. Tess found herself relaxing and joining in with their conversation. She even managed to laugh a few times, even if it did earn her a scowl from her mother.

They talked about her job, and Phil's. Tess didn't understand a word, even when he'd explained it twice, but Dan seemed amazingly impressed. Apparently Phil had designed some high-powered business software, and some educational packages that Dan used at college. He was even more thrilled when Phil promised to come round with a sneak preview of some of the latest stuff his company had been working on.

'So you're planning to stay around, are you?' Margaret cut in.

'Actually, yes,' Phil replied calmly. 'I've managed to combine coming here with a couple of business meetings.'

Her mother pursed her lips. 'I might have known there'd be money in it.'

'I'm not doing it for the money. I'm doing it so I can spend some time getting to know my son.'

That silenced her. Tess pushed her chair back and stood up. 'I'll just take these away, shall I?' She began gathering up the plates.

'I'll help you.' Before she could stop him, Phil was on his feet too.

He followed her into the kitchen, his hands full of dishes. 'Nice to see your mum doesn't bear a grudge.'

'You can't blame her. She knows how tough it was for me after you left—' she stopped quickly. The last thing she wanted was to sound self-pitying.

'But you don't hate me?'

'My feelings don't come into it.' Tess turned away from him and began scraping leftovers into the bin. 'I'm doing this for Dan.'

'So you do hate me?'

She straightened up and slid the plates into the sink. 'I don't feel anything,' she answered honestly. 'Maybe I did hate you once. But it was all a long time ago. I'm too busy to hold on to a grudge.'

'I wouldn't blame you if you did, after what you must have been through.' Phil lowered his voice. 'I didn't realise he was so—'

'So what? Handsome? Intelligent? Or do you mean disabled? It's all right, Phil, you can say the word. I'm not going to burst into tears.' Tess looked back over her shoulder at him. 'I did write and tell you, if you remember? About fifteen years ago?'

He winced. 'I know. I'm sorry. It was just a hell of a shock, walking in and seeing him – like that. I'm still trying to take it in.'

How do you think I've felt all these years? she wanted to shout. 'And would you have still come if you'd known how bad it was?'

'Of course.' He looked genuinely shocked. 'What kind of man do you think I am?'

Tess smiled. 'Do you really want me to answer that?'

'I suppose I asked for that, didn't I?' Phil took the plate she'd just washed and reached for the teatowel. 'So what exactly is wrong with him?'

'Spinal Muscular Atrophy. It's a bit technical to explain, but basically it means the cells in his spinal cord that carry messages from his brain to the muscles are dying off. Without the brain telling them what to do the muscles get weaker and weaker, until they stop working completely.'

Phil finished drying the plate and set it on the worktop. He seemed to be steeling himself. 'And will he die?'

'No, thank God. He actually has the mildest type, which isn't life threatening. We were lucky.'

'You call that lucky?'

Tess regarded him steadily. 'If you could see some of the babies who don't make it past their first birthday, you'd say we were lucky too.'

'So he was born like that?'

'He was certainly born with SMA, but we didn't notice the signs until he started to crawl. He just couldn't manage it the way the other babies did. But it took ages to get the doctor to admit something was wrong. He thought I was being neurotic.'

'You're not the neurotic type.' Phil picked up another plate from the draining board. 'It must have been a nightmare for you, bringing him up on your own.'

'I didn't have much choice, did I?'

'I'm sorry. If I'd known how bad things were—'

'You would have come back? I doubt that, don't you? Especially since you couldn't even bring yourself to answer my letter.'

'You're right.' He looked downcast. 'I probably would have left you to it. Just like I left you to it that night with my parents.'

The mention of his parents made her hackles rise. 'How are they, by the way? I don't suppose your mother was too pleased at Dan getting in touch?'

'She doesn't know. We kind of drifted apart after I went to university. I couldn't forgive them for what they'd done to you. What they'd made me do.'

'Nobody made you do anything. You didn't have to go along with it.'

'*You're* lecturing *me* on standing up to my mother?' Phil's eyebrows rose.

'Okay, maybe not,' Tess admitted. 'But there was nothing to stop you getting in touch later. We wouldn't have been too hard to track down.'

'I know. I was tempted a few times.'

'So what stopped you?'

'I didn't know how you'd feel about it. For all I knew you might have got married, had more kids. You might not have even told Dan about me.'

'I'd never lie to my son.'

'I know that now. But the longer I left it, the harder it was to get back in touch. In the end, I suppose I just took the coward's way out.'

'That sounds like you.'

Phil winced. 'I guess I deserved that.' He put the plate down and leaned back against the worktop. 'You didn't ever get married then?'

'No, I didn't. And you can stop looking at me like that, it wasn't because I've been pining for you all these years!'

'So why didn't you?'

'It just didn't happen.' She didn't want to point out that a single mother with a disabled son wasn't every man's idea of an ideal partner. 'What about you?'

'I was. We divorced three years ago.'

'Any children?'

'No. We split up because Angela couldn't have any.' His mouth twisted. 'Ironic, isn't it?'

Before Tess could answer, Margaret came barging into the kitchen with another armful of dirty dishes. By the way her narrowed gaze swept over them like a searchlight, she obviously expected them to be at it on the ceramic hob.

'Any chance of that lemon meringue pie?' she snapped.

The evening broke up fairly soon after that. Margaret refused Phil's offer of a lift home on the way back to his hotel.

'I promise I won't try any funny business,' he said solemnly.

'Where are you staying?' Tess asked, trying to stop herself smiling at her mother's outraged face.

'Middlethorpe Hall.'

'That's where all the rock stars and royalty stay, isn't it? Very posh. The software business must pay well.'

'It is pretty grand. Why don't you and Dan come over for dinner tomorrow night?'

'Well, I'm not sure—'

'That'd be great,' Dan leapt in while she was still thinking up a good excuse. 'You're always saying you never go out, Mum.'

Thanks for pointing that out, Tess thought. Fortunately Phil didn't seem to notice.

'I'll book us a table. About eight? And I'll drop that software round, okay?'

'He's very full of himself, I must say,' Margaret said as she prepared to go home.

'Why shouldn't he be? He's very successful.'

Margaret fiddled with the knot of her headscarf. 'Dan seemed very taken with him.'

'Yes, he did, didn't he?'

'That's not a good thing, you know. It will only lead to more hurt when he dumps him again.'

'What makes you think Phil's going to dump him?'

'He hasn't been interested for the past seventeen years, has he? No, you mark my words. As soon as he gets bored, he'll be off again and that's the last you'll see of him.'

I hope so, Tess thought. She'd enjoyed the evening, but she wasn't sure she could stand the idea of Phil popping round every five minutes. It would be a lot easier when he was safely back in London and Dan could arrange to visit a couple of times a year. That would suit her fine.

Dan was still on a high after her mother left. 'He was all right, wasn't he?'

'He seemed – okay.' Far better than she'd been expecting, actually.

'Didn't it feel weird, having him around? Almost – I dunno – like we were a proper family.'

'I wouldn't go that far.' Tess remembered what her mother had said and frowned. 'You do know this is just a visit, don't you, Dan?'

'Course I do. I'm not a kid.' He looked up at her slyly. 'Be nice if he did hang around though, wouldn't it?'

15

The school hall stretched before them, empty and silent. Tess sat with her A4 pad on her lap, eyes fixed on the double doors at the far end, willing them to open. The only sounds were the tick of the clock measuring the painfully long, drawn-out seconds, punctuated by the rhythmic click of Mrs Frobisher's ballpoint beside her. Tess gritted her teeth. If she clicked that bloody thing once more, she'd strangle her.

On her other side, Stephen Kwarme shifted in his hard chair, his legs stretched out in front of him, and stared at his Patrick Cox loafers. He felt as uncomfortable as she did.

'Oh dear. It doesn't look as if anyone's coming, does it?' Cynthia could scarcely keep the satisfaction out of her voice.

'There's still time.'

'We've been here ten minutes and they haven't exactly beaten a path to the door, have they?'

'Perhaps they're still finishing lunch?'

'Or perhaps they aren't interested. I did try to warn you this wasn't a good idea.'

Tess looked down at the pad on her lap. At the top of the page she'd optimistically written 'Audition Notes'. Underneath she'd doodled a house.

Maybe she'd got the date wrong on the posters? Or perhaps she hadn't made them eye-catching enough?

Or perhaps she should just admit Cynthia was right and the whole thing was a disastrous mistake.

She slumped back in her seat and stared at the clock. It would have been humiliating enough without Cynthia there to witness her utter defeat.

And of course, Cynthia had insisted on being there. Despite Tess' protests, she'd somehow convinced Mr Gant that she should be 'involved' in the production.

And she'd begun by laying down the law on exactly what the production should be.

'Maybe it's the thought of *Hamlet* that's put them off?' Tess ventured. 'Perhaps if we'd chosen something more suitable—'

'Nonsense, the Bard is always suitable. Besides, we've got all those doublets left over from the Jubilee pageant, we can't let them go to waste,' Cynthia said briskly. 'Not that it really matters anyway, since it's obvious no one is going to turn up.'

'Yes, but—'

'Excuse me a moment. I've just remembered something.' Stephen slid out of his seat beside Tess and hurried out of the hall.

'Like a rat deserting a sinking ship.' Cynthia voiced Tess' thoughts. Not that she blamed him. She felt like making a bolt for it too.

'He'll be back.'

'He'll be the only one.'

Five more excruciating minutes ticked by. Tess was just about to admit defeat when the double doors opened and Emily Tyler walked in.

She looked nervously around the empty hall. 'Am I too late for the auditions?'

'No!' Tess had to jam her backside into her seat to stop herself leaping up and hugging her. 'No, not at all, Emily. Come in.'

'Is it just me?'

'We're expecting a few more late arrivals,' Tess said firmly before Cynthia could interrupt. 'Why don't you read something for us while we're waiting?'

Emily was very nervous, but her voice was surprisingly strong and clear. Tess was thrilled. She didn't think she could have coped if she'd been dreadful. She glanced at Cynthia to see if she was similarly impressed. She wasn't. She hardly seemed to be listening. Her eyes were fixed on the clock in studied indifference, her thumb clicking her ballpoint, interrupting Emily's flow until finally the poor girl faltered to a stop.

'Thank you, Emily, that was very—'

'We'll let you know,' Cynthia cut her off rudely.

As she hurried out, Tess swung round in her seat. 'What did you do that for?'

'What? I only said we'd let her know. Isn't that what they usually say?'

'It wasn't just that. You were trying to put her off.'

'I most certainly wasn't!' Cynthia looked affronted. 'I can't help it if my attention wandered, can I? Her performance was hardly mesmerising.'

'I thought she was very good.'

'With respect, Tess, you don't have much to judge her against, do you? Anyway, since she's the only one who auditioned, it's rather irrelevant, don't you think? I mean, you can hardly have a school play with only one actor, can you?'

Suddenly it dawned on her, this was what Cynthia Frobisher had wanted and hoped for all along. Why else would she choose such a difficult play?

She wanted to put everyone off so she could run back to Eric Gant and tell him how spectacularly Tess had failed. Just as she'd predicted she would.

She stood up, pushing her chair back. Cynthia looked up at her in surprise. 'Where are you going?'

'I won't be a minute.'

'Don't be too long, will you? I'd hate to get caught up in an unexpected rush.'

Tess ignored her. She pushed through the double doors and looked up and down the corridor. Apart from a couple of Year 8s staggering up the corridor under the weight of a giant papier mâché camel, it was empty.

She caught up with Emily on her way back to the form room. The poor girl looked terrified when Tess came sliding round the corner behind her, red-faced and puffing like a steam train.

'Did you want me?'

'Yes – Emily – I – did.' Tess steadied herself against the wall and fought to get her breath back. 'Are the others – still in the form room?'

'I think so. Why?'

'Will – you give them a message – from me?' She put her hand to her chest where her heart was about to explode through it. 'Tell them I want them all at the auditions – now.'

Emily's mouth twisted. 'Yeah, right!'

'I'm serious. Tell them anyone who gets a part in the play will be excused English homework from now until Christmas.'

'Really? Cool.'

'Yes, it is, isn't it? Now hurry up and tell them.'

Emily headed for her form room, then stopped and turned round. 'But our next lesson's in ten minutes. We won't have time.'

Damn. Tess glanced at her watch. 'What is your next lesson?'

'PE.'

'Okay, leave it to me. I'll talk to Miss Wesley. She'll understand.' At least she hoped she would. 'Now get a move on!'

Cynthia was waiting impatiently when she got back to the hall. 'Where have you been?'

'Sorry, Cynthia, I had something important I had to do.'

'Haven't we all?' Cynthia stood up and began gathering up her things. 'I don't have time to hang around here waiting for something to happen. Besides, the lunch hour is almost over.'

'But there might be a last-minute rush.'

Cynthia raised a supercilious eyebrow. 'Tess, we've been sitting here for the last half hour. Somehow I don't think we're going to be trampled underfoot by a horde of would-be—'

She stopped, her head cocked towards the door. Tess heard it too. A sound like the low rumble of distant thunder. And it was heading their way.

'What the—?' Cynthia had barely reached the doors when they burst open and twenty Year 10s fought their way in, clamouring over each other to get to the front.

Tess smiled at Cynthia, plastered against the wall behind the door, hair askew.

'What were you saying about being trampled underfoot, Cynthia?'

Stephen crept back into the hall just as the auditions were ending. 'Did I miss something?'

'Only my utter vindication.' Tess grinned. 'You should have seen Cynthia's face when they all came rushing in.'

'They must have had a last-minute change of heart.'

'Or a last-minute bribe.' Tess told him about her plan. Stephen looked horrified.

'You didn't? Tell me you didn't?'

'Why not? Okay, I know it's not exactly orthodox, but half the time they don't do their homework anyway. At least this way they'll be absorbing some culture – why are you looking at me like that? Don't you think it's a good idea?'

'Brilliant,' Stephen agreed. 'Which is why I'd already thought of it. Where do you think I've been all this time?'

Now it was Tess' turn to look horrified. 'Oh God. You too?'

He nodded grimly. 'A fiver each for anyone who got a part.'

Tess took off her glasses and rubbed her eyes. 'Crafty little buggers. Oh well, at least it means we've got a cast. Now all we've got to do is wait and see how Cynthia tries to screw things up next.'

Jack stood in the middle of Saturday afternoon Tammy Girl Hell, waiting for Sophie to make her mind up between a pink spangled crop top and a blue one. He was jostled on all sides by determined ten-year-olds dressed like rock chicks, his brain scrambled by loud dance music. When he closed his eyes all he could see was glitter.

A young girl about Emily's age elbowed past him on her way to the changing room. As she passed, she dropped something from the pile of clothes in her arms. Jack bent down to pick it up.

'Excuse me,' he called after her. 'You dropped this.'

Everyone seemed to stop and look round at him as he stood there, dangling the maribou-trimmed thong from his finger. The girl went puce, grabbed the offending item and fled to the changing room. Everyone else stared at him as if he was a dirty old man. Including his daughter.

'Dad!' Sophie sounded more like her big sister than he'd ever thought possible. She rolled her eyes and headed for the changing room with a worryingly large armful of clothes.

Left alone, he felt even more like a pervert. A fairly conspicuous one, since he towered over all the other customers and most of the assistants. He didn't know where to put his eyes. If he looked one way, he was staring at a bra display. The other, he was gazing at a young assistant's bottom as she restocked the rails.

He shifted his gaze to the middle distance and found himself looking at the kind, bespectacled face of Tess Doyle.

She looked as harrassed as he felt, holding up two T-shirts. Relieved, he made his way through the throng to greet her.

'At last, a grown-up!'

Her smile lit up her face. 'Jack! What are you doing here?'

'Waiting for Sophie to finish trying on the contents of the shop.' He nodded towards the curtained cubicles. 'We've been here for the past hour and frankly I'm losing the will to live. I feel like handing over my credit card and telling her to buy the lot just so we can get out of this hell-hole.' He grinned at her. 'What's your excuse?'

'I'm trying to decide which of these to buy.' She held up the two tops. He squinted at them, his head on one side. One had 'Babe' emblazoned across the chest, the other 'Angel'.

'I would say you're more a Babe than an Angel,' he said at last.

Tess blushed. 'Thanks for the compliment, but it's for my niece, Lauren. She's ten on Wednesday.'

'Then I'd definitely go for the Babe. Although what do I know? I've already been told I have zero fashion sense.'

'You and me both.' She tucked them under her arm. 'The trouble is, she lives down south so I don't get to see her much. I'm not sure whether they'll even fit her.'

'I could get Sophie to try them on for you? God knows, she's tried on everything else.'

'No, it's okay. I'll take a chance.' She looked around. 'No Emily today?'

Jack grimaced. 'She took the money and ran, thank God. I don't think either of us could have coped with shopping together.'

Just then Sophie emerged from the changing room in a feather-trimmed halter top and a pair of jeans with glittery stars all over them. 'What do you think?'

Jack and Tess exchanged looks. 'It's hardly suitable for winter, is it?' he ventured. 'Wouldn't you be better off with a nice jumper?'

'Dad! You know nothing about fashion!' Sophie declared, and flounced back into the cubicle.

He turned to Tess. 'See what I mean? Is it my imagination or do all seven-year-olds want to look like Hollywood hookers?'

'She's growing up.'

'Don't I know it? Soon I'll be completely redundant. My only function will be to hand over money and embarrass them in front of their friends. Speaking of which, are you still coming to the party on Saturday?'

'Ah yes.' Tess shuffled her feet. 'I meant to talk to you about that—'

'Don't tell me you can't come?'

'I'm still not sure it would be a good idea. I'm Emily's teacher. That makes me even less cool than you are. I'm probably the last person she'd want there.'

'But I want you there!' He was surprised at how much he meant it. 'Go on. Emily wouldn't even know you were there. We could hide in the kitchen and bitch about how young people don't know how to enjoy themselves.'

'Sounds like an offer I can't refuse!' Tess grinned. Jack suddenly realised how desperate he sounded.

'I'm sorry. I didn't mean to put pressure on you. If you're too busy—'

'I'll see what I can do.' She smiled. 'I could probably do with a night out. Anything to take my mind off this wretched school play.'

'Emily told me you'd got the go-ahead. How's it coming on?'

'It isn't. I'm beginning to wish I'd never come up with the idea.'

'Sounds a bit like this party.' A thought struck him. 'Why don't we have a quick coffee? Then we can commiserate with each other.'

'I'd love to, but I'm with my mum.' She glanced back over her shoulder. A frowning woman in a brown raincoat and a headscarf was bearing down on them.

'She could come too?'

Tess smiled. 'I don't think so. My mother has a deep suspicion of coffee shops. Why pay a fortune when you've got a perfectly good kettle at home is her motto.'

'It's a hell of a motto.'

'She's got a million of them.'

Tess' mother was a slightly taller, less smiling version of her daughter. She looked at Jack appraisingly, then said, 'Are you ready yet, Teresa?'

'I've just got to pay for this.' Tess looked regretfully at Jack. 'Some other time, maybe?'

'I'd like that.' Before he could suggest anything, Sophie appeared at his side, her arms still full of clothes. It didn't look as if she'd rejected anything.

'Who was that?' Margaret wanted to know, as soon as they were out of earshot.

'His name's Jack Tyler. His daughter's in my class at school.'

Margaret's eyes sharpened. 'So he's married?'

'Widowed. His wife died last year.' Tess reached the cash desk and handed over her Switch card.

'And so young, too. That's tragic.' Her mother looked back over her shoulder at him. 'Still, I expect someone will snap him up soon.'

'Mum!'

'What? He's a nice-looking man.'

'I know, but he's still grieving for his wife. I shouldn't think he's even thinking about finding someone else. Did you, after Dad died?'

'That's different. It's always much harder for a man, I think. They need a woman to look after them.' She turned back to Tess. 'Speaking of which, is that other one still making a nuisance of himself?'

'If you mean Phil, he came round last night.' She glanced at the assistant, who seemed to be taking far too long to put her card through the machine.

'That's three times this week. Looks like he's got his feet well and truly under your table.'

'He came to see Dan.'

'That's what you think.' Margaret's mouth pursed. 'If you ask me, he's after crawling back.'

'After seventeen years? I doubt it.'

'He seemed interested enough the other night. You two looked very cosy, chatting away in the kitchen.'

'I was just being polite. What was I supposed to do, ignore him completely?' Tess snatched the receipt and pen from the assistant, who'd now given up any pretence and was blatantly earwigging.

'No, but it doesn't pay to be too friendly either. You say he's divorced?' Tess nodded. 'Well, there you are, then. He'll be looking for someone else.'

'I'm sure he's got enough women to choose from without me.'

'How many are the mother of his son?' Margaret looked at her shrewdly. 'I expect that would be very nice for him, wouldn't it, stepping into a ready-made family.'

'You don't know what you're talking about. I told you, he's only interested in getting to know Dan. And I'm not going to stop him coming round if he wants to see his son. This is nothing to do with me.'

'That's what you think,' Margaret said.

16

'For the last time, Emily, I'm not going out.'

'What's the matter? Don't you trust me or something?'

'Of course I trust you. It's everyone else I'm not sure about.'

'They're my friends, not a bunch of criminals.' Emily folded her arms across her chest. 'God, I knew it. This party's going to be a total disaster.'

Jack looked helplessly at Ros, who shrugged. 'Don't look at me. I'm only here to make the sandwiches.'

'You wait until your three are all teenagers.'

'Don't. I don't even want to think about it. I'm hoping they won't grow out of thinking Charlie Chalk's Fun Factory is the last word in party chic.'

'I might as well have my party there, the way *he's* going on.' Emily shot her father an evil look. 'Anyone would think we were going to have some mad sexy orgy the minute his back's turned.'

'What's an orgy?' Sophie asked.

Jack sighed and helped himself to one of the sausage rolls Ros had just taken out of the oven. Emily was already sulking because he'd refused to allow her to stock up on Bacardi Breezers at Sainsbury's.

'I know what teenage boys are like. I was one myself once.'

'Yeah, about a million years ago! They're not like that now.'

'I'm sorry? You mean they're not rampaging, hormonally crazed sex fiends?'

'Were you a rampaging, hormonally crazed sex fiend, Daddy?' Sophie asked.

'No,' Ros answered for him. 'Gran wouldn't allow it. He wore a tank top and ran the school stamp-collecting society.'

'That's a lie!' Jack protested. 'I had a haircut like that bloke from the Human League.'

'Only because you tried to do your own fringe and cut one side much shorter than the other.'

'I had my moments. And I never owned a tank top,' Jack insisted, but they were all laughing too much to hear him. At least it stopped Emily being furious with him, which was something.

'Anyway,' Ros said, 'your father can't go out. He's expecting someone, aren't you? Your friend Charlie, remember?'

'Oh God, I'd forgotten I'd even invited her.'

Emily stopped laughing. 'Who's Charlie?'

'Just someone from work,' Jack said dismissively. 'She probably won't even turn up.'

'Oh, she'll turn up. She seemed dead keen,' Ros smirked. It was too much to hope Emily hadn't noticed.

'Dead keen? Why is she dead keen?'

'Your Auntie Ros is just joking – again.' Jack glared at her. 'Haven't you got some vol-au-vents to check on, or something?'

Emily watched Auntie Ros taking another tray of sausage rolls out of the oven. There was no point asking her what was going on. She'd never tell.

And there was something going on, she was convinced of it. Why else would her dad look so shifty? He wasn't telling her everything.

She used to love secrets. A year ago they only meant good stuff – surprise outings, presents hidden on top of the wardrobe, that kind of thing. But a lot had changed since then. Her mum had died and now secrets were different, scarier. They meant whispered conversations that stopped when she walked into the room, tears behind closed doors, sudden house moves just when she thought she'd found her feet again.

These days, secrets meant change. And Emily had had enough of that to last a lifetime.

'You don't seriously expect me to go to this party, do you?' Dan asked.

'Why not? You'll have fun.'

'Fun? In a room full of giggling fourteen-year-old girlies?'

'Some boys your age would enjoy it.'

'Mother, some boys my age enjoy trainspotting, but that doesn't mean it's not pointless and laughable. Anyway, Phil said he might come round later.'

'Oh. Right.' That explains it, Tess thought. She might have known Dan would rather spend the evening with his father than with her. His wonderful, wealthy father, who knew all about computers and arrived laden down with state-of-the-art software and fabulous peripherals that made her carefully saved-for computer look like so much old hat. When the pair of them were together, they were like excited kids, talking in a language Tess couldn't understand, full of bits and bytes and binary codes. She was the only one in the house who couldn't converse in fluent Nerd.

Dan must have noticed her disappointment because he said, 'It's his last night. He's going back down south tomorrow.'

'I know.' Tess ruffled her son's hair. It was mean of her to begrudge Dan time with his father. But after seventeen years of having him to herself, she found it difficult to share him. 'You're not too upset about it, are you?'

'No way. He says he's coming back up to visit the first chance he gets.'

Don't hold your breath. Much as she hoped she was wrong, Tess couldn't help feeling her mother had a point. Once Phil was back at home and busy with work, it was likely Dan would slip into the background of his life, until he was reduced to a card at Christmas and a birthday gift when he remembered.

'I don't know why I'm going to this party myself,' she admitted, turning back to check her reflection in the mirror. 'Everyone will be half my age. Some of them will be in my class at school. How embarrassing is that?'

'Don't go, then. Stay here with me and Phil.'

That sounded even worse. Another evening of listening to them discussing gigabytes and megadrives and whether the X-Box would ever be as good as the Playstation, and she would go out of her mind with boredom.

'I can't. I promised I'd be there.' Although Jack Tyler had probably forgotten he'd even invited her.

It might have helped if she didn't feel so frumpy. Her black party dress was ages old, but since she only got to wear it once in a blue moon, it seemed extravagant to splash out on a new one. It still looked okay, but not exactly head-turning.

But whose head did she really want to turn anyway? Everyone was going to be under eighteen, apart from Jack. And she didn't think any woman was going to turn his head.

The party was in full swing by the time she got there. She could hear the thumping house beat halfway down the street. She wondered what the neighbours would make of it behind their discreetly drawn curtains.

There was a couple wrapped around each other in the front doorway. As Tess stepped past them to ring the bell, she caught a glimpse of the boy's profile in the porch light. It was Mark Nicholls, the troublemaker of 10A. Tess didn't recognise the blonde clamped to the rest of his face.

'Mark?'

'Bloody hell! Miss!'

Tess averted her gaze with a shudder. She didn't know who was most embarrassed – her, Mark or the blonde who was busy adjusting her clothing.

Sophie opened the door. Tess recognised her from Tammy Girl. She was wearing one of her purchases, a white sparkly shift dress with matching high-heeled mules.

'Daddy's hiding,' she announced. 'Me and my friends are dancing in my bedroom and Emily's friends are kissing everywhere else.'

She tripped off upstairs, leaving Tess alone. She followed the eardrum-crunching noise into the sitting room. Thirty pairs of hostile teenage eyes turned to look at her. What the hell are you doing here? they all said. Tess was beginning to wonder that herself. She had never felt so old or unwanted.

Thankfully, at that moment a dark-haired woman in a red dress appeared from the kitchen. 'You must be Tess? I'm Ros, Jack's sister. I'm afraid I don't know where my brother's got to,' she craned her neck to look around, 'but we're having civilised drinks in the kitchen, if you're interested?'

'Thanks. I brought this.' Tess handed over the bottle of Frascati she'd picked up from Oddbins on the way over.

'Great, I'll stick it in the fridge. Why don't you dump your coat upstairs with the others?'

All Tess really wanted to do was dive straight out of the door and go home. But the thought of meeting Mark Nicholls on the front porch again made her head upstairs.

The door to one of the bedrooms was open and she could see the coats piled on the bed. But as she reached the top of the stairs, a man's voice rang out from across the landing.

'Don't even think about sneaking into that room for a snog. I'm watching you.'

Tess swung round as Jack appeared in his bedroom doorway, a bottle in his hand. His frown disappeared when he saw her. 'Tess! Sorry, I thought you were one of those kids. You wouldn't believe how many I've turfed out from under those coats tonight.'

'So you're acting as bouncer, are you?'

'I've got no choice. Emily's banned me from the rest of the house. I don't suppose you noticed if they were wrecking the place, did you?'

'It all looked quite civilised to me.' Better not tell him about Mark Nicholls.

'That's only because I've confiscated all their booze.' He squinted at the label of the bottle he was holding. 'Have you ever had a Moscow Mule?'

'Can't say I have.'

'Don't bother, it's disgusting.' He swallowed the rest down in one gulp.

'Good to see you're putting them out of harm's way.'

'Someone's got to do it. I'm starting on the Bacardi Breezers next. Care to join me?'

Jack's bedroom was understated and masculine, in pale wood, dark blue and cream. A single photo of Emily and Sophie adorned his bedside table.

He reached down beside the bed and rummaged through the collection of bottles he'd stashed there. 'Lemon and Lime or Passion Fruit?'

'You choose. They both sound awful.'

'Passion Fruit it is, then.' He handed her a bottle and clinked it with his own. 'Cheers.'

Several bottles later, they'd come to the conclusion that a) they all tasted the same and b) they all tasted like bubble bath.

'And not even nice bubble bath,' Tess said. 'That cheap nasty stuff that comes in ten-gallon bottles and brings you out in a rash.'

Neither of them were in any hurry to join the party. They reclined on Jack's bed, chatting about life, work, children. The Bacardi Breezers must have been stronger than she thought, because by the end of the third bottle it seemed the most natural thing in the world to be lying on a king-sized bed next to a virtual stranger, confessing her innermost secrets.

'So how did you ever get to be a teacher?' Jack cracked the top from another bottle and handed it to her.

'It seemed like a good idea. Nice steady job, long holidays, hours that fitted in with Dan's school. Couldn't be better.' She took a swig from the bottle and grimaced. 'Ugh! What's this one?'

'Rhubarb and Red Cabbage, I think.' He rolled over and propped himself up on his elbow to face her. 'That doesn't sound like a very good way to choose a career.'

'It is when you've got a baby to think about.'

'So what did you want to do before he came along?'

Tess stared up at the ceiling. She could feel herself blushing. 'I don't want to tell you, it's too stupid.'

'Go on. It can't be any more stupid than what I wanted to do.'

She turned her head to look at him. 'What was that?'

'I wanted to fly Thunderbird Two. See? I told you it was stupid.'

'Why not Thunderbird One?'

He shook his head. 'Too flashy. If you watch the show carefully, you'll see it's Thunderbird Two that does the real work.' He looked so serious Tess could feel herself about to laugh. 'I was only seven years old at the time,' he protested. 'It's not like I went to the careers officer about it or anything. Although I did write an application letter to Mr Tracy asking to be considered if Virgil ever got too old for the job.'

'You didn't?' This time Tess couldn't stop herself laughing. She laughed so hard the bed shook.

'Come on, then,' Jack nudged her. 'What was your burning ambition?'

'If you must know, I wanted to be an actress.' She stopped laughing and wiped her eyes. 'I was pretty good when I was younger. I went to classes and everything. I even had a walk-on part in *Emmerdale* when I was ten.'

'Very impressive.'

'Not really. You only saw the back of my head in the end, but it was something. I didn't realise at the time it was going to be the pinnacle of my career.' She smiled. 'I had it all planned. I was going to be a big star and take the world by storm.'

'So what happened?'

She sent him a wry look. 'I'll give you three guesses.'

'You could have still been an actress with a baby.'

'Not very practical though, was it? I couldn't very well leave Dan with my mum for months on end while I went on tour. Always assuming I ever found work in the first place. You have to cut your coat according to your cloth, my mum says. So that's what I did.'

'Very sensible.'

'That's me.' Sensible Tess. Sometimes she felt as if she'd spent her whole life being reasonable.

'Sounds as if you missed out.'

'I suppose I did. There were a lot of things I couldn't do because of Dan. I couldn't go clubbing every night because it wasn't fair on Mum. I couldn't take a year out after school to travel the world. I couldn't even go on a week's package holiday to Ibiza because I had to get a job during the summer break.' She sipped her drink. 'Sometimes I think I only had one moment of madness in my life, and that ended up with me having Dan.'

'Do you regret it?'

'I've never regretted having him. But sometimes I wish things could have been different.' She looked across at Jack. 'Dan's disabled.'

'Ah.' At least he didn't say he was sorry like most people did. That always made Tess feel frustrated. What did they have to be sorry about? It wasn't their fault her son couldn't walk.

He didn't look at her with pity, either. That was something else that got on her nerves.

'What's wrong with him?' he asked.

He listened carefully as Tess explained about Dan's disability. 'It must have been tough for you, bringing him up on your own,' he said, when she'd finished.

'No tougher than bringing up two daughters,' Tess said.

'I'll take your word for that.' He leaned back against the headboard. 'It's the emotional stuff that's really hard, isn't it?'

'You mean constantly worrying you're doing the right thing?'

He nodded. 'It's not so bad when there are two of you to make the decisions, because at least there's someone to back you up. And it's so exhausting having to set boundaries and stick to them all the time. Sometimes I come home from work and I'm so knackered I don't really care if Emily's done her homework or if Sophie's watching TV because I just want five minutes' peace and quiet.'

'I know what you mean. I used to send Dan to bed just because I was the one feeling tired.'

'You too?' he grinned. 'The girls think I'm the meanest man in the world when I do that.'

They sank into wistful silence for a moment, listening to the music shaking the floorboards beneath them. Then Jack said, 'Listen to us. We're meant to be having a good time, remember?' He reached down and produced a large bottle of lurid pink liquid. 'How about an Aftershock?'

'What the hell is that?'

'God knows. But it looks pretty lethal.'

'Do you think we should? It doesn't seem very responsible.'

'I don't know about you, but tonight I really don't feel like being responsible.' Their eyes met. Tess looked away quickly.

She sat up, wrapped her arms around her knees and gazed around the room, so plain and lacking the personal touch of a woman. There was no stack of magazines on the bedside table, no jewellery or make-up on the dressing table. Just a solitary bottle of Eau Sauvage. Seeing it made her feel sad.

'What are you thinking?'

That you must be a very lonely man. She decided not to tell him what was really on her mind. 'I was just trying to remember the last time I was in a man's bedroom.'

'And when was it?'

'I can't even remember, it was so long ago. Isn't that tragic?'

'Nothing wrong with being choosy.'

'It's more a lack of opportunity than choice, I think.'

He nodded. 'Finding time for a relationship isn't easy when you've got kids.'

'Have you tried?'

'I don't think I'd know how any more.' He looked rueful. 'I expect the dating game's moved on a bit since I last did it.'

'You make yourself sound ancient!'

'Sometimes I feel it, believe me.' He drank his Aftershock without flinching. 'Anyway, it isn't just a lack of time for me. It's a lack of inclination too. I just don't feel ready for all that.'

'Don't you miss having a woman in your life?'

'I miss having *the* woman in my life.' He regarded her seriously. 'Sometimes I wonder if anyone will ever take Miranda's place.'

He sounded so intense, so full of unhappiness, Tess found she couldn't speak for a moment.

It was Jack who broke the silence. 'How about you? Have you had a serious relationship since Dan was born?'

'I've had boyfriends over the years. But they've always seemed to fizzle out before they got serious.'

'Because they couldn't handle you having a disabled son?'

'It's me who couldn't handle it.' She looked over her shoulder at him. 'Dan's always been my priority, ever since he was diagnosed. Everything takes second place to him. A lot of men find that difficult to accept.'

How many relationships had she backed out of as soon as she found them taking up too much of her time and energy? She couldn't make that final commitment, knowing Dan needed her more than any man she'd ever met.

'But he's getting older now, isn't he? Surely he doesn't need you as much?'

'Maybe. But that doesn't stop me worrying. If anything, I worry more because I know the day's coming when I can't look out for him the way I used to. He'll be on his own.' She suppressed a shudder at the thought.

'I think every parent feels like that. Emily's only fourteen and I'm already getting nervous about her getting hurt out there in the big bad world.'

'Believe me, the world seems a lot bigger and badder when your child's in a wheelchair. I've taught Dan to be independent and stand up for himself, but people can be so thoughtless. Do you know, we were out the other day and some horrible old man stared at us. Then he said, "Has your son always been retarded?"'

'What did you do?'

'I said, "No. Have you always been ignorant?"'

Jack laughed. 'I bet you're a wildcat when you're roused.'

'I've had to be.' She smiled. 'Trouble is, that doesn't make me every man's idea of the perfect partner.'

'Surely that depends on the man?'

He was so close she could see the dark rings around his pewter eyes, as if someone had outlined them with a black felt-tip pen.

'Jack?' There was a flash of scarlet on the landing and a second later Ros appeared in the doorway. 'There you are! I – oh!' She stopped short when she saw Tess. 'I'm sorry.'

'I only came up here to dump my coat.' Tess slid off the bed and looked for her shoes. Ros turned to Jack.

'I just thought you'd want to know – Charlie's arrived.'

'Oh. Right. Thanks.' Jack didn't move.

'You could come down and say hello. She's come all this way especially for you.'

As Jack got off the bed and followed his sister to the door, Tess heard Ros hiss, 'Thanks for leaving me to look after everything, by the way.'

'Sorry. We just got chatting.'

'So I see. Just as well I didn't bring Charlie up here, wasn't it? You really would have blown your chances if she'd seen you sprawled out on your bed with another woman!'

779

17

By the time she'd unearthed her shoes, he'd gone downstairs. Tess found him in the kitchen with a big fair-haired man and a willowy Nicole Kidman lookalike in a sexy cream dress.

No one noticed her as she slipped over to the makeshift bar by the sink and helped herself to a glass of mineral water.

'You don't have to stick to water, you know.' The fair-haired man appeared at her side. He was as tall as Jack, but not nearly so athletic-looking. His striped shirt didn't disguise his burgeoning paunch. 'We've got some hard stuff in the fridge. I just have to keep my eye on it so those little buggers don't get their hands on it.' He jerked his head towards the sound of the party in the next room. 'I'm Greg, by the way. Jack's brother-in-law.'

'Tess Doyle.'

He watched her add a handful of ice cubes to her glass. 'Are you sure you wouldn't prefer a glass of wine?'

'Water's fine.' Her head was already swimming, thanks to all the dodgy alcopops she and Jack had had. If she had any more, she might just keel over in the corner.

Not that anyone would notice. Tess glanced over to where Ros and Jack were engrossed with the glamorous redhead.

'Have you met Charlie?' Greg followed her gaze. 'She's a colleague of Jack's. Well, more than just a colleague, if you know what I mean?'

'I didn't know he was seeing anyone.'

'He isn't. Not yet, anyway. But he will be if my wife has anything to do with it. She's determined to throw them together,' he confided, his blue eyes twinkling.

I'm not surprised, Tess thought. They made a striking couple, both tall and good-looking, as if they'd stepped out of a Calvin Klein ad. Charlie's burnished beauty set off Jack's dark good looks perfectly. In fact, Charlie could have been a model. There wasn't a spare ounce of flesh on her elongated frame, and her legs seemed to go on for ever. Tess found herself unkindly hoping that perhaps she was a bit stupid or boring to make up for it.

'Let me introduce you,' Greg said.

'Oh no, I couldn't—' But he was already pushing her towards them, his guiding arm around her waist.

'Charlie, I'd like you to meet Tess. Tess, this is Charlie Ferguson, Crawshaw and Finch's fastest-rising star – apart from my brother-in-law, of course.'

'Greg! You're embarrassing me.' Close up she was even more gorgeous. Her creamy skin was flawless. She even had cheekbones – real ones, not put on with a splodge of blusher like Tess's. 'Ignore him,' she said. 'Except for the bit about Jack – that's true.' She turned to smile at him. Tess caught the adoring look in her eye and realised Ros wasn't the only one who was determined they should be together.

'Looks like my brother might have a rival soon.' Ros threaded her arm proudly through her husband's. 'Guess who we went out to dinner with last night? Peter Jameson!'

'Really?' Jack looked impressed, although Tess had no idea who they were talking about. 'How did that happen?'

'It's nothing, really.' Greg shrugged. 'He just invited us. Nothing special.'

'Excuse me? You call a posh restaurant nothing special?' Ros widened her eyes. 'I don't know what kind of social life you've been leading behind my back, but let me tell you it beats the hell out of fish fingers and beans with the kids!' She turned back to the others. 'He said he wanted to thank Greg for all the hard work he's been putting in on the Westpoint project. Seems he's finally noticed at last.'

'About time too.'

The four of them chatted about Peter Jameson and swapped office gossip while Tess nursed her mineral water and smiled blankly. She didn't want anyone to think she wasn't interested, but it was hard to follow a conversation peopled with characters she didn't know. And since everyone else seemed to know what they were talking about, she didn't like to halt the flow by asking questions. On top of which, her feet were beginning to hurt in her unfamiliar high heels. It had been such bliss to take them off on Jack's bed, she'd forgotten how uncomfortable they were.

She stifled a discreet yawn, but Charlie spotted it. 'Sorry, Tess. All this shop talk must be really boring for you.' Her smile lit up her tawny tiger eyes. 'I'm afraid that's what happens when we all get together.'

'I don't mind. It's – fascinating.'

'I wouldn't go that far!' She turned to face her. 'Tell us about yourself. What do you do for a living?'

'I'm a teacher.'

'Really? I bet you have some stories to tell.'

Why was it whenever people said that, her mind always went blank? Not that it would have mattered. They all seemed far too sophisticated to find life in the classroom enthralling.

'So where do you work?' Charlie asked.

'Haxsall Comp. I'm Head of English.'

'Tess is Emily's teacher,' Jack put in.

Charlie nodded in that thoughtful way people do when they're not quite sure what to say next. 'I have to say I absolutely hated English at school. It was my worst subject. Give me a quadrilateral equation any day!'

'I know what you mean,' Jack agreed. 'I could never tell my Aristophanes from my elbow either.'

They laughed. Tess fixed a smile. If she didn't sit down and get these wretched shoes off in one minute, her feet would be a bloody pulp.

She looked down at Charlie's shoes. Sandals with a fragile diamanté strap and tall, thin lethal heels like blades. So not only was she beautiful, intelligent and nice, she could also carry off killer shoes. Tess was beginning to develop an irrational dislike for her.

'Teachers get long holidays, though,' Greg said. 'Wouldn't mind a few of those myself.'

'You should have a word with your new friend Peter,' Jack teased. 'I'm sure he'd fly you out to his villa in the Algarve.'

Ros' eyes lit up. 'He's got a villa? I didn't know that.'

And then they were off again, talking about work. Tess shifted from one foot to the other and tried to keep the grimace off her face.

It was no good. She had to go. 'Would you excuse me a moment?' she said. No one noticed.

Outside in the garden, the cold night air penetrated the thin fabric of her dress. Tess sat down on the back step and eased her shoes off one foot, then the other. The light spilling from the kitchen window illuminated her mangled toes. She massaged them gingerly, wincing with pain.

What was she doing here when she could be at home in her nice comfy slippers? She'd turned up and done her bit. She'd even enjoyed it, more than she'd expected to anyway. But now it was time to leave.

She stood up to go back in. Her hand was on the door handle when she realised Jack and Charlie were alone in the kitchen. Ros and Greg must have sneaked off and left them to it.

She hesitated, watching them. Charlie suited Jack, she decided. But did he really need someone? His sister seemed to think he did, and she knew him better than anyone. But from talking to him, Tess could see it would take a very special woman to take his wife's place.

Maybe Charlie was that woman. She seemed to have all the right qualities. She was beautiful, intelligent, charming. And they obviously had masses in common.

Perhaps Ros was right. Not everyone was like her, destined to be alone.

At least that's what it felt like sometimes. For the first few years after Dan was born she hadn't had time to think about it. While most of her friends were getting into all kinds of romantic entanglements, dating men and dumping them and sharing weepy sessions over bottles of wine, Tess was too busy looking after her baby and keeping up with her college work. Then, when he'd been diagnosed with SMA, all her energies went into looking after him, making sure he got the right help and support and finding out all she could about the illness.

It was only in her mid-twenties that she started to think perhaps life and love had passed her by. All her friends were settling down, moving in with the men of their dreams, taking out mortgages and going on Sunday-afternoon trips to Ikea. Meanwhile Tess was moving in to her bungalow with Dan and worrying about getting the bathroom adapted. By the time he was older and she was ready for girly nights out at Café Rouge, her friends were holding couply dinner parties and heading off to antenatal classes together. Her whole adult life had been spent out of step with the rest of the world.

Not that she was short of offers from men. Being a single mother with a disabled son might have put some off, but there were others who were keen to stick around and even try to be a father to Dan. But sooner or later the relationship always ended.

As she'd told Jack, it was mostly her fault, not theirs. They were willing to commit, but she wasn't. Everything she had went into Dan. Not just looking after him – he was fairly independent these days – but worrying about him. She worried every time he caught a cold, in case it turned into a respiratory infection, or that he wasn't eating properly, or doing his physiotherapy. She worried that his spine would curve and he'd need surgery, that one day he would have to admit defeat and use a wheelchair permanently.

Mostly she worried about how he would cope when he was older. When he was living alone at college, when he had his first job. How would he fare when she wasn't there by his side to fight his battles for him, the way she always had been?

She was so preoccupied, she didn't have the space in her life to deal with anyone else's emotional demands. Worse than that, she'd forgotten how.

And then there was the fear. Dan's diagnosis had been a shock, and she knew that as a carrier of the gene there was a chance she might have another child with SMA. Next time it could be worse. The baby could be severely affected, or it could even die.

Or it could be perfect. Either way, she didn't think she could handle it. Irrational as it seemed, she knew having a 'normal' child would make her feel too guilty about what Dan had missed out on.

Which meant any man who came into her life would have to deal with her not wanting any more children. It was a lot to ask. Tess sometimes wondered if that was really why she backed off when things got too serious.

She looked back through the kitchen window. Jack was refilling Charlie's glass, laughing at something she'd said. Tess felt a stab of jealousy. Not for Jack, but for what he had. She felt like a kid outside a sweetshop, nose pressed against the glass, wanting all the goodies but knowing she could never have them.

'Where's Tess?' Jack looked around the kitchen. He hadn't noticed the room had emptied.

'I think she went home.'

'She didn't say goodbye.' He looked so disappointed Charlie felt wary. 'Is she a good friend of yours?'

'I told you, she's Emily's teacher.'

'Seems a bit odd, inviting her to this party. I would have died if my parents had invited any of my teachers to a party with my mates!'

'I needed moral support.' He helped himself to a sausage roll from what was left of the buffet. Charlie watched him carefully. He seemed very put out that Tess had gone home without telling him. A bit too put out, in fact.

'Is there something I should know about you two?' she asked lightly.

'In what way?'

'Are you an item or something?'

'You're joking? I hardly know her! Anyway, I'm not ready to be an item with anyone.'

Was that a warning? she wondered. If so, she wasn't about to be put off. She'd always enjoyed a challenge.

'Look, Jack—' They were interrupted by a little girl rushing in. She clutched a glass of Ribena, most of which had already gone down the front of her spangly white dress.

'Daddy, they're snogging in the spare room again!'

'Are they indeed?' Jack put down his glass. 'I'd better go and sort this out.'

Charlie put her glass down. 'I'll come with you—'

'No, you stay and talk to Sophie. I won't be a minute. Sophie, entertain Charlie.'

Great. Just great. She shot a sidelong glance at the small girl. In the uneasy silence, she could feel Sophie eyeing her up and down appraisingly while she stuffed a mushroom vol-au-vent in her mouth.

Finally she said, 'Why do they call you Charlie? It's a boy's name.'

'It's short for Charlotte.'

Sophie nodded, taking it in. 'I like your shoes.'

'Thanks.'

'Can I try them on?'

Charlie looked at her fingers, covered in greasy crumbs and sticky mushroom sauce, and winced. 'Why not?'

There was something slightly surreal about watching a seven-year-old girl clattering around in a pair of three-hundred-pound Gina slingbacks, slopping a glass of Ribena around at a dangerous angle. Charlie smiled tightly.

'Lovely,' she said. 'You should get your dad to buy you a pair.'

Sophie considered it. 'I might,' she said seriously. 'Do they do them in pink? That's my favourite colour.'

'I don't think so.'

Her lower lip jutted. 'Oh well, I've already got some pink shoes. My dad got them for me from BHS. They've got sparkly hearts on them.' She looked down at Charlie's sandals. 'Did yours come from BHS?'

'No, I bought them in London.'

'London!' Sophie looked impressed. 'I've got a lipstick from London. Mummy gave it to me. She's dead now, by the way.'

Charlie gulped. 'That's sad.'

'She had something wrong with her head.'

Seeing the troubled look in her eyes, Charlie quickly distracted her. 'What colour is your lipstick?'

'Pink, of course.' Sophie looked outraged, as if there was no other shade in the world. 'Do you want to see it?'

'I'd love to.'

Jack came back as Sophie raced past him and thudded upstairs. 'What did you say to her?'

'Girl talk. We've been discussing make-up and shoes.' She leaned against the worktop to pull her sandals back on again.

'How did I guess?' he groaned. 'That's all she ever talks about. I'm afraid Emily and I aren't much good at that kind of conversation.'

'You mean Emily's not into shoes?'

'Only if they've got a Nike label on them. My eldest is not what you'd call a girly girl.' She could feel him watching her, admiring her legs. 'Speak of the devil.' He swung round as a tall, sulky-looking girl slouched in. 'This is Emily. Em, this is Charlie Ferguson.'

'Pleased to meet you.'

'Hi.' Jack was right, no one could have described her as a girly girl in those baggy black jeans and T-shirt. She wasn't exactly pretty, but there was a haunting beauty in those big dark eyes.

Eyes that regarded her with extreme suspicion, if not downright hostility.

Ignoring the look, she said, 'Are you enjoying your party?'

Emily shrugged one shoulder. 'S'okay.'

785

'It must be nice to see all your old friends again?'

Another shrug.

'She does string two words together sometimes.' Jack glared at her. Emily scowled back and brushed past them to fish a Coke from the sink full of ice.

'Someone's been sick outside,' she announced casually.

'Oh great. Who was it?'

'I don't know, do I? I wasn't exactly watching them.' She popped the can and turned round to face her father. 'Aren't you going to do something about it?'

'No, Emily, I'm not. As you can see, I'm talking to Charlie at the moment.'

Emily shot another hostile glance at her. 'So you're just going to leave it?'

'For the moment, yes. Unless you'd like to clean it up? I'm sure I can find you a mop and bucket.'

'Ugh, gross!' Emily looked as if she was about to tell her father exactly what he could do with his mop when Sophie rushed back in, her eyes brimming.

'It's gone!' she cried. 'Mummy's lipstick's gone. I went to the place where I keep it and it wasn't there.'

'Come on, sweetheart, don't cry.' Jack crouched down and put his arms around her. 'It'll turn up again, I'm sure.'

'But I put it in a safe place! I always keep it there.'

Charlie watched Jack hugging his daughter. Was everything always such a drama in this house? It was like living in a soap opera.

'Tell you what,' she reached for her bag. 'Why don't you borrow mine until yours turns up? I know it's not nearly as good as yours, but it's better than nothing.'

'Oh no, we couldn't—' Jack began, but Sophie had already snatched the Clarins lipstick and was trying it on the back of her hand.

'It's not the same as Mummy's,' she said in a disappointed voice, 'but I'll keep it anyway.'

'What do you say, young lady?'

'Thank you.' Sophie gave her a gap-toothed grin, her eyes still fixed on the lipstick as she twisted it up and down in its case.

'No problem.' Charlie's smile went a little rigid around the edges when she saw how Emily was glowering at her. What was wrong now? Was she jealous? Did she want a lipstick too? She was just about to offer her a rummage through her make-up bag when Emily slouched off again, followed by a jubilant Sophie, still swivelling her lipstick.

'You do realise you'll never see that again?' Jack said, when they'd gone.

'I don't mind.'

'All the same, it was very nice of you.'

'I can be nice when I want to be.'

'I'm sure you can.' She held her breath as he moved towards her, only to let it out again in a frustrated sigh when he took her glass and said, 'Do you want another drink?'

'Please.'

She watched as he reached into the fridge for the wine bottle. He was a very attractive man, but he didn't seem to realise it. Not like the posers she met at the gym, who spent their whole time admiring their muscles in the mirrors. Or the slickly groomed types who knew their way around the Clinique counter better than she did. Jack was naturally fit and athletically built, and he probably spent no more than five minutes in the shower every morning.

God, wouldn't she love to find out?

'Here you go.' She dragged her mind unwillingly back from the image of him stepping out of the shower, his dark hair dripping, and took the glass he held out to her. 'So, what did you think of the kids?'

It was the question she'd been dreading. Charlie racked her brain for the right words. 'They – um – keep you busy, don't they?'

Jack grinned. 'You could say that! There's never a minute's peace in this house.'

Tell me about it. Charlie stared at the brightly coloured painting stuck on the fridge of three stick figures holding hands outside a house. She was used to being able to utter a whole sentence without being interrupted by a whining child or a sullen teenager.

'I don't really know much about children,' she admitted. All she knew was that she'd never wanted any of her own. As an only child, she'd grown up in a household full of adults, without the rough and tumble of brothers and sisters around her. Her parents were in their forties when she was born and not the kind to build their lives around a child. Charlie had soon learned to adapt to them, rather than the other way round. By the age of five, she was sitting down to dinner with them – real food; her mother would never have tolerated chips or chicken nuggets – and talking and listening to the grown-ups around her. She had perfect table manners, never clamoured for attention or spoke with her mouth full, and would never have dreamed of talking to her father the way Sophie and Emily spoke to Jack.

But it wasn't just her upbringing. She wasn't remotely interested in babies. As a child she'd preferred her pony to dolls, and even now she couldn't work up more than a polite interest when one of the girls in the office came back from maternity leave with tons of baby photos.

But she sensed none of that was going to win Jack over, so she added quickly, 'But yours seem very sweet.'

'I don't know if I'd call Emily sweet!'

Neither would I, Charlie thought.

A squawk from upstairs distracted them. 'Sounds like Sophie and her friends are fighting again.' Jack sighed. 'I'd better sort it out.'

'Couldn't you just leave them?' Charlie pleaded.

'If I don't go now, someone will be coming down in a minute with a broken nose. You stay here, I won't be long.'

She was still waiting for Jack and wondering if she should just cut her losses and go home when Ros came into the kitchen for a refill.

'All on your own? Don't tell me he's disappeared again?'

'He's doing his bouncer bit, I think.'

Ros shook her head. 'He's an elusive one, my brother.'

'You're telling me,' Charlie muttered. 'Sometimes I wonder if he's trying to avoid me.'

'Of course not. He likes you. No really, he does,' Ros insisted, as Charlie looked sceptical. 'But you know what men are like. They're useless when it comes to expressing how they feel. Especially Jack.' She leaned in confidingly. 'I think he's out of practice.'

'In what way?'

'You know. Being married all those years, he's forgotten how to ask a woman out, that kind of thing. He's terrified of putting a foot wrong. And, of course, he's got the girls to think about. I'm sure that's why he hasn't made a move. But trust me, he does like you. A lot.'

Charlie was pretty sure Ros must have downed an awful lot of Chardonnay, otherwise she wouldn't be talking quite so frankly. But it was nice to know someone was on her side.

'So what do you suggest I do?' she asked.

'You could wait for him to make a move, but if I know my brother, you'll probably wait a long time. Or you could make the first move yourself. Or you could leave it up to me.'

'You?'

'Why not?' She rested her hand on Charlie's arm. 'You leave it to your Auntie Ros,' she said. 'I'll get you two together if it kills me!'

18

It was nearly eleven when Tess limped home. She'd been looking forward to slipping out of her party clothes into her dressing gown and enjoying a blissful mug of cocoa in front of the last bit of *Newsnight*. So she was not amused to find Dan and Phil had taken over the sitting room and plugged the Playstation into the TV to play *Grand Theft Auto*.

'Hi, Mum.' Dan greeted her without taking his eyes off the screen. 'Good party?'

'Brilliant. If you like loud music and snogging teenagers.' Tess frowned at Phil. 'Are you still here? Haven't you got an early start tomorrow?'

'Not particularly.'

'Are you sure? I'd hate you to leave all that packing till the last minute.'

'But I don't have to be back down south until—' He caught her look. 'Sorry, you're right. I should be going.' He put down the games console. His car immediately spun off and crashed nose first into a street lamp.

'Do you have to?' Dan protested. 'Couldn't we have just one more game?'

'No, Dan, it's getting late. I should be making tracks.' Phil glanced at Tess as he said it. 'Besides, I don't want to be in your mum's way.'

'He's not in the way, is he, Mum?'

Tess looked from one to the other. Two extraordinarily similar pairs of green eyes looked back at her, silently appealing. She felt defeated.

'Do what you like,' she sighed. 'I'm going to put the kettle on.'

'Mine's a coffee. Milk, no sugar,' Phil called after her, picking up the console again. Tess' forthright reply was drowned out by the whine of car engines hurtling across the screen.

She flicked the switch on the kettle and stood staring out of the window at the night sky and the lights of the city twinkling on the horizon. She always looked forward to coming home to her little bungalow, but suddenly it didn't feel like her own any more. It had been invaded, taken over by a stranger.

And so, come to think of it, had her son. Dan had barely looked at her when she came in. Yet the moment it seemed Phil was leaving, he'd howled with protest.

It isn't fair! She'd never expected any thanks for bringing up Dan single-handed for seventeen years. But she hadn't expected to be cast aside like a battered old teddy when a brand-new toy came along either.

She was still silently fuming about it when Phil crept into the kitchen behind her. 'You know I was only kidding about the coffee, right?'

'All I want . . .' She swung round to face him, arms folded across her chest. 'All I want is to come home to my own space, soak my feet, enjoy my cocoa and watch *Newsnight* in peace. Is that too much to ask?'

'Not at all,' Phil said solemnly. 'I understand Naomi Campbell does exactly the same thing after a night out at the Met Bar.'

Tess felt her mouth twitching treacherously. 'Don't try to joke with me. I'm suffering a severe sense of humour failure,' she warned.

'I can tell.' He tilted his head sympathetically. 'Was the party that bad?'

She replayed the evening on fast forward through her head. 'Not really. I just wasn't in the mood, that's all. And my feet hurt.' She eased her shoes off and threw them into the corner. 'I am never, ever wearing those things again.'

'I'm not surprised. You look like you've walked barefoot through the Himalayas.'

'I feel like it, believe me.'

'Oh well, you know what they say. You have to suffer to be beautiful.'

'Stuff that. I'll stay plain and happy, thank you very much.'

'You could never be plain, Tess.'

The uncomfortable silence was broken by the pop of the kettle coming to the boil. Tess unhooked two mugs from the tree. 'You can have that coffee if you want.'

'No thanks. But there is something I can do for you before I go.'

'Oh yes? What's that?'

'A little trick I picked up from my ex-wife.' He winked at her. 'Come into the bedroom and I'll show you.'

'I beg your pardon?'

'Or we can do it on the sofa, if you prefer?'

Tess sighed heavily. 'Phil, I'm not in the mood for smutty innuendoes.'

'Who's being smutty? I'm only offering you a foot rub.'

'I don't think so.'

'Go on, you'll enjoy it.'

She finished making her cocoa and followed him reluctantly into the sitting room. 'I'm still not sure about this—'

'Stop moaning, woman. You'll enjoy it.'

'Enjoy what?' Dan turned away from the screen to look at them.

'I'm about to demonstrate some shiatsu on your mother.'

'Is that a good idea? She doesn't know any martial arts.'

'Shiatsu, Dan, not ju-jitsu. It's a form of Japanese massage.'

He knelt down in front of her. Tess jumped as he took her left foot in his hands. 'I think you ought to know I'm extremely ticklish.'

'I remember. I'll be careful.'

'Phil, stop it!' But as he gently massaged her foot, working his way slowly from heel to toes, she was overcome by a rush of unbelievable bliss. 'My God, that's heavenly. Where did you learn to do that?'

'My ex-wife was a masseuse. You'd be amazed what talents I've picked up over the past seventeen years.'

'I'm sure I would.' She closed her eyes and allowed the sheer ecstasy to wash over her.

He went on massaging for a few more minutes, gently caressing each toe. 'I'm sorry if it seems like I've taken over your space a bit recently.'

'Dan's enjoyed having you here.' She opened one eye and looked around. 'Where is Dan?'

'He sneaked out a minute ago. Between you and me I think he found your groans of rapture a bit much.' He slid his thumb up her instep, easing away the tension. 'How about you? Have you enjoyed having me here?'

'If Dan's happy, I'm happy.'

'So you wouldn't mind if I came back sometime?'

'If you like.'

'Actually, I was thinking of the middle of November?'

Both eyes flew open. 'That's only two weeks away.'

'Is that a problem?'

'No. I'm surprised, that's all.'

'I've got some more business up here, a couple of meetings I couldn't manage to sort out this time around. And I'd like to see Dan again as soon as possible.' He stroked her toes thoughtfully. 'He's a great kid.'

Tess smiled. 'I know.'

'You've done a fantastic job bringing him up.' He put her foot down gently and picked up the other. 'I wish now that I could have done more to help.'

Tess didn't answer. She was too sleepy for an argument and besides, there was nothing to argue about. She was beyond blame and recriminations. 'You're here now,' she said.

'I am, aren't I? It was really good of you to let me stick around. You always did have a big heart, Tess.'

'Like I said, if Dan's happy, so am I.'

He traced firm circles on the soles of her foot with his thumbs. 'So tell me about this party. Did anyone chat you up?'

'I don't think that's any of your business.'

Phil grinned. 'I take it that's a no, then? Otherwise you wouldn't have come home in such a foul mood.'

'Do you mind? I'll have you know I spent a great deal of this evening getting drunk in a man's bedroom.'

'On your own, or was he there too?'

'Funny!' Tess kicked out at him.

'Teresa Doyle, I'm ashamed of you.' Phil did a creditable impression of her mother. 'You of all people should know better than to get drunk in bedrooms at parties. Look what happened last time.'

It was too close to the knuckle to be funny, but Tess still couldn't help smiling ruefully. 'Watch it, you're on very thin ice. Anyway, for your information I wasn't drunk that night. I was—'

'In love?' Phil said.

'Incredibly stupid,' Tess finished firmly.

'You grew up a lot after that.'

'Someone had to, and I didn't see you volunteering.'

'I know.' He looked shame-faced. 'It took me a few more years than it did you. But I got there in the end, don't you think?'

His grey-green eyes met hers, full of appeal. Tess pulled a face. 'I suppose you didn't turn out too badly. In the end.'

Emily lay in bed, smiling up at the ceiling. Even though the house was silent, music still rang in her ears.

'Good party, wasn't it?' she said.

'Okay, I s'pose.' Her friend Katy sat cross-legged in her sleeping bag on the floor, rummaging through her overnight bag. Even in her tiger-print nightshirt she managed to look sophisticated. With all her slap on she looked about eighteen, which was how she'd managed to sneak into clubs so often. 'Shame there was no booze, though.'

'I know. I asked, but my dad wouldn't let me.' Emily sighed. The truth was, she wasn't that bothered. She couldn't see why everyone got so excited about alcohol. It always tasted horrible to her.

'Lucky I've brought my own then, isn't it?' Katy grinned wickedly and pulled a bottle out of her bag.

Emily stared at it in awe. 'What's that?'

'Vodka, dummy.' Katy unscrewed the top and took a swig, then offered it to her. 'Want some?'

'No thanks.'

'Suit yourself.' Katy put the top back on and stuck the bottle back in her bag. 'Not much talent, either. That Mark was fit, though.'

'He's all right.' This sleepover wasn't as much fun as she'd expected. She thought it would be a laugh to have Katy staying the night, so they could giggle and catch up with all the gossip. But all she wanted to do was talk about all the boys she fancied. She'd even tried to light up a cigarette, but Emily had stopped her. Her dad would go ballistic.

'Who was that girl you were talking to? The blonde one.'

'You mean Paris? She's really nice.'

'Looked like a bit of a dork to me,' Katy said dismissively. Emily thought Paris had looked anything but dorky, in a deep-pink dress that for once showed off her spectacular figure.

She was torn between defending her new friend and not upsetting Katy. She wondered if she was jealous. After all, they'd been best mates at school, she might not like the idea of being replaced by someone else.

'She's okay. We don't have a laugh like we used to, though,' she added quickly, but Katy wasn't listening.

'What about that woman your dad was with? The really glam one.' She hugged her knees. 'He was well into her, wasn't he?'

Emily knew exactly who she was talking about. 'She's just someone my dad works with.'

'Yeah, right! That's what he's told you!' Katy smiled knowingly. 'If you ask me, there's something going on there.'

'No, there isn't! He wouldn't do that.'

'Wouldn't tell you about it, you mean. Parents never tell their kids anything. Anyway, what's to stop him? It's not like he's still married or anything.'

Yes he is, Emily wanted to shout. He's married to my mum. And he always will be.

'And your mum's been dead nearly a year now,' Katy went on. 'He's bound to want a new girlfriend by now, if only for the sex.'

Emily squirmed down under the duvet and turned off the light. 'I don't want to talk about it.'

'I'm only saying, it's going to happen. You might as well face it. Emily?' Katy sighed in the darkness. 'You're not crying or anything, are you?'

'No.' Emily pulled the covers further over her head. Katy was wrong. There was nothing going on between her dad and that woman. He would have said something if there was. Wouldn't he?

Although, there was something about the way she'd looked at him that worried Emily. Her dad might not be interested, but Charlie definitely was. And then there was all that stuff Auntie Ros had said before the party . . .

'Anyway, if anything does happen, you'll probably be the last to know,' Katy said. 'I only found out about my mum and Roger when I came home from school and fell over his suitcases.'

'That's different. Your mum and dad are divorced.'

'So? He's not going to stay faithful to your mum for ever just because she's dead, is he?'

'I told you, I don't want to talk about it.'

'Suit yourself.' Katy burrowed down inside her sleeping bag. 'But don't be surprised if that one ends up being your new stepmother!'

19

'Not going? What do you mean, you're not going? Dan, he's come all this way to see you!'

Tess stared at her son in exasperation. Why did he have to choose now, twenty minutes before she was due at a Parents' Evening, to do this to her?

'I know, but I've got this really important college assignment that's got to be finished by tomorrow. I haven't got time to go out tonight.'

'And this really important college assignment has just happened, has it? I mean, you couldn't have done it at the weekend when you were lying around watching TV?'

Dan blushed. 'Look, I'm sorry, okay?'

'It's not me you should be apologising to. You do realise your father has travelled three hundred miles to see you? Now it's a wasted journey.'

'He's around for a few days. I can see him any time.'

'And what about tonight? He thinks you're having dinner with him in,' she consulted her watch, 'less than an hour.'

Dan looked sheepishly at her. It was the kind of look he usually gave her when he was about to ask for some horrendously expensive but vital piece of hardware for his computer. 'I thought maybe you could go instead?'

'Me?' Tess' voice rose an octave. 'Dan, this Parents' Evening won't finish until eight. Then I've got a mountain of housework to do—'

'Why can't you leave that till tomorrow?'

'Why can't you leave your college assignment?' Tess folded her arms. 'Anyway, your father's come all this way to see you. I'm sure he wouldn't want to spend the evening with me!'

'Oh, he doesn't mind,' Dan said quickly. 'And he says he can change the dinner reservation to eight-thirty, if that would help?' His voice trailed off under Tess' withering glare.

'You've already spoken to him?'

Dan hung his head. 'He's picking you up from the school at eight,' he mumbled.

'I see. Nice of you both to consult me first.' Tess sighed. 'Honestly, Dan,

794

why did you have to go and do a thing like that? You've put us both in a really difficult position.'

'Sorry. He said he didn't mind.'

'I don't suppose the poor man felt he could refuse, with you putting pressure on him. And what about me? Didn't it occur to you that we might not have anything to say to each other?'

'You seem to be getting on pretty well to me.'

'We're only being polite.' She wasn't sure she could stand the strain of being pleasant for a whole evening. It was bad enough having to keep a smile on her face for the next two hours while she was harangued by parents wanting to know why their little darling was in the bottom set for English when anyone could see he was practically a genius.

And it would mean getting changed. Her trouser suit was sensible and businesslike for a Parents' Evening, but not smart enough for the posh restaurant Phil had booked. That would definitely need a skirt. Or a dress. Which in turn would mean tights. She wasn't even sure she still owned an unladdered pair, it was so long since she'd worn them. And then there was all the hassle of make-up, and contact lenses, and – oh Lord, why tonight?

Dan must have seen the despair on her face because he said, 'You'll be fine, Mum. Anyway,' he added, less reassuringly, 'Phil's probably used to you looking like a wreck by now.'

Tess grimaced. 'Thank you very much. That makes me feel so much better.'

'Has anyone seen my shirt?'

'Is this it?' Emily pulled a rag from behind a cushion and held it at arm's length without looking up from *Bliss* magazine.

'What's it doing there?' Jack took it from her. 'Oh no, look at it! It's full of creases. It's going to need ironing again.'

'Looks all right to me,' said Emily, still not looking up. 'Anyway, I don't know what you're making so much fuss about. It's only a stupid Parents' Evening.'

'I want to make a good impression. What happens at these things anyway?' Jack shrugged on his shirt. He was mortified to realise he'd never been to one before. Like everything else, he left that kind of thing to Miranda.

'You all take your clothes off and dance naked round a burning pile of exercise books,' Emily said. 'Dad, it's just a bunch of teachers sitting around. You're meant to talk to them about my progress. Oh, and if you're really unlucky you might have to look at some really sad display.' She glared over the top of her magazine. 'You will try not to say anything embarrassing, won't you?'

'Me? Embarrass you?' Jack smiled at her in the mirror as he knotted his tie. 'As if I could!'

The Parents' Evening was just as Emily had described it. Tables were set up around the hall, each with a harrassed-looking teacher behind it. Depending on their subject, queues snaked across the hall as parents waited for their turn to praise, complain or defend their offspring. Some looked worried, others smug. Along the other side of the hall, display boards had been set up to show off the children's artwork.

Jack scanned the tables and spotted Tess. It was a relief to see a friendly face. She was at a corner table, talking to an anxious-looking couple. He imagined her listening to their troubles. A queue was building up in front of her. Lots of people like him, all keen to talk to her. She seemed to attract them, not like some of the other teachers who sat stony-faced, staring into space.

She suddenly looked up and gave him a little wave. Jack smiled back and pretended to study the art display, embarrassed at being caught staring. Unfortunately, he turned around a bit too quickly and knocked a wonky-looking vase off its plinth. He caught it just before it hit the ground.

'Oops!' He grimaced at the people next to him, a hairy-looking couple in matching anoraks. 'Some little darling's masterpiece.'

'Ours, actually,' the man said. They walked off.

He glanced back over his shoulder. Tess was still deep in conversation with the couple. They looked as if they were telling her their marital troubles too.

He filled in the time by talking to the other teachers. He spoke to the German teacher, the History teacher, and the Design Technology teacher, but only because no one else was and he felt sorry for him. He heard enough to reassure himself that even if Emily wasn't top of the class, she tried hard, turned her homework in on time and didn't disappear behind the bike sheds with the fifth-form boys.

All the time he kept glancing across at Tess. She was now talking to a ferocious-looking woman in a Burberry raincoat. The woman kept jabbing her finger at Tess, who somehow managed to keep smiling.

Finally she finished making her point and moved on. Jack dived into the vacant seat just as Mr and Mrs Anorak were closing in.

'Another satisfied customer?' He jerked his head towards the woman, who was now picking on the nervous-looking Head of RE.

'We aim to please.' Tess pushed her short dark hair off her face. She looked different tonight. She wasn't wearing her glasses for a start, and her brown eyes were fringed with thick dark lashes. 'How are you?'

'Great, thanks. Having a better time than you, by the look of it?'

'Oh God, do I look that bad?' She didn't. She looked very good. She was even wearing lipstick. And a flowery dress under her businesslike jacket. 'It's been a long day. And it isn't over yet.'

'Don't tell me you're going home to a pile of marking?'

'Not quite.' She gave him a funny little smile. She looked endearing with her glasses on, but he hadn't realised how pretty she was without them. 'How are things at home?'

'Oh, you know Em. She has her good days and bad days.' Like the rest of us, he thought. Except Emily could get away with slamming up to her room and crying on her bed while he had to get on with it.

'And how about you?'

Jack shrugged. 'I'm okay.' He looked around the crowded hall. 'I'm not sure I'm handling this very well, though.'

'In what way?'

'I don't think I'm asking the right questions. You know – intelligent ones.'

Tess laughed. 'You're not sitting an exam!'

'Are you kidding? Sometimes I feel as if I'm taking A Level child rearing, but I've missed most of the course and lost all my revision notes.'

Tess moved her hand and for a moment he thought she was going to reach out for him, then thought better of it. 'I'll let you into a secret, shall I? After two hours sitting here, your brain goes as numb as your backside. Most of us are just thinking of going home.'

'I'm sorry, I didn't mean to keep you—'

'Don't be silly, I wasn't talking about you. But I suppose we'd better get down to business.' She glanced over his shoulder at the hairy couple.

Tess quickly consulted her notes and they chatted about Emily's progress for a few minutes. Jack would have liked to go on talking, but Mr and Mrs Anorak were growing restive.

He got up and wandered aimlessly around the hall, pretending to look at the art. As the clock crept towards eight, the crowd of parents in the hall began to thin out and a few of the teachers started packing up to go home. Tess was one of them. Jack hurried over to her table as she was cramming her books into her satchel.

'Still here?' She looked up, surprised.

'I was so transfixed by your art display I completely lost track of time.'

'Year Eight's art tends to have that effect on people.'

He took a deep breath. 'I don't suppose you'd like a drink? We didn't get that coffee a couple of weeks ago and I just wondered if you'd prefer something stronger?'

He could already see the refusal forming on her face before he'd finished his sentence. 'I'm sorry, Jack, I can't. I'm afraid I already have plans for this evening.'

'Not your mother again?' He tried to hide his embarrassment behind a feeble joke.

'Not this time.' Tess glanced towards the doorway. A man had just walked in – tall, fair-haired, good-looking, in a tan suede jacket. He saw her, waved and made his way over.

'Hi, Tess.' Jack saw him swoop down to kiss her cheek and suddenly it all made sense. The dress, the make-up. She had a date.

He also realised how close he'd come to making a total fool of himself.

The man looked at Jack. 'Sorry, am I interrupting something?'

'No. Not at all.' Jack backed off. 'I was just going.' He turned to Tess. 'Have a nice evening, won't you?'

'Jack!' He stopped and looked over his shoulder. 'Some other night, maybe?'

He managed a smile. He'd already asked her twice and been turned down. He had no intention of making a fool of himself a third time.

'Who was that?' Phil asked, when he'd gone.

'Just a friend.' Tess kept her eyes fixed on the door.

'Are you sure about that? I could have sworn he was asking you out.'

'So? Friends can go out together, can't they? I'm going out with you.'

Phil smiled. 'Does that mean we're friends?'

'What else would we be?'

'I don't know. I got the distinct impression that as far as you were concerned I was only "Dan's father".' He imitated the slightly stroppy way she always said it. Tess gave him a not-so-friendly shove.

'Don't push it,' she warned. 'I might change my mind about going out with you at all.'

'What, and have me come all this way for nothing?'

Tess grew serious. 'I'm sorry about that. I could have killed Dan for letting you down. I hope you're not too disappointed he's not coming with us?'

Phil shrugged. 'Can't be helped. I'm glad to see he's taking his studies so seriously.'

'Hmm.' Tess had her suspicions about that. It wasn't like Dan to pass up the chance of a night out to stay in and finish an assignment. She had a vague feeling there was something else going on in her son's mind, but she hoped she was wrong. 'Anyway, we don't have to go out if you don't want to. I'm happy to cancel.'

She'd hoped he might agree so she could go home and tackle her mountain of ironing, but he didn't. 'It'd be a shame to waste a dinner reservation tonight. Especially when you've gone to so much effort.' He looked her up and down. 'You look great, by the way. I'd forgotten what gorgeous legs you have.'

'Phil!'

'Sorry. I didn't realise you were so touchy about compliments.' He spread his hands in a gesture of surrender. 'Look, I don't know about you, but I could do with a night out after the week I've had. Why don't we just enjoy ourselves for a few hours?'

Jack saw them emerge from the building and hunched down behind the steering wheel, but Tess didn't even look his way as she followed the fair-haired man to his car. A silver Porsche, of course. What else would a flash git like that drive?

He felt like a stalker, watching them. What did it matter to him what Tess did anyway? So she had a man. Big deal. He didn't know why he was so surprised. He didn't know why he was even interested. Just because everyone else had a life except him.

Sophie had gone to bed but Emily was waiting up for him when he got home. She was in the same position on the sofa, her feet up, still reading her magazine. Jack had the feeling she'd been staring at the same page since he left.

'Well?' she said.

'Well what?'

'How did it go? Am I going to be expelled? Did anyone notice your shirt? I hope you didn't say something stupid and make a complete fool of me?'

'No, you're not going to be expelled. No, no one noticed my shirt. And no, I didn't say anything stupid.' Apart from asking your teacher out when she blatantly wasn't interested. He poured himself a large drink.

'Good.' Emily sighed with relief.

'But I did snog your Geography teacher. That doesn't count, does it?'

'No, that's okay. Did his beard get in the way?'

'Not as much as Mrs Frobisher's.'

That made her giggle. It was a nice change from all the scowling and door slamming. He wished she'd try it more often.

Emily was in a surprisingly good mood. She even offered to make him a sandwich, something he could never remember her doing before. He hadn't even realised she knew where the kitchen was, from the amount of coffee cups that seemed to lose their way in her bedroom.

They were curled up companionably on the sofa watching *Taggart* when the phone rang. Jack reached for it, not taking his eyes off the screen. 'Hello?'

'Jack?' Charlie's voice on the other end made him sit up and reach for the remote control. He hit the mute button, much to Emily's disgust.

'I was watching that!'

'Shh!' He flagged her with his hand to be quiet and turned back to the phone. 'Charlie! This is a surprise.'

'Didn't you get my message?'

'What message?'

'I called earlier and spoke to Emily. I asked her to get you to call me back.'

'I expect she forgot.' Jack glared at Emily, who stared stony-faced at the silent screen. 'What can I do for you, anyway?'

'I just thought I'd warn you. Your sister's invited us both to dinner on Saturday.'

'Oh God.'

'I had pretty much that reaction too. I'm afraid she might be trying to fix us up.' She laughed. Jack didn't.

'I'll kill her when I see her,' he said. 'Look, Charlie, I'm really sorry. Ros is as subtle as a sledgehammer.'

'That's okay. You've got to admit, it's quite funny.'

'It's bloody embarrassing. I hope you told her where to go?'

'Of course not. I could hardly be rude, could I? Anyway, you never know. It might be fun.'

'I don't know about that.' Jack gritted his teeth. 'I'll call her and sort this out, okay?'

'Don't be too hard on her, Jack. I don't mind, honestly.'

'I do.'

He rang off, then dialled Ros' number.

'Oh, hi.' She sounded deceptively casual, a sure sign she was up to something. 'I was just about to call you.'

'I bet you were! What's all this about you inviting Charlie round to dinner?'

'Oh. You've spoken to her?'

'You bet I have. The poor woman was mortified, and so am I. Bloody hell, Ros, what made you do it?'

'I was only trying to help.'

'How? By making me look an idiot? By ruining my life?'

'For God's sake, Jack, calm down. You sound like you did when we were kids and I told everyone you had a thing about Sarah Greene.'

'Exactly. You embarrassed me then and you've embarrassed me now. For heaven's sake, Charlie's a work colleague!'

'But she likes you. And you like her.'

'Of course I like her!' He noticed Emily's ear cocked towards him and turned away. 'I like her as a friend.'

'So there's nothing wrong with coming to dinner with her as a friend, is there?'

'Except that's not what you had in mind.'

'I didn't have anything in mind. I just thought it might be a nice night out for you.' Ros sounded innocent. 'But of course if anything *did* happen—'

'Which it won't.'

'If you're so sure about that, what's the problem with spending an evening with her?'

Jack fumed silently. Ros had an annoying habit of running rings round him in an argument. She always had. 'You embarrassed Charlie,' he said again.

'She didn't sound embarrassed when I spoke to her. In fact she sounded dead keen.'

'She was just being polite.'

'And you're just being a coward. You'll thank me for this one day.'

'I doubt that.'

'You will. I mean, look how you were with Miranda. You would never have asked her out if I hadn't given you a push in the right direction. And that worked out all right, didn't it?'

'Charlie isn't Miranda,' Jack said sharply.

'I know.' Ros's voice was subdued. 'But she still seems like a nice woman. She's certainly very attractive, wouldn't you say?'

'I suppose so,' he conceded.

'And you've got masses in common.'

'I don't know about that—'

'Admit it, you do fancy her just a teeny bit?'

'Well—'

'So really I've done you a favour, haven't I?' Ros concluded brightly.

'Now, hang on—'

'Come on, Jack, I'm not asking you to marry her or anything. Just come round for dinner. It's not exactly a lifelong commitment, is it?' She took his silence for assent. 'Great. I'll see you on Saturday night. Oh, and don't worry about a babysitter for the girls. Mum says you can drop them off at hers with my lot.'

She rang off. Jack stared in frustration at the buzzing receiver. Maybe it was only dinner, but it was where it might end that worried him.

'What was that all about?' Emily asked, still not taking her eyes off the screen.

'Never mind that! Why didn't you tell me Charlie had rung?'

'I forgot.' There was something about the way she didn't meet his eye that made him suspicious. 'What did she want, anyway?'

'Auntie Ros has invited us to dinner on Saturday night.'

'All of us?'

'No, you're going to Gran's with your cousins.'

'Boring.' Emily made a face. 'So it's just you and that woman, is it?'

'I don't know. There might be some other people from work there.' He certainly hoped there would be.

'But it might be just the two of you?'

'Maybe.'

Emily frowned at the screen. 'Sounds like Auntie Ros is trying to fix you up with her.'

Jack sank wearily on to the sofa. 'Maybe she is.'

'And do you like her?'

He closed his eyes. He felt tired, his pleasant evening ruined. 'Emily, I don't really want to talk about this now.'

'Fine.' She jumped to her feet and stomped into the hall. A moment later she returned, shrugging on her denim jacket.

Jack looked up. 'Where are you going?'

'To see Paris. At least *she'll* talk to me!'

But Paris was too busy to talk when she got round to her flat. She was in the kitchen, cutting up slices of bread and jam. Her homework was spread out on the table. From the sitting room came the sound of two small boys squabbling over toys.

'Mum's gone out and those two haven't had their tea yet,' she explained, arranging the slices on a plate.

'Is that all they're having?'

'It's all we've got.' She picked up the plates. 'Put the kettle on, I won't be a minute.'

Emily followed her into the sitting room and watched as she calmly sorted out her brothers' argument and separated them to either end of the sofa with a plate each. Then she put on a *Star Wars* video and left them to it, with a stern warning not to make another sound.

'Do you have to do everything?' Emily asked, as they headed back into the kitchen.

'Only when Mum's out.'

'Where's she gone?'

'Out clubbing with her new boyfriend.' Paris fished two mugs out of the sink and rinsed them under the tap.

'What's he like?'

'Not bad. Better than the last one, anyway. He did a runner with the telly and Mum's child-benefit book.' She peered into the coffee jar. 'We're out of coffee. Will tea do?'

'Whatever.' Emily looked around. She'd never imagined Paris living in a place like this. Everything was so shabby and uncared-for. She took it for granted her home would always be clean and welcoming, and the food cupboards would always be full. It had never really dawned on her that anyone lived differently. How would she feel if she had to come home and take care of Sophie before she could get down to her homework every evening? She suppressed a shudder at the thought.

Paris must have guessed what she was thinking. She stiffened defensively. 'She's not out every night,' she said. 'And the only reason we don't have any food in the house is because she hasn't had time to go to the shops.'

'I'm not saying anything.'

'No, but that's what you're thinking.'

Emily blushed. She traced the chips on the rim of her mug with her finger. 'My dad's got a girlfriend,' she said. 'At least I think he has, anyway.'

She explained about the phone call. Paris listened, but didn't seem to grasp how shocking the news really was.

'So?' she said, when Emily had finished. 'Your dad's got a date. What's so wrong about that? Don't you want him to be happy?'

'Of course I do! It's just too soon, that's all.' Every step he took towards a new life was another he took away from his old one. Her mother's memory was like an old photo, fading more every day. Sometimes it felt to Emily as if she was the only one trying to hold on to it. 'My mum hasn't even been dead a year and he's looking for someone else.'

'Maybe he feels he needs someone.'

'Why? He's got us!' Emily blurted out. Paris gave her a look over her glasses.

'So you reckon he should forget all about women and dedicate his whole life to looking after you? Don't you think that's a bit selfish?'

Emily didn't answer. Maybe it was selfish, but it was the way she felt. She tried not to show it, but she felt very vulnerable. She'd already lost her mother and she was desperately worried about losing her father too. If this woman took him away, where would that leave her and Sophie?

She looked around the dingy flat. How long before she was in this position, taking care of her little sister while her dad hit the town with his new girlfriend?

20

'To be or not to be, that is the – oh, sod it!'

Tess Doyle stared at the Year 10 art display on the hall wall and pretended not to hear as Neil Wallis scrabbled through his script, his finger moving down the lines.

'The question,' she said patiently. Neil nodded and ploughed on, his heavy brows drawn in concentration.

He could have been reciting the lines in Serbo-Croat for all the feeling he put into them. He was a hefty fifteen-year-old, the most feared midfielder in the Under-16s football league and the unlikeliest Hamlet since Dale Winton.

Casting him hadn't been her idea. Cynthia Frobisher had insisted on it.

'But he's terrible!' Tess had protested, but Cynthia had merely raised her eyebrows.

'Really, Tess, I'm surprised at you. I thought you of all people would have been pleased to give him a chance. Isn't that what all this is about? Waking some dormant love of literature?'

From the longing way he stared out of the windows at the school playing field, it wasn't working. Poor Neil. How could he be expected to carry the production? Being a spear carrier would be too taxing for him.

The rest of the cast were just as bad, thanks to Cynthia's interference. Mark Nicholls, who was a natural as the brooding Hamlet, had been relegated to playing Guildenstern. And Emily Tyler, who Tess would have loved to cast as Ophelia, was filling up the background as one of the milling citizens of Elsinore. The fragile Ophelia was being played by Maeve Flaherty, a solid lump of a girl, who looked as if she could have floored Hamlet and probably half the Danish army. She sat at the side of the stage, chomping her way through a packet of Hobnobs as she waited for her cue.

The others were no better. As Hamlet stumbled through his lines, Claudius and Polonius sniggered in the background, while Queen Gertrude examined her split ends. She'd been dumped by Rosencrantz that morning and wasn't speaking to anyone.

'Not finished yet?' Mr Peake, the school caretaker stood in the doorway, tapping his watch.

'Not long now, Mr Peake.'

'It's all very well for you to say that, but I've got Weight Watchers in here at seven. I need to put the chairs out.'

'I'll make sure we're well out of your way by then.'

'And you'd better not leave a mess. I've got better things to do than tidy up after you lot. I hope you're not chewing gum?' He turned on Queen Gertrude. 'I'll have words with Mrs Frobisher if I find that on the stage.'

He shuffled off, mumbling. As if they didn't all have better things to do, Tess thought. She looked at her watch. Nearly six.

'Okay, let's call it a day, shall we?' She closed her book. 'Thanks everyone, you've all worked really hard.' But she was addressing an empty stage. As she looked out of the hall window, she could already see Neil Wallis sprinting across the playing field, leaping for imaginary headers and leaving a trail of script pages behind him.

The only one who hadn't disappeared was Emily. She took her time gathering up her things, dragging her feet as if she didn't really want to leave.

Tess watched her for a moment. She had a feeling she was waiting for her.

'Something on your mind, Emily?' she asked.

Emily lifted her shoulders in a half shrug. 'Not really.'

In other words there was, but she didn't want to come out and say it. Fine. Tess had too much to do to hang around trying to prise the problem out of her.

'You know where to find me if you want to talk, don't you?' She hiked her bag on to her shoulder and headed for the door.

Emily caught up with her in the car park. Tess heard her running foosteps behind her, but when she turned round Emily slowed down, dragging her feet again.

Tess stifled a sigh. 'Would you like a lift home?'

'S'pose.'

It took her five minutes of chatting about school, friends and family before Tess finally found out what was on her mind.

'Dad's got a girlfriend,' she said. 'That Charlie – you know, from the party?'

'How do you know?'

'I heard them talking on the phone. They're meeting up on Saturday.'

Blimey, that hadn't taken her long. 'And you're not happy about it?'

'It's not up to me, is it?' Emily stared out of the window. 'He doesn't care what Sophie and I think, so long as he's happy.'

'I'm sure that's not true.'

'It is! He never listens to us. Anyway, I think it's disgusting. He shouldn't have a girlfriend at his age.'

'He's hardly ancient!' Tess laughed, then saw Emily's face. 'Look, I know it can't be easy for you. But your dad was bound to meet someone sooner or later.'

'Why? Why does he have to meet someone?'

Tess searched her mind for a tactful answer, then gave up. It wasn't her place to explain any of this anyway. 'I think you should talk to your father about that.'

Emily looked down at her hands. Her nails were so bitten down she'd started nibbling the cuticles, Tess noticed. 'Why can't things just stay the same?' she said quietly.

Tess looked at the dark hair falling over her face, hiding her expression. Poor Emily, she'd been through so much upheaval over the past year, no wonder she clung on to the little bit of security she had left.

'Not all change is bad,' she said. 'Sometimes things can change for the better.'

'Not for me.' Emily shook her head. 'First Mum died, then we had to move here. And just when I'm starting to get used to it, that cow comes along and it all gets changed again.'

'I know it's bound to feel a bit strange at first, having another woman around. But you never know, this Charlie could turn out to be really nice. You might even get to like her.'

'I'll never like her!' Emily said bitterly. 'She's got no right to take Mum's place!'

'I'm sure she's not trying to do that.'

'I bet she is!'

So that's what this is about, Tess thought. It wasn't just Charlie. Emily would have hated any woman who usurped her mother. 'Have you tried talking to your dad about this?'

'I can't. He wouldn't listen anyway.' Emily twisted around in her seat. 'He might listen to you, though.'

'Me? What am I supposed to say?'

'I don't know. Tell him you don't like her. Tell him she's no good for him or something.'

'But I don't know her. Anyway, why should he listen to me?'

'He will, I know he will. He likes you.' Emily's face was full of hope. 'You've got to do something!'

It would have been so easy to say yes, to get involved. Tess steeled herself. 'I'm sorry, Emily. I can't help you.'

'But you can! I told you, he'd listen to you—'

'Maybe, but it's not my problem!'

She hadn't meant for it to come out so sharply. The light faded from Emily's eyes. 'Fine,' she said shortly. 'Sorry.'

They were silent all the way back to Hollywell Park. When they reached her driveway, Emily slammed out of the car without a backward glance.

''Bye, Miss Doyle. Thanks for the lift,' Tess muttered. She wrestled the awkward gear stick into reverse, fuming quietly.

It wasn't her problem. She hadn't even asked to be involved. This was something Jack had to sort out, not her.

Correction – Charlie should be dealing with the sulks and the tantrums, not Tess. Charlie had the man, she should put up with the kids too.

'I'm a teacher, not a flaming agony aunt,' Tess said aloud as she sat at the junction, waiting to pull out on to the main road. A gap appeared but as she edged into it, a Volvo full of kids and Labradors with a harrassed woman behind the wheel moved forward and filled it, blocking her exit.

'Selfish cow!' Normally Tess would have sighed at her stupidity but she was so wound up she leaned on the horn. The woman turned around, startled, and made a helpless gesture of apology. Tess gestured back, less apologetically.

The lights changed and the traffic shifted forward. The Volvo shot off, relieved to escape. The Toyota behind it hung back, allowing Tess out. Tess caught the frightened eyes of the man driving. He obviously thought she was a deranged maniac. Tess pulled in front of him, scarcely bothering to acknowledge his kindness.

She was deranged, all right. But it had nothing to do with the Volvo, or even Emily. It was because of Jack Tyler.

When had she started fancying him? She wasn't even aware she had until Emily's revelations about Charlie. No matter how much she tried to put her darkening mood down to annoyance at being involved in someone else's problems, she had to admit it came down to something far more basic – she was jealous.

The lights changed to red as she approached, and for a mad moment Tess was tempted to jump them. She fidgeted in her seat, fingers drumming on the wheel, cursing at the hold up, even though she was in no hurry.

All the time, she thought about Jack and Charlie. When did they get together? It must have been at the party, after she'd left.

She thought back to that evening. Maybe if she'd played things differently, she could have been the one Jack ended up with? But at the time she hadn't realised the depth of her own feelings. And she'd underestimated Jack's. While she'd been so convinced he didn't want another woman, Charlie Ferguson had steamed in and nabbed him.

But would she ever have stood a chance against Charlie? You only had to look at them to see she and Jack were made for each other.

Besides, she didn't envy her. She might be gorgeous, with a great job, a designer wardrobe and the man she wanted, but she also had Emily to deal with. Tess suspected she was going to be in for a rough ride.

'Oh, no!' Ros opened the oven door and fanned away the cloud of smoke with her oven mitt. Jack stood in the doorway, watching her.

'Can I help?'

'Only if you know the number of a decent Chinese takeaway.' Ros poked at the charred lamb shanks in the roasting tin. 'Oh well, I'll just cover them in sauce and maybe no one will notice.' She looked up at him. 'For heaven's sake, Jack, crack open another bottle and stop standing there like a wet weekend! You're supposed to be enjoying yourself.'

Jack reached for the bottle opener and started to peel the plastic wrapping from around the cork. 'I don't think this is a very good idea, that's all.'

'So you've said. About a million times.' Ros put the tin down on the worktop and closed the oven door with her foot.

'What if we don't get on? What if we've got nothing to talk about apart from work?'

'So? You can just say goodbye at the end of the evening and you've lost nothing.'

'Except my dignity,' Jack said gloomily. 'And a large chunk of my self-esteem.'

'But you'll never know if you don't try, will you?'

Laughter drifted from the other room as Greg dispensed the drinks generously to the other guests. Everyone was here.

Everyone except Charlie.

'She's late,' Jack said. 'I don't suppose she's coming.'

'Relax, she'll be here.'

'I expect she's decided not to bother.' She was probably on her way to a nightclub in Leeds right now, with some unencumbered, Porsche-driving twenty-something. That was the kind of man Charlie should go for, not a widower with two stroppy daughters and enough baggage to fill the hold of a jumbo jet.

He sipped his wine moodily. 'You do realise she knows this is a set-up?'

'How can she know? I've invited loads of people so it won't look obvious.'

'Obvious!' Jack spluttered into his glass. 'You couldn't be more obvious if you'd put a sign saying "Please Shag Me" round my neck.'

'That's Plan B.' Ros grinned. 'I just wanted to give you a helping hand since you're not getting anywhere by yourself.'

'Has it occurred to you I might not want to get anywhere?'

'Nonsense, I keep saying you need a woman in your life.'

'I've already got a woman in my life. In fact, I have two. And I don't suppose either of them would be too impressed at the idea of me seeing someone else so soon after their mother's death.'

He knew one of them wasn't. Emily had hardly spoken to him since Charlie's phone call three days earlier.

In the meantime, everyone kept telling him to go for it with Charlie. So what was stopping him? His old excuse, that it was too soon and he wasn't ready for another relationship, was beginning to wear thin. Miranda had been gone almost a year, and although the idea of sharing a bed with another woman still seemed strange, he'd started to think it might be nice to have someone to share his life with. If the right woman came along, he could even imagine himself falling in love again.

But he didn't know if Charlie was the right woman.

He said as much to Ros, who just laughed.

'What are you talking about? She's perfect for you. She's attractive, intelligent, and you've got so much in common.'

'Like what?'

'Well, you work together.'

'Great. We can discuss planning enquiries. I expect the long winter evenings will just fly by.'

'Look, she's interested in you. That's enough, isn't it?' Ros wiped her hands on a teatowel, picked up her glass, and put her arm through his. 'Come on, let's go and mingle with the guests. And for God's sake, try to look a bit more cheerful about it!'

Greg was handing round more drinks when they came in. Jack recognised Mike and Harry from work, plus their wives, one of whom was heavily pregnant.

He chatted with the other guests, but all the time he kept glancing at the door. He was painfully aware what everyone was thinking. They'd all totted up the numbers and worked out he must be the Spare Man. And where there was a Spare Man, there was usually a Spare Woman. Except this time there wasn't, because she hadn't bothered to turn up. He didn't know which was worse, her standing him up or her coming. Either way he felt sick.

And then the doorbell rang.

'That'll be Charlie.' Ros sent him an 'I told you so' look and went to answer it. Jack listened to their voices in the hall with rising panic and excitement.

Ros could barely keep the smirk off her face as she walked in, followed by Charlie. She was wearing a gold silk dress, which managed to look classy and sexy at the same time. Her hair flowed in silky amber waves over her shoulders.

'Sorry I'm late, everyone.' Her gaze swept the room. 'I had some paperwork to finish.'

'At the weekend? Don't you ever stop working?' Mike asked.

'It needed to be done by Monday.'

'You know what they say, all work and no play—'

'Makes me a senior partner one of these days?' Her gaze came to rest on Jack, who felt himself blushing like a schoolboy.

Greg poured her a drink and they sat down to dinner shortly afterwards. Jack cringed as Ros shoved the other guests aside so he could sit next to Charlie.

'Now you two can chat,' she said.

Chance would be a fine thing, thought Jack. His tongue was glued to the roof of his mouth, and he knew he couldn't make small talk if his life depended on it.

This was crazy. He'd never had any trouble talking to her before. But then, he'd never really thought of her as a woman before. She was Charlie Ferguson, a work colleague, a mate. Now she was someone else entirely. And he wasn't sure he liked the change.

Fortunately Charlie saved him the trouble of talking too much. She chatted easily, mostly about work. But as she gossiped away about who was in line for Alec Finch's job, Jack was appalled to find himself stifling a yawn.

What was happening to him? A few months ago he would have been only too happy to delve into office politics. But now he found his attention wandering to the other end of the table, where Harry's wife Elaine was explaining the best way to remove Ribena stains from a non-colourfast T-shirt. It was the kind of problem that played on his mind these days, far more than who was going to secure the senior partnership.

Jack wasn't the only one feeling out of his depth. Charlie was beginning to wish she'd never come. She'd been looking forward to having Jack to herself but now he barely seemed to be listening to her. He was monopolised by Harry and Mike's boring wives, droning on about kids. As if that was the only thing he knew how to talk about these days. He must be bored to tears, she decided, although he seemed to be hiding it well.

And they were so patronising! The way they went on like he was some kind of hero, taking care of two children all alone. As if thousands of single mothers didn't do it every day.

She tried to say as much, but everyone just looked awkward. 'Yes, but it's different for women, isn't it?' Harry mumbled.

'It certainly is,' Charlie agreed hotly. 'They don't usually earn as much as men so they can't afford decent childcare for a start. Or cleaners, or housekeepers. Yet no one's sympathetic to them. They're treated like the scourge of modern society. It's hardly fair, is it?'

Silence fell. Charlie looked round at all of them. She had the bad feeling she'd said too much.

'You're absolutely right.' Jack smiled at her. 'Single fathers get all the sympathy and single mothers just get a hard time. Maybe it's because we look as if we need all the pity we can get?'

That got everyone talking again. As the conversation flowed, Charlie leaned over to Jack and said, 'I don't suppose I'll ever be invited to join the Mother's Union now.'

'Would you want to?'

'No thanks! Sorry if it sounded like I was picking on you, by the way,' she whispered. 'I just find it so bloody condescending. I mean, you're an intelligent man. How hard can looking after kids be?'

He smiled. 'I'm not going to bore you by telling you.'

'I don't know how you stand it.'

'I don't mind. I'll tell you what I really can't stand, though.'

'What's that?'

'My sister watching us like we're the last pair of mating pandas in captivity!'

Charlie glanced up to the other end of the table. Ros was smiling encouragingly back at her. She couldn't help laughing. 'I see what you mean. I hadn't noticed it before.'

'I have! What does she have to keep looking at us for? I mean, what's she expecting us to do?'

'I shudder to think!'

At least he was talking to her again. But before Charlie had a chance to make the most of it, he was hijacked by Elaine, wanting to know if Sophie had picked up head lice, as her youngest kept getting them and she'd tried everything to no avail.

Head lice! Charlie felt itchy just thinking about them. What kind of topic was that for sophisticated dinner conversation? She was horrified when Ros and Jack joined in enthusiastically, and the three of them went into a group bitching session about mothers who didn't inspect their children's heads regularly, and the trouble it caused for the rest of the class.

In desperation, she turned to Jo, who was picking at her cheese and biscuits.

'So what do you do?' she said.

Jo blinked up at her. 'Sorry? Do about what?'

'What do you do for a living?'

'Oh! I'm a solicitor. Employment law. Or at least I will be for the next three weeks. Then I'm off.' She smiled blissfully and patted her bump. 'No more uncomfortable chairs. No more commuting. No more feeling faint in meetings. I can't wait!'

'It sounds awful,' Charlie agreed. 'How long are you taking for maternity leave?'

'I'm not.'

'Oh!' Charlie gazed at her with new-found admiration. She'd read about those supermums who delivered their babies in their lunch hour and were back at their desks masterminding a corporate takeover by two. But somehow Jo didn't strike her as that type. 'You're going straight back?'

'I'm not going back at all.'

'You're kidding? But what will you do?'

'Look after my baby, of course.'

'But your career—'

'I can't think of a more satisfying career than being a mother,' Jo said piously. 'I don't hold with these women who shove their babies on to a childminder three weeks after they're born and rush back to work. I mean, what's the point of having children if you don't intend to spend time with them?'

And what's the point of spending all those years studying for a law qualification if you don't intend to use it? Charlie felt like asking. But Jo was looking far too pleased with herself to argue.

'It just seems like a waste to me,' she said.

Jo smiled. 'I used to be like you. I thought my career was the most important thing in the world. But you wait until you're pregnant yourself. I'm telling you, it puts all your ambitions into perspective.'

Not to mention shrinking your brain, Charlie thought. She didn't like the way Jo and Elaine were looking at her, as if there must be something wrong with her. Just because she wasn't obsessed with being pregnant and having babies. Just because there was more she wanted to do with her life.

Jo poked at the brie with her knife. 'Do you think this is unpasteurised?'

'I haven't a clue. Does it matter?'

'Jo's not allowed unpasteurised cheese in her condition,' Mike said.

'Or liver, or peanuts or anything with raw egg in it,' Jo added.

'Doesn't that drive you mad?' Charlie helped herself to a hunk of brie.

'Oh no, it's only for nine months. And when you think what's at the end of it – a tiny, new person.' Jo glowed with bovine complacency. All the women beamed except Charlie, who felt slightly sick.

'How long have you got to go?' Elaine asked.

'Only another two months. We can't wait, can we?' Jo reached for her husband's hand. 'Another few weeks and we'll be welcoming our new son or daughter into the world.'

'Better make the most of your freedom while it lasts, then,' Charlie muttered. She would have been heading for the nearest nightclub to dance the night away before she was condemned to a tedious round of nappy changing and 4 a.m. feeds.

'Is it your first?' Ros asked.

Jo nodded. 'I didn't want to wait too long to start a family. I know they say you should wait until you're in your thirties, but I can't think of anything worse than being a middle-aged mum.'

For some reason all eyes turned to Charlie.

'What about you, Charlie?' Elaine spoke for them all. 'Haven't you ever thought about having children?'

'I've thought about it,' Charlie said. 'But then I've thought about trekking in Nepal or bungee jumping off the Golden Gate Bridge. None of them really appeals to me.'

The men laughed. The women were silent. Charlie had the bad feeling she'd put her foot in it again.

Poor Charlie, Jack thought. She looked as if she'd rather be a million miles away. He knew how she felt.

'Are you planning to be there at the birth, Mike?' Harry broke the silence.

'Of course he is,' Jo butted in. 'Mike's going to video it, aren't you, darling?'

'Bloody hell!' Greg said. 'Remind me never to come round to your place. It's bad enough watching your own, without seeing anyone else's.'

'There speaks a man who passed out when they showed the birthing film in the antenatal class,' Ros smiled.

'I'm not surprised. It was like watching a slasher movie. I kept expecting Freddie Kruger to jump out at any moment,' Greg said. 'No, as far as I'm concerned, the best place for a man during the birth is in the nearest bar with a large whisky.'

'So how come you insisted on being there for all three of ours?' Ros asked.

'You wanted me there.'

'No, I didn't. You were no use at all. He sobbed his eyes out the whole way through,' she told the others. 'And when the first one was born, he was so overcome the midwife offered him gas and air.'

Everyone laughed. Then Mike said, 'What about you, Jack? Were you there when your daughters were born?'

He suddenly had a flashback of the labour room, of Miranda squeezing his hand so hard her nails drew blood. And then Emily arriving into the world, red and wrinkled and angry-looking, and all three of them crying. The pain flashed through him, exquisite and intense.

'Why don't you all go through to the sitting room?' Ros said hurriedly, shooting him a worried glance. 'I'll bring the coffee through.'

As they all got up, Jack hung back. 'I don't think I'll bother with the coffee, if you don't mind?'

'Are you sure? It won't take five minutes.'

'No, really, I'd better collect the girls from Mum's and head for home. It's getting late.'

'But it isn't even ten—' Ros started to say, then saw Jack's face and thought better of it. 'Well, if you're sure?'

He sat behind his steering wheel, staring into space. What an idiot. First mention of anything to do with Miranda and he'd fallen to pieces. How could he think he was ready for another relationship? He wasn't even ready to face civilised company.

A sharp rap on the window brought him to his senses. He looked up. Charlie was staring in at him, her face full of concern.

He buzzed the window down. 'Are you okay?' she asked.

'I'm fine.' He forced a smile. 'I just had to get away, that's all.'

'I know what you mean.' The wind whipped at her hair and she tucked it back behind her ear. 'Why don't we have that coffee at my place?'

'I don't know—' he looked at his watch.

'Just coffee, okay? I promise I won't pounce on you or anything.' She smiled. 'Not unless you want me to.'

21

Charlie lived in a fabulously airy loft at the top of a converted warehouse overlooking the canal. Inside it was all high ceilings, big windows, wooden floors and white minimalist interiors. There was a high-tech kitchen area at one end of the vast living space, with an iron spiral staircase leading up to the bedrooms. It was the kind of place he might have liked to live in if he hadn't had to worry about sensible things like being near good schools and having space in the garden to play.

Not that you'd need a garden in this place. The girls could probably have a decent game of football in the space between the pale-cream sofas.

Charlie flicked on one of the halogen lamps, illuminating a fat ginger cat on the sofa. He blinked in the light, then tucked his head under his paws and went back to sleep.

Charlie dropped her coat over the back of one of the dining chairs. 'Make yourself comfortable. I'll get those drinks.'

Jack flopped down on the sofa next to the ginger cat. He put out a hand to stroke it. The cat opened one eye, then got up, stretched and moved pointedly to the far end of the sofa.

'I don't think your cat likes me,' he said, as Charlie returned from the kitchen area with a bottle of red wine in one hand, two glasses in the other.

'Don't be too upset about it. Clive doesn't like anyone except Tom. He's devoted to him.'

'Tom?'

'My flatmate.' She tipped Clive off the sofa and sat down next to Jack.

He looked at the bottle. 'I thought we were having coffee?'

'We were. But then I found this in the kitchen and I thought it would be so much nicer.'

'But I'm driving.'

'One glass won't hurt. You hardly had anything at dinner.' She handed him a glass. 'Anyway, you could always stay the night if you're over the limit. The sofa's very comfortable, so I'm told,' she added mischievously, before Jack could say anything.

He smiled back, admiring the way the low lamplight burnished her coppery hair. She really was beautiful, he thought. And bright and nice with it. What would be so wrong if he did stay the night? After all, it wasn't as if he had anyone waiting for him at home.

He gulped his drink, trying to drown the misery that welled up inside him.

'So where's your flatmate tonight?'

'No idea. Probably out with a woman. He's very popular with the ladies, is Tom.'

'How long have you known him?'

'For ever. We were at college together and we've been best friends ever since.'

'Just friends?'

She nodded. 'I love him to bits, but not in that way.'

'Very wise. It's not a good idea to get involved with your friends.'

'I didn't say that, did I?' She sent him a meaningful look and curled her long legs under her.

They talked about Ros' dinner party. They agreed it had been an excruciating evening, for all kinds of reasons.

'I'm really sorry Ros put you through that,' Jack apologised for the hundredth time.

'Don't be. I wanted to come. And I never do anything I don't want to do, you should know that. Besides, I had to do something. I got tired of waiting for you to ask me out.'

He looked taken aback. 'Sorry?'

'Oh, come on, Jack. You must have noticed me flirting with you?' She smiled. 'And there was me thinking you just weren't interested.'

Thankfully she changed the subject. They chatted some more, swapping life stories. As they talked, Jack hardly noticed Charlie refilling his glass twice, until she held up the empty bottle and offered to fetch another.

'Did we drink all that? I must be right over the limit.' He squinted at the dregs of ruby liquid in his glass. 'I'd better phone for a taxi—'

'Or you could stay the night? I meant what I said about sleeping on the sofa. If you want to?'

He eyed her doubtfully. She knew as well as he did that if he stayed the night, it wouldn't be on the sofa. He could already feel himself slipping, falling under her spell. 'I don't know if that's a good idea. The girls—'

'—are quite safe with their grandmother,' Charlie finished. 'You could always call and let her know where you are, if you think she'll be worried? Although you're a big boy now. I'm sure she knows you can take care of yourself.'

Can I? he wondered, seconds before her mouth closed on his. He didn't seem to be making a good job of it at that moment. Her mouth was soft and warm and tasted of red wine. It hot-wired sensation down his spine into parts of his body that had been dormant for months.

He pulled away. 'I can't. It feels wrong.'

'Are you sure about that?' Her eyes were a deep green in the lamplight. He looked down at her soft mouth and knew he wanted to feel it against his again, in spite of everything. 'It didn't feel wrong to me, Jack.'

She kissed him again. This time he didn't pull away.

It took him a moment to remember where he was the following morning. Sunlight streamed between the slatted wooden blinds, casting bars of light across the rumpled white bed.

Jack looked across at Charlie, sleeping beside him, her coppery hair fanned out across the pillow. He watched her for a moment, taking in her creamy skin, the curl of her dark lashes against her cheek, the sensuous curve of her mouth. Even asleep she looked fabulous. How many men would love to be where he was now? He was the luckiest man alive.

Except he didn't feel very lucky. Truth be told, he felt wretched, and not just because of the incipient hangover or lack of sleep.

Last night had been great, sensational even. But it also felt wrong. It felt like a betrayal. As if the harsh light of the morning had caught him cheating in another woman's bed.

He crept out from between the covers so as not to wake Charlie, dressed quietly and headed downstairs.

A man, bare-chested and wearing faded jeans, sat cross-legged on the floor, leaning against the sofa, eating a bowl of cornflakes. The Sunday papers were spread out on the floor in front of him. From the way the ginger cat was curled in his lap Jack guessed this must be the famous flatmate.

'It's Tom, isn't it?' he greeted him. 'I'm Jack. A friend of Charlie's.'

'I guessed.' Tom didn't look up from the papers. 'Good night, was it?'

Jack blinked. 'Sorry?'

'Your dinner party?'

'Oh. Right. Not especially. We left early, as a matter of fact.'

Tom shot him a glance. 'Where's Charlie?'

'Still asleep.'

'I hope you weren't planning to sneak off without saying goodbye?'

Jack stared at him. 'Actually, I was going to make us both some coffee. Would you like some?'

'Mm, coffee. That sounds like an excellent idea.' Charlie appeared down the stairs, wrapped in a brown towelling bathrobe that showed off her long tanned legs. Her hair fell messily around her face but she still looked gorgeous. 'Morning, Jack.' She reached up to kiss him. Jack moved his head so her lips landed on his cheek. He was uncomfortably aware of Tom watching them.

Charlie didn't seem to notice his awkwardness. 'He makes coffee, Tom. Isn't he wonderful?' she purred.

'Terrific,' Tom muttered. 'Next you'll be telling me he can walk and talk at the same time.' He closed the paper, tipped the cat off his lap and stood up. 'I'm going for a shower. Excuse me, won't you?' With another look at Jack, he disappeared upstairs.

Jack watched him go. 'I don't think your flatmate likes me very much.'

'He's probably just nursing a sore head after last night.' Charlie curled her arm through his. 'Shall we take the coffee and the papers and go back to bed?'

'I can't.' Jack looked at his watch. 'I should pick the girls up soon.'

'Really?' Charlie pouted. 'I was hoping we could spend the day together. There's a nice pub a bit further along the canal. I know it's not exactly Venice, but it's scenic.'

'What about Emily and Sophie?'

'They could come too, I suppose. Or we could go shopping. Do you think they'd like that?'

He could just imagine what Emily would make of a trip to the shops with him and Charlie. 'It's a nice thought, but I really should be heading home. The girls are bound to have homework they need to finish, and I have to get their uniforms ready for school—'

'A woman's work is never done.' Charlie's smile didn't reach her eyes. 'I suppose you'd better make a move, then.'

There was something about the way she said it that gave Jack a twinge of guilt. He shouldn't be running away. Charlie deserved better than that.

He made himself stay long enough to finish his coffee. The silence lengthened, became embarrassing. He could feel Charlie's darkening mood. He couldn't blame her for feeling put out. She had a right to expect something other than a hasty brush-off after last night. He felt like a heel for not being able to give it to her. But it was all happening way too fast for him.

They said an awkward goodbye at the door. 'I'll call you, okay?'

'You do that.'

He hesitated. 'I would have liked to stay, I really would—'

'I know. Mustn't let the girls down, must you?'

She knew it was an excuse. And a feeble one, at that.

She was on the sofa, staring into space, her hands curled around her cooling cup of coffee, when Tom emerged from the shower ten minutes later, towelling his hair.

He looked around. 'Has he gone?'

'As if you didn't know. Don't tell me you weren't upstairs listening to every word.'

'I couldn't help overhearing.' Tom's expression softened. He slung the towel around his shoulders and headed towards her. 'I'm sorry, Charlie.'

'Sorry? What for?'

'Well – he's dumped you, hasn't he?'

'Dumped me?' She managed a brittle laugh. 'Don't be stupid, of course he hasn't dumped me. You heard him. He had to go and pick up his kids.'

'Yeah, right.' Tom nodded solemnly. 'Sorry, but that sounded a lot like dumping to me.'

'That's all you know, isn't it?' Nobody dumped Charlie Ferguson. Ever. It was always her sneaking off in the cold light of dawn, shoes in hand, her making vague promises to call . . .

'So when are you seeing him again?'

'I don't know, do I? Tomorrow, probably. At work.' Although she wasn't sure how she was going to handle coming face to face with him. More to the point, how was he going to handle it?

'So you haven't actually made any plans, then?'

She twisted round to face him. 'What exactly are you trying to say?'

'Nothing.' He backed off. 'Except it doesn't look very promising, does it? You sleep with him; he disappears into the dawn without asking to see you again.' He sucked his teeth. 'Not promising at all.'

'Like you're an expert.'

'I know when I've been dumped.'

'You would, wouldn't you? It's happened often enough.'

'No need to take it out on me, just because Mr Wonderful doesn't want to know.'

Charlie stood up, wrapping her robe tighter around her. 'I don't have to listen to this. I'm going to have a shower. I hope you haven't used all the hot water?'

'There's plenty left. Enough to drown your sorrows, anyway,' he called after her, as she stomped up the spiral staircase.

She washed her hair, scrubbing away at the roots with her fingers, as if she could wash all the negative thoughts out of her head.

She was angry with Jack for walking out on her and making her feel humiliated. But she was even angrier with herself for reading the situation so badly. For once her instincts had let her down. She should have known Jack was wary of getting involved. She should have taken it slowly, not rushed right in there and come on strong. Now she'd frightened him off.

She knew he wanted her, in spite of his doubts. He just wasn't ready to face it yet. He still had a few emotional hurdles to get over first. She had to back off a bit, give him time to come to terms with the idea.

She held the shower over her head and let the hot water rush through her hair, washing away all the soap.

It wasn't her usual style, to play the waiting game. But Jack Tyler was worth waiting for.

On Monday morning, Jack was in his office when a call came through from the council's environment department with a query about the Westpoint site. Jack, up to his eyes in his own work, was impatient.

'Can't you talk to Bernard Sweeting about it? That's his department, not mine.'

'I've tried calling and emailing him, but I've had no answer. I think he's out of the office this morning.'

'What about Greg? He's supposed to be coordinating the project.'

'Same story. Sorry Jack, I wouldn't ask but I really need those figure by lunchtime.'

Jack sighed. 'Okay, I'll go down there and see if I can find something. I'll call you back.'

Bernard wasn't in his cubby-hole office, but his door was open. Jack was scribbling a note on a Post-it when he noticed Bernard's Westpoint file on his desk. Thinking the figures he needed must be in there, he flipped it open and began to read.

'What are you doing?'

He was so startled he dropped the file. 'Bloody hell, Bernard! You frightened the life out of me.'

Bernard Sweeting's face was ashen against his shabby jumper as he stood in the doorway. 'What were you looking in there for?'

'Just some figures.' He explained about the call from the council. 'I thought it would be quicker if I looked them up myself.'

'Well, you won't find anything in there.' Bernard snatched the file out of his hands, put it into his office safe and slammed the door. 'I keep all that information on computer.' He unlocked his battered briefcase, took out a disk and slipped it into the machine. 'If you tell me what you want, I can email it through to you.'

'It's okay, I can wait—'

'I said I'll email it!' Seeing Jack's face, he lowered his voice. 'It might – er – take a minute or two to find.'

'Fine. I'll leave you to it. Just send it direct to the council's environment people when you're ready.' Jack tried to look over his shoulder, but Bernard moved his bulky body around, blocking his view. He glanced furtively back at Jack.

'Er – was there something else you wanted?'

'No, that's all, thanks.' Jack watched his hands trembling over the keyboard. 'Are you all right, Bernard?' he asked.

'Of course I'm all right. Why do you ask?'

'No reason. You just seem a bit edgy, that's all.'

'Edgy? I'm not edgy. Why would I be edgy?' Bernard gave a strangled laugh.

Why indeed? Jack thought, as he left Bernard's office. He'd never seen Bernard looking so stressed, not even when he'd accidentally felled a four-hundred-year-old tree with a preservation order and a history that went right back to Charles II.

And why lock that file in the safe? Why not just shove it in the desk drawer? After all, it wasn't as if it was classified information.

Unless there was something in there. Something Bernard didn't want anyone else to see.

He was still pondering it when he rounded the corner and crashed into Charlie by the photocopier.

'Hello, Jack.'

'Charlie.' Embarrassment rushed through him. 'I've – er – been meaning to call you. Are you free for lunch?'

'Lunch? Today?' She pushed her hair back off her face. 'Sorry, Jack, I'm afraid I'm busy.'

'Oh. Right. Tomorrow, then?'

'I'm not sure. Why don't I get my secretary to check the diary and get back to you? Maybe we could get together later in the week?'

'Okay. Thanks.' He scratched his head as he watched her go. What was that all about? She'd seemed so keen the other day. And to think he felt guilty about letting her down!

Charlie allowed herself a small smile of satisfaction as she watched him head back to his office. It would mean going out at lunchtime to avoid him instead of having a sandwich at her desk and catching up with work as she'd planned, but it was worth it. She could even head up to the Victoria Quarter and treat herself to something nice from Harvey Nicks. She'd need a new outfit for her lunch date later in the week.

She was glad she'd decided to back off. Now she could have the pleasure of reeling him in all over again.

Jack called in at Greg's office on the way back to his own. He was behind his desk, surrounded by teetering piles of papers as usual. His in-tray spilled over with unanswered mail and more unanswered emails blinked urgently on his computer screen. How he ever kept track of it all Jack had no idea. His secretary must be on the verge of a nervous breakdown.

He looked up and grinned when Jack walked in. 'Just the man I wanted to see. How did it go with the Ice Queen on Saturday? Did you get her to melt?'

'I don't know what you're talking about.'

'Don't play coy with me, Jacko. I know you spent the night there.'

'How did you know that?'

Greg shook his head pityingly. 'Tyler family grapevine, old son. Your mum rang Ros to say you didn't pick the girls up until Sunday morning.' He leered. 'Anyway, let's hear it. Is it true she wears chain-mail underwear? Tell me everything!'

'So you can report straight back to my sister? No chance.'

'Spoilsport.' Greg said good-naturedly. He leaned back in his chair. 'So if you didn't come to gossip, what did you want to see me about?'

'It's about Bernard Sweeting.'

Greg rolled his eyes. 'Oh Lord, what's he done now? Don't tell me he's gone down with Dutch elm disease?'

'No, but there's definitely something odd about him.' He explained about Bernard's reaction when he found him flicking through his file.

Greg frowned. 'And did you see anything in there?'

'I didn't have time. He snatched it out of my hands before I could look. Then he locked it in the office safe. Doesn't that seem a bit strange to you?'

'It does. But our Bernard's always been a bit strange anyway.' He grinned. 'Maybe he's got some dodgy photos he's downloaded from the internet?'

'I don't know. But I definitely think he's hiding something. Couldn't you check it out?'

'What do you expect me to do? I can't just march in there and insist he shows me the contents of his safe, can I?'

'I suppose not. But there must be some way you can find out?'

Greg sighed. 'If you're that worried about it, I'll think of something.' He wagged a warning finger at Jack. 'But if I accidentally get sight of a load of disturbing porn, I want you to know I'm holding you personally responsible!'

22

'For heaven's sake, Neil, it's only a pair of tights. It's not like I'm asking you to wear a bra and thong!'

Neil Wallis folded his beefy arms across his chest and remained resolute. 'No way. No one said nothing about tights when I auditioned for this rotten play.'

The other boys all murmured agreement. Privately Tess agreed too, but there wasn't much she could do about it. It was another of Cynthia Frobisher's edicts from above; a wicker chest full of doublets and hose had been dragged out of the store room because, as Mr Peake explained, 'Mrs F reckoned they'd be suitable for costumes.' Apparently they were left over from the Haxsall Golden Jubilee pageant, when the lower school had inexplicably been dressed up as minstrels and maidens and made to cavort around a maypole on the village green. Quite what that had to do with the Queen's jubilee celebration Tess had no idea. But she was still left with several dozen manky pairs of tights, no costume budget and a mini rebellion on her hands.

'Why can't you lot just stop whingeing and flaming well get on with it?' Maeve Flaherty, aka Ophelia, bellowed from upstage, where she was passing the time giving herself a tattoo with the rusty nib of a fountain pen. She was desperate to get Neil Wallis in a clinch, so Tess had heard from Queen Gertrude. Poor Hamlet didn't stand a chance.

'It's all right for you,' Neil yelled back. 'You don't have to show your bleeding whatsits to the whole school.'

'That'll be a first if she doesn't,' Mark muttered.

'Oi, you, I heard that!' Maeve hitched herself off the box she was sitting on and advanced on him menacingly. 'One more word out of you and I'll knock your teeth so far down your throat you'll be talking out of your—'

'Let's take five, shall we?' Tess clapped her hands for silence. Her temples were beginning to throb again. She'd got into the habit of downing a couple of Nurofen before each rehearsal, as a precaution.

In the middle of it all, Stephen walked in. 'How's it going?'

'Fine.' Tess gritted her teeth into a smile. 'Apart from the fact I've got half the cast threatening to walk out.' She noticed his glum face. 'What's wrong with you?'

'I've just been called in to see Mrs Frobisher.'

Tess covered her eyes with her hand. 'Oh God, what does she want now? No, don't tell me. She's had another brainwave. She wants us to do this production backwards. In Polish. With balaclavas.'

'No,' said Stephen. 'But she does want us to do it by Christmas.'

'What? We agreed the spring term.'

'I know. But apparently she's told Mr Gant it's all going so well we'll be able to put it on for the parents at the end of this term.'

'Going well? I've seen better organised war zones.' Tess looked around at the chaos. Hamlet had disappeared, the gravedigger was dribbling the skull around the stage, and Ophelia was challenging all-comers to an arm-wrestling contest. 'She'll just have to go back to Mr Gant and tell him she got it wrong, won't she? The way this lot are going, we'll be lucky if we're ready in four months, let alone four weeks.'

'I get the impression she'd like nothing better than to do just that,' Stephen said. 'I expect she'll also tell him the reason we're not ready is because you and I aren't up to the job. She might even talk him into letting her take over.'

'I'd like to see her try.' Tess watched grimly as Polonius shuffled off the stage, clutching his wounded arm after being trounced by Ophelia. 'She'd probably just cancel the whole thing. Jason, will you stop kicking that skull around? I promised Mr Kramer we wouldn't let it come to any harm.'

She picked up her script wearily. 'Oh well, I suppose we'd better get this show on the road, hadn't we?' She looked around. 'Where's Hamlet? Has anyone seen Neil?'

There was a lot of feet shuffling and awkward looks. Then Jason piped up, 'Please, Miss. He's gone, Miss.'

'Gone? What do you mean, gone?'

'He's packed it in, Miss. Said he didn't want to be Hamlet any more.'

'I think it was the tights that did it, Miss,' Mark Nicholls sniggered.

'Great. Just great. So now I've got to do *Hamlet* with no Hamlet.' Her shoulders slumped. She felt like throwing down her script and following Neil Wallis' example.

Or maybe it was a blessing in disguise? Maybe Mrs Frobisher had done her a favour after all? 'Okay, we're going to have to adopt Plan B.' She turned to Mark. 'You can be Hamlet.'

'What?' He sat upright. 'I'm not wearing those tights.'

'Mark, no one is wearing the tights.' She picked up the offending pair and threw them over her shoulder. 'As of this moment, the tights are officially gone.'

A small cheer went up from the people on-stage. Stephen looked worried. 'But Mrs Frobisher—'

Tess swung round to face him. 'Do you know what? I don't really care what Mrs Frobisher thinks any more.' Stephen must have seen the wild glint in her eye because he backed away nervously. 'We haven't got time to argue. Let's just get this thing done, shall we? We'll try Act Three, Scene One, Hamlet and Ophelia. Don't worry about your lines, Mark. Just read from the script.' Everyone else is, she added silently. 'And Ophelia, remove that gum from your mouth. We'll take it from after the soliloquy.'

'The what?' Maeve stretched a long string of pink gum from between her teeth.

'From where you come in.' Give me strength, Tess thought.

The scene went quite well, considering Hamlet didn't know his lines and Ophelia had all the fragile grace of a New Zealand All Black. Tess was even beginning to feel quite hopeful until Mark put his script down and said, 'None of this makes sense.'

'It's not supposed to make sense, Mark. He's supposed to be ranting like a madman, remember?'

'I know that. But the rest of it doesn't make sense either. I mean this bit: "The power of beauty will sooner transform honesty from what it is to a bawd than the force of honesty can translate beauty to his likeness." What's that all about?'

'Much as I'd love to discuss the many interpretations of Shakespearean verse with you, Mark, I'm afraid we simply don't have time. So just say the lines, would you?'

'How can I say the lines if I don't understand what they mean?'

'What do you mean you don't understand? Are you thick or what?' Maeve snarled.

They carried on for another five minutes. Then Mark's script went down again. 'Why's he telling her to go to a nunnery?'

'He's telling her she might as well become a nun because all men are worthless liars,' Tess explained.

'He's right there,' Maeve muttered.

'Oh, and you'd know, wouldn't you? You've had enough of them.'

'What did you say? You take that back, Mark Nicholls!'

'Children, please—'

'Make me.'

'I will as well!'

'Ooh, I'm scared.'

'You flaming well ought to be. 'Cos I'm going to tell my brother and he'll come down and murder you.'

Tess turned to her sharply. 'What did you say?'

'Nothing, Miss.' Maeve turned red. 'I didn't say anything.'

'She said she'd get her brother on to Mark, Miss.' Queen Gertrude, ever ready with the gossip, stepped forward. 'He's a squaddie, up at Catterick.'

'He's just come back from Afghanistan,' Maeve added. She turned to Mark. 'He'd sort you out, no problem.'

'That's it!' Tess shouted. They both looked at her, baffled.

'Miss?' Maeve frowned. 'I was only kidding, our Lee wouldn't really murder anyone—'

'I don't mean that.' Tess beamed at them both. 'Look, let's call it a day, shall we? Why don't you all go home? And don't bother taking your scripts with you, you won't be needing them after today.'

They left with backward looks over their shoulders, as if they couldn't make their minds up whether Tess had flipped or not. Stephen didn't seem too sure either.

'What are you playing at? None of them know their lines.'

'That doesn't matter.' She flicked through the script. 'Mark's right, none of this is relevant. That's why they can't learn it. It means nothing to them.'

'So?'

'So I'm going to make it mean something.' She plonked down on the edge of the stage next to him. 'Maeve saying that about her brother gave me the idea. It was just like Ophelia in the play. Her brother was a soldier and ended up sorting out her love life, didn't he?' Stephen went on looking at her blankly. 'So, why not retell this story in a way the kids will understand? Make it modern-day?'

Stephen's expression slowly transformed from blank to horrified. 'You mean you're going to rewrite Shakespeare?'

'Only a bit. It'll be the same story, but just a bit – tweaked. I'm sure the kids will find it easier to remember the lines.'

Stephen shook his head. 'Mrs Frobisher's not going to like it.'

'Mrs Frobisher's not going to know, is she?' She smiled at his stunned expression. 'Don't worry, Stephen. I'm sure it will be a lovely surprise for her on opening night!'

Charlie was fifteen minutes late for lunch. Jack ordered a bottle of wine and chewed nervously on a breadstick as he waited for her.

Finally she arrived. All eyes swivelled to follow the tall, sexy redhead in the black trouser suit and spiked heels as she made her way through the crowded restaurant to his table.

'Sorry I'm late. Something came up.' She slid into the seat opposite. Ignoring the open bottle of Frascati on the table, she summoned the waiter and ordered a mineral water.

'So,' she said. 'What did you want to see me about?'

Jack stared at her blankly. Had he got it wrong? The way she was acting, it was as if Saturday night had never happened.

Her coolness unnerved him. 'It – it's about the other morning,' he stammered. 'I just wanted to say I'm sorry for rushing off like that.'

'It's fine, no problem.'

'It's not that I didn't want to spend time with you, but I had to collect the girls.'

'So you said.'

The waiter arrived and took their order. As he walked away, Jack said, 'I would have stayed if I could. But I'd already said I'd be home the night before, I didn't want them to worry . . .' He toyed with his knife and ended up dropping it on the floor. When he came up, Charlie was watching him, a slight smile curving her lips.

'I told you, it's absolutely fine. Look, I'm a big girl now, you don't have to fob me off with excuses.' She shrugged. 'It was a one-night stand, simple as that. We both knew what we were doing. It was fun, but it's over. End of story.'

'I'm not the kind of person who has one-night stands.'

'And you think I am?'

'I'm not saying that.'

'So what are you saying, Jack?' Her eyes were challenging and direct.

He only wished he knew. He'd been trying to work it out for the past three days, ever since he fled from her flat.

In the end the only thing he could think of was to be totally honest. 'That night . . .' His voice faltered. 'You were the first woman I'd been with – since Miranda died.'

Her expression softened a fraction.

'It felt like I was being unfaithful. That's why I panicked and ran. It was nothing to do with you.'

'Why didn't you tell me?'

'I don't know. But it was wrong of me to run away like that. I'm sorry.'

'I can't say it didn't hurt.' Charlie topped up her glass, this time from the wine bottle. 'Do you think you'll ever feel like you're not cheating?'

'I don't know.'

The waiter arrived with their food. A Caesar salad for her, sea bass for him. Neither of them touched it.

'How do you think your wife would have felt about all this? Would she have wanted you to spend the rest of your life alone?'

'Probably not.' They'd actually talked about it once, in the half joking way people did when they were young and thought they had their whole lives ahead of them. Miranda said she'd like to think of there being someone to take care of Jack and the girls after she'd gone. He said if another man so much as looked at her he would come back and haunt them both.

Thinking about it made him feel heavy with sadness. 'I don't know what

Miranda would have made of it,' he said. 'But even if she did give her blessing, I'm still not sure I'm ready for another relationship yet.'

'Who said anything about a relationship?'

Jack frowned. 'I'm sorry, I just assumed—'

'That I'd be trying to trap you into making a commitment? Do I look that desperate?' Charlie picked up her fork. 'If I'd wanted to find a man and settle down, I could have done it a long time ago. At the moment I just want to have fun.'

'Fun?' Jack looked rueful. 'I think I've forgotten what that is.'

'Then I'm just going to have to remind you.' Charlie reached across the table and covered his hand with hers. 'We're both grown-ups, Jack. What's wrong with us getting together and enjoying each other's company? No promises, no pressure. We'll just see what happens.'

'What about the girls?'

She withdrew her hand slightly. 'What about them?'

'They come as part of the package. Do you think you can handle that?'

'I don't see why not. They seem like very sweet kids.'

Jack grinned. 'We are talking about Emily and Sophie, aren't we?'

'Like you said, they come as part of the package. As long as I get you to myself occasionally, I'm sure we'll get along fine.'

He didn't share her optimism. 'It might be a bit difficult at first. Particularly with Emily. She took her mother's death especially hard. I don't know how she'll take to the idea of me with someone else.'

'We'll find out, won't we?' Was it his imagination, or did Charlie's smile seem a little fixed as she attacked her salad?

'Oh no!' Tess tapped frantically on her laptop keyboard. 'Where's it gone? Where's it gone?'

Phil and Dan looked over from where they were watching *Star Trek*. 'What have you done now?'

'Deleted all my notes, that's all. Everything I'd done so far. Bloody stupid computer!' She bashed the Return key a few more times in sheer panic.

'Can I help you?' Phil strolled over. 'What seems to be the problem?'

'If I knew that, I'd fix it, wouldn't I?' She hit the Return key again. Nothing happened.

'Calm down. Bashing the thing won't help, will it?'

'No, but it makes me feel a hell of a lot better!'

'She's hopeless with computers,' Dan called over from the sofa.

Tess shot him an evil look. 'Thank you, Dan,' she said. 'I think even I can spot when the wretched thing doesn't work.'

Phil sat down beside her at the table and pulled her keyboard towards him before she could do any more damage. 'Let's have a look, shall we? I'm sure it can't be too bad.'

Tess' shoulders relaxed. She understood why his clients loved him. She could have put a hatchet through the damn thing and he would have made it sound like a temporary blip. Whatever it was, Phil could fix it.

Or so she thought. His brows gradually lowered in a frown as he tapped a couple of keys, then a few more. Then he wiggled the connection cord in its socket. Always a bad sign. Tess only did that when she was truly desperate.

Finally, he said, 'What exactly did you do to it?'

'I didn't do anything. It's got a grudge against me. It's never liked me.'

'It isn't a person, Tess. It doesn't have feelings.'

'Want to bet? If that thing could talk, the first thing it would say would be "I hate your guts".'

'If that thing could talk, the first thing it would say would be "Get some IT lessons, woman, and stop being such a dinosaur," ' Dan said.

Phil straightened up, his eyes still on the blank screen. 'Well, I think I know what you've done to it.'

'Do you?'

'It's what we in techno-speak call well and truly buggered.' He grinned at her. 'But don't worry, I'm sure it's fixable. I'll take it away and tinker with it, if I may?'

'Would you? Thanks.'

'No problem. What were you working on, anyway?'

'*Hamlet.*'

He frowned. 'I hate to tell you this, but it's already been done.'

'Very funny,' Tess said. 'I need it for rehearsals on Friday, if that's possible?'

Phil sucked on his teeth like a builder who's about to tell someone their house is subsiding. 'Two days? That doesn't give me much time. But I'll do my best.'

'Thanks, Phil.'

He stayed for another glass of wine then headed home, earlier than they'd expected. 'I'd better make a start on your mother's computer,' he told a disappointed Dan. 'Looks like it might be an all-night job.'

'I feel sorry for him, having to go back to that hotel,' Dan said as they waved him off.

'All that luxury? I don't.' She could have done with a few days of pampering herself. Life was very pressured at the moment, with the mock GCSEs, Stephen and Marjorie both away on courses and, of course, the wretched school play. With the first night less than four weeks away Tess was beginning to realise just how much she'd taken on. She hadn't even finished writing it yet. 'It must be bliss to pick up the phone and order room service instead of going to all the hassle of cooking.'

'It's a bit impersonal, though. And it must be costing him a bomb.' Tess could see the way Dan's mind was working moments before he said, 'Why don't we ask him to stay here?'

'For a start, we only have two bedrooms. Where's he going to sleep?'

'On the sofa?'

'Oh, he'd love that. Why would he give up a nice comfortable hotel room for our sofa?'

'He wouldn't mind. At least he wouldn't have to keep going backwards and forwards all the time. And it would be nice to have him here,' he added wistfully.

Nice for whom? Tess wondered. Dan might be besotted by his new dad, but she couldn't imagine anything worse than sharing a house with Phil. Not because she disliked him or anything, but she was used to having her own space. The thought of meeting him bleary-eyed over the cornflakes every morning wasn't appealing.

Dan seemed to read her thoughts. 'You do like him, don't you?'

'I wouldn't go that far.'

'But you've got to admit he's a nice guy?'

'He's okay. He could be a lot worse. But that doesn't mean I want to live with him.'

'I thought you two seemed to be getting on really well?' Dan sounded casual, but he didn't fool Tess.

'What's that supposed to mean?'

'Nothing. Just commenting, that's all.'

'Dan!' Tess gave him a warning glare. 'I know what you're up to and I'm telling you now it's not going to work.'

'I don't know what you're talking about.'

'Really? So all this sneaking off and leaving us alone together isn't part of some great plan? What about dropping out at the last moment so we have to go out to dinner without you?'

'I told you, I had a college assignment.' Dan averted his face, but she could see he was blushing.

'You seem to have a lot of those at the moment. Usually when your father's coming round.' Tess folded her arms. 'There's no point in denying it. I know you're trying to set us up.'

'As if!' Dan looked indignant. 'Why should I care who you go out with?'

'Good question,' Tess said.

They lapsed into silence for a moment. Then he said, 'But what's so wrong about it anyway? Phil's an okay bloke, you said so yourself. And I like him.'

'Oh, so that makes it all right, does it? It doesn't matter what I think, as long as you like him.' Tess turned on him furiously. 'Dan, I don't need you to organise my love life for me!'

'Someone's got to. You're not making a very good job of it yourself.'

'Thanks a lot!'

'Okay, then. When was the last time you had a boyfriend?'

'I don't know, do I?'

'See what I mean? You're thirty-four, Mum. You're not getting any younger. You should find someone before it's too late.'

'You make me sound like a mangy old dog at the RSPCA no one wants! The only reason I don't have a man is because I'm too busy.'

'Doing what?'

'Looking after you, for a start!' As soon as she'd said it she wished she could bite the words back. She'd always been careful not to make Dan feel as if he was any kind of burden to her, because he really wasn't. And now she'd just gone and blurted out something like that. 'I'm sorry, I didn't mean that—'

'I know. But the thing is I can look after myself these days. It's you I'm worried about. This time next year I could be away at college if I get accepted. Then you'll be all on your own. I don't want to think of you like that.'

'I won't be on my own. I'll have my work and my friends. And I'll have Gran.'

'Great. You can go to the Over Sixties club together!' Dan smiled wryly. 'Seriously though, Mum, I don't like to think of you by yourself. I couldn't handle the guilt of you growing old alone and being eaten by your cats.'

'I don't have a cat. I don't even like cats.'

'You know what I mean.'

Tess smiled. How strange to think that all the time she'd been worrying about how Dan was going to cope when he left home, he'd been thinking the same about her.

'So you reckon I should grab your father while I can, so I don't end up alone and desperate. Is that it?'

'You could do a lot worse. And it's nice having him around, isn't it? Almost like we're a real family.'

'I thought we were a real family?'

'We are. But having Phil here sort of makes it more real. Now I know how all the other kids felt when they talked about their mums and dads.'

A lump rose in her throat. She'd never realised Dan felt the loss so badly. She'd done her best over the years to be mother and father to him, and it looked as if she'd failed.

He must have read her forlorn expression, because he said, 'I didn't mean that the way it sounded. You've been great, you really have. I didn't even think about Phil for years. Not until he was here. Now, I don't know – it feels right. I just wish we could make it permanent, that's all.'

'And how does your father feel about this? Or doesn't he get a vote either?'

'I'm sure he'd have you. And wouldn't it be nice for you to have someone to take care of you?'

'I can take care of myself, thank you very much!'

'Yes, but it'd be nice not to have to, wouldn't it?'

Yes, it would be nice, Tess thought, after Dan had gone to bed. It would be nice to have someone to share her worries with, to talk to at the end of a miserable, frustrating day. Another person to take some of the pressure off, to shout down the phone at repairmen to get them to turn up on time, to help carry the suitcases when they went on holiday and take the photos. All their holiday snaps were of either her or Dan, very rarely of them together, because one of them had to hold the camera.

It would also be nice to have someone to share the good times with, to laugh with, to get all soppy with on Valentine's Day.

But she knew Phil wasn't that someone. It sounded like Dan had got it all neatly sewn up in his mind. She and Phil would get together, he would have the two parents he'd apparently always wanted, and Tess wouldn't have to be lonely.

But surely you could be just as lonely with the wrong person as you could be on your own? And Phil was definitely the wrong person. They got on together, far better than she'd imagined they would. But she knew it could never go further than that. If it hadn't been for her getting pregnant, they would probably have split up anyway.

Sorry, Dan, she thought. Much as she would have done anything for her son, she couldn't make herself fall in love with someone.

23

Emily was very surprised when her father suggested a shopping trip to Leeds. He hated shopping, especially with her. They'd both agreed early on that the best way to avoid killing each other was for him to give her a wodge of cash and let her get on with it. But here he was, bundling them into the car, apparently looking forward to spending some quality time together.

Sophie was madly excited, of course, but Emily couldn't help wondering what he was up to. She sat beside him in the front seat, listening to him hum tunelessly to boring old Eric Clapton. He seemed in such a good mood. Too good for a Saturday-afternoon shopping trip anyway.

Then she found out why. He'd headed straight for Next, saying he needed to look for a new shirt. After browsing listlessly in the women's wear department for a few minutes, Emily had returned to find he still hadn't bought anything.

'Haven't you finished yet?'

'Hang on, I'm still deciding.'

That wasn't like him either. He usually dashed in and bought the first thing that came to hand. Most of the time he didn't even look at it until he'd got home. Now he stood there, a blue shirt in one hand, lemon in the other, as if his life depended on his choice.

'Buy the blue one.'

'What's wrong with the yellow?'

'Nothing, if you don't mind looking gay.' Emily stifled a yawn. 'Why don't you just buy them both? Come on, I'm starving.'

'Just a minute.' He kept looking around, craning over the heads of the milling shoppers. Emily frowned.

'Who are you looking for? The fashion police?'

'Jack! What a surprise.'

Emily swung round. There was Charlie, carrier bags in hand, her dark-red hair swinging glossily around her made-up face. She wore a cream sweater, high-heeled boots and chocolate leather jeans that looked as if they must have cost a fortune.

She watched Charlie move in to kiss her father. She was heading for the lips, but he averted his face at the last minute so she caught his cheek instead.

'Hi, Charlie. Fancy seeing you here.' Jack turned to Emily and Sophie. 'You remember Charlie, don't you, girls?'

Charlie beamed at them. Emily glowered back. Did they think she was stupid, or something? His surprised act didn't fool her for a second. This was a set-up. Why else would he be so keen to take them to Leeds? And why else would he be hanging around, dithering over a shirt?

And why, come to think of it, would Charlie Ferguson be in the men's department?

'I was just looking for a new shirt.' Jack held them both up. 'What do you think?'

Charlie considered them for a moment. 'The lemon one, definitely,' she said. 'It's very you.'

'Do you think so? Emily thinks it might be a bit much.'

'Nonsense, you could do with livening up your image. Don't you think so, Emily?' She turned her dazzling fake smile on to her.

'Don't ask me,' Emily shrugged, then added under her breath, 'Who cares what I think anyway?'

But no one heard her. They were already on their way to the cash desk, Sophie skipping happily behind them. With the hideous yellow shirt.

She'd hoped Charlie might disappear after that, but then her father said, 'We were just on our way to lunch in McDonald's. Would you like to join us?'

'I'd love to,' Charlie said. 'But you'll have to tell me what to order, I've never been there before.'

'Never been to McDonald's?' Sophie looked shocked. 'What, never ever?'

Charlie shook her head. 'Never ever.'

'Then you've missed one of the culinary treats of the century,' her father said. 'But don't worry. We'll look after you, won't we, girls?'

Sophie nodded enthusiastically. Emily rolled her eyes in disgust. This was supposed to be their day out, just the three of them. Now Charlie had hijacked it. Why couldn't she just butt out? They spent precious little time alone with him as it was, without her turning up and ruining everything.

Not that Sophie seemed to mind. She was already cuddled up next to Charlie in the queue, pointing things out in the illuminated overhead menu. Charlie was looking apprehensive.

'Don't they do salad?' she asked. Emily watched the way her father grinned at her. Almost lovingly, she thought. Her stomach flipped with anxiety. He couldn't. He just couldn't. It was like all her worst fears were coming true.

Charlie monopolised him all the way through lunch, talking about boring stuff to do with work. Even her father looked glazed, listening to her. Emily watched her pick at her fries – she'd refused even to consider a burger – and wished she'd choke on them. At least it might shut her up.

Why couldn't he see how fake she was, with her big smiles and pretending to be charmed by everything? And the way she looked at him, like he was Brad Pitt and Tom Cruise all rolled into one. It made her feel sick, but she couldn't stop watching them. Any second now Charlie was going to lean over and kiss him and then it really would be goodbye, Big Mac.

Sophie seemed to be won over. She stared up at her with an awed expression. Emily knew she was probably taking in every detail of her hair and make-up so she could copy them at home later. She was like a pathetic little puppy dog, admiring her shoes, her hair, her perfume.

'I like your trousers.' She stroked them with ketchupy fingers. Emily smiled as Charlie squirmed and tried not to look disgusted. 'Did you get them from London?'

'Actually, I got them from Milan.'

'Milan!' Sophie looked impressed.

'As if you even know where that is,' Emily said disgustedly.

'I do!'

'Go on, then. Where is it? She probably thinks it's the other side of Leeds.' She saw Charlie smiling and shut up. How dare she think she was making a joke for her benefit! 'I think wearing leather and fur is cruel,' she added loudly, to put her in her place. 'Animals die just so people can wear their skins. It's barbaric.'

'Some might think that burger you've eaten is pretty barbaric too,' Charlie pointed out coolly.

Emily looked down at the half-eaten Big Mac in her hand. It was difficult to square her belief in animal rights with her love of burgers and bacon sandwiches, but she couldn't give them up. She knew she was on dodgy moral ground, but Charlie had no right to point it out. 'That's different,' she muttered.

'Why? Because it's you and not me?'

'People need to eat. They don't need to wear leather.'

'They don't need to eat meat, either, but they do because they enjoy it. And it might interest you to know that the intensive cattle farming needed for those burgers causes a massive depletion in the Amazonian rainforest. They cut down areas the size of this country every day just to make room for the cows. How do you feel about that?'

Emily met her cool, challenging gaze across the table. She could feel her face burning with rage and humiliation.

'Would anyone like a McFlurry?' Her father tried to break the tension, but it was too late.

After lunch they headed for Top Shop, Charlie still trailing along with them. Why didn't she take the hint and go? Emily watched her trying on bandannas and belts with Sophie, as if she was remotely interested in them. Fake, fake, fake. Normally it would be her Sophie was pestering to try glittery eyeshadows on the back of her hand, but she'd forgotten all about her, she was so enchanted by her new best friend.

Emily sloped off to the other end of the shop and began trying on shoes, just for something to do. She tried on a pair of strappy wedge-heeled mules just for a laugh. They were hideous tart's shoes, about a million miles away from the trainers she usually wore.

'Very nice.' She looked up. Charlie was standing over her. For God's sake, couldn't she get away from that woman? 'You ought to get your dad to buy them for you. They make your legs look amazing.'

'I can make my own mind up, thanks.' Emily shook off the shoes as if they were infected and stuffed her feet back into her tatty trainers.

'Suit yourself. But they did look good.'

What would you know? Emily thought. She was ancient, thirty at least. As she stood up, Charlie said, 'Sophie's thinking of buying a T-shirt. She wants your advice.'

'What does she want my advice for? She's got you.' Emily elbowed past her and headed for where her father was loitering by the door, looking bored as usual. 'I want to go shopping on my own,' she announced flatly.

'Why? I thought this was meant to be a family trip?'

Emily shot a meaningful glance at Charlie. 'So did I,' she said.

'Well, I think that went rather well,' Charlie said wryly, as they watched Emily slope out of the shop.

'Take no notice of her. She's always like that. It's her hormones.'

'I don't think so. Not this time.' Charlie shook her head. 'I told you it wasn't a good idea to spring this surprise thing on them. She wasn't fooled for a minute.' At the time she'd allowed herself to be persuaded because it seemed a lot easier than facing them in a formal meeting. Now she was beginning to wish she'd just got it over with. She suspected she'd made an enemy for life.

And an enemy like Emily could make it even more difficult for her to get close to Jack.

'You've certainly won Sophie over.'

Charlie smiled. Sophie was sweet, if a little demanding. But there was only so long she could discuss the relative merits of pearly versus glittery nail polish without her brain exploding with boredom.

At least Sophie wasn't as sulky as Emily. The way she'd looked at her in that awful burger place! All she'd done was try to have a reasoned argument with her. Emily demanded to be treated like an adult, but she couldn't handle it.

Was it always going to be this hard? she wondered.

She looked at Jack. Being with him made up for it. Or so she hoped. They'd only actually been out together once, and that was only a rushed drink after work because he had to get back for some concert at Sophie's school.

She threaded her arm through his. 'As I've been such a good girl, do I get my reward?'

He grinned. 'Don't tell me you want that rhinestone tiara you and Sophie were trying on?'

'Not quite. I was thinking more of dinner tonight?'

'Tonight?' His face fell. 'Sorry, I can't. Sophie's got a friend coming to sleep over.'

When am I going to be invited to sleep over? she wondered. 'Couldn't you leave them with a babysitter?'

'I could – if I could find one with nerves of steel. No, I'd better be there in case they run riot. You know what kids are like.'

Charlie forced a smile. No, she didn't. But she was beginning to find out.

Two days later, Jack had to go up to the Westpoint site again, to meet the council's highways officers about a possible change to the traffic access. It was late afternoon by the time they'd finished. The trees at the edge of the site spread their skeletal branches against the darkening sky. The air had the November smell of burning leaves, mingled with the metallic tang of the factories' fumes. A sparrow hawk skimmed and dodged overhead. Jack watched it wheeling through the sky before it plunged like a missile towards the ground after its prey.

Beyond the trees, huddled behind a barbed-wire fence, he could make out the ramshackle shapes of the Second Chance buildings. He wondered if the barbed wire was to keep intruders out, or the workers in.

He trudged around the perimeter of the site, trying to imagine how it might all look with thousands of square metres of shops on it. All that activity, all those people. Cars streaming in and out, a complex network of roads and roundabouts cutting across the field, the still night air illuminated like daylight by the brightly lit shops, everyone coming to buy, to browse, to gawp at the spectacle. Piped muzak replacing the exuberant chatter of the starlings high in the trees . . .

Usually he was pretty good at visualising how things might look – that was part of his job, after all – but this time the picture jarred.

He turned away from the scene and headed back to his car. As he approached the gap in the fence, he disturbed a couple of blackbirds pulling at the ground. They rose into the sky with indignant, clattering cries. As Jack drew nearer he could see why they were so furious at being disturbed. They'd found a patch of ground where the earth had recently been turned over, making it a feasting ground for hungry birds.

He wouldn't have noticed it in the gathering darkness, but now he could see the blunt edges of where a spade had been. Whoever had dug the hole had obviously tried to cover their tracks; bits of turf had been hastily laid over the mound to disguise it. But they hadn't done a very good job. The shape was still clearly visible. A dark patch, roughly the size and shape of a grave ...

'What you doing?'

He swung round and found himself blinded by a torchbeam aimed straight at his eyes. He lifted his hand to shield the light. 'What the—'

'Oh, it's you.' Sam Dobbs lowered the torch. He was in his usual grubby duffel coat, his face grim under his knitted hat. 'What do you want? Come to dig it up, have you?'

'Dig what up?'

'I dunno. Whatever's buried down there.'

Jack took a step back from the mound. 'What makes you think there's anything buried down there?'

'Look at it, son.' Sam gestured towards the ground with his torch. 'It'd have to be a mole the size of a carthorse to do that kind of damage. And I don't think anyone would come all the way up here to make mud pies, do you?' He shook his head. 'No, there's definitely something down there. Question is – what is it?'

Jack looked at the dark, shapeless mound and felt his heart quicken. He knew what he thought it was. He just didn't like to say it out loud.

'Are you going to dig it up and find out, or shall I?'

He caught the amused glint in Sam's eye. 'Do you know anything about this?'

'Got nowt to do with me.' Sam was infuriatingly enigmatic. 'See nowt, say nowt, that's my motto.'

'I'm sure that comes in very useful in your line of work.'

'Being a vicar, you mean? I s'pose it does.'

'I was thinking more of your sideline as a latter-day Fagin.'

'Now hang about!' Sam advanced on him. 'Exactly what are you suggesting?'

'It seems a bit funny, that's all. This – thing – appears here, with your lot living next door.'

'So you think one of my lot, as you put it, has done someone in and buried them here? Is that what you're saying?'

'Maybe. Or it could be stolen goods or loot from a post office robbery. You tell me.'

They stared at each other for a moment. Then Sam threw back his head and laughed.

'Loot? Loot? You've been watching too many films, I reckon.' He wiped a tear from his eye with the sleeve of his coat. 'You're priceless, son, you know that? Those lads wouldn't know how to rob a post office. And they're about as likely to do a murder as you or me. They're strictly small time. And if they did do anything like that, most of them have got the good sense not to bury the evidence in their own back yard!' He shook his head. 'No, I reckon you want to look for your culprit a bit closer to home, before you go flinging your accusations around.'

Jack's eyes narrowed. 'Meaning?'

'Meaning the fella I saw up here with a spade wasn't one of my lot. He was one of yours.'

'You saw someone?'

'Course I did. I keep my eyes open and my wits about me, lad. Not like some people.' He tapped his temple. 'Loot, indeed! You're a funny one.'

Jack ignored him. 'So who was it? The man you saw?'

'How should I know? All I know is I've seen him hanging around with your bunch. The last time you were up here, as a matter of fact. Little bloke, round glasses. Bit like Himmler.'

'Bernard Sweeting?'

'Is that his name? I wouldn't know.'

Jack looked around. It made sense. Bernard was their environmental expert. He was probably just taking some soil samples or something.

He turned back to the mound. But that was one hell of a soil sample. It looked as if he'd dug up a wheelbarrow load.

'And you definitely saw him burying something?'

'Now I couldn't swear to that. But he looked a bit shifty when I came up and spoke to him.'

'You spoke to him? What did he say?'

'Nothing much. He wasn't too friendly, as a matter of fact. Told me in no uncertain terms that this wasn't my land or my business and I had no right poking about in it, either.'

Bernard had a point there, Jack admitted silently. And Sam Dobbs could seem a threatening character, with his squashed-in prizefighter's face and gruff manner. He was probably just trying to defend himself.

But something still didn't add up. Why would Bernard be taking more soil samples now? Unless there was something he wasn't telling anyone.

'So when was this?' he asked.

Sam shrugged. 'Not long. About a week ago. Maybe a bit longer. It was after you came up here with your little girl, anyway. How is she, by the way?'

'She's fine,' Jack answered absently, his thoughts racing.

'She's a lovely little kid. Still got that treasure of hers, has she?'

'Treasure?'

'That bone. The way she was clutching it you'd think it was the crown jewels.' Sam smiled fondly.

Jack didn't answer him. He looked around. Come to think of it, Sophie had dug it up somewhere around here . . .

Then he spotted it, sticking out of the ground, about ten yards away. The piece of stick Sophie had been digging with.

Fragments of disconnected thought rushed around in his brain. He tried to put them all together, to make sense of them. But it was difficult, like doing a jigsaw with half the pieces missing.

'Are you all right, son?' Sam watched him with a look of concern.

'I'm fine.' Jack thought for a moment. 'Sam, what do you know about cracking safes?'

Sam sighed. 'I already told you, my boys are all strictly petty crime—'

'What about you?'

'Who have you been talking to?'

There was something about the sharp way he said it that made Jack suddenly realise that maybe Sam Dobbs' shady criminal past hadn't been as small time as he liked to make out.

'Forget it,' he said. 'I shouldn't have asked you. I'll think of some other way of finding out what I need to know. Be seeing you, Sam.'

He started to walk away, but Sam called him back. 'This thing you need to know – there wouldn't be any mischief behind it, would there?'

'I don't know. That's what I'm trying to find out.'

'So it wouldn't be like you were trying to steal anything?'

He shook his head. 'I think someone's hiding something and I want to find out what it is.'

Sam scratched his stubbly chin for a moment. 'In that case, I don't suppose it would do any harm to give you a few tips, would it? Just in case you decided to have a go yourself, like?'

Jack smiled. 'I think the Almighty might overlook it, just this once.'

'I hope so, lad. He's overlooked enough in my life already, I'd hate to go blotting my copybook with Him all over again.' He looked back at the mound thoughtfully. 'You don't really think there's a body buried there, do you?'

'I don't know,' Jack said. 'But I've got a bad feeling about this place.'

24

'Where's Ophelia? Has anyone seen her yet?'

Stephen looked up from helping a soldier on with his boots. 'She's still at the rugby match. Helen says she'll drive her straight over as soon as the game's finished.'

'She'd better get a move on. The curtain goes up in ten minutes!'

Tess threaded her way amid the backstage chaos, tripping over strewn clothing and discarded props. Out in the front of house, the school orchestra was struggling through *Happy Days Are Here Again*.

'Not exactly appropriate for *Hamlet*, is it?' Stephen grimaced.

'I don't know. They're certainly murdering it.' Tess winced as the horn section tried and failed to hit a top C. It wasn't what she would have chosen, but Mr Herriman the music teacher had insisted it was the only thing he could manage. And since he was already on Prozac and heading for his second nervous breakdown, Tess had thought it wiser and kinder not to argue.

He wasn't the only one suffering with his nerves. Tess peered through a crack in the heavy velvet curtains. The audience was filling up as parents shuffled into their seats, each clutching their photocopied programmes. In the front row she spotted the Chair of Governors, flanked by Eric Gant on one side and Cynthia Frobisher on the other. Seeing her there made Tess feel sick with anxiety.

'Maybe this wasn't such a good idea after all,' she said to Stephen.

'Are you kidding? The kids love it.' He nodded to where Rosencrantz and Guildenstern were running through their lines behind the black curtain that screened the wings from the main stage. He was right. Her jazzed-up modern-day version had certainly captured their imaginations. The cast had not only turned up regularly for rehearsals, they'd even volunteered for extra sessions to make sure they were word perfect. For the last two weeks, Tess kept stumbling across little knots of them in corridors, corners of the school playground and even the toilets, testing each other on their lines.

'I just hope Cynthia feels the same.' Tess glanced back at her through the curtains. She was picking up her programme from under her seat, looking at the cover. Tess steeled herself. Any moment now she would open it, read the blurb and realise exactly what was going on.

But then Marjorie Wheeler arrived and Cynthia tucked the programme back under her seat without reading it. Tess watched them talking, their heads close together. Bitching about her, probably. They'd have plenty to bitch about by the interval.

She looked up and spotted Jack Tyler on the fifth row. Charlie Ferguson was beside him, dressed in a grey trouser suit that would have been mannish on anyone else but looked stunning on her. Jack was still in his work clothes. They must have come straight from the office.

She leant over and whispered something to Jack. He laughed, gazing straight back into her eyes. Tess imagined them driving up from Leeds together, discussing something high-powered that had happened at the office. And what had she been doing all day? Making cardboard swords.

She was just about to drag herself away from the curtain when she saw Helen Wesley come into the back of the hall, still in her ultra-short PE kit, blonde hair caught up in a girlish ponytail. She looked around, then hurried down to the stage, oblivious to the admiring stares of countless fathers that followed her.

'Psst!' Tess beckoned her over from between the curtains. 'Where the hell have you been?'

'I've just come from the hospital. There's been an accident.'

Tess' blood ran like ice through her veins. 'What kind of accident? Where's Maeve?'

'She was badly tackled during the match. Sorry, Tess, she's got a broken ankle.'

Tess reached out from between the curtains and dragged Helen through them. 'So where is she? Couldn't you just bring her anyway? She could have limped a bit, for God's sake. No one would have noticed.'

'No, but they might have noticed the two black eyes.'

Tess leant back against the lighting pillar. She suddenly felt very weak. 'Well, that's it, isn't it? It's over. We can't go on without an Ophelia.'

'Haven't you got an understudy or something?'

'Do me a favour! I had enough trouble finding one Ophelia, let alone two!'

'Excuse me?' Emily coughed behind them.

'Not now, Emily. Can't you see I'm having a crisis?' Tess said irritably. 'Why did you have to make her play in that stupid rugby match?' she asked Helen.

'Don't blame me!'

'Why not? You're the reason she's got a broken ankle!'

'Miss Doyle?'

Tess rolled her eyes and turned to face her. 'Yes, Emily? What is it?'

'I can do it.'

'I beg your pardon?'

'I can do Ophelia. I mean, I know all her lines.' Emily looked from one to the other and blushed to the roots of her hair.

'How come?'

'Never mind that!' Helen interrupted. 'She's the answer to all your prayers.'

But Tess wasn't used to having her prayers answered. It was too easy. 'Are you sure you can do this? It's a big role.'

'I think so.'

'Does it matter?' Helen said. 'For God's sake, get her in that costume before she changes her mind!'

For once it did seem as if God might be on her side. Emily turned out to be word perfect, and so was everyone else.

As the house lights dimmed and the soldiers – modern-day versions in fatigues 'borrowed' from Maeve's brother's barracks – took their places on the stage, Tess hung back in the wings to watch the audience's reaction.

Or more to the point, Cynthia Frobisher's reaction. While the parents' faces changed from glazed boredom to delight when they realised they were being treated to a shortened version of the story in modern language, Cynthia's grew rigid with displeasure. The lights were low but Tess was sure she could see steam rising from her ears.

In the interval, when she saw Cynthia rise from her seat and make her way purposefully towards the stage, flanked by an equally outraged-looking Marjorie Wheeler, she quickly dived down the back stairs, out into the corridor and outside before they could catch her.

The night was cold but clear. Beyond the dark ridge of the science block she could hear the whine of traffic on the bypass. The playground was illuminated by pools of sulphurous light from the street lamps.

She turned the corner and nearly fell over Jack Tyler sitting on the steps of the science block, smoking.

He jumped and dropped his cigarette when he saw her. Tess smiled. 'Shouldn't you be doing that behind the bike sheds?'

He looked ruefully at the cigarette he'd just ground under his heel. 'Stupid, isn't it? Old habits die hard in these places.'

'Do you mind if I join you?'

'Please.' He shifted along the step to make room for her.

'Where's Charlie?'

'Queuing for the ladies'. I just came out to get some air.'

Tess sat down beside him. 'I didn't know you smoked?'

'I don't. Only when I'm nervous.'

'What are you nervous about?'

'What do you think? My little girl's up there on that stage.' He took another cigarette out of the packet and lit it. 'She never told me she had a main part.'

'She didn't. Not until an hour ago.'

'You're joking?'

Tess shook her head. 'She took over when Ophelia dropped out. She's pretty good, isn't she?'

'Good? She's bloody amazing.' He took a drag on his cigarette and watched the smoke ring drift up into the night sky. 'I didn't realise how grown up she was until I saw her up there. Her mother would have been proud of her,' he said quietly.

He covered his eyes with his hand. It took a moment before Tess realised he was crying, his broad shoulders shaking with emotion.

Without thinking, she put her arms around him. He didn't resist. He let her pull him closer, hold him against her. She could feel his hair bristling against her cheek. He smelt of soap and freshly washed shirt.

After a few moments he pulled away from her. 'I'm sorry,' he said gruffly. 'I don't know what came over me.'

'Here,' she took a tissue out of her bag and handed it to him. 'It's crumpled but clean.'

'Thanks. God, I feel silly.' He wiped his eyes. 'You must think I'm an idiot.'

'Of course not.'

'Charlie will, if she sees me like this.' He stood up and brushed himself down. 'I'd better get back inside, before she thinks I've done a bunk.' He darted a quick glance at her. 'Thanks,' he said.

And then he was gone.

Tess watched him hurrying back to the school hall. She felt desperately sorry for him. What kind of relationship must he have with Charlie Ferguson if he couldn't let her see him cry?

She didn't go back inside for the second half. She stayed on the steps, hugging herself to keep the cold out and wishing she'd had the sense to grab her cardie before she made her escape. A thin shirt was no match for the biting December air. But she was too afraid to go back inside for it in case Cynthia was still prowling around backstage, looking for her.

She didn't know how long she sat there, her muscles seizing up with cold and cramp. But she still jumped when Stephen came round the corner.

'So this is where you're hiding! Everyone's looking for you.'

'I bet they are!' Tess' teeth chattered. 'And I expect Cynthia's leading them with my P45 in her hand.'

'Don't be so dramatic! They love it. Can't you hear them?'

Tess strained her ears. Sure enough, over the traffic noise, she could hear the muffled sound of applause.

'Aren't you going to take your bow?'

'I'd rather not.'

'Tough. You're coming.' Stephen dragged her to her feet and led her, protesting, back into the building and along the corridor to the side of the stage. The applause grew louder as they drew closer. By the time they reached the wings it was positively thunderous.

Tess peeped out at the cast, lined up on the stage. A few were bowing, others bobbed nervously, while the rest just looked dazed. Watching them, she suddenly felt a swell of maternal pride.

'Look at them.' Her voice was choked. 'Don't they look—'

She didn't have time to finish the sentence. Stephen shoved her in the small of her back towards the stage. She tripped over a trailing curtain cord and stumbled into the blinding glare of the footlights.

She stared out at the sea of faces. People were on their feet – clapping, not making for the doors in search of refreshments. Among them were the Chair of Governors and Eric Gant. Cynthia was still sitting down, and looked to be baring her teeth. Or was she? Tess risked another look. No, she was smiling. Tess looked away, unnerved, and found herself staring at Jack Tyler. He gave her the thumbs up. She grinned stupidly back.

She'd done it. They'd done it. In spite of all Cynthia's scheming and all the setbacks, it had happened. The faces blurred into a fog as her eyes filled with tears.

Afterwards there were drinks for the audience, provided by the PTA. Tess was so overcome by nerves she didn't want to go, but Stephen and Helen manhandled her into the crowded hall.

'You've worked hard for this, you deserve a bit of praise,' Helen told her firmly. 'If you don't go, Cynthia will only take all the credit.'

Not that there was much praise coming her way. Tess huddled in the corner, a plastic cup of warm Liebfraumilch in one hand, a bowl of peanuts in the other, while everyone milled past her. On the other side of the room, Cynthia was holding forth to a group of parents. Telling them all about her hard work, Tess guessed. She didn't care. She was just relieved it was all over and she'd escaped with her job.

She crammed a handful of peanuts into her mouth. She'd been too nervous to eat before the performance and now she was ravenous.

'Tess?' She turned round, mouth full of peanuts.

'Oh, hello, Jack.' She wiped her mouth with her sleeve. 'Sorry, I haven't had a chance to eat yet.'

'Don't let me stop you.' His grey eyes crinkled at the corners as he looked down at her. 'You did a great job tonight. How do you feel?'

'Like going home and sleeping for a week!'

'I just wanted to say how sorry I am about earlier. I don't make a habit of crying on people's shoulders, believe me.'

'At least you didn't do it in front of an audience.' She blushed to think how she'd burst into tears and had to be led away by a sniggering Polonius.

'I thought it was very touching.'

'You mean I made a complete idiot of myself!'

'I don't think anyone noticed.'

'Of course not. That photographer from the *Evening Press* was probably just taking pictures of the scenery.' She looked rueful. 'Anyway, you've got nothing to apologise for. It's been an emotional evening.'

'An emotional year, you mean.' Jack's face was bleak. 'Next week it'll be exactly a year since Miranda died.'

No wonder he was so upset. Tess regarded him sympathetically. 'How are you coping?'

'It depends. I thought I was doing okay, but I've had trouble sleeping lately. I can't stop thinking about it, going over it all in my head. Wondering what it would have been like if none of this had happened.'

'That's not surprising. Have you thought about seeing a doctor?'

'What could he do? Give me pills to make me forget?' Jack's mouth twisted. 'What really worries me is Christmas. It's only two weeks away and I don't know how we're going to manage.'

'What did you do last year?'

'Strangely enough it wasn't so bad. I think we were all too numb to feel anything, and the rest of the family rallied around to help. But my sister's going to visit her in-laws this year and my parents are off on a coach holiday to the Highlands.'

'I'm sure they'd cancel if you really wanted them to.'

'I expect they would. But they were meant to go last year and they put it off because of Miranda's death. I can't ask them to do it again.' He looked grim. 'It's my own fault. I've been going around telling everyone how brilliantly we're all coping, and they've started to believe me.'

'But you're not?'

'Most of the time we are, but it always seems worse at times like this.'

Tess nodded. She could still remember the first Christmas after her father died. Her mother had gone to so much trouble to make it as special as it always was. They had a tree, turkey, loads of presents. It had been a disaster. No one was in the mood to enjoy it. Everything they did reminded them someone important was missing. Tess had felt too guilty to play with her new toys, she and Frances had bickered all day and later they'd found their mother in the kitchen crying quietly as she made the stuffing.

'If I were you, I'd do something completely different,' she advised.

'Don't stay in the house, because you'll only get morbid. You should go out and make some new memories, instead of dwelling on the old ones.'

'What do you suggest?'

'I don't know.' She searched her mind for ideas. 'Couldn't you go on holiday? Somewhere hot and exotic?'

'I thought of that, but everything's fully booked. I can't even get a place on my parents' coach to the Cairngorms!'

'What about Charlie? Couldn't you spend Christmas with her?'

Jack frowned. 'Not a good idea. Emily hasn't exactly taken to her.' His look spoke volumes. 'I think spending Christmas together would ruffle a few too many feathers.'

Emily's or Charlie's? Tess wondered. She pondered the problem for a moment, then it came to her. 'Why don't you come round to ours?'

Jack shook his head. 'We couldn't impose on you—'

'You wouldn't be. My mum's going to spend Christmas with my sister in London, so it'll just be Dan and me. We could pool our resources. It'll be fun. That is, if you want to?'

'I'd love to. And I'm sure the girls would too.' He looked doubtful. 'But wouldn't your boyfriend mind?'

'I'm sure he would, if I had one. But since I don't that's not a problem, is it?'

'What about that man at the Parents' Evening?'

'You mean Phil? He's not my boyfriend. Well, not for the past seventeen years, anyway. He's Dan's father,' she explained.

'That's him, is it? So Dan got in touch with him, then?'

'I couldn't stop him! Actually, it's worked out quite well. He's not the monster I thought he would be.'

'You seemed to be getting on well when I saw you.'

'Not as well as my son would like us to,' Tess said.

'Really? Why's that?'

Before she could reply Charlie drifted up, a cup of wine in each hand.

'Here you are, darling. Sorry I've been so long, but I got collared by some strange little man over by the refreshments – oh, hello. It's Tess, isn't it?' Her smile widened. 'Great play. I thought I'd be bored senseless, but I loved every minute.'

'Thank you.' Why did she have to be so nice? It didn't give Tess a chance to hate her. 'Emily was very good, wasn't she?'

'Very. Although since she's such a drama queen that's hardly surprising!'

Tess glanced at Jack. Either he hadn't heard, or he'd stopped reacting.

They made small talk for a while, but Jack seemed less talkative when Charlie was around. As for Charlie, it was obvious, in spite of her niceness, that she wanted Jack all to herself.

In the end Tess decided to leave them to it. 'Oh well, I suppose I'd better go and mingle.'

Charlie made a brave stab at looking disappointed. 'It was nice meeting you again, Tess.'

'And you.' She turned to Jack. 'Let me know about Christmas, won't you? We can make some arrangements.'

'What arrangements, Jack?' she heard Charlie say as she walked away. Oops. Tess ducked quickly into the crowd.

'So I said to Miss Doyle, what we really need is something more modern, more on their wavelength,' Cynthia was telling the Chair of Governors as she hurried past. Tess didn't stop to set them straight. She was more worried about the conversation that was going on on the other side of the room.

Or rather, the lack of it. Charlie and Jack were half turned away, jaws set, eyes looking everywhere but at each other.

25

Charlie was still simmering in the car on the way back to Jack's. She knew she was being childish but she couldn't help it.

What made it worse was that Jack couldn't see why she was so angry.

'It's not as if we made any plans together,' he said. 'You're going skiing without me.'

'I asked you to come.'

'What about the girls?'

'They could have come too,' she said, less convincingly.

'I bet your friends would have loved that!'

'Or you could have left them with someone.'

'They're children, Charlie, not a pair of Labradors. I can't just dump them in boarding kennels whenever I feel like it.'

More's the pity, Charlie thought. She glanced in the wing mirror. Emily was hunched on the back seat, pretending to listen to her CD player. But Charlie knew she could hear every word they said. And was probably loving every minute.

Naturally she'd been very enthusiastic about the idea of spending the day with Tess. Especially when she saw how wound up Charlie was about it.

It wasn't just the thought of him not being with her that irked her. It was the thought of him being with Tess. Charlie wasn't sure about her. She had a feeling Tess had a crush on Jack. She wasn't seriously worried about her as a rival, but who knew what could happen if he was left alone with her on Christmas Day? Christmas was an emotional time, it could do strange things to people. As could copious amounts of champagne and cooking sherry.

'You should have talked to me first,' she insisted. 'We're supposed to be a couple.'

Jack didn't reply, but his frown gave his feelings away. It wasn't what they'd agreed. They were supposed to be keeping their relationship casual, but she wanted more. She wanted the dreaded C word. Commitment. The word she didn't dare utter to Jack.

She knew she was falling for him. She'd never felt like this. She was usually in control of her emotions, but for once she could feel them running away with her. She was even starting to feel jealous, something she'd always dismissed as a waste of time.

She glanced across at Jack's unsmiling profile as he concentrated on the road ahead. She was sure he could feel the same too, if only he'd allow himself to let go of the past.

And if it wasn't for another couple of small problems . . .

Her favourite REM track came on the CD and Charlie leaned forward to adjust the volume. Emily immediately snatched the headphones off her head. 'Do you mind? I can't hear my music.'

'No, but we can.' The tinny 'tsch tsch' of Emily's CD player had been driving her mad ever since they left school. 'Do you have to have it so loud? God knows what it's doing to your ears.'

'They're my ears,' Emily snapped back. She turned up the volume so the tinny beat filled the car.

'That's enough, Emily.' Jack warned. Emily clamped her headphones back on and retreated into angry silence.

Charlie stared at him. Was that it? If she had been rude at that age to an adult, her father would have given her a reprimand she wouldn't forget in a hurry. But somehow Emily was allowed to get away with murder. Jack didn't seem to care how awful she was to Charlie. As long as his precious baby wasn't too traumatised.

They were silent until they got back to Jack's house. He reversed his car on to the drive beside hers and turned off the engine. 'Are you coming in for coffee?'

'Are you sure you haven't made other plans?' she asked shrewishly.

Jack sighed. 'Obviously I haven't, or I wouldn't be asking.'

Charlie thought about refusing. If any other man had treated her like that she would have slammed the car door in his face and told him never to call her again. But she had a horrible feeling Jack wouldn't call her anyway. Hating herself for her lack of pride, she meekly said, 'Okay.'

Ros was babysitting. She was snuggled up with Sophie, watching *Friends* and flicking through a magazine. She smiled wearily when they came in.

'How was the play?'

'Great.' Charlie took off her coat, draped it over the back of the sofa and sat down. Ros immediately closed her magazine and tapped Sophie on the backside with it.

'Come on, little minx, it's time you were in bed. And me.' She yawned and stretched her arms wide.

'Aren't you going to stay for coffee?' Jack asked.

'No thanks. I'm working at the library tomorrow morning, and it's quite a drive back to Leeds.' She was already struggling into her coat. She reached up and kissed her brother on the cheek. 'Night, Jack, night, Em. Night, Charlie,' she added as an afterthought.

'Goodnight,' Charlie said, but she was already gone. It was very strange. After trying so hard to throw them together, Ros had seemed cool towards her since the dinner party. Charlie wondered if she'd said or done anything to upset her.

Probably because she hadn't said she was dying to have a baby or acted fascinated enough in the conversation about headlice, she decided.

Jack saw Ros to the door, then went upstairs to supervise Sophie's teeth-cleaning, leaving Charlie and Emily to sit in frozen silence. She'd been hoping for some time alone with Jack, but it didn't look as if it was going to happen. Emily seemed as if she was there for the rest of the night, stretched out on the sofa, the remote control in her hand.

'Shouldn't you be in bed by now?' she hinted.

'Dad always lets me stay up on a Friday.' Emily pointed the remote at the screen and flicked through the channels.

I bet he does, she thought. Emily was turning into a wilful little brat and Jack was doing nothing to stop her. But there was no point talking to him about it. He wouldn't hear a word said against her.

And Charlie didn't feel it was her place to tell Emily off, much as she felt like it. So all she could do was put up with her rudeness and tantrums, or try to ignore them. Neither of which came easily to her.

Jack came back downstairs and went straight into the kitchen to make the coffee. Charlie followed him.

'Is Emily going to sit there all night?' she asked.

'It's Friday. She always stays up on a Friday.'

'So she said. I just feel a bit uncomfortable with her watching us all the time.'

'It is her home.'

'It would be nice to have some time to ourselves, don't you think?'

'I know. But it's difficult. We have to be discreet.'

You're telling me, Charlie thought. Spending the night together had to be planned like a covert military operation, involving babysitters, clandestine phone calls and the smuggling of toothbrushes. It always had to be at her place, never his, and even then he left in the early hours so he could be home before the girls woke up. They'd been seeing each other for a month, and apart from that first night they'd never woken up in the same bed.

'Discreet? Bloody hell, I'm barely allowed to hold your hand as it is. What do you suggest, we become pen pals?'

'Now isn't the time. It's coming up to the anniversary of their mother's death. It's an upsetting time for them.'

For them, or for you? Charlie watched him as he made the coffee. She sometimes wondered if the real reason why he kept her at arm's length was because he still felt guilty about their relationship, not because he was worried about upsetting the children.

'Emily's fourteen years old. And she's not stupid. If she hasn't worked out we're sleeping together by now—'

'Shh! Keep your voice down, she'll hear you.'

'So what? The sooner she gets used to the idea, the better. Then maybe she'll stop looking at me like I'm some kind of nasty lab experiment.' She cuddled up against him. 'Still, we won't have any chaperones when we go away for the weekend, will we? I'll have you all to myself.'

'You make it sound like a dirty weekend.'

'That's up to you, isn't it?'

Jack grinned. 'We are talking about Crawshaw and Finch's team-building weekend in the Lakes, aren't we? The only chance we'll have to get dirty is when we're face down in mud being trampled underfoot by a bunch of gung-ho accountants.'

'Oh, I don't know. I could let you share my sleeping bag.' As Charlie lifted her face to kiss him, Emily walked in.

'Ugh! Don't mind me.' She pushed past them and headed for the fridge.

'For heaven's sake!' Charlie couldn't stop herself snapping. 'Don't you ever knock?'

'Don't you ever stop slobbering over my dad?'

'You see what I mean?' Charlie turned to Jack. 'At least we won't have to put up with this when we're away.'

She hadn't meant to say it; she knew Jack hadn't told Emily about the team-building weekend. He was still waiting for the right moment to break it to her, he said.

Well, she knew now. And she didn't look too pleased about it.

'Who's going away?'

'It's just a work thing,' Jack said quickly. 'And it's not until January. Not for another month.'

'Nice of you to tell me,' Emily muttered.

'He's telling you now, isn't he?' Charlie said. Although she hadn't meant to blurt it out, she couldn't help feeling an unworthy twinge of satisfaction that Emily was the one being put out for once.

But her triumph disappeared when Emily slammed out of the room and Jack turned on her. 'Thanks a lot,' he said.

'It's not my fault. I thought you would have said something by now.'

'I told you, I hadn't found the right time.'

'And when would that be? As you're on your way out of the door? For God's sake, Jack, you can't go on protecting her for ever. Sooner or later she's got to learn that you're a grown man and you've got your own life to lead.'

'I've also got two daughters who need me.'

'I know what she needs!'

She saw the look on his face and knew she'd said the wrong thing. He put down his coffee cup and headed for the door.

'Where are you going?'

'To see my daughter.'

'But we need to – talk,' she said, as the door slammed.

Charlie tipped her coffee down the sink. She held the cup in her hand for a moment, then turned around and hurled it at the wall in sheery fury.

She stormed out and sat in her car for a few minutes, waiting to calm down. Secretly she was also hoping Jack would come out and beg her to stay, but he didn't. The lights in the upstairs windows blazed. As she watched, Jack's silhouette appeared at one of them and pulled the curtains closed. He didn't even look down into the street.

Charlie turned the key in the ignition and sped off, furious as hell.

Tess, meanwhile, was still struggling to deal with the enormity of what she'd done. Less than two weeks until Christmas, and she'd invited three people she barely knew to join them. This meant her low-key Christmas with Dan had suddenly turned into a full bells-and-whistles affair.

Dan wasn't too pleased about it either. 'Who are these people, anyway?'

'Jack's just a friend. His daughter's in my class at school.'

'Since when did you start inviting kids from school round for Christmas?'

'Her mother died a year ago. I felt sorry for them.'

Dan grunted. 'I don't know why you don't just turn this place into a soup kitchen and have done with it.'

'Stop it, Dan. I've got enough on my mind without you giving me a hard time.' She ticked off the list on her fingers. 'I'm going to have to buy some presents for them, although God knows what they'd like. And we'll need a bigger turkey. How big will it have to be to feed five, do you think?'

'Six,' Dan said quietly. 'I've invited Phil.'

'What?' Tess sank down on to the sofa. 'When did this happen?'

'He rang the other night. We got talking about Christmas, he said he wasn't doing anything so I invited him.'

'Thanks for telling me!'

'Sorry. I didn't think you'd mind.'

Tess took it all in. Six people. She'd never cooked a huge Christmas dinner before. A horrible image of herself wrestling with a giant turkey formed in her mind.

But it wasn't just that. For reasons she couldn't fathom, the idea of Jack and Phil sitting around the dinner table together filled her with unease.

'I wish you hadn't invited him, Dan. This makes things very awkward. I don't even know if we've got enough chairs, for a start.'

'So call your friends and tell them they can't come.'

'I can't do that! They'll be so disappointed.'

'So will Phil.' Dan looked stubborn. 'Besides, I think he has more right to be here than that lot.'

'He could come on Boxing Day instead?' Tess suggested hopefully.

'No chance,' Dan said. 'This is the first Christmas I've ever had with my father. I'm not missing out on it for anyone.'

He had a point, Tess thought. Much as she hated to admit it.

She thought about phoning Jack to cancel. She actually got as far as dialling his number, but her nerve failed her when he picked the phone up.

'Tess. Thank God it's you.' He sounded weary. 'I thought it might be Charlie and I haven't got the strength to deal with her at the moment.'

'Have you two had a row?'

'You could say that. Actually, she and Emily had the row; I got caught in the crossfire as usual.' He sighed heavily. 'I don't blame Charlie for being pissed off. Emily was being stroppy with her and I didn't do much to help. But it's so difficult not to take sides, I always end up upsetting someone.' He brightened up. 'Anyway, I'm glad you called. I wanted to talk to you about Christmas.'

'Ah yes, I'm glad you mentioned that.'

'Thanks so much for inviting us. The girls are really looking forward to it and so am I. I can't tell you what this means to me,' he said quietly.

'Actually, that's what I was calling about.' Tess bit her lip. She couldn't bring herself to do it. 'I – um – just wondered if you could bring a couple of spare chairs with you?'

26

It was noon on Christmas Day, and Tess was at the kitchen sink humming tunelessly along to the carol service on the radio while she tackled the potato mountain. Apart from the veg, which had yet to be peeled, everything was suspiciously under control. The monstrous turkey was cooking nicely, having been in the oven since the crack of dawn. She'd had a bath and washed her hair, using the posh Aveda stuff her sister had sent, treated herself to a Clinique face pack – a present from Dan – and dressed in the black trousers and bronze sparkly top she'd bought for the staff Christmas party. She'd cracked open her first bottle of champagne an hour ago and toasted herself with a Buck's Fizz to celebrate her brilliant organisational skills.

The only thing spoiling her good mood was Dan. He was in his room – playing on his computer so he said, although Tess suspected he was sulking because Phil had called to say he'd had a water main burst outside his home and he couldn't leave in case his house got flooded. From the way Dan was acting, anyone would think Tess had deliberately burst the flaming thing herself.

He ignored the doorbell when Jack and the girls arrived. Tutting, Tess went to the door, wiping her hands on a teatowel.

'Merry Christmas!' Jack waved a bottle of Bollinger at her. Emily and Sophie stood behind him, their arms full of presents.

'Thanks. I've already opened a bottle.'

'Is there any left?'

'Cheek! Do I look as if I've been face down in the broccoli?'

She stepped aside to let them into the narrow hallway. 'Dan!' she called. 'Our guests are here.' No answer. 'He's probably got his headphones on,' she said, knowing full well he was in the middle of a major strop.

She led them into the sitting room. 'Nice place,' Jack commented, shrugging off his black leather jacket. He was wearing black jeans and a chunky grey sweater that matched his eyes.

'Thanks. It's not quite as grand as yours, but we like it. Ah, here's Dan.'

She smiled brightly as Dan wheeled in. 'Dan, this is Jack, Emily and Sophie.'

'Hi,' Dan grunted. 'Have you seen my Eminem CD?' he asked Tess.

'I imagine it's in your room.'

'Well, I can't find it.'

'Perhaps if you tidied up in there occasionally, you might be able to find things?' Tess was tight-lipped.

'Perhaps if you didn't tidy up, I might know where I'd left them?' He spun the wheelchair round and headed back to his room.

Jack's eyes twinkled. 'It feels like home already!'

They chatted for a while, then Tess prised Dan out of his room to hand out the presents she'd bought for Jack and the girls. After much thought, she'd settled on some glittery make-up and hair accessories for Sophie and a CD for Emily.

'I hope it's okay?' She watched her face as she unwrapped it. 'I'm afraid I don't know one band from another, but Dan assures me they're the latest thing.'

'It's brilliant, thanks.'

'My turn.' Jack picked up the large, gift-wrapped box in front of him and shook it gently. 'It's big enough. Are you sure it's mine?'

'I can't think of anyone else who'd want it. I hope you like it,' Tess said shyly. She'd been so certain he would when she spotted it in the Discovery Store. But suddenly she wasn't so sure. What if he didn't understand? What if he didn't get the joke?

But he did. He ripped off the paper and his face broke into a grin. 'I don't believe it,' he said. 'Where did you find this?'

'What is it?' Sophie and Emily clamoured to see. 'It's a toy rocket!' Sophie looked disappointed.

'Not just any old rocket. This is Thunderbird Two.' He gazed at it lovingly.

'It has lots of features, apparently,' Tess said. 'Almost as good as the real thing, the boy in the shop said.' She blushed. 'I hope you don't think it's too silly?'

'It's just what I always wanted,' he said.

'Open yours now.' Sophie, eager to move on to the next diversion, handed her and Dan their gifts. Dan's was a computer game; hers was a bottle of *Trésor*.

'How did you know this was my favourite?' she asked.

'I just recognised it.'

'Liar!' Emily said. 'He went round Fenwicks three times sniffing everything before he found out which one it was!'

Tess laughed, flattered. 'I didn't realise it was that memorable.'

'I'd know it anywhere.'

She turned to her son. 'What about yours, Dan? You wanted that game, didn't you?' He grunted. 'I'm amazed you found one he didn't have,' she said quickly, to cover his sullen response.

Tess went off to check on dinner and Jack followed, leaving Sophie playing with the new Barbie she'd got from her grandparents, and Emily and Dan in awkward silence in front of the TV.

He flicked channels. 'Anything you want to watch?'

'Not bothered.' Emily hardly dared speak to him, he was so rude. As if it was her fault they were here. His mum had invited them.

At the same time, she couldn't take her eyes off his wheelchair. She kept sneaking sideways glances at it. She had no idea Miss Doyle's son was disabled.

'You can try it out, if you're that interested?' he said, not looking round. 'What?'

'The wheelchair. You're obviously fascinated by it.'

Emily averted her eyes back to the screen. 'Sorry,' she mumbled.

'S'okay. Everyone stares. Why should you be any different?'

She hesitated. 'Were you in an accident or something?'

He nodded. 'I did a bungee jump and the rope broke.'

'Really?'

'No, I just said it to be interesting. I was actually born like this.'

'Oh. Right.' She couldn't think of anything else to say. 'So – um – do you mind being in a wheelchair?'

'No, I love it. I love that I can't go into shops because they've got steps outside. I love that I can't get my money out of the bank because I can't reach the cashpoint. Most of all I love that people like you talk to me as if I'm retarded!'

'I don't know, do I? I've never met anyone like you before!'

'Well, I've met lots of people like you, believe me.'

They sat in silence, both glaring at the TV screen. Sophie pulled Barbie's party dress off, revealing a pair of unsexy big white knickers.

'You would have thought she'd wear a thong, wouldn't you?' she said, disappointed.

Dan grinned. So did Emily. 'Sorry,' he said. 'Take no notice of me. I'm just a bit pissed off at the moment.'

'Because we're here?'

'Because my dad isn't.' He picked up the TV remote control and hit the Off button. 'Stuff this,' he said. 'I don't suppose you fancy a game on the computer?'

'They sound as if they're getting on okay,' Tess listened from the kitchen a few minutes later. 'I'm sorry, I don't know what's got into my son today. He isn't usually such a Kevin.'

'Don't apologise. Believe me, it's nice to know I'm not the only one with a surly teenager.'

'Like I said, he isn't usually that bad.' Tess opened the oven and pulled out the roasting tin to turn the potatoes. A whoosh of heat rose up, melting what was left of her make-up.

'Emily is. She's been even worse since I started seeing Charlie.'

It doesn't take a genius to work out why, Tess thought. 'How are things between you at the moment? Have you made it up?'

'We're speaking, but she's being a bit frosty.' Jack took the champagne bottle out of the fridge and refilled their glasses. 'I don't know what to do for the best. It always seems to be me having to take sides. I just wish she and Emily would get on with each other. She doesn't seem to have any trouble with Sophie.'

'That's because she's not at an awkward age. Emily's bound to be wary of anyone new,' Tess said.

'You try explaining that to Charlie. She thinks I should be a bit more heavy-handed. But the way I see it, that will only make Emily resent her more.' He sipped his drink. 'I'm not going to drive my daughter away, especially when I'm not sure if Charlie and I even have a future together.'

'You're not?' Tess came up so fast she nearly hit her head on the oven door. 'I thought you liked her?'

'I do. That's the problem. I don't want to hurt her, but I don't know if I can give her what she really wants.'

'Which is?'

'Commitment. She wants us to start making plans for the future as a couple. It's not unreasonable, I suppose. But I'm not ready for all that.'

'Because you're still in love with Miranda?'

'Because I'm not in love with Charlie.' He sent her a level look over the rim of his glass. 'I'm not saying I couldn't fall for someone. But she's not the woman I want.'

They looked at each other and a flash of heat rose in her face that had nothing to do with the oven.

The doorbell rang, breaking the tension. Tess heard Dan rush to answer it. 'Dad's here!' he yelled.

'I left the water board sorting out the burst main and drove straight up.' Phil stood in the hall, smartly dressed in a cream shirt and charcoal-grey trousers, his floppy fair hair brushed back off his face. 'Dan sounded so disappointed on the phone I thought I couldn't let him down.'

His smile faded when he saw Jack. 'Oh, hello. We've met, haven't we? At the Parents' Evening?'

'This is Jack,' Tess said. 'Jack, this is Phil, Dan's father.'

They shook hands. Neither of them looked terribly pleased to see the other.

'Sorry, I didn't know you were expecting anyone else,' Phil said.

Jack frowned. 'Neither did I.' They both looked at Tess.

'I'll just go and check on the potatoes again,' she said, and ducked back into the kitchen.

By the time she got back Phil was unloading Dan's present from the boot of his Porsche. Judging by the size of the box, there was no surprise about what it was.

'A new motherboard!' Dan gazed at what looked to Tess like the gubbins from the back of an old TV set. 'I've been wanting one of these for ages. And it's got dual BIOS, a twelve-volt connector and an optical S/PDIF output.'

'Sounds marvellous.' Tess smiled. For all she knew about computers, he could have told her it was a 2.5 GHz camel with USB ports, Athlon socket and an optional third hump.

'And it's got onboard RAID for faster hard disk drive arrays,' Phil pointed out. 'You'll have to update your software to take account of the increased memory, of course. But I can let you have a lot of that stuff. We've just got the new version lying around the office, straight from the States. It's not available in this country yet.'

'Actually, Mum's already bought me some for Christmas.' Dan gave her a shy, sideways glance.

'Oh. Right.' Phil had the grace to look embarrassed. 'Well, the existing version's just as good, of course. Even better, in some ways.'

Tess knew she was being placated. She also knew she'd just wasted nearly a hundred quid on something Phil had 'lying around' the office.

She wasn't going to throw a tantrum about it. The atmosphere was fraught enough already.

'Dinner's nearly ready,' she announced. 'Get your father a drink, Dan. We'll be eating in ten minutes.'

It was hardly the jolly affair she'd planned. There were long, tense silences, punctuated by awkward small talk. Dan ignored everyone else and chatted to Phil about motherboard installation and the relative merits of the dual CPU system. Tess played with her food and gazed at Jack, marooned at the other end of the table. She would have liked to talk to him but Dan had manoeuvred her as far away as possible, next to Phil.

Jack was trying to keep up a show of good spirits for the girls, but he'd gone quiet since Phil arrived. And yet she felt there was still so much to say. Especially after what had happened in the kitchen.

It was no surprise to her when, shortly after lunch, Jack announced he was going home.

'But you haven't been here long!' Tess protested. 'At least stay and have another drink?'

'No, I'd better be going. You'll want some family time.' He looked across at Dan and Phil, who'd cleared the dining-room table and were engrossed in dismantling Dan's computer on it.

He leaned forward and pecked her awkwardly on the cheek. 'Thanks for a lovely day, Tess. And for the presents.'

'You're welcome. Thanks for mine.'

She watched them go, burning with frustration. Family time, indeed!

She went back inside and slammed the door. Phil looked up vaguely from the instruction manual. 'Have they gone?'

Tess was too angry to answer him. 'I hope you're not going to leave all this stuff here? It's meant to be a dining room, not the head office of Microsoft!'

'Oops,' Phil whispered. 'Someone's in a bad mood.'

'Yes, I am. And do you want to know why? Because you two made my friends feel so uncomfortable they've gone home.'

'Hang on a minute! I haven't done anything.'

'You didn't help. Whispering in corners like a pair of schoolkids, sharing your little private jokes. Even I felt as if I didn't belong and I live here! And as for you—' She squared up to Dan, hands on hips. 'I was ashamed of the way you behaved. Sulking and snapping at Jack whenever he tried to talk to you. I've never brought you up to be rude to people.'

Dan stuck out his chin defiantly. 'I never asked him to come, did I?'

'No, but I did. They were my friends, Dan. And you made them feel unwelcome.' She took a deep breath, trying to contain her anger. 'I think you should call him and apologise.'

'No way!'

'Dan!'

'I didn't want him here. He can get stuffed for all I care!'

'Daniel Doyle! You come back here this minute!' But he'd already slammed out of the room. Phil and Tess stared at each other.

'Would it help if I left too?' he asked.

'I don't think things can get much worse, do you?' She sat down at the table, all the fight gone out of her.

This had started off as such a good day. Everything had gone so well, she'd had so much to look forward to. Now it was all ruined.

Phil came round the table to sit beside her and handed her what was left of his champagne. 'I wouldn't have come if I'd known it was going to be awkward,' he said.

'It's not your fault. It's Dan I'm really angry at.'

'He can't help being a moody teenager.'

'It's not just that. It's what he's trying to do that annoys me.'

'What's that?'

'You mean you don't know he's trying to push us together?'

Phil looked taken aback. 'What? I hadn't noticed.'

'Then you must be blind. Think about it. All those times he's managed to work it so we're left alone together? Like that night we went out to dinner?'

'You mean he didn't have a college assignment?'

'I don't know. But it seems a bit strange that he's suddenly become so keen on keeping up with his homework.'

Phil shook his head. 'Why would he want to do that?'

'Because he wants a happy ending. He wants you and me to walk off into the sunset and give him the perfect nuclear family he's apparently always wanted.' She couldn't keep the bitterness out of her voice.

Phil regarded her carefully. 'And don't you believe in happy endings?'

Tess thought about the mess that today had turned out to be. She thought about Jack, heading for home with the girls when she so badly wanted him to stay.

'Not today,' she said bitterly.

It looked as if it was about to snow. The sky had a threatening, yellowish-grey tinge to it, and the raw wind whipped at them as they trudged homewards towards Hollywell Park.

'Why did we have to go?' Sophie trailed along behind them, her arms full of half-naked Barbies. 'I was having a nice time. I wanted to stay.'

'I know, but Tess had another guest. We would have been in the way.'

He didn't want to stay and watch Phil worm his way back into Tess' affections anyway. It was fairly obvious that was what he was after.

'Do you think Tess will get back with Dan's father?' Emily surprised him by asking the question that had been going through his mind.

'I don't know. She might.'

'I think she should. She needs someone.'

'She wouldn't thank you for saying that!'

'It's true, though. That's what Dan says, anyway.'

'How do you know that?'

'He told me. While we were playing on the computer. He wants his dad to marry his mum so they'll stay together. He says he's always wanted two parents.' She looked wistful for a moment. 'I think they'll get together.'

So do I, Jack thought. He was amazed how glum the idea made him feel.

'What are we going to eat when we get home?' Sophie demanded, as they turned off the main road and into the wide, sweeping avenues of Hollywell Park. The streets were deserted, apart from a gaggle of small boys trying out their new bikes around the cul-de-sac. Lights blazed in every window. Jack could imagine all kinds of merriment going on behind those closed doors, with families getting together to enjoy the festivities. It made him feel achingly lonely.

He summoned a smile for Sophie's benefit. 'You've just had a big dinner. Haven't you eaten enough?'

'Yes, but I might want turkey sandwiches later. We always have turkey sandwiches on Christmas night.' She looked subdued, remembering.

'Maybe we could have festive beans on toast instead?' he suggested.

Sophie shook her head. 'It's not the same. I bet Tess has got turkey sandwiches,' she said.

As they turned the corner, it was Sophie who spotted her first. 'Charlie!' She ran towards the sporty Audi TT parked beside Jack's BMW on the drive.

Charlie got out of the car. She was wearing a long cream coat, her hair tucked up inside a pale fur hat. She smiled wanly at Jack. 'Surprise!'

'I thought you were meant to be skiing?'

'I was, but I came home. I missed you.' She moved into his arms for a hug. Jack held her briefly, then made a show of rummaging in his pocket for his key.

As he unlocked the door, she said, 'I'd better get the presents out of the car.'

'Presents!' Sophie jumped up and down.

'Don't get too excited. I didn't have much time to shop so I got them at the Duty Free.'

'So it's a bottle of Glenfiddich for me and a couple of hundred cigarettes each for the girls, is it?' Jack said.

'Not quite that bad. I do have some imagination, you know.' Jack opened the door and the girls rushed inside. He went to follow them, but Charlie held him back.

'Sorry I've been such a bitch,' she said. 'I should be more understanding about the children. I know how important they are to you. It's just I wanted to feel I was important to you too.'

Jack instantly felt a twinge of guilt. 'I'm sorry I didn't back you up more with Emily. I realise she can be a nightmare at times.'

'I'm just not very used to dealing with kids, I'm afraid.' She smiled shakily. 'I've always assumed they were like little adults, but they're not, are they?'

'Sadly no.' Jack looked rueful. 'And you can't just ignore them when you've had enough either.'

They laughed. It almost felt like old times, when they were friends, before all this complicated stuff began.

'I will try with the girls, honestly,' she promised.

And I'll try with you, Jack thought. It must have taken a hell of a lot for her to come here, he decided. Emily had been a monster to her, yet she still had the guts to come back. And to interrupt her skiing holiday. That must mean something.

He gazed into her tawny green eyes. He'd been so negative about their relationship, he hadn't really given her a chance. But he was lucky to have her. Charlie Ferguson could have had any man she wanted, yet she'd chosen him. The least he could do was try to make a go of it.

Once inside, he poured them both a glass of wine and they sat down to open the presents. Sophie was thrilled with her grown-up bottle of perfume, and Jack liked his leather briefcase.

'Sorry it's nothing more exciting,' Charlie said. Leaning closer, she added, 'I'm wearing your other present. I picked up some La Perla underwear in Val d'Isère.'

Jack smiled tightly and glanced around to make sure Emily and Sophie hadn't heard. He could feel himself blushing to the roots of his hair. He quickly handed Charlie her present, a businesslike Palm Pilot. She looked pleased, but he sensed she would have preferred something more personal. He'd meant to buy her something special, until he realised he had no idea what kind of jewellery she liked, or even if she ever wore any. He was also dismayed to realise that he could recognise Tess' perfume across a crowded room, but not hers.

Charlie had bought Emily a CD. Unfortunately, it was the same one Tess had got her.

'Oh well, I can always change it,' Charlie said brightly. 'Or I might keep it for myself and buy you another one. Who knows, I might even get to like garage music!'

Jack waited tensely for Emily's sarcastic reply. Her lip curled but thankfully she said nothing.

'I'm surprised you came home so early,' Charlie said, when all the gift-wrapping paper had been cleared away and they were relaxing with their wine. 'What happened? Did Tess burn the turkey?'

'No, but her ex turned up.' He explained about Phil. Charlie listened, wide-eyed.

'Really? How interesting. Do you think they'll get back together?'

'How should I know?' He felt subdued and changed the subject. 'Why don't we all have a game of something, to pass the time?'

Charlie looked as if she could think of better ways of passing the time, but she smiled brightly and said, 'Why not? I haven't played a board game for years. What shall we play?'

They finally settled on Monopoly, as it was the only game Charlie could remember. It turned out to be a bad choice. Monopoly was one of those games that brought out the worst instincts in people anyway. But with Charlie and Emily pitted against each other it was a definite needle match.

It began when Jack handed over the deeds of Old Kent Road and Whitechapel to Sophie.

'Why has she got those?' Charlie asked. 'We haven't started playing yet.'

'We like to give her a head start,' Jack explained.

Charlie wasn't happy, although she was trying not to show it. 'That's hardly fair, is it?' she said with a fixed smile.

'It's only a game!' Emily rolled her eyes. 'It's not like she's got Park Lane or anything.'

They finally began to play, but Jack could see Charlie was getting more and more wound up that Emily was buying the properties she wanted.

'What do you need Leicester Square for?' she demanded. 'You know I've got Piccadilly and Coventry Street.'

Emily shrugged. 'That's the game.'

'Yes, but I can't build any houses or hotels if I don't own them all.'

'So?'

'So they're not doing you any good, are they? You can't build anything either!'

Jack caught the glint in Emily's eye. That wasn't the point as far as she was concerned, he guessed. The point was to wind Charlie up until she exploded.

'Let's calm down, shall we?' he pleaded. 'Who really cares about winning anyway?'

Charlie sent him a perplexed look. 'What's the point of playing if you don't care who wins?'

Later, she retaliated by nabbing Mayfair before Emily could land on it.

'But I've got Park Lane!' Emily protested.

Charlie smiled maddeningly. 'So?'

Jack could see Emily about to reach boiling point and stepped in quickly. 'Come on, you two. Let's not fall out over a daft game.'

'Tell her that,' Emily jabbed an accusing finger. 'Anyone would think it was the Olympics, the way she's going on!'

'Just because you're a bad loser.'

Emily stood up, knocking the board and upsetting all the pieces. As she stomped off, slamming the door behind her, Jack wearily got to his feet. But Charlie stopped him.

'No,' she said. 'I'll go.'

'You?'

'Don't panic, I'm not going to start a row.' Charlie glanced at the door. 'But I think it's about time your daughter and I had a little heart to heart.'

She tapped on Emily's door. There was no answer, but she walked in anyway.

The bedroom was in darkness and the first thing Charlie did was trip over a pile of clothes strewn on the floor. She kicked them to one side and looked around. In the faint light from the street lamp outside she could make out posters stuck haphazardly all over the walls, and a dressing table overcrowded with books, CDs without their covers and rows of empty mugs. Charlie suppressed a shudder. If Emily was her child, she'd never stand for that kind of mess in her home.

But if Emily was hers, she would probably have left home a long time ago.

Emily was in bed, a huddled shape under the duvet, a pillow pulled over her head.

Typical, Charlie thought. She starts World War Three then runs away to hide. 'Emily?'

'Go away!' Her voice was muffled by the pillow.

'That's the point. I'm not going anywhere.' She sat down on the edge of the bed.

'I hate you! You're a horrible old cow!'

'To be honest, I'm not that keen on you, either. But since we're stuck with each other I think we should try to make this work, don't you?' Emily didn't reply. 'Not for my sake, of course. Frankly, you can be as big a nightmare as you like and you still won't beat me. I'm thinking about your father.' She shifted a little further down the bed. 'He feels he can't love us both because you're making him choose.'

'He doesn't love you!' Emily spat. 'He only sleeps with you! He'll never love you.'

'That's where you're wrong.' Charlie searched for the right words. 'Look, I'm not very good at talking to kids, so I'm just going to say this straight. I know you're pissed off because your dad's going out with me, but that's just the way it is. I'm sorry things have worked out this way. I'm sorry your mum's dead. But you hating me won't bring her back, will it?'

Silence. Charlie waited a moment, then gave up.

'Fine. If that's the way you want it.' She stood up. 'I've tried talking to you like an adult, but I can see I'm wasting my time. You're just a spoilt little kid who can't deal with the truth. But I'm telling you this, Emily. If you think you can get rid of me, you've got another thing coming.'

Jack was waiting anxiously for her when she got downstairs. 'How did it go?'

'How do you think?'

'Maybe you didn't handle it right?'

Or maybe she's just a manipulative little cow, Charlie thought. 'To tell you the truth, I'm sick of trying to handle it. Now it's your turn.' She grabbed her coat from the banisters. 'You sort it out, Jack, and let me know when you've done it. I'll be waiting.'

27

Emily sat in her Maths class, staring at the clock. Nearly ten past two. Her dad would be in the Lakes by now.

Would Charlie be with him? Stupid question. She never left him alone these days. At least she and Emily had given up pretending to be nice to each other. Now they just tried to stay out of each other's way. Not that it was easy, as Charlie seemed to be around more and more. How long before she moved in permanently? Emily wondered.

She'd tried to talk to her dad about it, but he just laughed. 'Why on earth would she want to move in with us when she's got a fabulous flat of her own in Leeds?' he said. He could be very naïve sometimes. Emily knew Charlie was slowly getting her claws into him, even if he couldn't see it. And she also knew she and Sophie weren't part of the package.

She was too afraid to mention it to her dad, but it was clear Charlie didn't like them being around. Even Sophie, who adored her. And now she had their father to herself for a whole weekend. All weekend to show him how wonderful and easy life could be without children cluttering it up. How long would it take her to make him see he'd be better off without them?

Maybe even as she sat there, pretending to tackle her trigonometry test, Charlie was sweet-talking him into letting them go and live with Auntie Ros while he moved into her fabulous flat. He might not take much convincing; if he could forget their mum, he wouldn't have much trouble abandoning them.

And Emily had played right into her hands by being such a stroppy cow. She'd been so insecure about everything, she'd turned into a monster to live with. Her dad would probably jump at the chance to be rid of her.

At least she was spending the weekend with Katy in Leeds rather than going to Gran's with Sophie. It was her reward for not kicking up a fuss about him going on this team-building weekend. She couldn't wait. Katy was so wise and grown-up, she'd know what to do. She'd probably come up with a million plans to get rid of evil Charlie.

Katy met her from the station. She looked even older than Emily remembered from the party in November. She was dressed in tight jeans, strappy sandals and a skimpy T-shirt, even though an icy January wind was blowing. Emily felt very young in her sensible coat and trainers.

After much squealing, jumping up and down and hugging each other, Katy announced they were going to McDonald's for tea.

'It's okay, I'm paying,' she said.

'But won't your mum be expecting us?'

'Where do you think I got the money from, dummy?' Katy laughed. 'Besides, Mum never cooks. She's crap at it. Mostly we just microwave stuff out of the freezer.'

It came as a shock to Emily. Her dad might not be the best cook in the world, but at least he tried.

Katy lived in the same area Emily once had. As they approached the terrace of tall Victorian villas, she felt an unexpected stab of panic. She found it hard to breathe, as if her lungs were squashed against her ribs.

Katy stared at her worriedly. 'Are you feeling all right? You're not going to be sick or anything?'

'I'm fine.' She took a deep, steadying breath, and the moment passed.

Did her dad ever feel like that? she wondered. If he did, she could almost understand why he'd been so desperate to move.

As Katy put her key in the door, her mother appeared in the hall, a glass of wine in her hand.

'Alan? Oh, it's you.' Her look of disappointment was quickly masked when she saw Emily. 'And you've brought a little friend with you. How nice.'

'This is Emily. I told you she was coming, remember?'

'Did you? You know I can't remember everything you tell me, darling.' Her voice was slurred. 'Well, come in, anyway. Welcome to the mad house.'

'Thank you, Mrs Jefferson.'

Katy's mother smiled. 'Call me Vanessa, darling, everyone does.' There was a shriek of laughter from the sitting room. Vanessa glanced over her shoulder. 'I've got some friends round, so—'

'Don't worry, we won't get in your way.' Katy dumped her school bag in the hall and pushed Emily in the direction of the kitchen.

'The coven,' she explained. 'Mum's cronies. They always come round to get pissed and sympathise when my stepfather's working late again.'

'My dad's always doing that.'

'Yeah, right!' Katy snorted. 'You don't get it, do you? Working late means he's probably shagging his secretary in some hotel.' She threw open the fridge door. 'Do you want anything to drink? I expect that lot have had all the wine, but we've got beer.'

'Won't you get told off?' Emily glanced back at the door.

'Do you really think they take any notice of what I do? They're too busy screwing up their own lives.' There was a bitter edge to Katy's voice as she helped herself to a can of Stella. She popped it open and handed it to Emily. 'Don't tell me you don't drink either?'

Emily steeled herself and took a swig, gagging as it hit the back of her throat. How did adults drink that stuff and not throw up?

'You get used to it,' Katy grinned. 'Anyway, you drink it for the effect, not the taste.'

There was another shriek from the sitting room. 'Listen to them.' Her voice was full of contempt. 'In a couple of hours they'll all be crying and wondering why they've never managed to stay married for more than five minutes. Come on, let's go up to my room.'

The attic had been converted into a bedsit for Katy. It had everything – TV, computer, stereo, video, telephone, even her own bathroom. Emily looked around in admiration. 'You're so lucky.'

Katy shrugged. 'It's okay, I s'pose. They mainly give me all this stuff to keep me out of their way.' She sorted through her video collection. 'What do you want to watch? I've got some good horror movies.'

Emily would rather have watched something funny, or romantic. But she shrugged and said, 'You choose.' After all, how scary could it be?

Forty blood-curdling minutes later, she found out. She was huddled in the dark on Katy's bed, watching the film from behind a cushion and wondering why the stupid heroine had gone into the empty school at midnight, as it was obvious the hideously deformed, hook-handed psychopath was prowling the corridors, when the front door suddenly banged.

Katy's shoulders stiffened and her head went up. 'He's home,' she said. 'They'll start in a minute.'

Sure enough, a moment later, Emily heard raised voices in the hall below, followed by the coven making their escape. The voices grew louder until they reached screaming pitch. Katy's mum seemed to be doing most of the screaming.

Emily glanced anxiously at Katy, but she just picked up the remote and cranked up the volume.

The row went on long after they'd gone to bed. Emily lay in her sleeping bag, listening. She didn't know which terrified her more, the thought of the hook-handed psychopath lurking in the darkness, or the screeching coming from downstairs.

She couldn't remember her parents ever fighting like that, but Katy seemed used to it. She even managed to go to sleep, while Emily stared at the unfamiliar shadows and wished she were back in the safety of her own bed. She'd never missed home so much in her life.

Home. When had she started to think of it as that? If anyone asked her, she would have vehemently insisted that Leeds was still her home. But now it felt unreal, unwelcoming. As if she didn't belong. Her real home was back in Haxsall, with her dad and Sophie.

She dozed fitfully and woke in the grey early dawn. She uncurled her cold, stiff limbs and listened. At least the house was quiet. She was ragingly thirsty, but she didn't like to venture downstairs on her own in case she found a couple of bodies with kitchen knives sticking out of them.

It was hours until Katy woke up and they went downstairs. There were no bodies, but there was a man in the kitchen, slumped at the table. He looked as if he'd had even less sleep than Emily.

'Hi, babe,' he greeted Katy with a weary smile. 'Be an angel and put the kettle on, would you?'

'Where is she?' Katy flicked the switch. 'Still in bed, I suppose?'

'Your mother has a headache this morning.'

'A hangover, you mean.' Katy opened the nearest cupboard and looked inside. 'We're out of bread.'

'Are we? Oh dear. I suppose your mother must have forgotten to buy it.'

'Typical. I bet there's no bloody cereal, either.'

Emily held her breath and waited for Katy's stepfather to give her a lecture on language, but he just cradled his head in his hands and groaned, 'Not so loud, sweetheart.'

'We'll just have to get something when we're out.' Katy went to her mother's handbag and helped herself to a handful of notes out of her purse. 'We're going.'

'Fine.' He didn't ask where, or how long they'd be. Emily had often wondered what it would be like to have so much freedom. Now she wasn't sure she liked it.

'Won't your mum mind?' she asked, as they left the house.

Katy looked wistful. 'I shouldn't think she'll even notice.'

They caught the bus into the city and wandered around for a couple of hours, browsing through the CDs in Virgin Megastore and trying on clothes in Miss Selfridge. It was boring when she didn't have any money to spend. Katy offered to share hers, but that didn't feel right either.

'Your mum will be expecting it back, won't she?'

'I wish you'd stop going on about my mum,' Katy snapped. 'She doesn't watch my every move, you know. What do you think of these jeans?'

They went back to McDonald's at lunchtime. From the way Katy flirted with the spotty boys behind the counter, Emily thought she must go there an awful lot. It was a wonder she wasn't twenty-five stone and covered in acne.

They sat side by side in the window, watching the shoppers in Briggate. While they ate their burgers, Emily tried to tell Katy about her problem with Charlie. She kept having to repeat herself because Katy was distracted by the boys deliberately clearing tables close by them. After Emily had been through the whole thing for the third time, Katy shrugged and said, 'So? I told you it would happen, didn't I?'

'But what am I going to do about it?'

'Not much you can do. If he likes her, he's going to go on seeing her whatever you do or say.' She bit into a chip. 'Look at my lot. I don't remember any of them ever asking how I felt.'

'How long has your mum been married to your stepdad?'

'Too long.'

'Have they always argued like that?'

'Suppose so. They wind each other up all the time. My mum's always drinking, so Alan stays out late and sleeps around. And because he's out shagging around, my mum drinks. It's a vicious circle really.'

'Don't you get sick of it?'

'I've got used to it. At least he's better than the last bloke she went out with. He used to lech all over me.'

'Ugh, gross!'

'It was. Very. Anyway, when they're on at each other, they leave me alone, so it has its good points.' She finished her milkshake and slid from her stool. 'Come on, I need to do some serious shopping.'

'What about your dad?' Emily ran to keep up with Katy's long strides as she crossed the street.

'What about him?'

'Do you still see him?'

'Sometimes. Although my mum doesn't like it. She can't stand him because he left her in the lurch with me and married a blonde bimbo. And the bimbo doesn't like it because she wants him all to herself. Her and the new baby,' she added bitterly.

She hurried on ahead, leaving Emily trailing behind.

Poor Katy, she thought. And to think she had always envied her for being so cool.

Could her life turn out like that? What if her dad moved in with Charlie and they had a baby? She and Sophie would definitely get pushed out then. Except when they needed a babysitter. She felt sick at the thought. No way would she want anything to do with Charlie's kid!

And what if it all went wrong? What if her dad ended up like Katy's mum, hitting the bottle and brooding about the terrible mistake he'd made? The thought of listening to those earth-shattering rows night after night made her feel ill too.

Her dad was all she had. That was why she was so afraid of Charlie coming between them. It was different for Katy. She still had two parents, even if they were both useless. Emily only had one. If he was taken away from her, she would be all alone. And alone meant vulnerable.

They wandered into various shops and Emily watched as Katy treated herself to a pair of jeans and a couple of new tops with her mum's money. The last place they visited sold accessories – cheap hairslides and bobbles, bangles and brightly coloured plastic things. They had some fun trying on the jewellery and nail polishes. Then Emily spotted a belt she liked.

'Have it,' Katy said.

'Dur, I don't have any money, remember?'

'So?'

'So what do you expect me to do, just walk out with it?'

'Why not?'

She saw the look in Katy's eyes and realised she was serious. 'I couldn't!'

'I do it all the time. It's fun.'

'But it's stealing! What if you get caught?'

'That's part of the buzz, dummy. Anyway, no one's ever caught me, have they?'

'No, but—'

'Look, it's easy. You just have to be really cool about it. Act natural.'

Emily wondered how she could act natural when she already felt as if she had the word 'Thief' emblazoned in neon across her face.

'Very natural,' Katy said sarcastically, as Emily stood rigid with fear, her eyes bulging. 'Why don't you just go up to that girl there and tell her you're going to nick something?' She tutted. 'Honestly, it's easy. I'll stand behind you, so they don't see what you're doing. Then just slip it in your bag.'

'But what if I get caught?' Emily's tongue was already stuck to the roof of her mouth.

'You won't. No one's going to chase you up the road for something worth a couple of quid, are they? Especially not this lot.' She looked around at the dull-eyed assistants picking at their nail varnish. 'Look, I'll do it if you're scared. Just stand behind me and I'll slip the belt to you, okay? Then get ready to run.'

She didn't think she could run anywhere. Her legs had turned to the consistency of custard. 'I don't want—' she began, but Katy was already in front of her. The next second she felt something being pushed into her bag.

It all happened very fast after that. Emily saw one of the assistants moving towards her across the shop, forcing her way past the girls trying out eyeshadows.

'Leg it!' Katy bolted for the door. Emily tried to follow, but she cannoned into a jewellery display. As earrings showered down around her, she suddenly felt a rush of adrenaline to her legs and sprinted to the door. She made it and briefly felt the daylight on her face before a hand descended on her shoulder and a voice said, 'Excuse me, Miss. Do you mind showing me what's in your bag?'

28

Margaret Doyle was very big on honesty. She didn't believe in make-up to conceal her ageing face, and wouldn't give house room to underwear designed to conceal her various lumps and bumps.

But she was looking decidedly shifty when Tess confronted her that Saturday morning.

'What do you mean, where did I spend Christmas? You know where I went. Down to your sister's in London.'

'But you told me you weren't coming back until Saturday. And I've just spoken to Frances and she mentioned you left on Wednesday. I just wondered where you'd been for those three days?'

'Does it matter where I went?' Margaret bristled defensively. 'Honestly, Teresa, I'm sixty-five years old. Anyone would think I was a child, the way you're checking up on me!'

'I'm not checking up. I'm just curious, that's all.' It wasn't like her mother to disappear off the radar for seventy-two hours. After Frances happened to mention it on the phone, she'd come straight round to find out what was going on.

She'd found her mother in the kitchen as usual, tackling some hand-washing at the sink. She did it the old-fashioned way, scrubbing on the stubborn stains with soap and a hard brush.

'Don't trust machines. Hand-washing is the only way to get them really clean,' she always said when she saw Tess piling her laundry willy-nilly into the washer-dryer. Tess sometimes wondered if her mother was born in the wrong century. She'd be much more at home down on the banks of the Ouse, beating her whites with a stone.

She seemed to be scrubbing particularly hard in her agitation. 'Yes, well, if you must know, I decided to have a couple of days in London. That's not a crime, is it?'

'Not at all.' Tess was taken aback. 'Were you on your own?'

'No, I was with my fancy man! There. Are you satisfied now?'

Tess smiled. The idea of her mother with any man, let alone a fancy one, was too ridiculous to be true.

Then Margaret held up the garment she was washing against the light to inspect it for stains, and Tess suddenly saw what it was. 'Mum – is that a man's shirt?'

'Happen it is.' Margaret plunged it quickly back into the bowl of soapy water. 'I'm doing them for Ronnie. His machine's broken down, and since he's been good enough to do a few odd jobs for me, I offered to return the favour. Although it comes to something when you can't even rinse through a few shirts without getting the third degree,' she grumbled.

Tess was still pondering this when her mobile rang. It was Phil.

'Where are you?' he asked.

'At my mum's.'

'Is Dan with you?' She could hear from the rush of traffic in the background that he was in his car.

'No, he's at home. Phil, what's all this about?'

'I'll tell you when I see you. Where can we meet?'

'Can't you just come round to our place?' Tess glanced up. Her mother was wielding the scrubbing-brush like a piston, her spine stiff with disapproval.

'I'd rather not. This is between you and me.'

Tess thought for a moment. 'Well, I'm supposed to be off to the supermarket after I leave here—'

'Give me directions and I'll meet you there.'

She pressed the Off button and looked up. 'It's all right, you can spare me the lecture.'

Margaret blinked. 'What lecture?'

'The one about me not getting too friendly with Phil.'

'It's nothing to do with me,' Margaret said. 'Your private life is your own concern.'

Tess stared at her. Now she really was convinced there was something wrong with her mother.

Phil was at the supermarket before her, waiting in the customer car park, his gleaming Porsche standing out among the everyday Volvos and Fords.

'What's all this about? I thought you weren't coming up until Monday?' she said, steering her trolley in through the automatic doors. Phil followed her.

'I needed to talk to you before then. It's about Dan.'

'What about him?'

Phil looked troubled. 'I don't know if I should be telling you. I promised Dan I wouldn't, but you've got to know sometime.'

Tess stopped dead. Several trolleys cannoned into the back of her. 'Know what? What's going on?'

'He's decided he doesn't want to go to university.'

Her first thought was, Is that all? Phil looked so grave she'd suddenly had the wild idea that Dan was seriously ill and hadn't told her. Then she realised this was serious. This was about Dan's future.

And he hadn't told her.

'Don't be ridiculous,' she said. 'He's got to go to university. It's all planned. He's got all the prospectuses and everything. We've been looking through them for months.'

'Apparently he's changed his mind. He wants to get a job working with computers instead. He says that'll teach him more than three years at uni.'

She pushed her trolley round the fruit and veg department, throwing in apples and carrots at random, her mind elsewhere.

'How long have you known about this?' she demanded.

'He told me when I came up at Christmas.'

'Christmas!' She stopped again. There was a lot of tutting as everyone manoeuvred their trolleys around her. 'You've known since Christmas and you're only telling me now?'

'Dan asked me not to.'

'But I'm his mother!' She'd been sorting out his problems since he was a baby. Every time he hurt himself, she was there with a plaster and a kiss to make it better. Every time someone was cruel to him, she was the one who crashed heads together. And now he'd made one of the biggest decisions of his life and he'd turned to Phil, not her. Phil, whom he'd only known five minutes.

She stared at the artichoke she'd picked up by mistake. 'I'm his mother,' she repeated.

Phil must have noticed her hurt and confusion. 'I had to prise it out of him,' he said quickly. 'He didn't want to tell either of us.'

'I'm not surprised. He probably knew I wouldn't allow it.' She did a three-point turn with the trolley and headed up the next aisle.

'I don't think you've got much say in the matter.'

'Of course I've got a say! Do you think I'm just going to stand by and let him make the biggest mistake of his life?' She pitched a can of beans into the trolley, crushing a packet of chocolate digestives.

'It's his life,' Phil said quietly.

'He's seventeen years old! How's he supposed to make those kind of decisions at that age? He's far too young to know what he wants.'

'You were that age when he was born. I seem to remember you knew exactly what you wanted.'

Tess ignored him. She charged into frozen foods, randomly helping herself from the freezer cabinets. 'It's ridiculous,' she muttered. 'I'm going straight home to talk some sense into him—'

'Hang on a minute.' Phil held her back as she cut a swathe through the microwaveable ready meals like Boadicea slicing through the Roman army.

'And you wonder why he didn't feel he could talk to you? You can't just rush in there and start laying down the law. He wants to handle this himself.'

Tess looked shaken. 'But he needs me!'

'Not this time.' Phil's voice was gentle, reasonable. All the things Tess wasn't feeling at that moment. 'He's almost grown up, Tess. You've got to let him think for himself.'

Tess looked around at the supermarket shelves, slightly dazed. If Dan didn't need her, she'd lost her purpose in life. She'd been his champion, his protector for so long she wasn't sure she knew how to do anything else.

Phil put his finger under her chin and turned her forlorn face up to meet his. 'You look like you could do with a drink.'

They paid for the shopping and headed for the pub. Tess was still in a state of shock but Phil steered her to a seat and put a brandy in front of her.

She looked down at it. 'Ugh, I hate brandy.'

'Drink it, it'll make you feel better. It's good for shock.'

'I haven't had a shock.'

'Want to bet? You haven't seen your face.'

She glanced at her reflection in the mirror. Come to think of it, she did look a bit wan.

They talked about Dan, and his future. 'He's so young,' Tess wailed.

'He's nearly eighteen.'

'But what if all this turns out to be a horrible mistake?'

'Then he can go back to college and start again. Anyway, it's the only way he's going to get on in life, by making mistakes and learning from them. You can't take that away from him.'

'I'm not trying to take anything away from him.' All she wanted to do was to protect him, just as she'd always done.

Phil managed to calm her down. He was good at that, Tess thought. But then he could afford to be detached. He wasn't as close to Dan as she was.

She said as much to Phil, who looked hurt. 'Just because I haven't known him long doesn't mean I don't love him,' he said.

'I know that.' Tess was instantly contrite. 'But you don't feel for him the way I do. We've been together so long, just the two of us. I know what he's thinking, how he's feeling.' Or she thought she did. Now she wasn't so sure.

'Then maybe it's time you both had some space?'

'Are you trying to say I want him to depend on me?' Tess snapped. 'I've spent seventeen years fighting for just the opposite.'

'And you've done a great job,' Phil said. 'But you've got to let go now. He'll never learn to cope on his own while you're around to fight his battles for him.' He sipped his beer. 'He's willing to give it a go. Why can't you?'

Because I don't know how, she wanted to wail. She stared disconsolately into her drink. It was awful not to feel needed any more.

Phil seemed to understand. 'Maybe it's time you stopped being Dan's mum and started being yourself?' he suggested gently.

'Oh yes? And what do you suggest I do? Take up yoga? Write a novel? Find myself a man?'

'Why not, if that's what you want?'

She smiled. 'And have you anyone in mind, oh great and wise one?'

Phil's face was serious. 'Me,' he said.

Her mobile rang before she had time to take in what he'd said. Tess fell on it, punching the buttons.

'Yes? Hello? Yes, this is Tess Doyle. What? You're joking? Oh my God, when did this happen? Have you contacted her father? Oh, I see. Yes, well, tell her not to worry. I'll see what I can do.'

She pressed the Off switch and turned to Phil. 'That was the police. They've arrested Emily Tyler for shoplifting.'

He frowned. 'Who?'

'You remember, she came round to my place at Christmas?'

'Oh, right.' His face clouded. 'So why are they calling you? Where's her father?'

'Away on some business trip. And Emily's refusing to give the police her surname or a contact number for him. The only number she'd give is mine.'

She gulped down her drink and stood up. Phil watched her. 'I suppose you're going to race down there and help her? Take on the local constabulary if you have to?'

'Of course. What else can I do?'

'What else indeed?' Phil pulled a wry face. 'Another helpless soul with a problem to solve and you can't resist jumping in to help.'

'That's unkind, Phil.'

'It's true, though. Good old Tess Doyle, always doing and fixing. But when are you going to do something about your own life?'

'We're not charging her, because we've nothing to charge her with,' the duty sergeant explained. 'According to the shop assistant, it was her mate who actually pinched the thing. Not that we've got any chance of catching her.' He looked at Tess hopefully.

'Sorry, I can't help you. I don't know any of her friends in Leeds.'

'Anyway, we might have got all this cleared up a long time ago, if she'd been more cooperative.' The sergeant looked grumpy. 'Are you sure you don't have a contact number for her father?'

'I'm afraid not,' Tess lied, hoping her blushing face wouldn't give her away.

'Well, at least you've given us a name and address. We'll send someone round tomorrow to have a word with him.'

'You do that.' By which time, hopefully, she would have managed to calm him down. 'Sergeant, Emily's not usually like this.'

'Hmm.' The police officer looked unconvinced. 'Wait here, I'll get her for you.'

Tess sat in the grim waiting room, staring at the posters telling people to mark their property and lock their valuables away in their cars, and tried to work up some indignation. She'd broken every speed limit to get here, but now her panic had subsided, she realised Phil was right, it was none of her business. Jack should be here sorting this out, instead of playing soldiers in the woods with Charlie.

But any shred of anger disappeared the moment the door opened and Emily came out beside the police officer, pale-faced, her eyes huge with apprehension. When she saw Tess she burst into tears and rushed into her arms. They hugged each other for a moment, then Tess whispered, 'Come on, let's get out of here.'

'Thanks for coming,' Emily mumbled as they got into the car. 'I couldn't think of who else to ring.'

'Why not your dad?'

'I didn't want him to know.'

'He's got to find out sometime. The police will tell him, even if you don't.'

'I know.' She chewed her thumbnail. Tears rolled down her cheeks. Tess fished in her bag for a tissue and handed it to her.

'It's okay,' she said. 'We'll think of something. It's not as if it was your fault, was it?' Emily said nothing. 'I suppose your mate Katy was behind it? It's all right, I'm not going to go back in there and tell them.'

'I was so scared,' Emily sobbed. 'I thought they were going to lock me up. They kept asking me all these questions. I didn't know what to do.'

'It's over now.' Tess put her arm around her. 'Come on, let's get you home.'

'Where can I go?' Emily pulled away from her. 'I can't go home until Dad gets back, and I – I don't want to go back to where I was staying.' Her voice trailed off.

'What about your Gran's? Sophie's there, isn't she?'

Emily shook her head. 'I can't face it. They're bound to ask all kinds of questions and I wouldn't know what to say.' She looked at Tess, biting her lip.

She sighed. 'In that case I suppose there's only one place we can go, isn't there?'

'Where's that?'

Tess started up the car. 'My place,' she said.

29

Jack stuck his head out of the bushes and ducked back again as a paint pellet whizzed past his ear and splatted on the tree trunk behind him. He sat down and pulled off his helmet. He was cold and wet, he ached all over, and he was sick to the teeth of squelching around a muddy field being shot at by a bunch of overgrown kids. He wanted to go home.

So much for team-building. In the past twenty-four hours, he'd been drenched after his team's hastily constructed raft fell to bits halfway downriver, he and Greg had nearly come to blows in the rain when their tent collapsed in the middle of the night, and he'd been dangled off a bridge on the end of a piece of abseiling rope by a sadistic bunch of bastards from Accounts.

And now those same sadistic bastards were stalking him through the woods. He was fed up with being yelled at and shot at, and most of all he was fed up with wearing bloody silly army fatigues like Action Man.

He desperately missed his kids. He'd already sneaked out of base camp the previous night to call his mother and speak to Sophie, only to have his mobile confiscated by the over-enthusiastic platoon leader.

'No phoning home!' he'd barked.

'But my family—'

'Sorry, soldier. Your team is your family now.'

How he'd resisted the urge to knock his teeth down his throat Jack didn't know. But he did know that if he met him in the field now he'd probably ram the butt of his paintgun somewhere the sun didn't shine.

The team didn't feel like his family. Not any more. Not since he'd seen what was in Bernard Sweeting's Westpoint file.

Cracking the safe had been easy, thanks to Sam Dobbs' instructions. But now he was beginning to wish he hadn't done it.

Running footsteps crashed through the undergrowth a few yards from where he crouched. Jack ducked down and waited for them to pass. This wasn't a game any more. Since reading that file, he'd begun to wonder who was really on his side.

He'd watched them all last night, gathered around the camp fire, laughing over their barbecue in the rain. Who else knew? he wondered. Who was in on it? He felt as if he couldn't trust anyone any more.

He'd been tempted to talk to Greg about it last night, when they were alone in their tent. His brother-in-law had guessed something was wrong.

'Anything on your mind, Jacko?' he'd said. 'You've been very quiet all evening.'

Jack thought about telling him. But in the end he couldn't bring himself to do it.

'Just thinking about the kids,' he'd said.

There was a rustle in the bushes. Jack couldn't even be bothered to pick up his gun. He didn't care any more. Let them shoot him. At least it would put him out of his misery.

The undergrowth parted and Charlie appeared, looking lean and menacing, like Lara Croft in her fatigues, her paintgun braced at her hip.

'Jack!' She let her gun barrel drop. 'Are you injured?'

'No.'

'Then why aren't you out there in the field, fighting with the others?' God, she was beginning to sound like something out of *Saving Private Ryan*.

'Because I can't be bothered.'

She looked shocked. 'But your team needs you. We're already a man down, thanks to Rav catching a pellet in his backside.'

'I don't care.'

She stared at him. 'But we can't let Accounts beat us!'

'Why not? What does it really matter if they do beat us? I mean, it's not as if we're actually at war, is it? What are they going to do, tie us to chairs and force us to listen to the basics of double-entry bookkeeping?'

'That's not the point.'

'Then what is? What does any of this crap really matter?'

'It's a team-building exercise.'

'Team? Don't make me laugh. We're not a team. Teams don't keep secrets. And they don't lie to each other.'

Charlie frowned. 'What are you talking about?'

He thought about telling her, then decided against it. It was bad enough he knew, without burdening her with it too.

'Nothing. Just battle fatigue, that's all.' He rubbed a weary hand over his eyes. 'Or maybe I've just realised how utterly pointless my job really is.'

'You can't say that! You're the best in the company.'

'The best at what? At designing buildings no one wants? At putting profits before people?'

'I don't know why you're talking like this.' Charlie said. 'It isn't like you.'

'That's just it. It *is* like me. You just don't realise it.'

He stood up. She looked up at him in alarm. 'Where are you going?'

'Out there.' He strapped his gun to his back.

'You're going back to fight?'

'No, I'm going to pack.'

'You're not leaving? You can't. It's against the rules.'

'Maybe I'm tired of playing by other people's rules.'

'What shall I tell Humphrey?'

'Tell him I've gone AWOL.'

He stood up. A paint pellet whizzed past him, narrowly missing his ear. 'Jack?'

He turned. The crack of gunfire was followed by a split second of pain between his eyes, which sent him reeling backwards.

'Bloody hell!' He clapped his hand to his forehead, expecting to see blood. But all he saw was a splodge of bright-yellow paint in the palm of his hand. 'Jesus, what did you do that for?'

She glared at him. 'For being a fucking deserter.'

By the time he got back to the tent he was spattered in so much neon paint he looked like the Berlin Wall. He peeled off his fatigues and tossed them into a corner. He was just pulling on his jeans when Charlie walked in, her combats pristine.

'You survived, then?'

'Of course. And I brought down a whole battalion of bought-ledger clerks single-handed.' She tossed her forage cap on the bed and shook out her red hair. 'I pinned them down in a foxhole. They were begging for mercy by the time I'd finished with them.'

'I bet they were. So does this mean war's over?'

She nodded. 'Everyone's gone to the mess hall to get cleaned up. We won, by the way, in case you're interested?'

'I'm not.'

She watched him throwing his things into his bag. 'You're really going?'

'Looks like it.'

'Can I ask why?'

'I told you, I'm tired of playing games.' He sniffed his sweater, which smelt of musty damp, then flung it into his bag.

'You do realise, if you walk away now, you can kiss goodbye to that senior partnership?'

'To be honest, I don't really care.' The sooner he got out of Crawshaw and Finch the better.

'And are you walking out on me too?' He didn't answer. 'I'll take that as a yes then, shall I?'

'I'm sorry, Charlie.'

There was a long silence. 'Is it because of the girls?' She looked down at her hands, but he could hear in her voice that she was fighting back tears. 'Is it because I didn't try hard enough with them?'

'Maybe it's because you had to try.' He sat down on the camp bed beside her. 'You did everything you could and I'm grateful for that. But it wasn't you, was it? You were always putting it on, having to make an effort.'

'I didn't mind.'

'Not now, maybe. But you would have, sooner or later.' He reached for her hand. 'We don't fit into your life, Charlie. And you don't fit into ours. No matter how hard we both tried, sooner or later we would have ended up resenting each other.'

She snatched her hand away. 'So you're doing this for my benefit, is that what you're saying?'

'No. But I hope one day you'll see why I had to do it.'

'Oh, don't worry. I can see it now!' Her voice spat venom. 'I've had a lucky escape from you, Jack. A bloody lucky escape. You're not the man I thought you were!'

'You're probably right.' He stood up, stuffed the last of his clothes into his holdall and zipped it up. 'I'll be seeing you, then.'

'Don't count on it. I don't waste my time with losers!'

He turned and walked out. As he pushed through the tent flap a boot whizzed through the air, narrowly missing him.

He could still hear her crying when he reached the gate. His heart contracted with pity, but he kept on walking.

Charlie lay under the camouflage netting on the assault course and wept. Tears ran down her cheeks and dropped into the mud. She didn't need this. She didn't need to be face down in filth, she didn't need the cold and wet seeping through her combats. And most of all, she didn't need that prick of a platoon leader standing over her, yelling in her ear.

'Move it, soldier!' He prodded her with the butt of his pretend rifle. 'You're letting your team down. They're already twenty seconds behind thanks to you! This is not time to stop and put your make-up on!'

She found the strength and edged forward, propelling herself through the freezing ooze with her elbows. She kept herself going by thinking of all the choice things she was going to say to him when she got out of this wretched hell-hole.

It wasn't just the fact that Jack had walked out that upset her. It was the fact that she'd been dumped so humiliatingly. Everyone knew they were supposed to be an item, and Charlie found it very hard to hold it together when people kept giving her sidelong looks and asking her in hushed tones if she was all right.

In the end she couldn't stand it any more and had phoned the only person she could think of who could make her feel better.

'Well, if it isn't Rambo!' Tom laughed when he answered the phone.

'And what have you been doing today? Fashioning rabbit traps out of your underwear?'

The sound of his voice, so cheerful and welcoming, had been enough to make her burst into tears. Tom was instantly all concern.

It took her ten minutes to tell him everything, because she had to keep breaking off to sob and blow her nose. Tom was the only person she would ever have cried in front of. She didn't have to put on a front, pretend to be Charlie Ferguson the go-getting, hard-nosed bitch. He'd lived with her, seen her at her best and at her worst. He was absolutely her best friend.

Being her best friend, he was full of outraged vehemence about Jack's desertion and called him some choice expletives, which made her feel a lot better. He also gave her a pep talk that wouldn't have disgraced the evil platoon leader.

'Now look here,' he said in his best Colonel Blimp voice. 'You're in the army now, soldier. So you'd better bloody well get on with it. You didn't see me blubbing like a girl when I lost a leg in El Alamein, did you?'

Charlie smiled, wiped her tears. Trust Tom to cheer her up.

'What are you smirking about, soldier? This is no laughing matter, you know!' Another prod with the rifle butt. Charlie inched forward and at last emerged from the netting – only to be faced by a towering wall.

'Don't just stand there! Start climbing!'

'Who do you think I am? Spiderman?' Charlie craned her neck to look up. There didn't seem to be any visible footholds. Feeling the platoon leader bearing down on her, she pushed herself forwards and started climbing.

Somehow she managed to scramble up to the top – and froze. She clung on to the rough timber, looking down at the sea of faces looking up at her, and wondered what the hell she was doing there. She was a planning consultant, not a bloody commando. What the hell did this have to do with putting together traffic-impact assessments?

Rebellion boiled inside her. She began to think Jack Tyler had the right idea walking out, even if he was a treacherous bastard.

'What are you doing up there? Get down immediately!' The platoon leader's red, stubbly face appeared beneath her. As did the ground, which seemed to be coming up to meet her.

'How do you suggest I do that without a parachute?'

'Don't be such a fucking wimp! Get down here now!'

Angry tears sprang into her eyes. 'Don't you call me a fucking wimp! I've just broken a fucking nail, and I'm not prepared to break my fucking neck too!'

The platoon leader opened his mouth, but his yell of rage was drowned out by another sound. The triumphant, stirring sounds of *Ride of the Valkyries*, just like *Apocalypse Now*. Everyone turned to see where it was coming from. Charlie, still clinging to her narrow perch, risked a look. She half expected to see a fleet of American helicopters throbbing across the sky, spraying them all with bullets.

The music grew louder until it was deafening. Then, out of the trees crashed a battered old Volkswagen Beetle, music blaring from the boom box in the back, Tom grimly hanging on behind the wheel.

Charlie laughed so hard she nearly fell off the wall. Tom brought the car to a halt and got out.

'What are you doing up there? Don't jump, you silly cow, he's not worth it!' he called up.

Still laughing, she managed to slither to the ground, not caring that she scraped most of the skin off her hands and shins as she did. By the time she reached solid ground, Tom was in the middle of an altercation with the platoon leader.

'What the hell are you doing here? You can't bring that car in here. This is private property!'

'I'm from Military Intelligence.' Tom flashed a card at him. 'This young lady is needed for a special mission. A matter of national importance. All very hush hush. Strictly need-to-know basis.' He tapped the side of his nose.

'What the—'

'Sorry, old boy. No questions.' He bundled Charlie into the passenger seat and closed the door. 'If I tell you any more, I'd have to kill you.'

They drove off, leaving the platoon leader speechless behind them. Charlie could see him in the wing mirror, watching them, his mouth hanging open.

'You're an idiot, do you know that?' she laughed, as they sped out of the compound and on to the open road. 'And I've left all my stuff back in my tent.'

'We can always go back for it.' Tom stepped on the brake.

'No! They'll probably have the military police out looking for me. Besides, I can't face eating another meal out of a bloody billycan.' She relaxed back against the seat. 'I couldn't believe that bullying bastard's face when you suddenly appeared out of nowhere! What was that card you showed him?'

'My library card. He seemed quite impressed, don't you think?'

Charlie giggled. 'Fool!'

'At least it brought a smile to your face,' Tom commented.

'True.'

'So does this mean you're over Mr Wonderful?'

She thought about it for a moment as she watched the scenery flash past. 'I wouldn't say that. But now I think about it, I suppose Jack had a point. I don't think I'm cut out to be anyone's stepmother.'

'Only in the evil Cinderella and Snow White sense,' Tom agreed.

'I wasn't that bad!' She prodded him in the shoulder. 'But I never realised how much kids restrict you. Just think, I'll be able to go to pubs and not sit outside in the freezing cold to be near the swings. And I'll be able to eat in restaurants that don't have laminated kids' menus.' She smiled blissfully. 'I can't wait. Talking of which, where shall we eat tonight?'

'I told you, we're on a special mission.'

'If it involves eating out of a billycan, count me out.'

'Where's your sense of adventure?' Tom grinned.

'I left it on top of that wretched wall. Along with half a set of acrylic nails.' She examined her hands. 'So go on, what's this special mission?'

'At eighteen hundred hours we're due to rendezvous at this rather nice little country hotel I spotted in a village on the way here. We will proceed to the bathroom where you will take a shower. Between you and me, you're not smelling your best.'

'Thanks very much! And then?'

'Then at twenty hundred hours we will make a pincer attack on the restaurant. And having successfully completed our mission we will retreat to the bedroom where I will make love to you for the rest of the night.'

Charlie laughed. 'Yeah, right!'

Tom's eyes twinkled. 'You think I'm joking?'

30

'What do you mean, she's not here?'

'She's gone home. That's what she said, didn't she, Katy?'

'S'right.' Katy scuffed her boot against the front door mat. When Emily did that, it was a sure sign she was lying.

'And you just let her go, knowing there was no one there?'

'What did you expect me to do? Tie her to the bed?' Jack caught a faint whiff of alcohol on Vanessa Jefferson's breath. 'Anyway, I didn't see her leave. As a matter of fact, her things are still upstairs. I thought you'd come to collect them.'

'You're telling me she's disappeared without taking her stuff with her, and you didn't ring the police?' Sweat broke out all over Jack's body. He glanced back at the car where Sophie was waiting, reassuring himself she was still safe, at least.

'Of course not. Look, don't worry about it. Katy wanders off all the time, don't you, darling? They always turn up in the end.'

'Your daughter might, but mine doesn't.' Jack looked at Katy. 'Are you sure you don't know where she's gone?'

'I told you, didn't I?' Katy couldn't meet his eye.

'I hope you're not calling my daughter a liar?'

Jack looked back at Vanessa, clinging to the doorframe. 'That's exactly what I'm saying. Now she can either tell me what she knows, or she can tell the police. It's her choice.'

'Not the police!' They both turned to face Katy, who looked panic-stricken. 'It wasn't my fault,' she whimpered.

'What wasn't your fault?'

Katy stared at the ground. 'I think Emily might have been arrested.'

And then it all came out. Jack felt the blood drain to his feet, leaving him light-headed as Katy explained what had happened.

'It was her idea, not mine!' she said. 'I didn't want to nick anything, but she thought it would be a laugh. I'm telling the truth this time,' she insisted, as Jack looked sceptical.

'Why should I believe you?'

'*My* daughter isn't the one in the police station,' Vanessa Jefferson said with asperity.

No, but she should be, Jack thought, and held on to his temper. 'Do you know where they took her?' Katy shook her head. 'So you just ran off and left her, is that it?'

'I don't blame her. The poor child must have been frightened to death.' Vanessa put a protective arm around Katy's shoulders. 'If I were you, I'd stop interrogating my daughter and try to track down your own. Oh, and you'd better take her things with you,' she added, as Jack turned to leave. 'I don't want her here any more, leading my Katy astray.'

Jack caught Katy's sly look. 'I think it's a bit late for that,' he muttered.

It took him two frustrating hours before he finally tracked down the police station where Emily had been taken, only to find that she'd been released without charge. Even more bizarrely, it had been Tess Doyle who'd taken her. What the hell was going on?

The duty sergeant must have sensed he was close to breaking point, because he offered him a cup of coffee while he explained what had happened. But Jack still left feeling dazed.

Why hadn't Tess called to tell him what was going on? Didn't she think he had a right to know if his own daughter had been arrested? Didn't she stop to wonder how it would make him feel, knowing she'd gone through all that and he wasn't there?

'Daddy, slow down!' Sophie pleaded from the seat beside him. Jack glanced at the speedometer. He hadn't realised he was doing well over ninety, his fingers white on the wheel. He eased his foot off the accelerator and forced himself to calm down. This time it was anger, not fear, making his heart race.

His mobile rang just as he reached the turn-off to York. It was Tess.

'Where are you?' she said.

'On my way home.'

'Thank God for that. Listen, Jack—'

'If it's about Emily, I already know.'

'You do? How?'

'Never mind that! Why the hell didn't you tell the police to phone me?' She sounded taken aback. 'Emily wouldn't give them your number.'

'But you could.'

'She didn't want me to.'

'So what? I'm her father, for Christ's sake! Don't you think I have a right to know if my daughter's locked up in a prison cell?'

'I didn't want to interfere.'

'Fucking hell, Tess!' He was so angry he didn't think of toning down his language for Sophie's sake. 'You bailed my daughter out of jail without telling me! If that's not interfering, what is?'

'What should I have done, left her in there?'

'You know what I mean. Why didn't you pick up the phone and let me know?'

'What do you think I'm doing now?'

Her calmness made the blood sing in his ears. 'We'll talk about this later,' he threatened and hung up. The second he pressed the button he realised he hadn't even asked how Emily was.

Shit, shit, shit! He banged his hands on the steering wheel. Sophie gave him an old-fashioned look.

'You nearly hit that blue car,' she said.

By the time he got to Tess' bungalow, he was so eaten up with tension and anger he was ready to explode.

'Where is she?' he demanded as soon as she opened the door.

'In Dan's room, listening to CDs. I thought we should talk first.'

'Oh, did you? Since when did you start making the decisions in my family?'

Tess flinched. 'I just wanted to give you the chance to calm down before you said something you might regret, that's all. Look, I realise you must be angry—'

'No, Tess, I don't think you can even imagine how angry I am right now.' The muscles in his jaw ached from where he'd been clenching them for the past hour. 'Let me ask you something. What if it was your son caught shoplifting and I didn't tell you? How would you feel?'

'As pissed off as you, probably. But of course I was going to tell you—'

'When? When were you going to tell me?'

Her confidence faltered in the face of his blazing anger. 'When I felt the time was right.'

'What gives you the right to decide that? I'm Emily's father. I should have been the first to know, not the last! How do you think I felt, going round to pick her up and finding she'd disappeared off the face of the planet?'

'I didn't know you were coming home early, did I?'

'Just as well I did, isn't it? Otherwise I might not have found out at all.'

'What's that supposed to mean?'

'Well, it makes sense, doesn't it? My daughter's arrested and you're the first person she calls. Then you rush off and collect her and don't bother to tell me. How do I know this wasn't going to be a little secret between the two of you?'

'Now you're being ridiculous.'

'What's ridiculous about it? She obviously feels far closer to you than she does to me—' He broke off, furious at himself for letting his hurt show.

Tess' expression softened. 'Look, why don't you have a drink or something? You look like you need it.'

'No, thank you. I'd like to take my daughter home, please. If it's all right with you?' he added sarcastically.

'Of course. I'll call her.' Tess stiffened. As she headed for the door, she said, 'And you wonder why Emily didn't want the police to call you.'

'What's that supposed to mean?'

'You're hardly the easiest person in the world to talk to, are you?'

He opened his mouth to answer, but she was already gone.

'He didn't sound too happy,' Dan remarked after they'd left.

'He wasn't.' Tess watched them through the window as they drove off. 'Poor Em. I don't think I made a very good job of calming him down.'

'A lifetime's supply of Prozac wouldn't have calmed him down, the mood he was in.'

'Maybe I should go round there, try to explain—'

'Are you mad?' Dan stared at her. 'He'd only bite your head off again. No, I reckon you'd better stay well out of this one, Mum.'

'How can I? Besides, he's right. I should have told him as soon as I found out. I'd be furious if it happened to you.'

'Not much chance of that, with the disabled access in most of the shops around here. Besides, glittery belts aren't really my thing.'

'It's not funny, Dan.'

She went on looking up the empty street through the window until Dan said, 'You're going to do it, aren't you? You're going to go round there?'

'I can't leave it like this.'

'Why are you so bothered? No one's asking you to get involved.'

'I know. But I can't help caring, can I?'

Dan looked at her shrewdly. 'About her or about him?'

She decided to leave him to calm down before she went round. She was having a glass of wine and mindlessly watching *Blind Date* when Phil arrived.

'Sorry, Dan's round at a friend's,' she said as she opened the door. 'I can call him, if you like?'

'It's you I came to see.'

'In that case, you'd better come in.'

He shrugged off his suede jacket. 'How's that girl? The one you rescued.'

'Emily's fine, I think. Can't say the same about her father, though.' She poured him a glass of wine and told him about her confrontation with Jack.

Phil gave her an 'I told you so' look. 'After you went all that way to help her? Don't know why you bothered.'

'Because I can't resist a helpless soul with a problem to solve?' Tess parroted back at him. 'And since my son no longer needs me, I'm forced to inflict myself on strangers.'

Phil smiled. 'I didn't mean to be so harsh. Have you talked to Dan?'

'No, and I'm not going to. I'll wait for him to tell me, if he wants to. I won't push it.'

'Very sensible.'

'But that doesn't mean it's not killing me,' she went on. 'As you may have gathered, patience isn't my strong point.'

'That's why you need me.'

'Excuse me? I wasn't aware I needed anyone.'

He didn't reply. He got up and went over to look at the photos ranged on the mantelpiece. He picked up one of Dan and studied it for a long time.

'He's a great kid, isn't he?'

'The best. But then I am biased.'

'I've really enjoyed spending time with him, more than I ever thought I would.' He put down the photo and picked up another. 'I never really thought about what it would be like to be a father. When Angela and I found out we couldn't have kids, I wasn't that bothered. I couldn't imagine wanting that kind of responsibility.'

Tell me about it, Tess thought bitterly. He'd been quick enough to run away when he found out she was expecting Dan.

'But things have changed now. I've realised what I've been missing all these years. I don't want to lose that.'

'How could you? Dan's part of your life now.'

'I wish he could be a more permanent part.'

Tess laughed. 'You're his father. What could be more permanent than that?'

He put the photo back. It was a picture of her, she noticed. She suddenly had a spooky premonition about what he was going to say, seconds before he turned round and said, 'We could get married?'

She was too shocked to speak for a moment. Finally she asked, 'What's brought this on?'

'I've been thinking about it for a while. I want to be a more permanent part of Dan's life. And yours.'

'Phil, has Dan put you up to this?'

'No! I haven't even spoken to him about it. It was you who made me think, when you said he was trying to bring us together. At first I thought it was a joke, like you. But then I got to thinking some more and I thought, Why not? We make a great team, Tess. We could be good for each other. We're both alone, we're both lonely and—'

'Who said I'm lonely?' Tess interrupted him.

'Aren't you?'

She shook her head. 'Just because I'm alone doesn't mean I'm lonely.'

'Maybe it's just me, then.' He looked wistful.

'So you thought you could pick up where you left off with me?' Tess said. 'A nice ready-made family for you to walk in to?'

He looked uncomfortable. 'That's part of the reason, yes.'

'I see. You split up with your wife and you're feeling as if you've missed out. Then we come along and suddenly you're a family man. You've got a wife to look after you, and a grown-up son you can be proud of, without any of the hassles that go with bringing up kids.'

'If that's what you think, then you don't know me at all!' Phil's eyes blazed. 'All right, I'll admit I'm lonely, but I don't need anyone to look after me. And as for not having the hassles of bringing Dan up, don't you think I'd turn the clock back if I could? I'd give anything to have those years back and for you not to have to go through all that alone.'

Tess stared at the drink in her hand.

'I'm sorry.' He put his glass down on the coffee table and sat down beside her. 'I know I can't make up for the past, but I can share your future. I can make things easy for you, Tess. You and Dan can have the life you should have had.'

Tess bristled. 'Our life has been absolutely fine, thank you,' she snapped. 'We don't need you to come along and make everything okay for us!'

'That's not what I meant at all.' Phil was instantly contrite. 'Of course you've done a brilliant job, you only have to look at Dan to see that. I'm just saying I want to share it. I want to be part of your lives, instead of always feeling like I'm a visitor, on the outside looking in.'

'You can be part of Dan's life without me.'

'But I want you too.'

She regarded him suspiciously. His face was open, sincere, as if he really meant it. It would be so tempting to take him up on his offer. He was a funny, kind, attractive man and they didn't come along every day. They got on well and she knew now that he would be a good husband and father. But still ...

She smiled. 'You're a lovely man, Phil—'

'Why do I sense a but?'

'But ... you're doing this for all the wrong reasons. You don't really want me. You've just talked yourself into it because you feel guilty for abandoning us and you think it's the right thing to do.'

'That's not true!'

'Okay, then. Answer me one thing.' She looked him squarely in the eye. 'Do you love me?'

She saw his gaze flicker away, just for a fraction of a second, but it was enough. 'Yes,' he said.

'Sorry, I don't believe you.'

'I do love you,' he insisted. 'I'm just not – in love with you. Not yet. But it could happen,' he added hopefully.

Tess shook her head. 'It wouldn't work.'

'Why not? We're friends, aren't we? Good friends. Isn't that enough?'

'Not for me.'

'So that's it, then?'

'You know it isn't. There'll always be a place for you in Dan's life.'

'But not in yours?'

She shook her head sadly.

They finished their wine in near silence. There wasn't a lot more either of them could say. She asked Phil if he wanted to stay and wait for Dan, but she was relieved when he refused.

They said goodbye at the door. 'I don't suppose there's any chance you might change your mind?' he said. Tess shook her head. 'At least think about it for a couple of days, won't you?'

'I will.' But she already knew her answer would be the same if she thought about it for the next thousand years.

It was just as well Phil didn't stay. Twenty minutes later, Dan called to say he was staying overnight at his friend's. Tess instantly went into Mother mode, checking he'd remembered everything he needed.

'For God's sake, Mum! Stop fussing! I can take care of myself, you know!'

'Of course you can.' She remembered what Phil had told her that morning and checked herself. He was right. Dan was nearly eighteen. But old habits die hard.

She had a bath while she psyched herself up to see Jack. But as she was about to get dressed, the doorbell rang.

Jack looked more exhausted than angry now. The strain of the day was etched into every line of his face.

'Sorry for calling so late,' he said. 'Only I felt we needed to clear the air.'

'Of course. Come in.' She stepped aside. 'I was going to come round myself but I thought I'd give you some time first.'

'Time to calm down, you mean?'

'Something like that.' She led the way into the sitting room. 'Would you like a glass of wine? I think there's some left in the bottle.'

'Drinking alone? That's not a good sign.'

'Not quite. Phil came round.'

He looked from the bottle to her dressing gown. 'I see.'

'How's Emily?'

'In bed. She was worn out after everything that's happened today.'

'I'm not surprised. I guess you must be too?'

'You could say that.' He took the glass she handed him and sank on to the sofa beside her.

Tess chose her next words carefully. 'I wanted to see you, to say I'm sorry. You were right, I should have given the police your number or phoned you straight away. I had no right to interfere like that. I don't blame you for being furious.'

'That was supposed to be my line! I'm the one who should be apologising. You were only doing what you thought was best. But I was in such a state of shock, I hardly knew what I was saying.' He leaned back against the sofa cushion and stared at the ceiling. 'It's not every day your fourteen-year-old daughter gets arrested for shoplifting.'

Tess twisted her glass around in her hands. 'I've been thinking about what you said – about me keeping it a secret. I really would have told you, you know. There's no way I would have kept something like that from you.'

'I know. Like I said, I wasn't thinking too clearly.'

'It's not that Emily feels closer to me than she does to you. If anything, it's because she feels too close to you that she didn't want you to know.'

He turned to look at her. 'How do you work that out?'

'Think about it. The reason she didn't call you is because she didn't want you to see her in that situation. She felt ashamed and didn't want to hurt you. Would she do that if she didn't care?'

He ran his hand through his hair. 'I don't know. I'd like to think you're right.'

'I'm always right.'

At least that coaxed a reluctant smile from him. 'I just wish I wasn't always wrong.'

'You're not.' Impulsively she reached over and covered his hand with hers. Their eyes met and suddenly it felt like the most intimate gesture in the world.

Gingerly she pulled her fingers away and wrapped them around her glass. 'I'm sorry if it spoilt your team-building weekend.'

'That was already over as far as I was concerned.'

'Is that why you came home early?'

He nodded. 'I'd had enough of playing soldiers.' He took a deep breath. 'I've finished with Charlie.'

She suddenly felt light-headed, and it was nothing to do with the wine. 'How did she react?'

'She shot me.'

'What?'

'I made the mistake of telling her when she had a paintgun in her hands.'

'Lucky for you it wasn't a real one.'

'I don't think that would have stopped her.'

He smiled ruefully. A smile that played havoc with her self-control. She held on to her glass even tighter. 'I'm sorry. I liked her.'

'So did I. I still do. But we were never cut out to be a couple.'

'So why did you go out with her?'

'I don't know. Everyone kept telling me it was a good idea, and in the end I believed them. As I said, I like her as a friend. Although whether she'll still be a friend after today I don't know.'

'Maybe you're not ready for another relationship?'

'Oh, I think I am.' His eyes held hers. 'I just don't think Charlie was the right woman.'

The air tingled with anticipation. Tess' gaze shifted from his eyes to his mouth and back again, knowing with absolute certainty that he was going to kiss her.

Then he seemed to change his mind, suddenly turning cool again.

'So what did your ex want?' he asked.

'Sorry?' It took her a moment to drag her thoughts away from her utter disappointment. 'Oh, you mean Phil? Actually he asked me to marry him.'

She waited for him to laugh, but he didn't. 'What did you say?'

'I told him I'd think about it. But he already knows what my answer will be.'

He sipped his drink and thought about it for a long time. 'It might be a good idea,' he said at last.

Her heart plummeted. 'What makes you say that?'

'It makes sense, doesn't it? He's a nice man and he obviously cares about you. And you've already said Dan would like the two of you to get together.'

'And that's a good enough reason, is it?' Frustration made her snap.

'Isn't it?'

'I've spent the last seventeen years putting my son first. Don't you think it's time I thought about what *I* want?'

'And what do you want?'

You, she wanted to shout. But what was the point when he obviously didn't feel the same way?

They finished their drinks and Jack left. Tess watched him walk to his car, still hoping that he might turn around. But he didn't even look back at her.

So that was it. At least she knew where she stood with him now. Absolutely nowhere.

She went back into the sitting room and picked up the empty glasses. She was carrying them back to the kitchen when the doorbell rang again.

Sighing, she dumped the glasses in the sink and went to answer it.

'Don't do it,' Jack said.

'Sorry?'

'Don't marry him.'

'But—'

But she never managed to get the rest out because the next second he'd gathered her into his arms and kissed her.

31

He pulled away. 'I'm sorry, I shouldn't have done that.'

Tess didn't answer. Her heart was thundering like the Grand National winner heading for Becher's Brook.

'I've got no right to barge my way into your life like this,' Jack went on. 'It's selfish. And it's ridiculous.'

'Jack—'

'I mean, I'm probably the last man you'd want to get involved with, right? What have I got to offer, apart from two stroppy kids and a lifetime of emotional baggage?'

'Jack, listen—'

'You're right. You're a free agent now. You could probably have anyone you wanted—'

'Jack Tyler! Will you shut up?'

Before he could react she trapped his face between her hands and kissed him. Then she took his hand. 'You'd better come inside before the neighbours start talking.'

They cracked open another bottle of red wine as Jack talked.

'I didn't just come round to apologise,' he said. 'I came round because I needed to see you. That's partly why I split up with Charlie. I realised she wasn't the woman I wanted to be with. It's you I want.'

Tess stared into the ruby depths of her glass. 'When did you work that out?'

'I don't know. It kind of crept up on me. But by the time I'd plucked up the courage to ask you out your ex had got there first.'

'There was nothing going on with me and Phil.'

'I didn't know that at the time, did I? I was jealous as hell when he turned up at that Parents' Evening.'

'Ah yes, the Parents' Evening.' Tess smiled. 'I really did want to go out for that drink with you. But you never asked me again.'

'There didn't seem to be much point. That was when I gave in and started seeing Charlie. I didn't think I had much choice.'

'That wasn't very fair on her.'

'Why do you think I finished it? It wasn't just that I didn't think we were suited. I couldn't stop comparing her to you.'

Tess felt herself blushing. 'I'm not sure we'd bear much comparison. She's so beautiful.'

'Not as beautiful as you.' He laced his fingers between hers. 'At Christmas I realised you were the woman I'd been looking for.'

'It must have been the enticing aroma of turkey giblets that did it!' Tess joked feebly, to cover her raging nerves. 'But if you felt like that, why did you do a disappearing act?'

'Because I couldn't handle seeing you and Phil together. I could see how well you got on and I knew Dan wanted you to be together, so I decided to back off. But it was hell,' he admitted gruffly. 'I spent the rest of the day thinking about the two of you here, alone.'

'And all the time I was thinking about you,' Tess admitted quietly. 'How stupid are we?'

'Very.'

He took her hands in his, pulling her closer to him. It all felt so unreal, as if all her daydreams had come true. Tess was almost afraid to speak.

'So where do we go from here?' she whispered.

He gazed down at her, his eyes warm with desire. 'I know where I'd like to go,' he said.

Somehow they made it to the bedroom. Her body was already molten with longing as they fell on the bed, clothes discarded, mouths fused together.

This was how she'd always imagined it would be, but never thought it would happen. She kept wondering if she was dreaming and had to keep reassuring herself by touching him. But as her fingers moved over every inch of him, feeling the silken skin, the taut sinews, the hard play of muscles under her hands, she still couldn't believe it was real.

But if it was a dream, she wanted to remember every perfect, sexy, delicious moment. She closed her eyes, trying to imprint it all on her memory – his clean scent, his tongue making tantalising circles on her bare skin, the touch of his strong fingers stroking her, sending exquisite sensations shimmering through her body. How perfectly they moved together, his body against hers. It had never felt so right, so perfect. She wanted it to go on for ever.

But finally it was all too much and raw, explosive pleasure took over, blanking out her mind to everything else as their sweat-drenched bodies moved together, harder and faster, spiralling towards oblivion.

Afterwards they lay amid the tangled sheets. Tess was almost afraid to move, worried that the slightest shift would make the blissful illusion disappear.

'Are you okay? You're very quiet.' Jack looked at her, his eyes full of concern.

'I was just worried I might have imagined all this,' she admitted.

He lifted himself up on to his elbow and looked down at her. 'We could always try it again and find out?'

'That sounds tempting.' She smiled up at him. 'Are you sure you're up to it?'

'That sounds like a challenge, Miss Doyle. And you know I can never resist a challenge.' The glint in his eyes sent a tingle of anticipation down her spine, followed seconds later by genuine surprise and pleasure as his lips began to trail over her shoulder, her breasts, and down over the curved planes of her stomach.

God, but he was good at this. She tried to blank out the thought of him practising on Charlie, of her slender, perfect, elongated limbs. What did he make of her in comparison, with her less-than-perfect body?

The thought made her arch away from him. He came up, looking surprised. 'What is it? Don't you like it? Do you want me to stop?'

'It's not that . . .' What could she say? 'I was just – being stupid, that's all. Thinking about Charlie.'

His face darkened. 'What about her?'

'She's so gorgeous and everything, I'm not nearly as beautiful as her. I bet she was really good in bed, too,' she said lamely. She could feel herself blushing.

Jack shifted back up the bed until his face was level with hers. 'Yes, she was. Very good,' he said shortly. 'She gave a virtuoso performance every time.'

'Great.' Tess retreated under the covers and pulled them up to her chin.

'In fact, if sex was an Olympic event, I reckon she would have brought home the gold.'

'All right, you don't have to rub it in!'

'But that's not what it's about, is it? It isn't about pushing the right buttons and hitting the jackpot.'

'Isn't it?'

'No, it isn't. Or at least, it shouldn't be.' He reached out and brushed a damp strand of hair off her face. 'It's about chemistry, being with the right person. I don't suppose you'll believe me when I tell you this, but I never felt as close to Charlie as I did to you when we ended up on my bed during Emily's party.'

'Really?'

He nodded. 'Really. That's when I realised how much I wanted you. Even if you aren't nearly as beautiful as her.'

She caught the teasing look in his eyes. 'Bastard!' She reached for a pillow but he was too quick for her. He rolled on top of her, pinning her to the bed, his hard body crushing hers.

He looked down at her. 'Well, Miss Doyle?' he said. 'How about we try for that Olympic gold?'

By the time he left in the early hours, they must have achieved medals in a whole pentathlon at least.

'Do you have to go?' Tess pleaded as she watched him dress in the shadowy darkness.

'I'm afraid so. I meant to leave ages ago, but you kept dragging me back to bed.'

'Excuse me? I don't seem to remember you putting up much resistance.'

'I didn't, did I?' He stood up, pulling on his jeans. Tess lay back against the pillows and admired the sculpted muscles in his broad shoulders, tapering down to the flat stomach. She felt herself go weak with longing again. Now she knew what he was like, would she ever stop lusting after him? she wondered.

'So what happens now?' she whispered.

'I suppose we just go back to our own lives and forget this ever happened. Joke,' he said, as Tess' face fell. 'What do you think happens? Do you seriously think that I'm going to let you go now we've finally got together?'

Put like that, it did sound a bit unlikely. But Tess still couldn't believe her luck. 'What about the girls?'

'What about them?'

'Are you going to say anything to them – about us?'

'What do you suggest? "Guess what, girls? I've just spent the night making mad passionate love to Miss Doyle"?'

Tess blushed. 'You know what I mean.'

'Of course I'm going to tell them. Why shouldn't I?'

'They might not like the idea.'

'Then they'll just have to get used to it, won't they?'

'Like they did with Charlie? That didn't turn out too well, did it?'

'That was different. They never liked Charlie. They love you.'

Not for long, Tess thought. 'Only because I'm not a threat. Emily might feel differently if she knows we're – you know.'

He frowned. 'So what do you suggest? Do you want me to lie to them?'

'No! Of course not. I just don't know how to handle this.' Tess sat up and hugged her knees. 'Maybe we should slow things down a bit – give them a chance to get used to me being around before we make any big declarations?'

'Like an old-fashioned courtship, you mean?' He considered it. 'It might be fun. As long as I can still come round and ravish you every night, of course!' His eyes gleamed.

Tess smiled enigmatically. 'We'll see.'

After he'd gone, Tess lay back amid the sheets, her body still aching pleasurably. What a night. She couldn't remember when she'd ever been made love to so expertly, so thoroughly – or so frequently.

It was all perfect. Too perfect, in a way. Pragmatist that she was, in the back of her mind she couldn't help feeling that something had to happen to spoil it.

And she was pretty sure she knew what that something was. A stroppy fourteen-year-old called Emily.

That was why she was so keen to take things slowly. She didn't want to upset Emily or Sophie. They'd been through enough upheaval already, she didn't want to create any more for them to cope with.

But she knew that if she and Jack were going to make this work, they had to be very, very careful.

It was a few days before Dan finally confided in her about his plans. Tess, mindlessly working her way through a pile of ironing, forced herself not to pitch in straight away with advice.

'So what do you want to do?' she asked, when he'd finished telling her.

Dan eyed her warily. 'Are you feeling all right, Mum?'

'I'm fine. Why shouldn't I be?'

'No reason. It's just I thought you'd try to talk me out of it.'

Tess hid a smile. 'Do you want me to?'

'No.'

She could feel him watching her, still waiting for her to explode. 'It's your life, Dan.'

'So you're not disappointed or anything?'

'Well, of course I would have liked you to go to university. You're a bright boy.' She chose her words carefully. 'But if you really feel you'd be better off getting some hands-on experience—' And you can always go back to college if it doesn't work out, she added silently.

'I do,' said Dan. 'It's not just because I can't face another three years at school. I don't really need a degree for the kind of work I want to do.'

Tess attacked the collar of a blouse with the tip of the iron. 'Jobs aren't that easy to come by, Dan. You might find you need those extra qualifications.'

'I've already got a job. I'm going to work for Phil.'

Tess let the iron drop. 'You're what? Since when?'

'I talked it over with him a couple of days ago. It makes sense, doesn't it? I want to work in computers and he owns his own software business. He says I can go down to Basingstoke and learn the ropes. Then he might think about opening a new office up here. That would be great, wouldn't it?'

But Tess wasn't listening. 'So you two have got it all sewn up, have you? Thanks for talking to me about it! Or doesn't my opinion count for anything any more?'

'Of course it does,' Dan said quietly. 'I just wanted to get it all sorted out before I told you, that's all.'

'You mean you wanted to make sure I couldn't object! Well, I'm sorry, Dan, but I think it's a lousy idea. You and your father haven't thought it through at all.' She picked up the iron and flung the blouse back on to the pile. 'Where are you going to live while all this is going on?'

'With Phil.'

'And his place is suitable, is it? It's all specially adapted?'

'No, but he can easily get that sorted out.'

'Of course he can! Your father's brilliant, he can do anything!' Tess saw him wince, but she didn't care. 'Whatever the problem is, he can wave a magic wand and everything will be perfect! Shame he wasn't here seventeen years ago, then maybe you wouldn't have needed me at all!'

Dan stared at her. 'I thought you'd be happy for me. What's your problem?'

'My problem? My problem is no one seems to care how I feel any more.' Her voice was choked. 'Everyone's doing such a great job, sorting their lives out, and I'm just expected to go along with it.'

'Like you said, it is my life,' Dan pointed out quietly.

'And I'm expected to stand aside and watch you ruin it?'

She hadn't meant it to sound like that. Dan gave her a look of reproach and then left the room, closing the door behind him.

Tess picked up the next item on the ironing pile and slung it on to the board. It was one of Dan's T-shirts. Typical. She wasn't good enough to discuss her own son's future, but she was allowed to do his ironing for him. Maybe she shouldn't bother doing it? Maybe she should stick them all in a bag and pack them off to Phil to do, since he seemed to be calling the shots these days.

She propped the iron up on its stand, covered her face with her hands and allowed the tears to flow. Stupid, stupid, stupid.

She was more angry with Phil than Dan. How dare he take over her son's life without even consulting her! Didn't he think she had a right to have a say in his future? Maybe he'd planned it all, talked Dan out of going to college so he could take him away from her.

But she was even angrier at herself for being so selfish and needy. She'd spent so many years teaching Dan to be independent, but the moment he was, she tried to snatch it all away from him.

She could feel the beginnings of a headache nagging at her temples. She unplugged the iron and went to lie down before it took hold.

She must have fallen asleep because half an hour later she woke up to find Dan reaching over to put a cup of tea on her bedside table.

'I thought you might be needing this,' he said.

'Thanks.' She sat up, rubbing her eyes. 'What time is it?'

'Nearly seven. I've finished the ironing, by the way.'

'Really?' She'd never known him do that before. She didn't even think he knew what the iron was for. As far as he was concerned, clothes just appeared in his wardrobe, flattened as if by magic.

Dan watched her sip her tea. 'I'm sorry,' he mumbled. 'I didn't mean to upset you.'

'And I didn't mean to upset you, either.' Tess gave him a watery smile. 'Take no notice of me, I'm being stupid and selfish. I just can't bear the thought of my little baby leaving, that's all.'

'Mum!' Dan hesitated a moment. 'It doesn't have to be like this. You could come too?'

'What would I do in Basingstoke?' Tess laughed.

'You could find a job. I'm sure they have teachers down there. We could all be together.'

She sighed. 'We've been through all this, Dan. I already told you, it won't work. Your father and I will always be friends, but it can't be any more than that. That's not how relationships work.'

'I only want you to be happy.'

'I'm fine, honestly.'

'And you're sure you don't mind about me going?'

She swallowed hard. Of course she minded. After so long together she couldn't imagine an hour going by when she wouldn't miss him. But she had to let him go.

'I think it's a very good idea,' she said bravely.

It seemed enough for him. He swung his chair round, but as he headed for the door he turned and said, 'Anyway, I don't suppose I'll have to worry about you being lonely, will I? Not now you've got Jack.'

Tess spluttered into her tea. 'How did you know about Jack?'

'Come on, Mum, I might be in a wheelchair but I'm not blind! Someone's put a smile on your face the last few days.' He grinned. 'So how long's it been going on?'

'None of your business! You're not the only one who can have secrets, you know!'

32

Jack turned up on Sunday morning with an armful of Sunday papers. The day was cold, grey and wet, and rain dripped off his hair. He was wearing faded Levis, a white shirt and black leather jacket, and Tess felt herself melting with lust.

'Where are the girls?' she asked, after she'd kissed him.

'Sophie's back at the house with her gran. Emily's gone into York shopping with Paris. I thought we could go back to bed with these?' He held up the newspapers. 'Unless, of course, you have any better ideas on how to pass the time?'

'I'd love to, but Dan's here.' Tess glanced over her shoulder. He might be fine about her seeing Jack, but she didn't feel very comfortable about disappearing into her bedroom with him, much as she wanted to.

'In that case, why don't we forget the papers and go out for a walk?'

'A walk?'

'Apparently it's what people used to do before cars came along.'

'Very funny. Why would you want to walk in this weather?'

'Because it's romantic. And it's the only way we're likely to get any time alone. And I do want to be alone with you. Very badly.'

The look in his eyes made her catch her breath. 'In that case, I'll get my umbrella.'

She quickly changed into a skirt and put her contact lenses in. It was crazy, because Jack had seen her in jeans and specs a million times, but it was a long time since she'd had anyone to make an effort for and she wanted to make the most of it.

They made their way up to Haxsall Common. As it was so grey and wet, they had the place virtually to themselves, apart from a few determined dog walkers.

They talked as they trudged through the mulch of mud and wet leaves. Tess could tell Jack had something on his mind. He finally admitted it was a work problem, but wouldn't tell her any more.

'It's something I've got to sort out for myself,' he said grimly, then changed the subject. 'How are the preparations for the Basingstoke move going?'

'Anyone would think he was going next week, the way he's carrying on,' Tess grumbled. 'Actually, if he had his way, he probably would be going next week.' But she'd insisted he stay on at the sixth-form college to finish his A Levels. Tess had been adamant about that and Phil had agreed, much to Dan's chagrin.

'I suppose he can't wait to get out in the big bad world and start earning money?'

'Can't wait to get away from me, more like.' Tess kicked at a stone in her path.

'I'm sure that's not true.'

'Isn't it? You haven't heard him. It's "Phil says this, Phil says that." Apparently Phil is having the ground floor of his house specially adapted into a flat for him so he can have his own space.' She grimaced.

'You should feel flattered,' Jack said. 'It's a sign you've brought him up well if he's that confident. He obviously feels he can cope on his own.'

'I never thought of it like that. Maybe I've got it wrong. Maybe it's just me who can't cope on my own.'

'Then it's lucky you've got me, isn't it?'

He grabbed her, pushed her back against a tree and kissed her long and hard.

Tess came up for air, breathless and laughing. 'Jack! Someone might see!'

'I don't know if you've noticed, but it's pouring with rain and we're the only ones stupid enough to be out in it. Besides, who's going to care?'

'Someone from school? They might tell Emily.'

'So what?' Jack's face clouded. 'I don't like lying to my children. They deserve better than that, and so do you.' He traced the line of her jaw with his finger. 'I don't want this to be some kind of dirty secret. I want the whole world to know about us. Starting with the girls.'

'Are you sure about that?' Tess looked wary. 'I don't like lying to them either. But I don't want them to get hurt. Especially Emily.'

'They'll have to get used to it. Because there's no way I'm giving you up.'

He kissed her again, pushing her back against the tree, his body pressed against hers, their mouths merging together with pent-up desire.

Emily and Paris trailed back from the bus stop, their collars turned up against the rain.

'Well, that was a waste of time,' Emily grumbled. 'All the way to town to buy you a pair of shoes and you leave your purse at home.'

'I said I was sorry, didn't I?' Paris replied tetchily.

They walked in silence for a moment. 'What do you want to do now?' Emily asked.

'You could come back to my place?'

'Why don't you come back to mine instead?' She was secretly a bit unnerved by Paris' mum and her boyfriend, with their pierced eyebrows, noserings and tattoos.

'If you like.' They turned and retraced their steps up the road towards the common, which in turn led to Hollywell Park.

'Bet you're happy now your dad's split up with his girlfriend?' Paris said.

Emily thrust her hands into her pockets, her shoulders hunched against the cold rain. 'It wasn't my fault they split up.'

'You didn't help, did you?'

She shrugged. 'He's much happier now, anyway.' Really happy, in fact. Happier than she'd seen him in ages. And knowing she had nothing to fear made her happier too. She couldn't remember when the house had been so harmonious.

As they reached the road that skirted the common, a small terrier shot out of the undergrowth, narrowly missing the wheels of a passing lorry. The driver slammed on the brakes and yelled something to Emily about keeping her bleeding dog under control.

'He's not mine,' she shouted back. She gathered the shivering animal up in her arms. 'Poor little thing. Look at him, he's terrified.'

'I'm not surprised.' Paris came up behind her. 'Put him down, Em. You don't know where he's been.'

'But he's all cold and wet.' She pressed the dirty, bedraggled fur against her cheek.

'He's not the only one. Can we get home, please? Before I catch pneumonia.'

'What shall I do with him?'

'I don't know. Just put him down and let him run back to his owner.'

'What if he hasn't got one?' She felt under the damp fur. 'He hasn't got a collar. He might be a stray.'

'Well, I'm not taking him home. We're in enough trouble with the landlord.'

Emily peered into the dense undergrowth. 'We should see if we can find his owner.'

'I've got a better idea. Why don't we just let him go?' But Emily had already set off through the long damp grass. With a long-suffering sigh, Paris followed her.

It was only lunchtime, but the trees overhead blocked out what little light there was, making everything grey and murky as twilight.

'Did you ever see that film, *The Blair Witch Project*?'

'What about it?'

'That was set in a place like this. These three students kept going round and round in circles, getting more and more lost. And all the time this unseen horror was trailing them—'

'Snowy!' someone shrieked from the trees. Emily screamed with fright, and the dog leapt from her arms and bolted towards the undergrowth.

'You naughty dog!' A woman in a grey anorak appeared, a lead in her hand. 'Fancy slipping your collar like that!'

'We found her on the main road. She nearly got run over,' Emily explained. The woman ignored her. She bent down and slipped the collar over the dog's head. Then, with a last dirty look in their direction, she gathered Snowy up in her arms and marched off the way she'd come.

'Charming!' Emily said. 'Did you see that look? Anyone would think we were stealing her flipping dog, not saving its life!'

Paris turned around, distracted. 'Shall we get back now?'

'What's the matter? Did you scare yourself talking about that film?' Emily grinned, but Paris was already hurrying back up the path. 'Hang on a minute, wouldn't it be quicker to keep going down here and join the main road further along?'

'I want to go this way. Come on!'

'But—' Emily turned around and realised why Paris didn't want her to go down that path.

Strolling towards her, hand in hand like a pair of soppy teenagers, were her father and Miss Doyle.

She stopped dead. Every sound seemed to be magnified a million times – the lonely birdsong, the patter of rain, the muted sound of their laughter.

As if they knew they were being watched, they suddenly looked up and saw her.

'Emily!' Her father made a move towards her. She turned, pushing past Paris and fled down the path, her trainers slipping in the wet leaves.

The next moment seemed to last a lifetime. Tess didn't realise she was still clinging to Jack's hand until he pulled away. 'I'd better go after her.'

She let him go. 'Do you want me to come with you?'

'I don't think that's a good idea, do you?' Jack let out a long ragged breath. 'Jesus, what a mess.' He turned to her. 'Will you be okay making your own way home?'

'Of course. Ring me later,' she called after him. But he'd already disappeared out of view.

He found her in the play park on the village green, slumped on a swing. She looked so heartbreakingly young, her long legs dragging on the ground.

'Emily?' She didn't reply. 'Emily, I want to explain.' He sat on the vacant swing beside her. She turned away from him. 'Look, I'm sorry you had to find out like that. We were going to tell you, honestly. You know I wouldn't do anything to deliberately hurt you – Emily, are you listening to me?'

'Go away,' she growled, so quietly he could barely hear her over the creak of the swing.

Jack opened his mouth to argue, then closed it again. What was the point? It would only antagonise her.

'Fine.' He stood up. 'We'll talk about it later. I'll see you at home, shall I?' There was no answer, just an imperceptible shrug of the shoulders. 'Don't stay out too long, will you? You'll get cold.'

He headed off across the play park, forcing himself to stay nonchalant and not look back, even though his mind was racing with all kinds of terrors in which Emily didn't come home. What if she ran away? What if he never saw her again?

He fought the urge to rush back, haul her off the swing and drag her home, kicking and protesting but ultimately safe.

He reached the far end of the green and finally allowed himself to sneak a look over his shoulder at the forlorn, drooping figure on the swing.

Please come home, he prayed.

She sat on the swing all afternoon, too afraid to move. While she was here, everything around her was suspended, frozen. If she got up, it would all become real again and she didn't want that.

She felt utterly, devastatingly alone, more even than when her mum had died. The two people she'd trusted most had betrayed her. Now she had no one in the world to turn to.

Every time she closed her eyes she saw them again, holding hands, gazing into each other's eyes, as if no one else mattered. As if she didn't matter.

She felt such a fool, not knowing. It must have been going on for ages. They'd probably been laughing at her the whole time.

And to think she'd trusted Tess, confided in her about things she couldn't tell anyone else. She'd thought Tess was her friend. Now she realised she was only pretending to be nice to her so she could get close to her dad. How stupid could she be? She was probably the only one who didn't know what was going on.

It was late afternoon and getting dark when she finally went home. The cold and damp had seeped through her clothes right through to her bones, and her misery had crystallised into hard, implacable anger.

Her father was in the kitchen, loading the washing machine. She could hear Sophie playing upstairs.

He looked up as she walked in. His expression was carefully neutral but she could see the strain in his eyes. Good. She hoped she'd really worried him. He deserved to feel bad.

'You're back, then?' He sounded falsely jolly. 'Bet it was freezing out there?'

She ignored him and went to the fridge for some orange juice. She'd mentally rehearsed every bitter, cutting line she was going to say, but when she saw him again she was so angry she couldn't bring herself to speak.

He sighed and closed the washing-machine door. 'How long is this silent treatment going to go on? If you've got something to say, why don't you just come out and say it?'

She hitched herself on to the stool at the breakfast bar and filled her glass with juice, but still said nothing. She wanted to wind him up, to make him feel as angry as she felt.

She expected him to yell at her, but after a moment he went back to programming the machine. That showed how much he cared, didn't it? He couldn't even be bothered to lose his temper.

Emily stared at the glass in her hands. 'So how long's it been going on?'

'A week.'

'And when were you going to tell me? Or weren't you going to bother?'

'Of course we were going to tell you. We were just waiting for the right time.'

Emily snorted. 'And when was that going to be? A month? A year? Just before the wedding?'

'Don't be ridiculous.'

His dismissive remark made her hackles rise again. 'You're always lying to me,' she accused.

'That's not fair—'

'What about Charlie? You told me she was just someone from work and the next minute she'd practically moved in!' She stopped, a thought occuring to her. 'Is that why you split up with her?' She immediately saw from his guilty expression that it was. 'Did she find out you were shagging my teacher behind her back?'

'That's enough!' He so rarely shouted at her, it made her shrink back. 'I won't have you talking like that. You can show some respect.'

'Why? You never show me any!'

'I don't have to ask a fourteen-year-old's permission to live my life, do I? What I do is none of your business.'

'I'm not a kid.'

'Then stop acting like one!' He was losing his temper now, she could tell. A muscle pounded in his cheek.

'I suppose it was her idea to keep it a secret?' An image of Tess, all smiling and friendly, filled her mind. And all the time she was plotting to take her father away.

'And you wonder why, the way you're acting?'

'I think it's disgusting.'

'I don't really care what you think.'

She stared at him, furious. He used to care. It just showed how Tess had got to him, wheedled her way in between them.

'She's a bitch and I hate her.'

'You said that about Charlie. I'm not allowed to have anyone, am I?'

No, she wanted to shout. No, you're not allowed to have anyone. Not if it makes you turn against us.

Not if it makes you forget Mum.

'I'm not going to give her up, Em. Not like Charlie. It's different this time.'

'Are you in love with her or something?' Her mouth curled with contempt.

'Yes,' he said quietly. 'Yes, I think I am.'

She blundered to her feet, knocking the glass over. 'You can't!' she screamed. 'You can't say that, you can't!'

'Emily, listen. Just because I love Tess doesn't change the way I feel about you and Sophie. You still come first, you always will.' He reached for her but she pulled away. Panic clawed at her, clutching at her throat so she could hardly breathe.

'What about Mum?' The words were out before she could control them.

He flinched. 'What about her?'

What about her? Emily stared at him in disbelief. How could he even ask that question? It was like he'd already dismissed her.

'Emily, your mum's dead. Now, I wish that wasn't true as much as you do—'

'No, you don't! You're glad she's dead. I bet you never even loved her!'

His face lost its expression. 'Emily, don't say that. Don't ever say that.'

'It's true!' She backed away, out of his reach. 'How can you say you loved her when all you want to do is find someone else?' The words came tumbling out, angry and spiteful. She could see the raw pain in his eyes, but she wanted to hurt him, just like she was hurting.

'Emily, stop this. You don't know what you're saying.'

'Yes, I do. You never loved Mum. You never even—'

The stinging slap took them both by surprise. Emily recoiled and put her hand to her cheek. She could see the shock in her father's eyes, mirroring her own.

'Emily—'

'Leave me alone!' She stumbled backwards towards the doorway. 'I hate you! I wish you were dead instead of Mum!'

She thudded up the stairs. Just before she slammed her bedroom door, she heard his voice in the hall below.

'You know what? So do I.'

'Bloody hell, so what happened then?' Ros said. She'd dropped everything and come over as soon as Jack had phoned.

'Not much. She hasn't spoken to me since.' Jack collapsed back against the sofa cushions and nursed the drink Ros had given him. 'God, what have I done? A year ago I would never have raised my hand to her, and now—'

'Jack, you lost your temper. That doesn't make you a monster. Besides, from what you've told me, I'm not surprised you lost it.'

'That still doesn't make it right, does it?' Jack lifted his glass, his hand shaking. 'I feel I've let her down. And I've given her another reason to hate me. As if she needs one,' he said grimly.

'She'll get over it.'

'You think so? You didn't hear her. All those things she said were so cruel.'

'She was just lashing out because she was angry. And scared.'

'Scared?'

'I suppose she can see how serious you are about Tess. That's bound to be frightening.'

'But I thought she liked her?'

'Liking someone and wanting them to take your mum's place are two different things.'

'Tess could never take Miranda's place. She wouldn't want to.'

'I know that and so do you. But maybe Emily needs convincing?'

'If she ever listens to me again.' He looked up at the ceiling, then at Ros. 'Do you think she's right? Am I being disloyal to Miranda?'

Ros put her arm round his shoulders. 'Jack, no one could have loved Miranda more than you did. But she's gone now. And knowing her, she wouldn't have wanted you to be alone. I reckon if she could have picked someone, it would have been Tess. You two are made for each other.'

Jack managed a thin smile. 'I seem to remember you said that about Charlie.'

'Yes, well, I was wrong. And you don't have to look at me like that, I know I don't admit it very often. And if you breathe a word to Greg, I'll kill you.' She shook a warning finger under his nose.

'I think Emily might beat you to it.'

'She'll come round,' Ros promised.

The phone rang just as she was leaving. 'I expect that's Greg, fretting about me leaving him so long with the kids,' Ros smiled.

But it was Tess. 'I wondered if everything was all right?'

Jack suddenly remembered she'd asked him to call her and felt guilty. He mouthed goodbye to Ros as she let herself out. 'Quite peaceful at the moment. But only because Emily's barricaded herself in her room and won't speak to anyone.'

'Oh God. She hasn't calmed down, then?'

'It's all relative, isn't it? She's not actually shouting and throwing things now, but I think it's more simmering resentment than actual calm.' He felt very weary, exhausted by the day. He just wanted to go to bed and wake up and for it to be tomorrow.

Except he had the feeling tomorrow would be just as bad, if not worse.

'Would it help if I came round?'

About as much as throwing petrol on a chip-pan fire. 'Not unless you're a trained siege negotiator?'

'I'm afraid not.' There was a smile in her voice. 'Poor you. I feel so guilty.'

'Why should you feel guilty?'

'It's my fault you're going through this. I talked you out of telling the girls.'

'I don't think that would have helped somehow.' He didn't tell her about the things Emily had said. He didn't want to upset her.

He looked up at the sound of footsteps overhead. 'Hang on, I think something's stirring upstairs.' He lowered his voice. 'I'd better go.'

'Will you call me later?'

'I'll try.' He put the phone down and gazed nervously at the ceiling.

33

That evening Tess went to visit her mother. She didn't bother calling first because she knew Margaret Doyle always had her flat spick and span, ready for visitors. She frowned on Tess' habit of only tidying up when she was expecting someone.

It took a while for her mother to answer the door. She looked rather flustered to see Tess.

'Teresa! What are you doing here?'

'That's a nice greeting!' Tess looked her up and down. There was something different about her. Her hair was set in soft, flattering waves around her face and under her usual beige cardigan she wore a blouse in a racy shade of eau-de-nil. 'Are you going to invite me in, or do I have to stand out here freezing like a Jehovah's Witness?'

It was meant as a joke but Margaret looked as if she was seriously considering it. 'I suppose you'd better come in,' she said finally.

In the hall, Tess shook off her wet coat and sniffed the air. 'Something smells good?'

'I was just having a bit of dinner.'

'On your own? You don't usually go to all that trouble just for—' She stopped in the kitchen doorway. There were two plates on the kitchen table. Ronnie was filling the kettle at the sink.

'All right, lass?' he beamed at her. 'I was just making a brew, do you fancy one?'

Tess nodded, too dumbfounded by the flowery pinny around his waist to speak.

'Shame you weren't around just now, or you could've had something to eat with us. She cooks a grand piece of beef, your mum.' His blue eyes twinkled appreciatively at Margaret, who dimpled in response. Tess peered at her. If she didn't know better, she would swear her mother was blushing.

Margaret noticed Tess staring at her, pulled herself together and began clearing the plates.

Tess frowned at the bottle on the table. 'Is that wine?'

'It is, lass. Would you prefer a glass of that to tea? I think there's some left in the bottle, isn't there, Maggie?'

'No thanks.' Tess looked at her mother. 'I've never known you to drink wine?'

'I was very partial to a glass when your father was alive.' Margaret looked defensive. 'But there's no point opening a bottle just for yourself.'

'Why not? I do.'

'I know.' Margaret's severe look was back in place. 'And most of the time you end up drinking the lot.'

'I've been introducing your mother to the delights of New World wines,' Ronnie explained.

'Ronnie belongs to a wine club,' her mother added proudly, as if she'd announced he belonged to the Prime Minister's cabinet. 'I never knew there were such things.'

'Oh yes?' And what other delights had he been introducing her to? Tess wondered. She watched them moving around the kitchen together, fussing over the washing-up. She was sure Ronnie must be a regular visitor. He certainly seemed to know his way around her mother's kitchen; he put the dishes away exactly how Margaret liked them, something Tess hadn't managed in thirty-four years.

There was something very odd going on. It was as if her mother had been abducted by aliens and replaced by this strange, smiling creature with a taste for eau-de-nil blouses and Chilean Chardonnay.

'Your hair looks nice,' she said.

'Do you think so?' Margaret patted her soft curls.

'Takes years off her, doesn't it?' Ronnie piped up. 'I've been telling her she suits it like that, but you know what your mother's like about compliments.'

He smiled at her. Fondly. Almost lovingly, in fact. Tess looked from one to the other and suddenly it all added up.

'I'm just going to the loo,' she said.

On the way back she sneaked into her mother's bedroom to take a look around. It looked just the way it always did – neat, clean, unadorned, with faded floral-print wallpaper and a pink silk eiderdown on the bed. There were photos of her grandchildren on her dressing table, alongside a neatly arranged tortoiseshell-backed hairbrush and comb set, and a bottle of Yardley's lavender water – and a make-up bag.

Tess rummaged quickly through it. As far as she knew her mother had made the same pot of face powder and pale-pink Rimmel lipstick last all her adult life, rationing it strictly for special occasions. But the make-up bag contained light-reflecting foundation, cream blusher, mascara and a new lipstick in a very flattering shade of warm coral. Max Factor, no less.

Tess tried it on the back of her hand. Either Ronnie was a cross-dresser, or her mother had been on an unheard-of spending spree in Boots.

'If you tell me what you're looking for, I can help you find it.' She jumped. Margaret stood in the doorway, her arms folded across her chest. No amount of light-reflecting make-up could hide her scowl. 'Got lost on your way to the bathroom, did you? You should know where it is by now.'

'I – I –' Tess looked around, searching for an excuse. There wasn't one. 'I was just trying to find out what's going on,' she said.

'Why didn't you just ask me?'

Tess opened and closed her mouth, then opened it again. 'Okay, then. What's going on?'

'None of your business,' Margaret said flatly.

'But I'm your daughter!'

'That doesn't give you the right to go prying into my affairs.' Margaret snatched the make-up bag away from her and put it back down on the dressing table.

Tess sat down on the bed. 'What's going on between you and Ronnie?'

'I don't know what you're talking about. He's just a friend from the Over Sixties club, that's all.' Her mother's sheepish expression gave her away.

'You've got lots of friends from the Over Sixties club, but I've never known you to invite any of them over for dinner. And how come he's allowed to call you Maggie? And what are his shirts doing hanging over there?' She suddenly noticed the row of crisply ironed shirts hanging up on the wardrobe doorknob, ready to be put away.

'All right, all right!' Margaret looked irritable. 'Since you're that bothered I'll tell you. Ronnie and I are engaged.'

'What! When? How?'

'He asked me to marry him at Christmas. When we were in London.'

So she wasn't lying when she said she'd gone with her fancy man! 'Does Frances know about this?'

Margaret shook her head. 'I met up with Ronnie after I'd left your sister's. We wanted to keep it quiet until we'd set a date for the wedding.'

'And have you?'

'Not yet. We're hoping for some time in the early summer. You can't afford to wait that long when you get to our age. That's why we've decided to live together now.'

'Live together!' Without thinking she glanced at the other side of the bed she was sitting on. Her father's side. There were a packet of Rennies and a Len Deighton paperback on the bedside table. She shot to her feet.

'Don't look so shocked.' Her mother's eyes gleamed with amusement. 'It does happen these days.'

Maybe, but not to her mother. Margaret Doyle, sharing her bed with a man! And getting married! She never imagined in her wildest dreams she would ever see the day.

'I know it's probably come as a shock,' Margaret said.

'You could say that!'

'But I hope you and your sister can be happy for us?' Tess didn't answer. 'Ronnie's a nice man, once you get to know him.'

'I'm sure he is.' That wasn't the point. The point was her mother had made such a huge, life-changing decision and she hadn't been told. Just like Dan. Why was it that no one wanted to discuss anything with her these days?

'I'm lucky to find someone like him,' Margaret went on. 'Single men are difficult to come by once you get to my age. Ones who've still got all their faculties, anyway.'

Tess suppressed a shudder. She didn't want to think about Ronnie's faculties, or how well they worked.

'And we're company for each other. It's a long time since I had that.'

Tess was stung. 'You've got me.'

'I know, but you've got your own life.' That's a matter of opinion, Tess thought. It turned out what she had always thought of as her life had been built around other people's. And now they were all moving away from her.

'I didn't realise you were so lonely?' she said.

'You wouldn't, would you? I didn't know myself until I met Ronnie.' Margaret twisted the wedding ring on her finger. Her father's ring. 'I've been on my own for twenty-five years, Teresa. Longer than I was married. And in all that time I've never so much as looked at another man. Never thought I'd want to. Until now.' She smiled mistily. 'I know we're no Romeo and Juliet. We're both a bit old for that nonsense. But like I said, we're company for each other. You miss that when you get to my age.'

'Why didn't you tell me?'

'I don't know. I suppose I knew it was a bit foolish.' She smiled shakily. 'Anyway, look on the bright side. At least if I've got Ronnie, I won't be a burden to you in my old age!'

'Tea's up,' Ronnie called.

'Give him a chance. For my sake?' Margaret pleaded as they headed for the kitchen.

They drank their tea and chatted, and half an hour later Tess left, knowing she liked Ronnie. And she only had to look at the way he fussed around her mother to see he adored her. But that didn't stop her feeling hurt and upset.

Fairly or unfairly, her mother was always fixed in her mind as living alone, staying faithful to the man she'd lost more than twenty-five years before. A man who could never be replaced.

Until now. Now everything had changed, shifted around. Tess didn't know why it should unsettle her after so many years, but it did.

The light on her answer machine was blinking in the darkness when she got home. Tess dumped her bag on the floor and pressed the Play button.

'Hi, it's me.' Jack sounded weary. 'Just to let you know the war's still going on over here. Give me a call when you get in. Doesn't matter what time it is. I just need to hear a friendly voice.'

Tess went into the kitchen, found the half-empty wine bottle in the fridge and poured herself a glass. New World wines, indeed! What would Ronnie be introducing her mother to next: salsa dancing?

A stab of jealousy went through her and suddenly she thought of Emily. If she could feel like this after twenty-five years, how much worse must Emily be feeling after one? Her grief was still so raw. And she was so much younger than Tess, so vulnerable and unable to deal with her emotions. No wonder she hated Tess and her father for what they'd done. She thought she was the centre of her father's life, just like Tess did her mother. To find out things had changed so dramatically, and no one had told her about it, must have hurt her more than anyone could imagine.

Heavy-hearted, she picked up the phone and dialled Jack's number.

'I don't believe I'm hearing this.' Jack paced the room. He'd come straight over after Tess' call. 'After everything that's happened, you're saying we shouldn't see each other any more?'

'I didn't say that.'

'Well, excuse me, but that's how it sounds. Would you mind explaining to me exactly what your mother's marriage has got to do with us?'

'I told you. Seeing her with Ronnie just made me realise how Emily must be feeling. This must be so hard for her. All this sneaking around behind her back, she must feel as if we've betrayed her.'

'Right now I don't care how she feels.'

She stared at him, shocked. 'You don't mean that.'

'Don't I? You didn't hear some of the things she said to me. Hurtful, spiteful things. About me and Miranda.'

'She was angry and hurt.'

'Sometimes I think she really believes she has the monopoly on pain.'

'That's teenagers for you. They're not exactly known for their generosity of spirit.'

Jack sat down on the sofa and reached for her hand. 'Ironic, isn't it? You're sticking up for her and she doesn't have a good word to say about you.'

'You get used to it.' Tess shrugged. 'Once you've read the obscene graffiti about yourself on a boys' toilet wall, insults don't seem to touch you.'

'How obscene?' Jack raised his brows questioningly. The old sparkle was there in his eyes. It would have been so easy to forget about Emily and all their problems and just enjoy being together, but Tess knew it wouldn't solve anything.

'Never you mind.' She tried to slip her hand from his, but Jack held on to it.

'I don't want to lose you,' he said. 'I'm a grown man. I'm not having my life dictated by a fourteen-year-old.'

'But if it's making her this unhappy—'

'She'll get over it. If I have to stop seeing you, I'm not sure I will.'

She saw the look in his eyes and her stomach did a backflip. She forced herself to stay calm. 'I'm not saying it's for ever. Just until the dust settles—'

'How long is that? Should we put our lives on hold until she's sixteen? Or eighteen? Or shall we just wait until she's married with kids of her own before we broach the subject? I love you, Tess. I never thought I could feel like this about anyone after Miranda died. I'm not prepared to give you up.'

How long had she dreamed of hearing him say those words? She wanted to ask him to say them again, just so she could bask in them.

'So you think we should just tough it out? Tell Emily she's got to like it or lump it?'

He looked defensive. 'Why not?'

'And what if she doesn't forgive you? What if this ruins your relationship for ever?'

'It will ruin our relationship anyway if she drives you away.'

'She won't.' She squeezed his hand reassuringly. 'I told you, if we just leave it for a few months, it might give her a chance to calm down. Anything could happen in that time. She might grow up a bit, see things differently—'

'Or you could decide you're better off without me?' Jack's voice turned cold. 'Are you sure that's not what all this is about? You've seen what Emily can be like and you've realised you don't need the hassle?'

'If I felt like that, would I be bothering to have this conversation?' she snapped back. 'I want this to last, Jack. That's why I want to do it properly. For everyone's sake.'

She could see him wavering. Part of her – the stupid, romantic part – wanted him to take her in his arms, tell her he couldn't go through with it, that he didn't think he could last a day, let alone a month, without her.

But her practical side knew it was never going to be like that. He could see the sense in what she was saying, even if he wasn't ready to admit it.

'How many months?' he said finally.

'I don't know – maybe six?'

'Six months!' He released her hand and began pacing again. 'That's a bloody lifetime! Why should I put my life on hold for that long? If there's one thing Miranda's death has taught me it's that life's short and you have to grab happiness while you can.'

Tess waited quietly for the storm to pass. Finally he calmed down and said, 'You're serious about this, aren't you?'

'It's the only way.'

He thought about it for a moment. 'Couldn't we meet in secret?'

Tess rolled her eyes. 'How do you think we got into this mess in the first place?'

'I suppose you're right,' he admitted grudgingly. 'It's still going to be bloody hard, though. I mean, Haxsall isn't exactly a seething metropolis. We're bound to bump into each other—'

'We're both adults. I'm sure we can manage to be civilised.'

'And what about when the six months are up?'

'Then we'll talk about it, and if we both still feel the same—'

'So you're saying you might not?'

'I'm saying *you* might not.'

He was silent for a moment. 'I must be stupid to agree to this,' he groaned.

34

Jack sat in his office, looking down at the piece of bone in his hand. That harmless little fragment had changed everything. It had even made him rethink his future at Crawshaw and Finch.

It would be so simple to throw it away, pretend he'd never seen it. That would be the easy way out.

At least he had something to distract him. He didn't know how he would have got through the last five days if he hadn't had work to stop him going out of his mind. He'd thrown himself into it, spending fifteen-hour days making phone calls, preparing drawings and labouring on the computer. It helped him forget.

And it helped him avoid Emily. At least she was talking to him now, although things were still uneasy between them. But inside Jack still burned with anger. He was afraid if he had to look at her sulky face or listen to how badly life had treated her, he might say something he regretted.

Greg walked in while he was still deep in thought. 'Why aren't you in the boardroom? The Westpoint meeting's due to start in — what have you got there?' Jack put the bone down on the desk. Greg stared at it for a moment, then laughed. 'Sophie's missing treasure. Where did you find it?'

'In Bernard Sweeting's safe.'

Greg picked it up and turned it over in his hand. 'What was it doing in there, I wonder?'

'You tell me.'

He saw Greg's eyes flicker. 'Don't know what you're talking about.'

'Really? So it wasn't you who gave it to Bernard for analysis?'

'You know it wasn't.' Greg laughed uneasily. 'What is this? Is there some kind of conspiracy going on at Crawshaw and Finch?'

'If there is, you're right in the middle of it.'

There was a long silence. Then Greg sat down heavily in the chair opposite his, all the fight gone out of him. 'How did you find out?'

'I saw the trial pit up on the site. Bernard wasn't very good at hiding his tracks.'

'Stupid bugger. He always was too thorough for his own good.' Greg picked up the fragment of bone. 'I told him to get rid of this thing.' He looked at Jack. 'I suppose he's still got that bloody Environmental Impact Assessment report too?'

'No, he hasn't. I have.' Jack pulled the file out of his drawer and slapped it on the desk. 'Makes interesting reading, doesn't it? I'm amazed no one picked up on all this stuff earlier.'

'They wouldn't, would they? All the previous investigations were on a different part of the site. No one would ever have known it was there, if only—'

'If only Sophie hadn't dug that bone up. I'm amazed she didn't find anything else.' Jack flicked through the file in front of him. 'Quite a discovery, wasn't it? Traces of mosaic floor, fragments of pottery—'

'Don't rub it in,' Greg groaned.

'All pointing to this being the site of a Roman temple. Quite an important one, by all accounts.'

'I'm afraid so.'

Jack closed the file. 'So who else knows about this?'

'Bernard, of course. And Peter Jameson.'

Jack looked up sharply. 'Jameson knows?'

'Of course he knows. Who do you think told us to cover it up?'

'But why?'

'Work it out, Jack. If anyone finds out about this, all hell will break loose. The place will be swarming with archaeologists and the first thing they'll do is declare it a site of historical importance. Then it'll be goodbye, Westpoint.'

'So he told you to keep quiet about it?'

'He said in a couple of months it wouldn't make any difference. He promised he'd make it worth our while.'

Jack suddenly remembered Peter Jameson's new-found friendship with Greg. The cosy dinners, the games of golf, the invitations to his villa. It all made sense.

'You let him bribe you,' he said.

'Yes, I let him bribe me.' Greg's eyes were cold. 'You don't have to look so sanctimonious about it, Jack. We all know you'd never stoop so low.'

'I never thought you would, either.'

'Well, I did. And do you know why? Because it felt good to be noticed, instead of always being known as Jack Tyler's brother-in-law.'

Jack frowned. 'What are you talking about?'

'Oh, come on, Jacko! Do you have any idea what it's like, living in your shadow? No matter how hard I try, I know I'm never going to match up to you. Jack Tyler, the golden boy. Top of the class. The college babe magnet.

919

The would-be senior partner.' His face was bitter. 'And what am I? Greg Randall, the also-ran.'

'Humphrey put you in charge of this project.'

'Only because you turned the job down! Everyone knows he asked you first, Jack. How do you think that makes me feel, being second best again?'

Jack stared at him. He'd always got on so well with his brother-in-law, he had no idea his resentment went so deep.

'Look, don't feel bad about it. You can't help being a hero.' Greg smiled at him. 'Anyway, I've proved my real worth, haven't I? I've screwed up again.' He stood up.

'Where are you going?'

'To see Humphrey and tell him about all this.'

'But you could lose your job.'

'Maybe. But we can't keep this hushed up, can we?' Jack didn't answer. 'To tell the truth, it'll be a relief to have it all in the open. I always hated lying. And I was crap at it. Just like everything else, really.'

'I'm sorry,' Jack said.

Greg shrugged. 'Like I said, don't feel bad. This was my mistake, not yours.'

He'd got to the door when Jack called him back. 'Wait. Don't go just yet. There might be another way . . .'

Humphrey had already opened the meeting by the time they arrived in the boardroom. Jack looked around at the men in suits ranged around the table. Peter Jameson was at the far end, looking smug. There was no sign of Bernard Sweeting.

Jack wasn't surprised. He'd been on stress leave for the past two weeks. The strain of keeping his findings a secret must have been too much for him. Bernard was a conscientious man, and good at his job. Just like Greg.

'Ah, Jack.' Jack felt a twinge of irritation as Humphrey greeted him and ignored Greg. 'I was just saying, it looks as if the public inquiry is in the bag. The opposition are in disarray now we've got the council on our side.'

'With any luck the whole thing should be wrapped up soon, then you can get the contractors on to the site,' Peter Jameson concluded. 'The quicker we get started, the better.'

I'll bet, Jack thought. He glanced at Greg, who cleared his throat and said, 'There may be a problem with that.'

Peter's smile didn't waver. 'What kind of problem, Greg?'

Greg reached over and topped up his glass from the water jug in the middle of the table. Only Jack could see how much his hand was shaking. 'We've been doing some further investigations and we've come up with the possibility that the site may hold special archaeological interest.'

A ripple ran around the table. 'What kind of archaeological interest?' Humphrey asked.

'We're not quite sure yet.' Greg made a show of consulting his notes. 'But initial surveys lead us to believe it may be a Roman temple.'

He passed copies of the report around the table. There was much murmuring as everyone flicked through it. Peter Jameson didn't bother to open his, Jack noticed.

'Well,' Humphrey sat back in his seat. 'This puts rather a different spin on things, doesn't it?'

Jack glanced at Peter. He looked as if he was about to explode with frustration, but there was nothing he could do about it. If he tried to drop Greg in it, he would have to admit he already knew about the report himself.

'I wasn't aware we'd requested these extra environmental studies to be done?' He glared at Greg.

'You didn't,' Jack said. 'But it's just as well we did, isn't it? Or no one would ever have known it was there.'

'Quite.' Peter shot him a look of loathing. 'Couldn't we just build anyway? Surely if no one's found it by now they're not going to miss it for another couple of centuries,' he joked.

Greg regarded him steadily. 'I think the archaeological world might take a different view.'

'So do I,' Humphrey said. 'We're going to have to rethink this whole project in the light of these findings.'

The meeting broke up shortly after that. Jack left them still comparing notes outside the boardroom and went back to his office.

Vicky guiltily folded up her copy of the *Daily Mail* and began tapping on the keyboard as he approached. 'Meeting over already?' she asked.

'There didn't seem to be much more to say.' He looked around. 'Have you got any cardboard boxes, Vick?'

'There are probably some downstairs. Why, are you having a clear-out?'

'You could say that.'

Half an hour later, Humphrey walked in. 'Hello, Jack. Can I have a word?'

'Sure. Sit down – if you can find somewhere.' Jack cleared a pile of books from one of the chairs and Humphrey took it. He didn't look so fit and sprightly any more. He seemed to have aged twenty years in the last hour.

'That was quite a meeting, wasn't it?' he said.

'It was certainly interesting. Have you spoken to Jameson?'

'I didn't get the chance. He left in rather a hurry.' Humphrey frowned. 'D'you know, I had the strangest feeling he already knew what was in that report?'

'Really?' Jack deadpanned. 'How would he know?'

'I thought you could tell me?'

'I have no idea.'

'And even if you did, you wouldn't say anything?' Humphrey regarded him shrewdly. 'That's what I like about you, Jack. You're a loyal, honourable man. And there aren't many of them around these days.' He leaned back in his seat. 'That's why I wanted to offer you the senior partnership.'

Jack smiled. His whole career had been building up to this moment. But now it had happened, he felt nothing at all. 'I'm flattered. But I'm afraid you're going to have to find someone else. I'm leaving.'

'What? But you can't!' Humphrey stared at him in amazement. 'Don't you understand, I'm offering you the top job?'

'And I'm turning it down.'

Humphrey was silent for a while. 'May I ask why?'

'I just don't feel I fit in here any more.' He sat back on his heels and looked around his office. A year ago, the only way he would have been leaving it was to go on to a bigger and better one. But now . . . 'You told me once you expect one hundred and ten per cent from the people here and I don't think I can give that any more. I've got too much else going on in my life.'

He expected Humphrey to argue, but he didn't. 'I respect your decision, although I can't pretend I'm not disappointed,' he said heavily. 'So what are you planning to do with your life? Not giving up your career entirely, I hope?'

'God, no. I couldn't afford to do that. Actually, I'm thinking of starting up on my own.' It felt strange, saying it aloud. 'It's something I've been mulling over for a while now, and I quite like the idea of being my own boss.'

'It's not as easy as it looks, you know. What will you do for capital?'

'I've still got some money left over from the sale of the old house. And there was an insurance pay-out after Miranda's death.' It had sat in the bank for almost a year because he hadn't wanted to touch it. It didn't feel right. But he felt sure Miranda would approve of his plan.

Humphrey stood up. 'In that case, I hope it all works out for you. But I must say you've left me in a difficult position. Where am I going to find another senior partner?'

'How about Greg?'

'Who?'

Jack checked his impatience. 'Greg Randall. He's intelligent, ambitious, loyal. He deserves a chance.' And maybe with Jack out of the way he'd finally get it.

'Greg Randall, eh?' Humphrey considered it. 'I hadn't thought of him.'

No, Jack said to himself. That's the trouble, no one ever does.

The yard at Second Chance was deserted, although from one of the distant sheds came the muffled sound of hip-hop music punctuated by lots of swearing. Jack went round to what had been the office and peered in through the window. There was no sign of Melanie labouring over her keyboard. There wasn't even a keyboard. It was empty, apart from a pile of boxes filled with old files and other rubbish.

'Taking a last look round, are you?' He swung round. There was Reverend Dobbs. 'I suppose you couldn't resist having a gloat?'

'Not necessarily.' Jack rubbed at the dusty pane of glass with his sleeve. 'Looks like you've been having a clear-out?'

'No point in leaving it till the last minute, is there? You lot will be wanting to get started on the site as soon as you get your go-ahead.'

'What makes you think we'll get it?'

'Oh, come on! I may be a vicar but even the Almighty couldn't pull off a miracle like that. Of course you'll get it. Unless you've come to tell me you've changed your minds?'

Jack didn't answer. He looked up at the main building. 'See that crack in the wall up near the roofline? Looks like you've got some movement in the foundations. With any luck it's just a bit of settlement, but you'd have to check if it's still happening. If it is, you might need underpinning.' He looked around. 'And those sheds should go. You need some new workshops. Purpose-built, south-facing, with a bit more natural light so the lads can see what they're doing.'

'Nice idea. Maybe while we're at it we could put in a heated swimming pool too?' Sam gave him an odd look. 'Hello? This whole place will be reduced to rubble in a few weeks, or have you forgotten?'

'Like I said, not necessarily.' Jack looked around. 'Of course, you'd have to be careful about where you build, so as not to upset the temple. But you should be all right over here.'

'Temple?' Sam followed him across the yard. 'Jack, have you been drinking? What are you talking about?'

'You mean you don't know about the Roman temple?' Jack regarded him with mock surprise. 'Perhaps you should ask the Westpoint consortium. They know all about it. They're having to hand this site over for archaeological investigations.'

A look of understanding passed across Sam's face. 'And you say this temple is somewhere around here?'

'So I believe. Right over there, in fact.' He pointed towards the other side of the field.

'Is that right?' Sam said slowly. 'And it's important, is it?'

'Very.'

'So it wouldn't be a good idea to build a shopping centre on top of it?'

'There's no way anyone would get permission. The archaeologists will have to open the whole site up. It could take years.'

'Really?' Sam scratched his chin thoughtfully. 'I don't suppose you'd like to stay for a cup of tea, would you? I'm sure we could track down the kettle.'

As they trudged towards the gate half an hour later, Jack said, 'Of course, now Westpoint can't build much more than a rabbit hutch here, they might be keen to get rid of the land. They might even be prepared to let you have this corner of it at a knockdown price.'

'It's worth asking, I suppose.'

'Can't do any harm.'

Sam glanced sidelong at him. 'And who found out about all this?'

'Let's just say I did some digging.'

'This wouldn't have anything to do with cracking safes, would it?'

'Reverend Dobbs! I'm surprised at you. You know that's illegal?'

Sam smiled. 'So why go to all this trouble? I expect it's cost your firm a few bob, losing that contract?'

'A wise man once said there's more to life than making money.'

'Sounds more like an idiot to me.' Sam grinned. 'Honestly, who'd come out with a thing like that?'

'The same idiot who'd spend his days hanging out with juvenile delinquents.'

'Ex juvenile delinquents, please.'

'And there's another reason,' Jack said. 'A purely selfish one.'

'What's that?'

'I want you to be my first client. I've decided to leave Crawshaw and Finch and set up on my own. I feel like doing something worthwhile for a change.'

'You won't get rich doing that. I should know.'

'Maybe not, but it's got to be better than building shopping centres no one wants. Anyway, maybe I'll get my reward in heaven. That's what you lot say, isn't it?'

'I'll put in a word for you at Head Office myself.'

They reached the gate. 'Fancy that,' Jack said, looking down the road. 'My car's still in one piece.'

Sam smiled. 'See?' he said. 'It's working already.'

35

'Now are you sure you've remembered everything? What about all that stuff in the airing cupboard? Have you packed all that?'

'Yes, Mum!' Dan rolled his eyes heavenwards. 'I wish you'd stop fussing!'

'My only baby's leaving home. How can I not fuss?' She looked at the cases arranged around her. 'Have you packed enough jumpers? You don't know how cold it gets down there.'

'I'm going to Basingstoke, not Siberia!'

He might as well be going to Siberia, Tess thought. It felt far enough. She picked up a shirt and refolded it. It was early May and Dan was on study leave before his A Levels. And in spite of all her prayers that he'd change his mind, he'd decided to spend the time getting settled in down south with his father. He would be coming back in June to take his exams but basically, this was it. He was leaving home.

'Anyway, I'll be back in a few weeks if I've forgotten anything,' Dan reminded her.

Tess forced a smile. 'Don't expect to stay here, will you? I've already let your room to a bunch of asylum seekers!'

Dan laughed. She could tell in spite of his merry mood he wasn't looking forward to saying goodbye any more than she was. It was up to her to try and make it easy for him, no matter how hard it might be for her.

'I'm going to miss your rubbish jokes, Mum.'

'And I'm going to miss tidying up your mess.'

They were saved from getting maudlin when Phil stuck his head round the door. 'Hi. The front door was open so I let myself in.' He looked around the room. 'Blimey, I hope this is everything?'

'Almost.' Tess put the shirt back in the case and stood up. 'We've just got to unplumb the kitchen sink and that'll be it.'

'Why do I not feel you're joking?' Phil grinned. 'I'd better start packing the car.'

'Would you like a cup of tea?'

'No thanks, I'd rather get on our way so we miss the traffic.' He saw her desolate face. 'Oh well, maybe a quick cup wouldn't hurt.'

Tess hurried off to the kitchen to make it, relieved that she didn't have to watch Phil loading Dan's luggage into the car. She'd been hovering on the edge of tears ever since she dragged the suitcases out of the loft a week ago.

It's for the best, she told herself over and over again. Dan will have a great job, he'll be really happy, and Phil will look after him.

It was his turn now. She'd had Dan all to herself for nearly eighteen years. The time had come to share him.

She just hoped he was up to the job. Playing dad every other weekend was one thing, but he'd never been a full-time father.

She busied herself making tea. By the time she'd carried the tray through to the sitting room Phil had loaded the last of the luggage into the boot of his car. A people carrier, she noticed.

Tess frowned through the window. 'What happened to the Porsche?'

'I sold it. I thought that one might be more practical. I'm having it specially adapted so Dan can drive it.' He glanced at her anxiously. 'That's all right, isn't it?'

'It's very thoughtful of you.' Tess smiled back. Maybe Dan would be okay with Phil after all.

All too soon the time came to say goodbye. Tess stood on the doorstep to watch Phil as he loaded Dan's wheelchair into the boot. Dan was in his bedroom, taking a last look around to make sure he had everything.

'I flaming well hope so!' Phil said. 'There's no room for anything else in the car.' He looked at Tess. 'Are you okay?'

She nodded. 'I'm fine. You will look after him, won't you?'

'Of course I will.'

'You'll make sure he does his revision and his physiotherapy? Oh, and be careful if he gets a cold. It can so easily turn into something worse—'

'Tess, calm down. He's my son too, remember?'

Her smile wobbled and Phil pulled her into his arms for a reassuring hug. 'It'll be okay,' he whispered into her hair.

'I'm just worried I won't be able to say goodbye.'

'You could come with us for the weekend? Just to make sure Dan's settled in.'

Tess knew he was being kind and she appreciated it. 'He's not a child, Phil. He doesn't need me to hold his hand for him.' Not any more, she thought sadly.

'Here he comes.' He let her go and she turned around. Dan was coming down the path on his sticks, a bundle of rolled-up posters under his arm. Her little boy, so full of hope. She mustn't spoil this for him.

She fixed her smile back in place. 'I hope you've cleared all the coffee cups out from under your bed?'

'I think you'll find you're the one with all the cups under the bed, Mother.' He handed the posters to Phil. 'I'll be back in June. And you can always come and visit us before then, can't she, Dad?'

Dad. She'd never heard him call Phil that before. And from the emotional look on Phil's face, neither had he.

'Of course, son. Any time she likes.'

'I will. You wait, as soon as those summer holidays start, I'll be down there all the time. Do they have beaches in Basingstoke?'

Phil smiled. 'We'll find one.'

He moved around to open the passenger door for Dan. Just as she'd been afraid she would, Tess hugged him fiercely, not wanting to let him go, trying to imprint the feel of him in her arms for ever.

As he pulled away, there were tears in his eyes. 'You will be all right on your own, won't you, Mum?'

'Who said I'll be on my own? I plan to find myself a toyboy the moment you're gone.'

'Why don't you ring Jack?'

A painful lump rose in her throat. She'd spent the last three months trying not to miss him. 'I can't. We had an agreement.'

'A stupid one, if you ask me. You miss him and I bet he misses you too.'

Does he? Tess was beginning to wonder. She hadn't heard from him at all in the past three months, and even though she knew that was what they'd agreed, part of her still worried that he hadn't even attempted to break it. She'd felt tempted, hundreds of times. She'd even gone as far as buying him a Valentine's card a couple of months back. It was still in her bedside drawer, unsigned and unsealed.

Also, Emily seemed far less moody and hostile at school these days. Maybe Jack had realised how easy his life was without Tess to complicate everything and decided they were better off without each other?

'We'll have to see, won't we?' she said.

She'd never known what it meant to put on a brave face until that moment. She stood at the front gate, waving madly until the car turned the corner and disappeared. Then she went back into the bungalow and closed the door.

The silence closed in on her immediately. She'd been on her own millions of times, when Dan was at college or round at a friend's. But the house had never seemed as empty as it did now. It was as if he'd taken all the life and memories away with him.

She went into his room. It, too, looked strange and unfamiliar without all his clutter around. She thought about all the times she'd charged in to this very room, shouting at him to keep the noise down. Now she'd never hear it again. Next time Dan came he would be a visitor. There would be no more banging doors, no more loud music, no more troglodyte friends stomping through the house.

She sat down on the bed, looked at the big, empty spaces on the wall where his posters used to be, and cried.

Emily was on her way to the shop to buy a magazine when a car slowed down beside her and someone called her name.

It took her a moment to recognise the boy with the floppy fair hair leaning out of the passenger window. Then she realised it was Tess Doyle's son.

'Got a minute?' he asked.

She glanced past him at the fair-haired man behind the wheel. He shrugged.

'What for?'

'I want to talk to you.'

She turned away. 'I've got nothing to say.'

'No, but I have. And you're going to hear it.'

Emily started to walk away up the road. She didn't turn round, but she knew he was getting out of the car. It took him a long time to catch up with her, limping along on his sticks.

'I told you, I've got nothing to say to you.'

'Fine. I'll do all the talking then, shall I?' He sidestepped in front of her, blocking her way. 'Why do you hate my mum?'

'I don't.'

'You could have fooled me. So how come you stopped her seeing your dad?'

'That was nothing to do with me.'

'Like hell it wasn't! She really misses him, you know.'

He missed her too, Emily could tell. Even though things had settled down at home and he'd been busy setting up his new business over the past few months, she could tell he was miserable. Sometimes she'd wake up in the early hours to find all the lights still on and him sitting at his drawing board, staring into space. She knew he wasn't thinking about work.

She missed Tess too. They'd reached an uneasy truce at school, but it wasn't the same. Emily missed Tess' jokes, her laughter, the way she could talk to her about anything. Now she couldn't talk to her at all.

She'd screwed everything up and she knew it. But that didn't mean she was ready to admit it to Dan.

'So?' she said.

'So you could stop giving them both a hard time.' She was silent. 'Look,

I know you're not keen on the idea of your dad having a girlfriend, but you can't keep him to yourself for ever. Apart from anything else, it's selfish.'

She glanced sideways at him. 'Oh yeah? How do you work that out?'

'Think about it. In a few years you'll probably have left home and be at college somewhere. Do you really want your dad to be lonely?'

'He'll have Sophie.'

'And what happens when she grows up and moves on? It's going to happen. I'm moving away myself and leaving my mum on her own, and I feel like shit for doing it. Do you want that?'

'Your mum's on her own?'

Dan nodded. 'But she wouldn't have to be if you'd given her the chance. And you could do a lot worse than my mum, you know. She's not that bad once you get to know her.'

Emily managed a half smile at that. She did like Tess. Very much. Or she had, until all this happened.

'They lied to me,' she said.

'Big deal. Adults do it all the time. Anyway, do you blame them? They knew you'd hit the roof when you found out.'

'They still shouldn't have lied.'

'I think they've worked that out for themselves,' Dan said wryly.

They reached the shop. Emily said, 'Anyway, it's finished now. It's been over for ages.'

'That's what you think.'

'What do you mean?'

'I mean my mum's still mad about your dad and I reckon he feels the same. The only reason they're not together is because they don't want to hurt you.'

'So?' Guilt made her snap.

'So maybe you should think about that.' Dan turned and limped away, leaving her open-mouthed.

That Saturday afternoon, her dad dropped them off at Auntie Ros' while he went to meet a potential client. He worked at the weekends a lot these days. He said he had to work long hours to get the business going, but Emily sometimes wondered if he was trying to avoid being at home.

Auntie Ros was attempting to tackle the housework and seemed relieved when Emily said she wanted to go shopping.

'I don't suppose you'd like to take these with you?' She looked down at the three small children jumping over the vacuum-cleaner hose at her feet.

'No thanks,' Emily smiled. Where she was going was no place for kids.

It was a warm day and the cemetery was busy. No funerals, but lots of people visiting graves. Emily thought about the last time she'd come here, with Tess. She'd been so kind to her, buying flowers and listening to her troubles. She'd even gone into battle with her dad on Emily's behalf.

She remembered them squaring up to each other on the front drive. That wasn't someone who was using her because she secretly fancied him. That was someone who cared about her enough to put her job on the line to stand up for her.

But that didn't quell the anxiety lurking in the pit of her stomach. She liked Tess and she was sure she hadn't used her to get to her dad. And yes, if she had to choose someone for him to get involved with, it would probably be Tess Doyle.

But that only made it worse. Emily could imagine them all living together, being happy. She could see Tess fitting seamlessly into their family. She could picture them all talking and laughing around the dining-room table.

That was what frightened her. Because the more comfortable Emily felt having Tess around, the more she might forget her mother. She'd already slipped from her father's mind. Emily owed it to her to keep her memory alive.

She turned the corner and saw him. A tall figure kneeling beside her mother's grave. Her heart lurched. She dodged behind a yew tree and watched him arranging flowers around the headstone.

So he hadn't forgotten her after all.

She wondered if she should sneak away but he looked up and saw her. 'Emily? What are you doing here?'

What do you think? All her old defences of sarcasm and bitterness sprang up, but she quelled them. 'Same as you. I thought you were working today?'

'I was. But then I decided to come here.' He straightened up and brushed the dirt off his knees. 'I've been tidying it up.'

'It looks all right.' Emily looked at the half-dead bunch of flowers he'd just taken from the grave. 'Who left those?'

'I did. Last week.'

'You came last week?'

'I come every week.'

'I didn't know that.'

'I don't tell you everything.'

She could have said something cutting, but she didn't. She gazed down at the roses. 'They were her favourites.'

'I know. I used to buy them for her every Friday before you were born.'

She kept her eyes fixed on the grave. 'Do you miss her?'

'Of course I miss her. Not a day goes by when I don't think about her.'

She glanced sideways at his profile and realised how badly she must have hurt him when she accused him of being glad her mother was dead. A lump rose in her throat. 'I'm sorry,' she mumbled. 'About those things I said.'

She felt his hand come down on her shoulder. 'It doesn't matter.'

'I can't help it. I just get – frightened.'

'Frightened of what, Em?'

'That you'll forget her.' She looked up at him, her eyes wet with tears. 'I'm scared that if you meet someone else, you might get to love them more than you loved her.'

His dark gaze softened. 'Do you really think that could happen?'

'It feels like you're trying to forget her,' she rubbed her eyes on her sleeve. 'That's why we moved house.'

'I wasn't trying to forget her. I was just trying not to miss her so badly.' His arm slid further around her shoulders. For once she didn't try to shrug him off. 'I don't want to forget her. We had some really special times, me and your mum. She'll always be there. Nothing could change that. And I wouldn't want it to.'

He hugged her close. It felt good to be back in his arms. Whatever happened, he would always be there for her and Sophie. Nothing could change that, either.

'Come on,' he said gruffly. 'Let's go home.'

She chose her moment carefully. They were on the M62, stuck in a traffic snarl-up as usual. Emily pretended to flick through the CDs.

'I spoke to Dan today.'

'Who?'

'You know – Miss Doyle's son?'

'Oh.' He didn't take his eyes off the road.

'He says he's left home.'

He missed a gear. 'Dan's gone? Already? I thought he wasn't leaving until the summer?'

'Well, he's gone, anyway.' She stared out of the window. 'His mum's very upset, he said.'

'I bet she is.' Jack's face was grim.

'Maybe you should call her?'

'Are you feeling all right?'

'I mean it.' Emily plucked at a loose thread on her sleeve. 'I wouldn't mind if you saw her again.'

He frowned. 'You don't sound too sure about that.'

Emily thought about it for a moment. It was going to be hard for her, seeing her father with another woman. But Dan was right. She had to stop being selfish.

And if there had to be someone else, she would rather it was Tess than anyone. 'She's all right really,' she said.

'She is, isn't she?' He was smiling. The first real smile she'd seen in weeks.

When they got back, the first thing he did was call Tess' number. Emily pretended not to listen as he stood there, hanging on to the phone.

Finally, he put it down. 'She's not there.' He looked disappointed.

'She must have gone out. She's not expecting you to call, is she?'

'No.'

'So she's not going to be sitting by the phone waiting, is she? Don't panic, I'm sure she hasn't lined herself up with another bloke!'

'I suppose not.' He went on staring at the phone. Emily sighed.

'If you're that worried, why don't you go round there?' she said.

Tess looked at the phone and resisted the urge to call Dan. He'd phoned an hour ago to say they'd arrived safely and even though Tess had done her best to sound thrilled when he raved about his new home, she already missed him dreadfully. She'd tried going out for a walk to make herself think about something else, but it hadn't worked.

She decided to do what she always did in times of crisis and call her mother instead. She reached for the phone and was halfway through dialling the number when she remembered no one was home. She and Ronnie had gone on a honeymoon cruise of the Mediterranean. She'd got a postcard from them that morning, a colourful photo of the island of Madeira.

It made her smile to see it propped up on the mantelpiece. Margaret had never owned a passport or gone further than Scarborough for her holidays. Ronnie was opening up new horizons for her.

But it felt strange, not having her on the end of a phone whenever she needed her. She was lucky to catch her mother in these days. If she wasn't out at her conversational Italian classes, she was learning tennis or Tai Chi. Sometimes Tess felt like the old one, sitting at home feeling bitter and resentful that no one bothered to call her any more.

Not that she begrudged her mother her new life. She just wished she could be part of it. It felt as if everyone had moved on and left her behind.

But she couldn't sit moping about it. As Helen kept telling her, this was her chance to make a life of her own.

'Just think, you don't have any responsibilities any more,' she'd said. 'You can do what you like, when you like.'

Which all sounded wonderful, except that Tess couldn't think of a single thing she wanted to do. Maybe she should ask Ronnie and her mum if she could tag along to their Tai Chi class?

Her grumbling stomach told her it was time to eat, so she trailed into the kitchen in search of food. It wasn't until she was staring into an empty fridge that she realised she'd forgotten to go to the supermarket. All the fridge contained was some sliced ham that had curled up at the edges and a Tupperware container full of something that might once have been potato salad but was now curdled and dubious-smelling. And the usual half bottle of wine, of course. Tess resisted the urge to drink the lot.

This was ridiculous! Dan had only been gone a few hours and she'd already let herself go. If she carried on like this, by the end of the week she'd have stopped bothering to wash her hair or get dressed. She'd sleep all day and drink all night and probably live in her slobby old pyjamas. She might as well go out and buy those cats now, so they could eat her when she dropped down dead from starvation or alcohol poisoning.

Or she could just stop being over-dramatic and go out for a takeaway. She grabbed the car keys from the worktop before she could change her mind and decide it wasn't worth the bother.

She opened the front door and walked straight into Jack coming up the path, clutching a large flat pizza box.

'Jack!' She shot a quick look around, half expecting a vengeful Emily to appear from behind the hedge. 'What are you doing here?'

'I heard about Dan moving out,' he said. 'I came to see how you are.'

The tender concern in his face made her want to weep all over again. 'I'm fine.' Actually, I'm bloody terrible, she cried out inside. My mother's got herself a life, my son's left home and I'm all on my own. *And I miss you.* She hadn't realised how much until she saw him standing there, so tall and dark and damn good-looking it hurt.

He looked at her shrewdly. 'Are you sure about that?'

'I will be once I get a grip on myself and stop crying in his bedroom. I've had to hide the phone to stop myself calling him.' A thought occurred to her and she frowned. 'How did you know he'd gone?'

'Emily told me.'

'How did she find out?'

'She met Dan this morning. They had a good talk, apparently. He told her you missed me.' He gave her a look that made her toes curl inside her trainers. 'Is it true?'

'Jack—'

'Is it true?'

'Of course I miss you! But we agreed—'

'You shouldn't be on your own at a time like this,' he cut her off. 'Why don't you come round to our place? We're having a pizza.' He held up the box in front of her. The heavenly smell made her stomach groan.

'Jack—'

'Before you say anything else, it wasn't my idea.' He glanced back over his shoulder. For the first time Tess noticed Emily and Sophie were in the car, their faces pressed against the glass. Emboldened, Jack leaned across the pizza box and kissed her full on the mouth. 'We'd all like you to come,' he said quietly.

Tess looked from the girls back to him. 'In that case, I'd love to.'

It was only pizza. But it was a start.